Zamparo

HANDBOOK OF ADHESIVES

Edited by

IRVING SKEIST

Consultant
Skeist Laboratories, Inc.
Newark, New Jersey

New York

REINHOLD PUBLISHING CORPORATION
CHAPMAN & HALL, LTD., *LONDON*

Preface

An adhesive is a substance capable of holding materials together by surface attachment. Adhesives are essential to shoes and space ships and sealing wax as well as cars, cabinets, countertops, corrugated cartons, and curtain-wall construction.

To the dauntless adhesive technologist, this volume is dedicated. Like our founding fathers, he seeks ever to form a more perfect union. Daily he risks the occasional hazards of his calling, shrugging off the apocryphal warning, "He who toucheth pitch, to him it shall cling." There is romance in his heart as he recalls the lilting imagery of Rob't Herrick:

What is a Kisse? Why this, as some approve;
The sure sweet-Sement, Glue, and Lime of Love.

This compilation has been in preparation for more than three years. Almost fifty groups of authors, all busy people, recognized the need for this handbook and undertook the extra task of preparing chapters in their specialties. Unfairly, the promptest contributors have the oldest bibliographies. Perhaps the brilliant minds who have given the world atomic energy, extra-terrestrial flight and cigarette commercials can devise a scheme for collecting 59 manuscripts in a single year, without gaps because of procrastination or defection.

In a compendium by so many authors, one must expect variations in style as well as content. The book is more lucid and homogeneous in style because of the noteworthy editorial work of Mrs. Alberta Gordon of Reinhold. At the same time, the strong preferences of chapter authors have been respected on some details; thus we have both "carboxymethyl cellulose" and "carboxymethylcellulose," "reclaim rubber" and "reclaimed rubber," the traditional "latices" as well as the ACS-approved "latexes." The ASTM changed its name last year from "American Society for Testing Materials" to "American Society for Testing and Materials."

This volume is concerned more with "how to" than with "why." While the *art* of adhesive bonding can be discussed dispassionately, the polemics over adhesion *science* are still highly exothermic. Consider the basic question of what sticks best to what. Voyutskii stresses the importance of mutual solubility, permitting interdiffusion of adhesive and adherend. He agrees with de Bruyne that materials of comparable polarity are most likely to form strong bonds. The electrical theory of adhesion, proposed by Deryagin as well as Rutzler, leads one to expect materials of opposite charge to bond most readily. According to Bikerman, however, any "pure" polymer can stick to any clean surface. Space limitations have impelled the authors of Chapters 1, 3, and 14 to be eclectic rather than comprehensive in their extracts of adhesion theory.

In addition to the chapter authors, many individuals and organizations have helped the editor. Special thanks are due F. F. Van Atta of ASTM, Richard F. Blomquist of U. S. Forest Products Laboratory, John T. Goodwin of Corn Industries Research Foundation, Mel Lerner of *Adhesives Age,* Kenyon Loomis of Adhesives Manufacturers Association, Alan A. Marra of University of Michigan, Frank W. Reinhart, formerly of U. S. Bureau of Standards, H. F. Wakefield, formerly of Union Carbide Plastics Company; also ASTIA, "Modern Plastics Encyclopedia," and many industrial firms.

From abroad, N. A. de Bruyne of Ciba, Ltd. (England) and Yehuda Th. Radday of Technion (Israel) sent helpful communications.

The late John E. Rutzler was a friend and teacher to us all.

Summit, N.J.　　　　　　　　　　　　　IRVING SKEIST
June, 1962

Contents

Section C—ADHERENDS

Section D—BONDING TECHNOLOGY

Definitions of Terms

Standard Definitions of Terms Relating to Adhesives*

A-Stage, *n.*—An early stage in the reaction of certain thermosetting resins in which the material is fusible and still soluble in certain liquids. Sometimes referred to as Resol. (*See also* B-Stage and C-Stage.)

Adhere, *v.*—To cause two surfaces to be held together by adhesion.

Adherend, *n.*—A body which is held to another body by an adhesive. (*See also* Substrate.)

Adhesion, *n.*—The state in which two surfaces are held together by interfacial forces which may consist of valence forces or interlocking action, or both. (*See also* Adhesion, Mechanical and Adhesion, Specific.)

Adhesion, Mechanical—Adhesion between surfaces in which the adhesive holds the parts together by interlocking action. (*See also* Adhesion, Specific.)

Adhesion, Specific—Adhesion between surfaces which are held together by valence forces of the same type as those which give rise to cohesion. (*See also* Adhesion, Mechanical.)

Adhesive, *n.*—A substance capable of holding materials together by surface attachment.

Note—Adhesive is the general term and includes among others cement, glue, mucilage and paste. All of these terms are loosely used interchangeably. Various descriptive adjectives are applied to the term adhesive to indicate certain characteristics as follows:

Physical form, that is, liquid adhesive, tape adhesive.

Chemical type, that is, silicate adhesive, resin adhesive.

Materials bonded, that is paper adhesive, metal-plastic adhesive, can label adhesive.

Conditions of use, that is, hot-setting adhesive.

Adhesive, Assembly—An adhesive which can be used for bonding parts together, such as in the manufacture of a boat, airplane, furniture, and the like.

Note—The term assembly adhesive is commonly used in the wood industry to distinguish such adhesives (formerly called "joint glues") from those used in making plywood (sometimes called "veneer glues"). It is applied to adhesives used in fabricating finished structures or goods, or subassemblies thereof, as differentiated from adhesives used in the production of sheet metals for sale as such, for example, plywood or laminates.

Adhesive, Cold-Setting—An adhesive which sets at temperatures below 20°C (68°F.) (*See also* Adhesive, Hot-Setting; Adhesive, Intermediate Temperature Setting; and Adhesive, Room-Temperature Setting.)

Adhesive, Hot-Setting—An adhesive which requires a temperature at or above 100°C (212°F) to set it. (*See also* Adhesive, Cold-Setting; Adhesive, Intermediate Temperature Setting; and Adhesive, Room-Temperature Setting.)

Adhesive, Intermediate Temperature Setting—An adhesive which sets in the temperature range 31 to 99°C (87 to 211°F). (*See also* Adhesive, Cold-Setting; Adhesive, Hot-Setting; and Adhesive, Room-Temperature Setting.)

Adhesive, Pressure-Sensitive—An adhesive made so as to adhere to a surface at room temperature by briefly applied pressure alone.

Adhesive, Room-Temperature Setting—An adhesive which sets in the temperature range of 20 to 30°C (68 to 86°F), in accordance with the limits for Standard Room Temperature specified

* ASTM Designation: D 907–60

Published through courtesy of American Society for Testing Materials, 1916 Race St., Philadelphia, Pa.

in the Standard Methods of Conditioning Plastics and Electrical Insulating Materials for Testing (ASTM Designation: D 618). (*See also* Adhesive, Cold-Setting; Adhesive, Hot-Setting; and Adhesive, Intermediate Temperature Setting.)

Adhesive, Separate Application—A term used to describe an adhesive consisting of two parts, one part being applied to one adherend and the other part to the other adherend and the two brought together to form a joint.

Adhesive, Warm-Setting—A term which is sometimes used as a synonym for Intermediate Temperature Setting Adhesive. (*See* Adhesive, Intermediate Temperature Setting.)

Adhesive Dispersion—A two-phase system in which one phase is suspended in a liquid.

Aging Time—*See* Time, Joint Conditioning.

Aggressive Tack—*See* Tack, Dry.

Amylaceous, *adj.*—Pertaining to, or of the nature of, starch; starchy.

Assembly, *n.*—A group of materials or parts, including adhesive, which has been placed together for bonding or which has been bonded together.

Assembly Adhesive—*See* Adhesive, Assembly.

Assembly Glue—*See* Adhesive, Assembly.

Assembly Time—*See* Time, Assembly.

B-Stage—An intermediate stage in the reaction of certain thermosetting resins in which the material softens when heated and swells when in contact with certain liquids, but may not entirely fuse or dissolve. The resin in an uncured thermosetting adhesive, is usually in this stage. Sometimes referred to as Resitol. (*See also* A-Stage and C-Stage.)

Bag Molding—A method of molding or bonding involving the application of fluid pressure, usually by means of air, steam, water, or vacuum, to a flexible cover which, sometimes in conjunction with the rigid die, completely encloses the material to be bonded.

Binder, *n.*—A component of an adhesive composition which is primarily responsible for the adhesive forces which hold two bodies together. (*See also* Extender and Filler.)

Blister, *n.*—An elevation of the surface of an adherend, somewhat resembling in shape a blister on the human skin; its boundaries may be indefinitely outlined and it may have burst and become flattened.

    Note—A blister may be caused by insufficient adhesive; inadequate curing time, temperature or pressure; or trapped air, water, or solvent vapor.

Blocking, *n.*—An undesired adhesion between touching layers of a material, such as occurs under moderate pressure during storage or use.

Bond, *n.*—The union of materials by adhesives.

Bond, *v.*—To unite materials by means of an adhesive. (*See also* Adhere.)

Bond Strength—The unit load applied in tension, compression, flexure, peel, impact, cleavage, or shear, required to break an adhesive assembly with failure occurring in or near the plane of the bond.

    Note—The term adherence is frequently used in place of bond strength. (*See also* Adhesion and Bond.

C-Stage, *n.*—The final stage in the reaction of certain thermosetting resins in which the material is relatively insoluble and invisible. Certain thermosetting resins in a fully cured adhesive layer are in this stage. Sometimes referred to as Resite. (*See also* A-Stage and B-Stage.)

Catalyst, *n.*—A substance which markedly speeds up the cure of an adhesive when added in minor quantity as compared to the amounts of the primary reactants. (*See also* Hardener and Inhibitor.)

Cement, *n.*—*See* Adhesive.

Cement, *v.*—*See* Bond, v.

Closed Assembly Time—*See* Time, Assembly.

Cohesion, *n.*—The state in which the particles of a single substance are held together by primary or secondary valence forces. As used in the adhesive field, the state in which the particles of the adhesive (or the adherend) are held together.

Cold Flow—*See* Creep.

Cold Pressing—A bonding operation in which an assembly is subjected to pressure without the application of heat.

Cold-Setting Adhesive—*See* Adhesive, Cold-Setting.

Colophony, *n.*—*See* Rosin.

Condensation, *n.*—A Chemical reaction in which two or more molecules combine with the separation of water or some other simple substance. If a polymer is formed, the process is called polycondensation. (*See also* Polymerization.)

Conditioning Time—*See* Time, Joint Conditioning.

Consistency, *n.*—That property of a liquid adhesive by virtue of which it tends to resist deformation.

    Note—Consistency is not a fundamental property but is comprised of viscosity, plasticity, and other phenomena. (*See also* Viscosity Coefficient.)

Copolymer—*See* Polymer.

Copolymerization—*See* Polymerization.

Crazing, *n.*—Fine cracks which may extend in a

network on or under the surface of or through a layer of adhesive.

Creep, *n.*—The dimensional change with time of a material under load, following the initial instantaneous elastic or rapid deformation. Creep at room temperature is sometimes called Cold Flow.

Cross Laminated—*See* Laminated, Cross.

Cure, *v.*—To change the physical properties of an adhesive by chemical reaction, which may be condensation, polymerization, or vulcanization; usually accomplished by the action of heat and catalyst, alone or in combination, with or without pressure.

Curing Temperature—*See* Temperature, Curing.

Curing Time—*See* Time, Curing.

Delamination, *n.*—The separation of layers in a laminate because of failure of the adhesive, either in the adhesive itself or at the interface between the adhesive and the adherend, or because of cohesive failure of the adherend.

Diluent, *n.*—An ingredient, usually added to an adhesive to reduce the concentration of bonding materials. (*See also* Extender and Thinner.)

Doctor-Bar or Blade—A scraper mechanism which regulates the amount of adhesive on the spreader rolls or on the surface being coated.

Doctor-Roll—A roller mechanism which is revolving at a different surface speed, or in an opposite direction, resulting in a wiping action for regulating the adhesive supplied to the spreader roll.

Double Spread—See Spread.

Dry, *v.*—To change the physical state of an adhesive on an adherend by the loss of solvent constituents by evaporation or absorption, or both. (*See also* Cure and Set.)

Dry Strength—*See* Strength, Dry.

Dry Tack—*See* Tack, Dry.

Drying Temperature—*See* Temperature, Drying.

Drying Time—*See* Time, Drying.

Elastomer, *n.*—A material which at room temperature can be stretched repeatedly to at least twice its original length and, upon immediate release of the stress, will return with force to its approximate original length.

Extender, *n.*—A substance, generally having some adhesive action, added to an adhesive to reduce the amount of the primary binder required per unit area. (*See also* Binder, Diluent, Filler, and Thinner.)

Filler, *n.*—A relatively nonadhesive substance added to an adhesive to improve its working properties, permanence, strength, or other qualities. (See also Binder and Extender.)

Flow, *n.*—Movement of an adhesive during the bonding process, before the adhesive is set.

Gel, *n.*—A semisolid system consisting of a network of solid aggregates in which liquid is held.

Gelation, *n.*—Formation of a gel.

Glue, *n.*—Originally, a hard gelatin obtained from hides, tendons, cartilage, bones, etc. of animals. Also, an adhesive prepared from this substance by heating with water. Through general use the term is now synonymous with the term "adhesive." (*See also* Adhesive, Mucilage, Paste, and Sizing.)

Glue, *v.*—*See* Bond, v.

Gum, *n.*—Any of a class of colloidal substances, exuded by or prepared from plants, sticky when moist, composed of complex carbohydrates and organic acids, which are soluble or swell in water. (*See also* Adhesive, Glue, Resin.)

Note—The term gum is sometimes used loosely to denote various materials that exhibit gummy characteristics under certain conditions, for example, gum balata, gum benzoin, and gum asphaltum. Gums are included by some in the category of natural resins.

Hardener, *n.*—A substance or mixture of substances added to an adhesive to promote or control the curing reaction by taking part in it. The term is also used to designate a substance added to control the degree of hardness of the cured film. (*See also* Catalyst.)

Hot-Setting Adhesive—*See* Adhesive, Hot-Setting.

Inhibitor, *n.*—A substance which slows down chemical reaction. Inhibitors are sometimes used in certain types of adhesives to prolong storage or working life.

Intermediate Temperature Setting Adhesive—*See* Adhesive, Intermediate Temperature Setting.

Joint, *n.*—The location at which two adherends are held together with a layer of adhesive. (*See also* Bond, n.)

Joint Aging Time—*See* Time, Joint Conditioning.

Joint Conditioning Time—*See* Time, Joint Conditioning.

Joint, Lap—A joint made by placing one adherend partly over another and bonding together the overlapped portions. (*See also* Joint, Scarf.)

Joint, Scarf—A joint made by cutting away similar angular segments of two adherends and bonding the adherends with the cut areas fitted together. (*See also* Joint, Lap.)

Joint, Starved—A joint which has an insufficient amount of adhesive to produce a satisfactory bond.

Note—This condition may result from too thin a spread to fill the gap between the adherends, excessive penetration of the adhesive into the adherend, too short an assembly time, or the use of excessive pressure.

Laminate, *n.*—A product made by bonding together two or more layers of material or materials. (*See also* Laminated, Cross and Laminated, Parallel.)

Laminate, *v.*—To unite layers of material with adhesive.

Laminated, Cross—A laminate in which some of the layers of material are oriented at right angles to the remaining layers with respect to the grain or strongest direction in tension. (*See also* Laminated, Parallel.)

  Note—Balanced construction of the laminations about the center line of the thickness of the laminate is normally assumed.

Laminated, Parallel—A laminate in which all the layers of material are oriented approximately parallel with respect to the grain or strongest direction in tension. (*See also* Laminated, Cross.)

Lamination, *n.*—The process of preparing a laminate. Also, any layer in a laminate.

Lap Joint—*See* Joint, Lap.

Mechanical Adhesion—*See* Adhesion, Mechanical, and Adhesion, Specific.

Modifier, *n.*—Any chemically inert ingredient added to an adhesive formulation that changes its properties. (*See* also Filler, Plasticizer, and Extender.)

Monomer, *n.*—A relatively simple compound which can react to form a polymer. (*See also* Polymer.)

Mucilage, *n.*—An adhesive prepared from a gum and water. Also in a more general sense, a liquid adhesive which has a low order of bonding strength. (*See also* Adhesive, Glue, Paste, and Sizing.)

Novolak, *n.*—A phenolic-aldehydic resin which, unless a source of methylene groups is added, remains permanently thermoplastic. (*See also* Resinoid and Thermoplastic.)

Open Assembly Time—*See* Time, Assembly.

Parallel Laminated—*See* Laminated, Parallel.

Paste, *n.*—An adhesive composition having a characteristic plastic-type consistency, that is, a high order of yield value, such as that of a paste prepared by heating a mixture of starch and water and subsequently cooling the hydrolyzed product. (*See also* Adhesive, Glue, Mucilage, and Sizing.)

Penetration, *n.*—The entering of an adhesive into an adherend.

  Note—This property of a system is measured by the depth of penetration of the adhesive into the adherend.

Permanence—The resistance of an adhesive bond to deteriorating influences.

Pick-Up Roll—A spreading device where the roll for picking up the adhesive runs in a reservoir of adhesive.

Plasticity—A property of adhesives which allows the material to be deformed continuously and permanently without rupture upon the application of a force that exceeds the yield value of the material.

Plasticizer, *n.*—A material incorporated in an adhesive to increase its flexibility, workability, or distensibility. The addition of the plasticizer may cause a reduction in melt viscosity, lower the temperature of the second-order transition, or lower the elastic modulus of the solidified adhesive.

Plywood—A cross-bonded assembly made of layers of veneer or veneer in combination with a lumber core or plies joined with an adhesive. Two types of plywood are recognized, namely (1) veneer plywood and (2) lumber core plywood.

  Note—Generally the grain of one or more plies is approximately at right angles to the other plies, and almost always an odd number of plies are used.

Polycondensation—*See* Condensation.

Polymer *n.*—A compound formed by the reaction of simple molecules having functional groups which permit their combination to proceed to high molecular weights under suitable conditions. Polymers may be formed by polymerization (addition polymer) or polycondensation (condensation polymer). When two or more monomers are involved, the product is called a copolymer.

Polymerization, *n.*—A chemical reaction in which the molecules of a monomer are linked together to form large molecules whose molecular weight is a multiple of that of the original substance. When two or more monomers are involved, the process is called copolymerization or heteropolymerization. (*See also* Condensation.)

Pot Life—*See* Working Life.

Pressure-Sensitive Adhesive—*See* Adhesive, Pressure-Sensitive.

Primer—A coating applied to a surface, prior to the application of an adhesive, to improve the performance of the bond.

Resin, *n.*—A solid, semisolid, or pseudosolid organic material which has an indefinite and often high molecular weight, exhibits a tendency to flow when subjected to stress, usually has a softening or melting range, and usually fractures conchoidally.

Note—Liquid Resin.—An organic polymeric liquid which when converted to its final state for use becomes a resin.

Resinoid, *n.*—Any of the class of thermosetting synthetic resins, either in their initial temporarily fusible state or in their final infusible state. (*See also* "Novolak" and Thermosetting.)

Resite, *n.*—An alternate term for C-Stage. (*See also* C-Stage.)

Resitol, *n.*—An alternate term for B-Stage. (*See also* B-Stage.)

Resol, *n.*—An alternate term for A-Stage. (*See also* A-Stage.)

Retarder—See Inhibitor.

Retrogradation, *n.*—A change of starch pastes from low to high consistency on aging.

Room Temperature Setting Adhesive—*See* Adhesive, Room-Temperature Setting.

Rosin, *n.*—A resin obtained as a residue in the distillation of crude turpentine from the sap of the pine tree (gum rosin) or from an extract of the stumps and other parts of the tree (wood rosin).

Scarf Joint—*See* Joint, Scarf.

Self-Curing, *adj.*—*See* Self-Vulcanizing.

Self-Vulcanizing, *adj.*—Pertaining to an adhesive which undergoes vulcanization without the application of heat.

Separate Application Adhesive—*See* Adhesive, Separate Application.

Set, *v.*—To convert an adhesive into a fixed or hardened state by chemical or physical action, such as condensation, polymerization, oxidation, vulcanization, gelation, hydration, or evaporation of volatile constituents. (*See also* Cure and Dry.)

Setting Temperature—*See* Temperature, Setting.

Setting Time—*See* Time, Setting.

Shelf Life—*See* Storage Life.

Shortness, *n.*—A qualitative term that describes an adhesive that does not string, cotton, or otherwise form filaments or threads during application.

Single Spread—*See* Spread.

Size, *n.*—*See* Sizing.

Sizing, *n.*—The process of applying a material on a surface in order to fill pores and thus reduce the absorption of the subsequently applied adhesive or coating or to otherwise modify the surface properties of the substrate to improve the adhesion. Also, the material used for this purpose. The latter is sometimes called Size.

Slippage, *n.*—The movement of adherends with respect to each other during the bonding process.

Solids Content, *n.*—The percentage by weight of the non-volatile matter in an adhesive.

Note—The actual percentage of the non-volatile matter in an adhesive will vary considerably according to the analytical procedure that is used. A standard test method must be used to obtain consistent results.

Specific Adhesion—*See* Adhesion, Specific and Adhesion, Mechanical.

Spread, *n.*—The quantity of adhesive per unit joint area applied to an adherend. It is preferably expressed in pounds of liquid or solid adhesive per thousand square feet of joint area.

(1) **Single Spread** refers to application of adhesive to only one adherend of a joint.

(2) **Double Spread** refers to application of adhesive to both adherends of a joint.

Storage Life—The period of time during which a packaged adhesive can be stored under specified temperature conditions and remain suitable for use. Sometimes called Shelf Life. (*See also* Working Life.)

Starved Joint—*See* Joint, Starved.

Strength, Dry—The strength of an adhesive joint determined immediately after drying under specified conditions or after a period of conditioning in the standard laboratory atmosphere. (*See also* Strength, Wet.)

Strength, Wet—The strength of an adhesive joint determined immediately after removal from a liquid in which it has been immersed under specified conditions of time, temperature, and pressure.

Note—The term is commonly used alone to designate strength after immersion in water. In the latex adhesives the term is also used to describe the joint strength when the adherends are brought together with the adhesive still in the wet state.

Stringiness, *n.*—The property of an adhesive that results in the formation of filaments or threads when adhesive transfer surfaces are separated. (*See also* Webbing.)

Note—Transfer surfaces may be rolls, picker plates, stencils, etc.

Substrate, *n.*—A material upon the surface of which an adhesive-containing substance is spread for any purpose, such as bonding or coating. A broader term than adherend. (*See also* Adherend.)

Syneresis—The exudation of small amounts of liquid by gels on standing.

Tack, *n.*—The property of an adhesive that enables it to form a bond of measurable strength immediately after adhesive and adherend are brought into contact under low pressure.

Tack, Dry—The property of certain adhesives, particularly nonvulcanizing rubber adhesives, to adhere on contact to themselves at a stage in the evaporation of volatile constituents, even though they seem dry to the touch. Sometimes called Aggressive Tack.

Tack Range—The period of time in which an adhesive will remain in the tacky-dry condition after application to an adherend, under specified conditions of temperature and humidity.

Tacky-Dry, *adj.*—Pertaining to the condition of an adhesive when the volatile constituents have evaporated or been absorbed sufficiently to leave it in a desired tacky state.

Temperature, Curing—The temperature to which an adhesive or an assembly is subjected to cure the adhesive. (*See also* Temperature, Drying and Temperature, Setting.)

Note—The temperature attained by the adhesive in the process of curing it (adhesive curing temperature) may differ from the temperature of the atmosphere surrounding the assembly (assembly curing temperature).

Temperature, Drying—The temperature to which an adhesive on an adherend or in an assembly or the assembly itself is subjected to dry the adhesive. (*See also* Temperature, Curing and Temperature, Setting.)

Note—The temperature attained by the adhesive in the process of drying it (adhesive drying temperature) may differ from the temperature of the atmosphere surrounding the assembly (assembly drying temperature).

Temperature, Setting—The temperature to which an adhesive or an assembly is subjected to set the adhesive. (*See also* Temperature, Curing and Temperature, Drying.)

Note—The temperature attained by the adhesive in the process of setting it (adhesive setting temperature) may differ from the temperature of the atmosphere surrounding the assembly (assembly setting temperature).

Thermoplastic, *adj.*—Capable of being repeatedly softened by heat and hardened by cooling.

Thermoplastic, *n.*—A material which will repeatedly soften when heated and harden when cooled.

Thermoset, *adj.*—Pertaining to the state of a resin in which it is relatively infusible.

Thermoset, *n.*—A material which will undergo or has undergone a chemical reaction by the action of heat, catalysts, ultraviolet light, etc., leading to a relatively infusible state.

Thermosetting, *adj.*—Having the property of undergoing a chemical reaction by the action of heat, catalysts, ultraviolet light, etc., leading to a relatively infusible state.

Thinner, *n.*—A volatile liquid added to an adhesive

to modify the consistency or other properties. (*See also* Diluent and Extender.)

Thixotropy—A property of adhesive systems to thin upon isothermal agitation and to thicken upon subsequent rest.

Time, Assembly—The time interval between the spreading of the adhesive on the adherend and the application of pressure or heat, or both, to the assembly.

Note—For assemblies involving multiple layers or parts, the assembly time begins with the spreading of the adhesive on the first adherend.

(1) **Open Assembly Time** is the time interval between the spreading of the adhesive on the adherend and the completion of assembly of the parts for bonding.

(2) **Closed Assembly Time** is the time interval between completion of assembly of the parts for bonding and the application of pressure or heat, or both, to the assembly.

Time, Curing—The period of time during which an assembly is subjected to heat or pressure, or both, to cure the adhesive. (*See also* Time, Joint Conditioning; and Time, Setting.)

Note—Further cure may take place after removal of the assembly from the conditions of heat or pressure, or both; *see* Time, Joint Conditioning.

Time, Drying—The period of time during which an adhesive on an adherend or an assembly is allowed to dry with or without the application of heat or pressure, or both. (*See also* Time, Curing; Time, Joint Conditioning; and Time, Setting.)

Time, Joint Conditioning—The time interval between the removal of the joint from the conditions of heat or pressure, or both, used to accomplish bonding and the attainment of approximately maximum bond strength. Sometimes called Joint Aging Time.

Time, Setting—The period of time during which an assembly is subjected to heat or pressure, or both, to set the adhesive. (*See also* Time, Curing; Time, Joint Conditioning; and Time, Drying.)

Viscosity, *n.*—The internal frictional resistance of an adhesive to flow when that resistance is directly proportional to the applied force.

Note—Viscosity and consistency are erroneously used interchangeably. (*See also* Viscosity Coefficient and Consistency.)

Viscosity Coefficient—The shearing stress tangentially applied that will induce a velocity gradient. A material has a viscosity of one poise when a shearing stress of one dyne per square centimeter produces a velocity gradient of 1 cm per sec/sec. (*See also* Viscosity.)

Vulcanization, *n.*—A chemical reaction in which the physical properties of a rubber are changed in the direction of decreased plastic flow, less surface tackiness, and increased tensile strength by reacting it with sulfur or other suitable agents. (*See also* Self-Vulcanizing.)

Vulcanize, *v.*—To subject to vulcanization.

Warm-Setting Adhesive—*See* Adhesive, Warm-Setting.

Warp, *n.*—A significant variation from the original, true, or plane surface.

Webbing, *n.*—Filaments or threads that may form when adhesive transfer surfaces are separated. (*See also* Stringiness.)

    Note—Transfer surfaces may be rolls, picker plates, stencils, etc.

Wet Strength—*See* Strength, Wet.

Wood, Built-Up Laminated—An assembly made by joining layers of lumber with mechanical fastenings so that the grain of all laminations is essentially parallel.

Wood, Glued Laminated—An assembly made by bonding layers of veneer or lumber with an adhesive so that the grain of all laminations is essentially parallel.

Wood Failure—The rupturing of wood fibers in strength tests on bonded specimens, usually expressed as the percentage of the total area involved which shows such failure.

Wood Veneer—A thin sheet of wood, generally within the thickness range of 0.01 to 0.25 in., to be used in a laminate.

Working Life—The period of time during which an adhesive, after mixing with catalyst, solvent, or other compounding ingredients, remains suitable for use. (*See also* Storage Life.)

Yield Value—The stress (either normal or shear) at which a marked increase in deformation occurs without an increase in load.

Section A

FUNDAMENTALS

— 1 —

Introduction to Adhesives

Irving Skeist
Skeist Laboratories, Inc.
Newark, New Jersey

HISTORY

Adhesives were utilized in a sophisticated manner even in ancient times. Carvings in Thebes dating back 3300 years depict the gluing of a thin piece of veneer to what appears to be a plank of sycamore. The glue pot and brush are shown.[1] Still earlier, in the palace of Knossos in Crete, wet lime was the binder for chalk, iron ocher, and copper blue frit pigments with which the walls were painted.[2] The Egyptians utilized gum Arabic from the acacia tree, egg, glue, semiliquid balsams and resins from trees. Wooden coffins were decorated with pigments bonded with "gesso," a mixture of chalk and glue.

Papyrus was an early nonwoven fabric. Reeds 12 to 20 ft high and 3 in. in diameter were cut in thin slices, laid side by side, and beaten with a mallet. After these were brushed over with flour paste, fresh slices of reed were laid at right angles, and the beating was repeated. The finished papyrus was a luminous brown.[2]

We read in Genesis that slime (bitumen) was the preferred mortar of the builders of the Tower of Babel—the first adhesives technologists to have problems of semantics. Bitumen and tree pitches were the sealants for the vessels that plied the Mediterranean. In the days of the prophets, as now, the adhesive had to be specific for the adherend. "He that teacheth a fool is like one that glueth potsherds together," we are advised in the Apocrypha (Jesus ben Sirach, Ecclesiasticus, Chapter 22). Educators are still struggling with the first problem, but the latter has been solved with epoxy adhesives.

According to Pliny, the Romans caulked their ships with pine wood tar and beeswax. Anticipat-ing the laminate and the printed circuit, Pliny described the application of gold leaf to paper with egg white. We learn also that the Romans, like the ancient Chinese, made bird lime, an adhesive from the juice of the mistletoe, with which they smeared twigs to catch small birds.

Glues from fish, stag horns and cheese were known in the days of Theophilus for fixing together wooden objects. Here is his ninth century recipe for *glutine casei:*

> "Soft cheese is cut very small, and is washed with warm water in a small mortar with a pestle, until, being frequently poured in, the water comes away pure. Then this cheese, compressed by the hand, is put into cold water until it hardens. After this it is very finely ground, with another piece of wood, upon a smooth wooden table, and in this state it is again placed in the mortar, and is carefully ground with the pestle, water mixed with quick lime being added, until it is made as thick as lees. The tablets of altars fastened together with this glue, after they are dry, so adhere together, that neither heat nor humidity are able to disjoin them."

Except for the introduction of rubber and pyroxylin cements a hundred years ago, there was little advance in adhesives technology until the twentieth century. In these last few decades, the natural adhesives have been improved, and a spate of synthetics has poured from the laboratories. Adhesives are now essential components of plywood, envelopes and stamps, automobiles, shoes, masking and sealing tapes, furniture, cartons, nonwoven fabrics, and a thousand other products. One aircraft[3] requires more than 800 pounds of adhesives for bonded sandwich panels, interior doors, storage cabinets, baggage racks, floor panels,

3

partitions and cabin ceiling. The automated packaging line depends on adhesives for speed and smooth operation. Adhesives and sealants, which are essential to curtain wall construction, are finding increased usage elsewhere in building.

Wood Adhesives

The rapid development of wood-gluing technology has been traced by Brouse.[4] Until 1903, the woodworker had to rely on animal glue. It was applied in the form of a warm solution which set by cooling. The wooden parts had to be assembled at just the right time; consequently mass production was not feasible.

Then F. G. Perkins[5] found that tapioca starch could be converted by mild caustic soda solution into a liquid glue that was stable at room temperature. This made possible the economical production of plywood.

During and shortly after World War I, the proteins regained their leadership as wood adhesives. Casein glues were developed which were usable at room temperature, like starch, but had somewhat better water resistance. Casein is still the preferred adhesive for structural timber that will not receive undue exposure. The U. S. Forest Products Laboratory found that blood albumin produced bonds having superior water resistance, but that the plywoods had to be hotpressed. Inexpensive woodworking glues having moderate water resistance were developed by I. F. Laucks from soybean meal. These became the basis for the growth of the Douglas fir plywood industry.

The first completely synthetic resin, phenol formaldehyde, was invented by Baekeland more than 50 years ago. However, its large-scale application to the plywood industry was a development of the 1930's. Phenolic film was introduced in Germany by T. Goldschmidt and in the United States by Resinous Products, now Rohm & Haas Co. It is an aid in the bonding of thin or highly figured veneers, and in the manufacture of large wooden structures by the gluing together of smaller pieces. Liquid and powdered phenolic resins also came into wide use. When cured under heat and pressure, the phenolics produced the first bonds that could withstand outdoor weathering.

Also in the 1930's, I. G. Farbenindustrie presented urea-formaldehyde wood glues. While lacking the water resistance of the phenolics, they could be cured at lower temperatures, were somewhat cheaper, and provided a colorless glue line. Their chief outlet is in furniture and hardwood plywood for interior use. The more expensive melamine resins, introduced shortly thereafter by

Ciba, have served to upgrade the urea resins in durability.

Resorcinol-formaldehyde glues were first offered during World War II by the Pennsylvania Coal Products Company, now part of Koppers Company. Although expensive, these resins cure at room temperature or slight elevated temperatures to provide waterproof bonds. Mixtures of phenol and resorcinol resins have become standard for the production of outdoor grades of plywood and structural timber.

Following World War II, polyvinyl acetate emulsions began to supplant scarce animal glues in many woodworking applications. The vinyl acetate resins are applied cold, and they set by loss of water to produce a colorless glue line.

Paper Adhesives

Adhesives for paper are also undergoing rapid technological change.[6] Each year more than a billion pounds of adhesives go into cartons, boxes, bags, labels, packs, laminates, tapes and other packaging applications. Inexpensive sodium silicate, formerly preferred in the manufacture of corrugated board, is being superseded by starch. The vinyl resins, new to the packaging industry a generation ago, are now second in value and gaining rapidly despite their higher cost because they are easier to use with automatic packaging machinery. Animal glue is used in setup boxes and gummed tapes. Most labels utilize starch products or animal glues, but beverage and beer bottle labels require the cold-water resistance of casein. Hot-melts based on polyethylene, ethylene copolymers, vinyl acetate resins, or polyamides permit even faster operation of automated packaging lines. They are challenging the older synthetics as well as the vegetable, mineral and animal adhesives. Pressure-sensitive tapes and labels, patented in 1930 by Drew,[7] have developed into a $200 million industry. A variety of rubbers and resins, both natural and synthetic, vie for this market (see Chapters 2, 14, 51).

Metal Bonding

Metal bonding (Chapter 44) is another area in which the functional contribution of the adhesive to the finished product is vastly out of proportion to its own cost. Adhesives and bonding processes for metals were developed under the pressure of military requirements during World War II by Aero Ltd. in England, and by Cycleweld (Div. of Chrysler Corp.) and Goodrich in the United States. The first successful metal glues combined the high tensile strength and specific adhesion of phenolic resins with the extensibility and good adhesion of the polyvinyl formal, neoprene rubber, or nitrile rubber. These hybrids are tough materials having high peel strength. They are applied to both adherends from solution, then air dried and occasionally baked before the two surfaces are brought together.

In the 1950's, the epoxy resins (Chapter 25) were found to offer equal strength, toughness and adhesion. In addition, they are 100 per cent reactive, containing no solvent, so that the adherend surfaces can be mated immediately after coating with epoxy.

LITERATURE

The adhesives art of the 1940's and 1950's has been reported by Delmonte;[8] Morris, Weidner and Landau;[9] DeLollis;[10] DeBruyne and Houwink;[11] DeBruyne;[12] Luettgen;[13] Clark Rutzler, and Savage;[14] Koehn;[15] Thielsch;[16] Blomquist;[17] Koehler;[18] Reinhart and Callomon;[19] and Merriam.[3]

The economics of the adhesives industry was discussed by Donnelly and Skeen.[20]

Major reviews of the bonding of specific adherends were prepared by Knight,[21] Brouse[4] and Blomquist[22] on wood; Epstein[23] on metals; Perry[24] on reinforced plastics; and Buchan,[25] Weidner and Crocker[26] on elastomers.

Noteworthy among recent expositions of adhesion theory are the papers of DeBruyne,[27] the late Professor Rutzler,[28] and a book by Bikerman.[28a]

Testing methods are compiled by the American Society for Testing Materials.[29] *Adhesives Age*[30] is the monthly trade and technical journal of the United States adhesives industry. A guide to adhesives which are commercially available in Great Britain has been compiled by Hurd.[31]

ADVANTAGES OF ADHESIVE BONDING

The rapid growth of the adhesives industry (Chapter 2) has resulted from the following advantages over other methods of joining materials:

(1) Thin films and small particles, that would be impossible to combine by other techniques, are readily bonded with adhesives. Typical of such uses are:
Paper-labeled bottles and cans.
Abrasive wheels, sandpaper, and emery cloth.
Laminates of two or more films of cellophane, polyethylene, cellulose acetate, vinyl, aluminum foil, cotton scrim, paper, etc., for packaging.
Nonwoven fabrics.
Clay-coated paper for printing.
Particle board.
Veneer furniture.

(2) Stresses are distributed over wider areas, making possible lighter assemblies than could be achieved with mechanical fastening. For example, airplane wings, tails and fuselages may be constructed of sandwich panels comprising a honeycomb core bonded to thin faces of aluminum or magnesium; consequently the possibility of fatigue failure is decreased.

(3) The strength-to-weight ratios and dimensional stability of anisotropic materials can be improved by cross-bonding. Thus wood, inherently nonuniform and water-sensitive, is converted into warp-resistant, water-resistant plywoods. Nonwoven fabrics having the same properties in all directions are made by bonding a random web of fiber (Chapter 58).

(4) The glue line provides electrical insulation in capacitors, printed circuits, motors, potted resistors, etc.

(5) The glue line can be a moisture barrier, sealing window panels in curtain wall construction. In laminates for packaging, the glue line adds greatly to the moisture vapor resistance.

(6) Dissimilar materials can be joined, e.g., aluminum-to-paper, iron-to-copper. When two metals are bonded, the adhesive separates them and prevents corrosion. When the two adherends are markedly different in coefficient of thermal expansion, a flexible adhesive lessens the stress due to temperature change. Laminates of dissimilar materials give combinations superior to either adherend alone; for example, a polyethylene-cellophane composite has the heat sealability and water resistance of the former plus the grease resistance and printability of the latter.

(7) Finally, what is often the key consideration: adhesive bonding may be faster and cheaper than the weaving of cloth, soldering, brazing or welding of metals, or mechanical fastening with rivets, bolts, or nails.

TYPES OF ADHESIVES

Adhesives may be classified in many ways, e.g., by mode of application and setting, chemical composition, cost, and suitability for various adherends and end-products.

Application and Setting

The adhesive must be applied to the substrate in a fluid form to wet the surface completely and leave no voids, even if the surface is rough. Consequently, the adhesive must be low in viscosity at the time of application.

To develop high cohesive strength, however, the adhesive must set. In a completed joint with an organic adhesive, the latter layer is either a *thermoplastic, fusible* material of extremely high viscosity, or a *crosslinked, infusible* thermoset resin or rubber.

The transition from fluid to solid may be accomplished in several ways:

Cooling of a Hot-Melt. Thermoplastics soften and melt when heated, becoming hard again when cooled. The heating must result in a sufficiently high fluidity to achieve successful wetting. Wax paper is thus heated and sealed under moderate pressure to make bread wraps. Cellophane with a thin coating of plasticized nitrocellulose is also utilized in food applications but sealed at somewhat higher temperatures, yielding a product of higher bond strength. Labels for bottles and cans, coated with vinyl acetate polymers, facilitate high-speed packaging. Special formulations provide such labels with "delayed tack" so that they remain sticky for as long as a minute after exposure to heat.

Asphalt is used as either a hot-melt or "cutback" with solvents to bind aggregate in the building of roads.

Ethyl cellulose, cellulose acetate butyrate, and blends of paraffinic and microcrystalline waxes have been employed as hot-melt baths into which packages may be dipped to achieve both adhesive bonding and protection against moisture.

Ethylene polymers and copolymers, vinyl acetate polymers, and polyamides can be utilized as adhesives by extruding them as films, or in rope form. See Chapter 36.

Polyethylene-coated kraft paper and indeed polyethylene itself have rapidly achieved importance in heat-sealing applications.

Tears in clothing, sheets, sails, etc., can be mended with a hot iron instead of a needle, using cloth patches coated with vinyl plastisol.

Polyvinyl butyral, highly plasticized, is softened by heat and bonded under pressure to plate glass to make safety glass.

Release of Solvent. Solutions and latexes (Chapter 35) contain the adhesive composition in admixture with water or organic solvents. These liquids lower the viscosity sufficiently to permit wetting of the substrate. Once this has been accomplished, however, they must be removed. Porous substrates such as paper permit the liquid to be drawn away from the glue layer. If both adherends are impermeable, however, it is necessary to evaporate the water or solvent before mating the two surfaces, thus slowing down production. This is the great disadvantage of solutions and latexes in adhesive applications. In addition, organic solvents are undesirable because of cost and possible toxicity or flammability.

In a solution, the concentration of "solids"— i.e., material which will remain in the final adhesive layer—is usually well under 50 per cent for organic solvents but may be somewhat higher with water as the solvent. Too great a solids content results in such high viscosities that the dope has poor wetting characteristics. The higher the molecular weight of the dissolved polymer, the lower is the maximum permissible concentration. Therefore, in the manufacture of solvent cements, one employs resins having far lower molecular weights than those preferred for plastics and elastomers. The "half-second" cellulose esters and nitrocellulose are examples of short-chain polymers which are adequate as adhesives, but might be too weak as plastics.

Water is not only the medium for latexes but is also the most important of the solvents. Starches and dextrins, protein glues, and polyvinyl alcohol are the more significant water-soluble organic adhesives. Sodium silicates, comprising the most important family of inorganic adhesives, are water soluble.

To achieve concentrations above 50 per cent, it is necessary that at least a portion of the polymer be present in agglomerates of greater than colloidal size.

In a latex, the polymer is present in the form of globules existing as a discrete phase in an aqueous matrix. Natural and synthetic rubbers, vinyl resins, and acrylics are the most important of the adhesive latexes. The polymer is not limited in molecular weight since the viscosity does not depend on what is contained within the discrete particles. The viscosity of the latex depends primarily on solids content and the composition of the aqueous phase. Latexes are commonly available in concentrations of 35 to 55 per cent; nevertheless it is possible, in some cases, to go considerably higher before reaching an excessive consistency.

Many battles between adhesive materials are being lost or won on the basis of differences in solids content of a few per cent. For example, in the making of paper, machine speeds may be as high as 2000 ft/min. At these speeds, the elimination of water becomes a bottleneck. In choosing a binder for clay and pigment, there is an increasing tendency to abandon starch solutions in favor of combinations of casein with styrene-butadiene or acrylic latexes, even though these latter are more expensive.

Organosols are akin to latexes in being two-phase compositions, but with a continuous organic phase instead of water. Organosols are dispersions of vinyl chloride resin in plasticizers and volatile organic solvents. Once again, they are sufficiently fluid to promote good wetting of the substrate which may be paper, cloth, or metal. After application to the substrate, the coating is heated to flash off the solvent and fuse the resin.

Polymerization in situ. This is the group of bonding agents making the most rapid technological progress. All the thermosetting resins come under this heading, including those which are first applied to the substrate in solution form. This category also includes elastomers that are vulcanized to develop higher cohesive strength. In addition, some vinyl-type thermoplastics, e.g., polymethyl methacrylate and cyanoacrylate esters, can be polymerized *in situ.*

The main advantage of these materials over solvent-based adhesives is that strength can be developed in the glue line after the two adherends have been brought together. Faster production, lower cost, and stronger bonds may result from the elimination of solvents.

The reaction-sensitive adhesives fall into two groups:

(1) Those formed by condensation, usually with water as a by-product. This group includes the phenolic and amino resins, which are the oldest of the all-synthetic adhesives.
(2) Those formed by polymerization without by-product formation. Among this group are several of the most interesting of the new adhesives, including polyesters, epoxies, urethanes, cyanoacrylates. Conventional acrylics and vulcanizing rubbers are also in this category.

When a composite is made with an adhesive from group (1), it is necessary to apply pressure to overcome the deleterious influence of the water or other volatile by-product. On the other hand, adhesives of group (2) may be cured with only contact pressure. This is especially advantageous in the preparation of large objects which cannot be conveniently placed in a press.

Some of the curing adhesives require heat, whereas others react at room temperature with the help of catalysts, and in some instances with activation by light. Again, it is an advantage to make a bond without the aid of an oven. Among the adhesives which can be processed in this manner, with proper formulation, are resorcinol formaldehyde, unsaturated polyesters, methyl methacrylate, cyanoacrylate esters, epoxies, and urethanes. The polymerization reaction is usually exothermic so that the glue line may become somewhat warmer than the ambient temperature, especially if the adherends are poor conductors of heat.

CHEMICAL COMPOSITION

Adhesives may be either organic, inorganic, or hybrids. The organic materials may be classified according to origin as:

(1) Natural: starch, dextrins, asphalt, animal and vegetable proteins, natural rubber, shellac.
(2) Semi-synthetic: cellulose nitrate and the other cellulosics, polyamides derived from dimer acids, castor-oil based polyurethanes. We may look to this group for many new products in the future.
(3) Synthetics:
    (*a*) Vinyl-type addition polymers, both resins and elastomers: polyvinyl acetate, polyvinyl alcohol, acrylics, unsaturated polyesters, butadiene/acrylonitrile, butadiene/styrene, neoprene, butyl rubber, polyisobutylene.
    (*b*) Polymers formed by condensation and other step wise mechanisms: epoxies, polyurethanes, polysulfide rubbers, and the reaction products of formaldehyde with phenol, resorcinol, urea, and melamine.

Alternatively, adhesives may be categorized according to the solubility and fusibility of the final glue line:

(1) Soluble, including thermoplastic (soluble and fusible): starch and derivatives, asphalts, some proteins, cellulosics, vinyls, acrylics.
(2) Thermosetting (insoluble and infusible): phenol- and resorcinol-formaldehyde, urea- and melamineformaldehyde, epoxies, polyurethanes, natural and synthetic rubbers if vulcanized.

The range of formulation possible for curing at room temperature is limited. In the epoxies, for example, it is necessary to use curing agents which do not result in products of the highest heat resistance. However, for many applications, such objections are outweighed by the advantages of production without ovens or presses.

Pressure-Sensitive Adhesives. These adhesives, unlike the other classes, do not undergo a progressive increase in viscosity. Instead, they are permanently in the intermediate *tacky* stage. One of their chief merits, in fact, is that they wet so inadequately that they can be removed from the adherend surface without "mark off," i.e., without leaving a residue of adhesive on that surface. One of the important early advances in pressure-sensitive tape technology was the discovery that a slightly gelled adhesive layer would fulfill this requirement. See Chapters 14 and 51.

While this deficiency in *ad*hesive strength is deliberate, the low *co*hesive strength of pressure-sensitive materials is undesirable. Low bond strength precludes the pressure-sensitive tapes from heavy-duty applications. It is inevitable that a permanently tacky material will be easily deformed and ruptured.

COST

The cost of adhesives varies from 1 to 3¢ per pound for asphalt and sodium silicate to several dollars per ounce for the cyanoacrylates. The former two materials are utilized in mass production outlets such as multiwall bags and cartons; the precious cyanoacrylates are dispensed by eye dropper for the bonding of tiny metal and ceramic components. The prices (cents per pound, dry basis, unless stated otherwise) of some adhesive components, Table 1, were compiled from the *Chemical & Engineering News* quarterly price index of December 26, 1960, *American Paint Journal*, and other sources. The price ranges quoted reflect both the quantity differential as well as the variety of grades available for each commodity. The prices of some other ingredients are also included.

The cost per pound does not reveal the entire story. Adhesives differ in their yield, in the area that can be glued successfully per pound of adhesive. On this basis, the cost of bonding 1000 sq ft might be lower with a high priced synthetic rubber than with another adhesive at half the price. Furthermore, an adhesive containing water or solvent may require such a long drying time that it becomes far more expensive than a hot-melt adhesive having a higher pound cost.

MATCHING ADHESIVE TO ADHEREND

Finally, the adhesive and adherend must be compatible, if their union is to last.

When two materials are bonded, the resultant composite has at least five elements: adherend No. 1, interface, adhesive, interface, and adherend No. 2.

The strength of the adhesive joint will be the strength of its weakest member. If one of the adherends is paper, excessive stress will usually result in a "paper tear." With stronger substrates, however, the failure will be either *adhesive* at an interface or *cohesive* within the glue. Failure will not be at an interface if the adherend surface has been properly prepared and the adhesive is appropriate.[32, 27] In other words, the adhesion between glue and substrate should be greater than the cohesion within the glue line. This will occur provided the combining of adhesive and adherend has caused a decrease in free energy, and provided also that excessive strains are not built up when the adhesive sets.

Let us consider the latter requirement first. Adhesives usually shrink as they harden. (Inorganic cements are exceptions.) Polymerization, the loss of solvent, even the cooling of a hot-melt may cause the glue line to contract. Strains are set up which induce the adhesive to pull away from the substrate. In addition, strains are produced when the adhesive joint is flexed. Various remedies may lessen the danger of failure from these causes:

(1) Choose low-shrinking resins, e.g., epoxies rather than polyesters.

(2) Choose adhesives that are no more rigid than the adherends; otherwise flexing will cause a concentration of stress in the glue line. (However, excessive flexibility in the adhesive may be accompanied by low cohesive strength.)

(3) Keep the glue line as thin as possible, consistent with the smoothness of the adherends, if the stresses are chiefly tensile. Porous adherends require the application of sufficient adhesive to avoid a "starved glue line." If the joint is to be exposed to considerable shear stress, the glue line should be somewhat thicker, and the adhesive should be only one tenth to one half as rigid as the adherends.

(4) Incorporate inert and preferably inorganic fillers.

(5) After applying the adhesive to an impervious substrate, evaporate water or solvents thoroughly before mating with a second impervious adherend.

Turning now to the free energy requirements, let us examine the types of bonds that may exist between adhesive and adherend. These chemical bonds may be either primary or secondary.

Primary bonds include electrovalent, covalent, and metallic bonds. *Electrovalent* or *heteropolar* bonds may be a factor in protein adhesives. *Covalent* or

TABLE 1. PRICES OF ADHESIVE COMPONENTS.

Natural Products and Derivatives:	¢/lb	Natural Products and Derivatives:	¢/lb
Starch	6–7.5	Inorganic:	
Dextrin	9–10	Sodium silicate	3.3
Methyl cellulose	69		
Ethyl cellulose	69	Solvents:	
Nitrocellulose	33	Acetone	8.5
Carboxymethyl cellulose	40	Cyclohexanol	28.5
Animal glues	15–25	Cyclohexanone	33.5
Casein	18	Ethyl acetate	13
Blood albumin	13–14	Heptane	16/gal
Whole beef blood, dried	11.5–12	Methylethyl ketone (MEK)	12.5–16.5
Isolated soya protein	20–23	Toluene	25/gal
Soybean flour, adhesive grade	5.5–6.25	Xylene	28.5/gal
Rubber (smoked sheet)	24–30	Mineral spirits	25/gal
Rosin	15–17		
Ester gum	18.5	Waxes, Humectants, and Plasticizers:	
Rosin ester	23–25	Montan wax	22
Hydrogenated methyl ester of rosin	27.5	Paraffin	15
Gum Arabic	21	Low-molecular-weight polyethylene	27.5
Shellac	31–57	"Carbowax"	22
		Glycerol	29
Synthetics:		Ethylene glycol	16
Acrylic (emulsion, dry basis)	42.4	Diethylene glycol	15.25
Butadiene-acrylonitrile (latex, dry basis)	45–53	Tricresyl phosphate	35
Butadiene-styrene resin (latex, dry basis)	28.5	Dibutyl phthalate	26
Coumarone-indene	15.5–20	Dioctyl phthalate	28.5
Epoxy	62	Dioctyl adipate	40
Melamine-formaldehyde	32.75–40	Diethanolamine	24.5
Neoprene	37–42		
Petroleum resins	12–13		
Phenolics	25	Fillers:	
Polyamides	66–80	Whiting	0.9–1.0
Polyesters (unsaturated)	31–47	Bentonite	0.7
Polysulfide rubber	96	Kaolin	0.5–1.75
Polyurethane raw materials approx.	50	Magnesia (rubber grade)	28
Polyvinyl acetate emulsion, dry basis	29.1	Zinc oxide	14.5
Polyvinyl alcohol	57–58	Silica	1.1–1.7
Polyvinyl butyral	105.		
Polyvinyl chloride	18.5	Catalysts and Curing Agents:	
Resorcinol-formaldehyde	94	Phenylenediamine	110.
Styrene-butadiene rubber (SBR)	24–30	Tetraethylenepentamine	56
Urea-formaldehyde	13–20	Triethylenetetramine	49
Urea	5	Hexamethylenetetramine	23.3
Formaldehyde (aqueous, dry basis)	10	Borax	2.5

homopolar bonds may play a part in some finishing treatments for fiber glass (Chapter 33). The *metallic* bond is formed by welding, soldering and brazing. The inorganic materials for these purposes are essentially high temperature thermoplastic adhesives, but are outside the scope of this volume.

By far the most important of the adhesive bonds are the *secondary* or *Van der Waals'* bonds that give rise to attraction between molecules. Most significant of these are the *London* or *dispersion forces*. They are responsible for virtually all the molar cohesion of nonpolar polymers such as polyethylene, natural rubber, SBR, and butyl rubber. These forces act at a distance of approximately 4Å, and fall off rapidly, as the sixth power of the distance between atoms. Consequently, molecules must be in close proximity for London forces to be effective. This helps to explain why a very flexible molecule such as natural rubber is a better adhesive than a moderately flexible molecule such as SBR, and far better than a stiff molecule such as polystyrene. Low modulus, indicating freedom of rotation on a molecular scale that permits the adhesive to conform to the adherend, is advantageous to adhesion.

Crystalline polymers, e.g., linear polyethylene, tetrafluoroethylene, saran and nylon 66 are generally deficient in adhesive bond strength for the same reason that they are high in cohesive strength: the crystalline spherulites clasp the molecules of polymer together, hindering their contact with other materials.

Interaction of permanent dipoles (Keesom forces) results in strong bonds, especially if the positive dipole is an H-atom. The *hydrogen bond,* typified by

$$> \bar{N}-\overset{+}{H} \ldots \ldots \bar{O}=\overset{+}{C} < \, ,$$

accounts for the excellent success with polar substrates of such diverse adhesives as starch and dextrin, polyvinyl alcohol, polyvinyl acetals, cellulose nitrate, phenolics and epoxies. All of these adhesives contain phenolic or aliphatic hydroxyl. Among the adherends bonded with polar adhesives are wood, paper, leather, glass, and metals.

Induced dipoles (Debye forces) play a minor role in adhesion. They are of some significance with aromatic compounds.

Solubility Parameter

When the substrate is organic and not too polar, the solubility parameter is useful in helping to select an adhesive.

If the bond between adhesive and substrate is to be strong, there must be a decrease in free energy as a result of combining the two. The free energy change on mixing two materials is:

$$\Delta F = \Delta H - T \Delta S,$$

where ΔH is the heat of mixing and ΔS is the entropy change. In general, when two materials are mixed, there is an increase in entropy; consequently the second term on the right of the equation is negative. If we can ignore the heat of mixing term, the free energy will also be negative. This tells us that materials will tend to combine provided the heat of mixing is not too high on the positive side. We see, also, that raising the temperature makes the entropy term more negative, thus aiding the process of combination. This is particularly true when at least one of the materials being mixed or combined is a high polymer.

The heat of mixing depends on the attractive forces between adhesive and adherend. These forces may be either primary or secondary bonds. If the heat of mixing is zero or if it is negative as the result of hydrogen bonding or other chemical combination of adherend and adhesive, then wetting will surely be accomplished. For most nonpolar or moderately polar pairs of materials, however, the heat of mixing is positive; consequently the free energy will decrease only if this positive term is not too high.

Hildebrand[33] and others[34, 35, 36] utilized the concept of *solubility parameter,* δ, to show why some pairs of materials mix more readily than others. The solubility parameter is related to the *internal pressure* or *cohesive-energy density:*

$$\delta = (\Delta E/V)^{1/2}$$

where ΔE = the energy of vaporization, and
$\qquad V$ = the molar volume.

The term, $\Delta E/V$, the energy of vaporization per cc, is called the internal pressure or cohesive-energy density.

For liquids such as the fluorocarbons and hydrocarbons, this energy is very low; therefore low-molecular-weight materials of these compositions vaporize readily. The low molecular-weight fluorocarbons are thus used in aerosol dispensers, and low molecular-weight hydrocarbons are the main constituents of natural gas.

As soon as we incorporate polar groups, we find that it requires more energy to vaporize a molecule, i.e., to separate it from its companions. Thus, acetone has a higher boiling point than butane, and isopropyl alcohol is still higher, although all three molecules are approximately the same size and weight.

Hildebrand indicated that the greater the difference between the solubility parameters of the two materials, the greater the heat of mixing.

$$\Delta H = V (\delta_1 - \delta_2)^2 \, \phi_1 \, \phi_2$$

where V = the total volume, and
ϕ_1 and ϕ_2 = the volume fractions of the respective components.

Consequently, wetting is most likely to take place when adhesive and adherend are most alike in solubility parameter.

Table 2, compiled from the work of Hildebrand and Scott,[33] Small,[34] Burrell,[35] and others lists the solubility parameters of a number of *ad*hesive and *ab*hesive materials, along with a qualitative characterization of their crystallinity and modulus.

The technologist is more likely to succeed if he follows rules such as these in selecting an adhesive:

(1) Try to match the adherend as closely as possible in solubility parameter.
(2) Avoid the crystallizing polymers.
(3) Pick an adhesive that is no stiffer than the adherends.

But how does one go about bonding two materials of quite different solubility parameters, e.g., tire cord and rubber? The answer, as revealed in Chapter 42, is to blend a high-solubility parameter material, resorcinol-formaldehyde, for the

TABLE 2

	Solubility Parameter, δ	Crystallinity	Modulus at Room Temperature (after cure, for thermosets)
Polytetrafluoroethylene	6.2	High	Medium
Silicone, polydimethyl	7.3	Low-medium	Medium
Butyl rubber	7.7	Low	Low
Polyethylene	7.9	High	Medium
Natural rubber	7.9–8.3	Low	Low
Butadiene-styrene	8.1–8.5	Low	Low
Polyisobutylene	8.0	Low	Low
Polystyrene	8.6–9.7	Low	High
Polysulfide rubber ("Thiokol")	9.0–9.4	Low	Low
Neoprene	9.2	Varies	Low
Butadiene-nitrile	9.4–9.5	Low	Low
Polyvinyl acetate	9.4	Low	Low-medium
Polymethyl methacrylate	9.0–9.5	Low	High
Polyvinyl chloride	9.5–9.7	Medium	Medium-high
Amino resins	9.6–10.1	Low	High
Epoxy	9.7–10.9	Low	Medium-high
Ethyl cellulose	10.3	Low	Medium-high
Polyvinyl chloride acetate	10.4	Low-medium	Medium
Polyglycol terephthalate	10.7	High	High
Cellulose acetate	10.9	Medium	Medium-high
Cellulose nitrate	10.6–11.5	Low-medium	Medium
Phenolic	11.5	Low	High
Polyvinylidene chloride (saran)	12.2	High	Medium-high
Nylons	12.7–13.6	High	Medium-high
Polyacrylonitrile	15.4	High	Medium-high

rayon or nylon cord, with a moderate-solubility parameter material, butadiene-styrene-vinyl pyridine, for the rubber.

Table 3, from the excellent survey by Reinhart and Callomon,[19] summarizes the general commercial practice followed in matching adhesive to adherend. A more detailed guide to adhesives selection is presented in Chapter 59.

References

1. Gettens, R. J., and Stout, G. L., "Painting Materials," New York, D. Van Nostrand Company, Inc., 1942.
2. Laurie, A. P., "Materials of the Painters Craft," London, Poulis, 1910.
3. Merriam, J. C., "Adhesive Bonding," *Materials in Design Engineering Manual No. 162,* **50,** 111–130, (Sept. 1959).
4. Brouse, D., "The Ideal Glue—How Close Are We?," *Forest Products J.,* **7,** 163 (1957).
5. Perkins, F. G. (to Perkins Glue Co.), U. S. Patent 1,020,657 (Mar. 19, 1912); Reissue Patent 13,443 (July 16, 1912).
6. Anon, "Adhesives," *Modern Packaging,* **98** (L, 1958); *see also* Ch. 2.
7. Drew, R. G. (to Minnesota Mining & Manufacturing Co.), U. S. Patent 1,760,820 (May 27, 1930).
8. Delmonte, J., "The Technology of Adhesives," New York, Reinhold Publishing Corp., 1947.
9. Morris, V. N., Weidner, C. L., and Landau, N. St., Encyclopedia of Chemical Technology," New York, Vol. 1, p. 191, Interscience Publishers, Inc., 1947.
10. DeLollis, N. J., "Industrial Adhesives," *Product Eng.,* **18,** 117 (Nov. 1947), 137 (Dec. 1947).
11. DeBruyne, N. A., and Houwink, R., Editors, "Adhesion and Adhesives," New York, Elsevier Publishing Co., 1951.
12. DeBruyne, N. A., "Structural Adhesives," London, Lange, Maxwell, Springer, 1952.
13. Luettgen, C., "Die Technologie der Klebestoffe," Berlin-Wilmersdorf, Wilhelm Pansegrau Verlag, 1953.
14. Clark, J., Rutzler, J., E., Jr., and Savage, R. L., "Adhesion and Adhesives, Fundamentals and Practice," New York, John Wiley & Sons, Inc., 1954.
15. Koehn, G. W., "Design Manual on Adhesives," *Machine Design,* **26,** 143 (Apr. 1954).
16. Thielsch, H., "Adhesive Bonding," *Materials & Methods,* **40,** 113 (Nov. 1954).
17. Blomquist, R. F., "Encyclopedia of Chemical Technology," Supp. Vol 1, p. 18, New York, Interscience Publishers, Inc., 1957.
18. Koehler, R., "Systematic Survey of Synthetic Adhesives," *Kunststoffe,* **48,** (10), 441 (Oct. 1958).

TABLE 3. SELECTING ADHESIVES.[19]

	Leather	Paper	Wood	Felt	Fabrics	Vinyl Plastics	Phenolic Plastics	Rubber	Tile, etc.	Masonite	Glass	Metals
Metals	1, 4, 21, 24, 25	1, 21, 22	1, 4, 11, 13, 21, 31, 32, 33, 35, 36	1, 5, 22	1, 21, 22, 24	25, 36	3, 13, 21, 31, 32, 33, 35, 36	13, 21, 22, 31, 32, 33, 35, 36	5, 6, 13, 22, 35, 36	5, 6, 13, 22	13, 32, 33, 34, 35	11, 13, 31, 32, 33, 36
Glass, ceramics	1, 4, 13, 24	1, 21, 22	1, 13, 21, 31, 32, 33, 35, 36	1, 5, 6, 21, 22	1, 21, 22, 24	25, 36	3, 13, 21, 31, 35, 36	21, 22, 31, 35, 36	4, 22		4, 13, 32, 35, 36	
Tile, etc.	1, 4, 21, 24	1, 21, 22	1, 5, 6, 21, 22	5, 6, 21, 22	5, 6, 21, 22, 24	25, 36	3, 13, 36	21, 22, 31, 35, 36	4, 5, 6, 22	5, 8, 13		
Masonite	1, 21, 24	1, 21, 22	1, 5, 6, 21, 22	5, 6, 21, 22	5, 6, 21, 22, 24	25, 36	3, 13, 36	21, 22, 31, 35, 36	5, 6, 22			
Rubber	21, 24	21, 22	21, 22, 33, 35, 36	21, 22	21, 22, 23	25, 36	21, 22, 36	21, 22, 31, 35, 36				
Phenolic plastics	21, 24, 25	21, 22	11, 13, 21, 24, 32, 33, 36	21, 22, 25, 36	21, 22, 24, 25	36	13, 32, 33, 36					
Vinyl plastics	21	21	21	21	21	25, 36						
Fabrics	21, 22, 23, 24	21, 22, 23	21, 22, 23	5, 21, 22, 23	1, 21, 22, 23							
Felt	21, 22, 23, 24	21, 22, 23	21, 22, 23	5, 22								
Wood	21, 22, 23, 24	2, 21, 22	1, 11, 12, 14, 15, 36									
Paper	21, 22, 23, 24	2, 4, 21										
Leather	1, 4, 21, 22, 23, 24											

Adhesive number code for Table 3:

Thermoplastic
(1) Polyvinyl acetate
(2) Polyvinyl alcohol
(3) Acrylic
(4) Cellulose nitrate
(5) Asphalt
(6) Oleoresin

Thermosetting
(11) Phenol formaldehyde (phenolic)
(12) Resorcinol, phenol-resorcinol
(13) Epoxy
(14) Urea formaldehyde
(15) Melamine, melamine-urea formaldehyde
(16) Alkyd

Elastomeric
(21) Natural rubber
(22) Reclaim rubber
(23) Butadiene-styrene rubber
(24) Neoprene
(25) Buna-N
(26) Silicone

Resin Blends
(31) Phenolic-vinyl
(32) Phenolic-polyvinyl butyral
(33) Phenolic-polyvinyl formal
(34) Phenolic-nylon
(35) Phenolic-neoprene
(36) Phenolic-butadiene-acrylonitrile rubber

19. Reinhart, F. W., and Callomon, I. G., "Survey of Adhesion and Adhesives," WADC Technical Report, 58–450 (1959).

20. Donnelly, M. V., and Skeen, J. R., "A Market Survey of the Adhesive Industry," American Chemical Society Meeting (Sept. 1952).

21. Knight, R. A. G., "Adhesives for Wood," New York, Chemical Publishing Co., 1952.

22. Blomquist, R., F., "Annual Reviews," Feb. issues of *Forest Products J.*

23. Epstein, G., "Adhesive Bonding of Metals," New York, Reinhold Publishing Corp., 1954.

24. Perry, H. A. G., "Adhesives for Reinforced Plastics," New York, McGraw-Hill Book Co., Inc., 1959.

25. Buchan, S., "Rubber to Metal Bonding," London, Crosby, Lockwood & Son, 1960.

26. Weidner, C. L., and Crocker, G. J., "Elastomeric Adhesion and Adhesives," *Rubber Chem. and Technol.,* **33,** 1323 (1960).

27. DeBruyne, N. A., "The Physics of Adhesion," *Trans. of the Plastics Institute,* **27,** 141 (Oct. 1959).

28. Rutzler, J. E., "Types of Bonds Involved in Adhesion," *Adhesives Age,* **2,** (6), 34; (7), 28 (June and July 1959).

28a. Bikerman, J. J., "The Science of Adhesive Joints," New York, Academic Press, 1960.

29. "ASTM Standards on Adhesives," sponsored by Committee D-14, American Society for Testing Materials, 1916 Race St., Philadelphia, Pa., 1960.

30. *Adhesives Age,* 101 West 31st Street, New York 1, New York, monthly since Oct. 1958.

31. Hurd, J., "Adhesives Guide," London, Cable Printing & Publishing Company, Ltd., 1959.

32. Bikerman, J. J., *J. Colloid Sci,* **2,** 163 (1947).

33. Hildebrand, J., and Scott, R. L., "The Solubility of Nonelectrolytes," 3rd Ed., New York, Reinhold Publishing Corp., 1950.

34. Small, P. A., *J. Appl. Chem.,* **3,** 71–80 (1953).

35. Burrell, H., "Solubility Parameters for Film Formers," Federation of Paint & Varnish Production *Official Digest,* **27,** 726 (Oct. 1955); "A Solvent Formulating Chart," Federation of Paint and Varnish Production *Official Digest,* **29,** 1073–4 (Nov. 1957).

36. Skeist, I., "Choosing Adhesives for Plastics," *Modern Plastics,* **33,** 121–3, 126–7, 130 (May 1956).

Economics of
The Adhesives Industry

Margaret V. Donnelly and George E. Osburn
Hercules Powder Company
Wilmington, Delaware

Many factors have contributed to the growth of the adhesives industry. There is no end in sight to the new materials, new formulations, and new uses to which adhesives will be put in the future. There is no master adhesive that will solve all bonding problems; such a product will probably never be devised. Adhesives is a complex, fast-growing field offering challenge and rewards to those engaged in advancing adhesives technology.

Today's total adhesives market is estimated conservatively at from $300 to $350 million. More optimistic estimates put the figure closer to $500 million.

COMPARISON OF
STATISTICAL SOURCE DATA

Statistically, the industry is difficult to analyze; economic data are not precise. Adhesives and their raw materials are produced by several different kinds of businesses—starch, meat packers, vegetable processors, rubber, and by the chemical industry. Formulations generally are compounded to satisfy a special need or needs. Therefore, uniformity of neither product nor end use exists. Figures to describe the adhesives industry can do little more than indicate relative volumes of its various segments. There are two principal sources of production statistics: The U. S. Bureau of the Census[1] which compiles data on protein-type glues, vegetable-base, lacquer, rubber cement, various gums, mucilage, furnace cements, and the U. S. Tariff Commission[2] which reports on synthetic resins produced for adhesives. The Adhesives Manufac-

turers Association is a source also of statistics, particularly for data not collected by governmental agencies.

The Census Bureau's statistics cover finished products—glues and adhesives presumably ready for application—while the various synthetic resins for adhesives usage as reported by the Tariff Commission may be further compounded and, therefore, values are not strictly comparable with Census Bureau statistics. There is no single source of production or sales data for the many types of adhesives, glues, cements and pastes used industrially or by the public. By piecing together bits of available information, it is hoped that a picture will emerge.

While use of all adhesives has increased, the greatest gain has occurred in the synthetic resin category. Prior to World War II, adhesives consisted mainly of animal and other protein glues, starches, and dextrines. The early 1940's brought the first commercial production of synthetic resin adhesives, less than 9 million pounds of this type being produced in 1942. Growth has been constant since, with 1959 sales in the range of 400 million pounds.

A general idea of the industry's growth is depicted in Fig. 1 which is a rough approximation of sales of each major category. Sales figures for synthetic resin adhesives are subject to the widest margin of error due principally to the reporting methods in effect for this segment of the industry. Taken into consideration in arriving at 1958 sales of all adhesives is the gradual inflation in prices affecting adhesives along with practically every

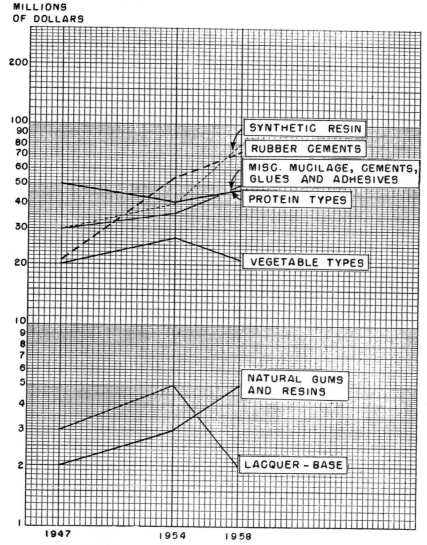

Fig. 1. Estimated adhesives sales, 1947–1958 (excluding laminating).

product of our economy. The estimated sales differ from the "value of shipments" figures reported by the U.S. Census Bureau mainly because of the addition of rubber cements, and the inclusion of estimates of adhesives made captively by synthetic resin producers. Census Bureau total values of shipments for the glue and adhesives industry are shown in Table 1.

By taking certain liberties with the Census of Manufactures reports covering glues and adhesives, it is possible to arrive at some idea of the relative importance of individual types of glues and adhesives making up the estimated totals. Recent Census reporting schedules were expanded considerably and, consequently, earlier years' figures are not sufficiently comparable to warrant inclusion in Table 2.

Table 3 gives data covering manufacturers' shipments of glues and adhesives for 1954 and 1958.

TABLE 1. VALUE OF SHIPMENTS OF ADHESIVES
IN THE U.S., 1927 . . . 1958.

Year	Value of Shipments*
	(Mil. $)
1958	$171
1957	148
1956	146
1955	140
1954	136
1947	116
1927	35

* Excludes value of rubber cements and captively produced synthetic resin adhesives.

TABLE 2. U. S. PRODUCTION OF GLUES AND ADHESIVES, 1954 AND 1958.

	1958		1954	
	Mil. Lb	% of Total	Mil. Lb	% of Total
Animal glues				
Hide, extracted and green bone	109	6.8%	109	8.3%
Flexible and nonwarp glue	38	2.4	28	2.1
Liquid glue	12	0.8	14	1.1
Total animal	159	10.0	151	11.5
Other protein (casein, soybean, blood, albumen, etc.)	129	8.0	57[1]	4.4
Vegetable adhesives (dextrines, starches)	200	12.5	245	18.8
Lacquer-base	8	0.5	13	1.0
Synthetic resins for adhesives[2]	400	25.0	225	17.3
Rubber and synthetic resin combinations	78	4.9	not reported separately	
Adhesives from natural gums and resins	23	1.4	26	2.0
Mucilage	3	0.2	12	0.9
Rubber Cements	390*	24.3	300*	23.0
Furnace and porcelain cements	37	2.3	127	9.7
Misc. and misc. formulated adhesives and glues	175(E)	10.9	150(E)	11.5
	1,600	100%	1,300	100%

* Authors' rough estimates. See "rubber cements."

(E) Authors' rough estimates arrived at by adding 25 million pounds of miscellaneous product for which dollars only were reported ($8.5 million) to 151 million lb reported covering "other formulated and prepared adhesives other than rubber cement" for 1958. The 1954 estimate of 150 million lb is made up of 76.6 million lb reported plus 75 million to cover "rubber and synthetic resin combinations" and miscellaneous adhesives. It should be noted that these are all rough estimates.

[1] 1954 not comparable with 1958. See "casein" adhesives.

[2] U. S. Tariff Commission statistics covering resins produced for adhesive formulations; not finished adhesives and, therefore, not strictly comparable with other statistics in Table 2. See footnotes to Table 3.

As in the case of Table 2, estimates have been included for the sake of completeness. Volume in 1958 shows a 23 per cent gain compared to a 35 per cent gain in value over the earlier year provided the various estimates are in a reasonable range of accuracy.

ANIMAL- AND VEGETABLE-BASE ADHESIVES

Protein Glues

Animal Glues. Animal glues, that is those produced from hides and bones of animals, are the oldest adhesive materials, having been produced in the United States since the early 1800's. Demand for these glues exceeded domestic supply during the 1920's and 1930's to such an extent that imports were necessary to supplement domestic production. In 1950, there were 36 plants in this country producing animal glues at an annual rate of 150 million pounds. Statistics on output, shipments, and stocks are made available on a regular basis by the Bureau of Census. In December, 1959, there were 22 animal glue plants in the United States distributed as follows:

4   in New York;
3   each in Nebraska and Pennsylvania;
2   each in Minnesota and Illinois;
1   each in California, Georgia, Indiana, Kansas, Massachusetts, Missouri, Ohio, and Wisconsin.

While the advent of newer type glues and adhesives has affected animal glues rather obviously, the tonnages being produced and consumed indicate that an impressive market still exists for these products. Hide glues, which today represent approximately 49 per cent of total animal glues even though they are more costly than extracted and green bone glue, actually show a slight percentage increase since 1947. In that year, hide glue production totaled 69 million pounds, or 45 per cent of the 153 million-pound total while, in 1959, hide glue output was 52.6 million pounds, or 49 per cent of the total 107 million pounds of animal glue produced.

Table 4 is a summary of production during the past three decades as reported by the U. S. Bureau of the Census.

Other Protein Glues and Adhesives. This group

TABLE 3. U. S. MANUFACTURERS' SHIPMENTS OF GLUES AND ADHESIVES, 1954 AND 1958.

	1958		1954	
	Mil. Lb Shipped	Value (Mil. $)	Mil. Lb Shipped	Value (Mil. $)
Animal glue	154.9	$ 32.0	147.1	$ 33.2
Other protein	126.7	14.7	56.5	7.3
Vegetable adhesives	197.4	20.7	241.3	26.8
Lacquer base	7.6	2.2	13.4	4.9
Synthetic resins (for adhesives)	400.0*	80.0	225.0*	40.0
Rubber and resin combinations	77.6	19.0	not reported separately	
Adhesives from natural gums and resins	22.9	4.9	25.4	3.3
Mucilage	3.2	0.9	12.2	1.9
Other formulated and prepared adhesives	145.7	16.1	77.8	13.9
Cements, furnace, etc.	37.1	5.6	121.0	11.8
Rubber cements	390.0(E)	73.4	300.0(E)	54.5
Misc. glues and adhesives	25.0(E)	8.5	70.0(E)	8.4
	1,588.1	$278.0	1,289.7	$206.0

(E) Authors' estimates.

*Authors' estimates based on volume of synthetic resins for adhesives as reported by Tariff Commission. The Census Bureau released the following statistics:

	1958	1954
Synthetic resin adhesives made from purchased resins (incl. all types of bonding and laminating adhesives)		
Production (Thous. lb)	239,983	147,552
Shipments (Thous. lb)	233,600	146,053
Value of shipment (Thous.)	$ 45,978	$ 24,496

comprises casein glues, soybean adhesives, flexible glues, blood, albumen, zein, fish, and possibly such products as glues based on cottonseeds, peanuts, wheat, even feathers.

Casein adhesives were used to an appreciable extent by the plywood industry several years ago but their use in this industry has declined steadily since 1950. Casein is still used in large quantities by the paper industry for its adhesive properties as a binder in paper coating. There has been little growth in casein adhesives other than the paper-coating use. The 4.7 million pounds of casein adhesives produced in 1954 as shown in Table 5 is thought to be greatly understated due to ambiguous reporting in that year. In Census Bureau statistics covering "plastic materials," figures are reported as follows:

Casein plastics (for ad- 1958—12,072,000 lb
hesives) production 1954—21,571,000 lb

When final 1958 statistics are released by the Census Bureau, it is possible that the casein adhesives statistics will be clarified somewhat. Casein adhesives find application in furniture, wallboard, carton and label glues particularly for labeling over ink and varnish.

TABLE 4. U. S. PRODUCTION OF ANIMAL GLUES,*
1927 . . . 1959.

Year	Mil. Lb
1959	107
1958	109
1957	116
1956	116
1955	115
1954	109
1947	153
1927	112

*Hide, extracted bone, and green bone.

TABLE 5. U. S. PRODUCTION OF PROTEIN GLUES,
1954 AND 1958.

(Thous. Lb)

	1958	1954
Animal glue		
Hide	52,363	52,384
Extracted bone	14,687	14,031
Green bone	41,873	42,825
Flexible and non-warp glue	37,745	27,855
Liquid glue (not glue stock)	11,846	13,577
Other protein adhesives		
Casein adhesives	35,126	4,726
Other (incl. blood, albumen, soybean, etc.)	94,057	52,368

There are so few producers of *soybean* glues and adhesives that data on output or sales are not available. The 94 million pounds of "other protein" adhesives reported for 1958 undoubtedly consists principally of soybean product. From statistics published through 1952 by the Census Bureau on consumption of various adhesives by the softwood plywood industry, it appears that well over 50 million pounds of soybean adhesives went into interior type plywood a few years ago. Various synthetic resin adhesives are competing with soybean and casein in that market now. Blood, zein, and albumen adhesives are reportedly small in comparison with the other protein types so that it is probably safe to assume about 80 per cent of the 94 million pounds represents finished soybean glues and adhesives. Additional quantities may be used also by companies formulating their own compounds for special industrial purposes.

Flexible and non-warp glues are usually compositions of animal glue, water and modifiers such as glycerin, sorbitol, cane sugar, invert sugars and syrups. Typical formulations are said to contain over 20 per cent animal glue. Production figures covering finished flexible glues have been reported by the Census Bureau. However, it is believed that the total may be somewhat understated since some users compound their own mixtures from purchased animal glue, various modifying agents, and water. The data serve to indicate growth in consumption during recent years, however:

TABLE 6. U. S. PRODUCTION OF FLEXIBLE GLUE, 1929 . . . 1958.

Year	Thous. Lb
1958	37,745
1954	27,855
1947	22,779
1939	11,178
1929	5,017

Flexible glues are used in bookbinding to impart permanently flexible backings to books, in luggage gluing, and in operations where a flexible adhesive film is required.

Liquid glues are usually derived from fish and animal glues which have been treated with acetic, nitric or hydrochloric acid. The 1954 Census of Manufactures contained a separate statistic indicating that 13.6 million pounds were produced in that year. Sales were 13.3 million pounds valued at $4.2 million, or a unit value of nearly 32¢. In 1958, shipments were 11.8 million pounds, valued at $2.5 million. These glues are made with varying properties depending on their ultimate use.

They are fluid at room temperature. Their main uses are for labeling bottles, and as a remoistening adhesive for specialty uses; other specialty uses include wood products and paperboard.

Vegetable-base Adhesives

Vegetable-type adhesives are based on starch, dextrin, and natural gums and resins; these last materials usually are imported. While any starch may be used as an adhesive base, the ones of importance are corn, potato, tapioca, wheat, sago and sweet potato. Vegetable gums such as imported arabic, tragacanth, and karaya are used usually in mucilage, pastes and glues. However, volume-wise, neither the vegetable gums nor water-soluble cellulose derivatives, such as the sodium salt of carboxymethyl cellulose, have reached the size of the starch and dextrin adhesives. The 1958 Census of Manufactures gave the information shown in Table 7.

As the figures indicate, production of starch and dextrin-based adhesives grew from 196.2 million pounds in 1947 to 244.8 million in 1954 but dropped to 200 million pounds in 1958. It is impossible to compare growth of adhesives from natural gums and resins since the earliest figures available are for 1954. Data on domestic water-soluble cellulose derivatives for adhesive usage have not been published separately.

Starch itself and dextrines made by roasting starch find their best market in packaging materials, mainly because of price and speed of adhesion. The three dextrines, "white," "canary" and "British gum," are used in sealing and winding paper and paperboard products, bag seams, labeling, envelopes, stamps, and in various paper and packaging applications. Recent advances in technology indicate a resurgence of importance in starch compositions. Improved quick tack and faster set are properties that allow wider usage on high speed, and continuous winding and packaging machines.

According to statistics compiled by the Adhesives Manufacturers Association of America, vegetable adhesives accounted for 60 per cent of the 425 million pounds of liquid adhesives used for packaging in 1958. The distribution by types of adhesives is shown in Table 8 with a comparison of the 1950 and 1958 usage.

SYNTHETIC RESIN ADHESIVES

Synthetic resin adhesives, second in importance for packaging uses, grew from 17 per cent of the total in 1950 to 36 per cent in 1958. Value-wise, the synthetics represented 52 per cent of the total

TABLE 7. U. S. PRODUCTION AND SHIPMENTS OF ADHESIVES FROM VEGETABLE AND NATURAL SOURCES, EXCEPT RUBBER, 1947 . . . 1958.

		Production	Shipments	
		(Thous. Lb)	(Thous. Lb)	(Thous. $)
Vegetable glues, adhesives, pastes:				
	1958	152,522	150,163	$15,597
Dextrins	1954	180,279	177,159	20,003
	1947	(figures combined with starches)		
	1958	47,809	47,291	5,194
Starches	1954	64,540	64,226	6,770
	1947	196,190	195,503	19,343
Adhesives made from natural gums and resins, except rubber				
	1958	23,376	22,944	4,900
	1954	25,779	25,415	3,332

$71 million consumption for 1958. While vegetable-type packaging adhesives chalked up an increase also between 1950 and 1958, this type actually lost ground percentage-wise. In 1950, vegetable-type adhesives accounted for 73 per cent of the total 307 million pounds while, in 1958, their share of the total dropped to 60 per cent. Obviously, synthetic resins grew at the expense of the two older types.

Synthetic resin adhesives are divided usually into two broad classes: thermosetting and thermoplastic. The thermosetting resins such as phenolic, urea and melamine, and resorcinol have achieved greater commercial importance than the thermoplastic type with the exception of vinyls.

Table 9 and Fig. 2 indicate the growth in production and consumption of selected synthetic resins in adhesives since 1942. The figures are those reported by the U. S. Tariff Commission in its annual survey. There have been some slight changes in reporting methods but the trend is obviously upward. The vinyls are reported on a net resin content basis. Prior to 1948, data covering urea and melamine resins as well as the phenolics were reported also on a net resin basis. Since 1948, the figures have been on a dry-weight basis. However, even with possible discrepancies in early years, one is still able to see the phenomenal growth that has

taken place in this segment of the adhesives industry. A detailed discussion of adhesive resins statistics is given by Margolis.[5]

Data for other adhesive resins, acrylics, epoxies, polyesters, isocyanates, and so on, are not reported separately.

RUBBER-BASE ADHESIVES

Rubber adhesives have evolved from formulations of raw natural rubber to a comparatively long

TABLE 8. U. S. SALES OF LIQUID ADHESIVES FOR PACKAGING, 1950 AND 1958.

	1958		1950	
	Mil. Lb	Mil. $	Mil. Lb	Mil. $
Vegetable type	250	$29	226	$20
Synthetic resin type	153	37	53	12
Animal	22	5	28	3
	425	$71	307	$35

TABLE 9. PRINCIPAL SYNTHETIC RESINS PRODUCED FOR ADHESIVES,* 1942–1959.

(Mil. Lb)

Year	Phenolics	Vinyls	Urea and Melamine Types	Total
1942	2.6	1.5	—	4.1
1943	12.7	10.0	—	22.7
1944	26.3	15.0	27.1	68.4
1945	22.0	13.0	30.4	65.4
1946	22.3	16.9	37.5	76.7
1947	31.9	10.0	45.6	87.5
1948	22.3	10.0	50.0	82.3
1949	28.6	11.9	40.8	81.3
1950	31.5	15.5	85.6	132.6
1951	41.9	22.8	78.7	143.4
1952	42.4	17.8	79.8	140.0
1953	106.6	26.9	63.5	197.0
1954	109.6	29.0	86.2	224.8
1955	166.7	37.7	106.7	311.1
1956	169.1	43.9	115.2	328.2
1957	183.4	46.7	107.8	337.9
1958	162.0	52.1	113.2	327.0
1959 (Prelim.)	209.6	59.5	134.1	403.2

* Excludes laminating.

Source: U. S. Tariff Commission statistics.

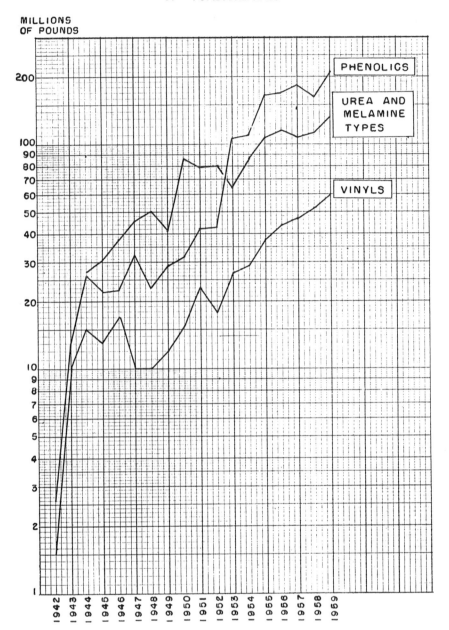

Fig. 2. Principal synthetic resins in adhesives, 1942–1959.

list of elastomeric materials ranging from butyl to reclaim rubber, including butadiene-styrene copolymer, neoprene, silicone rubber, isocyanate rubber, chlorinated rubber and blends of phenolic resins and elastomers. Applications are diverse and include items from pressure-sensitive tapes to metal-to-metal bonding used in aircraft assembly. Data on production and sales, however, are published only for rubber cement and reported by the Census Bureau in the rubber industry statistics. As stated earlier, the 1958 Census was expanded to include separate statistics on adhesives formulated from a combination of rubber and synthetic resins. These and undoubtedly other elastomeric-base adhesives were reported in miscellaneous categories in the 1954 Census.

Pressure-sensitive adhesives, a fast growing segment of the industry, should not be overlooked; they are important adhesive end products.

Statistics are reported as follows by the Bureau of Census for two specific products: adhesive plaster and rubber pressure-sensitive tapes.

TABLE 10. U. S. PRODUCTION OF RUBBER CEMENT (Sold as Such), 1939 . . . 1958.

Year	Production (Thous. Gal)	Shipments (Thous. Gal)	Shipments (Thous. $)
1958	not published	not published	$73,430
1954	39,990	39,984	54,542
1947	not published	17,650	20,982
1939	not published	17,218	9,165

An idea of production volume of adhesive coated paper, cloth, and plastic products can be had from the Bureau of Census data in Table 12. Unfortunately, growth trends are not available since detailed statistics of this kind were not collected for earlier years.

The "paper consumed" column may be useful to readers who are expert in this field by enabling them to calculate roughly the probable volumes accounted for by the dollar values shown.

LACQUER-BASE ADHESIVES

Lacquer-base adhesives refer usually to cellulosic materials such as nitrocellulose and cellulose acetate which are among the older adhesives. Principal users of this type have been the shoe industry for cementing soles to uppers, and the paper industry. Statistics separating nitrocellulose base from other "lacquer"-type adhesives appeared for the first time in the 1954 Census and were reported as follows in Table 13.

TABLE 11. ADHESIVE PLASTER AND RUBBER PRESSURE-SENSITIVE TAPE—VALUE OF U. S. SHIPMENTS BY MANUFACTURERS 1939 . . . 1958.

Year	Adhesive Plaster, Medicated and Nonmedicated (Thous. $)	Rubber Pressure-Sensitive Tape (incl. friction) (Thous. Lb)	Rubber Pressure-Sensitive Tape (incl. friction) (Thous. $)
1958	$47,835	n.p.	$20,285
1954	28,827	25,953	18,174
1947	20,300	35,711	16,506
1939	9,739	n.p.	4,339

n.p.—not published

GROWTH AND SIZE OF THE ADHESIVES INDUSTRY

Growth of the adhesives industry since 1947 has been about 4 per cent annually based on dollar values. Shifts in raw materials to combat increasing costs and to enable manufacturers to remain competitive have occurred to some extent, thus permitting logical use of dollar values in arriving at a growth rate for the industry. In Table 14 an estimated $350 million adhesives total has been broken down to indicate roughly the various types of adhesives sold in 1959.

The "industrial specialties" category covers the custom-made glues and adhesives formulated for specific customers' needs. There are actually no clear-cut lines of demarcation in adhesives; conse-

TABLE 12. GUMMED PAPER AND PRESSURE-SENSITIVE TAPES SHIPMENTS 1954 AND 1958.

	Value 1958 (Thous. $)	Paper Consumed (Short Tons)	Value 1954 (Thous. $)	Paper Consumed (Short Tons)
Gummed products				
Paper-base-gummed tape, all types	$ 46,642	103,374	$ 45,661	97,136
Cloth base-gummed tape	2,969	n.a.	5,841	n.a.
Gummed paper, incl. stock labels, unprinted*	26,180	34,844	14,889	14,625
Other gummed products	2,829	n.r.	n.r.	n.r.
	$ 78,620		$ 66,391	
Pressure-sensitive tapes				
Paper backing	$ 72,794	60,759	$ 50,861	n.r.
Cloth backing, excl. surgical	15,702	n.a.	10,289	n.a.
Plastic backing, incl. cellophane tape	88,859	n.a.	84,754	n.a.
Other, excl. rubber	6,072	n.a.	3,037	n.a.
Miscellaneous, not specified by kind	3,391	n.r.	n.r.	n.r.
	$186,818		$148,941	

n.a.—not applicable.
n.r.—not reported.
*1958 is not strictly comparable with 1954.

TABLE 13. LACQUER-BASE ADHESIVES PRODUCTION AND SHIPMENTS, 1947 . . . 1958.

Lacquer-Base Adhesives	Production	Shipments	
	(Thous. Lb)	(Thous. Lb)	(Thous. $)
Nitrocellulose types (collodion and pyroxylin)			
1958	4,257	4,257	$1,326
1954	9,534	9,582	4,075
1947	3,335	3,302	1,986
Other lacquer-base			
1958	3,370	3,387	921
1954	3,840	3,835	802
1947		figures not published	

quently, types and end uses cut across practically all lines.

During the past few years, several significant shifts in types of adhesives have occurred. To enumerate all of the changes that have taken place, particularly since the revolution brought about by the introduction of synthetic resins, would be an almost impossible task. The plywood industry and the aircraft industry, to mention only two important adhesive customers, have been responsible for many shifts in adhesive materials. Some idea of the rapid growth in adhesive formulations is evident from the number of United States patents issued on synthetic resin adhesive formulations during the 1937–1953 period. In the seventeen-year period, more than 500 patents were issued in this country, while over 2,000 patents were issued in the United States and abroad covering synthetic resin compositions in which adhesive applications were included in the claims.

The number of manufacturers of glues and adhesives is another indication of the size of the industry. *Modern Plastics Encyclopedia for 1959* listed the names of 146 manufacturers and/or suppliers of resins and adhesives. All types of glues and adhesives were included in the list and readers should consult the Encyclopedia for data on specific products, trade designations, as well as bonding classi-

TABLE 14. ESTIMATED SALES OF ADHESIVES
BY MAJOR USES IN 1959.

Type (or Use)	Mil. $
Paper and packaging	$100
Rigid	100
Wood	50
Over-the-counter	50
Industrial specialties	50
	$350

fications. The 1959 list, arranged by broad categories, is appended to this chapter.

The Bureau of the Census, in a special analysis of 1954 Census data, indicated that there were 189 companies reporting production of glues and adhesives for the year 1954. This total, of course, includes companies offering adhesives as products secondary to their principal lines. Total employment in the "glues (and gelatin)" category numbered 6,753 in 1954 with the four largest companies accounting for 27 per cent of total employment. The twenty largest companies employed 65 per cent of the 6,753 total. The four largest companies accounted for 22 per cent of the total value of glues and adhesives shipments ($136 million in 1954) while the 20 largest companies accounted for 56 per cent of the total. According to these figures, 20 companies had shipments of $76 million and 169 companies shipped $60 million, indicating a large number of medium and small producers in this industry. Another interesting point brought out in the 1954 Census concerns the proportion of total shipments accounted for by firms whose principal business is glues and adhesives. In 1954, such producers' shipments totaled $90 million, or two-thirds, of the $136 million total. Other manufacturers producing glues and adhesives as secondary products, and consequently classified in various other industries, shipped the remaining third, or $46 million. Neither rubber cements nor adhesive tapes are included in the statistics just described since the Census Bureau classifies such products in industries other than glues and adhesives.

The long-range economic outlook for adhesive resins, their plasticizers, and modifiers, and for modified starch adhesives is believed to be favorable. Several factors are responsible for this; the most important one is in the field of packaging. The over-all concept of packaging in units for both industrial and consumer markets should broaden in

TABLE 15. MAJOR USES OF VARIOUS ADHESIVES.

	Abrasives and Friction Materials	Book Binding	Construction and Industrial Fabricating	Fiber glass and Safety Glass	Furniture	Leather Products	Packaging	Plywood	Misc. Paper Products, Gummed Paper and Cloth (excl. Pkg.)	Textiles Incl. Tire Cord
Acrylates			x							
Alkyds (incl. oil free)		x		x		x	x			
Animal glues	x	x	x		x		x		x	
Asphalt			x	x			x		x	
Blood	x								x	
Casein					x		x	x	x	
Cellulosics		x	x	x		x	x			x
Epoxies			x	x						
Gums, natural							x		x	
Isocyanates			x	x					x	x
Phenolics	x			x	x	x		x		
Polyamides			x	x						x
Polyesters			x	x	x			x		x
Resorcinol	x					x	x	x	x	x
Rubbers	x	x	x	x		x	x		x	x
Silicone			x							
Soybean					x			x	x	x
Starch and dextrin	x	x			x		x		x	x
Styrene	x								x	
Urea			x	x	x			x		x
Vinyls		x	x	x	x	x	x		x	x
Waxes							x			

scope and open new avenues for growth. The ease of handling compact, standard-weight, containers through adhesive bonding instead of metal strapping materials is an example. Food packaging with requirements for adhesives to withstand mild acids and alkalies, alcohol beverages, oils and greases are all potential markets.

Industrial fabrication and assembly also offer attractive growth potential. Adhesives to replace rivets, bolts, for joining and ribbing are other outlets. Pressure-sensitive, or heat-curing, tapes for pipe insulation, and plastic film, such as polyethylene, as backing materials represent new markets.

Last, but not least, is the consumer "do-it-yourself" market. This field includes products designed for the industrial trade but which can, by minor modifications, be marketed through the hardware dealer and variety store. Adhesives for this growing market range from the simplest glues and mucilages for furniture-making and repair, to metal-to-metal bonding for frame construction.

In summary, the areas of greatest potential growth, in the foreseeable future as in the recent past, are synthetic resins and modified starches. Compounding technology will remain an integral part of the industry, and the technologist will be aided by the continuing emphasis of chemical companies in raw material product design in these broad areas. Animal and vegetable products will probably show growth in volume and unit value dependent to a large extent on the over-all economic picture; whereas, the growth in synthetics and starches will be based more on technology and competitive forces. A sales volume of $500 million for the adhesives industry by the early 1960's appears realistic on the basis of past performance and today's research.

Acknowledgments

Grateful acknowledgment is made by the authors to: Mr. Kenyon Loomis, Executive Secretary, Adhesives Manufacturers Association of America; Mr. A. Paul Peck, Managing Editor, *Modern Plastics Encyclopedia;* Dr. Frank H. Wetzel and Dr. W. G. Kinsinger, both of Hercules Powder Company.

References

1. *U. S. Census Bureau,* Washington 25, D. C.
   (*a*) Census of Manufactures.
   (*b*) Facts for Industry, Series M28W.2, "Animal Glues" (now called Current Industrial Reports).
   (*c*) "The Proportion of Shipments (or Employees) of Each Industry, or Shipments of Each Group of Products Accounted for by the Largest Companies as Reported in the 1954 Census of Manufactures (1957)."
2. *U. S. Tariff Commission,* Washington 25, D. C., Annual "Synthetic Organic Chemicals, United States Production and Sales."
3. *Modern Plastics Encyclopedia Issue for 1959,* New York, Breskin Publications, Inc., 1958.
4. Donnelly, M. V., and Skeen, J. R., "A Market Survey of the Adhesives Industry," paper presented at the Am. Chem. Soc. Meeting, Atlantic City, N. J., Sept. 1952.
5. Margolis, J. M., *Adhesives Age,* **2,** 22 (1959).

Adhesives Suppliers

(R)   indicates sources of bonding materials for compounding adhesives.

(A)   indicates sources of adhesive compositions prepared from the bonding materials.

Synthetic Resin—

(Acrylate, alkyd, coumarone-indene, epoxy, furan, petroleum polymer, isobutylene, isocyanate, melamine, oleo resin, phenolic, polyamide, polyester, resorcinol, silicone, polystyrene, urea, vinyl)

Acme Resin Corp., 1401 Circle Ave., Forest Park, Ill.   (A)

Acryvin Corp. of America, 470 E. 99th St., Brooklyn 36, N. Y.   (A)

Adhesive Engineering, San Carlos, Calif.   (A)

Adhesive Products Corp., New York 60, N. Y.   (RA)

Adhesive Products Inc., Albany 10, Calif.   (A)

Aero Research, Ltd., Cambridge-Duxford, England   (A)

Alkydol Laboratories, Inc., Cicero 50, Ill.   (RA)

American Cyanamid Co., Plastics and Resins Div., 30 Rockefeller Plaza, New York 20, N. Y.   (RA)

American Latex Products Corp., Hawthorne, Calif.   (A)

American Lucoflex Inc., 500 5th Ave., New York 36, N. Y.   (A)

American-Marietta Co., Adhesive, Resin and Chemical Div., 3400 13th Ave., S. W., Seattle 4, Wash.   (RA)

American Products Manufacturing Co., New Orleans 18, La.   (A)

Amoco Chemicals Corp., 910 S. Michigan Ave., Chicago 80, Ill.   (R)

Angier Adhesives, Div. of Interchemical Corp., 120 Potter St., Cambridge 42, Mass.   (A)

Arabol Mfg. Co., 110 E. 42nd St., New York 17, N. Y.   (A)

Archer-Daniels-Midland Co., Minneapolis 2, Minn.   (A)

Aries Laboratories, Inc., New York 17, N. Y.   (A)

Armour and Co., 1355 W. 31st St., Chicago 9, Ill.   (A)

Armstrong Cork Co., Lancaster, Pa.   (A)

Armstrong Products Co., P. O. Box 1, Warsaw, Ind.   (A)

Atlas Mineral Products Co., Mertztown, Pa.   (A)

Atlas Powder Co., Wilmington 99, Del.   (A)

Atlas Synthetic Corp., Long Island City 1, N. Y.   (R)

B. B. Chemical Co., 784 Memorial Drive, Cambridge 39, Mass.   (A)

Bakelite Co., Div. of Union Carbide Corp., 30 E. 42nd St., New York 17, N. Y.   (RA)

Allied Chemical Corp., Plastics and Coal Chemicals Div., 40 Rector St., New York 6, N. Y.   (RA)

Belding Corticelli Industries, Chemicals Div., 1407 Broadway, New York 18, N. Y.   (R)

Briggs Co., Inc., Carl H., Los Angeles 64, Calif.   (A)

Bloomingdale Rubber Co., Aberdeen, Md.   (A)

Bond Adhesives Co., Box 406, Main P.O., Jersey City 3, N. J.   (A)

Borden Chemical Co., Div. of The Borden Co., 350 Madison Ave., New York 17, N. Y.   (RA)

British Resin Products Ltd., London S. W. 1, England   (A)

Canadian Industries Ltd., Montreal, Canada   (R)

Carboline Co., 331 Thornton Ave., St. Louis 19, Mo.   (A)

Catalin Corp., 1 Park Ave., New York 16, N. Y.   (RA)

Celanese Corp. of America, Plastics Div., 744 Broad St., Newark 5, N. J.   (RA)

Chemical Coatings and Engineering Co., Inc., Edgemont, Pa.   (A)

Chemical Development Corp. (Devcon Corp.), Danvers, Mass.   (A)

Chemical Products Corp., King Philip Rd., E. Providence 14, R. I.   (A)

Ciba Co., Inc., Plastics Div., Kimberton, Pa.   (R)

Colton Chemical Co., A Div. of Air Reduction Co., Inc., 1747 Chester Ave., Cleveland 14, Ohio   (R)

Compo Chemical Co., Inc., Waltham 54, Mass.   (A)

Cordo Chemical Co., 34 Smith St., Norwalk, Conn.   (A)

Cycleweld Cement Products Div., Chrysler Corp., 5437 W. Jefferson, Trenton, Mich.   (A)

Dennis Chemical Co., 2701 Papin St., St. Louis 3, Mo.   (A)

Dewey and Almy Chemical Co., Div. of W. R. (A)
Grace and Co., Cambridge 40, Mass.

Dow Chemical Co., The, Midland, Mich. (RA)

Dow Corning Corp., Midland, Mich. (RA)

E. I. du Pont de Nemours and Co., Wilmington (RA)
98, Del.

Durez Plastics Div., Hooker Electrochemical Co., (RA)
888 Walck Road, North Tonawanda, N.Y.

Emerson and Cuming, Inc., Canton, Mass. (A)

Epoxylite Corp., El Monte, Calif. (A)

Farrington Texol Corp., Walpole, Mass. (A)

Flintkote Co., Atlas Adhesives Div., Philadelphia (A)
27, Pa.

Formica Corp., 4614 Spring Grove Ave., Cincin- (A)
nati 32, Ohio

H. B. Fuller Co., 255 Eagle St., St. Paul 2, Minn. (A)

Furane Plastics Inc., Los Angeles 39, Calif. (RA)

General Aniline and Film Corp, New York 14, (R)
N.Y.

General Electric Co., Pittsfield, Mass. (RA)

General Mills, Inc., Chemical Div., P.O. Box (RA)
191, Kankakee, Ill.

B. F. Goodrich Co., 500 S. Main St., Akron 18, (RA)
Ohio

Goodyear Tire and Rubber Co., Chemical Div., (A)
Akron 16, Ohio

Gordon-Lacey Chemical Products Co., Maspeth, (A)
Long Island, N.Y.

Griffin Chemical Co., Div. of Nopco Chemical (R)
Co., 1000 16th St., San Francisco 7, Calif.

Harwick Standard Chemical Co., Akron 5, Ohio (A)

Hercules Powder Co., Synthetics Dept., Wilming- (R)
ton 99, Del.

Heresite & Chemical Co., Manitowoc, Wis. (RA)

C. B. Hewitt and Bros., Inc., New York 13, N.Y. (A)

Houghton Laboratories, Inc., 322 Bush St., (A)
Olean, N.Y.

Hughes Glue Co., Detroit 7, Mich. (A)

Imperial Chemical Industries Ltd., London S.W. (R)
1, England

Interchemical Corp., Finishes Div., 67 W. 44th (A)
St., New York 36, N.Y.

Irvington Chemical Div., Minnesota Mining and (A)
Manufacturing Co., 500 Doremus Ave., Newark 5, N.J.

Koppers Co., Inc., Chemical Div., Pittsburgh 19, (RA)
Pa.

Lawrence Adhesive and Chemical Co., Lawrence, (A)
Mass.

Lebec Chemical Corp., Paramount, Calif. (A)

Lithgow Chemical Co., Div. of Reichhold Engineering and Plastics Co., 12827 E. Imperial
Highway, Norwalk, Calif.

Loven Chemical of California, Newhall, Calif. (RA)

Magic Chemical Co., Brockton 2, Mass. (A)

Marblette Corp., Long Island City 1, N.Y. (RA)

Marbon Chemical Div., Borg-Warner Corp., (A)
Gary, Ind.

Midland Adhesive and Chemical Corp., Detroit (A)
20, Mich.

Minneapolis-Honeywell Regulator Co., 2753 4th (A)
Ave. S., Minneapolis 8, Minn.

Minnesota Mining and Mfg. Co., Adhesives and (A)
Coatings Div., 411 Piquette Ave., Detroit 2,
Mich.

Miracle Adhesives Corp., 250 Pettit Ave., Bell- (A)
more, L.I., N.Y.

Mobay Chemical Co., St. Louis 4, Mo. (A)

Monsanto Chemical Co., Plastics Div., Springfield (RA)
2, Mass., and 911 Western Ave., Seattle 4,
Wash.

Multiplastics Div., Curd Enterprises, Inc., 3337 (R)
Lincoln St., Franklin Park, Ill.

Narmco Resins and Coatings Co., Costa Mesa, (A)
Calif.

National Adhesives Div., National Starch Prod- (RA)
ucts Co., 750 Third Ave., New York 16, N.Y.

National Casein Co., 601 W. 80th St., Chicago (RA)
20, Ill.

Naugatuck Chemical Div., U.S. Rubber Co., (RA)
Naugatuck, Conn.

Neville Chemical Co., Neville Island, Pittsburgh (R)
25, Pa.

Nova Chemical Corp., 147 Waverly Pl., New (R)
York 14, N.Y.

Nureco Inc., Cranston 10, R.I. (RA)

Ohio Adhesives Corp., New Philadelphia, Ohio (A)

Paisley Products Inc., Div. of Morningstar Nicol (A)
Inc., 630 W. 51st St., New York 19, N.Y.

Pennsylvania Industrial Chemical Corp., Clair- (R)
ton, Pa.

Perkins Glue Co., Lansdale, Pa. (RA)

Pierce and Stevens, Inc., 710 Ohio St., Buffalo 3, (A)
N.Y.

Pittsburgh Plate Glass Co., Paint Div., Pittsburgh, (R)
Pa.

Plastics Engineering Co., Sheboygan, Wis. (R)

Plastite Adhesives Corp., Chicago 10, Ill. (RA)

Poly Resins, Sun Valley, Calif. (R)

Polymer Corp. of Pa., 2140 Fairmont Ave., Read- (A)
ing, Pa.

Polymer Industries Inc., Springdale, Conn. (A)

Polypenco, Inc., Reading, Pa. (A)

Pyroxylin Products, Inc., Chicago 32, Ill.; Paoli, (A)
Pa.

Raffi and Swanson, Inc., Wilmington, Mass. (A)

Reichhold Chemicals, Inc., White Plains, N.Y. (RA)

Ren Plastics Inc., Lansing 4, Mich. (A)

Research Sales, Inc., 20 Fourth Ave., Hawthorne, (A)
N.J.

Reynolds Chemical Products Co., Ann Arbor, (A)
Mich.

H. H. Robertson Co., 2400 Farmers Bank Bldg., (R)
Pittsburgh 22, Pa.

Rohm & Haas Co., Resinous Products Div., 222 (RA)
W. Washington Sq., Philadelphia 5, Pa.

Rubba, Inc., 1015 E. 173rd St., New York 60, (A)
N.Y.

Rubber and Asbestos Corp., Bloomfield, N.J. (A)

Schenectady Varnish Co., Inc., Schenectady 1, (R)
N.Y.

Schwartz Chemical Co., Inc., New York 23, N.Y. (A)

Shawinigan Products Corp., New York 1, N.Y. (RA)

Shell Chemical Corp., New York 17, N.Y. (RA)

Silicones Div., Union Carbide Corp., 30 E. 42nd (R)
St., New York 17, N. Y.

Slomons Laboratories, Inc., Long Island City 1, (A)
N. Y.

Stein-Hall and Co., Inc., 285 Madison Ave., New (A)
York 17, N. Y.

Swift and Co., 4115 Packers Ave., Chicago 9, Ill. (A)

Synco Resins, Inc., Bethel, Conn. (RA)

Synvar Corp., 415 E. Front St., Wilmington 99, (RA)
Del.

Tylene Plastics, Inc., Freyer Rd., Michigan City, (A)
Ind.

UBS Chemical Corp., Cambridge 42, Mass. (A)

Union Paste Co., 1605 Hyde Park Ave., Hyde (A)
Park 36, Mass.

U. S. Plywood Corp., 55 W. 44th St., New York (RA)
18, N. Y.

U. S. Rubber Co., Rockefeller Center, New York (RA)
20, N. Y.

U. S. Stoneware Co., 100 Brimfield Rd., Akron (A)
9, Ohio

Varcum Chemical Corp., Packard Rd., Niagara (RA)
Falls, N. Y.

Velsicol Chemical Corp., Chicago 11, Ill. (R)

Watson-Standard Co., 225 Galveston Ave., Pitts- (R)
burgh 30, Pa.

Williamson Adhesives, Inc., 8220 Kimball Ave., (A)
Skokie, Ill.

Xylos Rubber Co., Div. of The Firestone Tire and (A)
Rubber Co., Akron 1, Ohio

Wm. Zinsser and Co., Inc., New York 19, N. Y. (A)

Rubber—

(Natural, reclaimed, chlorinated, cyclized, butadiene-
acrylonitrile, butadiene-styrene, butyl, polychloroprene, polysulfides)

Adhesive Engineering, San Carlos, Calif. (A)

Adhesive Products Corp., New York 60, N. Y. (RA)

Adhesive Products Inc., Albany 10, Calif. (A)

Alkydol Laboratories, Inc., Cicero 50, Ill. (RA)

American Latex Products Corp., Hawthorne, (A)
Calif.

American Products Manufacturing Co., New (A)
Orleans 18, La.

Angier Adhesives, Div. of Interchemical Corp., (A)
120 Potter St., Cambridge 42, Mass.

Arabol Mfg. Co., 110 E. 42nd St., New York 17, (A)
N. Y.

Armstrong Cork Co., Lancaster, Pa. (A)

Atlas Mineral Products Co., Mertztown, Pa. (A)

B. B. Chemical Co., 784 Memorial Drive, Cam- (A)
bridge 39, Mass.

Bloomingdale Rubber Co., Aberdeen, Md. (A)

Bond Adhesives Co., Box 406, Main P. O., Jersey (A)
City 3, N. J.

Borden Chemical Co., Div. of The Borden Co., (RA)
350 Madison Ave., New York 17, N. Y.

Carboline Co., 331 Thornton Ave., St. Louis 19, (A)
Mo.

Chemical Development Corp. (Devcon Corp.), (A)
Danvers, Mass.

Compo Chemical Co., Inc., Waltham 54, Mass. (A)

Cycleweld Cement Products Div., Chrysler Corp., (A)
5437 W. Jefferson, Trenton, Mich.

Dennis Chemical Co., 2701 Papin St., St. Louis (A)
3, Mo.

Dewey and Almy Chemical Co., Div. of W. R. (A)
Grace and Co., Cambridge 40, Mass.

E. I. du Pont de Nemours and Co., Wilmington (RA)
98, Del.

Farrington Texol Corp., Walpole, Mass. (A)

Formica Corp., 4614 Spring Grove Ave., Cincin- (A)
nati 32, Ohio

H. B. Fuller Co., 255 Eagle St., St. Paul 2, Minn. (A)

General Latex and Chemical Corp., Cambridge (A)
39, Mass.

B. F. Goodrich Co., 500 S. Main St., Akron 18, (RA)
Ohio

Goodyear Tire and Rubber Co., Chemical Div., (A)
Akron 16, Ohio

Gordon-Lacey Chemical Products Co., Maspeth, (A)
Long Island, N. Y.

Harwick Standard Chemical Co., Akron 5, Ohio (A)

Hercules Powder Co., Wilmington 99, Del. (R)

Hughes Glue Co., Detroit 7, Mich. (A)

Imperial Chemical Industries Ltd., London S. W. (R)
1, England

Lawrence Adhesive and Chemical Co., Lawrence, (A)
Mass.

Lebec Chemical Corp., Paramount, Calif. (A)

Loven Chemical of California, Newhall, Calif. (RA)

Magic Chemical Co., Brockton 2, Mass. (A)

Marbon Chemical Div., Borg-Warner Corp., (A)
Gary, Ind.

Midland Adhesive and Chemical Corp., Detroit (A)
20, Mich.

Minnesota Mining and Mfg. Co., Adhesives and (A)
Coatings Div., 411 Piquette Ave., Detroit 2,
Mich.

Miracle Adhesives Corp., 250 Pettit Ave., Bell- (A)
more, L. I., N. Y.

Narmco Resins and Coatings Co., Costa Mesa, (A)
Calif.

National Adhesives Div., National Starch Prod- (RA)
ucts Co., 750 Third Ave., New York 16, N. Y.

National Casein Co., 601 W. 80th St., Chicago (RA)
20, Ill.

Naugatuck Chemical Div., U. S. Rubber Co., (RA)
Naugatuck, Conn.

Ohio Adhesives Corp., New Philadelphia, Ohio (A)

Paisley Products Inc., Div. of Morningstar Nicol (A)
Inc., 630 W. 51st St., New York 19, N. Y.

Pierce and Stevens, Inc., 710 Ohio St., Buffalo 3, (A)
N. Y.

Plastite Adhesives Corp., Chicago 10, Ill. (RA)

Poly Resins, Sun Valley, Calif. (R)

Polymer Corp. of Pa., 2140 Fairmont Ave., Read- (A)
ing, Pa.

Polymer Industries Inc., Springdale, Conn. (A)

Pyroxylin Products, Inc., Chicago 32, Ill.; Paoli, (A)
Pa.

Research Sales, Inc., 20 Fourth Ave., Hawthorne, (A)
N. J.

Rubba, Inc., 1015 E. 173rd St., New York 60, N.Y. (A)

Rubber and Asbestos Corp., Bloomfield, N.J. (A)

Rubber Corp. of America, Latex and Chemical Div., New South Road, Hicksville, Long Island, N.Y. (RA)

Schwartz Chemical Co., Inc., New York 23, N.Y. (A)

Slomons Laboratories, Inc., Long Island City 1, N.Y. (A)

Swift and Co., 4115 Packers Ave., Chicago 9, Ill. (A)

UBS Chemical Corp., Cambridge 42, Mass. (A)

Union Paste Co., 1605 Hyde Park Ave., Hyde Park 36, Mass. (A)

U.S. Rubber Co., Rockefeller Center, New York 20, N.Y. (RA)

U.S. Stoneware Co., 100 Brimfield Rd., Akron 9, Ohio (A)

Williamson Adhesives, Inc., 8220 Kimball Ave., Skokie, Ill. (A)

Xylos Rubber Co., Div. of The Firestone Tire and Rubber Co., Akron 1, Ohio (A)

Cellulosics—

(Cellulose acetate, cellulose acetate butyrate, cellulose nitrate, ethyl cellulose, hydroxyethyl cellulose, methyl cellulose, sodium carboxymethyl cellulose)

Adhesive Products Corp., New York 60, N.Y. (RA)

Adhesive Products Inc., Albany 10, Calif. (A)

American Products Manufacturing Co., New Orleans 18, La. (A)

Angier Adhesives, Div. of Interchemical Corp., 120 Potter St., Cambridge 42, Mass. (A)

Arabol Mfg. Co., 110 E. 42nd St., New York 17, N.Y. (A)

Atlas Synthetic Corp., Long Island City 1, N.Y. (R)

B. B. Chemical Co., 784 Memorial Drive, Cambridge 39, Mass. (A)

Bond Adhesives Co., Box 406, Main P.O., Jersey City 3, N.J. (A)

Borden Chemical Co., Div. of The Borden Co., 350 Madison Ave., New York 17, N.Y. (RA)

Canadian Industries Ltd., Montreal, Canada (R)

Chemical Development Corp. (Devcon Corp.), Danvers, Mass. (A)

Compo Chemical Co., Inc., Waltham 54, Mass. (A)

Dennis Chemical Co., 2701 Papin St., St. Louis 3, Mo. (A)

Dow Chemical Co., The, Midland, Mich. (RA)

E. I. du Pont de Nemours and Co., Wilmington 98, Del. (RA)

Eastman Chemical Products, Inc., Kingsport, Tenn. (RA)

Farrington Texol Corp., Walpole, Mass. (A)

H. B. Fuller Co., 255 Eagle St., St. Paul 2, Minn. (A)

B. F. Goodrich Co., 500 S. Main St., Akron 18, Ohio (RA)

Gordon-Lacey Chemical Products Co., Maspeth, Long Island, N.Y. (A)

Hercules Powder Co., Wilmington 99, Del. (R)

Hughes Glue Co., Detroit 7, Mich. (A)

Imperial Chemical Industries Ltd., London S.W. 1, England (R)

Magic Chemical Co., Brockton 2, Mass. (A)

Midland Adhesive and Chemical Corp., Detroit 20, Mich. (A)

Miracle Adhesives Corp., 250 Pettit Ave., Bellmore, L.I., N.Y. (A)

Monsanto Chemical Co., Plastics Div., Springfield 2, Mass., and 911 Western Ave., Seattle 4, Wash. (RA)

National Adhesives Div., National Starch Products Co., 750 Third Ave., New York 16, N.Y. (RA)

Ohio Adhesives Corp., New Philadelphia, Ohio (A)

Paisley Products Inc., Div. of Morningstar Nicol Inc., 630 W. 51st St., New York 19, N.Y. (A)

Pierce and Stevens, Inc., 710 Ohio St., Buffalo 3, N.Y. (A)

Plastite Adhesives Corp., Chicago 10, Ill. (RA)

Polymer Corp. of Pa., 2140 Fairmont Ave., Reading, Pa. (A)

Polymer Industries Inc., Springdale, Conn. (A)

Pyroxylin Products, Inc., Chicago 32, Ill; Paoli, Pa. (A)

Raffi and Swanson, Inc., Wilmington, Mass. (A)

Research Sales, Inc., 20 Fourth Ave., Hawthorne, N.J. (A)

Rubba, Inc., 1015 E. 173rd St., New York 60, N.Y. (A)

Rubber and Asbestos Corp., Bloomfield, N.J. (A)

Schwartz Chemical Co., Inc., New York 23, N.Y. (A)

Slomons Laboratories, Inc., Long Island City 1, N.Y. (A)

Swift and Co., 4115 Packers Ave., Chicago 9, Ill. (A)

Union Carbide Chemicals Co., Div. Union Carbide Corp., 30 E. 42nd St., New York 17, N.Y. (R)

Union Paste Co., 1605 Hyde Park Ave., Hyde Park 36, Mass. (A)

Williamson Adhesives, Inc., 8220 Kimball Ave., Skokie, Ill. (A)

Starch, Dextrin, Soybean, Zein

Adhesive Products Corp., New York 60, N.Y. (RA)

Adhesive Products Inc., Albany 10, Calif. (A)

American-Marietta Co., Adhesive, Resin and Chemical Div., 3400 13th Ave., S.W., Seattle 4, Wash. (RA)

Arabol Mfg. Co., 110 E. 42nd St., New York 17, N.Y. (A)

Archer-Daniels-Midland Co., Minneapolis 2, Minn. (A)

Armstrong Cork Co., Lancaster, Pa. (A)

B. B. Chemical Co., 784 Memorial Drive, Cambridge 39, Mass. (A)

Borden Chemical Co., Div. of The Borden Co., 350 Madison Ave., New York 17, N.Y. (RA)

Corn Products Sales Co., Chemical Div., New York 4, N.Y. (A)

Hercules Powder Co., Huron Milling Division, Wilmington 99, Del. (R)

H. B. Fuller Co., 255 Eagle St., St. Paul 2, Minn. (A)

Hughes Glue Co., Detroit 7, Mich. (A)

Magic Chemical Co., Brockton 2, Mass.   (A)

Midland Adhesive and Chemical Corp., Detroit   (A)
20, Mich.

Monsanto Chemical Co., Plastics Div., Springfield   (RA)
2, Mass., and 911 Western Ave., Seattle 4,
Wash.

National Adhesives Div., National Starch Prod-   (RA)
ucts Co., 750 Third Ave., New York 16, N.Y.

Paisley Products Inc., Div. of Morningstar Nicol   (A)
Inc., 630 W. 51st St., New York 19, N.Y.

Perkins Glue Co., Lansdale, Pa.   (RA)

Polymer Industries Inc., Springdale, Conn.   (A)

Reichhold Chemicals, Inc., White Plains, N.Y.   (RA)

Slomons Laboratories, Inc., Long Island City 1,   (A)
N.Y.

Stein-Hall and Co., Inc., 285 Madison Ave., New   (A)
York 17, N.Y.

Swift and Co., 4115 Packers Ave., Chicago 9, Ill.   (A)

Union Paste Co., 1605 Hyde Park Ave., Hyde   (A)
Park 36, Mass.

Williamson Adhesives, Inc., 8220 Kimball Ave.,   (A)
Skokie, Ill.

Xylos Rubber Co., Div. of The Firestone Tire and   (A)
Rubber Co., Akron 1, Ohio

Animal, Blood, Casein

Adhesive Products Corp., New York 60, N.Y.   (RA)

Adhesive Products Inc., Albany 10, Calif.   (A)

American-Marietta Co., Adhesive, Resin and   (RA)
Chemical Div., 3400 13th Ave., S.W., Seattle
4, Wash.

Arabol Mfg. Co., 110 E. 42nd St., New York 17,   (A)
N.Y.

Archer-Daniels-Midland Co., Minneapolis 2,   (A)
Minn.

Armour and Co., 1355 W. 31st St., Chicago 9, Ill.   (A)

Borden Chemical Co., Div. of The Borden Co.,   (RA)
350 Madison Ave., New York 17, N.Y.

Corn Products Sales Co., Chemical Div., New   (A)
York 4, N.Y.

Formica Corp., 4614 Spring Grove Ave., Cincin-   (A)
nati 32, Ohio

H. B. Fuller Co., 255 Eagle St., St. Paul, Minn.   (A)

Harwick Standard Chemical Co., Akron 5, Ohio   (A)

C. B. Hewitt and Bros., Inc., New York 13, N.Y.   (A)

Hughes Glue Co., Detroit 7, Mich.   (A)

Lebec Chemical Corp., Paramount, Calif.   (A)

Magic Chemical Co., Brockton 2, Mass.   (A)

Midland Adhesive and Chemical Corp., Detroit   (A)
20, Mich.

Miracle Adhesives Corp., 250 Pettit Ave., Bell-   (A)
more, L. I., N.Y.

Monsanto Chemical Co., Plastics Div., Springfield   (RA)
2, Mass., and 911 Western Ave., Seattle 4,
Wash.

National Adhesives Div., National Starch Prod-   (RA)
ucts Co., 750 Third Ave., New York 16, N.Y.

National Casein Co., 601 W. 80th St., Chicago   (RA)
20, Ill.

Ohio Adhesives Corp., New Philadelphia, Ohio   (A)

Paisley Products Inc., Div. of Morningstar Nicol   (A)
Inc., 630 W. 51st St., New York 19, N.Y.

Perkins Glue Co., Lansdale, Pa.   (RA)

Polymer Corp. of Pa., 2140 Fairmont Ave., Read-   (A)
ing, Pa.

Polymer Industries Inc., Springdale, Conn.   (A)

Reichhold Chemicals, Inc., White Plains, N.Y.   (RA)

Slomons Laboratories, Inc., Long Island City 1,   (A)
N.Y.

Stein-Hall and Co., Inc., 285 Madison Avenue,   (A)
New York 17, N.Y.

Swift and Co., 4115 Packers Ave., Chicago 9, Ill.   (A)

Synco Resins, Inc., Bethel, Conn.   (RA)

Union Paste Co., 1605 Hyde Park Ave., Hyde   (A)
Park 36, Mass.

Williamson Adhesives, Inc., 8220 Kimball Ave.,   (A)
Skokie, Ill.

Xylos Rubber Co., Div. of The Firestone Tire and   (A)
Rubber Co., Akron 1, Ohio

Miscellaneous—

(Waxes, asphalt, shellac, sodium silicate, gum arabic)

Adhesive Products Corp., New York 60, N.Y.   (RA)

Adhesive Products Inc., Albany 10, Calif.   (A)

American Products Manufacturing Co., New   (A)
Orleans 18, La.

Angier Adhesives, Div. of Interchemical Corp.,   (A)
120 Potter St., Cambridge 42, Mass.

Arabol Mfg. Co., 110 E. 42nd St., New York 17,   (A)
N.Y.

Armstrong Cork Co., Lancaster, Pa.   (A)

Atlas Mineral Products Co., Mertztown, Pa.   (A)

Borden Chemical Co., Div. of The Borden Co.,   (RA)
350 Madison Ave., New York 17, N.Y.

Corn Products Sales Co., Chemical Div., New   (A)
York 4, N.Y.

E. I. du Pont de Nemours and Co., Wilmington   (RA)
98, Del.

Flintkote Co., Atlas Adhesives Div., Philadelphia   (A)
27, Pa.

H. B. Fuller Co., 255 Eagle St., St. Paul 2, Minn.   (A)

Harwick Standard Chemical Co., Akron 5, Ohio   (A)

Hughes Glue Co., Detroit 7, Mich.   (A)

Lebec Chemical Corp., Paramount, Calif.   (A)

Loven Chemical of California, Newhall, Calif.   (RA)

Midland Adhesive and Chemical Corp., Detroit   (A)
20, Mich.

Minnesota Mining and Mfg. Co., Adhesives and   (A)
Coatings Div., 411 Piquette Ave., Detroit 2,
Mich.

Miracle Adhesives Corp., 250 Pettit Ave., Bell-   (A)
more, L. I., N.Y.

Monsanto Chemical Co., Plastics Div., Springfield   (RA)
2, Mass., and 911 Western Ave., Seattle 4,
Wash.

National Adhesives Div., National Starch Prod-   (RA)
ucts Co., 750 Third Ave., New York 16, N.Y.

Naugatuck Chemical Div., U.S. Rubber Co.,   (RA)
Naugatuck, Conn.

New York Quinine and Chemical Works, Inc., (R)
The, 50 Church St., New York 8, N.Y.

Ohio Adhesives Corp., New Philadelphia, Ohio (A)

Paisley Products Inc., Div. of Morningstar Nicol (A)
Inc., 630 W. 51st St., New York 19, N.Y.

Pennsylvania Industrial Chemical Corp., Clair- (R)
ton, Pa.

Philadelphia Quartz Co., Philadelphia 6, Pa. (RA)

Polymer Industries Inc., Springdale, Conn. (A)

Pyroxylin Products, Inc., Chicago 32, Ill.; Paoli, (A)
Pa.

H. H. Robertson Co., 2400 Farmers Bank Bldg., (R)
Pittsburgh 22, Pa.

Rubber and Asbestos Corp., Bloomfield, N.J. (A)

Slomons Laboratories, Inc., Long Island City 1, (A)
N.Y.

Stein-Hall and Co., Inc., 285 Madison Ave., New (A)
York 17, N.Y.

Swift and Co., 4115 Packers Ave., Chicago 9, Ill. (A)

Union Paste Co., 1605 Hyde Park Ave., Hyde (A)
Park 36, Mass.

Xylos Rubber Co., Div. of The Firestone Tire and (A)
Rubber Co., Akron 1, Ohio

Wm. Zinsser and Co., Inc., New York 19, N.Y. (A)

Source: Modern Plastics Encyclopedia Issue for 1959.

The Adhesive Joint

Edmund Thelen

Laboratories for Research and Development
The Franklin Institute
Philadelphia, Pennsylvania

Purpose

Strong and permanent adhesive bonds are obtained only if a number of factors are favorable. Making good joints must be something like completing a steeplechase; that is, in order to score, every obstacle must be cleared. The main difference between bonding and steeplechasing is that from the horse's back you can see the hazards and estimate the speed and height required to clear them; whereas in bonding some of the most crucial obstacles are hidden. The purpose of this chapter, therefore, is to illuminate the factors conducive to good bonding and to suggest ways to overcome the obstacles.

Many companies have learned to make adhesive bonds that are very strong and permanent and have established reliable quality control. Some of the aircraft companies, for instance, adhesively bond, in lap joints, the thin aluminum sheets that comprise the skin of an aircraft's wings and control surfaces. When in the laboratory, such joints between thin metals deliberately are pulled under tension to destruction, it often is found that failure occurs only when the metal elongates and stretches away from the adhesive. In these cases, the strength of the joint is controlled by the rigidity and strength of the metal. In such joints, the stresses are distributed over the entire joint area, rather than being concentrated, as in riveted or spot-welded seams, around isolated places of attachment. Furthermore, as was learned a few years ago in England, when one of the aircraft models was crashing due to mechanical fatigue, the polymeric adhesives tend to dampen out vibration; therefore fatigue cracks in the metal panels were not propagated across the adhesive bonds.

Even in industrial applications of adhesive bonding where the ultimate in strength and reliability is not required, it is well to know how such performance can be obtained. With such knowledge, it may be possible to reduce costs by making a joint smaller, by using a cheaper adhesive or process, or by reducing the percentage of specimens that have to be tested to destruction to ensure quality control.

General Principles

As the other chapters in this book indicate, a wide variety of materials can be used as adhesives; in general, however, adhesive systems have these things in common:

(a) At the time the bond is formed between an adhesive and the solids being joined, the adhesive is either a liquid or a soft, readily deformed solid. This is a necessity because by flow or deformation the adhesive must shape itself intimately to the roughnesses of the solids, and practically all solid surfaces appear rough to an object as small as a molecule of adhesive.

(b) With few exceptions, e.g., pressure-sensitive tapes, the adhesives set, cure, cool, dry or otherwise become harder and tougher during the time the bond is formed or shortly thereafter. This must be true in all cases when high-strength joints are obtained.

(c) An adhesive must share some mutual attraction with the solid surfaces.

(d) An adhesive must have the toughness and strength to resist failure within the glue line under the conditions to which the joint will be subjected in service.

(e) As an adhesive cures, cools, dries, eliminates solvent, ages, etc., it must not shrink unduly, thereby setting up excessive internal stresses in the joint; furthermore the volume of adhesive in the joint must be sufficient to fill the joint.

(f) The adhesive must be suitably resistant to corrosion or swelling by ambient liquids or gases. It must either protect the solid surfaces to which it is applied, or these surfaces must themselves be resistant to such attacks.

(g) For strong bonds it is necessary at the time an adhesive is applied to the solid surfaces that these surfaces be free of dust, loose oxides or other weakly bonded materials, oils, and salts.

(h) Air, moisture, solvents, and other gases or volatile materials trapped in the interstices of the surfaces must have a way to escape.

(i) The design of a joint must be suitable to withstand the magnitudes and types of loads that it will be subjected to in service.

These various requirements, as well as the means by which they are fulfilled, are discussed in the succeeding sections of this chapter.

CONSIDERATIONS IN MAKING THE JOINT

For *maximum* strength of bond, it is essential that an adhesive have an affinity for the solid materials (substrates) being bonded, and that the adhesive be in physical contact with the substrate at all points. For the adhesive to be in intimate contact, the substrate must be free of dust, oil and other contaminatants; moreover the adhesive must displace air and water molecules from its surface. The factors involved when an adhesive displaces air and comes into intimate contact with the substrate are discussed in the following paragraphs.

Spreading

Provided a substrate is free of contamination, truly smooth, and flat, and the adhesive at the time of application is very low in viscosity, a drop of adhesive could be put on the substrate and in a short time the edges of the drop will form an equilibrium angle θ with the solid surface. The contact angle is at equilibrium when the surface forces at the edge of the drop are in balance. These surface forces, measured in dynes/cm, are dimensionally and numerically identical with the free energies of the same surfaces, expressed in ergs/cm². If the drop spreads into an immeasurably thin film, the contact angle is zero; indeed the adhesive has spread very well leaving no doubt that the adhesive wets the solid well and is in intimate contact with it. On the other hand, if the drop does not spread over a very smooth, polished surface, or even recedes causing its contact angle θ to be high, it indicates that the adhesive has little affinity for the substrate. The following equation enables us to define this lack more specifically:

$$\cos \theta = \frac{\gamma_{SV} - \gamma_{SL}}{\gamma_{LV}} = \frac{A}{\gamma_{LV}} \qquad (1)$$

When A, the adhesion tension $= \gamma_{SV} - \gamma_{SL}$

In other words, the cosine of the equilibrium contact angle θ is equal to the surface tension of the substrate γ_{SV} minus the interfacial tension between the adhesive and the substrate γ_{SL} divided by the surface tension of the adhesive, γ_{LV}. Spreading of the adhesive is favored, and the contact angle is low when (1) the substrate is free of contamination

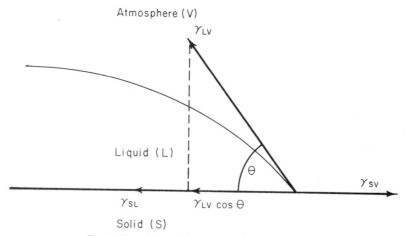

Fig. 1. Equilibrium of forces around a contact angle.[1]

and possesses a respectable surface attractive energy (high γ_{SV}), (2) the adhesive has a real affinity for the substrate (low γ_{SL}) and (3) the surface tension of the adhesive γ_{LV} is low. Measuring the contact angle is a convenient way to discover whether the relationships among these properties are suitable.

When the adhesive fails to spread over a very smooth surface to a low contact angle, the trouble might be that the substrate surface is oily or dusty, or that the adhesive either lacks affinity for it, has too high a surface tension, or is too viscous to flow readily. To determine whether the trouble is with the solid surface or with the adhesive, place a drop of pure water or other reproducible solvent on the substrate and measure its contact angle.

Metals, glass, china, metal oxides and silicates and most minerals by nature are hydrophilic; hence they have surface energies exceeding that of water, which is about 72 ergs/cm² at room temperature. Water will spread or form a very low contact angle on them when they are really clean. When the adhesion tension, A, Eq. (1), exceeds the surface tension of the droplet, γ_{LV}, the value for cos θ is greater than unity. Such a value which has no geometrical meaning, is called K and means that the surface is indeed avid for the liquid.

Organic solvents and polymers have lower surface tensions than water. Compared to water, their interfacial energies with hydrophilic surfaces generally are higher; however the over-all effect of substituting organics for water on a hydrophilic surface is to increase cos θ or K. An asphalt, for instance, had a surface tension of 26 ergs/cm² and an interfacial tension to water of 30 ergs/cm², from which its K to a hydrophilic surface is about 1.7. In general, if water will spread on a hydrophilic surface, the surface is free of any hydrophobic (oily) contamination. If the substrate is itself hydrophobic, a drop of water on it will have a high contact angle that is not very sensitive to contamination; in this case, a pure organic hydrocarbon solvent such as benzene or hexane would be a better test material.

If contact angles of water droplets are used to determine whether a hydrophilic substrate is "clean enough" for adhesive bonding, remember that, after the surface has been decontaminated so well that a water drop spreads on it, or forms a very low angle, it immediately thereafter starts adsorbing oily contamination from the surrounding air. In a matter of a few hours, the contact angle may be 30 to 45 degrees; yet a joint made from such substrates, with at least some adhesives, is as strong as a freshly-made one. If the substrate is initially clean, successful bonding can occur even after the contact angle has increased appreciably. This raises the question of how much contamination is required to raise the contact angle.

In a 1951 paper,[2] investigators at the University of Minnesota described experiments in which they embedded parallel strands of glass fiber in a matrix of clear methacrylate plastic and cut sections across the fibers thereby making plastic surfaces containing tiny dots of glass. They found that the contact angle of water changed from zero for a pure glass surface to 63½ degrees for the pure plastic. As illustrated in Fig. 2, a contact angle of 32 degrees was found when the glass was only 25 per cent covered by plastic and a 40-degree angle with about 38 per cent plastic. If adsorbed oils from the air act like polymethyl methacrylate, and other hydrophilic surfaces act like glass, it would seem that even with a 40-degree angle, two-thirds of the area of the hydrophilic surface is uncontaminated, and hence, available for bonding. Furthermore, organic adhesives should have at least some capability for dissolving the minute traces of contaminant on the other third of the surface.

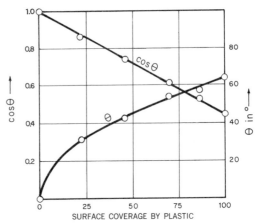

Fig. 2. Contact angles of water on a glass-acrylic plastic surface.

Roughness

We have discussed the spreading of liquids or adhesives over truly smooth polished surfaces. In practice, substrates other than fire-polished glass, mirror-like metal surfaces, etc., generally are appreciably rough, with peaks and valleys, or pores, or capillaries. Furthermore, etching baths, sand or vapor blasting or mechanical abrasion are sometimes used to remove contamination and to roughen surfaces to increase their bonding area and mechanical interlock with an adhesive.

When an adhesive droplet is applied to a rough substrate, it often will not spread as well as on a really smooth substrate since it cannot root out all the air between the asperities; hence, it actually bridges over pockets of air. The surface on which the adhesive rests in this case is partially air; just how much of it is air can be calculated from the following equation by Cassie:

$$\cos \theta_a = \sigma_1 \cos \theta_S - \sigma_2 \qquad (2)$$

When θ_a is the contact angle of a liquid on a "rough" surface

θ_S is the contact angle of a liquid on a truly smooth surface of the same material

σ_1 is the fraction of substrate surface that is air

σ_2 is the fraction of substrate surface that is solid

and $\sigma_1 + \sigma_2$ is approximately 1.

Just how much air will be trapped under a droplet placed onto a rough surface depends on a number of things. If the liquid has a strong affinity for the substrate, is low in viscosity, and if the valleys and capillaries get narrower as they get deeper, no appreciable air may be trapped. Conversely, droplets which are poorly wetted or are not very fluid set relatively quickly and may trap air on practically any surface.

If the substrate is porous or full of open capillaries which the liquid can wet, the liquid may well chase the air at the interface down the capillaries and itself follow far enough to get a good "grip." The danger here is likely to be not air entrapment but starvation of the joint due to too much adhesive flowing through the capillaries and leaving the bonding zone in a starved condition.

It is not to be inferred that really smooth surfaces necessarily are desirable in adhesive bonding. Rough surfaces are preferred when peel strengths are required (p. 39); in this case the conditions under which an adhesive is applied and cured can be chosen to minimize the amount of air that otherwise would be trapped (pp. 34 and 37).

Porosity

As previously mentioned when the substrate has open capillaries or passages which are wet by the adhesive, the adhesive will try to flow down them.

The pressure causing this flow in the case of cylindrical capillaries is equal to $2A/r$, where A is the adhesion tension as defined in Eq. (1), and r is the radius of the capillary. For most successful adhesive systems A probably is greater than 10 erg/cm^2; if r were 1 micron (40 millionths of an inch), the capillary pressure would be 200,000 dynes/cm^2, or about 3 psi. If the pore were closed at the bottom and originally contained gas or air at 1 atm pressure (14.7 psi), the imposition of an additional 3 psi pressure would compress the gas by about 20 per cent and the adhesive would penetrate about 20 per cent of the depth of the pore.

For open cylindrical capillaries, according to Poiseuille's law, the depth of penetration d is as follows:

$$d = \sqrt{\frac{A\,r\,t}{2\eta}} \qquad (3)$$

where t is the time of flow in seconds and η is the liquid in poises. Using the above values for A and r, and taking t as 10 min. and η as 30 poises, d would be 1 mm.

DeBruyne[3] in an extensive treatment of the effect of the shape of a substrate pore on the penetration of an adhesive points out, among other things, the effect of the angle of slope of the pore wall, ϕ, in conical pits. He states that when the liquid contact angle, θ, plus the slope angle, ϕ, add up to less than 180 degrees, some penetration of the pit tends to occur. If their sum is greater than 180 degrees, the liquid pressure will be negative, and it will not penetrate the pit (unless forced to by external pressure).

These relationships are indicated in Fig. 3 where θ in each case is 60 degrees and ϕ is 90 degrees for the cylindrical capillary, 135 degrees for the divergent cone, and 45 degrees for the convergent cone. The arrows show that for these cases the liquid will want to penetrate the capillary and the convergent cone, for which θ plus ϕ are 150 degrees and 105 degrees, respectively, but not the convergent cone, for which they are 195 degrees.

We can conclude that the depth of penetration of adhesive into a pore, and the amount of air trapped will depend not only on its shape but also

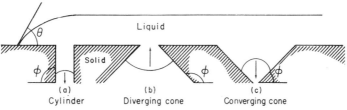

Fig. 3. Effect of pore shape on capillary pressure. Arrows indicate direction liquid wants to flow.

on adhesion tension, viscosity or consistency of adhesive, pore size, and set time. Control of these variables should provide control over air entrapment and mechanical interlocking of an adhesive to its substrates.

Diffusion

A solid in contact with reasonably mobile molecules of liquid or vapor will absorb and dissolve them until an equilibrium is reached between the absorbed molecules and their external vapor pressure. Once equilibrium is reached, no further absorption will occur unless external conditions are changed, or a gradient is applied which forces the absorbed molecules to migrate out of the solid (see discussion on thermal and shrinkage stresses, p. 40).

Diffusion processes are of considerable importance in adhesive bonding. Following are some situations where they can operate:

(1) When an adhesive hardens by eliminating water or other solvent, drying is accelerated if the solvent molecules are able to diffuse into the substrate. Wood, paper, leather, hard rubber and sometimes other polymers (depending on the solvent) are examples of substrates that can take up small liquid molecules relatively rapidly. This can occur even when the substrate is not wet by the solvent, e.g., when the adhesion tension between them is negative; when this is the case, the take-up cannot be due to porosity or flow of the liquid but rather to molecular diffusion.

Although drying by diffusion is useful and extensively practiced, it can cause difficulties if the substrate is degraded by the solvent. A decade ago we were experimenting on hard rubber with an adhesive containing methylene chloride. The solvent swelled the rubber to a depth of about one-eighth in. and when the joint was tested in tension, it failed where the swollen region joined the unswelled rubber.

When an adhesive joint fails in the substrate close to the adhesive, it is worth checking to determine if the adhesive contains a solvent or other migratable liquid which swells, dissolves or otherwise attacks the substrate.

(2) When air is trapped at an adhesive interface, and the adhesive is cured under pressure and heat, the air tends to dissolve into the adhesive, thereby increasing the real bonded area. Usually, both pressure and heat are required; heat alone may cause the air to expand into bubbles rather than to dissolve. The same effects can be observed in some cases when an adhesive is applied over a water or solvent-base primer that it not completely dry.

(3) A strong bond between a primer and an adhesive laid over it, or between two polymers that are heat or solvent welded, is undoubtedly created mainly by the diffusion of molecules in both directions, thereby wiping out the interface. The action of a solvent in the solvent bonding of thermoplastics is threefold: (a) it softens the polymer surfaces so they can be mated intimately, (b) it increases the mobility of the migrating polymer molecules, and (c) it probably increases the capability of the opposite polymer to absorb the migrating molecules.

Sometimes a joint is strong when freshly made, but becomes weak after aging a few days or weeks. Apparently the solvent has successfully softened and tackified the surfaces, but there has not been adequate diffusion of the polymer molecules. On aging, the solvent diffuses away from the joint, and the polymers at the interface shrink and pull away from each other.

(4) Some adhesives, before they are cured, will absorb water from the atmosphere and then on curing do not develop full strength; conversely at least one adhesive, Eastman's No. 910, presumably must absorb traces of water from the solid surfaces to which it applied in order to set hard

An instance of the former case was observed when a phenolic-type structural adhesive was laid in a thin film over a large number of primed panels which were then wrapped in kraft paper and stored. After the panels had aged for several weeks or months, they were mated to form joints and subsequently cured. Fluctuations in the strengths of the cured joints were found which correlated with variations in the humidity of the air during the few days before curing; high humidity at this time adversely affected joint strengths.

Deformation and Flow (Rheology)

It is essential that an adhesive flow or deform when the joint is made in order to penetrate the valleys and capillaries of the substrates, displace air, and come into intimate contact with the substrate surface. Also when the substrate is porous, the adhesive should not flow through the pores to such an extent that the joint is drained and starved. It is evident, too, that the adhesive consistency must be suitable for brushing, spraying, troweling or whatever method of application is to be employed for laying it on to the desired thickness.

Literature dealing with the deformation and flow of paints, thermoplastics, polymer solutions, and other adhesive-like materials is fairly extensive. Some of the recent compilations are by Eirich,[4] Hoekstra, Fritzius,[5] and Alfrey.[6] Here we shall try merely to present some of the rheological concepts most useful in understanding adhesives.

There are three ways in which an adhesive can resist flow or deformation under loads: it can be viscous, plastic, or elastic. Often it shows two and occasionally all of these characteristics simultaneously.

Viscosity. A viscous liquid is one that will flow at an infinitely small rate under an infinitely small stress for as long as the load is applied and will not try to recover its original shape when the load is removed.

If, in addition, the rate of shear increases proportionately as the shearing stress is increased, the fluid meets Newton's definition of a true liquid, and is referred to as "ideal" or "Newtonian" Fig. 4. Viscosity, η, is defined as the ratio of shearing stress F to rate of shear D, and is usually expressed in poises:

$$\eta = \frac{F}{D} \qquad (4)$$

A material having the characteristics of a viscous liquid, i.e., the ability to flow under very small loads without recoiling when the load is removed, may exhibit different viscosities at different shear stresses or rates of shear. In this case, the liquid is non-Newtonian, and the viscosity is often referred to as an "apparent" viscosity. Often a non-Newtonian liquid is perceptibly elastic or plastic as well as viscous.

As a liquid flows, each molecule continually changes neighbors and may itself wobble, tumble, or spin. The energy dissipated during these motions is converted to heat and is thought of as a "viscous loss." When shear stresses are small and the molecules slide over each other in parallel layers, or laminae, the flow is referred to as laminar or streamline.

Plasticity. A plastic solid is one that will not flow or deform appreciably unless the load that is applied exceeds a certain stress in it. When the load is removed, the material is inactive.

The critical stress that must be exceeded to cause flow is known as the yield stress or yield value, and is expressed in conventional stress units such as dynes/cm^2 or psi. When the shear stresses in the material exceed the yield stress f, the material will flow. If the rate of shear of this flow is proportional to the excess of shear stress over yield value, the material meets Bingham's particular definition of a "plastic solid," or "Bingham body:"

$$\eta = \frac{F-f}{D} \qquad (5)$$

Often it is found that the yield value of a so-called Bingham body is appreciable and constant over a moderate range of rates of shear, but at very low rates of shear is much smaller or even zero (Fig. 4); thus under creep conditions, some materials that would normally be classified as Bingham bodies behave like simple liquids. Because of this complication, yield values for an adhesive should be determined at the rates of shear at which it is to be applied and allowed to spread.

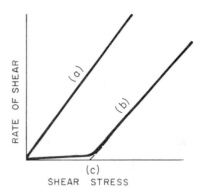

Fig. 4. Rheological diagrams.
(a) Newtonian liquid.
(b) pseudo Bingham body.
(c) apparent yield value.

Plastic solids generally are suspensions of solid particles in liquids, and their yield values are often thought of as a measure of the friction or interlock of the particles as they slide by each other. Yield values tend to be large if the particles are (a) rough, (b) nonspherical, e.g., plate-like or needle-shaped, (c) present in large volume, (d) swollen by liquid absorbed intersticially, or (e) increased in size by thick layers of liquid immobilized as an envelope around them.

With usual pigment and "inert" filler particles, the volume concentration in a liquid must be 20 to 25 per cent to produce a measurable yield value; conversely, less than 2 per cent by volume of a swelling bentonite or other thickening agent can markedly increase the viscosity of a liquid and may impart a yield value to it. Similarly, the addition of less than 1 per cent by volume of a chopped fiber glass was observed to impart a real yield value to a mortar slurry.

Two types of behavior may arise when a suspension is stirred: thixotropy (Fig. 5) or dilatancy (Fig. 6). If in a suspension at rest some of the particles touch each other and are interlocked, this lock must break when the system is stirred. The resistance to flow due to the initial interlock (or to other static equilibrium conditions) gives to the

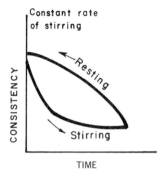

Fig. 5. Thixotropy.

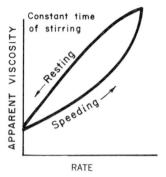

Fig. 6. Dilatancy.

suspension a higher yield value and/or viscosity than it would have after it has been stirred vigorously. The breakdown of this initially high consistency by stirring is known as thixotropy; usually it is reversible on aging at rest.

If, however, the suspended particles in the system at rest are separated from each other by adsorbed films such as ionic double layers, the apparent viscosity of the system may be small when the system is stirred slowly; nevertheless it may become large when stirring is vigorous and the protecting layers are ruptured. This increase in resistance to flow on stirring is called dilatancy; on aging the system reverts to its original fluidity.

Elasticity. An elastic material when loaded will deform to a degree proportional to the stress, and will try to recover its original shape when the load is removed. In a simple elastic or Hookean solid, the deformation and recovery occur instantly when a load is applied and removed. The elastic modulus for such a material is the ratio of stress to strain, and in essence describes its rigidity. A steel ball bearing and a rubber band are both basically elastic, but the elastic modulus of the steel is a hundred thousand or a million times greater than the elastic modulus of the rubber. A high elastic modulus means that the molecules, crystals or other structures in the material absorb a great deal of energy when they are deformed slightly. A low elastic modulus means that energy absorbed during deformation is small.

Young's modulus is the elastic modulus measured in tension; whereas an elastic shear or storage modulus is an elastic modulus measured in shear. For polymeric materials in general, at least under moderate loads, the Young's moduli are three times the shear moduli because only one-third of the energy applied in tension actually is directed parallel to the shear planes and causes shear. Adhesives, when both viscous and elastic, or "visco-elastic," exhibit a "delayed" elasticity. Instead of deforming immediately to a degree proportional to the stress, as a Hookean solid does,

they may take minutes or hours to attain their ultimate elastic deformation. For these materials the rate of "stretch" under constant load is fast initially, and then it slows down as the elastic deformation is completed; further flow is purely viscous at a rate proportional to the shear stress. Thus the material deforms slower; hence it appears to get harder as its stretch is taken up, This delayed elasticity has nothing to do with work hardening such as may occur in metals but is a normal characteristic of visco-elastic liquids and solids.

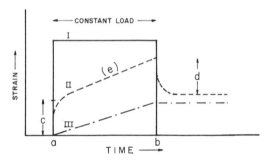

Fig. 7. Time effects on strain in materials.
   Load applied at *a;* removed at *b.*
   I. Hookean (Elastic) solid.
   II. Viscoelastic material (Maxwell model).
       Elastic deformation *c* equals recoil *d.*
       Linear portion (*e*) shows viscous flow.
   III. Simple liquid or plastic solid when shear stress is larger than yield value.

Figure 7 illustrates the differences among viscous, visco-elastic and elastic materials. When a load is applied suddenly at time *a*, the elastic material, I, deforms instantly and does nothing more as long as the load remains constant; when the load is removed at time *b*, it recoils to its original state. The viscous liquid, III, simply deforms at a constant rate until the load is removed and then stops. The visco-elastic material shows an initial, though not instantaneous elastic deformation *c*, followed by viscous flow *e* until the load is removed; then it recovers strain *d* equal to *c*.

Polymers, oxidized asphalts and their solutions, if reasonably concentrated, generally are viscoelastic in nature. The degree to which elasticity is present in a viscous liquid or a plastic solid can be estimated experimentally by calculating a value for n in these equations:

$$\eta = \frac{F^n}{D} \quad \text{or} \quad \frac{(F-f)^n}{D} \qquad (6)$$

When n is 1, the equations reduce to those for Newtonian liquids and plastic solids already given; when n has values of 2, 3, or more, a significant elasticity usually is present.

Thickness

Generally it is agreed that for maximum strength and rigidity an adhesive layer in a joint should be as thin as practicable without starving the joint. To prevent starvation, the amount of adhesive used must be sufficient to fill the declivities and level the asperities of the solid surfaces; furthermore the volume shrinkage of the adhesive as it cools or loses solvent, the possible loss of adhesive by diffusion or by flow into the pores of the substrates, and the roughness of the substrates must be taken into account.

Several reasons for the desirability of thin films are:

(1) It requires greater force to deform a thin film than a thick one.
(2) Probability of flow or creep is greater as thickness increases.
(3) Internal or "locked-in" stresses at the adhesive interfaces and thermal stresses due to differential expansion (see p. 40) are reasonably proportional to the thickness of the film.
(4) If the adhesive is hard or rigid, a thin film is more resistant to cracking when the joint is flexed.
(5) The greater the volume of adhesive in a joint, the greater the probability that it will contain an air bubble, unbonded solid particle or other source of weakness.

Pressure

The application of pressure to an adhesive joint before the adhesive is cured will promote its permeation into pores and valleys in the substrate surfaces, and the displacement or compression of air or other gases trapped at the interface. In conjunction with heat, pressure tends to mitigate bubbles and to promote the solution of gases trapped at the interface, or otherwise present in the joint.

In most adhesive joints, one or more edges are open and a liquid adhesive is not completely restrained from flowing out of the joint under pressure; hence the actual pressure in a joint, particularly near its open edges, is lower than would be calculated from the external force applied. If the periphery of the joint is open, and the adhesive is a viscous liquid, the pressure in the joint under a given external load will be proportionate to the viscosity, and inversely proportional to the third power of the thickness of the adhesive layer. In this case only a very thin layer of adhesive could persist in the joint under pressure, unless the adhesive sets extremely rapidly leaving no time for it to be squeezed out. To prevent joint starvation, various expedients are used: (a) fibers can be added to an adhesive to restrain its flow mechanically, (b) an adhesive formulation can be changed to impart a yield value, or (c) an adhesive applied to both substrate surfaces can be partially set before the surfaces are joined under pressure.

In (c) the pressure required to "weld" the semiset adhesive surfaces together is, at least in some instances, a function of the viscosity of the outermost layers of adhesive, the temperature (which promotes diffusion as well as lowering viscosity), and the time. When the adhesive surfaces are to be mated are at mating temperature, they should not be skinned over and usually should be discernibly tacky.

JOINT STRENGTHS AND PERFORMANCE

In service, an adhesive joint may be subjected to mechanical tension, shear or peel, to heat and moisture or to cycles of these, and to chemical or environmental attack. The substrates and adhesive with the passage of time eventually may interact with each other or alter themselves as they strive to reach an equilibrium with their surroundings. Also stresses "locked in" at the adhesive interfaces during the manufacture of the joint may significantly weaken it. Here we will discuss the strengths and permanence of a joint as well as the internal and external factors that affect its performances in service.

Hypothetical Strength

Let us assume that absolutely smooth and flat surfaces on solid blocks of two different materials are bonded together by an adhesive; furthermore both the solids and the adhesive are completely rigid, i.e., non-deformable. Blocks are clamped into the jaws of a tensile test machine and ever-increasing force is applied to pull them apart. Since the materials are completely rigid, the only elongation that will occur is due to the distances between the molecules and atoms becoming greater as the tensile load is increased. When the load becomes sufficiently high, a loud bang is heard and there is a crack through the weakest part of the joint, i.e., either through one of the solids or the adhesive or at one of the interfaces between adhesive and solid. If the failure is through either the substrate or the adhesive, it is referred to as a cohesive break; if it is at one of the interfaces, it is an adhesive break.

Presume the break were clean through the adhesive between adjacent "layers" of molecules under a load P of 5000 psi or 3.5×10^8 dynes/cm^2. The work or energy put into the system prior to the break would be $P \times d$, when d is the increase in distance between the adjacent layers just as the break occurs. Since we do not know with certainty the value of d, we shall assume it is 3×10^{-8} cm; consequently the energy required to cause the break would be $3.5 \times 10^8 \times 3 \times 10^{-8} = 10.5$ ergs/cm^2. Since the crack occurred in a single material, the energy causing it is equal to the cohesive energy of the material, and is equal, by definition, to twice its surface tension. Actually the energies calculated in this way are generally much too small, presumably because bubbles, internal stresses, impurities, and other defects in the material cause it to fail under an insufficient external force. In the case cited, a typical polymer adhesive with a tensile strength of 5000 psi would have a surface tension greater than 30 ergs/cm^2 and a cohesive energy of twice that.

The reason the cohesive energy is defined as being equal to twice the surface tension is as follows:

A liquid or solid material is held together by attractive energies within and among its molecules or crystal lattices. When a material is cracked in a vacuum, the attractive energies that had been operating across the plane of the crack to hold the material together, now become concentrated on the surfaces that form on either side of the crack, with half the cohesive energy going to each surface. Since surface tension is defined as the free energy of a surface in equilibrium with its own vapor, it must be half the cohesive energy of the material.

Consequently the work or energy required to break a material in cohesion is equal to the sum of the free energies of the newly formed surfaces; the force required to cause the break is considerably less than the theoretical value because of bubbles, local internal stresses, and other imperfections.

If in the hypothetical example above, the crack occurs at the interface between the adhesive and one of the solids, the same conclusions are true. In this case, however, the crack occurs at an interface which already possesses some free interfacial energy. When the adhesive and solid are cleaved apart, this interfacial energy goes to the new surfaces; and the energy that must be put into the system to cause the break is reduced by a like amount. Thus, for absolutely smooth surfaces 1 cm^2, the work of adhesion W (or energy to cleave along the interface) between a solid and an adhesive in an atmosphere V is defined as follows:

$$W = \gamma_{SV} + \gamma_{AV} - \gamma_{SA}, \text{ in ergs} \qquad (7)$$

When γ_{SV} and γ_{AV} are the free surface energies of solid and adhesive, respectively, in air or another ambient medium, and γ_{SA} is the interfacial energy between solid and adhesive. Obviously, if the pieces being bonded are large and the area of the interface is greater than 1 cm^2, W will be increased in proportion. The interfacial area can also be increased by roughening the surfaces; however this may introduce complications as previously discussed (pp. 32–33).

Mechanical Loads and Responses

In the hypothetical system just discussed, it was assumed that the adhesive and substrates were completely rigid and under these conditions it was observed that joint strength should depend on the cohesive or adhesive strengths of the system. This concept is useful, even though no materials are completely rigid; if they were, they would crack under the slightest deformation while being clamped into the test machine.

Organic adhesives generally become softer and more easily deformed when: (a) the temperature is raised, (b) the rate of shear is reduced, (c) the frequency or "abruptness" of the load application is reduced, or (d) the concentration of water or solvent in them is increased. Similarly, their tensile strengths tend to decrease and their elongation at break to increase under these conditions; however in comparing different materials, there is not necessarily any correlation between tensile strength and softness or deformability. For example, a polyurethane-type adhesive could have the same stiffness as an asphalt under similar conditions; yet it could have a tensile strength twenty times greater.

Adhesives which, under use conditions, are essentially viscous liquids (with or without a degree of elastic or plastic response) will creep or flow under continuously applied loads of any magnitude. Adhesives which do not have this short-

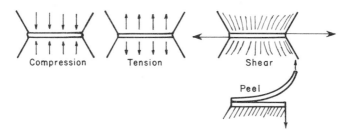

Fig. 8. Modes of stressing a joint (conventional).

coming are generally elastic solids (sometimes with a degree of viscous or plastic response). Among the elastic solids we can distinguish between are: (a) the relatively brittle materials, e.g., mortars, some asphalts, and resins at low temperature which have very small elongations at break and high rigidities, and (b) the tough resilient materials, e.g., rubbers and numerous resins at normal temperatures which have moderate rigidities and greater elongations at break.

In general, excessive creep on the one hand or brittleness on the other, could limit the durability and strength of an adhesive joint under load. Conditions which promote creep are usually high temperatures and loads applied for a long time; whereas conditions for brittleness usually are low temperatures and fast rates of loading (impact).

While load applications can be quite complicated, the simple modes (Fig. 8) are: (a) tension, when the substrates are pulled apart by forces perpendicular to the plane of the adhesive, (b) compression, when the substrates are pushed together by forces perpendicular to the adhesive planes, and (c) shear, when one substrate is slid parallel to the other. The amount of deformation under these modes of loading is minimized by using thin adhesive layers.

A very destructive type of loading, when one or both of the substrates is flexible, consists of peeling a substrate away from the adhesive. The interface is stressed in tension and shear and the force is concentrated along the zone of contact of the substrate to the adhesive. If the substrate is soft or thin, its radius of curvature approaches zero, the contact zone degenerates into a very small area, and the local tensile stress is almost infinitely high, even when the total peeling load is relatively small. When peel loads are contemplated, the substrate surfaces should be etched or otherwise relatively rough, to prevent cracks from propagating in the interface ahead of the line of contact.

When an otherwise strong lap joint between substrates that are thin or low in modulus is stressed in apparent tension, as shown in Fig. 9 (I), the principal stress plane may not be parallel to the adhesive interfaces. As the load is increased, the substrates try to stretch, bend, and peel before the shear strength of the joint is reached, Fig. 9 (II). In this case, the strength of the joint depends on the modulus and thickness of the substrate. An example of this is shown in Fig. 10, which compares the strengths of joints made from high modulus steel and lower modulus aluminum of various thicknesses.[8] The limiting strength, approximately 8000 psi, was near to the cohesive strength of the adhesive. Considering that the adhesive layer was only about a hundredth of an in. thick, the lap was a half in. wide and the substrate pieces were 4 in. long, the degree of tilt of the principal stress plane was much less than that shown in Fig. 9 (I).

Fatigue loading occurs when the joint is stressed alternately in opposite directions, or is periodically stressed in one direction with rests between load applications. Tough polymeric adhesives are known to have excellent resistance to fatigue. Apparently, because of their high elastic moduli they can store considerable energy without much strain, and release it during the return part of the load cycle. It is not expected, however, that fatigue resistances can be calculated from deformation and strength properties alone because eventually fatigue failure probably involves a change in molecular orientation or "crystallinity" which is more readily undergone by some polymers than by others. For example, we have noticed that asphalts, when split by fatigue, displayed dull lumpy surfaces; whereas the same materials, cleaved by a single blow, had bright glossy surfaces.

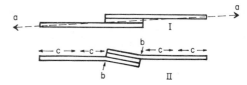

Fig. 9. Effect of tension on lap joint.
a–a. principal stress plane.
b. peel stress regions.
c. regions of stretching.

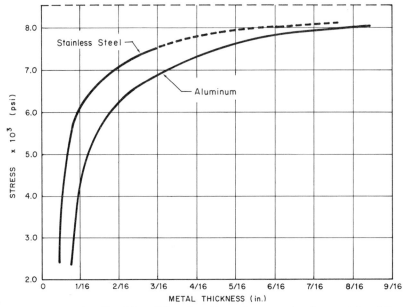

Fig. 10. Strengths of lap joints. When the adhesive is strong, the characteristics of the substrate may control the joint strength.

Thermal and Shrinkage Stresses

The coefficients of expansion of adhesives and of substrates frequently differ with minerals having low values, metals intermediate, and organics having highest coefficients; consequently as a joint is heated or particularly when it is cooled, stresses may build up, especially at the adhesive interfaces. If an adhesive occupies a certain volume when it is hot and becomes rigid on cooling, this rigidity may prevent it from shrinking to the smaller volume it should occupy at room temperature. Subsequently, it may continue to shrink at room temperature for long periods of time until it reaches its equilibrium volume.

When an adhesive in a joint contracts relative to the substrates, it tends to pull inward from its edges toward the center; thus shear forces are generated at the interfaces and tensile forces within the adhesive. These forces consequently subtract from the load-carrying capacity of a joint even when they are not strong enough themselves to cause failure.

Visco-elastic materials, if not too rigid, tend to relieve their stresses on aging. This process probably cannot be completed in a thin joint where the most highly stressed molecules are bonded to solid surfaces and hence immobilized. The addition of glass fibers or mineral fillers to organic adhesives is sometimes a useful way to make their thermal coefficients more nearly equal those of metal substrates.

Shrinkage stresses may also result from decreases in volume of an adhesive due to the evolution of solvent or to molecular orientation on aging. These stresses, like the thermally induced ones, subtract from the capacity of the joint to carry external loads.

Penetration and Corrosion

Previously, it was noted that adhesives and substrates are capable of dissolving small molecules, i.e., water, solvents, gases, etc., until the concentration of sorbed molecules is in equilibrium with their external vapor pressure. If the external vapor pressure (humidity, in the case of water molecules) is increased, more molecules will be sorbed. The swelling of rubbers by certain solvents and the hydrogen embrittlement of certain metals are spectacular examples of such diffusion. Other examples are given in the discussion on p. 34.

Once a substrate or an adhesive in a joint has sorbed a concentration of water or other molecules, energy gradients of various sorts can drive the sorbed vapors to the adhesive interface, where they may cause corrosion, blisters, or other damage:

(1) Liquids and gases in most materials tend to migrate from a hot zone to a cold zone. If one side of a joint is hot and the other cold, the migration will be through the hot substrate to its adhesive interface, and in the adhesive, to the cold interface.

(2) Inorganic salts and other soluble material at the interface will tend to pick up water molecules from the adhesive, and dissolve; the solution tends to become more and more dilute by osmosis, and can result in blisters. One purpose of cleaning substrates before bonding is to remove all soluble materials from their surfaces.

(3) If the sorbed vapors in the adhesive can react with the substrate and thereby be used up chemically, this will create a concentration gradient in the adhesive which will cause more vapor to be sorbed, possibly resulting in rusting or corrosion of the substrate.

Another type of reaction is the hydration of substrate metal oxides at the interface, converting them into a form which may lack cohesive or adhesive integrity in the joint.

(4) If air is trapped at the adhesive interface, and the walls of the bubble have a lower interfacial tension to water than to air, water will tend to be pulled into the bubble.

(5) In the presence of strong electric potentials, the migration or orientation of polar molecules and ions might be suspected.

While water vapor diffuses rapidly through cellulosic and protein materials, its progress through relatively nonpolar bitumens and polymers is slow. When corrosion shows up relatively soon at an interface with a polymeric adhesive, it often will be found that it penetrated not by diffusion but by capillary action through voids in the adhesive or along the interface itself. In such cases, if voids cannot be avoided, sealing the open edges of an adhesive joint is sometimes helpful.

Syneresis

Syneresis is the migration of relatively incompatible molecules out of a gel or poorly solvated solution. The elimination of hydrophobic oils and waxes from certain highly oxidized asphalts is one example. The self-elimination of a "bleeding" plasticizer or a poorly solvating solvent from an organic adhesive would be another example; moreover if this resulted in an accumulation of liquid molecules at the interface, it would weaken the joint.

Assuming an adhesive possesses this sort of instability, trouble still is avoided if the ejected liquids are able to diffuse into the substrate, thereby leaving the interfacial bonds intact. Of course, if the migrating liquid attacks the substrate, it could weaken the joint. In this case, when the joint is pulled in tension, the plane of failure often will be just inside the substrate.

CAPABILITIES OF FORMING ADHESIVE BONDS

Not all solid materials are capable of being adhesively bonded, and most that are must be cleaned or otherwise treated before really good bonding is possible. Here we will discuss the nature of adhesive bonds, the role of adsorbed films and oxides, and the preparation of surfaces for bonding.

Attractive Energies

On p. 31 it was shown that a liquid will spread over a solid when the surface tension of the solid is high and the surface tension of the liquid and the interfacial tension of the liquid to the solid are low. This immediately indicates that while a low surface energy material may spread over one with high surface energy, the opposite is untrue: oil will spread on water, but water will not spread on oil.

Some solids, e.g., untreated "Teflon," polyethylene, paraffin wax, etc. do not lend themselves to adhesive bonding because their surface energies are lower than those of any useful solvents or adhesives. Solids with high surface energies, e.g., clean metals, minerals, glass, and other hydrophilic materials, are very readily contaminated by oils with low surface energies. Since adhesives usually will not spread over these adsorbed oil films, the films must be removed if strong bonds are desired. That is why degreasing is a common first step in preparing such materials for bonding.

Similarly, in bonding molded plastics or plasticized ones, any molecular films of mold release agents or of plasticizers bled to the surface should be removed so that the adhesive will spread.

All liquids and solids attract each other to some extent; there are no pairs of materials that actually repel each other. The mechanisms responsible for attraction among materials are basically electronic in nature, e.g.:

(a) Groups of atoms, such as radicals in an organic molecule, may be balanced electronically, yet still share their electrons to some extent with adjacent groups. In this case, the magnitude of the attraction depends on the number of electrons in the group and the positive charges in the atomic cores. These nonpolar forces which occur among all atoms are known as London forces.

(b) When an electrostatically positive (electron-deficient) or electrostatically negative (electron-excess) group in a molecule comes in contact with a metal, the highly mobile electrons in the metal arrange themselves to compensate for the excess or deficiency. This arrangement is called a dipole mirror image and probably accounts for the ability of clean metal surfaces to attract any electrostatically unbalanced group.

The above are merely some illustrations of the ways in which attractions arise between materials. One point of considerable interest is that attractions are between active spots on molecules and therefore can result in bonds only when these spots are brought close together. For example, if the active spots on a substrate surface are 6 Å units apart, and those in a polymerized resin are 4 units apart, obviously the resin molecule cannot be fitted onto the substrate so as to mate all the active spots. Thus positional hindrances can prevent full adhesive strengths from being realized.

Another consequence of the idea that bonding occurs between active spots is the fact that liquid molecules will try to orient themselves to bring their active spots into juxtaposition with those on a substrate surface. Molecules in a solid, of course, are restrained from any extensive reorientation by the mechanical rigidity of the solid structure.

A layer of fatty acid soap molecules, which are polar at one end and nonpolar at the other, will be adsorbed from a soap solution by a metal substrate. This adsorbed layer will have its molecules oriented with their polar ends toward the metal and their nonpolar ends toward the solution. However if another layer of soap molecules is deposited on the first one, the second layer will try to orient itself with its nonpolar ends toward the nonpolar surface of the first layer. In such cases, the orienting influence of a solid surface may sometimes be felt across a number of adsorbed molecular layers, and the surface tension of the adsorbed film depends on the end of the molecule which is exposed in the outermost layer.

Actually, after the first layer of a liquid fatty acid is adsorbed on a metal, and the nonpolar ends of its molecules form a new surface, this surface has a lower energy than average for fatty acid in bulk; hence if bulk fatty acid is simply dropped onto this surface, its drops will not spread over it. This situation whereby unoriented molecules do not spread over an adsorbed film of identical molecules has been named by Zisman;[9] he refers to the adsorbed film as autophobic (self-hating).

Adsorbed films of water on hydrophilic surfaces are of special interest. If the layer of water is just thick enough so its outermost molecules cannot feel any attraction from the substrate, these outermost molecules will have the properties of free water, and the layer is called "duplex."[10] In experiments designed by Dr. W. Philippoff at The Franklin Institute,[11] it was found that the film of water adsorbed on powdered quartz is about 1.4×10^{-7} cm thick, which corresponds to about 4.5 molecular layers of water. The experiments were run by first bringing the powdered quartz into equilibrium with normal clean air (about 75°F, and 40 per cent relative humidity) and then heating it slowly until no more water was driven off, while measuring the weight of water evolved during heating. The results, Fig. 11, show that heating had to be continued above 1000°C to drive off the last water, which gives some idea of the attractive force between quartz and water molecules directly on its surface. Further experiments showed that the "tightly bound," or highly adsorbed, molecular layers could not be removed effectively at lower temperatures by applying a vacuum; the water molecules must have high thermal energies in order to escape from the quartz surface.

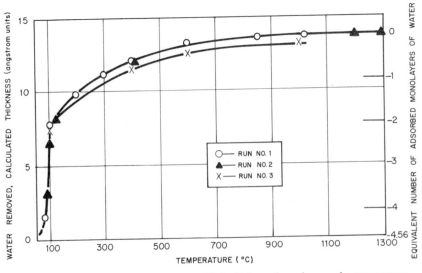

Fig. 11. Equilibrium water films on quartz. Their thickness depends upon the temperature.

It is reasonable to presume that most drying of water from hydrophilic surfaces preparatory to adhesive bonding will be at too low a temperature to drive off the last molecules of water; yet if the remaining molecules of water absorb the attractive force of the substrate and the adhesive does not know the substrate is there, resulting bond strengths should be inferior. The solution to this problem apparently is to use relatively polar or reactive adhesives that are capable of dissolving the water film, or of destroying it by chemical reaction, thereby getting right down to the substrate.

Surface Preparation

Much of the art of adhesive bonding is concerned with preparing the substrate surfaces before the adhesive is applied. Objectives are one or several of the following:

(1) To remove dust, scale, soils and liquids that could trap air or prevent the adhesive from contacting a "solid" surface.

(2) To etch or roughen the surface thereby giving the adhesive more surface area and more interlock with the substrate.

(3) Conversely, to plane or otherwise smooth rough surfaces so they can be brought into closer contact, and so an adhesive will flow better on them.

(4) To prime the surface by applying a thin, penetrating coat which will displace air from deep pores or cracks and/or inhibit corrosion.

(5) To seal the surface, bridging over or plugging large pores that otherwise would draw the adhesive away from the interface; also to size the surface so that the adhesive will not penetrate it too quickly.

(6) To treat the surface chemically so as: (a) to raise its surface energy (by oxidizing a polyethylene surface), (b) to coat it with an inert, firmly bonded layer, e.g., oxides or metals or (c) to passify the surface by the chemisorption of chromate ions, oxides, etc.

(7) To dissolve from the surface any airborne organics, mill oils, bleeding plasticizers, mold lubricants, etc., which lack mechanical integrity or attraction for the adhesive.

(8) To dry the surface, not only to remove gross layers of water but to remove as much as possible of any adsorbed liquid films.

(9) To electroplate the surface, thereby coating it with a metal which has greater attraction for the adhesive.

(10) To prime the surface after it has been prepared for bonding so that the substrates can be stored without fear of recontamination before they are bonded.

(11) Following any chemical treatments, to rinse the surfaces thoroughly to remove residual corrosive materials or soluble salts.

Although this is a formidable list, it is clear that some of these steps usually are unnecessary. The necessary action depends on the substrate, the adhesive, the performance desired in service, the subsequent bonding cycle, and the probable nature of the contaminants.

For glass, ceramics and minerals to be bonded with a water-based or hydrophilic adhesive, it often is sufficient to degrease (if necessary), wash in detergent solution, rinse copiously in hot water, and dry in relatively clean (dust and oil free) air. If the adhesive is relatively nonpolar and cannot take up water (asphalt or wax for instance), drying should be carried to well above 212°F, to drive off as much adsorbed water as is practical. Since these substrates are rigid, peel strength is unlikely to be a problem; moreover there is no real advantage to be gained by roughening the surface.

Metals can present three additional complications:

(1) The surfaces of base metals rapidly become coated with oxides which sometimes are too loose or too unstable chemically to be bonded.

(2) Metal surfaces, particularly with reactive adhesives, or adhesives that pick up water readily, or in joints containing voids, sometimes need to be protected or inhibited against corrosion by the adhesive, water, or other environmental vapors.

(3) Thin or soft metal substrates can be bent, and peel strength is important.

For relatively inert metals like stainless steel and titanium, which do not present oxide problems, (1) and (2) above are not serious. For these, degreasing followed by etching or sand or vapor blasting may suffice. If peel strength is unimportant, degreasing followed by a detergent wash and good rinsing and drying should be adequate.

With base metals that rapidly form oxides, the trick is to form on their surfaces an oxide which is well-bonded, strong, and inert to hydration or corrosive attack. If peel strength is required, the chemical bath also should etch the metal. The nature of the hydrated oxide that forms on aluminum, e.g., after acid-chromate etching, depends on the temperature of rinsing and drying. Temperatures above 160°F are likely to yield a hydrated oxide of poor mechanical integrity. Similar specific situations may be anticipated for other base metals.

It has been observed that if a hydrophilic surface is dried of water at a temperature as low as 160°F, it will possess three or four molecular layers of water as an adsorbed film. With relatively polar adhesives this water apparently dissolves in the adhesive during curing, since it does not appear to weaken the joint.

The various treatments that have been exploited for the passivation or protection of metals against corrosion will not be discussed here.

The practice of priming a prepared metal surface so as to protect it until it can be adhesively bonded has introduced flexibility into plant operations. Without protection, a prepared metal surface can become seriously contaminated by exposure to shop air for less than 24 hr. If a priming coat is used, but is not cured until after the adhesive is applied, it may be necessary to wrap the piece in a moisture-proof barrier so the uncured primer will not adsorb excess moisture from the air.

Most plastic and rubber substrates have lower surface energies than hydrophilic materials; hence they will not, if at all, strongly adsorb water films. Oxide formation and corrosion in normal environments similarly pose no problem. Depending on the material and design of the substrate, the special problems they may present are: (a) peel strength if the piece is flexible, (b) bleeding or syneresis if the substrate is plasticized and the adhesive cannot absorb the bleeding oils, (c) contamination by mold lubricants if such are used in their manufacture, (d) too low a surface energy to let the adhesive spread, as in the case of completely nonpolar resins such as "Teflon," polyethylene, etc. Here the approach is to convert, chemically, the surface to a higher-energy material.

Highly porous substrates may be sized or sealed to prevent drainage of the adhesive from the joint, or the adhesive may be plastic enough to not flow. If, however, one is relying on the suction of the substrate to pull solvent or water out of the adhesive, sizing may be required to keep it from leaving too quickly, i.e., before the adhesive has accommodated itself to the surface.

CHECK LIST

The following check list is offered as a review of the fundamentals of adhesive bonding:

(1) The adhesive or primer is in intimate contact with the substrate at all points.
  (a) The substrates before bonding are free of dust, oils, or other contaminants.
  (b) The adhesive or primer wants to spread on and wet the substrate.
  (c) The adhesive or primer is sufficiently fluid, under the pressures used and before it sets, to penetrate among the asperities of the surfaces.
  (d) The adhesive layer is not starved.
  (e) The adhesive layer does not contain gas bubbles.
(2) The adhesive joint is suitably strong.
  (a) The materials want to form a strong joint.
  (b) Modes of loading in service have been taken into account in the design of the joint.
  (c) The adhesive neither creeps at high temperatures or over long periods of time, nor cracks at low temperatures or under abrupt loading.
  (d) The joint is not weakened by thermal stresses or shrinkage stresses due to mismatch of expansion coefficients, evaporation or bleeding of oils and solvents, or orientation on aging.
  (e) If the substrates are flexible, their surfaces are etched and the adhesive is flexible and thin.
  (f) There are neither loose oxides at the interface nor attack of the substrates by the solvents or adhesives.
  (g) The adhesive has not picked up excess water or solvent during storage before curing.
  (h) Bonding occurred before the prepared surfaces could be recontaminated.
  (i) If the substrates were coated and dried partially before being mated under pressure, dry time and pressures were adequate.
(3) The joint is permanent.
  (a) It is free of voids where vapors and liquids could enter it.
  (b) It is not subjected to damaging gradients, and the materials are not unduly capable of diffusing oxygen, water, etc.
  (c) The substrates, if susceptible to corrosion, are passivated or inhibited.
  (d) There are no salts or soluble materials at the interface to cause blisters by osmosis.

References

1. Adam, N. K., "Physics and Chemistry of Surfaces," London, Oxford University Press, 1941.

2. Philippoff, W., Cooke, S. B. R., and Cadwell, D. E., "Contact Angles and Surface Coverage," *Mining Eng.,* **4,** (3), 283–286 (Mar. 1952); *Trans. AIME,* **93,** 283–286.

3. DeBruyne, N. A., "The Extent of Contact Between Glue and Adherend," Aero Research Technical Notes, Bull. No. 168 (Dec. 1956), Aero Research Limited, Duxford, England.

4. Eirich, Frederick R., "Rheology: Theory and Application," Vols. 1–3, New York, Academic Press, 1956–1959.

5. Hoekstra, J., and Fritzius, C. W., "Rheology of Adhesives," in Adhesion and Adhesives, edited by DeBruyne, N. A., and Houwink, R., New York, Elsevier Publishing Co., 1951.

6. Alfrey, Turner, Jr., "Mechanical Behavior of High Polymers," New York, Interscience Publishers, Inc., 1948.

7. Bingham, E. C., "Fluidity and Plasticity," New York, McGraw-Hill Book Co., 1922.

8. Thelen, E., "Preparation of Metal Surfaces for Adhesive Bonding," WADC Technical Report 57–513; Astia Document No. AD 142152 (1957).

9. Hare, E. F., and Zisman, W. A., "Autophobic Liquids and the Properties of their Absorbed Films," *J. Phys. Chem.,* **59,** (4), (1955).

10. Harkins, W. D., "The Physical Chemistry of Surface Films," New York, Reinhold Publishing Corp., 1952.

11. Thelen, E., "Surface Energy and Adhesion Properties in Asphalt-Aggregate Systems," Highway Research Board Bull. 192 (1958), National Academy of Sciences, Washington, D. C.

4

Roll Application of Adhesives

Raymond R. Myers
Lehigh University
Bethlehem, Pennsylvania

Adhesives application is a rheological problem, complicated to a certain extent by interfacial considerations. The technological difficulties that confront the adhesives producer are more intimately related to the application problems faced by the consumer than to performance characteristics of the adhesive; consequently, this chapter is devoted to the deformation and flow of liquid and plastic adhesives rather than to the behavior of the essentially solid end-product.

Adhesives application differs basically from adhesives performance in the state of matter under consideration. During application an adhesive must be in a permanently deformable state, and therefore, it must possess most of the features of a liquid. Proper performance, on the other hand, almost always demands that the adhesive yield little or not at all under stress, and therefore that it be essentially a solid.

The desired end result of roll application is the creation, on a substrate, of a uniform film of liquid which may then be cured as a coating, or joined subsequently with another film to form a sandwich. Therefore, expediency dictates that all sorts of coatings be considered as adhesives in uses which involve their application by rolls. Included in this broad category of adhesives are paper coatings and impregnants, textile sizing agents, paints, plastics, printing inks, linoleum, paper and cellulose tapes of the moisture-set and pressure-sensitive varieties, glazes, and sandwich constructions of all kinds. The common denominator in this heterogeneous listing is *surface coating*. The incident problems encountered in making suitable coatings are spreading, wetting and setting.

PHYSICAL PROPERTIES OF UNCURED ADHESIVES

In order to determine what rheological and interfacial conditions control the application of adhesives, one must be able to list and then measure the important physical properties of the adhesive which control the quality of the coating. Most properties involved in the transfer of material are mechanical properties, and this is certainly the case with wet adhesives. These properties determine the stresses encountered as the material is forced through a roll nip, and involve the shear-rate history of the adhesive during the short time in which contact is made between the roll and the substrate. The important mechanical aspects are discussed later in considerable detail. It is necessary, first, to describe the basic parameters which control transfer.

Viscosity

The important properties of the adhesive, itself, are the viscosity, elasticity, yield value, and their dependencies on shear rate. All of these parameters are familiar in the qualitative sense, but none of them are applicable with complete quantitative rigor to industrial problems of the type encountered in film application. For example, viscosity means resistance to flow in the minds of most users of rheological information, and yet the quantitative definition of viscosity reads something like this: *if two parallel plates situated one centimeter apart are gliding past each other with a velocity of one centimeter per second, and if the force per unit area on the plates is one dyne per centimeter squared, then the viscosity is one poise.*

Fortunately, this statement is expressible in simple mathematical terms,

$$S = \eta \dot{D} \tag{1}$$

if one disregards the possible dependence of η on instrument dimensions. Here $S =$ force per unit area, F/A; η represents the viscosity, or more precisely, the *shear viscosity*; and $\dot{D}$ is the shear rate in reciprocal seconds, because it is the quotient of a velocity term and a linear term representing the clearance:

$$\dot{D} = v/d \tag{2}$$

On the other hand, when a material is subjected to the type of stress that superimposes a compression or tension on the simple shear denoted by Eq. (1), a new type of viscosity, called *volume viscosity*, is introduced. The stress required to move an adhesive through a nip then depends not only on η, but also on the second coefficient of viscosity. At once, the mathematical expression becomes so complex that few physical scientists are willing to work with it. Technicians are even less inclined to turn to abstract mathematics for answers to everyday problems. And yet mathematical rigor is the main purpose of all of the research currently being conducted in rheology laboratories, especially in pursuit of an elusive quantity called *tack*, discussed below. It is necessary to express dynamic quantities in terms of quantities of motion called kinematics.

The objective, simply stated, is to express adhesive application in quantitative terms. In the simple case of Eq. (1), a *Newtonian liquid* is applied to one surface by another parallel surface. If the applicator is tilted so that the liquid is buttered onto the substrate, the kinematics of the operation become complex because the sharp trailing edge no longer tolerates laminar shear. Inertial effects and ultimate properties of the adhesive then become magnified out of proportion with viscous effects. Moreover, the adhesive is not likely to be a Newtonian liquid, in which case some viscous property or properties, which create a variable η, may play a major role.

Many industrial applications of adhesives are done by even more complicated procedures, such as spraying or rolling, than by the doctor blade described above. This chapter considers only rolling. Even if the adhesive is Newtonian, its application by rolls brings into play a perpendicular motion, involving a compression-tension sequence, which is added to the laminar shear situation described by Eq. (1). In fact, most of the force required to split the adhesive film from the departing face of the roll, is perpendicular to the roll face.

Therefore, the problem of roll coating evolves as a splitting of a liquid between two faces moving in opposition to each other. Volume viscosity, as well as shear viscosity, must be considered in roll application.

Elasticity

Some of the energy supplied by the application of stress to a material is stored energy, in contrast to that which is dissipated in overcoming viscous drag. The two recognized means of storing mechanical energy are by inertia (kinetic) and elasticity (potential), of which elasticity commands most attention as a possible determinant of the transfer and quality of the adhesive layer. Elasticity is not the sort of parameter one usually associates with the liquid state, and yet it is always present. If the time scale of the measurement is short enough to prevent relaxation of the applied stress (as, for example, with ultrasonics), any liquid will respond elastically. Polymeric materials have even longer relaxation times, and one would logically expect to find examples of adhesives which do not relax completely during their passage through a nip.

Tack

The behavior of all liquids under the circumstance just described is manifested as *tack*. Understanding starts with a qualitative definition which merely states that tack is the resistance to splitting; here again, one is confronted with the problem of supplying a quantitative definition so that tack can be measured and expressed in proper units. *Tack is the impulse* ($F \times t$) *per unit area necessary to separate two planes initially in contact through an intervening liquid or plastic layer.* If Ft is one dyne second per square centimeter, the tack is one unit.

The question, which presents itself, is whether tack is a true physical property of the adhesive, for it has not yet been demonstrated that fundamental material constants control the Ft product. Considerable evidence has accumulated which indicates that cohesive failure cannot be correlated with molecular quantities. Moreover, one can never be sure that the roll application of adhesives involves only cohesive failure. In many cases, adhesive failure at the applicator surface is sought.

The initial condition in the separation of surfaces is that the planes be in contact. The establishment of contact is not a condition which can be set arbitrarily, for then the tack impulse would depend on experimental conditions. In this regard, the means of measuring tack differs fundamentally from viscosity, where the spacing between the planes may be set arbitrarily. Most of the evidence regarding the formation of sandwich joints favors the concept that all materials possess a natural *contact point* which sets a maximum on the impulse which must be exerted in order to separate the surfaces. This concept serves as the starting point in measuring the *Ft* product of a given adhesive. Most frequently, the experiment tests *Ft* for a given *joint,* which depends on the fabrication conditions. The most convincing evidence of the existence of a contact point was provided by Heidebroek (Fig. 1).[1]

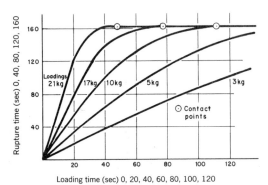

Fig. 1. Establishment of a natural contact point in an adhesive joint. Rupture load of 20 kg always requires 160 sec, regardless of compressive load, provided contact has been established. (*Adapted from Heidebroek and Pietsch*[1])

Even though the fundamental definition of tack involves true contact, and basic research must progress in this direction, the technology of roll application does not require the idea of a contact point to be invoked as a basis for understanding how tack influences adhesives application. This is a fortunate circumstance in studying the kinematics of the application of an adhesive by rolls, where a sudden impression is made and then broken, all in a fraction of a second. Clearly, any subjective estimate of tackiness which characterizes the application of a given adhesive under an arbitrary setting of the rolls will depend on the operating conditions; but conversely, the measurement will reflect the conditions fairly accurately.

The principal unresolved question is how can the artisan's measure of tackiness be reconciled with what the rheologist measures on an instrument. The subjective test may not coincide at all with the material parameters that constitute tack; the test may measure a different aspect of "resistance to splitting" than the *Ft* product. It may, for example, measure the maximum tension exerted on the substrate during application. Of course, the subjective test reveals important data, or else it would be discarded, but it does not necessarily measure tack.

Interfacial Properties

The adhesives manufacturer encounters a problem akin to the attainment of true contact, when adhesion to a specific substrate is to be achieved. Considerable controversy exists over the relative importance of the so-called interfacial aspects of adhesion and the rheological aspects, but this chapter cannot resolve the conflict. It seems sufficient to point out that a formulator who has not solved the problem of initial spreading of the adhesive and its wetting of the substrate should not be in the adhesives business; and therefore, one can conclude that the rheological aspects of adhesion are the only ones that govern the application step.

Interfacial aspects *are* important in the formulation of a commercial paste, however. The flow properties of any dispersed system depend on how well the particles are wetted by the liquid.[2] A short buttery adhesive results from a poorly wetted, flocculated dispersion. This type of dispersion will invariably be described as less tacky than a long, stringy fluid, yet either type may develop greater tensile pull on a substrate during its application, depending on the rate of separation of the applicator surface from the substrate. The presence of a trace of water can exert an enormous influence on the consistency of a paste, especially one made from a solid of high-surface energy and an oil of low surface tension.[3]

The *spontaneous wetting* of a substrate (Fig. 2a) is facilitated if the surface has high free energy and the adhesive possesses a low surface tension γ, for then the substrate surface S gives way to a substrate-adhesive interface SA and an adhesive surface A, with a concomitant gain in stability. The stabilization results from the net decrease in energy which occurs from the destruction of the high en-

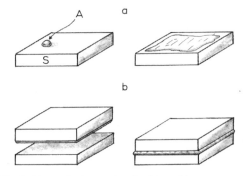

Fig. 2. Energetic changes involved in wetting.
  (a) Spontaneous wetting: $E = \gamma_S - \gamma_{SA} - \gamma_A$.
  (b) Induced wetting: $E = \gamma_S - \gamma_{SA} + \gamma_A$.
High surface tension opposes spontaneous wetting, but aids induced wetting. A high energy substrate S is beneficial in both cases.

ergy S surface. This overbalances the formation of a moderate energy A surface. If the surface free energy of S and the surface tension of A are about equal in magnitude (as they rarely are, since γ_A averages around 30 dynes/cm and γ_S can mount into the hundreds), then spontaneity in spreading is favored by a low interfacial energy γ_{SA}.

On the other hand, *induced wetting* of an interface (Fig. 2b) is favored by a large γ_A value. Here the new adhesive surface is preformed. The initial surfaces are S and A, and the final "surface" is the interface SA. Energetics of the process are favored by a high γ_A, and wetting occurs whenever γ_S and γ_A exceed γ_{SA}.

These considerations, and others in the realm of interfacial chemistry, all apply to specific problems in adhesion, rather than to the generalities. They enable one to postulate beforehand whether a particular adhesive-substrate combination will adhere if given a chance. They tell nothing of the overriding influence of cohesion in many practical adhesion problems, nor of the stresses which develop when an adhesive changes state after application.

The *breaking* of a freshly applied adhesive is the antithesis of induced wetting, and is the main subject of this chapter. The controlling interfacial parameter in a strictly cohesive break is the surface tension of the adhesive, and the energy required is 2γ. Subsequent sections reveal that surface tension cannot possibly account for the variety of responses shown by adhesives and other materials to cohesive fracture, despite the fact that roll application generally involves this type of failure, as stated earlier.

Ultimate Properties

Elasticity and viscosity are parameters which describe how an adhesive behaves inside certain prescribed limits, but they do not define the ultimate strength of an adhesive. Inasmuch as this property is the one which the consumer pays for, at least in structural adhesives, a certain amount of attention must be given to the parameters which determine the ultimate strength of an adhesive.

In the first place, it must be recognized that the ultimate strength of a material often depends on its geometry and on the rate of application of strain. These factors are important in the testing of structural adhesives, which by the nature of their function are necessarily solids. The major concern regarding ultimate strength in the application of viscous adhesives involves the maximum tension which the adhesive can maintain under the dynamic conditions of roll coating.

Ultimate strength and related properties are exceedingly hard to measure with even a fair de-

gree of reproducibility, in contrast to the remarkable constancy in viscosity and elasticity. Reasons for this difficulty are varied[4] but they all stem from the fact that breakage involves a physical discontinuity of stress, of extension, and of the material under study. This discontinuity creates difficulties of a mathematical nature, superimposed on the experimental problems and on the disconcerting fact that thermodynamic calculations of ultimate strength invariably are several orders of magnitude higher than the measured strength.

The fact that roll coating smooths out the incidences of rupture into a steady state condition is not a complete solution to the problems enumerated above. The statistical nature of the process of roll coating alleviates the experimental problem, and somewhat reduces the mathematical difficulties, but the thermodynamic objection remains. In theory, the tensile strength, P, of a liquid can be expressed in terms of the coefficient of thermal expansion α and the compressibility β[5].

$$P = T\left(\frac{\alpha}{\beta}\right) - P_A \qquad (3)$$

The last term represents the ambient pressure, which usually is 1 atm. For most liquids β is of the order of 10^{-4}/atm and α is about 10^{-3}/deg; consequently, the theoretical value of P is thousands of atmospheres, inasmuch as the temperature, T, is several hundred degrees Kelvin.

The technologist engaged in adhesives applications which involve the ultimate strength of liquids finds that he must temporize by dealing in yield value[6] in place of ultimate strength. This substitution is not wholly acceptable because yield value is also a property which one associates with solids under static loading, not with liquids under transient strain. The more closely an adhesive approximates a solid, the more closely yield value approximates tensile strength.

Yield values are most appropriately derived from the point of breakage under static loading (Fig. 3a), but more frequently (and less rigorously), they are obtained from the intercept of a flow curve (Fig. 3b), whose slope is called the plastic viscosity. In essentially liquid systems, this latter method is the only one available at the present time.

If an adhesive has a large yield value, it generally exhibits *shear-thinning** characteristics[7] to a high degree. A certain amount of shear thinning is desirable in paper coatings, wall paints, plastisols, printing inks, tile adhesives, and the like. *Shear*

---

* This property is described in the literature under various names: plasticity, pseudoplasticity, thixotropy, and shortness.

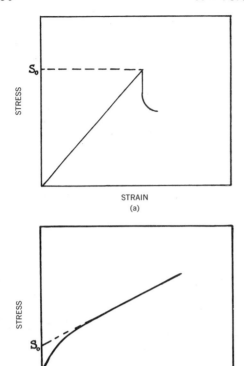

Fig. 3. Determination of yield value.
        (a) Yield under static loading.
        (b) Yield values from flow curves.
Both of these schematic drawings are idealized. Hookean
behavior is not likely to be obeyed up to the yield point
in Fig. 3a, and the flow curve of a shear-sensitive liquid
does not usually become linear in the high shear region
as indicated in Fig. 3b.

thickening is to be avoided in high-speed applications
because blockage and chattering of the rolls will
result, and the adhesive layer will be uneven.

Numerous other adhesive properties could be
considered, but those not mentioned here are all
of special, rather than general, interest. One such
property is the temperature coefficient of viscosity[8]
and the similar response of elasticity. Another is
the time dependence of structure buildup, which
is often described as thixotropy, and which controls
the post-application qualities of a coating, such as
paint leveling or sagging, or the preservation of the
integrity of printed halftone dots, or the stipple
effect which often accompanies roll application of
heavy-bodied adhesives.

Transfer Constants

The end result of the interplay of physical properties is the transfer of the adhesive from roll to
substrate. Walker[9] has analyzed the transfer of ink
from printing plates to paper and has produced a
reasonably accurate transfer equation of the form

$$Y = b + f(x - b) \qquad (4)$$

where Y, the amount of ink transferred, depends
in a linear fashion on x, the film thickness of material on the plate. Transfer constant, b, determines
the amount of coating immobilized by the substrate, and the constant, f, reflects the location of
the split with respect to the plate and substrate.

An equation of this nature should be of great
value in adhesives technology, where the thickness
of a given coating must be controlled closely either
for economic reasons or for the purpose of securing
maximum performance.

THE NATURE OF FILM SPLITTING

Most early investigations of tacky phenomena
were done with flat plates[10]. Equations have been
developed for the tension on two such plates supporting a single column of liquid, such as one encounters in a taffy pull, for instance. The basic

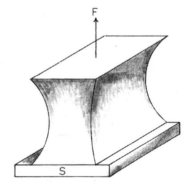

Fig. 4. Extension of a single filament. Tension, F, per
unit area determines the pull on the substrate, S. Filaments do not have circular cross sections in the roll
application of adhesives until near the end of their lives.

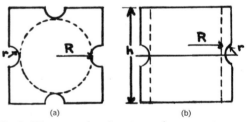

Fig. 5. Filament and cavity cross section parameters.
        (a) Cross section through center of filament.
        (b) Side view of filament and cavity.
Equivalent cylindrical radius is approximated by R as
long as cavities are small; cavity radius is approximated
by r as long as cavities are spherical. (*Courtesy Transactions
of the Society of Rheology*)

equation for the extension to rupture of a single filament (Fig. 4) is a result of the work by Stefan[11]:

$$F = \frac{3\eta R^4}{4th^2} \qquad (5)$$

where tension, F, is observed to depend on the time of separation, t, the viscosity, η, and two geometric quantities: the initial clearance, h, and the radius, R, of the filament.

Note that both sides of Eq. (5) can be multiplied by t to produce a relation for the impulse, Ft.

Filamentation

At high separation rates, the situation described by Stefan fails to apply. Rapid separation is accompanied by the breaking of the film into numerous, closely spaced filaments. Here the rheological equation of state must take into account some factor other than η, for the tendency of the liquid to split into filaments must be accounted for in a quantitative sense. This area of study is the objective of research described later in this chapter, in which the cavitation process, which produces the multiplicity of filaments, is discussed. Under conditions of copius filamentation the pillars of liquid occupy the interstitial region between cavities (to be described later), and therefore have cusped cross sections. In this case, R is the equivalent cylindrical radius as shown in Fig. 5.

Roll application of adhesives begins with essentially turbulent* conditions in the bank (or bead) upstream from the nip, progresses through a laminar shear region in which progressively larger shear

---

* Turbulence involves the density of the adhesive as a material parameter; however, this term varies little, and is of no great consequence in this discussion.

rates are encountered as the liquid passes the nip center, and ends with the normal or perpendicular shear that is necessary in the development of tack. Filaments are present at this last stage of separation. They are easily visible at the free boundary of splitting liquids (Fig. 6), and form webs or streamers as the material is drawn back into the nip.

Cavitation

The emergence of a freshly applied adhesive from the nip of the applicator roll is inevitably in the form of discrete filaments, as described above. Prior to filamentation, the adhesive may cavitate, depending on separation velocity. In order to demonstrate and further study the cavitation region, Miller and Myers[12] designed a film-splitting apparatus which permitted the innermost reaches of the roll nip to be viewed. A cone was rotated without slippage on the surface of a glass disc (the "Discone"). Each surface was covered with a polymeric material simulating an adhesive. They were able to secure microsecond exposures of the nip action from a vantage point *inside the nip*.

Figures 7a and 7b are four-microsecond photographs taken at two different roll velocities with a 200 poise hydrocarbon, polybutene. The roll velocity in Fig. 7a is approximately 0.2 cm/sec, and the direction of motion of the contacting cone and disc surfaces is toward the bottom of the photograph in the form of arches, concave downward. The merging boundary of the films is represented by the wavy line. The smooth area with striations is the contact area or nip of the rolls. These striations are polishing marks on the metal cone. Separation of the film at low speeds proceeds by simple flow into

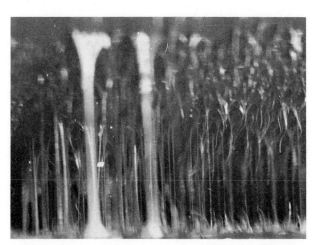

Fig. 6. Termination of film splitting by filamentation. Head-on view of filamentation, downstream from the applicator nip. (*Courtesy of the Interchemical Corporation*)

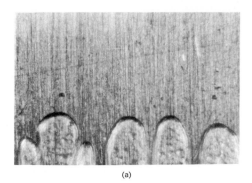

(a)

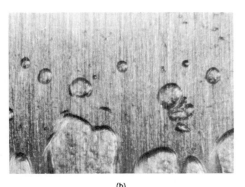

(b)

Fig. 7. High speed photographs of film deposition on a substrate. Microsecond exposures from beneath a transparent substrate at the moment of impression show a) the presence of filaments at low-rim velocities, and b) the onset of cavitation at U product greater than critical. Direction of motion is from top to bottom. (*Courtesy Transactions of the Society of Rheology*)

a unique web pattern perpendicular to the rolls. This pattern of flow is called the *first regime of splitting*.

Figure 7b portrays the splitting mechanism at roll velocities above 20 cm/sec. The formerly clear-cut boundary flow at the nip exit has disappeared and in its place is a discontinuous pattern which is the result of the filamentation shown in Fig. 6. Cavities whose size depends on the distance in the direction of flow from the splitting or cavitation line can be seen in the contact area between cone and disc. A definite increase in cavity size can be observed from the line where the cavity is first visible to where its life ends. This pattern of flow is called the *second regime of splitting*.

High-speed motion pictures also showed two additional characteristics of the free boundary which can only be observed by projection of the sequences on a screen. When a cavity grows to a large size and approaches the splitting interface, an implosion of the cavity occurs because its pressure is considerably less than atmospheric. The distance from the nip at which this implosion oc-

curs is not apparent from the still photographs, but is evident in motion pictures.

The Four Regions of a Roll Nip

Analysis of the area of contact between a roll applicator and the substrate with an intervening sandwich of adhesive is so complex that it is convenient to divide the area into four regions, as shown in Fig. 8. These regions are discussed independently.

The bank region precedes the point of juncture of the wetted applicator and the substrate. Adhesive flows in opposition to the motion of the surfaces in this region. More material contacts the approaching roll surfaces than can pass through the nip, and consequently some of it is rejected. This region is of no further interest as far as the thickness or evenness of the coating is concerned, although considerable attrition of floccules if any are present occurs in the turbulent streams which characterize the bank region.

The shear region exists between the point of nominally initial contact of adhesive with substrate and the point where this contact is nominally lost. Adhesive flows in the same direction as the surfaces, but at a more rapid rate, thereby creating a parabolic velocity gradient throughout the region. This condition obeys the established relations for laminar shear, and is most appropriately called the hydrodynamic shear region. Shear rates rise from zero to a maximum at the center of the region, then decrease again to zero at the end.[2]

The cavitation region appears as soon as the distance between applicator and substrate equals the film thickness of the adhesive. Film thickness is established by the clearance at the point of initial contact. Its effect on the location of the boundary between the cavitation and shear regions is readily visualized if a material balance is made of the material entering and leaving the nip. In the cavita-

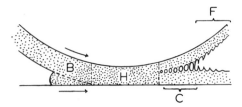

Fig. 8. Four regions inside a roll nip. Bank region, *B*, exists to left of first plane of no shear (vertical dashed line on left); hydrodynamic shear region, *H*, extends to second plane of no shear, at which cavitation begins. Cavitation region, *C*, gives way to filamentation region, *F*, when the adhesive becomes the discontinuous phase.

tion region, the cavities exist as a rarified discontinuous phase in a continuous matrix of adhesive.

The filamentation region is characterized by the inversion of the roles played by the adhesive and the cavities. As the cavities emerge on the downstream side of the nip they coalesce and become the continuum; on the upstream side, the adhesive remains as a collection of pillars or filaments extending between the freshly covered substrate and the departing applicator surface. Localized shear gradients are experienced inside the individual filaments. The lines of principal strain are directed at a 45° angle from the surfaces, thereby producing a reduction in cross-sectional area of the filaments as elongation proceeds. The consistency of the adhesive is of paramount importance in this region because the filament length and its pull on the substrate are determined by the relative contributions of elasticity and viscosity.

Shear Inside the Nip

Profiles of velocity and pressure[13] through the nip are particularly revealing of the way the liquid is sheared (Fig. 9). They show, for example, that in virtually every application of an adhesive by rolls, the liquid passes through a *plane of no shear* at the boundaries between the bank/shear regions (Fig. 10) and the shear/cavitation regions. Cavitation has recently been demonstrated to be a necessary consequence of high-speed roll application because no liquid is able to maintain the enormous tensions created downstream from the nip center. Dispersed or pigmented systems are even less capable of maintaining great tensions because the pigment particles act as nucleants for the film rupture.

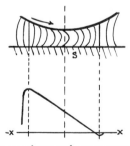

Fig. 9. Velocity envelopes and pressure profile through a roll nip. As adhesive passes from $-x$ to $+x$ the shear rate, D, decreases from finite values to the left of the plane of no shear, to zero, then to a maximum in the center of the hydrodynamic shear region, then back through zero to finite values in the cavitation region. Bowing of envelope to the left indicates negative shear rates in the vectorial sense. Pressure rises to a maximum at the first plane of no shear, then drops to a minimum at the point of cavitation. (*Courtesy Journal of Colloid Science*)

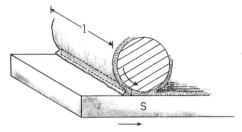

Fig. 10. Plane of no shear at the bank/shear region boundary. A hypothetical plane of width, h, exists at the nominal line of initial contact of adhesive (of thickness h) and substrate. Material to the left of this plane moves in opposition to the roll direction and forms a bead at the leading boundary of the nip.

Cavities are much more copious and are much smaller when solid particles are present.

Because of the breaking up of the fluid into discrete filaments, the kinematics of roll application are enormously complex. The rheology of film application is deeply involved in hydrodynamic theory, in nucleation phenomena, in tensile strength, and in surface chemistry. The role of viscosity is exceedingly great, but in searching for the dynamic components that make up tack, one must not overlook elastic components such as surface tension, the pressure-volume product of any gas present in the cavities, and the rigidity modulus (elasticity) of the adhesive. Because roll application is of such a sudden occurrence, the presence of elasticity is likely to be felt since the passage of material through the nip may occur in a time shorter than the relaxation times of some of the more unwieldy molecular species. The flexing of a roll occurs as often as hundreds of times per second. At this rate many commercial adhesives respond within a large portion of their relaxation time "spectrum."[14] In brief, rapid roll application brings out some of the elastic characteristics of polymeric materials, but not all.

ROLL COATING OF ADHESIVES

The practical aspects of roll application of films are numerous. The calendering of tile and plastics,[15] the finishing of leather, the manufacture and application of paints and printing inks,[16] the coating of paper, gear lubrication[17] and gear pumping are a few areas in which the passage of liquids through a roll nip is of vital interest.

Regimes of Flow

The velocity-viscosity ($U\eta$) product is the most important variable in roll applications. The flow of a liquid through the nip and its subsequent splitting obey one pattern when the $U\eta$ product is low, and another pattern if it is high. The difference between these two patterns lies in the onset of cavitation which characterizes the second regime. Factors other than $U\eta$ which control cavitation are the tensile strength of the film, irregularities of the surface, film thickness, nip clearance, force on the roll, and the amount of slippage of the roll on the substrate.

In the first regime, the adhesive undergoes alternate compression and distension, neither of which is very great. The entering material takes on the shape of a wedge in conformity with the approaching roll and substrate surfaces. As it moves toward the constriction, it accelerates. The pressure peak coincides with the zero shear situation described above as the plane of no shear (Fig. 10). To the left of the pressure peak, the net flow is outward, away from the nip, and upstream. To the right of the pressure peak, all the material is caught up in the streamlines that pass all the way through the nip. The acceleration is greatest in the interior of the liquid with the result that the velocity profile is bowed into a parabolic envelope, as shown in Fig. 9.

The pressure profile possesses a center of symmetry. Originally, the pressure was thought to describe a sine wave.[18] Later, a wave of the form $\sin\theta\cos^3\theta$ (where θ is a dimensionless parameter related to the horizontal distance from the nip center) was introduced to describe a pair of rolls.[19] It is not constructive to consider other variations.

Practical interest centers on the second regime, which describes high-speed roll application. In this regime the stresses which are applied to the adhesive and to the substrate alternate between high compression and weak-to-moderate tension. The pressure profile is asymmetric.

Lack of symmetry is of no great practical consequence, however. The important aspect of second regime kinematics is that the formation and subsequent enlargement of cavities is the only means of providing transfer of adhesives from the applicator to the substrate. Whereas plenty of time exists at low-application rates for the free boundary of adhesive to alleviate the tension by flowing backward toward the nip, the time allotted for stress relief at high rates is too small, and fracture occurs inside the liquid.

Dynamic Aspects of Roll Application

Stresses involved in roll coating can be calculated for supposedly Newtonian adhesives, although the calculation need not be restricted to Newtonians.

In fact, it is not at all evident that viscosity will retain its place as the prime determinant of tack in second-regime dynamics. Elastic responses become increasingly important as the critical $U\eta$ product is exceeded by a wider and wider margin. Acceleration terms, while present, are conveniently disregarded in elementary considerations of roll nip dynamics. Both of these factors must be considered in actual practice.

In the bank region of the nip, most of the film is in turbulent motion. Flow of the adhesive is characterized by swirls or eddies, where acceleration terms cannot be ignored; consequently, analysis of the bank region cannot be performed adequately at the present time. Fortunately, this facet of roll application does not appear to be as important as those discussed below.

In the hydrodynamic shear region of the nip, most of the adhesive is in steady laminar motion, and consequently the neglect of acceleration is permissible. The equation describing the pressure, P, of adhesive on adherend at any point inside the nip is given by[13]:

$$P = \frac{12U\eta\,(2Rh_0)^{1/2}}{h_0{}^2}\left[1/4\,(1 - h_1/h_0)\sin 2\,\theta\right.$$
$$\left. + 1/2\,(1 - 3h_1/4h_0)\,\theta - \frac{h_1}{32\,h_0}\sin 4\,\theta\right] + C \quad (6)$$

where U is the rim velocity, h_0 the minimum clearance, R the applicator radius, and h_1 the entrance clearance. The term θ is a dimensionless function of the two clearances; for example,

$$\tan\theta_1 = \left(\frac{h_1}{h_0} - 1\right)^{1/2}$$

The quantity h_1 is a constant. It represents a particular value of h at a distance x_1 from the nip center where the pressure profile attains a maximum. The distance x_1 represents the point of initial contact of the adhesive. The ratio h_1/h_0 is a parameter of the system varying between 1 and 4/3.

The pressure is a complex function of the distance from the nip center, but is not too difficult to interpret in physical terms. First of all, the coefficient of the terms in the bracket determines the span between maximum pressure and maximum tension; it is the amplitude term within which the undulations in pressure described by the bracket must operate. Second, the bracket contains two additive terms in θ (or distance from nip center), the first of which describes the differential between inlet and outlet pressures, or pressure head maintained by the roll. The other superimposes a sigmoidal pressure profile on the steady increase. It is this rapidly changing pressure decrease which supplies the main characteristics of the pressure profile and is responsible for the hydrodynamic shear through the nip which terminates in the cavities described above.

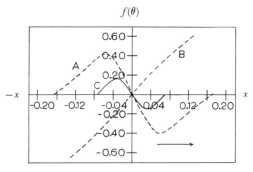

Fig. 11. The two characteristic terms of the nip pressure profile Curve A represents the characteristic term, $\sin \theta \cos \theta \, (0.74-2.17 \cos^2 \theta)$, which has the essential features of the pressure profile in Fig. 9. Curve B represents the characteristic term, 0.740, which denotes the overall pressure head imparted to the adhesive as it is pumped through the nip. The composite is indicated by Curve C.

TABLE 1. TYPICAL ADHESIVES APPLICATION CONDITIONS.

$\eta = 150$ poises

$U = \quad 8$ cm/sec (rim velocity)

$R = \quad 2.5$ cm (applicator radius)

$h_o = 3 \times 10^{-3}$ cm (center clearance)

$x_1 = -x_e = 3.5 \times 10^{-2}$ cm (entrance distance)

$\sqrt{2\,Rh_o} = 0.12$ cm

$$\frac{h_1}{h_o} = \frac{x^2}{2\,Rh_o} + 1 = \frac{(0.035)^2}{(0.12)^2} + 1 = 1.085$$

$$\theta_1 = -\theta_e = \arctan\left(\frac{x_1}{(2\,Rh_o)^{1/2}}\right) = \arctan 0.29 = 0.28$$

Table 1 gives a particular evaluation of Eq. (6) from conditions found on a typical low-speed application of an adhesive.*

Eq. (6), with these values substituted, becomes

$$P = 2.4 \times 10^7 \, [\sin \theta \cos \theta \, (0.74 - 2.17 \cos^2 \theta)$$
$$+ 0.74\, \theta] + C \qquad (7)$$

where 2.4×10^7 is an amplitude term† in dynes/cm² established by the material and geometrical constants of Table 1. It is called the *coefficient*. C is a constant which can be adjusted to bring the magnitude of the minimum pressure to the experimental value. The major task is to identify the two θ terms inside the bracket. They are called *characteristic terms*.

Figure 11 is a plot of the two components of Eq. (7) within the brackets as a function of x, the distance from the center of the nip.

The graph shows clearly that two characteristic terms of the equation play opposite roles. The first term behind the bracket is responsible for the *pressure gradient through the nip*, which establishes the amount of shear imparted to the adhesive. The second term establishes the *pressure head* imparted by the applicator, and is of more concern to a designer of gear pumps than coating machinery. The physical consequence of this term is an overall pressure increase, or pumping action.

The effect of the *wedge parameter*, h_1/h_0, on the composite curve is of interest. When the ratio is

* One atmosphere is 10^6 dynes/cm².

† The author is indebted to R. D. Hoffman for assistance in this analysis.

unity, the film just passes between the rolls at the center, and no discernible pressure is created because the wedge of liquid has no taper. The pressure cannot exceed the limit imposed by a wedge parameter of 1.33 (or 4/3). A "maximum effective film thickness" is attained which even complete immersion of the applicator does not affect (except for a small hydrostatic effect). In the operating conditions of Table 1, a maximum pressure of roughly 50 atm occurs at a maximum effective film thickness of 40 microns.

The adjustable constant, C, imposes a *bias* on the pressure. It is necessary because the equation must fit a determined value of the minimum pressure at x_e. The pressure at this point cannot be determined from the equation because it reflects a cohesive property of the liquid, while the theory considers only viscous properties.

Pressures as high as hundreds of atmospheres are attained, but tensions approaching those magnitudes are unknown; and yet, the pressure gradient through the nip maintains a steady downward trend between the entrance and exit planes of no shear. Cavitation not only sets the absolute limit on tension, but it also reduces the pressure gradient all the way through the nip.

Cavitation Dynamics

Viscosity is the only material constant which was considered in the calculation of nip pressure. On the other hand, if viscosity were the only mechanical property involved in tack, excellent correlations would have appeared in the literature between η and performance characteristics of adhesives. They have been conspicuously absent. Not only must the inconstancy of η be invoked as a partial explanation of this dilemma, but also the possible role of the other mechanical properties discussed earlier must be considered. The degree of involvement of these other parameters can be considerable. They enter the picture at a point at which Eq. (3) breaks down, namely, at the onset of cavitation which characterizes all high-speed roll applications.

Reference has been made earlier to the enormity of the problem of fitting a rheological equation of state to the cavitation region. The solution to the problem came with the discovery of a certain degree of order in the spacing of the cavities, and consequently in their size. Subsequently, the growth rates of the cavities have been analyzed and have provided excellent agreement with the deductions from cavity count. These two approaches are described separately.

Analysis by Cavity Population. If the number of cavities per unit area is denoted by B, the dynamics of film splitting in the cavitation region can be calculated from the simple relation between cavity population and $U\eta$ (velocity-viscosity) product:

$$B = K(U\eta - U_0\eta) \tag{8}$$

This equation is vaguely similar to the Von Weimarn equation for the rate of nucleation[20]

$$\text{Rate} = \frac{C - S}{S} \tag{9}$$

which states that the extent to which the instantaneous concentration, C, of the separating phase exceeds its saturation concentration, S, determines the rate of formation of nuclei per unit volume. The cavity count, B, in the Discone[12] was based on area, rather than volume, in which case the dynamic term of Eq. (8), $(1/K)$, emerged with the dimensions of ergs per cavity:

$$\frac{1}{K} = \frac{\eta}{B}(U - U_0) \tag{10}$$

However, when a direct dependence of tack energy on film thickness, h, was observed, both on a gross scale[21] and in the Discone (transparent substrate) analysis, the only way in which a constant energy of separation could be obtained, free from experimental variables, was by introducing the thickness term to give:

$$\frac{h}{K} = k = \frac{h\eta}{B}(U - U_0) \tag{11}$$

In order for k to have the dimensions, ergs per cavity, $1/B$ must be expressed as centimeters per cavity. This intuitive approach to the significance of the cavities is not as rigorous as one would prefer, but the conclusions which can be drawn from the constancy of k are entirely plausible. The constant spacings between cavities are substituted for the steadily decreasing filament radii, R, which are the chief determinants of stress in a pull normal to the surface.

Inspection of photographs of numerous cavitating conditions has revealed that for a given liquid type, the $U\eta$ product is truly prophetic of the cavity population, which in turn, practically fingerprints the conditions of split. With liquid adhesives one can judge at least semiquantitatively how much tensile pull has been imparted to the substrate. This knowledge may be important in paper impregnation, for example. Critical $U\eta$ products of hydrocarbons of widely varying η fall close together; linseed oil and other fairly polar liquids behave similarly, both in $U_0\eta$ and in the slope of the $U\eta$ versus B relation. In general, the types of vehicles used in formulating adhesives will all have $U_0\eta$ around 25 dynes/cm (about the same magnitude as surface tension); on the other hand, $U_0\eta$ for pastes generally falls below 2.0. Surface tension is not the only cavitation variable, but it appears to impose a limit on the cavitation resistance of a liquid.

Pigmentation of course complicates the situation. $U_0\eta$ drops practically to zero with the introduction of these excellent nucleants, as observed above, and the slightest separation velocity leads to more or less brittle fracture of the sandwich. One must not be led to the conclusion that pigmentation weakens an adhesive, for the true test of ultimate strength lies in the ability of an adhesive to withstand static loading where U is virtually zero. The lowered $U_0\eta$ value reflects increased shortness in the system; first regime kinematics simply do not prevail in this type of material.[22]

Analysis by Cavity Growth. An alternative to the calculation of tack dynamics via cavity population is to perform a statistical analysis of the growth of single cavities as a function of time. This analysis can be performed by the projection of high-speed cinematographic sequences, one at a time, and measuring the dimensions of selected groups of cavities.

In this analysis[23] the averages of the major and minor axes of the cavities were measured as a function of distance from the center of the applicator nip in the Discone.[12] Distance was divided by the roll velocity to convert the argument into the time variable, and when cavity size was plotted versus time, the growth rate was found to be constant. This fortunate circumstance permitted the velocity term, dr/dt, to be used in the same sense that U was employed in the earlier analysis. For simplicity,

dr/dt is given the symbol v. An early analysis of cavity expansion into an infinite viscous medium by Westerfield and Pietenpol[24] expresses the expansion tension as

$$P = \frac{4\gamma}{r} + \frac{12v\eta}{r} \qquad (12)$$

where P represents the pressure difference between the cavity wall and infinite depth in the adhesive, and r is the cavity radius, as before. This equation neglects changes in kinetic energy, which is tantamount to assuming low growth rate.

More recently, Poritsky[25] developed a more general equation including acceleration (inertial) terms, which when simplified, resembles Eq. (12) in all respects except the constant term and the fact that kinetic energy is considered:

$$P = \frac{2\gamma}{r} + \frac{4v\eta}{r} + \frac{3}{2}\rho v^2 \qquad (13)$$

The ρv^2 term describes the kinematics of cavity expansion as revealed by the sequential photographs. It was insignificant in the case under consideration, but must be reckoned with in high-speed applications. Density is represented by ρ.

Under conditions in which the kinetic energy term can be discarded, the term which governs the tension is the quantity, $\frac{\gamma + 2v\eta}{r}$. In general, the surface tension contribution is about 7 per cent of the viscous contribution. Both have the same dependence on cavity radius.

Filamentation Dynamics

Theoretical considerations of pressure profiles in the hydrodynamic shear region of the nip, and of the cavity spacing in the cavitation region, have shown that the tension exerted by an adhesive on a substrate cannot vary over wide limits. On the other hand, considerably more energy (in contrast to force) is expended in the rupture of filaments if the adhesive is of a "stringy" nature than if it is "short" or "buttery." The net result of a relatively long period of filament elongation is to provide a larger impulse (Ft) for a given force of separation. Consequently, one can say with a certain amount of quantitative rigor that a resilient, elastic, adhesive is more tacky than a soft, plastic, adhesive. The instantaneous tension on the substrate may not deviate widely between the two compositions, because the tension is defined by the ultimate strength of the adhesive, and yet the expenditure of energy during filament elongation may be many times larger in the case of the tacky adhesive. Tensile strength, in conjunction with the separation velocity and the nip geometry, determines the spacing of the filaments.

The viscous forces retarding the elongation of the filaments, Equation (5), also die out rapidly as the clearance, h, increases. Therefore, the only means of prolonging the tension in the cavitation-filamentation region is by incorporating elasticity in the adhesive formulation. This term was not considered in the developments based on the splitting of Newtonian liquids, nor has it been adequately studied experimentally. The main unsolved problem in the splitting of materials of commercial interest concerns the isolation and evaluation of the elastic response.

A demonstration of the effect of elasticity in an adhesive has been provided by Erb and Hansen.[26] These investigators used high speed cinematographic sequences to show the onset of cavitation from a different vantage point than that used by Miller and Myers. By photographing a sandwich of the material at the instant of split, they detected not only a marked difference in cavitation behavior among polymeric materials, but also a strong elastic pull in certain instances.

The existence of an elastic response was unmistakable. The apparatus was constructed so that an impact loading of the top block of the sandwich separated it catastrophically from the bottom block, which was not anchored. Then, when an impulse of sufficiently long duration (literally, of large Ft product) was transmitted through the intervening liquid layer, the energy was great enough to propel the bottom block away from its cradle.

An unexpected bonus of the Erb and Hansen studies was that differences between adhesive and cohesive failure were demonstrated.

The chief proponent of the filament elongation approach to tack dynamics is Voet.[27] His work has culminated in the concept of "tack energy density," which is reminiscent of the cohesive energy density sometimes used in connection with the testing of cured adhesives under static loading. The dynamic situation encountered in measuring tack energy is more complex than that encountered in tensile testing of solids because viscosity is superimposed on elasticity. Moreover, force is a rapidly decaying function of distance of separation in the dynamic case.

APPLICATION PROBLEMS

Whether one measures the dynamics of adhesives application or calculates them from kinematic information is not the most important question facing the adhesives manufacturer. The real problem is to employ this knowledge in laying down the optimum amount of adhesive in a perfectly even layer with a minimum of surface asperities. The possible role of interfacial properties must be understood and exploited to its fullest extent while the rheological mysteries are being unfolded.

Some of the application problems to be solved in roll applications are discussed below insofar as rheology and surface chemistry can help in their solution.

Coating Thickness

The consumer wants "mileage" out of the expensive stuff he applies to surfaces. Moreover, he wants the strongest bond possible as a premium. The answer is found in coating thickness, where an optimum depth must be achieved in order to maintain proper balance of all the desired conditions. In routine applications the control of coating thickness will continue to be done subjectively by arbitrary settings of roll clearance and viscosity. In putting new adhesives on stream these two variables may not permit sufficient latitude in operation, and the technologist may have to learn more about the relaxation time of the adhesive, or the wettability of the roll and substrate.

Percentage transfer of adhesive from roll to substrate may turn out to be the prime determinant of whether a large coating operation is marginal or not. Transfer is particularly important in moving large quantities of low-viscosity material onto porous substrates, as in the coating or impregnating of paper. Coating thickness cannot be increased beyond reasonable limits imposed by the rapid viscous response of thin, watery, materials; consequently, the only avenue of exploration is to improve the percentage transfer at a given roll thickness. A few per cent improvement may effect great economies.

Pick

Perhaps the most troublesome problem encountered in the coating of weak substrates such as felt, paper or a fresh coating of another adhesive is the problem of pick. No other problem is more amenable to improvement by rheological analysis than this one. Certain types of substrate failure undoubtedly arise from the inability of the microstructure to withstand large transient tensions. Other failures occur because of the persistence of force over a long period of time relative to the sojourn time in the nip.

The $U\eta$ product provides some insight into the causes of pick, especially in operations on the threshold of picking. After the onset of cavitation, however, $U\eta$ appears to be more instrumental in establishing the spacing of the cavities than in setting the force requirement. The energy dissipated during separation may actually decrease as a result of increased cavity population. On the other hand, the energy stored in the filaments undoubtedly increases at a fast rate as U increases.

Coverage

The most important interfacial property is the efficiency with which the adhesive wets a substrate. This problem can be misleading because the spreading of the coating over a surface is often confused with wetting in the thermodynamic sense. The problem of coverage may be a composite of the difficulties encountered in spreading (rheological) and those in wetting (interfacial). Poor coverage may be manifested as (1) adequate overlay of adhesive but a paucity of attachments, (2) a clear distinction between bare and covered areas, but still, with an adequate quantity of adhesive to cover the area with a uniform layer if the interface were so disposed, or (3) a starved condition in which wetting and spreading both appear to be satisfactory, and yet an insufficient amount of adhesive is present to establish the necessary contact with both surfaces of a joint.

Patterning

The difficulties in securing an even coating are inherent in all the problems described above. Sometimes the uneven texture becomes the main problem. Different trades use different names for the development of a pattern in a coating, such as mottle, tracking, herringbone, etc., and the causes may be just as varied. The filamentation region is involved in this aspect of adhesives application, for the pattern left after impression often resembles the webs in the free boundary of the nip. The existence of this problem suggests that one of the rigidity phenomena (yield value, elasticity) is involved, or else, that the viscosity of the adhesive is much larger after deposition than during its passage through the nip.

Pattern is not uniquely found in roll coating. Brush marks can be found in paints whose viscosity or yield value are too high to permit the disappearance of the striations before the advent of drying. The best evidence of gross patterning is supplied by the separation of two wetted flat plates. Incidentally, cavitation minimizes gross pattern by providing centers for the migration of liquid into the filaments as they lengthen, rather than requiring all of the flow to be directed inward from the periphery.[28]

Power Requirements

The effect on the substrate of the expenditure of energy has been mentioned, but an equally important consideration in high-speed application of heavy bodied adhesives is the necessity of shearing the material at high rates inside the nip. The fact that the stress requirements are directly proportional to the shear rate, attests to the magnitude of the problem if the proportionality coefficient (η) is high, but at the same time it suggests that there are only two ways to alleviate the power requirement: either the viscosity at high shear, or else, the shear rate must be lowered. Conceivably, one can lower η at high shear rate without changing the post-application consistency of the adhesive (by increasing the shear sensitivity of the adhesive); or one can reduce the shear rate at a given roll speed (by increasing the clearance). These solutions are not independent of each other; in fact, the variety of interactions among the geometrical factors, operational variables, and material constants is quite large.

Ways of Measuring Tack

The final problem is an academic one. Tack has not yet been satisfactorily defined in absolute units as, for example, have elasticity and viscosity. The elusive nature of tack undoubtedly stems from the fact that it is a composite of these two material parameters if not more; but this complication is not as serious, fundamentally, as the dependence of the tack impulse on clearance. Removal of this dependence by using Heidebroek's criterion of contact is not a complete answer because of doubts which still exist regarding its generality.

Two basically different ways exist for the measurement of tack dynamics. They are (1) measurement of the transient pressure-tension sequence during the fleeting moment of contact, and (2) measurement of the gross, steady torque imparted to the rolls by the resistance of the adhesive to passage through the nip.

Transient pressure studies were used by Bergen and Scott[15] to study the pressure profile of tile calendaring. The information obtained by this method appears to be most useful in delineating the stresses of a compressive nature which are transmitted by the adhesive. It has not been successfully applied to the cavitating situation chiefly because tile is not supposed to cavitate.

Another transient method has been developed by Curado,[29] but this development has not been formally reported. It utilizes a small flat hammer oscillating normal to the surface of a flat anvil, whose response to the oscillation is detected by means of a strain gage. Strasburger[13] has measured transient responses to impact loading, with particular emphasis on recording the tension portion of the pressure profile. Eschenbach[30] has recently contributed to the piezoelectric measurement of transient tensions.

Steady state dynamics have not been as popular as transient measurements. Some of the conventional adhesive tests could be (and no doubt are) used in testing uncured adhesives, but the resulting information is likely to be too compromising to be useful. The one instrument specifically designed for measurements on the entire roll system, in contrast to the innermost reaches of the nip, is the Reed inkometer.[31] This instrument rates tackiness according to the torque imparted to an idler roll by the cavitating liquid and elongating filaments. It appears to be based on sound principles, but some controversy exists over its applicability, possibly because the torque which is developed is excessively responsive to the latter stages of elongation of the filaments where the stress has decayed to a small value, but the lever arm which provides the torque has increased several fold.

Steady state methods are so different fundamentally from transient methods that a comparison of the two is out of the question. The hardest decision which the adhesives technologist has to make in developing or purchasing a tack instrument is to clarify in his own mind the question which he wished to ask of Nature before putting that question to an expensive test. Transient studies are oriented more toward the fundamental aspects of tack, and are, therefore, less immediately applicable as referee methods than steady state measurements. Each approach has its drawbacks.

Future work should be directed toward developing a tack-measuring device which incorporates the best features of both methods. One logical starting point is the roll system of Reed with provision for measuring directly the stresses normal to the roll surfaces, rather than the tangential components of those stresses. Either the steady normal pull could be recorded by means of a balance, or some form of integrated output of a crystal should be displayed on a dial or counter.

A large untapped source of knowledge exists in the realm of *dynamic properties,* one example of which is dynamic viscosity.[32] The propagation of stress waves through adhesives will reveal at least twice as much information about their mechanical properties as will simple shear. The development of a tack measuring apparatus may have to wait until more is learned about bulk properties of polymeric systems. Bulk properties are usually studied dynamically, and are valuable because they provide a new dimension for the characterization of liquids and pastes. The second coefficient of viscosity, as this new dimension is called, may eventually become the most valuable parameter in the evaluation of the application behavior of adhesives.

References

1. Heidebroek, E., and Pietsch, E., *Forsch. Gebiete Ingenieurw.,* **12,** 74 (1941).
2. Myers, R. R., Miller, J. C., and Zettlemoyer, A. C., *J. Appl. Phys.,* **27,** 468 (1956).
3. Kruyt, H. R., and Van Selms, F. G., *Rec. trav. chim.,* **62,** 407–415 (1943).
4. Alfrey, T., Jr., "Mechanical Behavior of High Polymers," Vol. VI, 476–525, New York, Interscience Publishers, Inc., 1948; Bull, T. H., *Phil. Mag. Ser.* 8, **1,** 153 (1956); Bull, T. H., *Brit. J. Appl. Phys.,* **7,** 416 (1956).
5. Glasstone, S., "Textbook of Physical Chemistry," 2nd Ed., 480, New York, D. Van Nostrand Co., Inc., 1946.
6. Green, H., "Industrial Rheology and Rheological Structures," New York, John Wiley & Sons, Inc., 1949.
7. Myers, R. R., Brookfield, D. R., Eirich, F. R., Ferry, J. D., and Traxler, R. N., *Trans. Soc. Rheol.,* **III,** 205–206 (1959).
8. Andrade, E. N. da C., *Nature,* **125,** 309, 582 (1930).
9. Walker, W. C., and Fetsko, J. M., *Am. Ink Maker,* **33,** 12, 38 (1955).
10. Banks, W. H., and Mill, C. C., *J. Colloid. Sci.,* **8,** 139 (1953).
11. Stefan, M. J., *Sitzber. Akad. Wiss. Wien, Math.-naturw. Kl. Abt.* **II,** 69, 713 (1874).
12. Miller, J. C., and Myers, R. R., *Trans. Soc. Rheol.,* **II,** 77 (1958); Myers, R. R., Miller, J. C., and Zettlemoyer, A. C., *J. Colloid Sci.,* **14,** 287 (1959).
13. Frazer, R. A., *Phil. Trans. Roy. Soc. London. Ser. A.,* **225,** 93 (1926); Ardichvili, G., *Kautschauk,* **14,** 23 (1938); Gatcombe, E. K., *Trans. Am. Soc. Mech. Engrs.,* **67,** 177 (1945); Cohn, G., and Oren, J. W., *ibid.,* **71,** 555 (1949); Gaskell, R. E., *ibid.,* **72,** 334 (1950); Finston, M., *J. Appl. Mechanics,* **18,** 12 (1951); Paslay, P. R., *ibid.,* **24,** 602 (1957); Parish, G. J., *Brit. J. Appl. Phys.,* **6,** 256 (1956); Strasburger, H. J., *Colloid Sci.,* **13,** 218 (1958).
14. Baker, W. O., and Heiss, J. H., *Bell System Tech. J.,* **31,** 306 (1952).
15. Bergen, J. T., and Scott, G. W., *J. Appl. Mechanics,* **18,** 101 (1951).
16. Zettlemoyer, A. C., and Myers, R. R., "The Rheology of Printing Inks in Rheology, Theory and Applications," Eirich, F. R., ed., Vol. 3, Chapter 5, New York, Academic Press, 1960.
17. Gatcombe, E. K., ref. 13; Hersey, M. D., and Lowdenslager, D. B., *Trans. Am. Soc. Mech. Engrs.,* **72,** 1035 (1950).
18. Sjodahl, L., paper presented at the first annual meeting of the Technical Association of the Lithographic Industry, Chicago, Ill., Apr. 15, 1949.
19. Banks, W. H., and Mill, C. C., *Proc. Roy. Soc.,* **223A,** 414 (1954).
20. Von Weimarn, P. P., "Die Allgemeinheit des kolloiden Zustandes," Dresden, Th. Steinkopff, 1925.
21. Voet, A., "Ink and Paper in the Printing Process," p. 68, New York, Interscience Publishers, Inc., 1952. See also Ref. 27.
22. Miller, J. C., *Ph.D. Dissertation,* Lehigh University, June 1956.
23. Hoffman, R. D., unpublished data.
24. Westerfield, E. C., and Pietenpol, W. B., *Phys. Rev.,* **55,** 306 (1939).
25. Poritsky, H., *Proc. First Intern. Congr. Appl. Mechanics* (1951).
26. Erb, R. A., and Hansen, R. S., *Trans. Soc. Rheol.,* **4,** 91–116 (1960).
27. Voet, A., and Geffken, C. F., *Ind. Eng. Chem.,* **43,** 1614 (1951).
28. de Bruyne, N. A., *Paint Technol.,* **9,** 211 (1944), Hoffman, R. D., unpublished data.
29. Curado, J. G., private communication.
30. Eschenbach, W., and Wagenbauer, K., *International Bulletin for the Printing and Allied Trades,* to be published.
31. Reed, R. F., *Am. Ink Maker,* **17,** 27 (1939).
32. Ferry, J. D., *et al., J. Colloid Sci.,* **8,** 1, 224 (1953); **9,** 479 (1954); **10,** 1, 474 (1955); **12,** 53, 327, 400 (1957); **13,** 103, 459 (1958); **14,** 36, 135, 147, 222, 239 (1959); *J. Am. Chem. Soc.,* **72,** 3746 (1950); **77,** 3701 (1955); *J. Phys. Chem.,* **58,** 987 (1954); **59,** 658 (1955); **60,** 289, 294 (1956); *J. Appl. Phys.,* **24,** 679 (1953); *Rev. Mod. Phys.,* **31,** 130 (1959).

— 5 —

Properties, Testing, Specification and Design of Adhesives

Marco Petronio

U. S. Army Ordnance
Frankford Arsenal
Philadelphia, Pennsylvania

PROPERTIES

There are a number of general factors that require consideration in the evaluation of an adhesive. These factors pertain to the behavior of an adhesive from the time the adhesive is made to the moment the ultimate bond is accomplished. They are commonly referred to as the working properties and include such characteristics as viscosity or consistency, storage life, working life, coverage, blocking, tack, penetration, and curing rate or rate of strength development. Their importance becomes apparent when one seeks to obtain the same adhesive from batch to batch with respect to its physical properties and application. Several standard test methods are available for obtaining this information. Unless otherwise specified, the atmospheric conditions surrounding the specimen prior to and during the test shall be 73.5 ± 2°F and 50 ± 4 per cent relative humidity.

Consistency (Viscosity). Adhesive materials are not simple fluids. In general they consist of polymers, usually in solvents and often compounded with powders of various physical or chemical properties. It is not surprising therefore that adhesive materials do not exhibit Newtonian flow, and the characterization of the rheological properties of adhesives requires more than one measurement. To characterize fully the rheological properties of a non-Newtonian adhesive for practical purposes, it may be necessary to plot curves of strain rate versus shear stress and thixotropic shear stress versus time, in addition to accumulating a family of curves at various temperatures and degrees of cure. Obviously, except for special circumstance, this procedure would be too time-consuming and costly when many adhesive materials are involved. Instead devices which are flexible in their operation and adaptable to a wide variety of measurements are used.

There are a number of test methods available for evaluating the flow properties of adhesives. ASTM method D-553 describes two procedures for determining the viscosity of rubber cements containing organic solvents as differentiated from latex cements or dispersions of rubber in water. The "funnel" method gives closely duplicable results but is limited in use to those cements having viscosities which permit sufficient rapid flow through the funnel to avoid excess loss of solvent. The "falling cylinder" method is adaptable to rubber cements having a wider range of viscosities and offers some advantages in control testing due to ease of manipulation.

ASTM test method D-1084 is intended for determining the consistency of free-flowing adhesives. Three methods are covered, of which the first is applicable only to adhesives that will deliver 50 ml in a steady uninterrupted stream of the sample adhesive in from 30 to 100 sec at standard conditions. The apparatus consists of a set of four consistency cups, one of which is shown in Fig. 1, each having an orifice of one of four diameters ranging from 0.07 to 0.25 in.

Consisting of a Brookfield synchrolectric viscometer, the second method is intended for measuring the consistency (viscosity) of Newtonian

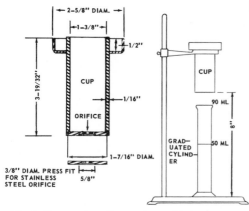

Fig. 1. Cross section of cup and assembled apparatus.

adhesives ranging from 50 to 200,000 cps. The third method is intended primarily as a control method for determining the consistency of adhesives which are Newtonian liquids. The apparatus consists of a Stormer viscometer with a double flag paddle-type rotor actuated by a falling weight. This method is limited, however, to self-leveling adhesives thereby eliminating thixotropic and plastic materials the viscosity of which is a function of rate of stirring and previous history of the adhesive.

Storage Life. When an adhesive is stored for a considerable length of time under extreme temperature conditions, physical and chemical changes may occur. Storage life of an adhesive is the time during which an adhesive can be stored, preferably under controlled conditions, and remain suitable for use. ASTM method D-1337 provides a means for determining the storage life of an adhesive. This is realized by requiring the measurement of either the consistency of an adhesive or the bond strength, or both, before and after storage at a specified temperature and for various periods of time. The adhesive and all of its components, if there are any, are stored in their original and unopened containers.

Some adhesives may be seemingly impaired by exposure to low temperature but can be restored to satisfactory service by slight warming and agitation. Some solvent-based adhesives, for example, separate at temperatures of 30 to 40°F but can be reconstituted by stirring at room temperature. The undesirable effects of low temperature are not limited to water-based adhesives. Although adhesives may be apparently unaffected by being frozen and thawed once, they may be affected by repeated cycling.

Often it may be impractical to conduct extensive room temperature storage tests. The only alternative is to conduct the test at elevated temperatures. Accordingly, it is not uncommon to expose adhesives to a temperature of about 120°F for 30 days. Although an accelerated test of this nature will shorten the storage life test from 6 months or a year to 30 days or so, it may also cause changes in the adhesive which may not occur at room temperature. Generally, it is advisable that the adhesive be stored at a temperature close to actual service conditions and the time when changes in the adhesive occur be observed. To determine these changes both the consistency test and bond strength test should be periodically conducted.

Working Life. The working life of an adhesive is the time elapsing between the moment an adhesive is ready for use and the time when the adhesive is no longer usable. *Pot life* is another term commonly used for working life. ASTM method D-1338 covers two procedures applicable to all adhesives having a relatively short working life. This method purports to determine whether the working life conforms to the minimum specified working life required of an adhesive by determining the change in consistency or bond strength or by both. The method applies to self-contained liquid or paste adhesives, to adhesives requiring addition of a catalyst, hardner, filler, thinner, etc., or combinations of two or more of these materials just prior to use, as well as to powdered or flaked adhesives which are dissolved in water or other solvents and are used as liquid or paste adhesives.

Coverage. Coverage is that property of an adhesive which determines the extent to which an adhesive can be uniformly spread over an area to be bonded with a unit weight or volume of adhesive. Two ASTM methods exist. D-898 describes a procedure for determining the quantity of adhesive solids applied in a spreading or coating operation; whereas D-899 describes a procedure for determining the quantity of liquid adhesive applied in a spreading or coating operation. The amount of spreading or coating weight is expressed in pounds per thousand square feet of surface area to be bonded and is the solvent-free gross weight of the adhesive on the surface, whether resulting from a single spread, double spread (spread on both contacting surfaces) or multiple applications of adhesives.

Blocking. Blocking is the undesirable adhesion between touching layers of similar or dissimilar materials such as that which occurs under moderate pressure or during storage. In some applications, adhesives are applied to one or both of the surfaces to be bonded and stored until ready for use or assembly. It is essential that the coated surfaces do not bond or block during storage even if subjected to slight contact pressure or minor variations in humidity or temperature. Adhesives will block in various degrees, from none at all to complete bonding. Invariably impairment of the adhesive will occur when an attempt is made to separate members which have completely bonded.

ASTM method D-1146 is intended for determining the blocking point of a coating of potentially adhesive material, i.e., those materials in a substantially nonadhesive state which may be activated to an adhesive state by application of heat or solvents. Since some potentially adhesive materials are both thermoplastic and hygroscopic, this method provides means for estimating both thermoplastic and hygroscopic blocking. Since some requirements are more strict than others, two varying degrees of blocking are defined. First degree blocking is an adherence between surfaces under test to such an extent that when the upper specimen is lifted, the lower specimen will cling thereto but may be parted with no evidence of damage to either surface. Second degree blocking is an adherence between surfaces to such an extent that when the surfaces under test are parted, one surface or the other will be found to be damaged. The two types are referred to as cohesive and adhesive blocking, the former being blocking between two similar, potentially adhesive faces and the latter being the blocking of a potentially adhesive face and a standard test surface.

Tack. Tack is that characteristic of an adhesive which causes one surface coated with an adhesive to adhere to another on contact. Essentially it is the "stickiness" of an adhesive. An adhesive having this characteristic to a high degree is spoken of as having *quick tack* or an *aggressive tack;* moreover, it is one of the most important properties in determining the suitability of an adhesive for particular applications. Associated with tack are *dry tack,* which is the property of certain adhesives to adhere on contact to themselves, at a stage in the evaporation of volatile constituents even though they seem dry to the touch, and *tack range,* which is the period of time in which an adhesive will remain in the dry tack condition. The measured value of tack may vary with time, temperature, and film thickness.

ASTM has published[1] a suggested method of test for the measurement of tack of adhesive. The method makes use of a weighted cantilever bar machine[2] whereby tack is determined by the pull required to effect cohesional parting of the adhesive.

Penetration. The control of adhesive penetration into porous materials is important to manufacturers of asphalt laminated kraft paper, multilayer corrugated board, fiberboard, grocery bags, and multi-wall shipping bags. The foremost requirement for an adhesive is to "wet" or intimately contact both surfaces to be bonded. An adhesive which penetrates far below the surface of the material being coated contributes nothing to the bonding of two materials and is wasted. When excessive substrate penetration occurs, adhesive costs are increased; furthermore, a starved "glue line" or adhesive layer may result and a wet or soggy product may be obtained which could lead to warpage, reduced production speeds, and processing delays.

Claxton[3] has devised an interesting penetration test which is in the process of adoption by ASTM. The method consists of applying a measured quantity of adhesive, normally 0.20 ml, on the topmost layer of a stack of four or five sheets of Whatman's No. 4 laboratory filter paper. Immediately thereafter the entire assembly is placed in a hydraulic press where 100 psi pressure is applied for a period of 15 sec. After the assembly is removed from the press, each sheet of filter paper is examined for depth of penetration. As an aid in detecting the presence of adhesive on each of the papers, special techniques are used, such as an iodine staining solution for use with starch adhesives or phenolphthalein solution for silicate and other alkaline adhesives. Usually a comparison is made of adhesives having different antipenetrants or of any two adhesives being evaluated.

Curing Rate. Many adhesives require curing by either the application of heat or the addition of catalyst, or both, with or without pressure for specified periods of time. Since it is often desirable to know the variation in bond strength with rate of cure, ASTM has issued a recommended practice, D-1144, which provides a means of determining the rate of strength development of adhesive bonds when cured at time intervals of $\frac{2}{3}$, $\frac{3}{5}$, $\frac{4}{5}$ and $1\frac{1}{5}$ the time prescribed by the adhesive manufacturers. The specimens used for determining the strength properties of the adhesive bonds may be either the tensile specimen (D-897) or the lap shear specimen (D-1002).

TESTING

Evaluation of the chemical, physical and other characteristics of adhesives helps in predicting the performance and reliability of an adhesive bond. Testing provides a measure of quality control of the adhesive material, adequacy of the bond formed, acceptability against specifications and other criteria of economic importance.

Perhaps more than most other classes of materials, evaluation of adhesives requires specialized test methods. In testing, not only is the adhesive material evaluated but also the bonding technique which includes preparation of the surface, application of the adhesive, and the curing of the adhesive.

There is considerable and useful literature on test methods for measuring the physical as well as other characteristics of adhesives. Almost without exception, these methods utilize specimens of standard dimensions, shape and design prepared specifically for the purpose. The resulting data are important in establishing comparative characteristics of adhesives.

It is difficult however from these standard test data to predict the performance of adhesives when subjected to varying stresses and environmental conditions. Few, if any, adhesive bonded configurations will even remotely resemble the standard test specimen in shape or dimension. Even when it is feasible to cut specimens from a larger object, the tests of such specimens cannot be relied on to reveal the probable performance of the integral object itself. Recognizing the difficulty of evaluating with reliability the probable performance of an adhesive assembly on the basis of either the standard test specimens or tests of specimens cut from the article itself, one must arrive at a test method which is adaptable to the specific case at hand and at a specimen design that most closely resembles the particular article to be used.

The accuracy and reproducibility of test results will depend on the conditions under which the bonding process is performed. Before starting any evaluation, the individual conducting the tests should have complete information on each of the following variables:

(1) Procedure for preparing the surfaces prior to application of the adhesive, including the moisture content of wood, the cleaning and drying of metal surfaces, and special surface treatments.

(2) Complete mixing directions for the adhesive.

(3) Conditions for application of the adhesive, including the rate of spreading, thickness of film, number of coats to be applied, whether to be applied to one or both surfaces, and the conditions of drying where more than one coat is required.

(4) Assembly conditions before application of pressure, including the room temperature, per cent relative humidity and whether there should be any open or closed assembly time. Unless otherwise specified, the atmospheric conditions surrounding the specimen prior to and during the

test shall be $73.5 \pm 2°F$ and 50 ± 4 per cent relative humidity.

(5) Curing conditions, including the amount of pressure to be applied, the length of time under pressure, and the temperature of the assembly when under pressure. It should be known whether this temperature is that of the glue line or of the atmosphere at which the assembly is to be maintained.

(6) Conditioning procedure before testing unless a standard procedure is specified, including the length of time, temperature, and relative humidity.

Numerous test methods have been developed by government and industrial investigators and task groups. Many have been prepared under the auspices of ASTM Committee D-14 on Adhesives, and a continuing effort is being made to develop new test methods. Therefore the reader is advised to consult the latest publication of ASTM and Federal Test Standards for the most recent amendments and revisions. Described below are some essential features of existing test methods in determining the strength properties of adhesives and factors which affect the permanence of adhesives.

Strength

Tensile. An adhesive is in tensile loading when the acting forces are applied perpendicularly to the plane of the adhesive. The tensile strength of an adhesive bond is the maximum tensile load per unit area required to break the bond. It is expressed in pounds per square inch. ASTM method D-897 is intended for determining the comparative tensile properties of adhesives when tested in standard shape specimens and under defined conditions of pretreatment, temperature and testing machine speed. The method describes spool-type specimens for both wood-to-wood and metal-to-

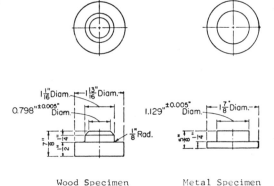

Wood Specimen   Metal Specimen

Fig. 2. Adherends for tensile test specimens.

metal adhesives. Figure 2 illustrates the shape of one adherend of each specimen. The test specimens are similar in shape except that in order to minimize the probability of wood failure, the bond area is reduced proportionally to the cross-sectional area of the adjacent wood. The specimen is loaded by means of two U-shaped grips which fit over the annular boss at the end of each half of the specimen.

Either the wood or metal specimen can be adopted for determining the tensile strength of adhesives between dissimilar materials, and this is readily accomplished by interposing the dissimilar material between the two adherends. Thus by applying adhesive to both sides of a thin material such as rubber, plastic, leather or glass and sandwiching it between the two wood or metal adherends the bond strength of two different materials can be determined. This technique is particularly advantageous when one of the materials to be bonded cannot be used as an adherend either because of lack of strength, e.g., rubber, or a material difficult to machine such as glass.

A variation of the sandwich specimen for dissimilar materials just described is a specimen for determining the bond strength between two low strength or difficult-to-machine materials. Thus, for example, by bonding a 1 in. square of glass cut

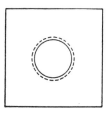

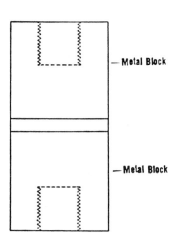

—Metal Block

—Metal Block

Fig. 3. Centered and axially loaded tensile specimen.

from a microscope slide to one metal adherend and a thin sheet of rubber to the other metal adherend, bond strength determinations can be obtained for glass-to-rubber adhesives, the only limitation is that the bonds between the glass and metal and between the rubber and metal be greater than the adhesive bond between the glass and rubber. Similarly, tensile bond strengths between glass-to-glass, plastic-to-plastic, rubber-to-rubber, etc., can be determined.

One major difficulty arises with the spool-type tensile specimens. Cleavage is introduced in testing the specimen, which results in substantially lower strengths. For example, an adhesive that will demonstrate a tensile strength of 6500 psi when tested in a center and axially loaded specimen illustrated in Fig. 3 will fail at about 3700 psi using a spool-type specimen, even though self-aligning grips are used. Koehn[4] has demonstrated by means of high-speed motion pictures (3000 frames per sec.) that cleavage does occur, and concludes that with rigid adhesives the spool-type specimen gives significantly lower values than the center-loaded specimen. However, when a nonrigid or low modulus adhesive is used, the difference between the spool-type and the center-loaded specimens is not large.

ASTM method D-1344 describes cross-lap specimens for determining the tensile properties of adhesives. This test was especially designed for the adhesion of glass either to itself or to other materials. The glass block (1 by 1½ by ½ in.) is easily cut from plate glass; the cross lap consists of two glass blocks assembled at right angles to provide a 1 sq in. of bonded area. Self-aligning grips holding at the extending edges of each block pull the specimen apart in testing. The maximum tensile load is expressed in pounds per square inch.

Shear. Shear stresses are those forces which act in the plane of the adhesive layer and reflect the total stress exerted by the adherends along the adhesive plane which tend to slide the adherends in opposite directions. A pure shear stress actually cannot be attained with specimens commonly used in adhesive tests, but since pure shear stress is rarely encountered in adhesive assemblies, conventional test specimens are adequate for most purposes. The shear strength of metal-to-metal adhesives is determined by ASTM method D-1002. This method is intended for determining the comparative shear strengths of adhesives for bonding metals when tested on a standard specimen and under specified conditions of preparation and testing. The form and dimensions of the specimen are illustrated in Fig. 4.

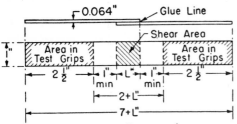

Fig. 4. Lap shear tensile test specimen.

The recommended length of overlap (L) for most metals of 0.064 in. thickness is 0.5 ± 0.05 in. The maximum permissible length of overlap between metal strips may be computed from the following relationship:

$$L = \frac{Yt}{r}$$

where
L = length of overlap in inches
Y = yield point of adherend (or the stress at proportional limit)
t = thickness of adherend in inches
r = 150 per cent of the estimated average shear strength in adhesive bond in pounds per square inch

This formula also may be used with some nonmetallic adherends where the yield point of the material will permit its use. It is undesirable to exceed the yield point of the adherend in tension testing. A variation in thickness of the metal and the length of overlap will influence the test value and make direct comparison of data questionable.

Bond strengths of lap shear specimens are directly proportional to the width of the specimen but as the length of overlap increases, the unit strength decreases due to stress concentrations at the edges of the overlap. It is possible to illustrate the distribution of stress in a lap shear specimen by showing the relative portion of the load carried by the edges of the overlap. Lap shear specimens with a 1 in. overlap were prepared with an adhesive which when tested resulted in a tensile shear strength of 3000 psi. Specimens were then prepared with the same adhesive by coating only the lapped edges with a ¼ in. band of adhesive, making a total bonded area of ½ sq in. The specimens now averaged 2500 lb or failed at a unit stress of 5000 lb/sq in. In other words, the center ½ sq in. of bonded area of a completely bonded specimen contributed only 500 lb of strength to the total 3000 lb. This illustrates in a simple manner the high stress concentration in the specimen.

In lap shear specimens an optimum film thickness exists. Bond strengths will decrease when films are very thin or thick. For maximum bond

strengths the optimum will vary with adhesives of different moduli. The thickness varies from about 2 mils for high modulus materials to 6 mils for low modulus materials.

Lap shear specimens can be used for determining the shear strengths of dissimilar materials in a manner similar to that which was presented for the tensile specimens. Thin and inherently weak materials such as plastics, leather, and fabrics are sandwiched between the metal adherends and tested. It is important to maintain the thickness of the overlap to a minimum in order to reduce deflection in the specimen during testing.

Wood-to-wood specimens are tested in shear by tensile loading in a plywood construction as outlined in ASTM method D-906. The specimens conform to the shape and dimensions shown in Fig. 5. There are several reasons for this choice of specimen. The plywood construction is one of the more typical applications of glued wood construction and the cross-laminated construction results in moderately severe and typically stressed assembly. The 1/16 in. veneer thickness for the specimen in this test was selected somewhat arbitrarily because it was considered to be quite typical of hardwood veneer in actual use; it was relatively easily obtained; it was thin enough to permit rather rapid penetration of heat and moisture to and from the glue lines; and it was thick enough to prevent excessive failures in the face of the specimen when a 1-sq in. shear area are used. The specimen size also was small enough to handle efficiently in large volume tests.

Shear strength of adhesives can be determined also by compression loading, rather than tensile loading. ASTM method D-905 describes a standard specimen for determining the compression shear strengths of adhesives for wood and other similar materials. The specimen conforms to the shape and dimensions shown in Fig. 6 and is tested between self-aligning bearing blocks of the testing machine to ensure uniform lateral distri-

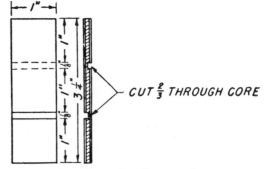

Fig. 5. Plywood tensile test specimen.

bution of the load. An adhesive will demonstrate higher bond strengths when tested in compression shear specimens than when using tensile lap shear specimens. The higher bond strength is ascribed to better stress distribution.[5]

Peel. The peel test involves the stripping of a flexible member of an assembly that has been bonded with an adhesive to another member that may be flexible or rigid. For example, cloth bonded to cloth or cloth bonded to metal may be tested in peel. The test consists of pulling the flexible member at an angle of 90 or 180 degrees so as to induce peeling. Failure may occur in the flexible member, in the adhesive, or in the rigid member. The 180 degree test for peel or stripping strength of adhesives is described in ASTM method D-903

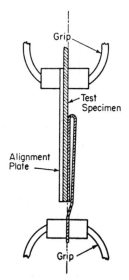

Fig. 7. Peel specimen in test grips.

and strength is expressed in pounds per square inch of width. The 90 degree stripping test is described in ASTM method D-429, which provides a means for determining the pull necessary to separate a rubber strip from a metal plate. Strength values are expressed also in pounds per inch of width. Figure 7 illustrates a peel specimen under test.

A recent test method has been published by ASTM for determining the peel strength or stripping characteristics of adhesive bonds by the climbing drum technique. This method is intended primarily for bonds between metal facings and cores of sandwich constructions and between metal laminates when one member is flexible. Furthermore, it can be used for determining the peel resistance or bond strength of a laminated material having one member flexible enough to bend smoothly over the surface of the drum and strong enough to withstand the peel loads. The peel torque includes both the forces required to break the bond and to bend the flexible member. The average peel torque is reported in inch-pounds per inch width of specimen.

The stress distributions in a peel test are complex, and the force required to initiate and maintain stripping is influenced by the width of the specimen, the mechanical properties of the adherends, and the strength of the adhesive. The width of the flexible adherend is usually specified as 1 in. Care must be taken in cutting the adherend to avoid overheating or mechanical damage to the bond. In testing, the flexible adherend is bent sharply (180 degrees) on itself causing deformation as its yield point is exceeded and resulting in undue stresses in the exposed adhesive layer. A small

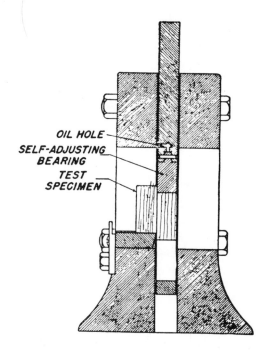

OIL HOLE
SELF-ADJUSTING
BEARING
TEST
SPECIMEN

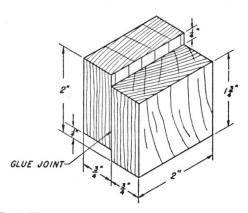

GLUE JOINT

Fig. 6. Shearing tool and compression shear specimen.

change in adhesive strength or thickness of adherend will result in a large variation of the peel force. For this reason the average force over a 5 or 6 in. length pull is taken as an indication of the peel strength. An alternate method is to calculate the area under the stress versus distance curve as a measure of the work done or the strength of the bond.

Another precaution is necessary in the 180 degree peel test. The flexible member is rubbed on itself as the test is performed. To reduce the friction created, a suitable fluid may be used such as oil, glycerin or soap solution, provided it does not deleteriously affect the adherends or the bond. When the flexible member is a porous material such as cloth, the thickness of the adhesive layer and the degree of penetration of the adhesive into the cloth are difficult to control. This is another source of variation in peel strength. When one considers all the conditions which require careful control, it becomes apparent that the peel test is a very sensitive method for the determination of bond strength.

Impact. The standard method of evaluating the impact strength of adhesives is described in ASTM method D-950. The specimen consists of two blocks, which may be made of wood or metal, bonded together as shown in Fig. 8. In testing, the lower and larger block is held in the vise-like grip of the machine and the upper block is struck by a pendulum hammer traveling at a velocity of 11 ft/sec and in a direction parallel to the plane of the adhesive layer. The impact energy absorbed by the specimen is reported in foot-pounds per square inch.

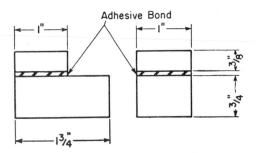

Fig. 8. Block shear impact test specimen.

The shear impact specimen has been found to give reproducible values, and it is quite generally used despite one limitation. By high-speed photography Koehn[6] has shown that frequently the bond at the moment of failure actually is being stressed in cleavage, with the back of the specimen being lifted. Silver[7] has obtained reproducible results with flexible adhesives showing that impact

strengths increase with film thickness over a range of 10 to 30 mils. This was ascribed to the greater deformability of the heavier films.

The impact strength of adhesives may also be tested in tension. Several types of specimen can be used, of which a modified spool-type tensile specimen (D-897) is the most generally employed. Another common specimen is the butt-joined rods with gripping ears at the extreme ends. At Frankford Arsenal, lap shear specimens (D-1002) have been used informatively for impact (dynamic shear) strength values. The only modification required was the attachment of a cross bar at each extremity of the specimen. Impact strength values averaged 10 per cent lower than the block shear specimens.

Falk[8] describes an apparatus which can be used for repeated impact tests. It makes use of a falling weight from a known height on a tension test specimen. A repetitive loading test such as this simulates an impact fatigue test.

Cleavage. The cleavage test is conducted by introducing a prying force at one end of a bonded specimen to split the bond apart. A suitable cleavage test is described in ASTM method D-1062. The test specimen, shown in Fig. 9, is pulled apart by tensile loading, and the cleavage strength is specified in terms of pounds per inch of width. Specimens are ordinarily made of metal, but other rigid materials can be employed as well. With low modulus adhesives, a lap length of 1 in. is sufficient. The stress distribution in a cleavage test is complex and the forces required both to initiate and continue separation are considerably influenced by the dimensions of the specimen, the mechanical properties of the adherends as well as the strength and elastic characteristics of the adhesive.

Creep. The deformation or dimensional change occurring in an adhesive-bonded specimen under stress and over a period of time is referred to as creep. A standard test for creep does not exist. It is customary, however, to determine creep by subjecting a bonded specimen to a constant load for a given period of time and at a specified temperature. The length of time for conducting such a test depends on the properties of the adhesive and the service requirements for which it is being evaluated. Thermoplastic adhesives may be tested for weeks or months until either failure occurs, or the test is terminated after a specific amount of deformation. Creep performed at room temperature is usually referred to as "cold flow."

Periodically it is desirable to determine the rate of creep, in which case the dimensional change occurring in a bonded specimen is determined

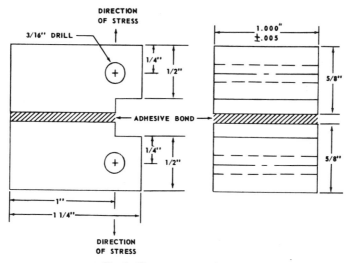

Fig. 9. Cleavage test specimen.

regularly during the length of the test. Usually the test is performed at various temperatures because the effect of temperature on creep is appreciable.

It has been found[9] that long time stressing of thermoplastic adhesives results in reduction of the initial strength of the assembly. This is readily understandable when it is realized that during the process of stressing, shear or tensile loads are rupturing the adhesive bond, thereby leading to excessive deformation and eventually to separation. Bonds made with rigid thermosetting adhesives possess no creep or negligible creep under stress. Highly plasticized adhesives are more apt to creep than rigid adhesives.

By unloading the specimen and allowing it to remain unstressed, one can determine the amount of relaxation or recoverability of an adhesive. Direct numerical correlation between creep and relaxation is not available; therefore, relaxation design of adhesive bonds is not yet on a sound basis.

Fatigue. The repeated application of a given load or deformation imposed on an adhesive specimen, which is known as fatigue testing, is a measure of the ability of an adhesive specimen to resist failure. This test does not measure mechanical properties such as elastic modulus or damping characteristics; furthermore, it may be used for comparing the behavior of bonded assemblies under repeated loading and for evaluating the effects of environmental conditions on the ability of a specimen to withstand repeated loading without failure.

A variety of fatigue testing machines have been developed for determining the fatigue endurance limits of materials, of which several types may be used for adhesive specimens. In these machines a suitable specimen is held in such a manner that a cyclic axial load is applied[10] or an alternating bending stress is applied.[11] Since fatigue life is known to be dependent on frequency, amplitude, temperature and mode of stressing as well as the magnitude of the stress, these variables must be controlled and specified. An adequate fatigue strength test is described in Method 1061 of Federal Test Method Standard No. 175. Loads are selected such that failure occurs within a range varying from at least 5000 cycles to not more than 10 million cycles. A cyclic axial load is applied and the maximum rate of cyclic loading is 3600 cycles per minute. Although the standard lap shear specimen given in ASTM method D-1002 is generally used for fatigue testing, other bonded specimens may be used. Some may require modification for suitability in fatigue testing. The number of cycles to failure and the corresponding loads, calculated in psi are recorded and plotted on stress-log cycles coordinates. The point at which a smooth curve connecting the points of minimum stress crosses the 10 million cycle ordinate is referred to as the fatigue strength.

Flexural Loading. ASTM method D-1184 is intended for determining the shear strength of adhesive bonded strips (8 strips of 0.01 in. thick) of metal or wood by testing as a simple beam loaded at mid-span. The span-to-depth ratio is 8:1. The maximum shear stress is developed at the neutral surface approximately midway between the top and bottom of the specimen; therefore, delamination or failure will occur in the center layer of adhesive.

The shear strengths obtained by this method are usually much higher than the values obtained with lap shear specimens (D-1002) or with compressive loaded block shear specimens (D-905). The reason for this is that substantial compressive stresses normal to the adhesive layer exist which increase the resistance of the adhesive to failure by shear.[12]

Nondestructive. One principal difficulty associated with mechanical testing of adhesive bonds has been that the structure (or specimen) is destroyed in tests made to determine its properties. Several research programs have been sponsored to develop nondestructive methods for testing adhesive bonds in structures, thereby determining whether or not an adhesive bond is satisfactory without destroying the structure. Therefore, if the bond is found to be adequate, the tested component can be put to use. The advantage of nondestructive testing is that complete inspection of bonded assemblies can be made.

Evidently the ultimate strength of bonds cannot be measured by nondestructive techniques; however, there are some useful properties such as the dynamic elastic, viscous or complex moduli as well as dielectric constants which can be measured nondestructively. Dietz[13, 14] has determined by means of ultrasonics the moduli of polyvinyl butyral-phenolic adhesive bonds in metal rod specimens after various periods of heating to degrade the adhesive layer. The dynamic moduli and dielectric constants may be used to differentiate between bonds of high and low tensile strength; thus they were used to determine the deteriorating effect of prolonged heating.

D'Agostino[15] has explored the photoelastic properties of adhesives and Norris[16] has investigated dielectric constants by measuring the change in electric capacitance of the adhesive layer as stress is applied to the test specimen.

These and other nondestructive investigations are the precedents of the basic research required to yield acceptable and meaningful test methods for nondestructive testing. There is no standard test method at present, although a first draft of a proposed test method is under consideration by Committee D-14 of ASTM.

Permanence

No test or series of tests is known to exist which will accurately foretell the service life of an adhesive bond. There are, however, a number of tests which may be used to measure the effects of various destructive or deteriorating influences, thereby helping to ascertain which adhesives will survive best under various conditions. Oxidation, water, oils, chemicals, sunlight, mold, and temperature changes are factors which can be measured thus giving definite indications that an adhesive will be satisfactory for specific periods under controlled conditions. Strength tests with any of the test specimens described in the previous section can reveal quantitative changes. The selection of the test specimen will depend on the information being sought. For example, metal tensile or shear specimens would be used if information were desired to determine the effect of water penetration at the exposed edges of the thin adhesive; however, the specimen must be appropriate. Aluminum specimens would not be suitable for testing the alkali resistance of an adhesive.

Chemical. Chemical factors may affect the permanence of an adhesive bond in two ways, i.e., (1) external chemical agents may affect the properties of the adhesive or the adherend and (2) chemical reactivity of the adhesive itself may affect the adherend. The resistance of adhesives to chemical reagents may be determined by exposing films of adhesives or by exposing bonded specimens to a chemical environment. The exposed films can be used to determine qualitative effects only; whereas strength tests on the bonded specimens will yield quantitative data.

ASTM method D-896 describes certain standard reagents in which strength test specimens are soaked for 7 days at room temperature. The most commonly encountered reagents are water, sea water, oil, gasoline, and hydraulic fluid. The concentration of the reagent is important because some adhesives may be resistant to diluted reagents and vulnerable when exposed to the concentrated form of the reagent; however, the degree of deterioration may not be proportional to the concentration.

An adhesive bond can be affected by chemical reagents in other ways. External chemical reagents may attack an adhesive bond by action on the adherend, e.g., when glass assemblies are in contact with water, the glass may hydrate and cause adhesive failure. Some adhesives may be affected by chemical constituents contained in the adherends. For instance, vinyl compounds or rubber compositions may contain plasticizer which will migrate to the adhesive-adherend interface and cause loss of adhesion. Similarly, plasticizer in the adhesive may affect the bond by migration to the adhesive-adherend interface. Plasticizer or other ingredients of the adhesive may cause crazing in plastic adherends. A simple test can be used to determine whether crazing in acrylic plastics will occur, i.e., an adhesive is applied to a stressed specimen of an acrylate under controlled atmospheric conditions. After 4 days the specimen is examined for crazing.

Service Life. An adhesive-bonded assembly must perform satisfactorily under all conditions of weather, heat and humidity. In order to determine accurately the service life expectancy of an adhesive, test specimens would have to be exposed for specified periods of time to all the conditions which the bonded assembly would be expected to encounter in service. Tests of this nature are usually long, often impractical, and sometimes impossible. There are some tests which can be utilized for judging and predicting the performance of a bonded assembly under various predetermined conditions, of which typical tests consist of exposure to light, water, salt spray, bacterial attack, etc. Judicious care must be exercised in using these test methods, e.g., light may have little effect on adhesive specimens which are protected by light-impervious adherends such as metal. Light, however, is an important factor with glass and other transparent or translucent materials. ASTM method D-904 provides a means for determining the effect of artificial and natural light on the permanence of adhesive assemblies; whereas ASTM method D-822 provides a means for the uniform operation of an accelerated weathering apparatus which exposes specimens to intermittent light and water spray. The extent of deterioration can be measured quantitatively by determining the change in bond strength of exposed specimens using any of the standard specimens such as the tensile specimen (D-897), the peel specimen (D-903), or the lap shear specimen (D-1002).

Salt spray tests are useful for evaluating specimens which are intended for use in coastal areas or which are to be shipped overseas. A standard salt spray atmosphere test is described in ASTM method B-117 for exposing specimens in a salt spray (fog) apparatus.

Exposure to an atmosphere of high ozone concentrations can have a deteriorating effect on adhesive specimens. A standard test method for ozone resistance is not available; however, it is the general practice to expose adhesive films on specimens to ozone concentrations of up to 50 part per hundred million in air. Deterioration is known to occur more rapidly when the specimens are stressed during exposure.

Undoubtedly, the greatest volume of data on long-term exposures of test specimens has been developed under laboratory conditions, and these data are probably reliable from the standpoint of accuracy and duplicability of results. However, since test exposures are selected somewhat arbitrarily in an effort to simulate one or more of the factors previously discussed, the validity of the results concerning actual service conditions can always be queried.

Long-term exposure of test specimens to actual weathering is generally considered to be a reliable indication of the durability and permanence of the bond. Unfortunately, such service information is often difficult or impossible to interpret accurately because specimens are subjected to uncontrolled exposure and wide variations over extended periods of time. In fact, results may not be repeatable due to nature's varying behavior from time to time. Also results in one locality may be different from those obtained elsewhere; nevertheless, exterior weathering represents a useful service-type test. A continued program of supervised and properly recorded service testing is an important requirement to more adequately understand the durability of adhesive bonding, since the results of such a program would be expected to serve as a standard for correlation with all other durability tests.

Accelerated test procedures whereby the time of exposure is reduced from years and months to days and hours are highly desirable to both the adhesive manufacturer and the consumer. Obviously, the reliability of accelerated tests is dependent on the degree of correlation that can be established with long-term service tests and on the degree to which they adequately simulate the pertinent factors influencing durability of the adhesive bond.

Under laboratory conditions the Weatherometer is commonly used to expose materials to various cycling weather conditions. The cycle which consists of a combination of simulated rain, sunlight, and dry heat serves to provide information in a comparatively short time for general evaluation and study. The Weatherometer can be used for testing bonded assemblies of dissimilar adherends to determine the variation in stress and endurance caused by the differing coefficients of thermal expansions. Cyclic testing, which should also include a study of the effects of extremes of temperature on the durability of the adhesive bond, can be adapted to evaluate wood bonds. Wood is susceptible to dimensional change with variations in moisture content depending on the surrounding atmosphere. ASTM method D-1183 contains a group of cyclic tests of varying severity for evaluating the resistance of wood adhesives. High and low temperatures as well as high and low relative humidities under laboratory conditions are specified. The extent of deterioration is ascertained from the change in strength properties of plywood shear specimens (ASTM-906) as a result of exposure to the test conditions.

A test method for determining the quality of adhesive bonds in laminated wood products when subjected to continuous exposure at specified conditions of moisture and temperature is presented in ASTM method D-1151. The performance is expressed as a percentage based on the ratio of strength retained after exposure to the original strength.

Since there are many factors that influence test results, it is important to weigh the major considerations. In a test which involves subjecting bonds to either water or high humidity, the specimen, the adhesive, and the duration of exposure are all important. For example, short-lived exposures may not permit the moisture to reach the adhesive; furthermore, a thick block of wood requires a longer exposure than a thin veneer. When the bonded assembly is composed of materials such as metal, which are relatively unaffected by water, a cyclical test involving exposure to water or water vapor is of doubtful value unless the adhesive is highly susceptible to the test conditions. Exposure to extremes of temperature will induce physical or chemical changes in adhesives and lead to deterioration of the bond. Short-time exposure to sub-zero temperatures can quickly indicate the ability of adhesives to absorb gross differences in thermal coefficients of adherend materials. This low temperature test also can be used to evaluate the effects of embrittlement and crystallization of adhesives. However, it must be recognized that some adhesives crystallize within minutes after exposure to low temperatures; whereas others require long periods of time. The strength tests should be conducted at the temperature to which the specimen is exposed rather than permitting the specimen to return to room temperature and then testing.

At elevated temperatures a number of changes may take place which can affect the adherends as well as the adhesives, thus influencing the bond. The adhesive or the adherend may decompose at elevated temperatures. Long exposure to moderately high temperatures may cause changes in degree of polymerization of the adhesive. Physical as well as chemical changes, which may occur, can result in stresses at the adhesive-adherend interface which will influence the bond strength; moreover, these reactions can occur in days, weeks, or years. The best tests for evaluating the permanence of bonds are those which reflect service temperatures. Exposure tests conducted at temperatures substantially higher must be considered on a comparative basis rather than an absolute one.

Whatever test method is employed, it must be recognized that no accelerated procedure for determining deterioration of a bond correlates perfectly with actual service conditions, and that no single or small group of laboratory test conditions will simulate all actual service conditions. Consequently, care must be exercised in the interpretation and use of data obtained in tests.

Biological. Adhesives composed of dextrin, soybean, casein, or protein, etc., may be subject to attack by mold, fungi and bacteria as well as by rodents and insects. As early as 1943, Kaufert and Richards[17] found that accelerated mold tests can be quite useful in evaluating the performance of casein and soybean adhesives in plywood under mold conditions, and that they appeared to correlate well with long-term exposures at high relative humidities. The accelerated mold tests consisted of impregnating birch veneers with a diluted casein adhesive and inoculating them with mold organisms. Plywood shear specimens were made and maintained in a closed chamber over water at 72 to 80°F. Significant losses in bond strength were observed after 14 days of incubation. Since this early work, standard laboratory methods have been developed to determine the effect of these deteriorating agents on the strength of bonds. The tests appear to be useful also in evaluating the relative effectiveness of preservatives for protein adhesives.

ASTM method D-1286 is intended for evaluating the effect of mold contamination on the permanence of adhesive preparations by determining the change in viscosity of adhesives and the comparative bond strengths of contaminated and uncontaminated specimens when tested under defined conditions. The organisms used are Aspergillus niger, A. flavus, and Penicillium luteum; the incubation period is 28 days with weekly inspections.

ASTM method D-1174 is intended for evaluating the effect of bacterial contamination on the permanence of adhesive preparations and bonds as determined for the mold contamination test just described. The organisms used are Pseudomonas fluorescens, Bacillus subtilis, and Proteus vulgaris, and the incubation period is 28 days with weekly inspections.

ASTM method D-1383 describes a procedure for evaluating the susceptibility of dry adhesive films to attack by laboratory bred, starved, white, male rats. Damage is determined by calculating the per cent destruction (weight loss) of the test specimen. Comparison is made between adhesive-impregnated filter paper and blank filter paper.

ASTM method D-1382 describes a procedure for determining the extent to which adhesive impregnated filter paper, compared to blanks, is damaged by starved male and female Periplaneta Americana roaches. As in the previous test with rodents, damage is determined by calculating the per cent weight loss of test specimens.

Radiation. Although there is considerable published literature on the effect of nuclear radiation on high polymers, little research has been conducted on structural adhesives. The literature on the general subject of radiation effects on polymers and elastomers however should be a helpful source of information. Kinderman and Radding[18] report that polystyrenes are resistant to radiation showing less than 50 per cent reduction in shear, impact and tensile strengths after exposure of 3×10^{10} rad. Polymethyl methacrylate, on the other hand, shows 50 per cent reduction in shear and impact strength after only 10^8 rad exposure and a 50 per cent reduction in tensile strength after a 5×10^7 rad exposure.

Borders[19] studied the effect of high-density gamma-radiation (up to 10^9 roentgens) on aluminum lap joint specimens using nine commercial adhesives. His study showed that an acrylonitrile rubber-phenolic and a vinyl-phenolic adhesive "have usable properties after exposure up to 10^9 roentgens." An epoxy-phenolic withstood temperatures up to 500°F and gamma dosages up to 10^9 roentgens.

Mixer[20] reported on what occurs chemically when epoxy resin structural adhesives are subjected to nuclear radiation using lap shear specimens, thereby attempting to improve the irradiation resistance of adhesives with protective agents. Nine per cent of 2,5-diphenyloxazole in an epoxy resin showed a "marked improvement in the radiation resistance of the adhesive."

Brophy and Perron[21] discovered that irradiation of an adhesive formulation *in situ* may result in an adhesive bond. Satisfactory bonds to leather were obtained with adhesives of the polyester, natural rubber, and synthetic rubber types.

SPECIFICATIONS

An adhesive specification, like all material specifications, is a document which specifies values for all the important properties of an adhesive together with limits of variability and methods for determining these values. Specifications are looked upon differently by producers and consumers. The producer is concerned with his ability to meet the specification and to supply the adhesive competitively. The consumer relies on the specification to assist him in procuring a satisfactory adhesive at a reasonable cost.

In general, a procurement specification can be prepared based on composition or performance requirements. Sometimes specifications contain requirements based on both composition and performance.

The well-informed consumer prefers the composition-type specification. He knows exactly what is wanted because he has complete information on the reliability, performance and merit of the specific adhesive composition desired.

Performance specifications can be extremely useful provided that discriminating physical and chemical requirements are specified, and that reproducible test methods and standard conditions are clearly defined and specified. There are many advantages attributable to performance-type specifications. One is the ease with which changes from one material to another may be made in times of critical shortages or when new and improved materials become available. Another is that manufacturers have complete freedom in formulating their product and can provide engineering and manufacturing skills in accordance with best scientific and technological practices.

Specifications which contain both composition and performance requirements will usually specify the adhesive by its chemical type, e.g., identifying the basic ingredient contained in the adhesive formulation. Periodically, the basic ingredient is referred primarily as a thermosetting or thermoplastic adhesive and the chemical type is given parenthetically, if at all.

There is no adequate single system of classification for adhesives. In the trade, adhesives may be classified broadly in terms of end use, such as wood adhesives, metal adhesives, shoe adhesives, general-purpose adhesives, or label adhesives. This practice is inadequate since one end-use adhesive may be useful in several other fields. Another system which has been used to classify adhesives has been based on the temperature required by the adhesive to establish a bond, e.g., reference has been made to a cold-setting adhesive (below 68°F), room-temperature setting (68 to 86°F), intermediate-temperature setting (87 to 212°F), and hot (above 212°F) adhesive. A variation of this system is found in MIL-A-5090 which specifies adhesives according to exposure to various temperatures. Type I is for long-time exposure to temperatures from −67 to 180°F; Type II for long-time exposure to temperatures from −67 to 300°F; and Type III for long-time exposures to temperatures from −67 to 300°F as well as for short-time exposures to temperatures from 300 to 500°F. Lastly, another classification is based on the method used for establishing the bond, of which typical groups are the pressure-sensitive adhesives, chemical-setting adhesives, and solvent-release adhesives.

There are many adhesive specifications, of which the most prominent are the industrial and government specifications, which describe and establish the technical and physical characteristics or performance requirements of adhesive materials, including prescribed methods and conditions of tests, packaging, marking and other essential characteristics. When qualification approval is required, appropriate qualifications tests are specified. These specifications frequently are revised or amended; moreover, to list the presently existing specifications here would be futile. Listings of these specifications are readily available from most government agencies (including foreign governments) and from ASTM as well as from large industrial manufacturers and users of adhesives.

A test can be no better than the sampling technique. Test methods regardless of accuracy can produce valid data regarding the nature and condition of the adhesive only when performed on samples which are truly representative of the adhesive material. It is important therefore that every sample be obtained and processed in strict accordance with standard procedures. Recommended practices apply to the sampling of liquid, semisolid, solid, or powdered adhesives based on judgment, skill, and experience. The basic principle of each procedure is to obtain a sample or composite of several samples from locations in the container which will guarantee that the sample or composite will be representative of the entire batch of adhesive being tested.

The larger the number of tests the higher the cost and the longer the time required to perform the tests. The problem of sampling consequently is one of finding a median between the minimum number of tests required for reliability and the value of increased reliability gained by larger sample testing.

There are good reasons therefore for using statistical methods in the preparation of specifications. The rejection of a quantity of adhesive that is satisfactory will result in an increase in material cost to the consumer; furthermore, the acceptance of low quality adhesive may result in failure or in poor quality assemblies for the consumer. There is a cost associated with each of these errors although the costs are often difficult to determine. Statistical methods are methods of probability and when considered in terms of odds, they can be related to cost advantages resulting from their use. Testing is expensive, but statistical methods will provide the maximum information from a given number of tests.

There exists a variety of statistical methods designed to cope with crucial questions that often cannot be answered by a more reliable, less expensive and less time-consuming procedure—particularly in cases where a choice must be made from among comparable materials or processes. Statistical methods often provide the only means of answering the question: Is an observed change in the mean value of some physical trait attributable to some peculiarity of the material or method, or is this change reasonably expected as a result of the chance fluctuations inherent in the experimental procedure? The only objective basis available for making the selection or providing the answer is in many cases the "t" test, the "F" test or the "Chi-square" (χ^2) test.[22]

The "t" test provides a measure of the significance of a difference between means. The usefulness of this test stems from the fact that it establishes the probability with which one material or process can be regarded as different from another with respect to a single trait. If the variances associated with the respective means are not approximately equal, this test is invalid.

By providing a measure of the significance of a deviation from one of the ratio of two variances, the "F" test performs nearly the same service as the "t" test; moreover it has an advantage over the "t" test in that it is applicable when the variances are not approximately equal.

The "χ^2" test offers a measure of the significance of a discrepancy between the amount of a quantity obtained and that expected in addition to representing an invaluable means of determining the relative efficiency of different processes. For example, the "χ^2" test can be used to determine how consistently the yield from one process is larger than from another.

Since they constitute a reliable source of pertinent information, these tests should always be applied where appropriate. Although statistical design is an important aspect of any experimental program, it is neither necessarily expensive nor time-consuming.

DESIGN OF ADHESIVE BONDS

No set rules can be established for the design of adhesive assemblies since it involves a judicious understanding and regulation of the factors that influence the strength of both the structural member and the adhesive itself. It includes the geometry of the bond, the selection of an adhesive and its bonding process, the properties of the adhesive and the adherends, and finally an analysis of the stresses which the bond is likely to encounter in service.

The design of an adhesive bond may be a very simple or an involved one depending on the adhesive's function. For example, in a simple case, very little must be done to design a bond for a label since all that is needed is a suitable adhesive and a clean surface. At the other extreme, the complexities in the bonding of an airplane wing or a helicopter rotor blade or a honeycomb sandwich panel require design considerations based on calculations of stresses, the geometry of the bond, the properties of materials and their behavior under environmental conditions. For maximum effectiveness and success, adhesive bonds should be designed with the following general principles:

(1) Stress the adhesive in the direction of maximum strength.
(2) Provide for the maximum bond area.
(3) Make the adhesive layer as uniform as possible.
(4) Maintain a thin and continuous adhesive layer.
(5) Avoid stress concentrations.

Rigid Materials

The major factors influencing the bond design of rigid members are the duration, magnitude and direction of the load. Most of the adhesives used for structural purposes are relatively strong in shear and weak in peel or cleavage. Therefore, bonds usually are designed to place the adhesive in shear and to prevent or minimize peel and cleavage stresses. The magnitude of the shear stress influences calculations of the bond area and total stresses influence the geometry of the adhesive bond.

The thickness of the adhesive film is important because it affects the bond strength, e.g., thin films demonstrate high shear strength. But "starved" adhesive layers must be avoided. Thick films will improve impact and peel strengths but may also increase creep tendencies; furthermore, the shape and finish of faying surfaces also affect design considerations. Grooves, slots, waviness and protuberances in faying surfaces may interfere with the attainment of optimum film thickness thus nullifying over-all design considerations.

The most common bond assembly is the straight overlap, which has the tendency of subjecting the adhesive to tensile stresses at the extremities of the lap as the bond is loaded. Stress concentration points are shown in Fig. 10. As demonstrated previously, the edges of the lap carry a high portion of the load; consequently, the load at which a specimen fails is substantially below the true strength of the adhesive.

The strength of a lap assembly in shear is directly proportional to the width of the bond. Strength is also improved by increasing the length of the overlap, but the relationship is not linear. Unit strength will not continue to increase at the same rate with successive increase in overlap. The curves in Fig. 11 illustrate the typical relationship between failure load and overlap, thereby indicating how this relationship compares with what might be expected if the relationship were linear. *Note:* The curves are typical but not actual, and the data are hypothetical.

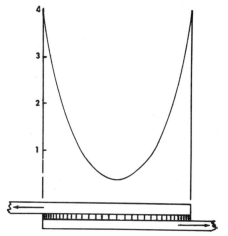
Fig. 10. Stress distribution in a lap specimen.

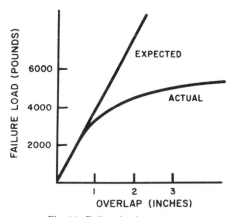
Fig. 11. Failure load *vs* overlap.

The strength of the overlap depends not only on the length of lap, but also on the thickness of the metal and its yield strength. Since the yield strength depends on modulus and thickness of the metal, the lap strength must not exceed the yield strength. With adhesives which may exhibit a tensile shear strength of several thousand pounds per square inch, the yield strength of thin gage metals can be exceeded even with relatively short overlaps. The typical interrelationship between length of lap, loads, and thickness of metal is demonstrated in Fig. 12. *Note:* The curves are typical.

The relationship of thickness and overlap to stress, which has been analyzed by De Bruyne,[23] has been referred to as the "joint factor," i.e., the ratio of the square root of the thickness to the length of the overlap. A uniform curve is obtained when the joint factors obtained with steel, aluminum alloy and clad aluminum, using several overlaps, are plotted against the mean failing stress as shown in Fig. 13. At high values of joint factor, the failing stress asymptotically approaches a value

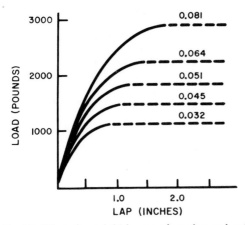

Fig. 12. Effect of metal thickness and overlap on bond strength.

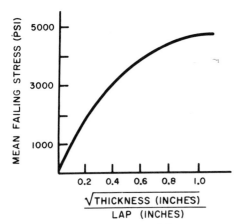

Fig. 13. Joint factor *vs* mean failing stress.

that is characteristic of the adhesive, which means that a small overlap shows a high apparent failing stress approximating the true failing stress or strength of the adhesive. The linear relationship between a joint factor of zero and one of about 0.3 indicates that the apparent failing stress is proportional to the joint factor and that the failing load is independent of the overlap and proportional to the square root of the thickness. Apparently, the design engineer can, within limits, vary the length of overlap and gauge of metal to obtain a desired strength.

There are a number of joint designs that can be adapted to specific design problems, of which a group is illustrated in Fig. 14. The scarf joint, the most efficient of the simple joints, permits uniform stress distribution over the entire bonded area thereby eliminating the stress concentrations characteristic of the lap joints. The beveled lap joint also demonstrates good stress distribution and possesses strength advantages in comparison with the straight lap joint. Nevertheless, both the beveled

lap and scarf joint present several production problems, e.g., thin sections of metal cannot be machined easily, the feather edges tear rapidly, and the bonding pressures must be applied with care.

Fig. 15 presents several designs of angle joints evaluated for their resistance to cleavage. Each design is analyzed for its effectiveness against four directions of stress application. When heavy sections are bonded, the parts should be designed so that the adhesive is in shear. Whenever possible, cleavage stresses should be avoided or minimized in bond design. Angular joints such as corners are also subject to peel or cleavage stresses. The designs shown in Fig. 16 illustrate how corners can be reinforced for improved strength and durability.

Butt joining of solid rods may be affected by cleavage forces. In order to improve the performance of the bond, designs such as those illustrated in Fig. 17 are recommended. Lastly, cylindrical or tubular joints have limited contact area unless they are designed with heavy wall thickness. The strength of the bond can be improved by machining a more adequate bonding area and subsequently utilizing designs similar to those shown in Fig. 18. In this type of bond there must be adequate clearance for the adhesive. Although pressure during bonding may be applied by compression from the ends, radial pressure is impractical. With some designs, high-solids content or gap-filling adhesives may be required.

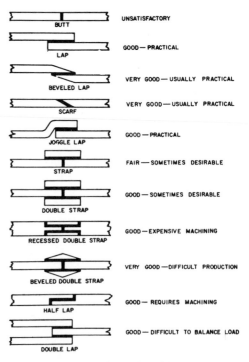

Fig. 14. Types of lap joints.

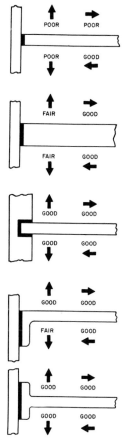

Fig. 15. Joint stress evaluation.

Wood

Wood is an anisotropic material and therefore presents problems in bonding. Strength properties and changes in dimensions due to moisture absorption vary with grain direction. The tensile strength of wood perpendicular to the grain is approximately one-tenth the strength of the wood in the grain direction. In the design of laminated assemblies, bonds are usually designed with the adhesive in shear either parallel or perpendicular to the grain or in compression in any grain direction. Both tension and cleavage bonds which are perpendicular to the grain are avoided because of the natural weakness of the wood in this direction.

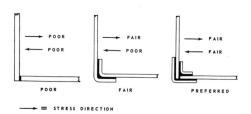

Fig. 16. Corner joint stress evaluation.

	A	B,C,D,
TENSION	GOOD	GOOD
COMPRESSION	GOOD	GOOD
TORSION	GOOD	GOOD
BEND	POOR	GOOD

Fig. 17. Joint design for solid rods.

Scarf joints are the common method for joining wood end-to-end. Since the slope of the scarf controls the ratio of end grain to face grain, the efficiency of the scarf in tension (the adhesive being in shear) depends on the slope. A slope of 1 in 12 is commonly used for wood members in tension. Generally, the slope of scarf joints in compression members should not be greater than 1 in 5. The efficiency of plain scarf joints varies with the type of wood, but these variations are insignificant. In multiple laminations scarf joints should be well distributed so that they do not occur adjacent to one another.

Assembly bonding of wood members with adhesives requires special joint designs. The strongest joints are formed with parallel grains such as in face-to-face or edge-to-edge bonding. Often the

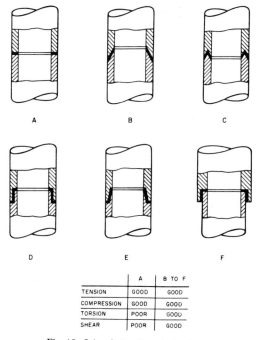

	A	B TO F
TENSION	GOOD	GOOD
COMPRESSION	GOOD	GOOD
TORSION	POOR	GOOD
SHEAR	POOR	GOOD

Fig. 18. Joint design for tubular forms.

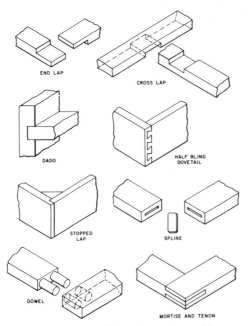

Fig. 19. Typical joints for wood assembly.

bonding of end grain members perpendicular to each other is unavoidable. Figure 19 illustrates a few representative assembly joints.

Flexible Materials

The bonding of flexible materials such as rubber and plastics to each other and to various rigid

materials involves several design procedures and practices. Thin rubber sheets and plastic sheets which can not be heat sealed may be edge joined by a simple lap, or they may be butted and a strap or doubler of the same material applied over the seam. The butting of thick sheets is impractical because butt joints in tension generally have inadequate strengths. In such cases, scarf joints are the most practical. Dissimilar adherends may be bonded with a scarf joint with a minimum sacrifice of uniform stress distribution if the ratio of the thickness is inversely proportional to Young's modulus. Rubber as well as metals may be formed with this design. Figures 20 and 21 illustrate the stress distribution of various lap joints using materials of equal and unequal modulus. It also illustrates that uniformity of stress distribution can be obtained with materials of unequal moduli by tapering the materials symmetrically in proportion to the modulus of each material.

In summarizing considerations in adhesive bond design, it can be stated that the strength of bonded joints is dependent on the properties of the adherends and the adhesives, the geometry of the joint, and the environmental conditions. The material properties of the adherends are modulus of elasticity, elongation, tensile yield strength, Poisson's ratio, and surface conditions; whereas the material properties of the adhesives are modulus of elasticity, shear strength, tensile strength, peel strength, elongation, and fatigue characteristics. The geometric factors include length of lap, thick-

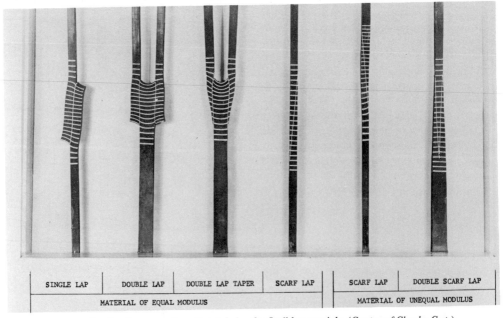

Fig. 20. Graphical presentation of joint design for flexible materials. (*Courtesy of Chrysler Corp.*)

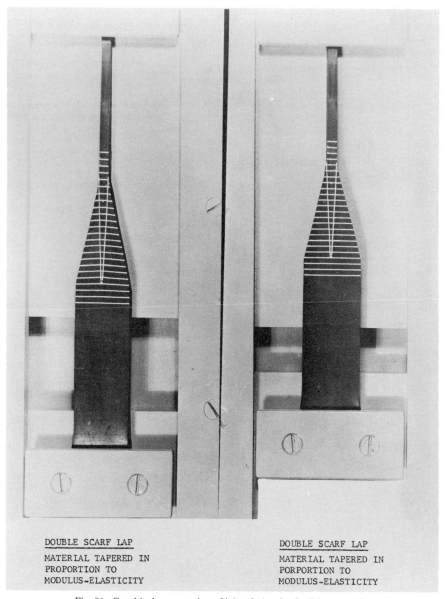

DOUBLE SCARF LAP

MATERIAL TAPERED IN
PROPORTION TO
MODULUS-ELASTICITY

DOUBLE SCARF LAP

MATERIAL TAPERED IN
PORPORTION TO
MODULUS-ELASTICITY

Fig. 21. Graphical presentation of joint design for flexible materials.
(*Courtesy of Chrysler Corp.*)

ness of adherend, joint flexibility, joint symmetry, and thickness of the adhesive. The environmental conditions are time dependent on loads, temperature, and exposure conditions.

References

1. ASTM Standards on Adhesives, p. 228, Philadelphia, Pa., Am. Soc. for Testing Materials, 1957.
2. Green, Henry, *Ind. Eng. Chem.,* **13,** 632 (1941).
3. Claxton, A. W., "The Functional Behavior of Clays in Adhesives," *Tappi,* **40,** 180A (June 1957).
4. Koehn, G., in Clark, Rutzler and Savage, Symposium on "Adhesion and Adhesives: Fundamentals and Practice," Society of Chemical Industry, p. 120, New York, John Wiley & Sons, Inc., 1954.
5. Meissner, H. P., and Baldauf, G. H., "Strength Behavior of Adhesive Bonds," *Trans. ASME,* **73,** 697 (1951).
6. Koehn, G. W., "Behavior of Adhesives in Strength Testing," Adhesion and Adhesives, p. 123, New York, John Wiley & Sons, Inc., 1954.
7. Silver, I., "Shear Impact and Shear Tensile Properties of Adhesives," *Modern Plastics,* **26,** 95 (1949).
8. Falk, A. H., *ASTM Bull. No. 141,* 42 (Aug. 1946).

9. Bikerman, J. J., "Strength and Thinness of Adhesive Joints," *J. Soc. Chem. Ind.* (Trans. and Comm.), **60,** 23–24 (1941).

10. Templin, R. L., *ASTM Proc.,* **39,** (1939).

11. Buhler, H., *Welding J., Research Suppl.,* 52s to 54s (1953).

12. Perry, H. A., "Adhesive Bonding of Reinforced Plastics," p. 116, New York, McGraw-Hill Book Co., Inc., 1959.

13. Dietz, A. G. H., *et al., ASTM Special Technical Publication,* No. 138, 40 (1952).

14. Dietz, A. G. H., *et al., ASTM Proc.,* **50,** 1414 (1950).

15. D'Agostino, J., *et al., Proc. Soc. Exp. Stress Analysis,* **12,** 115 (1955).

16. Norris, C. B., *et al., ASTM Bull. No. 218,* 40 (1956).

17. Kaufert, F. H., and Richards, C. A., Forest Products Laboratory Report No. 1344 (Sept. 1943).

18. Kinderman, E. M., and Radding, S. B., "Nuclear Radiation Effects on Structural Plastics and Adhesives," WADC Report 56–534 (1957).

19. Borders, D. F., "Nuclear Deterioration of Structural Adhesives," WADC TR 57–513, p. 142 (1957).

20. Mixer, R. Y., "Nuclear Deterioration of Structural Adhesives," WADC TR 57–513, p. 163 (1957).

21. U. S. Patent 2,668,133 (Feb. 2, 1954).

22. Croxton and Cowden, "Applied General Statistics," 2nd Ed., New Jersey, Prentice-Hall, 1958.

23. De Bruyne, N. A., and Houwink, H., "Adhesion and Adhesives," p. 98, London, Elsevier Publishing Co., 1951.

Section B

ADHESIVE MATERIALS

—— 6 ——

Inorganic Adhesives and Cements

John H. Wills

Philadelphia Quartz Company
Philadelphia, Pennsylvania

The natural world around us has many examples of inorganic bonds which have lasted for centuries. Most of the common building stones are formed from aggregates bonded with siliceous compositions, both crystalline and amorphous. Commercial inorganic cements and adhesives are employed in large quantities. Their general properties are widely known as well as the facts that they are economical, fire resistant and usually resistant to water and many other chemicals. The hydraulic cements such as Portland cement are probably the most common of the commercial forms, and soluble silicates are the primary inorganic adhesives.

Differentiation between adhesives and cements is difficult. Cements have greater thickness than adhesives, but both include an adhesive bond or "thin film uniting surfaces nearly in contact."[1] In a cement, three-dimensional, isotropic cohesion is also important. Cements contribute the behavior of a rigid solid to the cemented body. With rare exceptions, cements are composed of network structures, predominantly oxygen or hydroxyl polyhedrons which follow the theoretical requirements for random glassy structures with respect to low co-ordination and high bond strength. Nonstoichiometric compositions, network flexibility and residual force fields all are characteristic of cements.

A good cement forms a continuous skeleton rather early in the process, subsequently building upon and filling in the skeleton. The reaction rate must be slow in order to achieve a strong bond. With the soluble silicates, therefore, a silicofluoride of low solubility is often used. Calcium chloride reacts very rapidly and usually does not form a bond. In acid phosphate cements, mildly basic elements (active oxides) form good bonds by direct reaction with phosphoric acid. However the most basic elements react too violently. The pozzuolanic cements are not used alone because they require a long time to react and to reach high levels of strength.

Inorganic cements may be grouped as air-dried cements, reaction cements, precipitation cements and hydraulic cements.[2] The air-dried cements, of course, set by loss of water or other solvent. Reaction cements form bonds through the reaction of two components other than water. Examples are the oxy-phosphates and phosphoric acid bonds, other acid salts including nitrates and sulfates, oxy-bonds such as the oxy-chloride and oxy-sulfate, as well as basic carbonate utilized in the 85 per cent magnesia insulation and anhydrous calcium silicate, also used in insulation.

The third group, the precipitation cements, form gels thrown out of solution or colloidal dispersion. They are essentially single-component systems and include the siliceous silicate precipitated by sodium silicofluoride and other materials. Zircon and phosphoric acid bonds apparently depend on solution of silica by the acid followed by precipitation of a gel. Silicon esters as well as titanium and zirconium esters can be precipitated as gels. They can be used as temporary bonds for refractories and in numerous formulas for precision metal molds. Gamma-alumina and silica-alumina bonds may also be classified here.

In the last group are the hydraulic cements which set by reaction with water. This includes the gypsum cements such as Keene's cement and plaster of Paris, calcium silicates and aluminates which are the primary hydraulic cements, barium compounds, ferrites, ferrates, pozzuolana and slag cements.

This chapter has been divided into the soluble silicates, which are used both in adhesives and cements, and the other inorganic cements such as the insoluble salts in hydraulic and sorel cements, silico-phosphate or dental cements and other phosphate cements, etc. In most of the applications, setting is by chemical reaction; however in the simple adhesive uses of the soluble silicates the bond is formed by dehydrating the colloidal solution.

SOLUBLE SILICATES

There are two factors among the properties of the soluble silicates and silicate cements which have an especial appeal to development chemists. One is the relatively low cost of the adhesive itself, and the other is the total resistance to combustion. In the case of many cements which set by reaction there is the additional factor that the bond is extremely resistant to deterioration under most conditions. When dehydrated to the glassy state, a soluble silicate bond is resistant to attack by water; however continued exposure to high humidities or aqueous solutions will destroy it. All siliceous bonds are liable to attack by strong caustic solutions and by solutions of hydrofluoric acid. In the form of glasses, they will become plastic as they approach the softening point. This upper temperature limit can be increased by the use of additives which react with the silicate to form insoluble compounds. The addition of silica itself raises the softening limit by increasing the proportion of silica in the soluble silicate. Other factors in favor of the use of the soluble silicates are their ready availability, general ease of application, and relatively rapid set.

With materials like paper, the soluble silicates are termed adhesives, whereas with refractory materials, they are considered cements. In both fields the reactivity of the silicate as well as the increase of viscosity by dehydration are important characteristics.

Properties

The ordinary commercial soluble silicates are prepared by melting purified silica sand with soda ash or sodium sulfate (or the potassium analogue) and then, if desired, dissolving the glass in water. The preparation and use of the soluble silicates is described in some detail by Vail.[3]

The soluble silicates are available commercially either as glasses or as liquids and, in either case, vary over a wide range of composition and ratio of SiO_2 to Na_2O (Table 1). They are technically pure chemicals and contain as impurities most of the components present in the purest glass sand available and in the soda ash. Typical analyses of commercial glasses are as follows (% by weight):[3]

SiO_2:Na_2O	2.00	3.31
Na_2O	33.04	23.53
SiO_2	65.64	75.56
Al_2O_3	0.21	0.36
Fe_2O_3	.033	.055
CaO	.14	.14
MgO	.03	.07
TiO_2	.009	.02
Cl	.08	.14
SO_3	.06	.08
Ignited loss	.56	.11
Total	99.80	100.07

The highly alkaline solids, which are crystalline materials and generally much more soluble than the glasses, are detergents and find little use in the adhesives and cement field. In any application it is necessary to consider the effect of the water content and the proportion of silica to alkali in order to secure optimum results. One often finds in the literature reports that some authors have been unable to use soluble silicates, whereas others have been completely successful. The difference is usually in the choice of commercial soluble silicate.

The relatively siliceous soluble silicates are characterized by empirical *weight ratios of the silica to the alkali* content, since their compositions are not those of molecular chemical compounds. A solution containing 1 mole of Na_2O for each 3.3 moles of SiO_2 will, on a weight basis, have a ratio of 3.22 per cent SiO_2 to 1 per cent Na_2O; thus it will be referred to as a 3.22 ratio silicate.

In general, only the silicates with a ratio higher than 1.5 are employed as cements and adhesives, although some of the more alkaline crystalline materials are found in special cements. Powders formed from dehydrated liquors have a place in dry preparations which must be mixed with water prior to application. The commercial liquid sodium silicates are generally used over the weight ratio range of 2 to 3.5 and at concentrations providing viscosities at the temperature of use varying from about 1 to 10 poises. The sodium silicates with ratios more alkaline than 2 are usually too alkaline and tend to crystallize. However, in some cases mixtures of the liquid silicates or even a liquid and powdered silicate have been found to have advantages. The more alkaline silicates have

TABLE 1. STANDARD COMMERCIAL SOLUBLE SILICATES.
(Philadelphia Quartz Co.)

% SiO$_2$/% M$_2$O % by wt.		Gravity Be	Sp. Gr.	Viscosity Poise	% Na$_2$O	% SiO$_2$
				Liquids		
M = Na 1.60		67.5	1.87	587,000	24.2	38.7
1.60		58.5	1.67	70	19.5	31.2
2.00		59.3	1.69	700	18.0	36.0
2.00		50.0	1.53	2.8	14.5	29.0
2.40		52.0	1.56	17	13.8	33.1
2.54		50.5	1.58	11.2	12.8	32.6
2.90		47.0	1.48	9.6	11.0	31.9
3.22		42.2	1.41	4.0	9.2	29.5
3.22		41.0	1.39	1.8	8.9	28.7
3.25		42.6	1.42	7.6	9.2	29.9
3.40		39.7	1.38	3.3	8.3	28.2
3.75		35.0	1.32	2.2	6.8	25.3
	Mole				% K$_2$O	
M = K 2.10	3.29	40.3	1.39	11.4	12.5	26.2
2.20	3.45	30.0	1.26	0.07	9.1	19.9
2.50	3.92	29.8	1.26	0.4	8.3	20.8
				Solids		
			lb/ft^3		% Na$_2$O	
M = Na 2.00		lumps	80		33.0	66.0
2.00		powder	62.2		32.4	64.8
2.00		powder	55.6		27.5	55
3.22		lumps	88		23.5	75.7
3.22		powder	62.2		23.1	74.4
3.22		powder	52.3		19.4	62.5
	Mole				% K$_2$O	
M = K 2.50	3.92	powder	75.0		28.3	70.7
2.50	3.92	lumps	88.0		28.4	71.0

a higher wetting power while the more siliceous ones reduce the tendency to absorb water and allow drying at normal, atmospheric temperatures. At the concentrations suitable for adhesives, the pH is fairly constant because it changes little when the solids content of the sodium silicate solution exceeds about 10 per cent. For the adhesive compositions, the pH will range between approximately 11 for the more siliceous liquids and 13 for the more alkaline ones.

Potassium silicates are seldom used as adhesives because of their greater cost; nevertheless they do appear in a number of special cements. They are also sold on a weight per cent basis, but in their case the molecular ratio is quite different from the weight ratio. A potassium silicate with a per cent by weight ratio of 2.10 has a molecular ratio of SiO$_2$:K$_2$O of 3.29.

Liquid films having viscosities initially as low as 50 centipoises dry to hard, vitreous films which do not readily redissolve even though they still contain water in amounts depending on the drying conditions and on the ratio. The commercial sodium silicate adhesives are generally agreed to be composed of colloidal electrolyte particles having a fairly high negative charge and becoming barely electro-positive as the pH approaches zero. These colloidal characteristics of the sodium silicate give their films the property of deformability which is necessary for a good adhesive bond. The presence of sodium may be considered as stabilizing the silica micelles until time of contact when hydrogen bonds form or the silica reacts with the substrate.

Even in those cements which set by reaction, the amorphous colloidal structure is recognized. The silicon atom is rather small, with a strong positive force field which accounts for the low

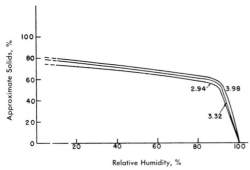

Fig. 1. The equilibrium moisture content of sodium silicate solutions at room temperature depends on both the ratio of the silicate and the relative humidity. (*Wills and Sams*[4])

polarizability and difficult adjustment to new conditions. The normal coordination number is 4, but 6 is often found. The tetrahedrally spaced bonds are more readily deformed than the analogous carbon bonds. The glass structure is considered a more or less random network of silica with intervening alkali metal ions which account for the electrical conductivity and a decrease in the softening temperature as the proportion of the cations increases. The rate of solution, viscosity, and surface tension increases more rapidly as the cation content increases; whereas density, refractive index, dielectric loss and specific resistance decrease less rapidly.

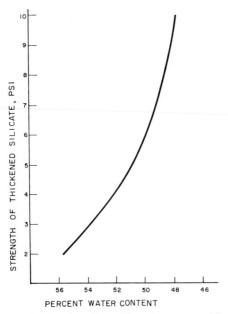

Fig. 2. A 3.2 ratio sodium silicate increases rapidly in tensile pull as the water content is reduced. (*Boller, Lander and Morehouse*[6])

A soluble silicate film will continue to hold some moisture until heated to about 1000°F (550°C), which means that the adhesive bond will have some resiliency and be less brittle than the anhydrous glass. Figure 1 shows that at ordinary humidities the silicate bond may contain as much as 40 per cent water; in fact, even at only 10 per cent relative humidity, it will have approximately 20 per cent water.[4, 5] The bond becomes stronger as the water content decreases as shown in Fig. 2.[6] Such strengths are quite sufficient for many adherends. Extenders in the form of sodium chloride, clay or talc are occasionally added to maintain the viscosity in a diluted silicate. Much higher strengths, 600 psi or more, have been indicated for free films. A strength of 300 psi was obtained with maple blocks. Values as high as 1500 psi have been reported on some metals and up to 1000 psi on glass. In these cases the bond failure was primarily in the adherend.

Working Properties. The viscosity of silicate solutions in adhesive applications varies from a few centipoises to several poises depending on the condition of the surface, temperature, humidity, and time available for setting. The ordinary commercial solutions in carefully sealed metal containers have a life which is substantially limitless although if stored at rather high temperatures for several years, crystallization may occur. If frozen, the solution must be thoroughly remixed and is then just as satisfactory as before. These solutions are all viscous liquids showing no definite yield point.

The viscosity varies with the concentration of Na_2O and SiO_2 solids, the ratio of $SiO_2 : Na_2O$ and the temperature. Figure 3 shows the increase of viscosity with increasing solids content.[7] The rapid reduction of viscosity with increasing temperature appears in Fig. 4.[4] At a constant solids content, viscosity drops sharply to a minimum as the ratio is reduced. At ratios lower than about 2.1, the viscosity rises again.

The viscosity can be increased by adding a neutral salt such as sodium chloride.[8] Miscible organic materials such as sugar[3, 9,] react quite differently as the ratio changes. Cane sugar added to 3.8 ratio sodium silicate reduces the viscosity; but in more alkaline 3.2 ratio solution, the viscosity is increased. At the latter ratio, however, small amounts of glycerin rapidly reduce the viscosity. Sugar, glycerin, sorbitol and other materials tend to retain moisture in the film and thus increase its flexibility or pliability. They usually reduce the viscosity but at the same time increase the tackiness, the setting time and the toughness of the

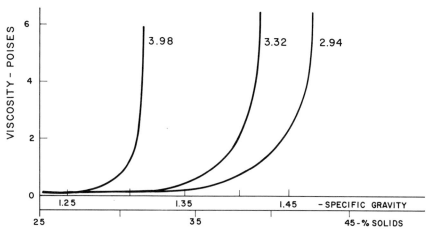

Fig. 3. A "knee" occurs in the viscosity curve as the solids content of a sodium silicate solution is increased. (*Vail and Baker*[7])

coating or film.[3] The addition of 0.25 to 5 per cent of glycerin, cane or beet sugar, molasses, a trisaccharide or invert sugar is usual. One to 15 per cent of "Nulomoline" (an invert sugar) or 5 to 15 per cent of ordinary sugars may be incorporated. Five to 30 per cent of sorbitol gives good flexibility, but the silicate needs first to be diluted to avoid excessive thickening. Sodium alginate or algin in the amount of 0.5 to 1 per cent first must be swelled in water and then worked into the silicate by rubbing or milling.

Starches and dextrins or latices of either natural rubber or the various synthetic polymers may usually be mixed with the silicate although the amount is in some cases restricted. Suspensions of wax and other less soluble polymers may be formed in a more or less stable state. The working properties are primarily those of the continuous silicate phase. However, after the films have been dried they may be heated above the melting point of the suspensoid forming a continuous film of the original dispersion on the surface of the silicate. The films may also be modified by the addition of inorganic powders such as various clays and reactive materials such as limestone.

While, in general, tackiness of the silicate solutions is not nearly as pronounced as with animal glues, the more alkaline silicate solutions have a definite tack, which, as Stericker has shown, is not entirely related to the viscosity.[1, 10] Using the practical thumb and forefinger test, strings 1 in. long can be obtained with viscous 2.0 ratio solutions; whereas for the very siliceous 3.9 ratio, the strings will not be longer than about a quarter of an inch and will appear only at a rather short interval during the dehydration of the film.

Wetting. Soluble silicate adhesives have relatively good wetting properties in themselves. The wetting rate can be increased by adding a small amount of a more alkaline silicate or by diluting the silicate. The relative ease of wetting standard filter paper by a more alkaline adhesive is compared in Fig. 5.[5, 11] If necessary, the viscosity can be maintained by adding fillers such as clay.

Additional wetting agents are sometimes added to increase the effectiveness of the silicate as an adhesive for metal or to accelerate the rate of wetting paper. Anionic or nonionic wetting agents generally increase the viscosity slightly so that

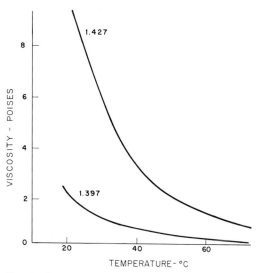

Fig. 4. A 3.2 ratio sodium silicate with a specific gravity of 1.427 approaches the viscosity of the more dilute solution at 1.397 as the temperature increases. (*Wills and Sams*[4])

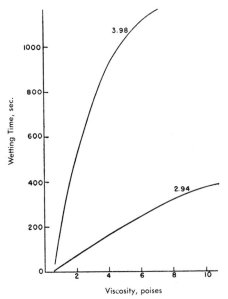

Fig. 5. The time to wet a standard filter paper increases as the viscosity increases, but less rapidly for the more alkaline 2.94 ratio than the siliceous 3.98 ratio sodium silicate solution. (*Wills*[11])

more water must be added to maintain the initial viscosity. Organic wetting agents lower the strength of the bond in corrugated paperboard:[12, 13]

% Wetting Agent	Spread in lb/1000 sq ft	Tensile Strength in lb/ft Glue Line
0.0	14	40.2
0.1	24	43.3
0.0	24	44.3

The amount of adhesive absorbed by an adherend will depend on the pore sizes as well as the wetting properties. A dry finish Fourdrinier kraft will absorb the adhesive more slowly than will jute since the former has larger pores; nevertheless the larger pores will absorb more adhesive. The effect of these larger pores can be overcome by the addition of a filler such as clays. The rate of penetration into the paperboard can be regulated by control of viscosity of the liquid phase and temperature as well as the moisture content of the board itself.

Setting. Sodium silicates set by loss of moisture unless other reactive materials are present. The closeness of approach to the characteristics of a glass depends on the humidity of the surrounding atmosphere and the temperature of drying. Even at low humidities resilience may be obtained by the incorporation of glycerin and other materials as already mentioned. The film can be attacked by CO_2 and other acidic acids of the atmosphere; generally however it will be only a surface effect, and experiments with rather thin bonds on corrugated papers in atmospheres of CO_2 have shown

that the bond can be retained under very adverse circumstances.[12]

Some understanding of the effect of loss of water on the viscosity of a silicate adhesive bond may be obtained from Figs. 6 and 7. A conchoidal fracture appears above about 40,000 poise for a 3.32 ratio sodium silicate.[4, 5, 11] About 2 lb of water must be lost from 17 lb spread to reach an initial set at this ratio. It is possible to utilize the effects of the temperature and water loss by heating the adhesive in order to employ an adhesive with very high solids content. If such an adhesive is applied to paper, the adhesive will not only increase in viscosity on cooling as the paper is cooled but will also lose moisture to the paper. If the paper is also initially hot, a flash set may be obtained by rapid evaporation of the water on initial contact with the paper. Only half of the water loss required to reach equilibrium is needed for initial set in a 3.32 silicate bond at room conditions.[11] (Figs. 1 and 7).

Resistance to Pests. Inorganic alkaline adhesives resist the growth of molds and fungi as well as attack by ants and other cellulose-destroying insects. Rats and mice usually show little interest in boards made with these stiff, glassy films although given sufficient incentive, they may chew through them. The addition of certain fungicides such as sodium pentachlorophenate will protect that portion of the paper adherend not wetted by the silicate itself. The presence of silica inherent in certain woods as well as the addition of siliceous

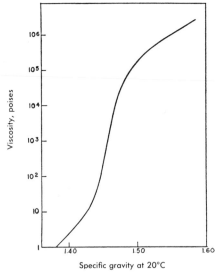

Fig. 6. The change in slope of the viscosity of a 3.2 ratio sodium silicate solution at about 1.48 is sometimes considered an initial set, and coincides with the appearance of conchoidal fracture. (*Wills*[11])

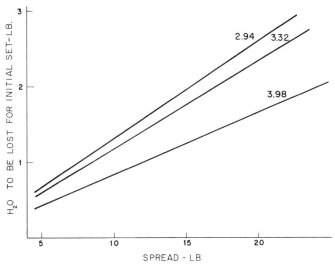

Fig. 7. Conchoidal fracture or initial set in a bond occurs with less water loss at lower spreads and higher ratios of soluble silicate. (*Wills and Sams*[4])

extenders to plywood glues has been shown to prevent penetration beyond the first ply by various ship worms and other pests.[13]

Anhydrous Silicates. The most nearly insoluble silicate bonds are obtained by drying at temperatures sufficiently high to remove all of the water. They have the characteristics of glasses. The linear thermal expansion of sodium and potassium silicate glasses from room temperature to 400°C is 10 to 19°C $\times$ 10^{-6}.[14] The annealing temperature for such compositions is about 440 to 600°C.

TABLE 2. SOLUBLE SILICATES COMMONLY USED IN REFRACTORY CEMENTS.

(Philadelphia Quartz Co.)

Weight % Ratio SiO_2/Na_2O	Silicate to Make 100 lb Solids (lb)	Liquidus Temp. of Solid without Filler (°C)	Approximate Softening Temp. (°C)	Order of Fluxing Effect on Fillers
3.75	323	1099	675	1
3.22	266	857	650	1
3.22	258	857	650	2
2.90	233	820	633	3
2.40	213	829	620	3
2.00	185	871	600	4
1.60	190	843	570	5
3.22	121	857	650	2
3.22	101	857	650	2
2.00	121	871	600	4
2.00	101	871	600	4
SiO_2/K_2O				
2.5	366	762	660	1
2.5	366	762	660	1
2.1	254	860	640	2

In drying a sodium silicate film in air, about 15 to 20 per cent of water will ordinarily remain. Baking at 100°C will leave approximately 1 to 10 per cent water. Complete dehydration requires heating to 550°C. To prevent deterioration of the bond in this drying process, care must be taken to stay below the boiling point at all times. Table 2 gives the liquidus temperature of glass formed from the ordinary soluble silicates, the approximate softening temperature, and the order of fluxing effect on usual filler materials.[15] Higher alkali contents reduce the viscosity of a sodium silicate glass melt as would be expected (Fig. 8).[16, 17] Mixed sodium and potassium glasses have a lower viscosity than either of them alone (Fig. 18).

Cost. The 41°Bé solution of sodium silicate (37.6 per cent concentration) sold in the largest volume was $0.012/lb, f.o.b., in tank-truck quantities, in 1961.

Applications

In these applications of soluble silicates as adhesives the silicate is supplied as a thin film and is set primarily by the loss of moisture.

Glass. The anhydrous sodium silicates are the simplest silicate glass systems, with structures similar to ordinary window glass. When liquid soluble silicate dries out in contact with glass, failure usually occurs in the glass rather than in the bond. Provision must be made for the silicate to dehydrate until the bond retains sufficient strength. The silicate usually reacts to some extent with the glass, and it is difficult to remove dried spots of soluble silicate. Acetic acid, 2 per cent hydrogen

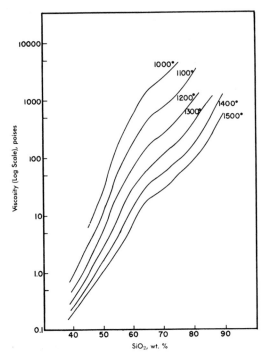

Fig. 8. The viscosity of melts of anhydrous silicates rises rapidly with increasing silica ratio and decreasing temperature. (Temperature in °C given on lines.) (*Heidtkamp and Endell*[16])

fluoride, or ammonium bifluoride may facilitate removal of spots.

While the bond is not resistant to long exposure to moisture, the liquid 2.9 ratio sodium silicate has often been used for the temporary repair of ceramic materials. McBain achieved a strength of 1000 psi with a 2.9 ratio silicate between glass sheets.[18] Occasionally it is useful to insert a sheet of paper impregnated with a sodium silicate between two impervious faces, thus retaining the silicate in the bond and perhaps permitting more complete drying.

Sodium silicate sprayed on a glass surface has been used as the binder in forming a safety glass sandwich with cellulose acetate.[19, 20, 21]

Very dilute solutions of potassium silicate are employed to bind phosphors to the face of television tubes. The silicate is sensitized by the addition of salts such as barium nitrate. A coating of aluminum metal powder may be bonded to glass with a thin film of soluble silicate in the alkaline range of 1.6 to 2.0 ratio.[22]

An adhesive formed by heating 40 parts by weight of 37° Bé 3.22 sodium silicate with 1 part by weight of fine filament glass wool for about 2 days at 60 to 70°C in a water-jacketed steel kettle[23] could be used to bind leather-to-metal,

glass-to-glass or porcelain, leather, textiles, stoneware, etc. It is recommended especially for optical work such as the bonding of lenses or the preparation of multilayer shatter-proof glass as it has approximately the same refractive index as Canada balsam. A clear layer may be concentrated by evaporation at 15 to 20°C with constant stirring; this more viscous adhesive may be used for setting jewelry.

Another adhesive to be applied under pressure and at elevated temperatures to a glass surface consists of 65 per cent feldspar, 11 per cent precipitated silica powder, 24 per cent calcium carbonate, mixed with 3 parts of sodium silicate and 1 part of potassium silicate.[24]

Similarly, spun glass or asbestos served as a filler to give increased water resistance in a soluble silicate adhesive.[25, 26, 27, 28] Glass-lined equipment may be patched with thin layers of the 3.2 ratio sodium silicate solution at about 30°Bé,[29] dried by radiant heat and then treated with an acidic agent.

Soluble silicates used for bonding fiber glass may attack the fiber glass surface and weaken it. The higher ratio silicates such as a 3.3 ratio silicate solution with 25 per cent clay may be used at the rate of about 1 lb/sq yd to bond fiber glass to a steel surface.[30]

Metal. Liquid soluble silicates will wet clean metal surfaces and will generally form strong bonds with such surfaces since the metallic silicates form readily and there is some attack at the metal surface.

The soluble silicates have bonded decorative sheets of copper to walls, plywood to steel or soft metals and, in large volume, aluminum foil to paper for such uses as cigarette packages and insulation board. For this, the soluble silicates have the advantage that they are odorless, nonpoisonous, fire resistant, noncorrosive to soft metal and resistant to vermin and molds. Either the 2.89 ratio at 47°Bé or the 3.22 ratio sodium silicate at either 41 or 42°Bé is usually suggested. Protective coatings may be removed by cleaning electrolytically or with a dilute sodium silicate solution of 5 to 10°Bé.[32] A 1 per cent solution of sodium metasilicate at 70 to 80°C is also recommended.

The silicate is applied to aluminum foil with a knurled applicator roll and a hard doctor roll which wipes the surface clean of excessive adhesive. Two to 4 lb/1000 sq ft is a desirable spread. The foil-paper laminate is dried over a large steam-heated or electric dryer or infrared lights. The bond formed will resist some immersion in water, and if torn, will fail in the adherend. Fig-

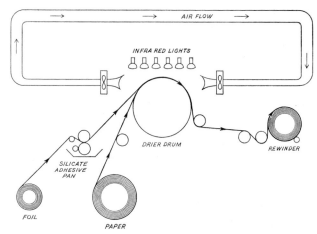

Fig. 9. Laminated aluminum foil is carefully dried to a low moisture content with a specified degree of negative curl by equipment similar to that indicated in this schematic diagram.

ure 9 is a schematic diagram showing the arrangement and equipment for this operation.[33]

A fairly heavy silicate of high ratio, that is, about 3.3 is recommended for bonding aluminum to concrete, and if 25 to 40 per cent of calcium carbonate (whiting) is added to such a silicate slightly diluted, the final bond will be more resistant to water and carbon dioxide.[34, 35] Fabric is bonded to metal with soluble silicate and next coated with 20 or more coats of polyvinyl halide to give an impermeable acid-resistant surface.[36] A dextrin-coated fabric is pressed into a silicate-latex coating on metal to form a permanent bond.[37, 38]

Watch screws are held in position in a polishing head by a coating of a silicate such as the 2.9 ratio. Rock bits are hardened by facing the teeth with tungsten carbide held on the surface with the same silicate adhesive until the particles can be fused into position with an oxyacetylene flame.[39] A chromium alloy surface on a casting was formed by first binding a film of chromium metal granules on the inner surface of the mold. Metallic aluminum in a silicate vehicle makes a good heat-resisting paint with 3.9 ratio silicate at 22 to 28° Bé.[40] Suspensions of metal powders in the silicate solution are sprayed on a metallic surface and then heat-treated by drying at 800°C, e.g., zinc powder with 0.1 to 0.8 per cent of zinc bicarbonate is used for rust-proof coatings in marine use.[3, 41]

Aluminum or zinc powder mixed with alkali silicate solutions should never be held in closed containers. The formation of hydrogen may be counteracted by the addition of strong oxidizing agents.

Tetrafluoroethylene coatings are bonded to metal without cracking by interposing a layer of potassium silicate solution and polytetrafluoroethylene[42] as a primer coat sprayed on a panel and cured for 3 min at 400°C. The panels were then coated three times with the usual polytetrafluoroethylene composition. With no primer, the pull required to separate a 1 in. strip from the panel was less than ½ lb. With the above primer, the pull was 3.8 lb for a copper strip and 4.5 lb for a steel panel.

The development of glass-to-metal sealing has achieved rapid progress in recent years. Anhydrous sodium silicates having ratios varying from about 1.6 to 2.4 wet the more noble metals in inverse proportion to the polarizing power of the metal in a helium atmosphere.[43] Where other atmospheres are used, the degree of wetting depends on the formation of a surface film such as the oxide or hydride. A high temperature adhesive which fuses and welds to stainless steel at 927°C but will not flow at 1100°C for a short period has been formed from a silicate with stainless steel filler.[44]

Of numerous formulations suggested for reducing the adhesion of silicate to metal surfaces, the best results are obtained using a combination of about 5 per cent urea, 0.5 per cent of an amyl phosphate and a few tenths of a per cent of a wetting agent such as triethanolamine.[45]

Wood. A good bond can be obtained with most wood surfaces if care is taken to be sure that there is sufficient adhesive present to fill the surface pores and yet leave a continuous film in the bond area itself. Pressure is usually required. With good placement, maple blocks have tested in shear as high as 3000 psi with 58 per cent of failure in the wood itself.[46] Bonds with an initial tensile strength of 750 psi gradually dropped to 300 psi in 8 months but subsequently maintained that strength for the 4 years during which the test was continued.[1] Tests seem to show that CO_2 is a minor factor even in 100 per cent CO_2 atmosphere.[47]

Unmodified adhesives cannot be recommended for long-term applications but are very satisfactory for many industrial operations. In the manufacture of box shooks, a 3-ply veneer is formed by applying 85 to 90 lb of 3.2 ratio adhesive to each side of the center sheet.[3] The stack is then left at about 60 to 200 psi for several hours.

For plywood heads for barrels, a suspension of calcium carbonate may be added to the sodium silicate adhesive to increase the viscosity.[48] Hardwood veneer has been made satisfactorily with a more viscous and tacky adhesive such as the 2.9 ratio. The addition of some algin may permit slightly longer working periods.[49] For bonding rubber-to-wood flooring, a clay silicate adhesive is composed of a 3.3 ratio sodium silicate, having about 7.8 per cent of Na_2O, and 8.5 per cent of clay.[34] A water- and fire-proof coating of diatoms is bound to cork or balsa wood life preservers with sodium silicate containing spun glass or asbestos.[50]

Soya flour adhesives used for interior-type plywood frequently contain soluble silicates for the improvement of wetting and dispersion of the protein, providing a buffered alkalinity, a biocide, reduced viscosity, increased bond strength and water resistance. The usual formula[51] involves mixing approximately 100 lb of finely ground soybean flour with 200 lb of water, adding an additional 110 lb of water with 36 lb of a 33 per cent lime dispersion, and then 16 lb of 50 per cent flake caustic solution. Subsequently 30 lb of sodium silicate is added, and finally 2.5 lb of 25 per cent carbon tetrachloride-75 per cent carbon bisulfide is stirred in. This hot-press formula is spread at about 20 lb/1000 sq ft of glue line. For a cold-press glue, the spread is about 60 to 120 lb wet mix per 1000 sq ft of double glue line. Such interior plywoods have withstood immersion under flood conditions for over a month. Hot-press protein adhesives are also made with combinations of blood albumin and soya protein which may vary from 15 to 60 per cent of blood albumin.

A dry, readily soluble, blood albumin adhesive made with five parts of powdered commercial blood albumin mixed with 5 parts of powdered 5-hydrate sodium metasilicate[52] can be used immediately after stirring into a paste, or it may be dusted in dry form on the wet surfaces to be joined. The bond is coagulated by the alkaline solution rather than by heat. Fertilizer grades of blood albumin need alkaline adhesives, and lime is often

mixed with 3.2 ratio silicate solutions in such compositions.[53, 54] Three-ply fir panels tested after 5 days storage and following an additional 2 days of soaking in water had a dry strength of 249 psi and a wet strength of 142 psi.

An adhesive for bonding paper to wood veneer contains approximately 200 lb of soya flour by weight, 20 lb of "Vinsol" resin blended into a mixture of 525 lb of water and 10 qt of kerosene at 80 to 90° F and 26 lb of lime slaked in 50 lb of very hot water, and 13 lb of flake caustic dissolved in 25 lb of water.[55] Following a preservative, 30 lb of sodium silicate of the 3.22 ratio is worked in and then 0.10 lb of cresol dispersed in 2 lb of water.

With a nearly pure protein, the silicate will form a good bond even at ordinary temperatures, but a mixture of 15 per cent ordinary soy flour dispersed in water and approximately 12 per cent of a siliceous 3.22 sodium silicate added will rapidly form a bond if the temperature is raised to above about 70°C.[56] A birch veneer with such a formulation can have a wet tensile shear strength of 151 psi, and fir veneer may have a strength of 175 psi after soaking for 2 days.[57]

A representative casein formula is composed of 100 parts by weight of casein, 150 to 250 parts of water, 20 to 30 parts of hydrated lime, an additional 100 parts of water and 70 parts of 3.2 ratio sodium silicate at 40°Bé.[3]

Paper. The most important application of soluble silicate adhesives is that of bonding paper, e.g., laminated solid fiber sheets, sealed box flaps, wound cans and tubes, or, and certainly the largest in volume, corrugated board for conversion into boxes. Half a billion pounds are shipped, for this purpose annually, principally by tank car.

The soluble silicate sets rapidly requiring only a small loss of water even at room temperature, and the final bond increases the structural strength of the product. Stiffness may be increased as desired by impregnating one or more of the sheets with the silicate. The simplicity of handling the adhesive as prepared by the manufacturer, without additional formulation or mixing, saves labor. The silicate adhesive bond acts as a barrier to vermin of various sorts and increases the fire resistance of the finished board.

The usual corrugated board sheet consists of two flat outer sheets or liners and an inner sheet which is formed in waves or corrugations. This inner sheet is usually about 9 point (.009 in. thick). It is softened by steaming before forming on a fluted brass, steam-heated roll. The standard corrugating adhesive is a 3.2–3.4 ratio sodium silicate solution with a specific gravity of 40 to 42°Bé. It is applied to the flute tips by a glue roll and a sheet of liner, 0.010 to 0.030 in. thick, is immediately pressed on this wet tip at a pressure of about 150 psi. This so-called single-facer sheet is passed over a drying bridge to the double-backer glue station where additional adhesive is applied to the opposite flute tips and pressed onto the second liner or double backer through a continuous felt belt weighted with iron rollers giving a pressure of about 15 psi. The usual glue line spread at the single-facer may be about 7 to 10 lb/1000 sq ft whereas at the double-backer it is likely to be 10 to 12 lb/1000 sq ft.

In a dual adhesive system, an ordinary 3.2 ratio silicate may be diluted to 37 to 40° Bé for use on the single-facer, while on the double-backer, the original silicate of 41 to 42° Bé is used to give an increased spread with decreased penetration.

As the speed of corrugating machines is increased to improve production rates, the adhesive must change from a liquid to a solid at an increasingly rapid rate. At 500 ft/min there is less than 20 sec available. The final bond is set by passing over steam-heated hot plates and then over a cold curing section after which the board may be cut and stacked. A properly balanced board will not warp and may be made into boxes immediately.

Addition of clay not only raises the viscosity to improve placement but also prevents the adhesive from penetrating too deeply into the open pores of the board. Approximately 8 to 10 per cent of a kaolin clay has been found most satisfactory[3, 7, 11, 58] (Table 3).

Raw starch, added in small amount, plasticizes

TABLE 3. EXPERIMENTAL AND COMPUTED COMPRESSION STRENGTH OF CORRUGATED PAPERBOARD BOXES. (McCready and Katz)[61]

| Board | | Strength (lb) Computed | | Experimental |
Adhesive	Application	Column Modulus	Beam Modulus	Top to Bottom
Silicate	Normal	1021	1021	1021[a]
Silicate clay	Normal	1115	1063	1082
Starch	Normal	910	817	916
Silicate	Heavy	1235	1030	1229
Silicate clay	Heavy	1324	1160	1074
Starch	Heavy	965	790	899

[a] This board was used as the standard.

the bond and effects a preliminary grab with the loss of less moisture. The addition of borax is also said to improve the operating characteristics[59] (Fig. 10). As an example of these more complicated adhesives, one formula calls for 4 to 7 per cent water, 2 to 7 per cent raw corn starch, 7 to 8.5 per cent kaolin clay and 87 to 78 per cent of 3.3 sodium silicate at 41° Bé. The adhesive is heated to 150 to 165° F before entering the adhesive pan. The low moisture loss needed for initial set permits 50 per cent higher operating speeds on heavy corrugated boards and double-wall combinations, increases compression resistance 15 to 20 per cent, and provides smooth, flat printing surfaces.

To ensure a permanent dispersion of clay, it is advisable to make an initial dispersion using a small amount of sodium silicate merely to wet the

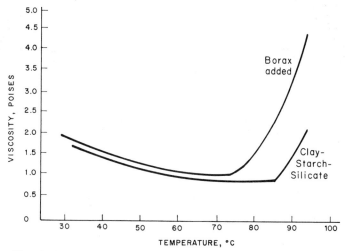

Fig. 10. A clay-starch-silicate adhesive on corrugated board will require only two-thirds of the heat needed for initial set of a clay-silicate adhesive, and the addition of 1% borax will lower this requirement to one-third. (Kreyling[59])

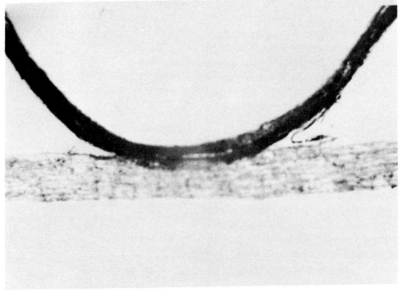

(a)

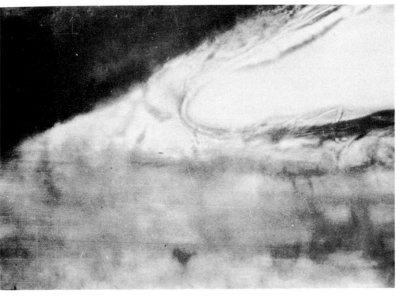

(b)

Fig. 11. The mechanical support provided by a dry bond of sodium silicate is indicated by bonds sectioned in Canada balsam. (*Boller, Lander and Morehouse*[6])
   Single face bond. (a) Corrugated member depressed below liner surface with truss outlined at edges. (b) Edge of bond magnified showing placement of dry bond.

clay and water.[60] Subsequently the rest of the sodium silicate can be added without causing the clay to flocculate. A short heat treatment at 10 to 75°C also helps to develop a stable suspension.

   The joint of a corrugated bond has been studied in detail. If the adhesive is too thin or has too little clay causing it to penetrate too greatly, the shoulder does not form satisfactorily and the bond is brittle[6, 61] (Fig. 11).

   A well-dried silicate adhesive bond is quite resistant to high humidity for a considerable length of time, but it cannot be soaked indefinitely[13, 62] (Fig. 12). When paper bonded with silicate adhesive is stored at a high humidity for a long time,

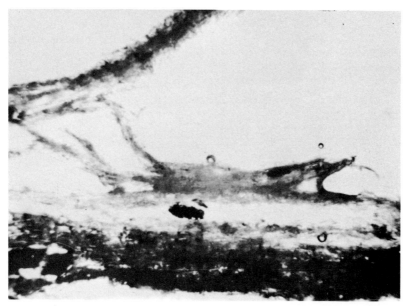

Fig. 12. After soaking a silicate-clay dry bond for 25 min in water, the truss structure attached to the fibers may be separated intact from the main body of the paper. (*Vail and Wegst*[3])

the alkali may migrate through the paper and react with the rosin sizing in the surface; moreover if the ink is not alkali resistant, it may discolor.[13, 63]

It is possible to reduce or preclude staining by treating the board surface with reactive chemicals such as ammonium sulfate or magnesium or iron chloride. A water-resistant bond can be formed by treating the surface with an aqueous aluminum chloride, then drying and combining with 3.2 ratio sodium silicate solution (40.5°Bé).[64]

Combinations of soluble silicate and partially degraded vegetable protein flour, e.g., soya are somewhat water resistant.[65] Protein flour which has a lower water-soluble protein content and is almost wholly free from degradation is more insoluble.[56] Such a heat-setting adhesive for corrugated board may contain 14.5 per cent of soy flour, 66.5 to 69.5 per cent water, 3 per cent raw corn starch and 16 per cent of 41°Bé 3.3 ratio sodium silicate. A similar adhesive will set cold if formed from the natural protein. Prepared simply by mechanical dispersion, these adhesives have a pot life of 8 hr or more at 20°C. Peanut flour has also been used, giving bonds which have maximum wet strength at low alkali concentrations.

A corrugated paperboard house,[3, 66] disposable pallets, and a corrugated unit for heat insulation[67] suggest unusual applications of corrugated board.

Solid Fiberboard. Fiberboard thicker than 0.016 in. is usually built up by lamination or pasting to about five plies as a maximum.[15] Although the components are very similar, adhesive viscosities and machine pressures are much higher than in corrugated board: the viscosity is built up to approximately 2 to 5 poises by the addition of clay. Pressure may be as high as 800 psi. The adhesive is applied either by passing the ply through a bath or by the use of transfer rolls, applying about 6 lb of adhesive per 1000 sq ft of single glue line. As much as an 11 lb spread can be used without discoloring or desizing the outer surface of a 0.016 in. ply. The laminated board is cut into sections and stacked until dry.

A desired stiffness can be obtained more economically with silicate supported paper than by increasing the amount of fiber stock.[68] Under standard conditions, crushing resistance was increased to 240 lb of adhesive per 1000 sq ft and stiffness as determined by bending reached an optimum at about 90 lb of adhesive per 1000 sq ft, using commercial sodium silicates ranging from 2.0 to 3.7 ratio (Figs. 13, 14).

Fiber Tubes, Cans and Drums. If the diameter of a finished tube is less than 6 in., it is considered a tube, or a can if equipped with closed ends. A drum has a diameter exceeding 6 in. Convolute or straight wound tubes are generally stronger than spiral wound tubes, but are prepared by an intermittent operation wherein the width of the paper determines the length of the tube and the length of the paper governs the number of plies for a given mandrel. Those with a diameter greater

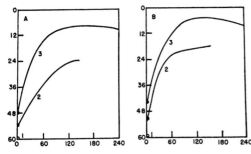

Fig. 13. Laminated board is markedly stiffened in proportion to the amount of sodium silicate in the bond. The single 0.01 inch ply of straw board (A) had about the same sag as the single ply of kraft board (B), i.e., 60 units. The curves show increasing amounts of adhesive. (*Sams and McCready*[68])

ordinate—Sag of a 10 in. span of 1, 2, and 3 plies under a center load of 10 g (16th in. units)

abscissa—Spread of a 3.3 ratio sodium silicate solution (39.7° Bé), lb per 1000 sq ft of laminated board. board.

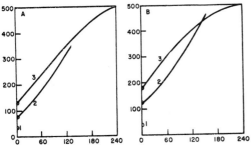

Fig. 14. The resistance to deformation of 0.01 in. thick 2 and 3 ply laminated straw (A) and Kraft (B) board is increased by including more sodium silicate in the structure. The unit (1) shows the initial strength of one untreated ply. (*Sams and McCready*[68])

ordinate—Ring crush strength for 6.25 in. paper ring 0.5 in. high with 1, 2, and 3 plies, lb.

abscissa—Spread of 3.3 ratio sodium silicate (39.7° Bé), lb per 1000 sq ft of laminated board.

than 2 in. are made with unmodified sodium silicate adhesives.

When spirally wound, paper tubes are made continuously at high speeds and require very careful attention to details.[15] The tube is moved along the steel mandrel by the pressure of belts traveling around the freshly formed tube. The adhesive must not allow the paper layers to slip at this stage and must set fast enough to prevent separation of the lamination when the tube is cut off with a saw at the end of the mandrel. For this purpose a sodium silicate having a medium tack such as a 3.4 ratio silicate is recommended. In general, the thinnest possible spread, usually less than about

20 lb/1000 sq ft of glue line, is used. The inner plies of paper are passed through a bath of the adhesive where the silicate penetrates the stock before the excess is removed by notched scraper blades that control the thickness of the film on the ply. Notches 0.05 in. deep every 0.2 in. across the edge of the blade permit beads of silicate to come in contact with the paper. Under pressure of the belt, the beads spread to a thin continuous film that sets quickly to a tight bond.

Tubes less than 3 in. in diameter require much longer mandrels to provide time to form a green bond before the cut-off knife. With a 3 in. or larger tube, 5 sec is satisfactory for set but 10 sec is needed for a tube 1 in. to 3 in. in diameter. In initial operation, a 2.90 ratio sodium silicate diluted from 47° Bé down to about 35 to 37° is usually recommended. Papers that resist wetting need a more dilute silicate. If the distance to the cutting saw is short, it may be important to raise the temperature of the adhesive to 50°C.

Borax reacts with the silicate apparently forming a metaborate and effectively raising the silica ratio of the sodium silicate.[69] This reaction does not occur immediately so that there is some working life. The best quick adhesion was obtained with 27 per cent borax in a 2.4 ratio sodium silicate diluted to 48° Bé; however it gelled in a month. A 2.0 ratio silicate at 50° Bé mixed with 27 per cent borax did not change viscosity for at least 2 months and remained tacky for 2 min on kraft fiber. Seventy-five per cent of the surface of both jute and kraft paper was torn in 2 min.

Sealing. Since the paperboard tears before the adhesive bond fails, pilfering is detected. The inorganic character of the bond sets up a barrier against rodents, bugs or insects as well as against fire.[70] The silicate employed will depend on whether the boxes are being sealed manually or by automatic machines,[15] the surface properties of the paper liner, the time required for set, and the handling system during setting.

For hand sealing, the very tacky 2.9 ratio sodium silicate at 47° Bé is applied evenly with a flat 4-in. brush at the rate of about 0.011 lb/sq ft over one flap; then the other flap is immediately closed and held with a pressure of 10 to 50 psi for from 1 to 5 min. Eighty to 90 per cent of full strength is developed in 30 min or less.

In automatic sealing machines the less tacky but faster setting 3.22 ratio sodium silicate at 42° Bé finds general use. Transfer rolls apply the minimum spread and then the flaps are closed and maintained in a pressure section for 1 or 2 min. If the cases tend to open, it may indicate that excessive adhesive is being applied. When cold, the silicate has a higher viscosity than when warm and will require a different adjustment. In special cases, dilute adhesives with viscosity increased by the addition of clay or borax have been found helpful. Similar adhesives are used for capping rolls of toilet tissue, newsprint and other sealing operations.

Labeling. Labels may be applied with either the 2.9 ratio or 3.2 ratio silicate. Further protection may be provided by a surface coating. Ink colors which are sensitive to alkali should be avoided. Discoloration of some papers by the alkali may be overcome by addition of 0.5 per cent peroxide to the silicate.[71]

For labeling wooden barrels, a mixture of 100 parts of 3.7 ratio silicate with 20 parts of sugar diluted to the required viscosity has been recommended.[13] The 2.0 ratio solution will serve alone on clean tin surfaces but the addition of 5 per cent rosin added hot with an equal weight of water improves flexibility, tack and clean up. A silicate of about the 2.4 ratio is used for attaching labels to grinding wheels.[51]

Wallboard. Thick, highly absorbent chip filler paper stock is formed into wallboard with 25 to 40 per cent kaolin clay in the silicate adhesive formulated to meet the requirements of a slow drying time and a slow setting speed.[72] If 25 parts of the 2.0 ratio silicate at 60° Bé are diluted with 25 parts of water and 60 parts of whiting are added, the bond becomes insoluble in about a week. The initial bond is not as strong as with the clay-silicate adhesive.

Various other wallboards of asbestos, cork, kapok, vulcanized fiber, etc., have been developed with silicate adhesives.[3, 13] An after-treatment with magnesium or calcium chloride will result in an insoluble bond. Chips of wood are first dipped in a 3.2 ratio silicate at about 3° Bé, then mixed with a Portland cement and molded. Plates are formed from ground wood fiber by applying silicate solutions as a spray, then compressing into a sheet, and passing through a flame. Laminated boards of felt or paper impregnated with bituminous material are bonded with a cement prepared from 150 parts of the 3.2 ratio silicate solution at 40° Bé, 65 parts of Portland cement and 10 parts of trisodium phosphate with 3 parts of sodium fluoride.[73]

Floc. The practice of covering evergreens such as spruce, hemlock and pine boughs with a floc of powdered rayon or cellulose is becoming popular for Christmas decorations.[15] For variation, a metallic powder may be substituted. The 3.2 ratio silicate at 41° Bé is diluted with up to 1 part of water per part of silicate and sprayed at a pressure of 40 psi from a distance of about 3 ft. Through a second gun the floc is directed into the silicate spray at about a 45 to 90 degree angle and thus is driven onto the silicated surface. A quick finish coat of the silicate is applied. If bare branches are to be coated, they may be sprayed with silicate, tumbled in the powdered floc material to save waste and occasionally given a final surface spray.

Insulation. Numerous insulating sheets and bodies have been developed with soluble silicate as a binder.[3, 13] Fragments of paper have been blown together with a silicate spray against wood, paper or metal backing to form insulation or cushioning. A sound deadening composition composed of 12 parts of emulsified asphalt, 60 parts of the 40° Bé 3.2 ratio silicate and 28 parts by weight of clay is applied by brush or spray on the underside of automobile bodies and withstands a temperature of 200°C.[74] Cotton and wool felt filters are formed similarly.

The fire-resistant properties of silicate adhesives are especially helpful in the preparation of mineral sheets such as those formed by asbestos, mica, etc. Asbestos insulation formed with sodium silicate withstands continuous temperatures of 370°C and about 538°C under intermittent conditions.[13] Insulating pipe coverings built up with 4 poise 3.2 ratio silicate are sawn in half, placed around a pipe, bound with a sheet of cotton and finally coated with the 3.2 silicate solution at 41° Bé or a higher gravity if the temperature is very warm.

Mica, vermiculite, zonolite, kieselguhr, etc., have been bound similarly, forming lightweight insulation.[13]

Heterogeneous Mixtures

The development of greater water resistance in the final silicate adhesive by addition of whiting or aragonite is aided by reaction with the 2.0 ratio sodium silicate. Such alkaline silicates react more rapidly than 3.2 ratio solutions and have a sharp upturn in viscosity after an initial period of slow reaction.[3, 13] A mixture which barely shows evidence of action at 20°C may set very rapidly at 40°C. These adhesives are satisfactory for laminating paper if given time to set. For gluing northern hardwoods such as birch or maple, 25 lb of lime-free, finely ground whiting with 100 lb of neutral 3.2 ratio silicate is suggested. Mixtures of sodium silicate solutions are sometimes recommended.[75]

The addition of raw or ungelatinized starch to silicate adhesives has been mentioned for laminating paper. An adhesive having equal weights of 3.2 ratio sodium silicate solution and raw starch also bonds to metal surfaces, rock sponge, etc.[13]

Mixtures with animal and vegetable proteins have been mentioned both for wood and paper adhesives.

Rubber. Aqueous latices of rubber and other high polymers may usually be mixed with liquid silicate solutions in any proportions, but synthetic latex may require more care in formulation than natural latex. The stability of latices to coagulation by silicate solution has been studied.[76] One recommended composition contains 100 parts of latex (60 per cent solids), 10 parts of ammonium hydroxide (28 per cent) and 10 parts of 2.0 ratio sodium silicate at 52° Bé.[77]

The sodium silicate should be added to the latex a little at a time with constant stirring although the agitation should not be vigorous. The temperature should be maintained at about 25°C. In warmer weather, 0.27 part casein or 0.03 part borax acts as a stabilizer. Compositions containing 4.7 lb of latex (60 per cent rubber content) and 5.6 lb of sodium silicate[37] were used for gluing metals and in bonding plywood to dull galvanized iron or aluminum. An elastic coating of the latex-silicate solution should be applied to the metal surface, permitted to dry, and then additional adhesive spread or sprayed on one side.

A 50 per cent vulcanized latex having 60 per cent solids plus 50 per cent of 2.0 ratio sodium silicate at 50° Bé adheres tightly to paper but may be peeled cleanly with ease. This is characteristic of palletizing adhesives. Increasing the silica content tends to decrease flexibility, while increased alkali results in staining and reduced water resistance.[12] The strongest bonds between cold set birch veneer were achieved with 30 per cent of the 3.7 ratio silicate at 6.3 per cent Na_2O and 70 per cent of natural latex (60 per cent solids). Latex-silicate adhesives have been used in shoe soles and trim, foxing on tennis shoes, gauze bandages, fabric layers, etc.

Polyvinyl Acetate. The soluble silicate solutions are more compatible with vinyl acetate copolymer solutions than with the homopolymers.[78] They are also more compatible in the presence of ethylene glycol and higher ratios of silica to alkali.

Polyvinyl acetate emulsion paint has been gelled by the addition of soluble silicates.[79] The 3.2 ratio and more siliceous sodium silicates were found effective in 0.5 per cent concentration. An adhesive on a fabric belt to hold abrasive particles has 15 lb of sodium silicate, presumably 3.2 ratio, mixed at a medium speed with 6 lb of kaolin clay, 1 lb of sorbitol, 1.5 lb of sodium carboxymethylcellulose and 6 lb of 56 per cent polyvinyl acetate emulsion.[80]

The addition of a polyvinyl chloride to a silicate coating increases the resistance to temporary high temperatures.[81, 31]

Methylol Urea. Water resistance of soluble silicate coatings has been increased by the addition of methylol urea.[82] Dimethylol urea has also been mixed with soluble silicates to form an adhesive for flexible abrasive-coated material.[83] A paper backing of 130 lb cylinder paper was roll-coated with 3 to 4 lb per ream of a 50 per cent solution of 2.0 ratio sodium silicate at 60° Bé. To this, 100 grit-fused aluminum abrasive grain was applied electrostatically. After drying at 38°C for ½ hr, the coated paper was sized with 8 to 10 lb per ream of a mixture of 43 per cent by weight of dimethylol urea and 57 per cent by weight of the 2.0 ratio sodium silicate, dried at 45°C for 5 hr, gradually raised to 110°C and cured for 2 hr at that temperature. This paper was effective for wood sanding 1 year later, whereas a straight sodium silicate adhesive had deteriorated in storage.

Ceramic Cements

Adhesives for ceramic materials—inorganic, amorphous or crystalline matter—are usually termed cements. Silicate cements may be divided into three general types.[3] In the first, *air-dried,* the viscosity is increased and hardness developed merely by loss of water. Such low temperature bonds may have a tensile strength of about 3000 psi, depending greatly on the gradation in size of the inert additive. They will be more or less resistant to water, depending on how thoroughly they have been dried and the time during which they may have been able to react with the more or less inert filler or treated with mineral acids to increase the insolubility. In such processes, crystalline materials do not usually develop.

The second type, *dehydrated,* is a high temperature bond free of water. Thus, it is a glass formed by reaction between the soluble silicate and other parts of the mixture. The original silicate becomes solid at about 20 to 30 per cent water when the bond may have a tensile strength of about 2000 psi. At about 300°C below the liquidus, the strength decreases until a vitreous bond is formed by fluxing; then very high strength may be obtained.

The third type depends on *chemical reaction* between the soluble silicate and the materials added. The reactant product is usually a gelatinous material whose strongest bonds are obtained in the presence of a minimum of water. The particle size of the added reactant is also important since the set usually occurs before complete reaction has occurred.

Drying. To avoid intumescence, the temperature of a liquid silicate bond should be raised only a few degrees per hour until well above the boiling point. Above 130°C the temperature may be increased rapidly.[3] The proper drying sequence varies according to composition and thickness of the bond, rate of transfer of heat and air, and character of the substrate. If the proportion of silicate solution is too low, the aggregate may not be adequately wetted, whereas if it is too great, a weak gelatinous bond may result. If the solution is too thick, distribution and wetting will be poor; and if it is too dilute, the cement will be slow in drying and may run away from the interface and form a weak bond with the aggregate.

Carefully dried silicate-sand mixtures tend to have a higher strength than cements formed by chemical reaction with silicate.[3] It is recommended that the filler contain 20 per cent of material passing 200 mesh and a similar amount between 100 and 200 mesh. This should be used with about 20 per cent of the 3.2 ratio sodium silicate.

Chemical Reactions. Unreactive additives include quartz, barium sulfate, oxides of iron, chromium and manganese, silicate minerals such as clays, carbon black, etc. Some of these react slowly but do not cause a rapid setting of the cement. However, the soluble alkali silicates react directly with many compounds such as precipitated calcium carbonate, preferably in the form of aragonite, lead oxides or carbonates, alkali metal fluorides, alkaline earth metal fluorides and fluosilicates, calcium sulfate, soluble salts of the heavy metals, and many silicates. The fluosilicates set quickly and form cements of highly acid-resistant character. Most of the reactions result in gels or gelatinous precipitates. The lower the water content at the critical stage of setting, the stronger the bond tends to be, and the denser cements are more resistant to water and acids.

At 90°C zinc oxide powders formed the hardest compositions with 3.2 ratio sodium silicate, but at 242°C 2.4 ratio silicate was hardest. After reaction at 900° for 15 min, all mixtures showed a definite crystal change to more insoluble products. The finest zinc oxide particles, 0.1 micron, gave the fastest reaction.[3, 84]

Physical Factors. A high strength combination was made with 79 per cent of graded cement clinker, 3 per cent of fines at 100 to 200 mesh and 3 per cent of clinker fines through 200 mesh, with 12 per cent of anhydrous calcium sulfate and 3 per cent of borax.[85] 6.3 ml of the 2.0 ratio sodium silicate at 54 per cent solids and 7.3 g of water were added to each 100 g of the dry mixture.

After pressing at 5000 to 10,000 psi and heating to 104°C, the brick had a compressive strength of 4720 psi. The compressive strength decreased at higher drying temperatures and increased with higher molding pressures. The maximum strength of a 3.8 ratio silicate solution with balanced sieve fractions of grog and fire clay was obtained at approximately 29 per cent H_2O.[86] (Fig. 15).

A study of soapstone slabs bonded with soluble silicates demonstrates many of the properties of similar combinations[87] (Fig. 16).

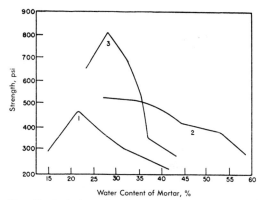

Fig. 15. Inclusion of sodium silicate in a refractory mortar at the optimum water content increases the strength after drying at 105 to 110°C. (*Heindl and Prendergast*[86])

(1) Ohio fire clay and grog
(2) Ohio fire clay
(3) Ohio fire clay, grog and 3.8 ratio sodium silicate solution.

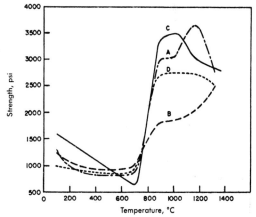

Fig. 16. The ratio and physical characteristics of the sodium silicate bond must be chosen for optimum strength. Soapstone bonded with 10 per cent sodium silicate (with optimum water) and vitrified at 700 to 900°C. (*Phillips*[87])

A. 2.0 sodium silicate (60°Bé)
B. 3.3 sodium silicate (17.5% H_2O)
C. 2.0 sodium silicate (17.5% H_2O)
D. 2.0 sodium silicate (anhydrous glass powder)

The addition of small amounts of other salts to the sodium silicate binder frequently increases the tensile strength of the final bond.[88] Presumably the sodium bicarbonate acts to increase the effective silica ratio. Sodium nitrate and potassium salts also are beneficial. They probably affect the water balance since they are known to be active in coacervating soluble silicate solutions. Alkali phosphates and borates also increase the strength and toughness of the bond.[89]

The change in volume on drying frequently can be almost completely avoided by the proper control of grain size and filler. The tendency to expand increases with silicate binder content and alkalinity[90] (see Fig. 17). A periclase refractory bound with a 2.0 ratio sodium silicate[91] showed less shrinkage and a higher strength than when a 3.2 ratio silicate or a silica sol was tried.

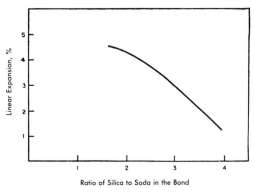

Fig. 17. The linear expansion of a fired dry-press refractory mixture of calcined grog, Tennessee ball clay, with a liquid sodium silicate binder can be controlled by varying the proportion of Na_2O in the binder. (*Norton*[90])

In studies of pyrophyllite refractories, the compressive strength increased with increasing concentration of binder.[92, 93]

A refractory brick which will maintain a reasonable strength over the temperature range from the formation of a viscous glass to the normal ceramic set is composed of 80 per cent olivine and 20 per cent of a bond composed of 25 parts of colemanite, 35 parts of 3.2 ratio sodium silicate powder, 20 parts of kaolin and 20 parts of potter's flint.[94] A formula with carefully sized magnesite or chrome ore which resists temperatures up to 1590°C regulates expansion and contraction by the presence of zircon sand.[95]

Plastic Cements. The age hardening of plastic cements can be caused by a number of phenomena.[96] In some cases, soluble impurities in the raw clay or grog may react with the silicate. If these reactions occur by base exchange, sequestering agents will improve the storage life. In other cases, a preliminary treatment with sodium carbonate will eliminate the reactive material. Any increase in the effective ratio of the silicate also tends to shorten the storage life. This may occur through adsorption of the alkali by the clay or grog or through the release of a soluble silica from the calcined grog. This release may sometimes be controlled by regulating the calcining time and temperature. Acidic materials may be introduced from fuel oil or through the water, which also may contain hardness factors that react with the silicate.

Mortars for setting fire brick are classified as (1) ground plastic fire clay, (2) heat-setting, (3) wet air-setting, and (4) dry air-setting.[97] In general, air-set bonds are somewhat stronger than heat-set, at 25 to 1100°C. At 1425°C and above, they have about the same strength. The composition and properties of three mortars meeting all criteria are listed below together with four other representative mortars (Table 4).

Potassium Silicates. The application of potassium silicates to refractories is beginning to receive attention now that they have become readily available and their properties are better understood.[96] The liquid potassium silicates tend to have a higher mole ratio, and therefore show less fluxing effect. Furthermore, a potassium silicate glass has a higher viscosity at a given temperature than its corresponding sodium equivalent. The potassium silicates are indicated for the very highest temperature conditions and in clay-type ramming mixes. Potassium silicates are also substituted for sodium silicates in air-set mortars or plastic cements primarily because they make a less tacky cement which is more desirable for the brick mason. They are also more hygroscopic; the potassium silicate glasses dissolve more rapidly than sodium silicate glasses having the same molecular ratio. It has been long recognized that potassium silicate in cements and coatings does not cause bloom, since potassium carbonate hydrate readily deliquesces instead of forming visible crystals.

Mixtures of the liquid potassium and sodium silicates may show either maximum or minimum viscosities, depending on the ratios involved.[3] In the anhydrous systems, mixed sodium-potassium glasses show a minimum viscosity,[17] (Fig. 18), usually at about 30 mole per cent K_2O. These mixtures have found use in low-fired refractory bonds and in coatings. The mixed sodium-potassium silicate glasses also have minimum dielectric constants at a ratio of about 3 moles Na_2O to 4

TABLE 4.

The best commercial refractory mortars fall within a narrow range of composition. The first three met all of the selected criteria; the other four were the best of other types of mortars tested. (From Eusner ET AL).[97]

Refractory Mortar Type	1 Heat-set	2 Air-set	3 Air-set	4 Air-set	5 Heat-set	6 Air-set	7 Air-set
Composition							
Al_2O_3	54.7	48.7	43.9	58.5	81.3	40.1	4.2
SiO_2	40.9	46.2	50.2	35.3	16.6	51.6	91.9
Na_2O	0.1	2.6	2.3	0.8	0.6	2.0	2.0
K_2O	1.1	0.1	0.6	0.9	0.1	1.3	0.2
Fe_2O_3	1.1	1.1	1.4	1.4	0.5	2.2	0.5
TiO_2	2.0	1.0	1.3	2.5	0.4	1.8	0.4
Major aggregate	Mullite grog, kyanite clay	Raw and calcined kyanite	Raw kyanite	Mullite grog, clay (sulfate bond)	Corundum	Fire-brick grog, kyanite	Quartz
Linear shrinkage							
100°C	1.8	3.4	3.4	1.6	1.8	3.1	1.6
1400°C	0.5+	0.0	1.0	0.8	2.1	4.7	1.0
Apparent porosity, % (1400°C)	42	40	39	47	42	27	16
Bulk density (1400°C)	1.63	1.64	1.69	1.52	1.97	1.73	1.55
Load test subsidence, % (1370°C)	10.4	11.2	25.6	21.6	12.0	13.6	20.6

moles K_2O. At this same ratio, the potassium glasses have a lower electrical conductivity than do the sodium glasses.[3, 96]

Applications. Soluble silicates are used as refractory cements for laying bricks for tanks, boilers, ovens, furnaces, and chimneys; for repairing and protecting stoves, dissolvers and plating tanks, drains, floors and sewers, etc; for boiler setting; or repairing broken saggers. Ready-mixed cements of silicon-carbide, firesand, raw fire clay and powdered hydrated 3.3 ratio sodium silicate are used in large amounts.

A simple acid-proof cement is made from a fine, pure quartz sand and a 3.7 ratio sodium silicate in equal proportions. Such cements resist concentrated and dilute hydrochloric, nitric and sulfuric acid. Linings for sulfite digesters used in paper mills are made with the solution of 2.4 ratio sodium silicate, one part to one part of Portland cement, and two parts of 20 mesh quartz sand.[13, 98]

Silicon carbide, metallic silicon powder and sodium silicate liquid have been combined in a neutral self-baking refractory.[96] The hydrogen gas from the reaction is ignited and burns off.

Basic refractory mixes must be kept dry until they are ready for use.[96] Gunning mixes of chrome ore and magnesia take advantage of the low fusion point of hydrated sodium silicate powders. Magnesite mixed with hydrated or anhydrous sodium silicate powdered glass forms the bottom of an open-hearth furnace. This mixture is rammed into

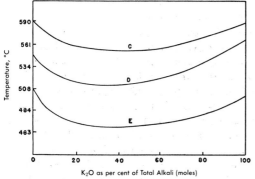

Fig. 18. A "double glass" of $Na_2O:K_2O:nSiO_2$ reaches a given viscosity (10^{10} poise) at a lower temperature than either single glass. (Poole[17])

C. 18 mole per cent of alkali (total)
D. 25 mole per cent of alkali (total)
E. 35 mole per cent of alkali (total)

place and sets by reaction when the furnace is heated.

Carbonaceous cements are used to fill spaces in electrode joints.[3] A cement is suggested containing 31 per cent petroleum coke (60 per cent through 200 mesh screen), 28 per cent coal tar pitch having a melting point of 175°C and passing a 35 mesh screen, 3 per cent of 3.2 ratio silicate, 23 per cent molasses and 15 per cent water.[99]

Coatings for welding rods utilize silicate cements. A high cellulose coating for electrodes may contain medium amounts of sodium silicate and/or potassium silicate, ferromanganese, asbestos and titanium dioxide, small or optional amounts of calcium carbonate, magnesium silicate (talc), feldspar and gum and large amounts of cellulose.[3]

The colored pigments which brighten the roofs of many housing developments are bound to inert granules by silicate adhesives which permit a life expectancy of 25 years or more. For example, a mixture of warm (45°C) crushed rock granules (−10M) 2000 parts, ultramarine blue 15, blue phthalocyanine paste (20 per cent solids) 1.2, titanium dioxide 2, aluminum fluoride 11.4, white Portland cement 4, sodium silcofluoride 5.7, and 2.85 ratio sodium silicate solution 50 parts was placed in a rotary mixer and then dried in a rotary kiln between 120 and 315°C.[100] Other simpler, wholly inorganic formulas are fired at temperatures up to about 1000°C.

Monolithic Structures

Molds. In foundry practice, "hot-tops" prevent the development of hollow "pipes" during the cooling of ingots. They are molded typically from 12 parts of 3.3 ratio sodium silicate solution with a small amount of zinc oxide and the rest silica sand,[101, 102, 103] and baked at about 260°C providing a refractory cover with sufficient porosity to allow the escape of gases. The Antioch process which employs gypsum molds results in fine surface contours and is applicable to the casting of aluminum for engine parts, etc.[104]

To form thin shell molds, Watertown Arsenal sprays a molding sand wet with 5 per cent of a 3.75 ratio sodium silicate (35°Bé) and 2.5 per cent water on a hot metal pattern.[105]

In the carbon dioxide process for foundry molds, the sand is mulled with a viscous soluble silicate, then formed and the silicate binder caused to set partly by air drying and partially by effecting a reaction of a portion of the alkali with CO_2 passed through the porous mold as a gas. The carbon dioxide rapidly develops the green strength.[106]

Commercial binders include other additives which are usually carbonaceous materials, preferably invert sugars.[3, 9, 107]

Abrasives. The binding of abrasive wheels with 2.0 soluble silicate is an old art, but the difficulties of controlling the bond have been such that few wheels are now so made.[3, 108]

Silicate-base polishing wheel cements will withstand higher temperature in drying and use and can be dried more rapidly than wheels formed with organic glues.[3] The silicate cements are favored for fast, tough, coarse polishing. The cloth layers are assembled with glue between them and after drying or baking, the cutting edge is coated with the adhesive, first as a dilute solution to fill the porous cloth and, after drying, with full strength thick viscous adhesive. This coated wheel is rolled back and forth in a trough of abrasive grain. Along with mixed sodium or potassium silicates, the formulation may include china clay and talc or asbestos.[109]

Briquettes. In some cases, moistening with water before pressing is sufficient to hold particles together; in others, pressure alone may serve the purpose; occasionally dilute solutions of starch or resins are sufficient. Taconite is prepared for the replacement of higher grade ore by the addition of a small percentage of bentonite clay as an inorganic adhesive.[110] Serpentine has been pelleted with 0.5 to 1.5 per cent borax and fired at 650°C. In the briquetting of coal dust, a dispersion of 20 to 25 per cent of ground pitch passing a 100 mesh sieve is formed with 30°Bé 3.4 ratio sodium silicate solution.[3] Metallurgical briquettes use about 5 per cent of 3.2 or 2.9 ratio silicate. Glass batches have been briquetted using 3 per cent of the 2.9 ratio sodium silicate and 0.9 per cent water,[3] as well as 1.6 ratio liquid sodium silicate.[111]

Soil. Soil may be conditioned or impermeabilized with soluble silicate mixtures designed to set by reaction with additives or with the soil itself.[3, 15] The most widely known of the soil stabilization processes is the so-called "Joosten Process" in which soil is impregnated at a pressure of 50 to 125 psi first with a sodium silicate of the 3.2 ratio and following this by a solution of calcium chloride, thus forming a calcium silicate mass which hardens and prevents the passage of water as well as strengthens the soil structure.[112] A trench prepared for housing foundations was stabilized similarly.[3] Secondary roads have been formed by mixing soluble silicates with soils containing calcium.

A less permanent type of solidification is brought about with sodium bicarbonate,[15, 113] which is particularly useful where loose sands are met during a tunneling operation. The 3.2 ratio sodium silicate is diluted 50 per cent by weight with water to about 21.0°Bé and mixed with 6.6 lb of the bicarbonate in 93.4 lb of water. Usually the solutions are mixed on the job and immediately forced into the ground, since the gel time is only 30 sec to 70 min, varying with the proportions used.

Chemically Resistant Cements

Three types of chemically setting silicate mortars have been differentiated.[3, 114] The first type sets by drying in air; acid resistance is developed by treating with an acid solution to remove the sodium carbonate from at least the outer surfaces and form an SiO_2 bond.

The second group, in which the silica is gelled by the slow hydrolysis of an organic ester, finds little commercial application because a 3-part package is needed and the ethyl acetate, for instance, is highly flammable and anaesthetic.[115, 116]

The third comprises a reaction with the fluosilicates such as sodium fluosilicate. Because these set more rapidly, they have found wide usage during the past 30 years, and many installations in corrosive systems have held up for 10 or 15 yr of continuous service. For superior performance, the sodium silicate is replaced by potassium silicate or by a silica cement formed with a silica sol containing 30 to 35 per cent SiO_2 and practically no alkali; the maximum is about 0.7 per cent Na_2O. Before immersion in concentrated sulfuric acid, each of these mortars will have approximately the same strength, i.e., about 2100 psi. After immersion for 56 days in 94 per cent sulfuric acid containing ammonium, sodium and iron sulfates, the sodium silicate mortar had a strength of 1560 psi and the potassium silicate 1240 psi, while the silica sol mortar had increased to 6530 psi. It is said that these silica mortars set without loss of water but the strength is not developed until a large part of the water is lost.

Silica gel as a bonding agent is precipitated by hydrolysis from organic silicate esters such as ethyl orthosilicate.[115, 116] Addition of magnesia accelerates the hydrolysis. Esters of titanium and zirconium have similar properties.[2]

Acid-resistant cements formed by the reaction of the soluble silicates and the silicofluorides, fluorides or silica, etc. may have three or four times the adhesive strength of Portland cement.[13] Shrinkage is low, and the thermal expansion approaches that of steel. Such an adhesive loses strength at about 400°C and vitrifies at 980°C. A representative formula which had a compressive strength of about 7000 psi was of 93.4 g of powdered quartz, 4.6 g of sodium silicofluoride, 2.0 g of calcium silicofluoride and 30 ml of 2.4 ratio sodium silicate at 48°Bé.[117] A substantially insoluble cement for uniting porcelain and glass with metal was made by mixing 62 parts of powdered flint, 14 parts of 3.7 ratio soluble silicate solution at 1.4 specific gravity, 14 parts of water and 10 parts of aluminum fluoride. After mixing and applying, the cement is baked preferably at about 100 to 175°C.[118]

The silicate and silica cements are not resistant to strong alkaline solutions such as calcium hydroxide or caustic soda, sodium peroxide, sodium hypochlorite or fluorides.

PHOSPHATE CEMENTS

Five types of phosphate bonds are recognized: silicate-phosphoric acid, zinc phosphate, oxidephosphoric acid, acid phosphate and other miscellaneous phosphates.

Silico-Phosphate

The silicate-phosphoric acid bonds are porcelaintype "silicate" dental cements formed from alumina, lime and silica glass frits ground with phosphoric acid just prior to use. They set through the formation of a silica gel. While these are not suitable for refractory applications, a refractory patching cement for vertical retorts was made of ground silica brick, silica flour and ball clay with ½ gal phosphoric acid per 100 lb on the dry weight.[119] Other bonds have been formed with complex silicates such as zircon by reaction with phosphoric acid. With zircon the composition is fired at 982°C and does not volatilize or soften at temperatures up to 1650°C.

Dental Cements. A cement for this application must resist solution by fluids in the mouth. It must have a coefficient of thermal expansion comparable to that of a normal tooth, a low heat of conductivity, and a surface similar to that of normal dentine. It must be capable of easy molding during placement but set rapidly once in position. Since these cements do not appear to bond to the tooth surface, it is thought they are held by mechanical interlocking and by frictional resistance. Dental cements have been grouped as:

(1) Zinc oxychloride and zinc oxide-eugenol. (See basic salts.)
(2) Copper phosphate and zinc phosphate. (See zinc phosphate.)

(3) The above classes 1 and 2 together with silver, copper or mercury salts.

(4) Silicate and zinc phosphate-silicate. (See silicate-phosphoric acid and zinc phosphate.)

The so-called "silicate cements" are the least permanent but most widely used of the so-called "permanent materials," primarily for fillings. The brittle mixed silicate-zinc phosphate cements are utilized as translucent cementing material. The silicate cements are generally even more brittle and about two-thirds as strong as the zinc phosphate-silicate cements. The average compressive strength is 24,000 psi. Most silicate cements appear to reach nearly maximum strength in about a week when stored in distilled water. After 6 months in distilled water the strength was 25,000 psi; stored in saliva, it was 26,000 psi; and in oil, 30,000 psi.[13, 120]

Although the average life expectancy of a silicate cement is about 4.5 years, it is considered possible to place silicate fillings which will last 20 or more years. The cement has an opacity of 25 to 57 per cent and a hardness of 54 kg/mm² compared to 100 per cent opacity and 36 kg/mm² hardness for zinc phosphate, and 70 per cent opacity and 55 kg/mm² hardness for dentine.

Metal Phosphate

The principal metal phosphates are the zinc phosphate bonds in dental cements and household appliances, which are probably mainly dibasic zinc phosphate $ZnHPO_4 \cdot 3H_2O$.[13, 119, 120, 92] A mixture of zinc oxide powder and H_3PO_4 reacts violently with considerable heat development when mixed, but small amounts of dental cement are spread on a chilled slab so that the temperature is kept down to that of the body tissues. The setting time increases as the amount of acid is increased, but decreases with dilution.

Zinc phosphate cements form a crystalline material when setting, whereas the "silicate" cements appear to form primarily colloidal materials of gelatinous character. Copper phosphates containing 2 per cent cupric oxide have a short life and are used primarily for their antiseptic value.

Oxide-Phosphoric Acid

An oxide bond is formed with phosphoric acid and aluminum, chromium, magnesium or zirconium oxide or halide at 200°C.[121] These bonds, matured at about 300°C, are relatively insoluble in boiling water. The phosphate bond decomposes and converts to a sintered alumina bond with the high refractoriness of pure corundum as well as excellent thermal stability and strength at high temperatures.

Cements for ramming, troweling or gunning may be formed by mulling phosphoric acid with alumina. With a prepared dry mix, reaction between water and P_2O_5 is highly exothermic. Mixing and ramming are carried out above 70°C because the very concentrated phosphoric acid will freeze below this temperature. A preliminary bond is formed at about 230°C and a final bond at 300°C. The 85 per cent H_3PO_4 may constitute 10 to 13 per cent of the mixture with tabular alumina.

For cementing casings in wells, slurries of gypsum or Portland cement are conventionally employed; but in very deep wells temperature and pressure conditions as well as contamination from the formation interfere with normal setting. A cement which will seal off such contamination, will hold firm at 260°C and is easily controlled in setting time, is formed by mixing 41 parts by weight of bauxite, 10.2 parts of calcium fluoride and 41 parts of a filler such as coal with 27.6 parts of water and 23.1 parts of 85 per cent phosphoric acid.[122]

Similar compositions with kaolin are more suitable for temperatures of about 90°C.

Acid Phosphates

Acid phosphate cements may be prereacted or formed *in situ* by reactions of acids with oxides, hydroxides or salts of basic elements. When added as prepared solutions, drying is required. The water in water-soluble aluminum phosphates must be low enough to permit the solids to precipitate but high enough to form a soluble compound.[123] They are made by suspending fine aluminum hydrate and phosphoric acid or oxide in separate portions of kerosene, toluene, etc. using enough organic diluent to maintain the temperature in the range of 70 to 80°C when the components are mixed. The aluminum phosphate, $AlPO_4$, which separates as a secondary liquid phase is drawn off and solidified by evaporation to 10 to 30 per cent free water.

Acid phosphates which form reaction bonds include the aluminum, beryllium, cadmium, calcium, copper, chromium, iron, lanthanum, lead, tin, thorium, vanadium, yttrium, zinc and zirconium salts, both monobasic and dibasic.[119, 124] On heating beyond the dehydration temperature, they usually gain strength. Magnesium and aluminum, which have small ionic radii, provide optimum bonding as the phosphate. Cement mortars of fire clay grog and Florida kaolin with $Al(H_2PO_4)_3$ or

$Mg(H_2PO_4)_2$ retained good strength properties up to 1500°C and 1850°C, respectively. Above those temperatures, the shrinkage and expansion on heating became greater than desirable. These mortars are more expensive than the ordinary high heat-duty mortars but are valuable for extremely high temperature use.

Aluminum acid phosphate, $Al(H_2PO_4)_3$, forms solutions of very high viscosity at concentrations of 60 to 70 per cent. Precipitation of mono- and dibasic phosphates results in the strongest hydrogen bonds known.

A composition of abrasive grain or powdered glass, plastic clay, aluminum acid phosphate solution and sodium silicate glass powder formed artificial stone with strength of 24 psi green and 120 psi after firing, compared to a sodium silicate bond of 12 psi green and 114 psi fired.[125, 126] Aluminum hydroxide sol as a binder showed a strength of 17 psi green and 86 psi fired.

Powdered talc may be bonded into a monolithic product using from 8 to 22 per cent of phosphoric acid fired at up to about 1200°C.[127] At 9 per cent phosphoric acid the compressive strength fired was 31,800 psi and the water adsorption was 7.3 per cent, whereas at 22 per cent phosphoric acid the compressive strength was 51,500 and the water adsorption was 9.0 per cent. The green strength was 825 and 980 psi, respectively.

A quick-setting refractory composition for precision casting was prepared from an aggregate bonded with sodium, calcium, magnesium, zinc, ammonium or organic acid phosphates, phosphoric acid or sulfuric acid plus water and zircon or various zirconium silicates.[124] The addition of fluosilicates increased the setting time.

Silica or siliceous materials with phosphoric acid are set by heat to form $SiO(PO_3)_2$.[2] Phosphoric acid with asbestos probably forms a magnesium acid phosphate as a bond. Phosphorus pentoxide and ethyl alcohol with magnesia makes a gelatinous refractory bond which may be an acid phosphate.

HYDRAULIC CEMENTS

The principal types of cements which set by hydration are calcium silicate or Portland cement, calcium-aluminate cements, pozzuolanic cements, slag cements, natural lime-silica cements, barium silicate and barium aluminate cements, ferrites and ferrates, lime and gypsum cements. In these cements, time for hydration must be permitted but the heat developed must be kept to a minimum. Plenty of water must be maintained at the surface to retard evaporation. Calcium aluminate cements have higher heats of hydration than Portland cements and require more caution to prevent early drying, as well as more water for completion of hydration. High alumina cements contain considerable iron and silica. Dried Portland cements or hydraulic cements are usually more or less porous depending on the compaction and gradation of the aggregate and the initial water content. These pores may be filled by impregnation with sodium silicates or with metal fluosilicates which react with the free calcium and precipitate silica gel or calcium silicate in the pores.[128] The treated surfaces are more resistant to penetration by water and to attack by acids.

Portland Cement

The essential constituents of Portland cement are $3CaO \cdot SiO_2$ and $2CaO \cdot SiO_2$ with some minor proportions of $3CaO \cdot Al_2O_3$ and $4CaO \cdot Al_2O_3 \cdot Fe_2O_3$ which is probably either a solid solution or an undercooled liquid. The dry powder is made by fusing limestone and clay into a clinker which is finely pulverized with about 2 per cent SO_3 as gypsum. Five types of Portland cement are recognized in ASTM and other specifications[129] (Table 5). Type I is for general construction; Type II has a moderate heat of hardening and will withstand moderate sulfate action; Type III is a high early strength cement; Type IV is a low heat of hydration cement and Type V is sulfate resistant. If air-entraining agents such as extract of pine wood or a triethanolamine salt of a sulfonated hydrocarbon are added, the letter "A" is appended to the type number.

In the process of hydration, the tricalcium silicate hydrolyzes forming calcium hydroxide and a certain amount of silica gel plus dicalcium silicate. Setting occurs by crystallization of the solution formed from the hydration products of the calcium silicates and aluminates. Gypsum is present to prevent the rapid solution of the tricalcium aluminate which would otherwise produce a high heat of hydration and flash set with a weak bond. The whole process of setting and heat evolvement has been studied carefully and is quite well understood.[2, 130]

The cements are usually used in concrete, which is a conglomerate of coarse aggregate with sand, Portland cement and water. Mortar may be defined as a mixture of cement, water and fine aggregate while grout is usually a neat cement paste which is creamy at the time of mixing and placing. It may also be a thin mortar. The proportion of cement used with sand and the amount of water added varies considerably but a 1:3::

TABLE 5. FIVE STANDARD PORTLAND CEMENTS.*

	Type I	Type II	Type III	Type IV[a]	Type V[a]
SiO_2, % (min.)		21.0			
Al_2O_3, % (max.)		6.0			
Fe_2O_3, % (max.)		6.0			
MgO, % (max.)	5.0	5.0	5.0	5.0	4.0
SO_3, % (max.)					
$3CaO \cdot Al_2O_3$, $\lesssim 8\%$	2.5	2.5	3.0	2.3	2.3
$3CaO \cdot Al_2O_3$, $< 8\%$	3.0		3.0		
Insoluble residue, % (max)	0.75	0.75	0.75	0.75	0.75
Loss on ignition, % (max.)	3.0	3.0	3.0	2.3	3.0
$3CaO \cdot SiO_2$[b], % (max.)		50		35	50
$2CaO \cdot SiO_2$[b], % (min.)				40	
$3CaO \cdot Al_2O_3$[b], % (max.)		8	15	7	5[c]
Specific surface, cm^2/g					
turbidimeter test, average value	1600	1600	1600	1600	1600
Autoclave expansion, % (max.)	0.50	0.50	0.50	0.50	0.50
Setting time—Vicat, minutes, $\gtrless$	45	45	45	45	45
Air content by volume, %, $<$	12.0	12.0	12.0	12.0	12.0
Compressive strength (psi)					
1 day in moist air			1700		
1 day in moist air, 2 days in water	1200	1000	3000		
1 day in moist air, 6 days in water	2100	1800		800	1500
1 day in moist air, 27 days in water	3500	3500		2000	3000
Tensile strength (psi)					
1 day in moist air			275		
1 day in moist air, 2 days in water	150	125	375		
1 day in moist air, 6 days in water	275	250		175	250
1 day in moist air, 27 days in water	350	325		300	325

* As specified by ASTM C150-56 (not complete). Tests methods are also specified.

[a] IV and V are not normally carried in stock.

[b] Estimated from chemical analysis.

[c] $4CaO \cdot Al_2O_3 \cdot Fe_2O_3 + 2(3CaO \cdot Al_2O_3) < 20\%$

Portland cement: standard sand mixture is usual and requires about 36 to 46 per cent water. The amount of water required to form a workable stiff paste is generally about that necessary for complete hydration of the cement. To obtain a dense, strong concrete, it is necessary to have the right amount of water present during the period of setting. Five gallons of water are recommended per sack of cement for the most severe exposure, or 7.5 gal per sack for less severe exposure. The surface is then kept moist for at least 1 wk. Selection and grading of the aggregate are important.

For road building or for bridge piers, etc., a mushy grout is forced into a graded stone foundation. Oil wells are cemented, and the contraction joints of concrete dams are filled with grout. Grouts have also been used for stabilization of bridge abutments, etc. Soil cement roadways and runways are built by mixing cement in the proportion of about 7 to 16 per cent of the soil. Sandy or gravelly soils with 10 to 35 per cent of silt are recommended. High organic content is undesirable. For an earth cement grout, about one sack per cubic yard of soil may be used to support a pavement slab, etc.

An ordinary concrete will weigh between 145 to 155 lb/cu ft. A light structural concrete may weight 50 to 140 lb/cu ft.[131]

Lightweight Concrete

Concrete blocks have made deep inroads on brick production. They air-dry in 2 to 4 weeks, but modern plants use autoclaves at 175°C and steam at 150 psi to finish the cure in 8 to 12 hr, thus cutting inventory 75 per cent. The economy of using lightweight concrete with 40 per cent saving in weight and 12 per cent in volume compared to ordinary concrete has led to the inclusion of such aggregates in half of all the concrete block now made in the United States[131] (Table 6). In

TABLE 6. REPRESENTATIVE PROPERTIES OF LIGHTWEIGHT CONCRETE.[131]

Aggregate	Cement, Sacks per cu yd	Compressive Strength (psi)	Lb/cu ft Dry	Modulus of Elasticity (Million psi)	Shrink-age (%)	Conductivity, BTU/hr/sq ft (gradient 1°F/in.)
Ordinary concrete of sand, gravel and stone	8	5000–8000	133–143	4–6	.04–08	8–12
Expanded shale, clay, etc.	8	4000–6500+	85–102	2.1–3	0.02–.08	2.5–4
Expanded slag	8	3000–4000+	75–100	1.5–3	0.04	2.5–5
Pumice	8	2000–3000	68–85	0.8–2	+0.1	2–2.8
Perlite	8	250–1000	35–60	0.1–0.3	+0.1	1–1.7
Vermiculite	8	300–500	30–45	0.1–0.2	+0.1	0.6–1.3

1957, 50 million cubic yards or 5 per cent of the total cast or structural concrete was lightweight. Expanded shales, slags, clays and slate, etc., are the usual aggregates and will withstand heat up to 1100°C. Pumices are used principally in insulation blocks, perlite and vermiculite form insulating plasters and honeycomb sandwich materials having strengths of 1000 psi. The lightest aggregate weighs 10 lb/cu ft, whereas a middleweight aggregate weighs 45 to 70 lb/cu ft and costs a tenth as much. To obtain the same strengths, 4.4 sacks of cement are required per cubic yard of expanded clay, 6.7 sacks per cubic yard of expanded slag and 6.4 per cubic yard of shale.

Lime Cements

Sand-lime bricks and other calcium silicate products resistant to high temperature result from the reaction of calcium oxide and sand under pressure and heat in the presence of steam.[3, 130] They are usually improved by incorporation of sodium silicate. Calcium silicate refractories will withstand temperatures of 650°C compared to 315°C for 85 per cent magnesia.

Slag Cements. Slag cements or "ciment sursulfates" are made of chilled blast furnace slag, usually mixed with Portland cement, lime, or anhydrite. Ten to 30 per cent of anhydrite gives the "ciment sursulfate." The addition of 5 to 8 per cent caustic soda in the mixing water produces a high early strength slag cement with an extremely low heat of hydration, high resistance to aggressive waters and high impermeability to water, all compared to Portland cement.[132] The caustic soda is added to the water and acts as a catalyst to promote the rapid crystallization of the glass. Slag cements formed by mixing blast furnace slag with Portland cement are well known in Europe. In Germany these include Eisen Portland Zement

and Hochofen Zement, and in France, Ciment Metallurgique de Fer, Ciment Metallurgique des Hauts Fourneaux and Ciment Delaitier a Base de Ciment Artificial. Iron ore mixed with Portland cement is "Erz" cement or Ferrari. Bauxite and Portland cement with high early strength is Kuhl cement or Bauxitland cement.

A slag cement of greatly improved strength was made by treating the powdered slag in soluble silicate and steaming for 8 hr.[133]

Pozzuolana Cement. Pozzuolana is a loosely consolidated siliceous rock of volcanic origin which imparts to Portland cement an improved resistivity to corrosive waters. The trass cements, 30/70 or 50/50 trass/clinker, with high dimensional stability and small exothermic reaction, are especially valuable for dams, bridge piers, etc., as well as coatings for walls.[3] With densities of about 2.65 to 2.75, they are somewhat lighter than Portland cement.

Lime Mortars

These are mixtures of sand and hydrated lime, $Ca(OH)_2$. Stucco is usually a Portland cement-lime mortar or plaster. The N or normal type hydrated lime is differentiated from Type S or special hydrated lime, which has a limited amount of unhydrated oxides present.[134] Hydraulic hydrated lime is also designated as high calcium and high magnesium. The MgO content is below 5 per cent in the former and greater than 5 per cent in the latter. They contain 14 to 26 per cent SiO_2, less than 12 per cent $(Fe_2O_3 + Al_2O_3)$, and less than 10 per cent CO_2. Quick lime or calcium oxide is cheaper and although dangerous to handle is widely used on large-scale work.

A lime putty is formed with water, aged, and mixed with sand as needed. A lime mortar usually contains about 1 part of hydrated lime to 3 parts of sand and may contain from 0.3 to 1 part of cement with additional sand.[130] Lime plasters are made with about 1 volume of lime putty, 2 volumes of plastering sand and 7.5 lb of fiber or hair per cubic yard of mortar. Keene's cement (see gypsum) may be added if a harder or quicker set is desired. The finish coats use 4 to 4.5 volumes of lime putty with 1 volume of gypsum or gauging plaster.

Lime putty is a dispersion of colloidal calcium hydroxide in a saturated solution of lime. This will slowly take up CO_2 and become carbonated; however in that case the internal strength is low.[135] In the carbonation of a high calcium lime, a gel forms which has a higher solubility than anhydrous calcium carbonate. This gradually recrystallizes to the anhydrous calcium carbonate. Where the carbonation is controlled along with the evaporation of water to keep a thin film of water present during the recrystallization of the gel, very strong products can be formed.

A lime putty binder for foundry molds, set with CO_2, has been reported to have moderate green strength, good dry strength, low gas content, and low retained strength.[136]

Gypsum

Plaster of Paris or gypsum is also known as wall plaster, dental plaster, etc., according to use.[3, 130] There are also hard finish plasters for flooring and tiling such as Keene's cement, Parian cement and Martin's cement. The best known of these is Keene's which is made by burning gypsum at about 110°C to form the hemi-hydrate, dipping in a solution of papermaker's alum and then reburning to 400 or 500°C.[138] In Parian cement, borax is used instead of alum and in Martin's cement, potassium carbonate is used. These hard finish plasters are very hard and white when dry. A mixture of plaster of Paris and Portland cement is known as Spence's plaster. It contains aluminum sulfate and sand and has a low expansion on setting and a high dry crushing strength.

Plaster of Paris or dehydrated gypsum ($CaSO_4 \cdot 0.5H_2O$) is quite soluble in water at low temperatures. It crystallizes rapidly to form the dihydrate, gypsum, and thus forms a strong lightweight material quickly. While gypsum will set under water and is thus a hydraulic cement, it has enough solubility to make its use unsatisfactory at high humidity or continuous exposure to water, unless impregnated with resins. If gypsum is heated at about 123°C under steam pressure, finely divided separate and nonporous crystals of the half hydrate composition are formed ("Hydrocal") which require somewhat less water to make up the plaster[137] and develop a crush strength of 7500 psi.

TABLE 7. THE EFFECT OF THE RATIO OF WATER TO PLASTER ON THE PROPERTIES OF PLASTER OF PARIS USING A MIXING TIME OF 1 MIN. (Skinner)[137]

Water: Plaster Ratio (cc/g)	Setting Time (min)	Setting Expansion (%)	Dry Crushing Strength (psi)
0.45	3.25	0.51	3800
0.60	7.25	0.29	2600
0.80	10.50	0.24	1600

The setting time of plaster of Paris varies with the water content, as well as possible additives (Table 7). Accelerators are zinc sulfate, potassium sulfate, sodium chloride, papermaker's alum, sodium carbonate, or hardened plaster. Retarders are borax, tartaric acid and other organic substances.[138a] Mortar mixed with sand in a ratio of 1:1 to 1:2 showed swelling while others mixed at the 1:3 to 1:4 ratio shrank.

The thickening or setting time of the plaster of Paris can be controlled within short limits, and full strength is obtained rather quickly. For these reasons, plaster of Paris may be used to shut off water in oil well bore holes, to "kill gas wells," for shot tamping, and to plug cavernous limestone in addition to its major applications in wall plaster and cast products. In the ceramic industry, plaster of Paris molds extract water from the plastic clay. They also permit the precise casting of metals and metal alloys, and the reproduction of wax designs in the preparation of dental inlays. The amount of expansion and contraction is controlled by the addition of cristobalite; such mixtures can be formulated to give a constant volume over a considerable range of temperature. The composition can also be adjusted to allow for the shrinkage of a gold or similar alloy. The smooth surface of the gypsum allows reproduction of minute details.

Gypsum also forms a fire-proofing coating with high insulating value on structural steel. Lightweight plasters are used for thermal and acoustical insulation. Permanent metal molds may be formed from the reaction of plaster of Paris moistened with sodium silicate.

High Alumina

Calcium aluminate cements have been developed for refractory concrete applications in place of the calcium silicate cements, which break down at relatively low temperatures, e.g., 270°C. The ordinary impure calcium aluminate cements formed by fusing limestone and bauxite are primarily the 1.0 ratio $Al_2O_3 : CaO$, often with as much as 20 per cent of impurities, principally iron oxides and silica which act as fluxes.[2, 139] Imported ciment-fondu has also been used. The aggregate is usually a calcined refractory clay such as a high alumina-flint clay in the proportion of 3 or 4 parts to 1 of calcium aluminate. Accessory binders such as clays increase the plasticity and may be added for temperatures below 700°C. For higher temperatures, cements with additives such as chromite, kyanite, magnesium oxide, aluminum oxide, mullite and spinels attain 90 per cent of their strength within 3 days after placement.

Calcium aluminates prepared from chemical grade limestone and (Bayer) tabular alumina by grinding and sintering have less than 2 per cent impurities and may be used above 1650°C.[140] This cement has 2 to 6 times the fired strength and 10 to 18 cones higher refractoriness than commercial calcium aluminate cements; it can be stored for a year without deterioration. It is as erosion and abrasion resistant as phosphate-bonded alumina castables.

Basic Salts

A Sorel cement is a basic salt of a heavy metal, usually magnesite or magnesia cement or magnesium oxychloride cement.[2, 13, 44, 91, 141] It is suitable for dry locations where 2 to 8 hr hardening will permit immediate use. The final strength will be in the range of 7000 to 10,000 psi. Magnesium oxychloride cements are made by reacting magnesium oxide with magnesium chloride, probably forming $3MgO \cdot MgCl_2 \cdot 11H_2O$. The addition of copper powder, forming insoluble blue-green $3CuO \cdot CuCO_2 \cdot 3H_2O$, overcomes some of the problem of expansion due to active lime and the tendency to dissolve in the presence of water. Without copper, Sorel cements are too soluble to withstand weathering or washing and have a large coefficient of thermal expansion. However, they are 3 to 4 times as strong as Portland cement; they set rapidly; are resilient and bond to many materials. The strength of adhesion to sand-blasted glass exceeds 100 psi. A typical formula contains 17 to 18 per cent by weight of plastic magnesia, now usually a blend of magnesia from magnesite and from seawater, about 10 per cent dendritic copper powder, about 72 per cent of aggregate and 22°Bé magnesium chloride solution in a ratio of $6:1::MgO:MgCl_2$. These cements resist damage by cooking fats and greases, repel vermin and prevent the growth of mold and bacteria. They also conduct static electricity from hospital operating room floors.

Similar compositions have been used instead of sodium silicate to bind colors to roofing granules without the high degree of heat treatment usually required.[142] Addition of 20 per cent by weight of finely divided silica on the weight of MgO improves the strength, volume stability and moisture resistance of Sorel cement.[143] Unfired refractories may be bound permanently with the fired reaction product of magnesium sulfate or chloride and sodium silicate or with magnesium acid sulfate.

Basic magnesium carbonate is a bonding agent for 85 per cent magnesia insulation. It may be written as $Mg(OH) \cdot (CO_3H)^2$. An adhesive composition similar to Sorel cement is made up by mixing MgO, $BaSO_4$, chalk, $MgCl_2$, HCl, and H_2SO_4.[144] It forms a hard, durable cold-setting cement for use in flooring and for stucco faced with crushed stone to resist weathering, water, and hydrocarbons.

The bond in magnesium oxysulfate cements prepared by the reaction of the magnesia and magnesium sulfate is primarily $Mg(OH)_2$ gel.[141] These cements are used in prefabricated structural products processed at relatively high temperature since they are less sensitive to elevated temperatures than is the oxychloride.[130] They are lightweight and strong, have a low modulus of elasticity, a high water of crystallization, stability at high temperatures and are easily cured by heat.[145]

Zinc acid phosphates formed *in situ* are also known as Sorel cements. These and other similar dental cements are sometimes known as oxyphosphates. They frequently contain minor additions of cations other than zinc which appear to add randomness to the structure.

Zinc oxychloride, similar in properties to Sorel cements, is a saturated solution of zinc chloride made up with zinc oxide. It cannot be used in contact with soft tissues and is limited to cavity linings and root canal fillings. Zinc oxide with eugenol is rather soluble and is used only as a temporary cement or a pulp cavity material. A representative formula is 99.8 per cent zinc oxide and 0.2 per cent of zinc acetate mixed with liquid 100 per cent eugenol.[13, 146a]

A cement for dental impressions is made with sodium alginate, set with basic lead silicate sulfate, diatomaceous earth, Na_2SiF_6 and tetrasodium pyrophosphate at 21°C.[146b] This mixture has a working time of 1.5 min and sets in 2 min.

MISCELLANEOUS CEMENTS

Metal Powder Cements

Lutes and sealing compositions containing iron powder are of increasing use in automobile radiators, iron covers and connecting lines. The setting appears to occur by corrosion of the iron and crystallization of solids which provide adhesion between the adherend and the remaining iron particles. Such cements are not strong, nor do they resist acids. A simple formula for use with wrought iron is iron filings 62 per cent, NH_4CL 1 per cent and H_2O 37 per cent.[146, 147, 148]

Numerous formulas for attaching iron to stone for high temperature use, for resistance to alkali and acids, etc., are available.[13]

Litharge Cements

Mixtures of glycerin and litharge are used as a lining to protect cellulose digesters against acids and as paints resistant to hydrocarbons, as well as for the repair of tubs and sinks, pipe valves, glass, stoneware and ammonia gas conduits. A mixture of 1 part of slightly diluted glycerol with 2 to 3 parts of lead oxide, (PbO), requires approximately 1 day to form what is considered a crystalline compound.[13, 98, 148, 149] Such a cement will resist weak acid and nitric acid but reacts with sulfuric acid.

Sulfur Cements

Where liquid sulfur is allowed to crystallize as a cementing layer, it is quite vulnerable to thermal shock.[13] The addition of graded aggregates will reduce the normal 12 per cent volume decrease to about 4 per cent. Such cements may be used only at temperatures below 93°C because of the increase in coefficient of expansion when rhombic sulfur changes to monoclinic sulfur at 96°C. The melting point of sulfur is low—that is, 110°C. The λ form which is in greater proportion in molten sulfur at temperatures of about 160°C has poor binding strength, whereas the feathery crystals of the μ form which are prevalent at temperatures lower than 140°C are much stronger. Sulfur cements set up rapidly at low temperatures and have high resistance to many chemicals. Improved physical properties are obtained by adding fine carbon black and "Thiokol" polysulfides.[150] A sulfur cement has about 600 psi tensile strength and will still have a strength of 440 lb when held in water for 2 years at 70°.

The outstanding use for sulfur cements is in tanks holding mixtures of nitric and hydrofluoric acid at 72°C.[151] Of the organic acids, oleic acid is destructive at higher temperatures. The sulfur cements are not resistant to oxidizing agents and have little resistance to strong base or lime in continuous use. A sulfur cement adheres well to metals, particularly well to copper. It has a strength of adhesion of 30 to 37 psi to terra cotta. Representative formulas have been evaluated.[13]

A sulfur-silicate cement for protecting and bonding tile liners for concrete sewers was fused with a hot iron. It prevented the entrance of roots as well as presenting an acid-resistant surface.[152] Eye bolts which serve as a base for cables holding boulders threatening to destroy the Great Stone Face of New Hampshire were set in base rock with a sulfur adhesive compound.[153]

Oxides, Nitrides, Etc.

Efforts to raise the temperature limits for refractories have been directed toward increasing the purity and perfection of the crystallized material. A bonding agent which is lost on firing such as phosphoric acid or starch is occasionally used; however much study has gone into the recrystallization of the material itself. Mullite refractories of the highest quality are made by bonding with mullite formed from heating an excess of silica in the original body and added aluminum oxide to about 1700°C.[154] Zircon bodies are extruded with starch and an aqueous jelly to give an initial bond. They are pressed hydrostatically and fired at 1750°C. A zircon binding may be formed by adding zirconia and finely divided silica in zircon sand aggregates. For zircon to be used in pressing or ramming, phosphoric acid, zirconium chloride or sulfite may be used as binders. For thoria formed either by pressing or slip casting, thorium chloride may be used as the binder; for alumina, hydrated aluminum oxide is suggested.

Silicon nitride has high temperature stability and resistance to thermal shock. It will resist molten aluminum at 980°C or over for 3000 hr and will also resist most acids; consequently it has been used as the bond for silicon carbide in the manufacture of a pump to handle molten aluminum. The nitride bonded silicon carbide refractory undergoes practically no volume change between the green and dried states. The coefficient of thermal expansion at 1500°C is 6.7×10^{-6}. It has a modulus of rupture, at 1350°C, of 5000 to 7000 psi.[155]

Bonds less than 0.001 in. thick between stainless steel and ceramic bases may be prepared from ceramic frits to withstand tensions exceeding 1000 psi for 1000 hr at temperatures of above 540°C. The inclusion of 20 per cent carbonyl iron in the slip increases the resistance to immersion in boiling water for 1000 hr.[156]

References

1. Vail, J. G., "Soluble Silicates In Industry," ACS Monograph No. 46. p. 165, New York, Chemical Catalog Co. (Reinhold) 1928.
2. Wygant, J. F. in Kingery, W. D., Ed., "Ceramic Fabrication Processes," p. 171, New York, John Wiley & Sons, Inc.

3. Vail, J. G., "Soluble Silicates," ACS Monograph No. 116, New York, Reinhold Publishing Corp., 1952.

4. Wills, J. H., and Sams, R. H., *Ind. Eng. Chem.,* **41**, 81 (1949).

5. Wegst, W. F., unpublished work of Philadelphia Quartz Co.

6. Boller, E. R., Lander, J. G., and Morehouse, R., *Paper Trade J.,* **110**, (12), 51 (1940).

7. Vail, J. G., and Baker, C. L. (to Philadelphia Quartz Co.), U. S. Patent 2,239,358 (1941).

8. Malcomson, J. D., *Ind. Eng. Chem.,* **12**, 174 (1920).

9. Carter, J. D. (to Philadelphia Quartz Co.). U. S. Patent 2,078,836 (1937).

10. Stericker, Wm., Ph.D. Thesis, University of Pittsburgh (1922).

11. Wills, J. H., *Paper Trade J.,* **127**, (2), 47 (1948).

12. Sams, R. H., unpublished work of Philadelphia Quartz Co.

13. Wills, J. H. in N. A. DeBruyne and R. Houwink, "Adhesion and Adhesives," Chap. 6, Amsterdam, Elsevier, 1951.

14. Shermer, H. F., *J. Research Natl. Bur. Standards,* **57**, (2), 97 (1956).

15. Philadelphia Quartz Co. Bulletins.

16. Heidtkamp, G., and Endell, K., *Glastech. Ber.,* **14**, 89 (1936).

17. Poole, J. P., *J. Am. Ceram. Soc.,* **32**, 230 (1949).

18. McBain, J. W., Great Britain, Dept. Scientific Ind. Research, Adhesives Research Comm., 1st, 2nd, 3rd Reports, 1922, 1926, 1932.

19. MacFarlane, W. S., and Sewell, J. F., in Clark, J., Rutzler, J. E., Jr., and Savage, R. L., "Adhesion and Adhesives, Fundamentals and Practice," p. 203, John Wiley & Sons, Inc. (1954): Thornton, J. E., British Patent 308,117 (1928).

20. Fix, E. L., and Dennison, B. J. (to Duplate Corp.), U. S. Patents 2,003,288 (1935) and 2,009,441 (1935); Dennison, B. J., Fix, E. L., and Zola, J. C. (to Duplate Corp.), U. S. Patents 2,005,075 (1935) and 2,006,348 (1935).

21. Fix, E. L., and Dennison, B. J. (to Duplate Corp.), U. S. Patent 2,072,583 (1937).

22. Stericker, Wm., private communication (1957).

23. Albert, K., German Patent 848,064 (1952).

24. Strain, R. N. C., and Sewell, J. H. (to Natl. Research Development Corp.), British Patent 791,530 (1958).

25. Farber, H., and Blum, W., *J. Research Natl. Bur. Standards,* **4**, 27 (1930).

26. Rife, P., *Industry and Power,* p. 75, June 1943.

27. Walters, H. W., U. S. Patent 2,350,654 (1944).

28. Ware, W. C., U. S. Patent 1,989,833 (1935).

29. Meier, E. F., *Chem. Eng.,* **54**, (12), 116 (1947); Calera Mining Co., *Lead,* **21**, (4), 4 (1957).

30. Jos. Crosfield & Sons, Ltd., Silicate Survey, Warrington, England, 1955.

31. Monsanto Chemical Co., British Patent 803,369 (1958).

32. Rojas, F. A., U. S. Patents 2,285,053 (1942) and 2,318,184 (1943).

33. Philadelphia Quartz Co., Bull. T-7-4 (1959).

34. Jos. Crosfield & Sons, Ltd., Bull. (1956).

35. National Board of Fire Underwriters, "Report on Investigation of Corrosion in Metal-Clad Paneled Firedoors," Subject 10, Chicago, 1936.

36. Benson, D. G. (to B. F. Goodrich Co.), U. S. Patent 2,278,345 (1942).

37. Jones, W. I. (to Roddis Lumber & Veneer Co.), U. S. Patent 2,006,770 (1935).

38. Stevens, W. H., *Rubber Developments,* **1**, (3), 10 (1948); Kliefoth, M. H. (to C. F. Burgess Laboratories, Inc.), U. S. Patent 2,028,397 (1936).

39. Steadman, G. E., *Welding Eng.,* **33**, (8), 40 (1948).

40. Edwards, J. D., "Treatise on the Physical Properties of Aluminum Paint and Its Uses in Industry," Pittsburgh, Aluminum Co. of America, 1924.

41. Nightingall, V. C. J. (deceased), Nightingall, R. V. N., Old, A. M., and Nightingall, C. M. G., executors (to Di-Met Proprietary Ltd.), U. S. Patent 2,440,969 (1948); Nightingall, V. C. J., Nightingall, R. V. N., Old, A. M., Nightingall, G. M., Aitken, J. B., and McKenzie, M. G. (to Di-Met Proprietary Ltd.), U. S. Patent 2,462,763 (1949).

42. Hockberg, J. (to E. I. duPont & Co.), U. S. Patent 2,710,266 (1955).

43. Zachay, V. F., Mitchell, D. V., Mitoff, S. P., and Pask, J. A., *J. Am. Ceram. Soc.,* **36**, (3), 84 (1953); **40**, (4), 118; (8), 269 (1957).

44. Mitchell, L., *Ind. Eng. Chem.,* **47**, 1956 (1955).

45. Sams, R. H., and Jeglum, C. H., Patent granted; Lander, J. G. (to Diamond Alkali Co.), U. S. Patents 2,671,747 (1954); 2,772,177 (1956); 2,788,285 (1957); 2,870,033 (1959).

46. Browne, F. L., and Brouse, D., *Ind. Eng. Chem.,* **21**, 80 (1929).

47. Sams, R. H., unpublished work of the Philadelphia Quartz Co.; Knight, R. A. G., *Timber Tech.,* **62**, (2177), 124 (1954).

48. Carter, J. D. (to Philadelphia Quartz Co.), U. S. Patents 1,676,727 (1928) and 1,681,570 (1928).

49. Stericker, Wm., unpublished work of Philadelphia Quartz Co.

50. Walters, H. W., U. S. Patent 2,350,654 (1944).

51. Philadelphia Quartz Co. Records.

52. Cleveland, T. K., and Stericker, Wm. (to Philadelphia Quartz Co.), U. S. Patent 2,044,466 (1936).

53. Cone, C. N. (to I. F. Laucks, Inc.), U. S. Patent 1,976,436 (1934), 2,400,541 (1946).

54. Jarvi, R. A. (to Monsanto Chemical Co.), U. S. Patent 2,705,680 (1955).

55. Christian, M. B., and Ladd, H. F. (to Chicago Mill & Lumber Co.), U. S. Patent 2,784,106 (1957).

56. Wright, R. E. (to Philadelphia Quartz Co.), U. S. Patent 2,894,847 (1959).

57. Burnett, R. S., and Parker, E. D., *Trans. Am. Soc. Mech. Engrs.,* **68**, 751 (1946).

58. Kreyling, R. L. (to Philadelphia Quartz Co.), U. S. Patent 2,554,035 (1951); *Fiberboard Containers and Paperboard Mills,* **42**, (12), 82 (1957); *TAPPI,* **32**, (5), 238 (1949).

59. Sams, R. H., U. S. Patent 2,772,996 (1956), and Kreyling, R. L. (to Philadelphia Quartz Co.), 2,669,282 (1954).

60. Vail, J. G., and Baker, C. L. (to Philadelphia Quartz Co.), U. S. Patent 2,133,759 (1938); 2,205,609 (1940); Boller, E. R., and Remler, R. F. (to E. I. duPont de Nemours & Co.), U. S. Patent 2,287,411 (1942).

61. Schupp, O. E., and Boller, E. R., *Ind. Eng. Chem.*, **30,** 603 (1938); McCready, D. W., and Katz, D. L., University of Michigan, *Eng. Research Bull.*, No. 28 (1939).

62. Vail, J. G., and Wegst, W. F., unpublished records of the Philadelphia Quartz Co.

63. Vail, J. G., and Carter, J. D., unpublished records of the Philadelphia Quartz Co.

64. Carter, J. D. (to Philadelphia Quartz Co.), U. S. Patent 1,676,727 (1928); 2,015,359 (1935); 2,099,-598 (1937); 2,231,562 (1941); 2,414,360 (1947).

65. Baker, C. L., and Sams, R. H. (to Philadelphia Quartz Co.), U. S. Patent 2,681,290 (1954); 2,457,108 (1948).

66. Howells, T. A., Institute of Paper Chemistry, private communication, 1951; van den Akker, J. A., and Wink, W. A., *Paper Ind. and Paper World*, **30,** 231 (1948); *Laboratory*, **20,** (4), 91 (1951).

67. Laminite Products Inc., *Ind. Eng. Chem.*, **39,** (2), 5A, 8A (1947).

68. Sams, R. H., and McCready, N. W., *TAPPI*, **34,** (2), 67 (1951).

69. Wills, J. H., and Cohen, R. H., unpublished work of Philadelphia Quartz Co.

70. Roederer, H., *Das Papier*, **11,** 492 (1957); *Worlds Paper Trade Rev.*, **144,** 213 (1955); Kalmback, E. R., U. S. Dept. Agr. Yearbook, p. 894 (1943–1947); U. S. Wildlife Research Lab. U.S.D.A., private communication (1949).

71. Stericker, Wm. (to Philadelphia Quartz Co.), U. S. Patent 2,647,069 (1953).

72. Carter, J. D. (to Philadelphia Quartz Co.), U. S. Patent 1,188,040 (1916); Thickens, J. H. (to Beaver Co.), U. S. Patent 1,377,739 (1921).

73. Johnston, G. B. (to Philip Carey Mfg. Co.), U. S. Patent 2,414,533 (1947).

74. Torri, J. A. (to J. W. Mortell Co.), U. S. Patent 2,175,767 (1959).

75. Ware, W. C. (to Industrial Abrasives, Inc.), U. S. Patent 2,311,272 (1943).

76. Nazzaro, R., *Paper Trade J.*, **121,** (21), 90 (1945).

77. Teague, M. C. (to American Rubber Co.), U. S. Patent 1,550,466 (1925).

78. Spencer, R. W., unpublished work of Philadelphia Quartz Co.

79. Edbrooke, P. C., Fair, J. A., and Grimshaw, F. P., *Paint Technol.*, **20,** (11), 395 (1958).

80. Porter, P. W. (to D. & H. Scovil, Inc.), U. S. Patent 2,611,689 (1952).

81. Martens, C. R., and Bellamy, J. G. (to Sherwin-Williams Co.), U. S. Patent 2,699,407 (1955).

82. Tovee, E. H., and Ford, E. G. (to Canadian Westinghouse Co., Ltd.), U. S. Patent 2,694,020 (1954).

83. Robie, N. P. (to Carborundum Co.), U. S. Patent 2,452,793 (1948).

84. New Jersey Zinc Co. of Pennsylvania, private communication (1949).

85. Work, L. T., U. S. Patent 2,083,180 (1937).

86. Heindl, R. A., and Pendergast, W. L., *Bull. Am. Ceram. Soc.*, **19,** 430 (1940).

87. Phillips, J. G., Canada Dept. Mines, *Invest. in Ceramics and Road Materials*, **31,** (726), 67 (1936).

88. Lathe, F. E., Pitt, N. P., and Hodnett, L. (to Canadian Refractories, Ltd.), U. S. Patent 2,218,-242–4 (1940).

89. Pitt, N. P., and Gill, A. F., U. S. Patent 2,077,258 (1937).

90. Norton, F. H., Natl. Defense Research Comm., Off. Sci. Research and Development, Div. B., No. 107 (1941).

91. Pole, G. R., Beinlich, A. W., and Gilbert, N., *J. Am. Ceram. Soc.*, **29,** 208 (1946).

92. Greaves-Walker, A. F., and Amero, J. J., *N. Carolina State Coll. Record*, **40,** (10); *Eng. Expt. Sta., Bull.* No. 22 (1941).

93. Greaves-Walker, A. F., Owens, C. W., Jr., Hurst, T. L., and Stone, R. L., *N. Carolina State Coll. Record*, **36,** (3); *Eng. Expt. Sta., Bull.* No. 12 (1937).

94. Harvey, F. A., and Birch, R. E. (to Harbison-Walker Refractories Co.), U. S. Patent 2,077,793 (1937).

95. Comstock, G. F. (to Titanium Alloy Mfg. Co.), U. S. Patent 1,952,119 (1934); Weidman, V. W., U. S. Patent 2,773,776 (1956).

96. Schleyer, W. L., *Ceram. Bull.*, **38,** 341 (1959).

97. Eusner, G. R., and Bachman, J. R., *Bull. Am. Ceram. Soc.*, **37,** 12 (1958).

98. Merrill, R. C., *TAPPI*, **32,** (11), 520 (1949); Stephenson, J. N., ed., "Preparation and Treatment of Wood Pulp," Vol. 1, New York, McGraw-Hill Book Co., 1950.

99. Bushong, R. M., Clark, C. W., Holloway, F. P. (to Union Carbide Corp.), U. S. Patent 2,890,128 (1959); Schwartzwalder, K., and Ortman, C. D. (to General Motors Corp.), U. S. Patent 2,793,956 (1957).

100. Buzzell, M. E., and Swenson, G. W. (to Minnesota Mining & Mfg. Co.), U. S. Patent 2,417,058 (1947).

101. Wolcott, E. R. (to Texas Co.), U. S. Patent 1,617,696 (1927); Dominion Magnesium Ltd., British Patent 602,062 (1945).

102. Vallak, E., U. S. Patent 2,821,758 (1958).

103. Pursall, F. W., and Hawthorn D.H.R.W. (to Foundry Services Ltd.), British Patent 793,022 (1958); Tigerschold, B., and Werner, K., Tholand, Inc., Bull. (1958).

104. Bean, X. L. (to Antioch College and M. Bean, X. Bean, A. D. Henderson, A. E. Morgan, and W. Beatty), U. S. Patent 2,531,496 (1950).

105. Ahearn, P. J., and Gartner, G. I., *Foundry*, **86,** (2), 98 (1958).

106. Wulff, C. E., *Modern Castings*, **33,** (3), 81 (1958); Morey, R. E., and Lange, E. A., *Foundry*, **87,** (4), 188 (1959); Atterton, D. V., *J. Research Brit. Cast Iron Assoc.*, **6,** 267 (1956).

107. Neil, J. M. (to Alexander M. Hay), U. S. Patent 1,030,114 (1912); Brewster, F. S. (to Brumley-Donaldson Co.), U. S. Patent 2,861,893 (1958).

108. Carlton, R. P. (to Minnesota Mining & Mfg. Co.), U. S. Patent 2,536,871 (1951).

109. Ware, W. C. (½ to M. R. Ware), U. S. Patent 2,278,158 (1942); Ware, W. C. (to Industrial Abrasives, Inc.), U. S. Patent 2,311,271-2 (1943).

110. Joseph, T. L., *Blast Furnace and Steel Plant*, 43, (6), 641 (1955).

111. Kolb, A. R., Communication from Philadelphia Quartz Co. of California (1956).

112. Joosten, H., U. S. Patent 2,081,541 (1937); Jeziorsky, J., German Patents 39,732 (1886); 42,513 (1887); 52,711 (1889) Cl.5.

113. Wright, R. E., *Eng. News-Record*, 143, (5), 42 (1949); Polivka, M., M. S. Thesis, University of California, 1948.

114. Mercer, R. S., *Corrosion*, 14, 455t (1958).

115. Glass, H. M., *Brit. Ceram. Soc.*, 48, 161 (1949).

116. Farkas, L. V., and Szwarc, M. M. (½ to Ellis-Foster Co.), U. S. Patent 2,492,790 (1949).

117. Dietz, K., and Frank, K. (to Penn-Chlor, Inc.), U. S. Patent 2,208,571 (1940).

118. McCulloch, L. (to Westinghouse Electric & Mfg. Co.), U. S. Patent 2,032,142 (1936).

119. Kingery, W. D., *J. Am. Ceram. Soc.*, 33, (8), 239 (1950); Watts, C. H. (to Pre Vest Inc.), U. S. Patent 2,928,749 (1960).

120. Souder, W., and Paffenberger, G. C., NBS Circular C433, Natl. Bur. Standards (U. S.), Washington, Govt. Printing Office, 1942.

121. Gitzen, W. H., Hart, L. D., and MacZura, G., *Bull. Am. Ceram. Soc.*, 35, (6), 217 (1956); Sheets, H. D., Buloff, J. J., and Duckworth, W. H., *Brick & Clay Record*, 133, (1), 55 (1958).

122. Beale, A. F., Jr., Eilers, L. H., and Abel, W. T. (to Dow Chemical Co.), U. S. Patent 2,868,294 (1959).

123. Greger, H. H., U. S. Patent 2,405,884 (1946).

124. Kingery, W. D., *J. Am. Ceram. Soc.*, 35, 61 (1952).

125. Eubank, W. R., U. S. Patent 2,880,081 (1959).

126. Greger, H. H., U. S. Patent 2,425,151 (1947).

127. Comeforo, J. E., Breedlove, J. B., and Thurnauer, H., *J. Am. Ceram. Soc.*, 37, 191 (1954).

128. Ocrietfabriek, N. V., Dutch Patents 75,384 (1954) and 78,558 (1955); *Chem. Eng.*, 66, (12), 84 (1959).

129. ASTM Spec. C150-56, ASTM Standards, Pt. 4, Philadelphia, Am. Soc. Testing Materials, 1958.

130. Kirk, R. E., and Othmer, D. F., ed., "Encyclopedia of Chemical Technology," Vols. 1–15, New York, Interscience Publishers, Inc., 1947–1956.

131. *Architectural Forum*, 107, (3), 163 (1957).

132. Purdon, A. O., *J. Soc. Chem. Ind.*, 59, 191 (1940).

133. Brock, A. S., and Meinzer, C. F. (to Wallace L. Caldwell), U. S. Patent 2,016,796 (1935).

134. ASTM: C5-26, C6-49, C206 and 207-49, C141-55; see *Ref.* 129.

135. Zalmanoff, N., *Rock Products*, 59, (8), 182; (9), 84 (1956).

136. Moren, R., *Foundry*, 87, (5), 152 (1959); *Gjuteriet*, 59, (Jan. 1959).

137. Skinner, E. W., "Science of Dental Materials," 3rd ed. rev., Philadelphia, 1946; *J. Am. Dental Assn.*, 58 (1), 27 (1959).

138. Lemmon, E. M. (to James L. Palsgrove), U. S. Patent 2,868,660 (1959).

138a. Ridge, M. J., and Surkericius, H., *J. Appl. Chem.*, (11), 420 (1961).

139. Wygant, J. F., and Bulkley, W. L., *Bull. Am. Ceram. Soc.*, 33, (8), 233 (1954).

140. Gitzen, W. H., *J. Am. Ceram. Soc.*, 40, 158 (1957).

141. Hubbell, D. S., *Ind. Eng. Chem.*, 29, 123 (1937); *J. Am. Chem. Soc.*, 59, 215 (1937); Paranjke, N. V., *Bombay Technologist*, 3, 7 (1952–1953); Hayek, E., and Schnell, E., *Ztg. Chem. App.*, 84, 697 (1960).

142. Denning, P. S. (to Frederic E. Schundler), U. S. Patent 1,876,630 (1932).

143. Austin, L. W., and Rhodes, D. (to Permanente Metals Corp.), U. S. Patent 2,466,145 (1949); Chisholm, H. E. (to Food Machinery and Chemical Corp.) U. S. Patent 2,939,799 (1960).

144. Bennett, H., "Chemical Formulary," Vol. 4, New York, Chem. Pub. Co., 1939.

145. Biefeld, L. P., Armstrong, M. C., and Shannon, R. F. (to Owens-Corning Fiberglas Corp.), U. S. Patent 2,717,841 (1955).

146. Kutscher, A. H. (to Olin Mathieson Chem. Corp.), U. S. Patent 2,937,099 (1960); Rabchuk, A. (to Kerr Mfg. Co.), U. S. Patent 2,878,129 (1959).

147. Mason, C. F., *Chem. Ind.*, 41, 605 (1937); 42, 177 (1938); Heuer, R. P. (to General Refractories Co.), U. S. Patent 2,952,554 (1960).

148. Delmonte, J., "Technology of Adhesives," New York, Reinhold Publishing Corp., 1947.

149. Peras, L. (to Regie Nationale des Usines Renault), U. S. Patent 2,906,907 (1959).

150. Duecker, W. W., and Payne, C. R. (to Texas Gulf Sulfur Co.), U. S. Patent 2,046,871 and 2,056,836 (1936); *Trans. Am. Inst. Chem. Engrs.*, 36, 91 (1940).

151. Curll, V. A., *Plating*, 35, 1008 (1948).

152. Smith, H. G., *Eng. News-Record*, 144, 444 (1935); Nicklin, R., *Coke and Gas*, 14, 323 (1952).

153. Little, A. D., Inc., Ind. Bull. No. 365, June 1959.

154. Kingery, W. D. ed., "Ceramic Fabrication Processes," New York, John Wiley & Sons, Inc, 1958.

155. Mitchell, L., *Ind. Eng. Chem.*, 46, 2056 (1954); Lennon, J. W., *ibid*, 1433 (1958); The Norton Company, *Bull. Am. Ceramic Soc.*, 39, 481 (1960).

156. Lefort, H. G., *Ceram. Ind.*, 72, (4), 98 (1959); Ekedahl, J. C., and Veale, J. H. (to Illinois Clay Prod. Co.), U. S. Patent 2,919,202 (1959).

Animal Glues

John R. Hubbard

Peter Cooper Corporations
Gowanda, New York

Animal glue is an adhesive of great versatility with broad acceptance in industry. This natural high polymer is an organic colloid derived from collagen—a protein constituent of animal skins, connective tissue, and bones, principally of cattle origin.

In use since earliest times and in good supply, the modern animal glue is a time-tested product for adhesive, sizing, composition, protective colloid, and flocculation applications.

Its wide acceptance as an adhesive stems from its unique ability to deposit a tacky viscous film from a warm water solution, which on cooling a few degrees passes to a firm jelled state providing an immediate, moderately strong initial bond. Subsequent natural or forced-air drying provides a permanent, strong, resilient bond between polar materials. Ease of preparation, ready application, good machining properties, relatively low cost, and high-speed operations are characteristics of prime importance and interest in its use.

Because of its many unique properties, animal glue is the subject of considerable fundamental, basic, and applied research as to its protein structure, configuration, and modification for constantly widening areas of application.

Animal glue is commercially available in a number of forms including the dry granulated products for use as hot glues, cold liquid glues for immediate use, and a wide selection of composition glues in cake or jelly form. These products are produced and marketed by a progressive group of manufacturers comprising the animal glue industry, including representation from the packing industry and strong independent producers. Recent domestic production and consumption runs close to 115,000,000 lb annually.

CHEMICAL COMPOSITION

Animal glue is a protein derived from the simple hydrolysis of collagen which is a principal protein constituent of animal hide, connective tissue, and bones. Collagen, animal glue, and gelatin are very closely related as to protein and chemical composition, and as a group is presently the subject of broad research in protein, adhesive, food, leather, and medical fields.

Hofmeister considers gelatin (glue) as hydrolyzed collagen:

$$C_{102}H_{149}O_{38}N_{31} + H_2O \rightleftarrows C_{102}H_{151}O_{39}N_{31}$$

which gives an approximate chemical composition for glue of:

	%
	%
Carbon	51.29
Hydrogen	6.39
Oxygen	24.13
Nitrogen	18.19
	100.00

confirmed within close tolerances by many other investigators.[19] More recent research has indicated that while there are minor variations in the composition of collagens from different sources, and in the composition of animal glues imparted by variations in processing techniques, the compositions of glues and gelatins having widely differing case histories are very similar.

As a protein, animal glue is essentially composed of polyamides of certain alpha-amino acids. The amino acids present in animal glue (gelatin) have been investigated rather thoroughly by Eastoe,[1] Neuman,[2] and Pouradier,[3] among others. It is believed that the amino acids are present in animal glues not in the free state but rather as residues which are joined together by the elimination of water to form long polypeptide chains. Table 1 lists the amino acids present in animal glue.

Animal glue is a polydisperse system containing mixtures of similar molecules of widely differing molecular weights. The molecular weight of animal glue is always an average. A wide range of molecular weights is reported, ranging from 20,000 to 250,000.

Ward's[5] work indicates that most glue molecules consist of single polypeptide chains terminated at one end by an amino group and at the other end by a carboxyl group. The possible existence of branched chains and cyclic structures cannot be precluded, although this would not prevent the existence of an essentially linear form. An elongated coil or spiral form has been suggested by Pauling[6] for collagen, the precursor of animal glue, and it is not unreasonable to consider the possibility of the polypeptide chains of glue conforming in part to the orientated chains in collagen. Crosslinkages between the glue molecule chains are a definite possibility including hydrogen, ionic, and covalent bonds.

The polar and ionizable R-radicals are believed to be largely responsible for the gelation and the characteristic rheological properties of animal glue, assisting in the formation of large aggregates even in dilute solutions. The solubility of animal glue in water is due in no little part to the fact that five of the major constituent amino acids present in glue possess high water solubility.

An ever-increasing interest in the chemistry of collagen and in the configuration of the animal glue chain molecular structure is noted as evidenced by recent publications.[7, 8] Continued further knowledge will unquestionably lead to increased understanding of the chemical and physical properties of animal glue in its applications.

TYPES

There are two major types of animal glue—hide and bone,—each of which is the hydrolysis product of the collagen found either in the hide or connective tissue, or in the bone structure of the raw material used. Both types are principally of cattle origin with the packing and tanning industries as the primary sources of the raw material.

Hide glues are prepared by initial cleansing of the raw stocks by water washing, followed by curing with milk of lime for the removal of non-glue proteins. The cured stocks are then lightly acidulated with acids such as hydrochloric, sulfuric, and sulfurous, followed by careful removal of excess acid by additional washing with water. The treated stocks are transferred to cooking kettles or tanks, hot water is added, and by a series of separate "cooks" under carefully controlled schedules of time and heat, separate successive dilute glue solutions are drained from the cook kettles until the glue stocks are completely extracted of glue. The separate glue extraction liquors are then filtered, evaporated to 16 to 45 per cent glue solids, and in the newer installations are dried in noodle form on

TABLE 1. AMINO ACIDS IN ANIMAL GLUE.[4]

Amino Acid	Residues Per 1000 Total of All Residues	Character of R-Radical	
		Polarization	Ionic Character
Glycine	335.0	Nonpolar	Neutral
Proline	128.0	Nonpolar	Neutral
Alanine	113.0	Nonpolar	Neutral
Hydroxyproline	94.5	Polar	Neutral
Glutamic acid	72.0	Polar	Acid
Arginine	47.0	Polar	Basic
Aspartic acid	46.5	Polar	Acid
Serine	35.0	Polar	Neutral
Lysine	27.0	Polar	Basic
Leucine	23.0	Nonpolar	Neutral
Valine	20.0	Nonpolar	Neutral
Threonine	18.0	Polar	Neutral
Phenylalanine	13.0	Nonpolar	Neutral
Isoleucine	12.0	Nonpolar	Neutral
Methionine	5.0	Polar	Neutral
Hydroxylysine	5.0	Polar	Basic
Histidine	4.5	Polar	Basic
Tyrosine	1.4	Weakly polar	Very weakly acid

continuous dryers within 2 to 2½ hr using conditioned, filtered air.

Bone glues, as the name implies, are processed from the collagen content of bones. Green bone glues are in greatest supply and are produced from fresh or "green" bones available as a by-product of the packing industry. Bone glues prepared from solvent-extracted degreased bones are known as extracted bone glues. To prepare the modern bone glues, the bones are cleansed in water and/or dilute acids, charged to pressure tanks, and by a series of alternate steam-pressure and hot-water extractions, separate successive dilute glue solutions are removed from the bone stocks. The dilute glue liquors are then filtered or centrifuged for removal of free grease or fat, followed by evaporation to high solids content for subsequent drying.

With either hide or bone glues the dried product is usually ground to 8 to 12 mesh for "coarse ground," 25 to 35 mesh for "fine ground," and bagged for inventory, blending and sales stocks.

The modern animal glues, whether of hide or bone type, are sound, uniform products, and are well preserved against bacterial or mold infection for their intended industrial applications. For high-speed adhesive applications, where control of foam is an important feature, defoaming agents and/or foam suppressors are incorporated. These surface-active materials are conveniently added after evaporation of the glue liquors and prior to drying, giving very uniform products with excellent foam control under the most exacting operations and conditions.

The addition of modifying agents to the glue after evaporation and previous to drying is an important trend in the manufacture of animal glues. Wetting agents, dispersing agents, plasticizers, and chemical reactants are frequently employed to "tailor" the product for specialized commercial applications. Considering the amphoteric nature and complex protein structure of animal glues, such modifications open limitless fields for specialized industrial adhesives based on animal glues.

While the major tonnages of animal glue are marketed in dry form, increasing volumes of cold liquid animal glues, flexible and nonwarp composition glues, and glue jellies are being offered by glue producers and specialty adhesive manufacturers. These adhesives are prepared from dry animal glues and modifying agents, and will be discussed later.

PROPERTIES

As commercially marketed in granular or pulverized forms, animal glues are dry, hard, odorless materials ranging in color from light amber to brown. Kept dry, they may be stored indefinitely without loss of strength or reactive values. The density of animal glue is approximately 1.27, and a moisture content of 10 to 14 per cent is considered commercially dry. An ash content of 2.25 to 4.00 per cent is normal; this consists principally of calcium sulfate from hide glues and calcium phosphate from glue of bone origin. Most hide glues are produced to yield a fairly neutral pH in water solution, usually in the range of 6.5 to 7.4 although wider variations are possible. Bone glues are generally slightly acidic with pH values of 5.8 to 6.3. The isoelectric point of commercial animal glues is usually in the range of pH 5.6 to 4.5.

Animal glues are soluble only in water, and insoluble in oils, waxes, organic solvents, and absolute alcohol, but may be emulsified in water-oil, or oil-water systems under proper conditions. One of the most interesting properties of animal glue solutions is that of passing from a liquid to a jelled state on cooling, and again reverting to a liquid on reheating. This jelling property is of primary importance in many adhesive applications.

Precipitants for animal glue include absolute alcohol, tannic, picric, and phosphotungstic acids, and a saturated solution of zinc sulfate. Aluminum, ferric, and chromic sulfates all thicken, coagulate, and in some instances will precipitate glue from solution; mild tannages and raising of the melting point of glue compositions are also possible with these reagents. Formaldehyde and formaldehyde donors added to glue solutions will provide an effective tannage of the glue film. A solution of aluminum sulfate, sodium acetate, and borax[9] used as an overwash on glue-bearing films and coatings provides an immediate, effective tannage with no adverse color change. Potassium dichromate added to glue solutions, followed by exposure to light, will effectively insolubilize the protein.

The Biuret test is commonly employed for confirming the presence of animal glue in the absence of other proteins. In the absence of other nitrogen-bearing materials or chemicals, the approximate commercial dry glue content of a composition is readily obtained by multiplying the per cent nitrogen content (Kjeldahl) by the factor range of 6.54 to 6.95.

The destructive heating of animal glue liberates free and bound moisture followed by a marked swelling, charring, and eventual disintegration, leaving only a residual ash. Being amorphous colloidal materials, dry animal glues do not possess a melting point, and will withstand drastic heat treatment. In fact, dry-glue films heated in excess of 220°F and below the charring point will become denaturalized without ill effect, with the added advantage of becoming appreciably water resistant. The so-called melting point of glue jellies and compositions range from below room temperature to over 120°F depending on the glue-water ratio, test grade of glue, the presence of plasticizers, and possible chemical modifications.

Animal glues possess many physical and chemical properties which as a group are unique to any class of adhesives and serve as desirable features for industrial applications.

Added to cold water, they swell to a marked degree, and will then readily pass into a uniform solution under gentle heat (110 to 140°F) and mild agitation. On cooling, glue solutions thicken, become very tacky, and pass to a jelled state providing an immediate temporary bond of considerable strength in adhesive applications. Dried films deposited from animal glue solutions are continuous, noncrystallizing, permanent, and possess great strength and resilience. Tensile strengths in excess of 10,000 lb have been reported, and shear tests in excess of 3,000 psi on glue-bonded maple blocks are not unusual, indicating strengths far in excess of common industrial requirements. Being soluble only in water, animal glue films are ideally suited as sizing barriers against oils, fats, and waxes, and when suitably treated with tanning agents are made water resistant.

A wide range of viscosities is possible, from that of water to in excess of 70 to 100,000 cps by variation of the dry glue concentration and the test grade. Available in several test grades ranging from the highest to lowest in inherent viscosity and jelling properties, animal glues are readily adapted to any specific adhesive requirement suitable to these products.

Animal glue solutions are readily compatible with, and are frequently modified by plasticizers such as glycerine, sorbitol, glycols, sugars, syrups, sulfonated oils, and emulsions of oils, fats, and waxes. Under controlled conditions they may be added to or extended with other adhesives such as starches, dextrins, and alpha-protein.

Since they are colloidal, amphoteric proteins, animal glues possess colloidal charges of considerable magnitude, and with suitable modification by simple chemical additives are highly effective as colloidal flocculants[10, 11, 12] and as protective colloids, particularly in water and industrial waste treatment, and in the paper and uranium mining industries.

TEST GRADES

Animal glues are conveniently and logically graded on the basis of their jelly and viscosity values. These properties, varying with the original degree of hydrolysis of the collagen precursor, have a marked bearing on glue application and best selection as to end use.

One of the earliest grading systems based on these properties was introduced by Peter Cooper, founder of the domestic glue industry, about 1844.

TABLE 2. GLUE TEST GRADES.

(Hide Glues)

Peter Cooper Standard Grade	National Association of Glue Manufacturers Grade	Bloom Grams		Millipoise Value (Minimum)
		Range	Mid-Point	
5A Extra	18	495–529	512	191
4A Extra	17	461–494	477	175
3A Extra	16	428–460	444	157
2A Extra	15	395–427	411	145
A Extra	14	363–394	379	131
#1 Extra	13	331–362	347	121
#1 Extra special	12	299–330	315	111
#1	11	267–298	283	101
1XM	10	237–266	251	92
1X	9	207–236	222	82
1¼	8	178–206	192	72
1⅜	7	150–177	164	62
1½	6	122–149	135	57
1⅝	5	95–121	108	52
	4	70–94	82	42
	3	47–69	58	
	2	27–46	36	
	1	10–26	18	

The Peter Cooper Standard Grades established the necessary stability for comparative values of animal glues, leading to rapid growth of the industry, and are commonly used today. The National Association of Glue Manufacturers in 1928 adopted standard methods for the testing of animal glues based on sound technical procedures for determining the viscosity in millipoises and the jelly value in Bloom grams.[13] This official testing method is the accepted standard of the industry. Numerical test grades based on these test procedures find trade acceptance. More commonly, the test grades for animal glue are designated by Bloom gram jelly values such as 85, 222, 315, 379, 411 grams (g), together with brand names of the various producers which most generally reflect particular Bloom gram values.

Hide glues range in test values from the highest to lowest, 512–50 Bloom grams, bone glues usually range from 220–50 grams. Viscosity values generally follow a definite pattern increasing with jelly test to give a "balanced" glue. The difference in jelly value between successive standard grades varies from 22 to 32 grams as a rule, reflecting a price differential of about 1 to 2 ¢/lb. The number of grades commercially available permits a wide choice as to specific selection. In most cases, however, four general groups may be considered: low test grades of 50 to 135 g, medium test grades of 164 to 251 g; medium high test grades of 283 to 315 g, and high test grades of 347 to 512 g.

Optimum grade selection involves consideration of the desired viscosity and jelly properties for the specific end use. High test grades have greatest water-taking values, high viscosities, strongest jelly compositions, rapid gel formation and speed of set, and greatest reactivity with tanning agents. Low test grades have longest tack life, slow speed of gel formation and set, and best laying of mobile high solids films. The medium high testing groups provide a broad choice of intermediate properties.

The prevailing practice is to market animal glues under brand or gram strength designations conforming to the mid-point values for Bloom gram strength as shown in Table 2. Most commercial animal glues are dry mixtures or blends of several lots, or production runs of glues, so blended as to give standard tests for the specific grade supplied, ensuring uniformity.

TESTING

All animal glues are tested and graded on the basis of standard methods developed and adopted by the National Association of Glue Manufacturers.[13]

The viscosity and jelly determinations are made on a 12.5 per cent solution of animal glue, employing 15 ± 0.01 g of commercially dry glue with 105 ± 0.2 g of distilled water at $25 \pm 2°C$ using a standard 150-ml test bottle. The viscosity is determined by timing the outflow of 100 ml of the glue solution at $60.0°C$ from a calibrated glass pipette under closely controlled conditions. The millipoise value is determined by proper reference to the time of outflow in seconds and the constants of the specially calibrated pipette. The jelly value in Bloom grams is obtained by subjecting the viscosity sample to rigidly controlled gelation in a water bath maintained at $10 \pm 0.1°C$ for 17 hr, followed by measurement of the force in grams required to depress the surface of the glue jelly 4.0 mm by a mechanically loaded plunger approximately 0.500 in. in diameter, using the Bloom gelometer.

The pH is preferably determined electrometrically on the melted glue jelly at $40°C$. The moisture content is determined on glue ground to 8 mesh or finer by drying for 17 hr at $105°C$.

Where considered essential, the relative foam value of animal glue may be evaluated. A 12.5 per cent sample, heated to $140°F$, is subjected to high-speed agitation with a milk shake stirrer for 15 sec, and the time is recorded for the foam to subside partially or completely. Many large users of animal glue require foamless or "defoamed" animal glue formulations.

PREPARATION OF GLUE SOLUTIONS

Modern dry animal glues are readily prepared for use.

The direct addition of dry glue to hot water in a jacketed mechanically agitated mixer or tank is recommended for fastest preparation. The hot water is preferably brought to 150 to $170°F$ before addition of the dry glue. As the glue dissolves under heat and moderate agitation, the temperature gradually drops to 140 to $145°F$, the optimum range for efficient running properties of animal glue. Thermostatic controls are recommended to hold the glue temperature at 140 to $145°F$. Following this procedure batch preparations are common within 30 to 60 min.

An alternate procedure is to pre-soak the dry glue in cold water until swollen (30 to 45 min), then transfer the swollen glue to a jacketed melting tank with agitator, melting and stirring the glue into solution. This procedure is recommended where a number of small, successive batches of glue are to be prepared. Using fine ground animal glues with hot water and high-speed agitation, almost "instantaneous" glue solutions are possible. The dry glue is usually poured into the vortex created by the single-shaft propeller, and the speed adjusted to prevent aeration of the glue solution.

For best results the dry glue should always be weighed. Measuring glue by volume introduces wide errors. The water should be weighed initially and may then be measured for successive batches after calibration of the tank.

Galvanized iron and stainless steel mixing tanks are preferred. Iron and copper tanks are used, but may cause discoloration of the glue on long heating. Vented water jackets with low-pressure steam injection are recommended for the larger mixers; electrically heated water jackets are usually preferred for smaller mixers and for bench pots.

Liquid Animal Glues

Liquid animal-glue adhesives for direct room-temperature application are preferred in many industrial applications. The newer type superior products are ready-to-use cold adhesives and possess the inherent strength, stability, and resilience of hot animal glue together with ease of use, controlled tack life, and varying speeds of set depending on the specific formulation.

These commercially available products are prepared from hot animal glue solutions by the addition of gel depressant chemicals which, in the presence of water, arrest or eliminate the natural jelling properties of the glue. On loss of water to the adherend and gradual drying, the physical action of the gel depressant is eliminated and the original unmodified properties of the animal glue take effect. The better products readily surpass Federal Specifications,[14] and are formulated to between 35 to 65 per cent dry solids, with a preferred viscosity range of 3000 to 5000 cps at room temperature. Many liquid glues contain clays or calcium carbonate for improved adhesive filming properties, with wetting and dispersing agents, plasticizers, and other modifiers as needed. Both fast and slow setting liquid glues are available; they are readily applied by syringe, brush, and mechanical spreaders. These tailored products find wide application in general adhesive fields and particularly in the furniture industry for assembly gluing, panel on frame, laminating, and cores.

FLEXIBLE, NON-WARP JELLY GLUES

Large tonnages of flexible and non-warp glues are used in the bookbinding, luggage, and set-up paper box covering fields. These products are prepared animal glue compositions available in cake, slab, or jelly form. They are produced from hot animal glue solutions by the addition of modifying agents such as glycerin, sorbitol, glycols, cane or invert sugars, syrups, dextrins, mineral fillers and the like. These compositions are available in a wide selection of basic properties as to viscosity, tack-life, speed of set, degree of flexibility or non-warp action, softness or hardness of deposited film, and are essentially tailored products. Being in jelly form, these adhesives are quickly and easily prepared for use by rapid melting in a melting tank, or by adding small pieces of the jelly directly to the heated applicator pan for ready solution.

Flexible glues are formulated to deposit a film possessing permanent elasticity and resilience, such as required in bookbinding, in the production of flexible notebook binders, and in soft luggage. Glycerin is usually the principal plasticizer, often combined with sorbitol, glycols, and tackifiers. The flexible glues are usually prepared from the higher testing grades of animal glue to provide great toughness and strength. The ratio of plasticizer to dry glue controls the degree of flexibility imparted, which can be varied from a moderate degree of resilience to a full soft rubbery state.

Cake non-warp glues are designed to provide a fast, strong initial tack yielding a hard, firm, dry film with minimum curling or warpage of the adherend on drying. These compositions are prepared by the addition of sugars, dextrins, and syrups to hot animal glue solutions, with, in many cases, fillers and extenders such as magnesium sulfate (Epsom salt), clays, and calcium carbonate. These tailored products find wide acceptance in the paper box industry on hand fed, semiautomatic, and fully automatic covering machines, for hard notebook binders, phonograph record cases, hard luggage, cloth coverings, and related applications. A wide variety of products is available.

Dry non-warp glues are finding increased acceptance. They are dry blends of fine ground animal glue with cane sugar and Epsom salt. These dry products are similar in working properties to the cake non-warp glues, and are prepared for use by dissolving directly in hot water, or by a preliminary slushing of the blended adhesive in cold or warm water and transferring the slushed material to the glue applicator pan for direct melting.

Jelly glues are commercially available for those users who desire to eliminate the equipment and supervision necessary in the preparation of hot glue solutions. These products are usually straight glue-water compositions in jelled form, and are readily melted to the liquid state in bench glue pots, small melters, or in the adhesive applicator pan.

APPLICATIONS

Adhesive

Animal glues have long been accepted as a standard product where economy, strength, permanence of bond, ease of use, and versatility are of prime importance. In the more common use of the dry glues of commerce, the usual adhesive solution is prepared at 25 to 50 per cent concentrations at 140°F to give a paint-like fluidity which permits ready spreading and deposition of a thin, continuous adhesive film at the joint. The inherent property of animal glues so applied to thicken on slight cooling permits the rapid development of desired tackiness and also serves to hold the adhesive at the joint surface, eliminating the danger of excessive bleeding from the joint on application of pressure.

The time-tested principles governing the use of animal glues as an adhesive are few in number:

(1) Deposit a thin continuous glue film on one surface only of the matching adherends or joint faces.
(2) Permit the glue film to thicken slightly to a tacky condition prior to applying pressure.
(3) Apply pressure adequate to squeeze out excess glue and bring perfect contact over the entire assembled area.
(4) Hold under pressure long enough to ensure an initial bond strength in excess of the stresses inherent in the specific glued assembly.

Observance of the above principles should result in perfect bonds on materials and applications suitable for the use of animal glue. Joint failures, should they occur, may be readily traced to failure to observe one or more of the basic steps discussed.

The choice of test grades and glue concentration is predicated on the specific adhesive application with reference to the gluing schedule, type of joint, conformance to specification, and cost. In general the higher testing grades are employed for maximum speed of operation where fastest set and fast gluing schedules are required, and the medium and lower testing grades where longer open or closed assembly periods are desired with long periods of high tack. While there is considerable evidence from practical experience that the higher testing grades of animal glue possess greater strength, resilience, and shock resistance, test grade selection is frequently made by matching the jelling rate of the animal glue solution with the required assembly time. The jelling rate and viscosity of animal glue solutions are usually closely related.

As the viscosity of the adhesive at the time of application plays an important part in the formation of ultimate sound bonds, the interrelation of glue test grade and water-glue ratio, or per cent glue solids, is of great practical interest. Table 3 shows such relationships between selected grades of animal glues. These data indicate also the differences in water-taking properties of the various test grades as reflected by the equivalent glue concentrations required to give equal viscosity values. It is evident that a wide choice of test grades of glue and per cent solids concentrations is available for any specific use of animal glue as an adhesive. The superior water-taking properties of the high test glues often permit lower adhesive costs; the lower test glues provide readily spreadable high solids adhesives when required.

For general adhesive applications Table 4 gives the relationships between glue test grade, water-glue ratio, and gluing schedules. Although this is specifically a guide for edge gluing in the woodworking industry, the data may be applied generally.

Woodworking. The continued widespread use of animal glue as a time-tested adhesive in the furniture and woodworking industries is well known and

TABLE 3. VISCOSITY IN CENTIPOISES AT 140°F FOR DRY GLUES OF GIVEN GRADE TEST AND MILLIPOISE VALUE.

Glue % Concentration	High Test (155 m.p.)	Medium High Test (102 m.p.)	Medium Test (63 m.p.)	Low Test (32 m.p.)
5	3.0	2.4	2.0	1.6
10	8.8	5.6	3.6	2.6
12.5	15.5	10.2	6.3	3.2
15	28.0	17.2	8.4	5.0
20	79.2	46.0	22.4	10.0
25	196	112	49.6	19.6
30	524	264	108	37.6
35	1360	612	224	72.0
40	3216	1320	476	133
50	16320	7240	2400	566

TABLE 4. RELATIONSHIP BETWEEN GLUE TEST GRADE, WATER-GLUE RATIO AND GLUING SCHEDULE.

Bloom Gram Test	Peter Cooper Standard Grade	Water-Glue Ratio by Weight for Rapid Assembly Times (0–15 sec closed)	Water-Glue Ratio by Weight for Slow Assemblies (1 min closed)
379	A Extra	2–1	2¾–1
347	1 Extra	1⅞–1	2½–1
315	1 Extra special	1¾–1	2¼–1
283	#1	1⅝–1	2⅛–1
251	1XM	1½–1	2–1
222	1X	1⅜–1	1¾–1
192	1¼	1¼–1	1⅝–1
164	1⅜	1¼–1	1½–1
135	1½	1⅛–1	1¼–1

Wood and room temperature—70–75°F.
Glue temperature   —145°F.
Pressure   —150 psi

reflects the strength, economy, and versatility of this adhesive in joining relatively rigid wood members. The wide range of products includes furniture, chairs, tables, desks, cabinets, patterns, toys, sporting goods, and musical instruments. The modern animal glues used with the newer type conveyerized spreaders and clamps provide even faster and more economical gluing operations. For high-speed assembly gluing, edge gluing, post laminations and gluing operations with short assembly periods, the higher testing grades in the range of 251 to 315 g are employed. Glue test grades of 135 to 225 g are usually preferred for the slower speed assemblies, veneering, and edge-banding operations. The highest testing grades of 347 to 379 gs are reserved principally for special conditions where an extremely fast jelling adhesive must be used.

The unfortunate practice of diluting fast-setting glue solutions prepared with high test glues to obtain slower setting adhesives with longer assembly times is to be avoided. Such excessive dilution under high pressures may lead to starved joints. A better choice is to employ a lower testing glue at the proper water-glue ratio. An alternate procedure for varying the rate of chilling or gelation of the glue film is to incorporate small quantities of a gel depressant such as thiourea in the glue solution. The addition of from 3 to 10 per cent of thiourea based on the dry weight of the glue, added directly to the warm glue solution and dissolved therein, will give effective control with no adverse effect.

Gill[15] in recent articles, concisely covers the use of hide glue in the manufacture of furniture. The newer type liquid animal glues are finding wide acceptance in this general field as well. These products, usually of 50 to 60 per cent solids, are available in either fast or slow setting types. They find particular application in panel-on-frame bonding of hardboards for cabinets, trailer assemblies, difficult laminations, and where small intermittent adhesive requirements preclude the use of the more economical hot glues.

Gummed Tape. Animal glue is the primary adhesive in gummed tapes. More than 50,000,000 lb of glue is consumed annually in the manufacture of gummed tapes for sealing of commercial solid fiber and corrugated shipping cases where fast machining and heavy-duty tapes provide the utmost in strength and permanence of adhesion, as well as in the more common lightweight tapes for retail packaging.

Green bone glues are used in greatest volume for the adhesive, testing in the range of 50 to 200 g jelly value, with greatest demand for the 85 to 120 g products. These animal glues possess the desired machining properties, quick, immediate tack with good tack life, and a speed of set and permanence of adhesion which are essential for these critical applications. Chrome-type hide glues and the regular hide glues are frequently used as well, either alone or in combination with bone glues for added properties, especially with heavy-duty tapes, stay tapes, duplex, veneer, and specialty tapes.

The adhesive is generally prepared at about 50 per cent solids concentration and may include from 10 to 20 per cent dextrin on the weight of the dry glue together with small amounts of wetting agents, plasticizers, and gel depressants if required. The amount of adhesive solids deposited is usually close to 25 per cent of the basis weight of the paper. The adhesive at 140 to 145°F is usually applied to the backing by a roll coater. The coated web is dried under tension over steam-heated rolls or by direct dryers with conditioned air, then reeled into jumbo rolls for subsequent slitting, printing, and rewinding into standard sized rolls for industrial use.

Coated Abrasives. The coated-abrasive industry consumes large volumes of animal glue in the manufacture of sandpapers and sand-cloths for widely diversified industrial applications. The role of abrasives in the rough and fine finishing of wood and metal products is of prime importance in the production of machinery, automobiles, household furnishings, appliances, etc.

The production of coated abrasives includes the basic steps of applying an animal glue film to the base paper or cloth backing, followed by deposition of the abrasive grain upon and within the glue film, partial drying of the base coat, and subsequent application of a dilute glue size to lock the grain in position, with final drying of the web. Modern equipment and close technical controls permit almost automatic operations at great speeds yielding uniform high quality products.

The great strength, resiliency, toughness, and ready machinability of animal glue play an important part in its selection for this critical adhesive application. Cloth backings such as jeans, drills and twills are usually "filled" and sized with animal glue, or starch and animal glue, to impart body and strength. For this work the lower to medium testing grades of glue are employed at 33 to 40 per cent glue concentration, imparting a pickup of from 10 to 33 per cent by weight.

For the base coat or "making coat," advantage is taken of the viscosity and gelling properties of the hot glue to deposit a tacky glue film which stays in place on the moving backing sheet, and which readily accepts the grain, holding it in place in random or oriented position during the passing of the "make coat" through the initial drying period. The glue film for the making coat serves as a "jeweled setting" for holding the grain. Accordingly, for fine grains a thin coating is applied and, conversely, a heavy coating for coarse grains thus ensuring good anchorage of the grain to the base web and permitting proper exposure of the cutting edges of the grain for effective work. Glue selection is predicated on type of grain, grain size, and industrial application, with the coated abrasive producers having very definite opinions and ideas as to best choice. In general, the high test grades of glue, 315 to 411 g, are preferred for the silicon carbide and aluminum oxide grains, the medium jelly grades testing 225 to 315 g for emery and garnet, and the lower jelly grades of 135 to 192 g for flint. Glue concentrations of from 25 to 45 per cent with or without fillers and extenders such as calcium carbonate[16] are most generally used.

The partially dried making coat is then passed through a second coating machine which applies a thin size film of animal glue to lock the grains securely in place. This sizing coat is usually a 10 to 15 per cent concentration of the same glue employed for the base or making coat, but other grades of glue may be used as desired. The fully dried continuous web is then rolled in jumbo rolls for inventory storage, and cut or slit as desired.

Closely allied with coated abrasives is the use of animal glue in the preparation of set-up polishing wheels. This general classification includes polishing wheels, discs, bobs and belts as "set-up" by the user. The principles involved, glue selection, and handling are quite similar to those employed in coated abrasives and permit the user to tailor his abrasive requirements to specific needs.

"Greaseless" abrasive composition sticks find considerable acceptance in industry for recoating cloth buffing wheels for finishing operations. These products are essentially a molded stick which when held against the revolving wheel melt by friction and deposit a thin layer of abrasive grain and adhesive on the surface of the wheel. In general such compositions contain from 6 to 8 per cent of high gram strength animal glue (411 g and higher), 24 per cent water, and the balance abrasive grain.

Other Adhesive Uses. Other large industrial users of animal glues for adhesive purposes include book and magazine binding-backing, casemaking, padding, loose-leaf binders; paper containers—folding and set-up boxes, spiral and convolute tube winding, heavy cartons; luggage covering, both hard and soft goods.

Sizing and Coating

Dilute water solutions of animal glues are widely used for sizing and coating applications principally in the textile and paper industries. Such applications range from imparting stiffness, body, and strength by saturation procedures to that of depositing a thin continuous film of glue as a protective surface coating for added strength and improved surface characteristics.

Textiles. Animal glues are employed in the textile industry in conjunction with softening oils for the "throwing" of skeined or coned rayon yarns for control of a pebbled effect in crepes. Here the glue acts as a size to hold in the twist imparted to the yarns until, on desizing of the woven goods, the glue is removed permitting the twist of the yarn to be released, causing a crepe effect. Large tonnages of animal glues are also used in the warp sizing of many of the synthetic fibers such as rayon, acetate, "Orlon," and in some cases nylon. Size concentrations of from 2½ to 8 per cent are usual, with the animal glue modified with from 20 to 45 per cent softening agents and lubricants such as sulfonated oils and wax emulsions. The plasticized glue film as deposited on the yarns as they pass through the application rolls followed by can dryers, imparts considerable strength, encases the filaments in a tough, smooth, elastic coating and promotes high loom efficiencies with freedom from fraying and breaking. The glue size deposited may average 2½ to 7 per cent of the weight of yarn. It is removed in the final finishing of the woven fabric.

Paper. The applications of animal glue in the paper industry aptly illustrate the versatility of this protein. Its interesting colloidal properties, amphoteric nature and charge relationships, and its excellent film-forming properties are all effectively applied in various phases of this industry.

In rag mills the protective colloidal property of animal glue facilitates the maintenance of clean beaters. Small quantities of animal glue are added to the stocks together with dispersing agents such as the neutral sodium salts of the formaldehyde condensation of naphthalene sulfonic acid. The protective colloidal action of glue on the rosin particle, especially in high free rosin sizings, particularly with hard-water conditions, has long been recognized. Small amounts ranging from 0.5 to 5.0 per cent based on dry rosin have proved to be effective stabilizers, preventing premature precipitation of the rosin with improved internal sizing.

Animal glue added at the beaters is an aid to internal rosin sizing, with the enhancement of toughness, density, formation of the sheet and improved resistance to scruffing and erasure, particularly on bond papers. The amount of glue required is very small, ranging from 0.3 to 0.6 per cent dry basis on the furnish. The dilute glue solution is preferably added to the beater just prior to completion of the beater operation and after the beater charge has been set at about pH 4.5. The negatively charged glue is precipitated on the paper fiber which at pH 4.5 or below is positively charged in relation to the glue.

Glue has been used as a wet-strength additive for beater application in conjunction with melamine resins. From 1 to 3 per cent of glue has been added at the beater employing the principles of opposite colloidal charges, followed by the introduction of small amounts of melamine resin at the regulating box or fan pump of the paper machine. Tannage of the retained glue is accomplished by the free formaldehyde released by the resin as the sheet passes over the dryer section of the paper machine.

The creping of tissues on cylinder drying machines such as the Yankee dryer is effectively promoted by the introduction of small amounts of animal glue to the hydrated cellulose soft tissue stocks. The amount of glue so furnished is generally not over 0.1 per cent on the dry furnish. The glue provides a very light tacky glue film at the dryer surface, enabling the sheet to hug the dryer without blowing or lifting to the doctor blade, which peels it off with desired creping effect. The glue may be added at the beater or as a 1 per cent glue solution fed to the fan pump.

Appreciable volumes of animal glue are used in the surface sizing of papers. Here the glue provides a protective film on the surface of the sheet to close the pores, eliminate feathering of inks, increase surface strength, resist picking of fibers during printing, increase bursting, folding, and tearing strength, and to provide better rattle and firmness. Usually the medium to high testing grades of glue are employed, particularly where it is desired to hold the sizing at the surface of the sheet. Such glues provide thin continuous films of good color with great strength, elasticity and cohesive value. Glue concentrations are customarily 3 to 8 per cent. The size films may be applied by "tub-sizing" of the paper web as a sectional part of the paper machine or as a separate operation for off-machine application. The sheet to be tub sized is immersed in the glue size tub, then passed through squeeze rolls and dried over the drying cans or through festoon dryers. The trend toward faster operations has resulted in the use of the size press as an integral part of the paper machine for surface sizing of many papers.

Animal glue is frequently employed in fortifying starches for the tub and size press sizing of combination rag and sulfite stocks. With offset printing grades the addition of from 5 to 20 per cent of animal glue based on starch solids provides a tougher surface film with improved wax pick values. Many direct line reproduction stocks are surfaced sized with glue only; others, where no moisture resistance is required, are frequently sized with a starch-glue, with the glue ranging from 25 to 50 per cent on the starch solids.

By proper use of hardening and tanning agents such as papermakers' alum and/or formaldehyde or combinations of these materials, moisture resistance is readily imparted to the glue size for blueprint, reproduction, map, indicator chart, currency, bank note and protection stocks. The addition of from 2 to 4 per cent papermakers' alum based on the dry weight of the glue provides improved hardness to the dried glue and also assists in holding the size film at the surface of the paper. The alum is preferably added to the preliminary soaking water in preparation of the size. Depending on the test grade of the animal glue employed, from 0.5 to 5 per cent of commercial formaldehyde may be added to the usual glue for improved water resistance of the size film, without undue thickening or arresting of normal working life. The presence of from 2 to 3 per cent alum in the glue size permits wider latitude in addition of the formaldehyde. Additional possibilities are offered in the patent literature[17] with further discussion of the underlying factors. A colorless hardening or tanning solution for glue protein films which has found wide industrial use[9] comprises a solution of aluminum sulfate, sodium acetate, and borax, which is applied as an overwash or as a secondary treatment.

The use of animal glue in coated papers has been limited in recent years to specialty items and some playing-card stocks. Smaller quantities are being effectively used as auxiliary adhesive aids in conjunction with starches, casein, and soya protein for improved fluidities and laying of colors for both "on-machine" and "off-machine" applications. Methods of formulating high solids coatings using animal glues for "on-machine" coating based on a controlled alkaline balance of deflocculated clay slurries are described in the patent literature[18] and in TAPPI Monograph No. 22, "Protein and Synthetic Adhesives for Paper Coating" (1961). In size press coatings for offset printing grades considerable animal glue is used in conjunction with starches and clay or clay-titanium mixtures for pigmented surface sizing.

Compositions

Tough, elastic, resilient compositions of animal glue are effectively used as printers' rollers. These compositions are essentially plasticized animal glue solutions in jelly form.

With slight modification these plasticized glue compositions are used extensively in the manufacture of paper gaskets as a seal for gases, air, gasoline, water, and oils.

Cork compositions, especially bottle cap inserts, are prepared from cork granules with a plasticized animal glue as the preferred binder and composition agent.

The match industry consumes large tonnages of animal glue for match head compositions. Here the particular colloidal and foaming properties of the glue provide the desired and required porosity, firmness, and resilience of the match head while serving as the adhesive to bond the ignition chemicals, oxidizing agents, and fillers therein combined. Book matches require the use of the highest test glues of very low free fat content. Medium to medium-high test grades of glues are preferred for

the older type stick matches for both the bulb and tip compositions.

Colloid and Flocculant

The particular complex protein structure and colloidal properties of animal glue are effectively employed in a wide range of industrial applications as a simple protective colloid and as a flocculant.

Possessing the lowest "gold number" of any colloid—0.005 to 0.1, (Zsigmondy[19])—animal glues are used in the electrolytic refining of metals, particularly copper. A glue concentration of from 0.03 to 0.15 per cent in the electrolyte will aid in the production of a smooth, dense cathode deposit eliminating production losses and needle growths. Its use as a dye leveling agent in the textile industry and its stabilizing effect in proprietary cleaning powders for the washing of paint and woodwork are well known.

Animal glue solutions are amphoteric, with an isoelectric point of 4.5 to 5.5. At a pH above the isoelectric point the animal glue is negatively charged; below it, positively charged. By suitable addition of alkalies or acids to normal glue solutions, enormous changes in charge relationships are possible, resulting in the flocculation of suspended solids by neutralization of charges upon the particles present in the system.

These principles are applied in the paper industry under the *Sveen System* for increasing the initial retention of fine-fibers, colors, pigments and fillers in the initial pass of the furnish over the Fourdrinier wire or into the cylinder vat, and for securing important savings by reclaiming through flotation save-alls such filterable solids as escape into the white-water systems on the paper machines. Sveen glues are essentially animal glue solutions of 0.5 to 1.0 per cent concentration, modified with small amounts of rosin size, with the pH set at the approximate isoelectric point of the glue (pH 4.7) with papermakers' alum.[10, 11, 12, 20, 21, 22]

For retention purposes the basic dosage is approximately 2 lb of dry glue, fed as the 1 per cent Sveen glue solution, per ton of paper.

Uranium Mining. The processing of uranium ores[23, 24, 25] for military purposes and for peacetime nuclear power reactors has been facilitated by the use of animal glues as a protective colloid and flocculant.

PRESENT TRENDS

The present potential of the animal glue industry is well in excess of 135,000,000 lb annually, with production and sales holding close to 120—

130,000,000 lb during recent years. Constant improvement in processing methods and production facilities, together with product and end-use research by individual companies and cooperatively through the National Association of Glue Manufacturers has strengthened the position of animal glue in its wide industrial acceptance as a chemical product. The present trend is toward increased chemical and physical modifications of the basic animal glue by the producers in developing and marketing tailored products for well diversified adhesive, sizing, composition and colloidal flocculant applications in industry.

References

1. Eastoe, J. E., "The Amino Acid Composition of Mammalian Collagen and Gelatin," *Biochem. J.,* **61,** 589–602 (1955).

2. Neuman, R. E., "Amino Acid Composition of Gelatins, Collagens, and Elastins from Different Sources," *Arch. Biochem.,* **24,** 289–298 (1949).

3. Pouradier, J., "Status of Knowledge of the Constitution of Gelatin," *Science et indus. phot.,* **19,** 81–91 (1948).

4. National Association of Glue Manufacturers—Private Survey of the Animal Glue Industry.

5. Ward, A. G., "The Chemical Structure and Physical Properties of Gelatin," *J. Photographic Sci.,* **3,** 60–67 (1955).

6. Pauling, L., "A Theory of the Structure and Process of Formation of Antibodies," *J. Am. Chem. Soc.,* **62,** 2643–57 (1940).

7. Gustavson, K. H., "The Chemistry and Reactivity of Collagen," New York, Academic Press Inc., 1956.

8. "Recent Advances in Gelatine and Glue Research," edited by G. Stainsby, New York, Pergamon Press, 1958.

9. Hubbard, J. R., "Waterproofing Composition and Process," U. S. Patent 2,043,324 (June 9, 1936).

10. Sveen, K., "Process of Effecting Agglomeration in Paper Pulp and Other Suspensions and Mixtures," U. S. Patent 1,622,474 (Mar. 29, 1927).

11. Tutt, R., Jr., "Composition for Effecting Agglomeration of Solids in Aqueous Suspensions," U. S. Patent 2,403,143 (July 2, 1946).

12. Tutt, R., Jr., "Composition for Effecting Agglomeration of Solids in Aqueous Suspensions, U. S. Patent 2,403,144 (July 2, 1946).

13. National Association of Glue Manufacturers, N. Y. C., "Standard Methods (Revised) for Determining Viscosity and Jelly Strength of Glue," *Ind. Eng. Chem.,* **16,** No. 3, 310 (Mar. 1924); *Ind. Eng. Chem. (Anal. Ed.),* **II,** No. 3, 348–351 (1930).

14. Federal Specification MMM-A-100b (Nov. 10, 1960); "Adhesives, Animal Glue."

15. Gill, R. C., "Animal Glues in the Modern Furniture Plant," *Furniture Manufacturer,* **78,** No. 2 (Feb. 1957).

Gill, R. C., "The Use of Hide Glues in Furniture Manufacture," *Furniture Manufacturer,* **79,** No. 2 (Feb. 1958).

Gill, R. C., "Trouble Shooting Animal Glues in Assembly and Edge Gluing Operations," Report presented at joint meeting ASME and FPRS, Syracuse, N. Y., Mar. 30–Apr. 1, 1958.

Gill, R. C., "Refresher Course on Animal Adhesives in Assembly and Edge Gluing Operations," *Hitchcock's Wood Working,* **60,** No. 9 (Sept. 1958).

Gill, R. C., "Spreading Animal Glues in Furniture Manufacture," *Furniture Manufacturer,* **80,** No. 2 (Feb. 1959).

Gill, R. C., "Bonding Wood with the Oldest High Polymer," *Adhesives Age,* **2,** No. 4 (Apr. 1959).

16. Oglesby, N. E., "Coated Abrasive," U. S. Patent 2,322,156 (June 15, 1943).

17. Hubbard, J. R., "Water Resistant Glue and Method of Making the Same," U. S. Patent 2,246,405 (June 17, 1941).

Hubbard, J. R., "Process for Forming Water Resistant Glue Films," U. S. Patent 2,334,098 (Nov. 9, 1943).

18. Tutt, R., Jr., "Coating Compositions and Method of Making the Same," U. S. Patent 2,513,121 (June 27, 1950).

19. Bogue, R. H., "The Chemistry and Technology of Gelatin and Glue," New York, McGraw-Hill, 1922.

20. Loddengaard, P. M., and Tutt, R., Jr., "Use of Sveen Glue," *TAPPI Papers,* 485 (1941).

21. Hutchinson, O. F., "Actual and Potential White Water System with the Sveen Pedersen Saveall," *Paper Trade Journal* (Dec. 2, 1948).

22. Tutt, R., Jr., "Sveen Glue," Technical paper presented Technical Section, Canadian Pulp & Paper Association Meeting, Montreal, Jan. 1954. *Pulp and Paper Magazine of Canada,* Convention Issue (Jan. 1954).

23. Clegg, J. W., and Foley, D. D. (editors), "Uranium Ore Processing," Addison-Wesley Publishing Co., Reading, Mass., 1958.

24. Lillie, D. F., "Two Years Milling at Biocroft Uranium Mines Ltd.," Technical Paper AIME Annual Meeting San Francisco, Feb. 1959.

25. McCreedy, H. H., "A Method of Comparing Reagents used as Aids to Pulp Suspensions in Agitation," Topical Report No. TR-143/57, Canada Department of Mines and Technical Surveys, Mines Branch, Ottawa, May 31, 1957 (Unclassified).

8

Fish Glue

Hugh C. Walsh

The Kendall Company
Polyken Division
Chicago, Illinois

There has been less technical information written about fish glue than probably any other known adhesive despite the fact that it has been used in volume, industrially, for nearly 100 years. This lack of reference material is undoubtedly due to the secrecy of manufacturing processes prevalent in the late 1800's and early 1900's.

With the advent of adhesive specialists and the general increased importance of adhesives, a renewed interest in the properties of fish glue has developed. The adhesive formulator is continually confronted with the problem of balancing his formula to obtain the ideal properties he is seeking, which include heat resistance, creep resistance, remoistenability, water resistance, solvent and oil resistance, wet tack, drying rate, and machinability to mention only a few. Most formulators consequently keep fish glue available for preparing their formulations since they feel it may well enhance the properties they intend to develop in the new product.

This section will cover the properties of fish glue and the effect to be expected when it is combined with other adhesives such as polyvinyl acetate emulsions, dextrines, animal glues, and latex emulsions.

Fish glue is derived from fish skins. Generally speaking, all fish skins will produce glue, although the properties often may be such that the glue is not considered industrially desirable. By selection of the proper fish skin species, it is possible to manufacture a product with reasonable uniformity, which exhibits the properties best suited for general use. In the selection of fish skins the following requirements are of utmost importance:

(1) Ready availability; continuous source of supply, in tonnage required.
(2) A non-oily type of skin, ruling out such species as mackerel.
(3) A skin of reasonable size, thus eliminating small fish.

The cod skin has been found to comply with the above requirements and to yield a good quality glue in expected volume per ton of skins. A ton of fish skins will yield approximately 50 gal of liquid fish glue.

The fish skins are salted and dried for storage to prevent bacterial degradation prior to use therefore necessitating the removal of the salt before extracting the glue from the skins. After the salt is removed, the skins are cooked in a hot liquor; the liquor, which is then drawn off, contains approximately 5 to 7 per cent glue solids. The glue liquor is further evaporated to increase the solids to the desired level between 40 and 50 per cent. A bactericide is added to the finished glue, which now has an indefinite shelf life capable of being safely stored for at least a year. The finished glue after successfully passing the following tests for gel point, salt concentration, viscosity, solid contents, and bond strength is ready for use.

Gel Point. The temperature, expressed in °C, at which the glue will start to solidify.

Salt Concentration. Expressed as per cent, salt, which should be maintained at less than 1 per cent, is usually 0.1 per cent salt.

Viscosity. Tested on Stormer viscosimeter at 18°C using a 600-g weight. Expressed as revolutions per minute.

Bond Strength. Tested on selected kiln dried maple wood blocks, the values average 2500 psi.

PHYSICAL PROPERTIES

Fish glue is generally available in liquid form containing 40 to 50 per cent solids, at which concentration, the glue will weigh from 9¾ to 10 lb/gal. Samples of dry-powdered fish glue have been prepared; nevertheless no use has been found for the product in its dry state. Dry films of fish glue are relatively brittle; however, the glue may be easily plasticized using glycerin to yield flexible films if desired.

The speed of set may be controlled within certain limitations. To accelerate the rate of set, high-grade animal glue can be added to fish glue; whereas to decelerate the rate of set, salt (calcium or sodium chloride) may be added to the glue.

The pH of fish glue is generally between 6.5 and 7.2 when shipped to the customer. Fish glue may be made either alkaline or acid by careful additions; however strong acids or alkalies degrade the natural protein fairly rapidly.

Alcohol or acetone may be added to the glue to assist in the penetration of the glue into certain coatings or finishes which are present on articles to be bonded. 100 g of fish glue will tolerate the addition of the following amounts of some typical solvents at room temperature before showing separation:

	gram
Ethyl alcohol	50
Acetone	25
Methyl "Cellosolve"	95
Dimethyl formamide	110

Liquid fish glue may be frozen and thawed repeatedly without affecting the performance characteristics of the glue.

Compatibility with Other Adhesives

Animal Glue. Fish glue may be added to hot animal glue in liquid state, e.g., in formulating the glue coating for gummed tape. Fish glue and animal glue may be mixed in any proportion; however the fish glue should be slowly added to animal glue to prevent cooling the latter below its gel point.

Dextrin Adhesives. Fish glue is fully compatible with some liquid dextrins, partially compatible with others, and incompatible with some. A liquid mixture of fish glue and dextrin can be prepared in advance by the adhesive manufacturer using fully compatible dextrins. For dextrins that are partially compatible with fish glue, 4 fluid oz of fish glue can be added to 1 gal of liquid dextrin. This addition is generally made by the adhesive user. The fish glue is added directly to the dextrin, with mild agitation, while it is in the glue pot. Examples of this exist in straight-line gluing operations as well as envelope front-seal and back-seam formulas for hard-to-stick papers.

Fish glue is also used in flat gumming formulas to improve adhesion and re-moistenability, but the addition is limited to about 5 per cent. Beyond this per cent the curl of the paper stock is noticeable even though the coated stock is run over a "breaker bar" to eliminate a continuous glue film.

Polyvinyl Acetate Emulsions. The number of acetate emulsions that are compatible with fish glue is somewhat limited. Generally, acetate emulsions which are dextrine-compatible are also compatible with fish glue.

The addition of fish glue to acetate emulsions will improve the following properties of the acetate emulsion:

(1) Cold flow and creep resistance.
(2) Heat resistance.
(3) Initial tack or quick stick.
(4) Glue penetration on paper stock that is hard to wet out.
(5) Resistance to aliphatic solvents.
(6) Cleaning of gluing equipment with water, especially dry glue films which normally require the use of a solvent such as methylethyl ketone.

Latex Emulsions. A supplier catering to the adhesive needs of the shoe manufacturer is using fish glue in conjunction with rubber latex systems. The addition of fish glue improves adhesion to leather as well as wet tack which is so important to achieve the instant holding power needed for many manufacturing operations.

Currently, very little is known concerning the full potential of fish glue as an addition to latex systems. Possibly fish glue can act as a stabilizer in latex emulsions thus prolonging the shelf life of these products. Every adhesive manufacturer today is constantly striving to improve the shelf life of adhesive products offered for sale.

APPLICATIONS

Gummed Tape

Fish glue is used extensively in conjunction with animal glue in the manufacture of gummed tape. Usually about 10 per cent of the glue formula consists of fish glue which improves re-moistenability of the tape. Fish glue re-moistens readily even with cold water; thus it is especially important during winter months when the water in tape dispensers is cold. Upon re-moistening, fish glue develops instant tack with high holding power and actually lengthens the tack period, allowing for positioning and alignment of the tape. On veneer tapes, stay tapes, and reinforced tapes, fish glue improves the adhesion level; furthermore it allows bonding of these tapes to a wider variety of surfaces such as wood, metal, and glass.

Make-ready

Fish glue is used throughout the paper-box field for adhering tympan sheets to steel cylinders in the make-ready operation. Not only does fish glue bond well to the steel cylinder, but after the run is completed, the tympan sheet can be removed by washing off the glue with water. Fish glue is readily re-moistened with water.

Shoe Boxes

Many shoe manufacturers receive shoe boxes and covers pre-cut but stacked flat to minimize warehouse space requirements. These boxes and covers are formed and glued on high-speed gluing and bonding machines. A very thin coating of glue is applied, and because of its very high wet tack, fish glue is capable of forming a tearing bond at the glued joints even before it has dried.

Straight-Line Gluing

Dextrin glues are used for many straight-line gluing operations, particularly when the stock being run is relatively porous and wets out easily. On the more difficult coated stock, it is often necessary to use synthetic adhesives. On intermediate types of board, dextrins are nearly adequate but require some strengthening. In this instance, fish glue is added directly to the dextrin in the glue pot. Since all dextrins and fish glues are not fully compatible in the liquid state, the mixture is kept under mild agitation while the glue is added. For this type of board, fish glue can of course be used straight or unblended, and it will also accept solvents such as alcohol or acetone to aid in penetrating finishes or coatings which extend on to the glue seam. Fish glue is easily cleaned from gluing equipment, using only water.

Graphic Arts

A special high grade of clarified fish glue is made for the graphic arts industry which is referred to as photoengraving glue. It is used to make such items as blueprint paper, tracing cloth, letterpress printing plates, and etched nameplates, the principal application letterpress plates. The properties which make photoengraving glue suitable for letterpress plate-making are:

(1) High quality and uniformity.
(2) Dried glue film readily soluble in water.
(3) Good adhesion to metal.
(4) Glue can be rendered photosensitive by chemical addition.

A brief description of the letterpress plate-making procedure follows since it not only points up the photosensitivity of fish glue, but also indicates that the glue can be made water-insoluble by chemical means.

Water and ammonium bichromate are added to photoengraving glue to render it photosensitive and contribute the desired flow viscosity. The metal plate is thoroughly cleaned with pumice and water to remove all residual oil, dirt, and oxides. The photosensitive fish-glue solution is flowed over one surface of the metal and allowed to dry on it in a smooth film.

A negative is placed in intimate contact with the coated side and the assembly is exposed to arc lamps which emit ultraviolet light. The actinic rays from the arc lamp insolubilize the glue film; however, there are dark or opaque areas in the negative which do not permit the passage of light. These protected areas are therefore unaffected by the exposure; hence the glue is still water-soluble. The finest details which can be captured on a negative are thus accurately transferred to the photosensitive coating on the metal plate.

In the next step, *development,* the exposed plate is placed under a flow of water. The soluble glue is loosened and washed away; whereas the insoluble glue remains on the metal plate. We now have areas of exposed metal and areas of protected metal on the plate. The insoluble glue remaining on the metal plate is further toughened by heating the plate to approximately 500°F.

The plate is then placed in an etching tank where the exposed metal is etched to the desired depth. The etching solution varies with different types of metal. On copper plates, which are used for the most detailed pictures, ferric chloride is used as the etchant. The glue-protected metal areas thus result in printing surfaces for transferring the image to paper.

During the exposure of glue and ammonium bichromate to actinic rays, the chrome complex changes from hexavalent chromium to trivalent chromium which reacts with the collagen of the fish glue rendering it water-insoluble.

Fish glue can also be rendered water-resistant by other tanning agents such as formaldehyde or chrome alum. Even formaldehyde vapors are sufficient to insolubilize dry films of fish glue.

— 9 —

Casein Glues and Adhesives

H. K. Salzberg

Borden Chemical Company
Bainbridge, New York

CASEIN MANUFACTURE

Casein, which is the main protein in milk, obtainable from no other source and sharply defined as to chemical constitution and reactivity, is readily obtained from skim milk after separation of cream for the market or for buttermaking. Thus as a by-product of the dairy industry casein is subject to the economics of the industry as determined by the demands for its products. Another commercial use of skim milk is its conversion to nonfat milk solids in the form of skim-milk powder for food uses. Even so, the supply of milk for casein production has remained ample; in fact, casein production is a convenient and profitable operation in seasons of surplus milk production where facilities for drying it are limited. This is the situation in many countries which together produce well over 100 million lb of casein annually for its well-established uses as an adhesive in many industries. The more important dairy countries of the world, having a surplus of milk for casein production and export include Argentina, New Zealand, Australia, France, and Poland. In many other countries casein is made for the domestic industry or for occasional export, as an alternative to the dumping of skim milk. World production annual figures indicate that casein, with its many useful properties, will continue to be a world commodity for industries that require adhesives.

For use as an adhesive casein is isolated from skim milk by acidifying the milk to about pH 4.5, the isoelectric point of this protein. A curd separates, which after washing, drying and grinding yields approximately 3 lb of raw casein from 100 lb of milk. Many factors determine the yield and quality of the product, now well stabilized at a high level of purity and uniformity.[109]

Casein is usually curded commercially by the addition of bacterial cultures which produce lactic acid from the lactose in the milk. Alternatively, if lactose is to be made from the whey and marketed, hydrochloric acid is used to precipitate the casein. The purity and quality of the casein depend more on the structure of the curd and the thoroughness with which it is washed free of occlusions than on the particular precipitating acid employed.

CONSTITUTION OF CASEIN

Casein is a protein; therefore it is essentially a condensation product of amino acids in which the main bond in the chain is the amide bond, $-CO \cdot NH-$, known as the peptide bond in proteins. Hydrolysis, the reverse of condensation, occurs when casein is subjected to alkali at pH values in excess of about 10, the macromolecule of several hundred amino acids splitting into peptides of low molecular weight. Certain proteolytic enzymes, notably trypsin in alkaline solutions and pepsin in acid solutions, also split the molecule. Enzymes naturally present in milk and carried over into the casein may degrade the molecule. The high molecular weight of casein, reported as high as 300,000, accounts for its colloidal properties and therefore for its value as an adhesive. Destruction of the molecule by hydrolysis reduces its worth as an adhesive.

Casein is also defined as a phosphoprotein, as it contains about 0.75 per cent phosphorus, part of which is inorganic phosphate, which becomes part of the ash of casein on combustion. Other elements in the ash of casein are potassium, sodium, and calcium. The ash of casein from different sources varies with the process by which it has been made, especially the degree to which soluble salts have been removed by washing of the freshly precipitated curd. Ash content may be as low as 0.2 to 0.3 per cent or as high as 2 to 3 per cent. Rennet casein, from which casein plastic is formed, has an ash value of 7 to 8 per cent because it is curded at the normal pH of milk of about 6.7 with the enzyme rennin instead of acid. Small amounts of butterfat, lactose and acid occluded from the curding operation can also be found in casein, but not in amounts that affect its performance as a glue. Methods for analyzing casein are detailed in Chapter 5 of the Sutermeister book.[110]

CHEMISTRY OF CASEIN

The amino acid condensation by which casein is formed in the metabolism of the cow does not include all the amine or carboxylic groups of the many different amino acids involved. There is a surplus of basic and acidic groups, and since both are present, casein is amphoteric, reacting with either basic or acidic chemicals. Since there are more free acidic than free basic groups, casein is more readily soluble in alkalies than in acids; hence this accounts for the almost exclusive use of casein in alkaline solution. Glues and adhesives, therefore, contain inorganic or organic alkalies which remain wholly or partly in the glue line. If the alkali is ammonia or a volatile organic amine, much of it is lost by evaporation during cure, yielding a film of almost pure insoluble casein. A fixed alkali such as the sodium alkalies remains in the glue line as sodium caseinate, a soluble salt. Calcium hydroxide, the alkali on which water-resistant wood glues are based, forms insoluble calcium caseinate in the glue line. Similarly, certain heavy metal ions, such as zinc, aluminum, and chromium, form insoluble casein compounds, and are used in casein adhesives for paper.

Many other reactions with casein are possible in view of its richness in free reactive groups, one of which is the reaction with aldehydes, particularly formaldehyde, which is a crosslinking agent, forming with casein a reticulated gel structure that dries to a water-resistant film. In general, reagents which are reactive with amino groups, such as organic acid chlorides and anhydrides, are useful in reducing the hydrophylic nature of the casein bond. These and other chemical reactions of casein are discussed in Chapter 2 of the Sutermeister book.[110]

HISTORY AND POSITION OF CASEIN GLUE IN INDUSTRY

The adhesive nature of the casein curd from milk was recognized early in the practice of the arts; in fact, casein has been identified as the glue in ancient museum pieces and as the pigment binding in old tempera painting. Early use required only the mixing of precipitated curd with alkalies, of which lime appears to have been the main one. The marketing of casein for gluing appears to have had its beginning in Switzerland and Germany in the early nineteenth century, and patents on casein glue formulas and processes began to appear in the United States during the middle of the nineteenth century.[14] As the twentieth century emerged, a mixture of dry casein, lime, and a sodium salt was formulated,[47] marking the beginning of the prepared casein glue industry; however it was not until a sharpened demand for water-resistant wood glues developed during World War I that casein glues assumed a high level of commercial importance. Here, the use of the word "glue" will be limited to the gluing of wood, and the term "casein adhesives" will be reserved for applications of casein to adherends other than wood, and primarily to paper.

Casein glue is distinguished from animal glue from hides and bones, not only as to source, but also by several rather sharp differences in properties, though both are of animal protein origin. Animal glues, commercially important for wood gluing long before casein came into general use, are gelatins. Gelatin differs from casein in that it is liquefiable with heat in the presence of only a small amount of water and in exhibiting no isoelectric point or pH value at which it is insoluble. The glue joint thus sets quickly as the warm glue cools; conversely animal glue cannot readily be made water resistant and therefore durable as can casein. Thus one or the other of the two glues is usually selected on the basis of the degree of durability which the particular job demands.

The relatively high degree of durability of casein-glued wood accounts for the current wide usage of casein in laminating lumber into large beams and arches, in door assembly, and in other glued members that become internal parts of a house or building. Earlier, casein glue acquired a good reputation as the bond for wood joints exposed to the weather, e.g., in the plywood used in the construction of airplanes during World War I. However, with the advent in the United States of synthetic glues of the phenolic resin type in 1935, and of the resorcinol-formaldehyde resins in 1943, casein glue for exterior exposure gradually gave way to these resins. Urea-formaldehyde glues, introduced for plywood gluing in 1937, further reduced the use of casein because of their lower cost without sacrifice of joint strength and durability. Then, about 1947, still another replacement for casein as a wood glue began to appear in the form of polyvinyl acetate resin emulsions, which have taken some of the market for furniture assembly gluing away from casein. Despite these strong competitors, a steady and not inconsiderable use of casein glue remains, particularly if the situation is viewed world-wide, as a result of its properties and attributes.

CLASSIFICATION OF CASEIN GLUES AND ADHESIVES

Lime-Containing Water-Resistant Casein Glues

A glue sets by changing from liquid or sol state to a gel which eventually becomes more or less rigid in the joint. Water-resistant casein glues gel as the result of a slow chemical reaction, a solution of sodium caseinate being gradually converted by lime to a gel of calcium caseinate. Some of the lime has previously produced sodium hydroxide from a sodium salt, and this strong alkali has dissolved the casein. Usually the chemicals are dry-mixed with the casein in the form of a powder, shipped by the glue manufacturer to the user as prepared glue for dispersing in water. Previously, pure dry casein was sold, and the gluing shop provided the same chemicals to make up so-called "wet-mix" glues, a practice currently in disuse. A classification of glues, based on their performance in the glue line, agreed upon in 1950 by the Forest Products Laboratories of the world, puts casein glues in the category of "Moisture-resistant but Mold-susceptible" glues.

Lime is added to dry prepared casein glue in excess of that needed to convert the sodium salt (NaX) to sodium hydroxide. As excess lime increases, the working life of the glue is shortened, but the water resistance of the glue line increases. The formation of a gel in the bulk glue on standing overnight at room temperature is a forecast of the attainment of a strong glue joint though maximum strength is not reached until the joint has aged for several days.

Numerous chemicals have been suggested for NaX.[110] Those in greatest commercial use are trisodium phosphate, sodium sulfite, sodium carbonate, sodium fluoride, and combinations of these. Skill in formulating a casein-prepared glue

to meet requirements as to viscosity, working life, and water resistance involves the knowledge of subtle differences in anion effects of these chemicals, in addition to use of the correct amount of excess lime in the formula.

Sodium Silicate as NaX in Lime-Containing Glues

Sodium silicate, usually of silica: soda ratio of 3 to 3.5 : 1, is a special and useful source of sodium hydroxide in casein-lime glues because it increases the working life of the glue at all levels of alkalinity. Typical formulas require the addition of 20 to 30 parts of calcium hydroxide to 100 parts of casein, soaked in 250 parts of water, followed immediately by the addition of 70 parts of sodium silicate. If the addition of the silicate is delayed beyond about 1 min after the lime, the glue will be too thick. A solution of casein in lime alone thickens rapidly to a gel in a matter of minutes, and although the final joint is strong and water resistant, the short working life makes this combination uninviting for commercial use.

Lime-Free Casein Adhesives

Casein adhesives not involving the lime reaction are made by dissolving casein with hydrolyzable sodium salts of weak acids, which provide a medium sufficiently alkaline to dissolve the casein. Salts commonly used and the ranges of parts to 100 parts of casein are: borax 10 to 15, anhydrous sodium carbonate 5 to 10, and trisodium phosphate 15 to 20. Adhesives are also used in which the casein is dissolved directly in strong alkali, such as sodium hydroxide 2.5 to 5 parts, or ammonium hydroxide 5 to 10 parts. Finally, organic amines dissolve casein, and there is some small use of alkyl amines, ethanolamines, and morpholine as solvent for casein adhesives.

In the absence of lime, casein adhesives do not gel to water-resistant films. To give them a measure of water resistance the following expedients are used: (1) inclusion of formaldehyde or carbon disulfide in the wet glue, or exposure of the wet glue line to formaldehyde fumes, (2) inclusion in the adhesive of a formaldehyde donor in the form of a formaldehyde-containing resin or hexamethylenetetramine, (3) inclusion in the adhesive of a salt or oxide, the cation of which forms an insoluble metal-casein complex such as salts of chromium, zinc, or aluminum. A typical glue is formulated with zinc oxide to compensate for the lack of lime.

Casein Blend Glues

Common usage of the term "casein blend glues" refers to combinations of casein with either soybean meal,[15, 16] blood albumin,[30] or both admixed with the chemicals which produce water-resistant bonds.

Blend glues assumed commercial importance in 1920 when by-product blood in dry soluble form was made available from animal processing plants and was found to make an excellent bond for hot-pressed plywood for airplane construction. Blends with casein and lime-NaX, to provide water resistant glue lines by cold pressing, were soon on the market. The blood constituent contributes to quick setting, reduction in clamp time, and both wet and dry strength of the glue joint. These glues are now quite generally used in the construction of flush doors, boxes, furniture, and other assembly work.

Blend glues comprise mixtures of casein with soybean meal, the residue remaining after the extraction of oil from soybeans. They have found a substantial outlet in the bonding of interior grades of plywood. The meal, of approximately 50 per cent protein content, has adhesive value of its own and responds to lime much in the same manner as casein; thus this blend is a way in which the cost of water-resistant glue lines can be reduced.

GENERAL VISCOSITY AND RHEOLOGICAL PROPERTIES OF CASEIN GLUES

The gradual viscosity change in a mixed casein glue is referred to as its "viscosity pattern." The initial viscosity depends on both the level of excess lime in the glue and the proportion of sodium hydroxide formed to casein. For any one combination of chemicals used to produce increasing amounts of sodium hydroxide, the solution reaches its highest initial viscosity at a pH value of approximately 9.[134] Casein glues for wood have pH values of 12 to 13; hence they are far beyond the pH of maximum viscosity and therefore workable at the relatively low ratio of water to casein of 2.0 to 2.5 : 1.

Highly alkaline solutions of casein do not require the presence of lime to gel. Sodium hydroxide solutions of casein gel above pH 12.5 through formation of a reticulated network of chain molecules held together by sulfur linkages.[51, 132]

Freshly mixed casein glue is essentially Newtonian in structure, of uncomplicated flow properties, and exhibits no yield value; however in the more concentrated solutions as thickening progresses, a yield value appears,[52] and the solution exhibits plastic flow, i.e., a certain minimum stress must be applied for the solution to begin to flow. The development of a yield value depends greatly on the NaX used. The straight lime system remains Newtonian to gelation. Casein solutions in the usual concentration range of 15 to 25 per cent do not exhibit thixotropy, that is, the relation between stress and flow rate is linear, even in solutions which show a yield value.

The viscosity of casein solutions and glues increases rapidly with the concentration and decreases rapidly as the temperature of the solution increases. The viscosity-pH relationship for freshly prepared casein solutions is much more complicated, especially in lime-containing glues. In a series of glues made by dissolving casein with varying amounts of sodium hydroxide, after which 15 g calcium hydroxide per 100 g of casein is added, the initial viscosity values in poises decreased as sodium hydroxide increased, as follows:[110]

NaOH, g	4	6	8	10	12
Viscosity, poises	200	90	20	6	5
pH		12.19	12.44	12.68	13.08	13.25
Time to gel, hr		0.5	1	2	4	No gel

Gel formation in the lime-containing glue is retarded by increase in alkalinity, which is the reverse of the change occurring in the absence of lime illustrated above. Prediction of the viscosity pattern of casein-lime glues of varying alkalinity, as they age, has been undertaken by Higgins and Plomley[52] for the non-Newtonian period of solution.

Viscosity Measurement

The Stormer rotational viscometer with the 500-g weight is most generally used for determining the viscosity of casein glues and adhesives. Alternative methods of expressing viscosity using the Stormer instrument are (1) in rpm of the rotor, in which case the higher the reading the thinner the glue, and (2) in minutes required for 100 revolutions of the rotor, in which case the higher the reading the more viscous the glue. Method (1) is universally used for wood glues, but method (2) is sometimes used for other casein adhesives.

The Brookfield rotational viscometer expresses viscosities in poises or centipoises. Many other types of viscometers, including efflux pipettes and cups, can be used to determine relative viscosity values of casein solutions. Narayanamurti and co-workers[83] use a penetrometer type of instrument to measure viscosity of the gelling glue and a torque pendulum to follow the development of rigidity in the glue film.

ADDITIVES TO CASEIN GLUE

Certain ingredients are either indigenous to dry prepared casein glues or are added to the wet mix:

Oils

Casein is usually treated with 1 to 3 per cent of nondrying oil before introducing the chemicals in making prepared glues. This treatment retards interaction between the casein and chemicals and promotes wetting out of the glue in mixing.

Fillers

Many prepared glues contain small amounts of wood flour, nut-shell flour, or cellulose, i.e., materials which have a bodying effect on the glue and a restraining action on its penetration into the wood. In the compounding of prepared glues the choice of filler is important in adjusting glue performance to the requirements of the job. Inorganic fillers are not ordinarily used because of their tendency to make the glue line abrasive to woodworking tools.

Viscosity-Adjusting Agents

Casein glues can also be thickened with alum, calcium chloride, sodium sulfate, or with formaldehyde; conversely, they can be thinned thereby extending the working life by adding sodium sulfite, sodium hexametaphosphate, or sugar, or by replacing some of the casein with seed meal to make a blend glue. Casein solutions to be used as adhesives of low alkalinity are sometimes thinned and stabilized by including urea at 20 to 40 per cent or dicyandiamide at 10 to 20 per cent on the casein.[1]

Preservatives

The susceptibility of casein as a protein to bacterial decomposition, resulting in putrefaction, is not evident in the highly alkaline, water-resistant casein-lime glues. However if the glue line is to be exposed to ambient conditions favoring the growth of molds and fungi, it may require protection. This is accomplished by including in the glue a strong fungicide, usually of the chlorinated phenol type, at levels of 3 to 5 per cent on the dry prepared glue. Alternatively, or supplementing the inclusion of a preservative in the glue, are treatments of the glued wood with conventional wood preservatives such as pentachlorophenol or creosote.

Casein solutions of lower alkalinity, such as those used as adhesives for paper, require the addition of preservatives if the solution is to be held for more than several days. Neutral solutions are most liable to spoil quickly. If the solution is to be an additive to some other aqueous adhesive, such as latex or resin emulsion, it must possess resistance to agencies of spoilage in the presence of all the ingredients and at the dilution of the full product formula. The concentration of the preservative to be used is determined by the weight of the solution containing all the ingredients, because its strength is dependent on its concentration in the solution rather than on its ratio to casein. Chemicals long used as preservatives for casein solutions such as beta-naphthol, thymol, and phenol have been largely superseded by derivatives of phenol such as o-phenylphenol and the chlorinated phenols, by esters of p-hydroxybenzoic acid, and by phenylmercuric acetate or other mercurials. The former are effective at concentrations of 0.5 to 1.5 per cent solution basis in protecting casein from putrefaction. The mercury compounds are effective at much lower concentrations. Of the chemicals customarily used for dissolving casein, sodium fluoride and borax possess marked bactericidal power.

Another type of damage to casein solutions arises from enzyme activity, i.e., proteolytic enzymes naturally present in the casein causing hydrolysis with resulting loss in viscosity of the solution and strength of the casein bond. This may occur in solutions which are well protected with preservatives against putrefaction; conversely, a casein solution of low alkalinity may slowly thicken with age, an effect explainable by the action of enzymes of other species which eventually predominate. The preservatives named above as commonly used to protect casein against bacteria and fungi, are insufficiently strong poisons to prevent whatever chain of events occurs in the thinning or thickening of the solution; no other chemicals or enzyme denaturants have been found however which in small amounts achieve the objective of stable viscosity in solutions of casein of low alkalinity.

Heat, however, causes irreversible inhibition of all enzymes. If in the preparation of casein solutions a period of wet heating in the range of 160 to 180°F is introduced, solutions of stable viscosity can be prepared. Concentrated solutions of casein of constant viscosity at room temperature are not attained solely by "cooking" the solution in this manner. The solution should also approximate neutral pH and contain preservatives which in themselves do not cause a slow thinning or thickening of the solution. A 13 per cent casein solution was prepared at pH 7.2 with sodium hydroxide by "cooking" for 20 min at 170°F. A combination of 0.5 per cent each of the methyl and the propyl esters of p-hydroxybenzoic acid was employed as the preservative. This solution maintained its original appearance and viscosity for a period of at least 3 months. Though casein solutions of unchanging properties have thus been made, success cannot be assured in view of the variable microorganisms in casein from lot to lot. To provide complete protection against all agencies of deterioration, the above solution may include also relatively high amounts of enzyme denaturants such as sugar or urea or may be made with alcohol as a partial replacement for water as the solvent.

Plasticizers

The dry casein film is inherently brittle, but this does not prevent it from forming a strong wood glue joint. Glycerin or sorbitol is sometimes added to casein glues and adhesives to impart a degree of softness to the joint. Sulfonated oils are also useful. Natural rubber latex, synthetic latices, and resin emulsions are equally compatible and contribute flexibility to the glue line.

GLUING WOOD WITH CASEIN GLUES

Success in gluing wood depends on a sequence of operations which have been long recognized as controllable. Specifically there must be control in consistency of the glue, in temperature of the glue and of the wood, in the manner and rate at which it is spread, in time intervals between spreading and assembly and between assembly and pressing, in time under cold or hot pressure, and in equilibration period after gluing.

Mixing and Spreading Casein Glue

Dry prepared casein glues are dissolved in cold water according to directions furnished by the manufacturer. The dry glue and water are weighed in commercial practice and usually measured out by volume in household gluing where the approximation of a 1:1 ratio of glue to water is convenient. Directions for commercial gluing call for adding the glue powder slowly to the water with constant stirring. When all glue has been added, stirring continues for about 5 min, followed by a rest period of approximately 10 min, which in turn is followed by a second period of stirring for about

5 min, during which the additives described above may be added.

In the preparation of wet-mix lime glue, the raw casein is soaked in water for up to 15 min; then the lime mixed with some of the water is stirred in. After approximately 1 min the glue begins to thicken, and the sodium hydroxide or sodium silicate must be added quickly to avoid overly thick glue. Stirring continues for 15 to 20 min to smooth out the lumps.

Lime-free casein adhesives with alkalies or hydrolyzable salts as the solvents are usually prepared with heat. Following a soaking period of casein in water in sufficient amount to provide a casein concentration of at least 15 per cent, the solvent is added and the mixture brought to 160 to 180°F with stirring. The solution is complete in 10 to 15 min. Additives to adjust viscosity, including water to thin if desired or to provide water resistance to the glue line, preservatives, plasticizers, or defoamers are added during the cooling period. As stated above, heating destroys enzymes naturally present in the casein which might subsequently cause rapid thinning or thickening of the adhesive. Solutions prepared with heat are of lower viscosity than those prepared at room temperature.

Mixing equipment for casein glues and adhesives is usually of a semiheavy-duty type, fitted with paddles that scrape the sides of the vessel rather than with propellors. Metals may be of ordinary steel, stainless steel, or enameled.

Casein glue can be spread by either fiber brushes or metal blades. For large-scale application mechanical glue spreaders are used, e.g., a roll spreader. Working life of the glue is defined as the time required for it to become too thick to spread. In the gluing of wood it is common practice to apply the glue to only one of the two surfaces to be joined. In the gluing of lumber laminations, however, the glue is customarily double spread to produce a more reliable joint in these large construction members. Single spread, as for plywood, veneering, door and cabinet work, requires 60 to 90 lb of liquid glue per 1000 sq ft of wood surface, corresponding to 20 to 30 lb of dry glue. Double spreading requires about 25 per cent more glue. In lumber laminating, a typical prepared casein glue, mixed with water at 1:2 by weight, having viscosity of 4 to 6000 cps, increasing to about 10,000 cps during its working life of 4 to 5 hr, is double spread at the rate of 40 to 50 lb per 1000 sq ft on each side of the lamination. At these spreads, glue line costs are estimated at $9 to $18 for casein glue as compared to $20 to $30 for synthetic resin glues, per 1000 sq ft of glue line, the spread varying for different species of wood.

Assembling and Pressing

The assembly and pressure periods in gluing constitute perhaps the most critical aspect of the entire sequence from compounding of the adhesive to inspection of the final product. Three time intervals are recognized:

(1) Open assembly, timed from the instant of spread to the joining of parts.
(2) Closed assembly, scheduled from the joining of parts to the application of pressure.
(3) Pressure period, during which the assembly is under pressure in clamps, in mechanical press, or under weights.

During open assembly the glue line is exposed to the atmosphere. Although casein glue lines do not dry out quickly, it is good practice to join the parts immediately after spreading. The closed assembly time for casein glue on wood is usually limited to 15 to 20 min and is not particularly sensitive to temperature of the glue or of the wood. Strong joints are attained with casein glue over as wide a range of wood temperature as 40 and 100°F. Too long a closed assembly period may result in "dried" joints as a result of excessive absorption of water from the glue into the wood surfaces so that when pressure is applied, the film is too thin and dry to respond. Casein glue has fairly good gap-filling properties, i.e., the surfaces' roughnesses are filled providing there is sufficient film thickness at the time of pressing. So-called "starved" joints result from excessive pressure on highly fluid glue; conversely, if the glue line has gelled before pressing, a weak "chilled" joint results. The consistency of the glue line at the time of pressing depends not only on the viscosity of the glue as mixed but on rheological changes occurring during the assembly periods. These changes are relatively slow in casein glue compared to warm animal glue or catalyzed resin glues, thus giving the woodworker more latitude in assembly time. This attribute of casein glue is especially attractive in lumber laminating. The balance between assembly period and time under pressure required for the glue to set changes with the gluing conditions as to temperature and humidity, moisture content and temperature of the wood, as well as with the species of wood; however it can be easily adjusted by variations in the choice of casein and the proportions of lime and filler.

Most wood gluing is done under cold pressure, i.e., without application of heat at the time of pressing. Hot pressing is impracticable for joining thick pieces of lumber because of the low heat conductivity of wood; however any casein glue may be hot pressed in making plywood, and as a rule the water resistance of the glue line is thereby improved. Under ordinary circumstances good results may be expected with casein by cold pressing at 150 to 200 psi. Usually mechanical pressure maintained for a few minutes is followed by a clamping or "dead stacking" period so that the press is not unduly tied up. In lumber laminating pressure is applied by clamps.[98] For a more adequate discussion of the technique of gluing with casein and other glues the reader is referred to the publications[118, 119] of the U. S. Forest Products Laboratory, Madison, Wisconsin.

Casein glues set quickly and produce joints sufficiently strong to be machined in a pressure period of 4 to 6 hr. Good practice calls for a seasoning period of the glued assembly after release of pressure to permit thorough drying of the glue line, which may require up to one week under normal atmospheric conditions.

Results with Different Woods

The joint strengths of casein glue in wood, produced under optimum gluing conditions as prescribed above, vary with the species of wood.[110] The percentage area of wood failure of the separated test joint is used as the criterion of success in gluing. The following woods average better than 90 per cent wood failure when glued with a lime-sodium silicate-casein glue: redwood, western red cedar, white fir, Sitka spruce, southern cypress, western hemlock, eastern red cedar, chestnut, red alder, and northern white pine, which are among the weaker woods. The stronger woods comprise red oak, soft maple, white ash, yellow birch, persimmon, and sugar maple, which all showed 30 to 50 per cent wood failure; however the block shear values were at least 2500 psi, values which approximate the shearing strength of the woods themselves. Bergin[10] found casein glue satisfactory for gluing twenty different species of Canadian woods.

All strongly alkaline glues stain oak, maple, and some other species of wood,[114, 118] and are especially conspicuous on thin veneer. Staining is avoided by using dry lumber, a thicker glue, by removing panels more quickly from the press, and by drying the panels immediately after pressing. Sodium perborate can be used to remove color from the bulk glue; moreover stained glue joints can be bleached by treating with dilute oxalic acid solution.

TESTING CASEIN WOOD GLUES

Specifications for the purchase of casein glue are usually confined to the determination of viscosity and working life, but may also involve dry and wet joint strength tests and resistance to microorganisms, particularly molds. The strength of a glued wood joint depends equally on the strength of the wood and the conditions under which the gluing was performed as it does on the properties of the glue;[69, 70] consequently tests of joint strength require well chosen and controlled techniques in addition to proper interpretation of the results. Although well glued joints are sometimes stronger than unsupported films of the glue itself, the fundamentals of adhesion as set forth in Chapter 3 can lead to predictions of strength values far in excess of experience. Failure to approach the theoretical strength potential is attributed to imperfections in the glue-wood interface. Test specimens approximating the type of stress to be encountered in service are most desirable, even though they may not show the adhesive to the best advantage. Blomquist[13] published much detail as to wood test specimen design and procedures, which had become generally standardized from pioneering work at the U. S. Forest Products Laboratory. Joint strength test procedures for wood and other materials have been reviewed by deBruyne and Houwink.[19]

Working Life and Setting Properties

U. S. Federal Specification MMM-A-125[122] defines the working life of a casein glue as the time to the closest one-half hour at which the glue can no longer be spread conveniently to a uniform film on the wood, or the time at which the glue reaches a viscosity of 800 poises at 71 to 75°F. Casein glue of Type I (water resistant) of this Specification shall set to a firm gel at 70 to 80°F within 24 hr; whereas glue of Type II (water and mold resistant) shall set in 48 hr. In this specification the designation "mold resistant" refers to casein glue containing preservative.

The Block Shear Test

U. S. Federal Specifications MMM-A-125[122] and MMM-A-175, Method 1031[123] rely on the well-known block shear test for strength requirements of wood glues.

Hard maple blocks having a minimum specific gravity of 0.65 based on oven-dry weight and volume and measuring ¾ by 2½ by 12 in., are cut from stock free from defects, with the grain direction parallel to the longest dimension and the moisture content between 10 to 12 per cent. The blocks are surfaced on a jointer just prior to gluing and remain unsanded. The adhesive is prepared and applied in accordance with recommendations from the manufacturer of the adhesive. If no rate of spread is recommended, 3 to 4 g of wet glue is applied to each contacting surface. The blocks are assembled for 5 to 10 min in closed assembly, then pressure is applied at 150 to 200 psi and the blocks held under pressure for at least 4 hr as specified in MMM-A-125 for casein glues. Upon removal from pressure the joints are conditioned at 50 per cent humidity and 73.5°F for the shorter of two periods: either 7 days or until specimens reach equilibrium as indicated by no progressive change in weight. The glued block is sawed into five offset specimens, and the testing machine is fitted with a shearing tool. The shear stress at failure, which is calculated in psi from the glue line area, is the average for at least eight specimens.

The Plywood Shear Test—Wet and Dry

U. S. Federal Specifications MMM-A-125[122] and MMM-A-175, Methods 1032 and 2031[123] are the source of first importance for directions on running the plywood shear test though the method is repeated in many other references.[3, 115, 121]

Sweet or yellow birch veneer, either rotary cut or sliced, ⅟₁₆ in. thick, is selected free from defects and used unsanded. The veneer is cut into suitable sizes and assembled in groups of three sheets, the grain of the center or core sheet running at right angles to the grain of the two face sheets. A convenient size is 4 by 12 in. from which 10 test specimens can be sawed. The grain in the face plies must be parallel to the smaller dimension. The veneer shall be at a moisture content of 10 to 12 per cent based on oven-dry weight. The glue is prepared in accordance with the procedure given by the manufacturer and is applied after 1 and 4 hr of pot life to both sides of the core. The spread is recorded from the weight of wet glue applied. A closed assembly time of 5 to 10 min is specified for casein glue (MMM-A-125), after which pressure is applied at 150 to 200 psi and held for at least 4 hr. The test specimens are cut from the panel. The cut specimens are conditioned at 50 per cent humidity and 73.5°F, either for 7 days or until specimens reach constant weight, whichever is the shorter period. The testing machine shall be capable of maintaining a rate of loading of 600 to 700 psi min and be provided with grips and jaws to enable the specimen to be gripped tightly and held in alignment as the load is applied. The load at failure and the estimated per cent of wood failure are recorded for each specimen. The load is expressed in psi. The number of panels and specimens tested and averaged is recorded.

A standard wet test long in use for casein glues merely required that the cut specimens be immersed in water at room temperature for 48 hr and subsequently tested while still wet. Other more severe conditions of wet exposure specified in MMM-A-175 for glues in general are: (1) immersion in boiling water for 3 hr followed by immersion in cold water for ½ hr, (2) four cycles of water immersion alternated with drying, (3) two cycles of immersion in boiling water alternated with drying, and (4) a vacuum pressure, accelerated wet and dry cycle test. These more extreme exposures to deteriorating conditions, however, are not usually applied to casein-glued plywood.

The Mold-Resistance Test

U. S. Federal Specification MMM-A-125[122] requires the testing of at least thirty dry plywood specimens made according to Method 1032 of Specification MMM-A-175:

The glued specimens are soaked for 1 min in a water suspension of mold spores prepared by brushing spores from a stock of moldy casein-soaked veneer into water. The soaked shear specimens are placed on wood stickers or glass rods individually so as to leave an air space above and below each specimen, placed in a cabinet having saturated atmosphere, and held at 72 to 80°F for 14 days. The specimens are tested according to Method 1032 immediately upon removal from the cabinet

The test was developed at the U. S. Forest Products Laboratory[60] as a quick method for comparing the preservative power of fungicides in casein glue. The test conditions are designed to favor the development of molds rather than bacteria, which cause rapid deterioration of the glue only when the moisture contents of the wood is higher than provided in this test. The British counterpart of this test is found in a report from the Princes Risborough Laboratory.[65]

Other Test Methods

Federal Specification MMM-A-175[123] can be consulted for other methods applicable to casein-glued wood joints as follows:

Method 1033: Single Lap Constructions
Method 1051: Impact Strength
Method 1061: Fatigue Strength
Method 2100: Chemical Resistance
Method 2021: Delamination
Method 3011: Applied Weight per Unit Area
Method 4011: pH of Adhesives and Bonded Assemblies

Wakefield[126] devised a plywood tensile test by which stress is applied normal to the glue line, i.e., the force required to pull vertically the face ply from the core is measured. Genin[43] uses a convenient and simple test for comparing two glues by merely applying the glues on each end of a lap joint and observing which fails first in applying a shearing force. Many of the standard test methods of the American Society for Testing Materials in the field of adhesives[3] are applicable to both casein glues and casein-glued wood; moreover they.can be applied alternatively to the methods of the Federal Specifications.

The adoption of casein glue for laminating lumber called for the designing of test procedures which supplement the standard block shear test. The tests which are used in controlling casein glues made with preservatives also apply in selecting a glue used in lumber laminations.[41] In addition, the joint strength tests have been elaborated to simulate service conditions for laminated structures such as cross-bending tests on small models and tests to destruction of full-scale structural members.[62] Furthermore, strength tests of end joints of various types peculiar to laminated lumber have been designed and applied.[75] Another test, particularly pertinent to glued lumber laminate, involves three cycles of immersion in water and drying to cause dimensional changes in the wood.[41] These changes may be accelerated by applying alternately vacuum and pressure to the immersed specimens.[3, 41, 112, 123] The percentage delamination is recorded.

DURABILITY OF WOOD JOINTS MADE WITH WATER-RESISTANT CASEIN GLUES

Controlled exposure tests of glued specimens and models have been conducted by investigators at the U. S. and Canadian Forest Products Laboratories. Under damp or alternately wet and dry conditions, casein glues last for sometime but gradually lose strength and finally fail from: (1) chemical hydrolysis, (2) destruction of the casein and the wood by microorganisms, and (3) mechanical failure as a result of alternate swelling and shrinking of the wood. The significance of moisture or wetness is evident when one considers that agencies (2) and (3) are destructive only in the presence of water.

Plywood Glued without Preservatives

The effect of atmospheric conditions on the rate of deterioration of plywood joints made with casein glue was investigated by Brouse.[18] After 3 yr of exposure up to 80 per cent humidity, the specimens showed no loss in strength. Specimens exposed to a 30 to 90 per cent humidity cycle failed in about 80 wk. When exposed to alternating 30 per cent relative humidity and soaking, failure occurred in about 15 wk.

In the exposures to higher humidity, a highly alkaline (lime-sodium hydroxide) glue failed somewhat more rapidly than a glue of low alkalinity, with chemical hydrolysis occurring in the highly alkaline glue line. Continuous soaking was a much less severe test than a dry-wet cycle because with the exclusion of air, fungi are inactive; thus progressive mechanical failure is less severe.

Comparative Rating of Casein Glue with Synthetic Resin Glues

The dominant position of casein glue for wood was maintained during post-World War I years though competition for the more durable work resulted from the emergence of another protein glue, i.e., soluble blood albumin. However when the chemists of Europe showed industry in the early 1930's how to make durable adhesives by reacting urea with formaldehyde at attractive costs and soon thereafter introduced phenol-formaldehyde resin in film form for additional boost in durability, casein was relegated to only a modest share in the business of gluing wood.

Selbo[102] compared casein with seven other plywood glues. In atmospheres not exceeding 65 per cent relative humidity, the casein glue, which contained no preservative, held up better in 3 or more years of exposure than some of the resin glues, particularly the urea resin glues. Exposure to high or low temperature alone was not particularly damaging to casein glue. It was only in very damp atmospheres and on soaking that casein glue failed rapidly, and it was here alone that the phenolic glues showed marked superiority.

Durability of Casein Glue with Preservative

When glued joints are exposed continuously to high humidity, both wood and glue are attacked by fungi and bacteria. Under this condition the performance of casein glue can be improved by incorporating preservative chemicals in the glue, or by impregnating the wood with preservatives. Beta-naphthol at 10 parts to 100 parts of casein or creosote at 20 parts are effective additions to casein glue and delay complete failure in moisture-saturated atmosphere. Impregnation of plywood

with creosote or beta-naphthol, after gluing, prevents loss of strength. Coating the plywood with asphalt paint or with aluminum paint is effective if the specimens are exposed to dampness only for short intervals as would be the case with plywood exposed to the weather.

Selbo[102] modified water-resistant casein glue by adding 5 per cent pentachlorophenol, glued birch plywood and determined the durability of specimens for a 2-yr period. The addition of a preservative had a delaying action on failure, except at highest humidity.

Tested in plywood-to-framing members, the casein glue with preservative withstood as well as hotpressed phenolic resin in dry-wet cycles up to 90 per cent relative humidity, and held up better than the room temperature-setting urea resin. Bergin[11] found casein glue more durable than urea resin glue at 194°F.

Selbo concludes from the plywood tests: "Casein glue is not considered suitable for exterior use in house construction or for interior use where the moisture content of the wood may be expected to exceed about 20 per cent for repeated or prolonged periods."

Joint Strength of Plywood Made from Treated Veneers

Kaufert and Hutchins[61] made plywood by cold-press gluing veneers of birch, sweet gum-spruce, and mahogany-spruce, which had been surface treated by immersion in oil solution of pentachlorophenol or other chlorinated phenol before gluing. On the majority of treated veneers, no significant differences were observed between casein glue, urea-formaldehyde resin, and resorcinol-formaldehyde resin.

Durability of Casein Glue in Laminated Beams

Southern pine beams laminated with casein glue containing no preservative lost all strength in 4 yr of outdoor exposure; whereas Douglas fir beams laminated with the same glue retained most of their strength after 8 yr of exposure.[102] A review of gluing conditions revealed that the fir beams had been glued at a substantially lower moisture content than the pine beams; this is offered as an explanation for the difference in durability.

Laminations are satisfactorily glued with casein glue over a wide range of moisture content of the wood and with wood temperature as low as 40°F.[34] Teak, pine, and yew are strongly bonded with casein glue because of its high alkalinity. Casein glue also has gap-filling properties; thus it forms a good bond on rougher surfaces as well as on planed surfaces. Prepared casein glue containing a preservative and meeting the requirements of Federal Specification MMM-A-125[122] is entirely adequate for gluing laminations for interior installation, or wherever the moisture content of the wood does not increase to more than approximately 20 per cent at which point deterioration by fungi may begin.[78, 111] Casein-glued laminates may be post-treated with organic preservatives, either creosote or pentachlorophenol in oil without losing strength;[89] aqueous solutions of preservatives do weaken the glue line, however.

A report from the Forest Products Laboratory of Canada[21, 62] showed casein glue to be initially stronger than urea-formaldehyde resin in spruce/spruce, pine/pine, fir/fir laminates, as well as in combinations of these species, and that planed surfaces gave the laminate higher strength than sawn surfaces. The Princes Risborough Laboratory in England has also completed long-time exposure tests on laminates made with casein glue with preservatives.[66] Jessome in Canada[57] investigated the efficiency of scarf joints as used in lengthening laminated members, and Stevens measured the shape accuracy of bent work made with different glues concluding that bent work accuracy was somewhat higher with resin than with casein glue. The U. S. Forest Products Laboratory[117] investigated the effect of dimension of the laminations of white oak on the strength and durability of the glue bond.

Durability of Casein Glue in Assembly Joints

An investigation of assembly glues was made at the U. S. Forest Products Laboratory in cooperation with the Office of Quartermaster General, Department of the Army. This agency supplies office and field equipment as well as furniture to widely separated world bases; moreover the glue joints are required to hold up under wide variations in climatic conditions. Provisions for the test were:

(1) Hard maple specimens glued at room temperature with casein glue, animal glue, or with one of five types of resin glues.

(2) Periodic determination of joint strength and wood failure for seven types of assembly joints, which are sketched by the authors.[103]

(3) Exposure for 3 yr to humidity cycles in which a damp period of 65, 80 or 90 per cent relative humidity for 4 wk is alternated with a dry period of 30 per cent humidity for 4 wk.

The data for the casein glue containing 5 per cent of pentachlorophenol as preservative are given in Table 1.

TABLE 1. RETAINED STRENGTH OF CASEIN GLUE JOINTS WITH PRESERVATIVE IN ASSEMBLY JOINTS AFTER 3 YEARS EXPOSURE.*

	(%)	(%)	(%)
High humidity (4 wk)	65	80	90
Low humidity (4 wk)	30	30	30
Type of Joint	Retained Strength		
	(%)		
Dowel	100	10	21
Mortice-Tenon	63	52	18
Block	48	10	1
Slip or lock	95	84	28
End grain-side grain	100	57	14
Side grain-side grain	100	—	81

* From Selbo and Olson.[103]

The initial strength of the casein glue in these assembly joints was generally lower than that attained by the synthetic glues; furthermore when exposed to high humidity, the casein glue lost strength faster than the synthetic glues. The comparative performance of the casein glue varied, however, with the design of the joint, the design most favorable to casein glue being side grain-to-side grain. Other designs favored the synthetic glues, particularly the thermoplastic polyvinyl-acetate emulsion glue and the resorcinol-formaldehyde resin glue.

Resistance of Casein Glue Joints to Vibration

Although dry casein glue is hard and brittle, joints made with it have been subjected for 40 hr to high frequency vibration without showing loss of strength. Olson and co-workers[90] studied the resistance of casein glue in lap joints to fatigue stressing. Glue lines 0.02 in. thick held up better than glue lines only 0.002 in. thick, though initial shear strength was higher for the thinner glue line.

SUMMARY—CASEIN GLUE IN WOODWORKING

Casein glue is used principally by the woodworking industries, where it is in competition with other glues. Its cost is higher than starch and soybean glues but lower than animal glues, blood albumin, or most resin glues. Casein glue is superior to starch in water resistance and speed of setting after a joint is made. While soybean glues are also water resistant, they are not as satisfactory as casein glues for making strong joints in the denser hardwoods. Animal glues and the polyvinyl emulsion glues are particularly adaptable to assembly gluing with short assembly periods and to the gluing of thin veneers where penetration of an alkaline glue may cause staining. Liquid animal and fish glues are convenient for repair work and household use; also prepared casein glues are marketed by retail stores for home use. Blood albumin glue is somewhat more water resistant than casein glue, but the highly water-resistant formulas require hot pressing; consequently their use is limited to plywood and veneered panels. Where the highest degree of water resistance is required, hot-pressed thermosetting phenol-formaldehyde or cold-pressed resorcinol-formaldehyde resin glues are currently in use. In general, casein glue may be chosen when a moderate degree of water resistance is required in cold pressing at a relatively low cost. Commercial categories of gluing which employ casein or casein-blend glues largely for this reason include lumber laminating, sash and door work, furniture plywood and veneered panels, as well as assembly and cabinet work. The general properties of casein glues used in these products are listed in Table 2.

Casein glues of government specification grades are those that meet the requirements of Federal Specification MMM-A-125[122] for wet strength (Type I) or strength after exposure to fungi (Type II). Type II glues contain a preservative and are used primarily for lumber laminating as described below. For general plywood, casein glue has been largely replaced by resins or blend glues not containing casein. A disadvantage of cold-pressed casein glue is that it introduces water into the wood plies, and good practice therefore dictates that, when casein glue is used, the plywood be dried after gluing.[94]

Hollow flush doors for interior installation are often glued with casein glue[120] or low cost blended glues containing casein. These glues give a good bond to birch or gum wood, or to hardboard; moreover they are so formulated that the required pressure period is shortened to as little as 30 min, thus earning them the sobriquet of "no-clamp glues." The short pressure period is followed by a period of "dead stacking" for several hours. Solid slab flush doors may be cored with laminations employing casein glue of Type I for edge-gluing the laminations.

Furniture plywood and veneering may be made with casein glue when more water resistance is sought than that provided by starch, animal glue, or resin emulsions. Assembly gluing of furniture was considered under "Durability of Wood Joints." In this category of gluing, the relatively high proportion of water to dry glue, compared to animal glue and vinyl emulsions, has militated against general usage, despite the better moisture resistance of the casein glue line. Casein glue holds a small position here, however, in the gluing of piano frames, caskets, butchers' blocks, cabinets, etc.

Home Building and Repairs

Casein and casein-blended glues find use in home building, in structural plywood for house sheathing, and for interior plywood. The additional protection against moisture possessed by the resin glues has brought them to the fore in exterior plywood; in fact, interior plywood can be more cheaply bonded with blend glues not containing casein. Most gluing in the building industry is done in plywood and millwork plants which supply units to be assembled on-the-job. The gluing technique is too exacting to be done adequately and economically by hand. Experimentation in construction methods led to the gluing of plywood

TABLE 2. CASEIN GLUES FOR WOODWORKING.

	Lumber Laminate Gov't Specs.	General Plywood Sash and Door	Furniture Plywood and Veneering	Assembly Cabinet
Contains preservative	yes	seldom	no	no
Contains filler	seldom	yes	yes	yes
Water ratio	1:2	1:2	1:2	1:2
Working life, hr	4 to 8	6 to 10	8 to 12	16+
Spread, lb/1000 sq ft	70 to 100	70 to 100	60 to 80	70 to 90
Maximum assembly time, min	20	20	30	40
Pressure, psi	50 to 250	50 to 250	50 to 250	50 to 250
Staining tendency	yes	yes	mild	very mild
Abrasive to tools	yes	yes	slightly	very slightly

walls directly to studs,[20] joining plywood wall panels by gluing splines at the joints,[18] and joining prefabricated wall units with glue. Much of this type of gluing has been done with water-resistant casein glues. A symposium entitled "Adhesives and Sealants in Buildings," sponsored by the Building Research Institute in 1958,[29] refers in several papers to the current use of casein glue in home construction. In the experimental prefabricated houses put up at the U.S. Forest Products Laboratory in 1935, and still in service, the plywood was glued to the framework with casein glue.

Home gluing of small wood parts can be done with prepared casein glue, which is put up in small packages for the householder. Repairs of furniture involving laminating, edge-gluing, dowelling, and mortice-and-tenon work are done with casein glue.

Laminating Lumber

Casein glue has regained a leading position in the woodworking industry as a result of its application in the gluing of lumber laminations for interior installation. Glue laminated lumber is defined[48] as "sawn wood laminations glued with grain parallel, the members being straight or curved, and face- or edge-glued." Construction of this kind makes it possible to use wood more economically for structural support over long spans. Large laminated columns, beams and arches are made of kiln-dried wood laminations, and select and common grades can be combined within the members in such a way as to achieve satisfactory utilization of the lumber without loss in strength from defects.

Some of the more striking examples of the functional side of this type of construction[49] include the Parr-Franconia Warehouse in Franconia, Virginia, the U.S. Naval Ordnance Station in Inyokern, California, the Union College Field House in Schenectady, New York, the Billy Graham Auditorium in Detroit, Michigan, and the U.S. Coast Guard Drill Hall in New London, Connecticut. One of the earliest structures, using casein-glued laminated arches 46 ft long, is the storage shed built in 1935 on the U.S. Forest Products Laboratory property in Madison, Wisconsin.[58] A very early construction laminated with casein glue was a 10-ft beam made in Bainbridge, New York in 1933[79] and tested at the University of Illinois.

Complementing the economical and purely functional advantages of the laminated type of construction is an esthetic value which is being exploited by alert architects and builders. Modern exotic building shapes have been made possible by constructions that are continuous for long spans, and which can be shaped by bending to produce beautiful contours impossible with sawn lumber.[74] Quoting Hanrahan of the American Institute of Timber Construction in 1954: "Glued laminated lumber is a new and superior structural material giving fresh scope to architecture and engineering, resulting in a Renaissance in Wood, a Revolution in Architecture, and a New Era in Wood Utilization."

For many years glued laminated structures were being erected in Europe, employing casein glue prior to the first structure made in the United States. The glue lines of these structures had remained sound for 30 yr when inspected in 1939,[40, 131] except where they might have come in contact with damp earth or where the moisture content of the laminate exceeded 20 per cent. Even laminated members as a part of the construction in locomotive repair shops and chemical plants remained sound, indicating good resistance of the casein glue line to coal and chemical fumes; also footbridges and railroad platforms were sound under conditions of good drainage and ventilation. The end uses of casein-glued laminates have now expanded to include trusses, girders, and columns in churches, schools, auditoriums, field houses, hangers, and towers,[41] where the members are not exposed to the weather or exceptionally high humidity. Conversely, waterproof resin glues are required for exposure to high humidity and condensation, e.g., in the ceilings of dairy barns.[116]

Established trade associations in the lumber field are active in support or progress in lumber laminating. The following have issued specifications applying to this type of construction: National Lumber Manufacturers' Association,[84] West Coast Lumbermans' Association,[128] Southern Pine Association,[107] Southern Hardwood Producers,[106] Appalachian Hardwood Manufacturers,[4] and Northern Hemlock and Hardwood Manufacturers Association.[87] Strong leadership in this field is exercised by the American Institute of Timber Construction,[2] founded in 1952, through the issuance of Fabrications Standards, which include the use of casein glues.

CASEIN ADHESIVES FOR BONDING PAPER

Here attention is turned from lime-containing casein glues for wood to casein-based adhesives for paper.[53] For the most part these are combinations of adhesives comprising casein solution as a major ingredient compounded with latex or resin emulsions and hardening chemicals other than lime to provide water-resistant bonds. Important packaging applications include bottle labeling, foil laminating, cap-liner laminating, cigarette pasting, match-book striker strips, and other paper-bonding operations. In all these applications the adhesive is of a low degree of alkalinity, often neutral or even slightly acidic. Of course, the reaction of these adhesives does not approach the pH of the isoelectric point of casein.

Foil and Paper Laminating

A rapidly developing packaging material is the aluminum foil-to-paper laminate. Ammoniacal casein solutions are compounded with latex of the styrene-butadiene or neoprene type to a predetermined and carefully controlled viscosity[64] so that they can be applied by machine as a continuous film at a fast rate of bonding to provide a water-resistant bond almost instantaneously. The adhesive must have no deteriorating effect on aluminum over long storage periods and for many applications must be free from color, odor, and toxic ingredients. Machine application and joining require a balance of rheological properties in the adhesive so that it will not "string" or "throw" on the machine, or foam, coagulate or skin over.[76] Aluminum foil is bonded occasionally to glassine, rubber, fiber glass, asbestos, vulcanized fiber, masonite, plastic sheet, and tissue paper, for which laminates casein-containing adhesives have been satisfactory.

Cap-liner stock is a paper laminate which can utilize casein compositions comprising resin emulsions to provide a bond that does not soften on contact with water or oils. Here also the rheological properties of the glue must be controlled to permit easy application on fast-running laminating machines.

Pastes for Bottle and Can Labels

Casein pastes for labels occupy a position of some importance in providing moisture-resistant paper-to-glass and paper-to-metal bonds that are relatively inexpensive. These pastes are solutions of casein from which the bond acquires water resistance at relatively low degrees of alkalinity by reaction of the casein with metallic salts or oxides.[6, 63, 68, 129] Rubber and rosin are possible ingredients;[80] moreover casein may be incorporated in the label paper to facilitate in the alkaline washing of returned bottles.[85] Casein pastes for labeling beer and soft drink bottles give a good bond and the labels do not fall off easily in damp atmospheres or when immersed in ice water. The glues must be adaptable to high-speed operations on specially designed labeling machines and possess quick tack for both paper and foil laminated labels. Great skill in formulation is thus required.

Paper labels can be applied to tin cans with a composition comprising casein and sodium resinate,[8] or with a casein solution containing sodium borophosphate.[55]

Other Paper Bonds Employing Casein

Casein is employed in special paper products applications in large fields of adhesive usage[59] where other materials may predominate. Mention is made[73] of paper-bag seaming where casein adhesives provide especially strong wet tack and a degree of water resistance. Case-sealing for rapid setting and water resistances to a degree that meets the requirements of Military Specification MIL-A-101A[113] include: spiral or convolute winding of paperboard to form water-resistant cups, cartons and tubes, and bonding paper cap liners to plastic or wood closures.

Also, casein has been used as a bookbinding adhesive,[99] in combination with vinyl chloride emulsion;[133] to edge-glue paper sheets into pads;[50] to bond paper milk cartons in place of the usual vinyl emulsion adhesives;[70, 96] to adhere waxy paper surfaces with alcohol-soluble casein derivatives,[54] with combinations of casein solutions and emulsions of chlorinated hydrocarbons,[86] or with water-miscible solvents;[88] in mucilage for gluing paper containing bentonite and cellulose;[82] in gluing "Papreg," the resin-impregnated paper developed at the U. S. Forest Products Laboratory;[35, 36] in laminating paperboard;[7, 17] as an adhesive for food packages[38, 46] and for cellophane.[22] Casein in dry, soluble form for compounding adhesives such as these was made available by extrusion with alkaline salts.[31, 32, 33] Casein is often compounded with resin emulsions for paper bonding operations. These compositions meet all requirements as to stability, machining properties, viscosity and tack, and they cure to permanent, flexible, water-resistant bonds.

The adhesive that bonds the abrasive to the edge of match-book covers may be an alkaline casein solution chosen for a moderate degree of water resistance. An important requirement of this bond is rapid curing of the rolled-on-strip to enable subsequent operations to occur without interruption of production.

The adhesive which holds the seam of a cigarette together is often an alkaline casein solution, also comprising wax to provide a moderate degree of water resistance. The requirements with respect to application are most demanding for cigarettes are seamed at an amazing speed; consequently the bond must set in the few seconds allowed between forming and packing. Also, the bond cannot contain ingredients that might give objectionable color or flavor to the cigarette.

CASEIN ADHESIVES FOR BONDING DISSIMILAR MATERIALS OTHER THAN PAPER

The field of adhesives for dissimilar materials has been an inviting one for both scientists and inventors. Reinhart and Callomon[100] in a survey of adhesives and adhesion provide a useful list of dissimilar adherend combinations most of which are commonly bonded with elastomeric materials, which may contain casein. De Lollis and co-workers[28] included casein glue in a comprehensive investigation of the comparative strength of adhesives in adherend systems comprising metals, glass,[104, 124] and rubber as well as wood and paper. Among the adherend combinations that are or have been bonded with casein-elastomer emulsion mixed adhesives are:[100] metal sheet-to-wood, cork-to-metal, cork-to-wood,[42] linoleum-to-wood[56] ceramic tile-to-wood, plastic sheet- to-wood, paper-to-stainless steel, corrugated board-to-metal, plastic-to-glass, vulcanized fiber-to-"Mylar," wood-to-stone,[92] vinyl sheet-to-plywood, and "Celluloid"-to-glass.[127]

Plymetal is plywood or hardboard with sheet metal glued to one or both faces, which may be bonded with casein glue to form panels for heat insulation, outdoor signs, truck bodies, and store fronts. The glue may be used either as a primer coat for other adhesives or as the adhesive itself.[67, 71] Wood veneer may be glued with casein glue to metal fire doors, elevator cabs, and other places where fireproof construction is required but where the decorative effect of wood is also desired. Plywood-to-metal bonded combinations are especially interesting because they possess greater stiffness and resistance to buckling than shown by metal alone.[37] In metal-to-wood bonding the casein bond is insufficiently elastic; however it is improved and made durable by the inclusion of latex or neoprene in the glue formula. The machine application of an adhesive for bonding metal to plywood requires close control of rheological properties, which depend primarily on the pH of the glue.

USE OF CASEIN TO MODIFY OTHER ADHESIVES

Combinations of casein with other proteins have been described as blended glues for wood. In a different category are the latex adhesives, either of natural or synthetic origin, which may contain casein as stabilizer or modifier. Latices of neoprene and nitrile rubber are frequently compounded with casein for adhesive purposes.[9, 27] The latex has a softening effect, whereas the casein hardens the glue line. The insolubility of casein in systems of pH 4 to 5 eliminates any use in conventional vinyl glues and adhesives. Latex adhesives proper are discussed in Chapter 35 of this book, and casein-latex adhesives for paper were discussed earlier in this chapter. An early use of casein with natural latex was as the "tie gum" to strengthen the bond of rubber to synthetic fiber tire cord. This adhesive combination is currently largely replaced by latex-resin compounds.[125] Latex-casein mixtures may serve as primers for other adhesives.[105] Rosin emulsions containing casein form a good bond between fabric and metal.[91] There are many patents claiming latex-casein adhesives.[12, 26, 77] Latex-casein adhesives may be used as the priming coat on cellophane tape over which pressure-sensitive adhesive is applied,[81] and casein-shellac combinations may be the nonadhesive backing coat on this type of adhesive tape.[39]

Combinations of casein with thermosetting resins are described in patents. The few that have been applied commercially include combinations with phenolic resins of the resole or water-dispersion type with casein and with urea-formaldehyde or other amino resin[5, 44, 45] in which casein either takes part in the resin condensation reaction[25, 72, 108] or is merely mixed in solution with the preformed resin.[23, 24] Since these resin glues contain free formaldehyde, mixtures with casein solution are stable only at pH values in the narrow range of 6 to 7.

ANALYTICAL METHODS APPLIED TO CASEIN GLUE

Casein glue, with its components of protein, salts and alkalies, organic fillers and oils, is easily separated into three fractions by merely dispersing the dry glue in chloroform.[95, 97] There appears a mineral sediment, a chloroform solution of the oils, and a floating fraction containing the casein, wood flour or other filler, together with other proteins if the glue is a blend glue. The ions are determined in the sediment; the oils in the chloroform solution; and the proteins in the upper layer. Through the microscope soy protein in the upper layer may be identified by the presence of soybean hull or kernel fragments.[93]

Casein and blood albumin are distinguishable in a glue line by viewing a cross section mounted in glycerol under crossed nicols.[101] The casein glue line is colorless, whereas the blood glue is green. Any casein in admixture with blood gives a sparkling appearance. Staining the glue line with a mixed solution of methylene blue and rosin in 50 per cent alcohol solution produces a purplish pink color with casein and a wine red color with blood glue.

The presence of casein in wood and its depth of penetration from the glue line can be detected by soaking the wetted wood in a solution comprising 4 g hematoxylin in 25 ml alcohol, 400 ml saturated ammonium alum solution, 100 ml glycerol, and 100 ml methyl alcohol.[130] Wood sections containing casein assume a violet color even after formaldehyde treatment. The usual protein color reactions do not develop with casein which has been treated with formaldehyde.

GOVERNMENT AND INDUSTRY SPECIFICATIONS FOR CASEIN GLUES AND ADHESIVES

The more frequently used specifications under which casein glues and adhesives are purchased and tested by government agencies or by industry are listed below for ready reference. The list also includes specifications for glued products. Federal Specifications, U. S. General Services Administration, Washington, D. C.

MMM-A-125: Adhesives, Casein-Type, Water- and Mold-Resistant
MMM-A-175: Adhesives; Methods of Testing
NN-P-515a: Plywood, Container Grade
NN-P-530: Plywood, Flat-panel
LLL-A-581: Doors, Exterior and Interior Wood, Flush Type, Veneered
PPP-B-566: Boxes, Folding, Paperboard

Military Specifications, U. S. Department, Army, Washington, D. C.

MIL-A-101A: Adhesive, Water-resistant, for Sealing Fiberboard Boxes
MIL-A-140A: Adhesive, Water-resistant, Waterproof Barrier Material

Commercial Standards, U. S. Department Commerce, Office of Technical Services, Washington, D.C.

CS-35-56: Hardwood Plywood
CS-45-55: Douglas Fir Plywood
CS-122-56: Western Softwood Plywood
CS-120-58: Ponderosa Pine Doors
CS-171-50: Hardwood Veneered Flush Doors
CS-200-55: Hardwood Veneered Hollow-Core Flush Doors

Douglas Fir Plywood Association, Tacoma, Washington

Same as commercial Standards CS-45-55 and CS-122-56 above

American Institute of Timber Construction, Washington, D.C.

Section 900: Guide Specifications-Structural Timber Framing
Section 901.1e: Adhesives
Section 1000: Heavy Timber Construction
AITC Sa 11.06: Selection of Adhesives

American Society for Testing Materials, Philadelphia, Pennsylvania. Standard Methods.

D-1084: Consistency of Adhesives
D-1338: Working Life of Liquid or Paste Adhesives
D-1183: Resistance of Adhesives for Wood to Cyclic Laboratory Aging Conditions
D-1174: Effect of Bacteria on Permanence of Adhesives and Adhesive Bonds
D-1286: Effect of Mold Contamination of Permanence of Adhesives
D-1151: Effect of Moisture and Temperature on Adhesive Bonds
D-805: Testing Veneer, Plywood, and Other Glued Veneer Constructions
D-906: Strength Properties of Adhesives in Plywood Construction
D-905: Strength Properties of Adhesives in Shear by Compression Loading
D-1344: Cross-Lap Specimens for Tensile Properties of Adhesives
D-1101: Integrity of Glue Joints in Laminated Wood Products
D-1580: Adhesives for Automatic Machine Labeling of Glass Bottles
D-1581: Bonding Permanency of Adhesives for Labeling Glass Bottles

British Standards Institute: Cold-setting Casein Glue for Wood, British Standard 1444:1948

Canadian Standards Association: Specification for Glued Laminated Timber Construction, Ottawa, Canada

Reichsausschuss für Lieferbedingungen: Lieferbedingungen und Prüfverfahren für pülverformige Kaseinkaltleime, Nr. 093c., Berlin, Germany

References

1. American Cyanamid Co., "Dicyandiamide in Pastes and Glues," New York, 1949.
2. American Institute Timber Construction, "Inspection Manual for Structural Glued Laminated Lumber," Washington, D. C.
3. American Society for Testing Materials, "ASTM Standards," Part 6, Philadelphia, Pa., 1958.
4. Appalachian Hardwood Manufrs., Inc., "Standard Specifications for Design and Fabrication of Hardwood Glued Laminated Lumber for Structural, Marine and Vehicular Uses," Cincinnati, Ohio.
5. Arnot, R., British Patent 225,953 (Sept. 15, 1923).
6. Atkinson, J. D., (to The Buckeye Cellulose Corp.), U. S. Patent 2,848,342 (Aug. 19, 1958).

7. Bain, W. M., (to The Glidden Co.), U. S. Patent 2,637,675 (May 5, 1953).

8. Becher, Carl, *Gelatine, Leim, Klebstoffe,* **3,** 163 (1935).

9. Becker, R. O., "Neoprene Latex Type 635," Du-Pont Rept. 57–2, 1957.

10. Bergin, E. G., *Canadian Woodworker* (Dec. 1953).

11. Bergin, E. G., Forest Products Lab. Canada, Tech. Note 8, 1958.

12. Biddle, Arthur, (to United Products Corp. of America), U. S. Patents 1,777,157–62 (Sept. 30, 1930).

13. Blomquist, R. F., A.S.T.M. Symposium: "Testing Adhesives for Durability and Permanence" STP No. 138, 1952.

14. Bogue, R. H., "Chemistry and Technology of Gelatin and Glue," New York, McGraw-Hill Publishing Co., 1922.

15. Bradshaw, L., and Dunham, H. V., U. S. Patent 1,703,134 (Feb. 26, 1929).

16. Bradshaw, L., and Dunham, H. V., (to The Casein Mfg. Co. of America, Inc.), U. S. Patents 1,829,258–9 (Oct. 27, 1931).

17. Bronson, F. L., (to The Fibre Can and Machinery Co.), U. S. Patent 2,300,907 (Nov. 3, 1942).

18. Brouse, D., U. S. Forest Products Lab. Rept. R 1125, 1931.

19. de Bruyne, N. A., and Houwink, R., "Adhesion and Adhesives," Elsevier Publishing Co., 1951.

20. Butterman, S., *J. Ind. Eng. Chem.,* **12,** 141 (1920).

21. Canadian Forest Products Laboratory, "Canadian Woods," Ottawa, Edmond Cloutier, 1951.

22. Charch, W. H., and Snyder, J. E., (to Du Pont Cellophane Co., Inc.), U. S. Patent 1,929,013 (Oct. 3, 1933).

23. Christopher, E. F., (to Industrial Patents Corp.), U. S. Patent 1,962,763 (June 12, 1934).

24. Ciba Ltd., Swiss Patent 248,194 (Jan. 16, 1948).

25. Ciba Ltd., Swiss Patent 248,212 (Jan. 16, 1948).

26. Clarke, R. B. F. F., Robinson, E. B., and Shepherdson, A., (to Imperial Chemical Industries, Ltd.), U. S. Patent 1,978,247 (Oct. 23, 1934).

27. Dede, J. B., and Watson, D. A., (to Monsanto Chemical Co.) U. S. Patent 2,862,896 (Dec. 2, 1958).

28. DeLollis, N. J., Rucker, N., and Wier, J. E., Natl. Advisory Comm. Aeronautics Tech. Note 1863. 1949.

29. Dietz, A. G. H., Building Research Inst., Publ. 577, Washington, D. C. 1958.

30. Dunham, H. V., U. S. Patent 1,892,486 (Dec. 27, 1932).

31. Dunham, H. V., U. S. Patent 2,005,730 (June 25, 1935); British Patent 453,305 (Sept. 8, 1936).

32. Dunham, H. V., U. S. Patent 2,103,153 (Dec. 21, 1937).

33. Dunham, H. V., U. S. Patent 2,108,582 (Feb. 15, 1938).

34. Eby, R. E., Building Research Inst., Publ. 577, Washington, D. C. 1958.

35. Eickner, H. W., U. S. Forest Products Lab. Bull. 1348, 1944.

36. Eickner, H. W., U. S. Forest Products Lab. Bull. 1538, 1950.

37. Eickner, H. W., and Blomquist, R. F., U. S. Forest Products Lab. Bull. R1768, 1951.

38. Franchi, F. A. R., Swiss Patent 259,447 (June 16, 1949).

39. Franer, V. R., and Steinhauser, A. H., (to Minnesota Mining & Mfg. Co.), U. S. Patent 2,785,087 (Mar. 12, 1957).

40. Freas, A. D., *ASTM Bull.* No. 170, 1950.

41. Freas, A. D., and Selbo, M. L., U. S. Dept. Agric. Bull. 1069, 1954.

42. Frink, N. S., McManus, C. E., and Weisenburg, A., U. S. Patents 2,121,791; 2,121,809–810; 2,121,844 (June 28, 1938).

43. Genin, G., *Lait* **30,** 574–8 (1950).

44. Golick, A. J., and Dike, T. W., (to I. F. Laucks, Inc.), U. S. Patent 2,368,466 (Jan. 30, 1945).

45. Golick, A. J., and Maas, J. J., (to Monsanto Chem. Co.), U. S. Patent 2,537,343 (Jan. 9, 1951).

46. Hall, W. A., U. S. Patent 609,200 (Aug. 16, 1898).

47. Hall, W. A., U. S. Patent 684,545 (Oct. 15, 1901).

48. Hanrahan, F. J., *Southern Bldg.* (Nov. 1954).

49. Hanrahan, F. J., *Southern Lumberman* (Dec. 15, 1954).

50. Healy, L. J. D., (to The Lee Hardware Co.), U. S. Patent 1,966,389 (July 10, 1934).

51. Higgins, H. G., Fraser, D., and Hayes, J. F. *Nature,* **169,** 1020 (1952).

52. Higgins, H. G., and Plomley, K. F., *Australian J. Applied Sci.,* **1,** 1 (1950).

53. Holt, F., *Paper Ind.,* **17,** 656 (1935).

54. Howard, H. W., and Salzberg, H. K., (to The Borden Co.), U. S. Patents 2,748,009; 2,750,374 (June 12, 1956).

55. Iddings, C., (to The Muralo Co., Inc), U. S. Patent 2,133,098 (Oct. 11, 1938.).

56. I. G. Farbenindustrie A-G., German Patent 577,885 (June 6, 1933).

57. Jessome, A. P., Forest Products Lab. Canada, Tech. Note 9, 1958.

58. Johnson, R. P. A., Building Research Inst. Publ. 577, Washington, D. C., 1958.

59. Jones, S., in "Adhesion and Adhesives," New York, John Wiley & Sons, 1954.

60. Kaufert, F. H., U. S. Forest Products Lab. Bull. 1332, 1943.

61. Kaufert, F. H., and Hutchins, W. F., U. S. Forest Products Lab. Bull. 1484, 1945.

62. Kennedy, D. E., Forest Products Lab., Canada. Mimeo 0–152, 1950.

63. Kinney, W. B., (to The Borden Co.), U. S. Patent 2,570,561 (Oct. 9, 1951).

64. Kinney, W. B., (to The Borden Co.), U. S. Patent 2,754,240 (July 10, 1956).

65. Knight, R. A. G., "Glues and Gluing Progress, Rept. 35," Princess Risborough, England, 1944.

66. Knight, R. A. G., Doman, L. S., and Soane, "Glues and Gluing Progress Rept. 47," Princess Risborough, England, 1948.

67. Koehn, G. W., Building Research Inst. Publ. 577, Washington, D. C., 1958.

68. Landecker, M., U.S. Patent 1,725,805 (Aug. 27, 1929).

69. Lee, W. B., *Ind. Eng. Chem.*, **22**, 778 (1930).

70. Leibfarth, R., Brit. Patent 362,011 (Sept. 10, 1930).

71. Leicester, W. R., "Influence of Modern Glues on the Utilization of Wood," Wood Products Conf., Syracuse, N. Y.

72. Leonardson, C. S., and White, D. J., (to The Borden Co.), U.S. Patent 2,332,519 (Oct, 26, 1943).

73. Lodge, R. J., "Casein Adhesives," *Modern Packaging (Encylopedia Issue)*, 1959.

74. Lundy, V., *Time*, (Apr. 4, 1960).

75. Luxford, R. F., and Krone, R. H., U.S. Forest Products Lab. Bull. R1622, 1946.

76. Lyon, J. R., *Fibre Containers and Paperboard Mills*, 110–116 (Feb. 1954).

77. McGavack, J., and Nikitin, A. A., (to The Naugatuck Chemical Co.), U.S. Patent 1,932,632 (Oct. 31, 1933).

78. MacLagan, C. F., "Laminated Structures—Adhesives," Forest Products Research Soc., Northeast Section, 1953.

79. MacLagan, C. F., "Future of Glues and Gluing," Am. Inst. Timber Construction, Annual Meeting, 1954.

80. Mark, J. G., (to Dewey & Almy Chemical Co.), U.S. Patent 2,279,256 (Apr. 7, 1942).

81. Minnesota Mining and Manufacturing Co., British Patent 427,700 (Apr. 23, 1935).

82. Mummery, W. R., *New Zealand J. Sci. Technol.*, **27B**, 55 (1945).

83. Narayanamurti, D., and Handa, B. K., *Kolloid-Z.*, **135**, 140 (1954).

84. National Lumber Manufacturers Assoc., "National Design Specification for Stress-grade Lumber and its Fastenings," Washington, D. C.

85. Nestor, L. R., (to Minnesota Mining & Mfg. Co.), U.S. Patent 2,654,171 (Oct. 6, 1953).

86. Noakes, H. F., and Martyn, J. R., (to E. I. du Pont de Nemours & Co.), U.S. Patent 2,436,596 (Feb. 24, 1948).

87. Northern Hemlock and Hardwood Manufacturers Assoc., "Standard Specification for the Design and Fabrication of Hardwood Glued Laminated Lumber for Structural, Marine and Vehicular Uses," Oshkosh, Wis.

88. N. V. de Bataafsche Petroleum Maatschappij, Dutch Patent 77,638 (Apr. 15, 1955).

89. Oliver, W. A., "Tests on Glued Laminated Wood Beams Impregnated with Cresote," *Am. Soc. Testing Materials, Preprint No. 99*, 1941.

90. Olson, W. Z., Bensend, D. W., and Bruce, H. D., U.S. Forest Products Lab. Bull. 1539; 1946.

91. Opie, W. J., in "Adhesion and Adhesives," New York, John Wiley & Sons, Inc., 1954.

92. Ott, W., and Dannegger, K., Swiss Patent 253,481 (Nov. 16, 1948).

93. Pangaro, Eva F., private communication.

94. Perry, T. D., "**Modern** Wood Adhesives," New York, Pitman Publishing Co., 1942.

95. Pfanner, H., *Gelatine, Leim, Klebstoffe*, **4**, 100 (1936).

96. Pichugina, N., and Korsakova, A., *Molochnaya Prom.*, **18**, (4), 36–7 (1957).

97. Pien, J., and Renvoise, G., *Lait*, **25**, 121–44 (1945).

98. Quick, L., "Mechanical Clamp Equipment," Southern Pine Assoc., Annual Meeting, 1953.

99. Rasmussen, R. T., U.S. Patent 2,302,378 (Nov. 17, 1942).

100. Reinhart, F. W., and Callomon, I. G., "Survey of Adhesion and Adhesives," Wright Air Development Center Tech. Report 58–450, 1959.

101. Rendle, B. J., and Franklin, G. L., *J. Soc. Chem. Ind.*, **55**, 105T (1936).

102. Selbo, M. L., *J. Forest Prods. Research Soc.*, **3**, 361 (1949).

103. Selbo, M. L., and Olson, W. Z., *J. Forest Prods. Research Soc.*, **3**, (5), 50 (1953).

104. Shikazono, N., *Rept. Govt. Chem. Ind. Research Inst., Tokyo*, **45**, 119 (1950).

105. Silver, I., *Modern Plastics* (May 1949).

106. Southern Hardwood Producers, "Standard Specifications for the Design and Fabrication of Hardwood Glued Laminated Lumber for Structural, Marine and Vehicular Uses," Memphis, Tenn.

107. Southern Pine Assoc., "Procedure, Equipment and Material Recommendations for Laminating Lumber," Annual Meeting, New Orleans, 1953.

108. Sparre, T., (to The Borden Co.), U.S. Patent 2,279,096 (Apr. 7, 1942).

109. Spellacy, J. R., "Casein Dried and Condensed Whey," San Francisco, Lithotype Process Co., 1953.

110. Sutermeister, Edwin, and Brown, F. L., "Casein and its Industrial Applications," 2nd ed., New York, Reinhold Publishing Corp., 1939.

111. Truax, T. R., Blew, J. O., and Selbo, M. L., *Proc. Am. Wood-Preservers' Assoc.*, 1953.

112. Truax, T. R., and Selbo, M. L., U.S. Forest Products Lab., Bull. D 1729, 1948.

113. U.S. Dept. Army, "Adhesive, Water-Resistant, for Sealing Fiberboard Boxes," Military Spec. MIL-A-101A, 1952.

114. U.S. Forest Products Laboratory, "Occurrence and Removal of Glue Stains," Tech. Note 146.

115. U.S. Forest Products Laboratory, "Testing and Mixing Aircraft Glues," Bull. 1338, 1941.

116. U.S. Forest Products Laboratory, "Durability of Glued Laminated Barn Rafters," Bull. R1232, 1945.

117. U.S. Forest Products Laboratory, "Effect of Width and Thickness of Laminations in Laminated White Oak Beams upon Strength and Durability of the Glue Bond," Bull. 1713, 1948.

118. U.S. Forest Products Laboratory, "Casein Glues: Their Manufacture, Preparation and Application," Bull. D280, 1950.

119. U.S. Forest Products Laboratory, "**Control of Conditions** in Gluing with Protein **and Starch Glues**," Bull. R1340, 1950.

120. U. S. Forest Products Laboratory, "Hollow-Core Flush Doors," Bull. 1983, 1954.

121. U. S. Forest Products Laboratory, "Wood Handbook," Madison, Wis., 1955.

122. U. S. General Services Administration, "Adhesives, Casein-Type, Water- and Mold-Resistant," Federal Spec. MMM-A-125, 1955.

123. U. S. General Services Administration, "Adhesives, Methods of Testing," Federal Spec. MMM-A-175, 1951.

124. Waine, A. C., in "Adhesion and Adhesives," New York, John Wiley & Sons, Inc., 1954.

125. Wake, W. C., in "Adhesion and Adhesives," New York, John Wiley & Sons, Inc., 1954.

126. Wakefield, W. E., Forest Products Lab., Canada, Mimeo No. 121, 1947.

127. Watkins, G. B., and Ryan, J. D., *Ind. Eng. Chem.,* **25,** 1192 (1933).

128. West Coast Lumbermen's Assoc., "Standard Specs for the Design and Fabrication of Structural Glued Laminated Lumber," Portland, Ore.

129. White, T. A. (to National Starch Products, Inc.), U. S. Patent 2,613,155 (Oct. 7, 1952).

130. Whitehead, T. H., *Ind. Eng. Chem.,* Anal. Ed. **5,** 150 (1933).

131. Wilson, T. R. C., "The Glued Laminated Wooden Arch," U. S. Dept. Agric. Tech. Bull. 691, 1939.

132. Wormell, R. L., *Nature,* **167,** 817 (1951).

133. Zhdanova, L. G., and Yurshenko, A. I., *Poligraf. Proizvodstvo,* **26,** 7 (1948).

134. Zoller, H. F., *J. Gen. Physiol.,* **3,** 635 (1921).

—— 10 ——

Soybean Glues

Alan L. Lambuth
Monsanto Chemical Co.
Seattle, Washington

Soybeans are the seeds of a leguminous, low-growing vine of the Glycine family. They occur one to several in a tough pod and are ripened and harvested in much the same manner as other field-grown beans. Although native to eastern Asia, soybeans are now extensively hybridized and grown as a major crop in many areas of the world where climatic conditions are favorable.

Dried soybeans are similar in appearance to the familiar navy bean except for their color, which ranges from green or yellow to mottled brown or black. Containing unusually large quantities of protein and triglyceride oils when mature, they are classified as oleaginous seeds. It is this combined assay of useful materials that makes soybeans such a unique and valuable crop resource.

Soybeans have been of great importance to man as a food for several thousand years; in fact, the earliest written record of their planting dates from nearly 3,000 B. C.[1] The Chinese considered soybeans the most valuable cultivated legume and one of the five sacred grains essential to the existence of their civilization. Soybeans are still an important food staple for both man and animal in most parts of the world, and by far the greatest percentage of soybeans grown today is used for nutritional purposes.

The use of soybean flour for adhesives and binders is a recent development in view of its long history as a food. This development was pioneered about 30 years ago by Otis Johnson,[2] Glenn Davidson, and I. F. Laucks.[3] It required a supply of soybean meal from which the oil had been extracted without altering the solubility of its protein, the principal adhesive ingredient. The original soybean meal for this purpose was a special hydraulic-pressed product imported from Manchuria. It contained a fair amount of residual oil that acted as a defoaming agent in the ultimate soybean glue. Since that time, the domestic soybean milling industry has been largely converted to moderate temperature processing and solvent extraction of the soybean oil. Currently this industry provides ample quantities of soluble oil-free soybean meal and purified soybean oil, which has become an important world commodity in its own right.

The soybean adhesives industry based on the discoveries of Davidson and Laucks has grown and diversified steadily over the years; however the technology has remained much the same. The annual consumption of soybean flour in wood adhesives, as opposed to paper coating adhesives, increased to a peak of about 60 million pounds during the early 1940's; subsequently it declined gradually to an average level of about 30 million pounds after World War II, primarily under the impact of synthetic resin adhesives and the growing demand for all-weather plywood. By 1950 the use of soybean adhesives was again increasing steadily, reaching a new peak of almost 100 million pounds in 1956 and remaining nearly constant to the present.[4] Although a long-term decline in consumption from this tremendous volume is anticipated, soybean glues are expected to remain an indispensable portion of the adhesive spectrum, contributing heavily in many phases of the wood utilization industry.

REQUIREMENTS FOR ADHESIVE-GRADE SOYBEAN FLOUR

To become a useful base for adhesives, whole soybeans must be cracked, dehulled, dried, flaked, solvent extracted, re-dried, and finally milled into flour. The temperature during all these processing operations must be held to a maximum of about 160° F to preserve the solubility of soybean proteins. When solvent-extracted soybean meal is intended for food uses, it is cooked or "toasted" at this point to denature the proteins and carmelize a portion of the carbohydrates, thus improving the nutritional qualities of the meal at the expense of the soluble or adhesive qualities.

A typical analysis for solvent extracted "untoasted" soybean meal is as follows:[5]

Protein (Nitrogen X 6.25)	54.0
Carbohydrates	29.7
Hemicellulose Cellulose ⎱ Fiber	2.6
Fats	0.7
Ash	6.0
Water	7.0
	100.0

The protein content of soybean meal varies considerably with the geographical source of the soybeans and the particular variety, ranging from about 35 to about 55 per cent on an as-received basis. The bulk of industrial soybean meal generally contains about 44 to 50 per cent protein. As an adhesive-base material, soybean flour reflects the variability of a natural product. It is usually blended in large quantities to minimize this variation; nevertheless close control during glue manufacture is still required to obtain soybean adhesives of uniform properties.

The fineness of an untoasted soybean flour has a distinct influence on its suitability for adhesive purposes.[6] Fineness of grind is more often expressed in terms of specific surface (square centimeters per gram, according to a standard test) than mesh size. A satisfactory range of specific surface is about 3000 to 6000 sq cm/g. Typical screen analyses corresponding to these limits for soybean flour are as follows:

	Specific Surface (sq cm/gm)	
	3000	6000
	%	%
0 to 60 mesh	10.7	0.1
60 to 100 mesh	15.8	0.4
100 to 200 mesh	17.0	2.2
200 to 325 mesh	14.9	14.8
Finer than 325 mesh	41.5	82.5

MANUFACTURE AND FORMULATION

A substance must be highly polar to be adhesive to polar adherends such as wood. The protein molecules of soybean flour, although containing many polar groups, are heavily coiled;[7] consequently these polar groups are unavailable due to internal (hydrogen) bonding with each other. For this reason, a simple paste of soybean flour in water is a relatively poor adhesive, hardly even as efficient as a wheat flour paste. A chemical change is required to break the internal bonds and uncoil or "disperse" the polar protein molecules. The most effective treatment for this purpose is an increase in pH of the soybean slurry to about eleven or higher.[8] At this pH the protein molecules are almost completely and irreversibly uncoiled, making available the entire adhesive potential of their complex polar structure.

Destruction of the soybean protein by hydrolysis also begins as the pH is raised; however the large increase in adhesive properties gained from complete dispersion more than offsets the moderate loss of protein activity by hydrolysis.[9] Both alkaline dispersion and hydrolysis are time reactions, the former proceeding at a rapid rate for a short time (1 hr or less) and the latter at a slower, steady rate on a continuing basis. Both are subject to the effect of temperature, the higher the faster, and conversely. These rate factors cause the typical viscosity curve for most alkaline protein glues; namely, low immediate viscosity increasing rapidly to a peak or plateau of maximum viscosity, then slowly returning to a low viscosity over a period of hours. By the time this cycle has been completed, hydrolysis has ended the useful life of the glue. Bond strength and water resistance are heavily impaired.

Almost any alkaline material will disperse soybean flour in water at least to a limited degree. Complete dispersions of ultimate adhesive strength generally require several per cent of a strong base such as sodium, potassium or lithium hydroxide, trisodium phosphate or a similar highly alkaline salt;[10] however these salts invariably cause an alkali stain or burn on cellulosic adherends. Hence ultimate protein bond strength is necessarily associated with staining of wooden joints. Soybean glues can be made stainless for bonding weaker adherends, i.e., paper, softboard, etc., by dispersing the glues with weak bases such as calcium hydroxide, monosodium phosphate or borax.[11] Typical formulations will be given later in this chapter.

Although simple alkaline dispersions of soybean flour in water are adequate adhesives and binders for some purposes, many improvements in glue properties can be gained from further refinements in the dispersing system. Assuming for the moment that sodium hydroxide is the best and cheapest strong base for dispersing most soybean glues, the addition of a slightly soluble calcium or magnesium salt such as calcium hydroxide with the sodium hydroxide improves both the water resistance and the assembly time tolerance of soybean adhesives by reaction with protein constituents to yield insoluble proteinates and altered glue consistency.[3] Adding several per cent of a liquid or readily soluble grade of sodium silicate (high ratio of sodium oxide to silicon dioxide), especially with a protein denaturant, increases the water-holding capacity, levels the viscosity, and prolongs the useful life of most soybean glues.[3] Several of the sample formulations shown later in the chapter are based on dispersing systems of this general type.

Protein denaturants and crosslinking agents play an important part in the technology of soybean glues. For example, sulfur compounds such as carbon disulfide, ethylene trithiocarbonate, thiourea and potassium xanthate are strong crosslinkers of dispersed soybean proteins, acting to increase their water resistance, stabilize their structure against hydrolysis and raise their viscosity.[3, 12, 13] Soluble copper,[14] chromium[15] and zinc[16] salts perform this function to a lesser but useful degree. Epoxide compounds, particularly aliphatic epoxy resins, are very active hardening agents for alkaline soybean dispersions, although they yield glues which are expensive and difficult to control.[17]

Formaldehyde donors, adducts, reaction products and some higher aldehydes form an important class of protein modifiers. They act to crosslink or denature soybean proteins for improved water resistance, longer useful glue life, altered (granular) consistency for improved assembly time tolerance and curing behavior, and increased water-holding capacity.[9, 18] Compounds typical of this group are tris-hydroxy-methyl nitromethane, dimethylol urea, sodium formaldehyde bisulfite, aldehydic starch, glyceraldehyde, hexamethylenetetramine, urea-formaldehyde resins, and methylolated phenols. Solutions of formaldehyde and paraformaldehyde are too active for many of the present soybean adhesive formulations, usually causing premature gelation. In general, very small quantities of these aldehyde-acting compounds are sufficient to produce the desired glue modification, on the order of $1/10$ to 1 per cent based on dry glue weight. They are usually added during the initial or final stage of the glue mix.

Soybean protein can also be denatured by the application of energy in many forms, and even by a change in physical state. Wet and dry heat, grinding, freezing, pressure, irradiation and sound waves are examples. Similarly the adhesive properties of soybean flour are degraded by contact with these denaturing forces, which is the main reason that soybean processing must be conducted under moderate conditions when a soluble (adhesive) end product is desired.

Organic solvents, particularly those at least partially soluble in water such as lower alcohols and ketones, denature proteins on contact.[20, 21] Their primary use in soybean glues at this time is to inhibit dispersion or viscosity produced by other compounds.

Soybean proteins enter into a number of specific reactions that yield new chemical compounds rather than simply denatured protein. Examples of these reactions are acetylation, cyanoethylation, sulfonation, diazotization, and alkyl silane addition. Almost without exception, however, reactions of this type decrease the adhesive properties of soybean protein in roughly direct proportion to the degree of completion, and consequently have little value in protein adhesive systems.[13]

Thus far, the discussion has been limited to the protein constituents of soybean flour, which are the active bonding constituents, but comprise only about half the bulk of solvent-extracted soybean flour. The other half is mainly carbohydrates, with small amounts of cellulose, moisture and ash. As with other starchy materials, the carbohydrates become tacky in alkaline solution and contribute useful consistency properties to the soybean glue, but little adhesion.[22] There is some indication that the water resistance of soybean glues is reduced by the presence of these carbohydrates. However the issue is clouded by the fact that even proteins in a cured glue line soften and swell on immersion in water, but do not dissolve.[23] Most of the special soybean glue additives listed earlier have been developed for the express purpose of reducing this tendency to swell in water, but none of them to date has entirely prevented it.

Several distinct mixing steps are necessary to make a useful glue from soybean flour. These are wetting, shearing, defoaming, dispersing and (optionally) denaturing or cross-linking. The wetting of soybean flour with water is best done in almost neutral solution to eliminate lumps prior to alkaline dispersion, which then renders them permanent by encapsulation. Shearing the wetted glue to reduce lumps is accomplished by an efficient mixer and a thick "batter" consistency of glue during at least one early mixing stage. Water additions are generally divided to provide this thick stage. Defoamer is added early in the mix to prevent frothing and fine bubble formation. The defoamer is frequently absorbed into the dry glue in a prior blending operation to reduce its dustiness. Dispersion is accomplished by adding one or more alkaline agents to the smooth soybean slurry. Finally, special ingredients such as mold inhibitors, denaturants and cross-linking agents are added to modify the properties of the dispersed glue, after which a mixing period of at least several minutes prepares the glue for immediate use.

A typical soybean interior plywood glue embodying these mixing principles is shown below:

	(lb)
Water at 60–70°F	175
Untoasted soybean flour	97
Pine oil or equivalent defoamer	3
Mix 3 min or until smooth	
Water at 60–70°F	145
Mix 2 min or until smooth	
Hydrated lime	12
Water at 60–70°F	24
Mix 1 min	
50% Sodium hydroxide solution	14
Mix 1 min	
"N" Brand sodium silicate (Philadelphia Quartz Co.)	25
Mix 1 min	
Carbon disulfide in	1¼
Carbon tetrachloride	½
Flake pentachlorophenol	4¼
Mix 10 min	

This glue is ready for use immediately after mixing and has a working life of about 6 to 10 hr depending on storage temperature. Hot- and cold-pressing schedules for this glue are listed below.

A variety of efficient preservatives are available for protecting protein glues from attack by mold. In addition to pentachlorophenol, such compounds as chloro-2-phenylphenol, copper naphthenate, ortho-phenylphenol, tributyltin oxide, copper-8-quinolinolate and others may be added to the dry glue blend or during any stage of glue preparation at the rate of 1 to 5 per cent of the dry glue weight depending on the degree of protection desired. Five per cent of almost any of these compounds will protect soybean glue from heavy mold exposure for a period of several months or many times longer for moderate exposure. The phenol-based inhibitors are initially insoluble in aqueous alkaline glue dispersions; however they dissolve rapidly through the formation of their soluble salts. About 1 per cent additional alkali per 5 per cent inhibitor is required in the glue mix for this reaction.

It should be clearly understood that mold inhibitors protect only the glue and the wood adjacent to the glue line, and not the bulk of the laminate which is still capable of supporting mold growth unless separately protected. Mold inhibitors also impart some degree of termite protection, but, again, only to the glue and not to the entire wood structure. A gradual loss of mold protection is normally experienced and is considered to be primarily a matter of leaching of the inhibitor from the glue film by moisture, together with the probable development of resistant mold and bacterial strains.[24]

Soybean dry glue compositions may contain other ingredients than just soybean flour and defoamer. Fillers such as clays, nut shell flours, wood flours, etc., may be added to reduce cost or modify working properties; however, in general, it is necessary to maintain the highest level of active ingredient (soybean flour) that the composition will permit if maximum adhesive performance is desired. Where maximum bond strength is not required or is secondary to cost, the dry glue can be extended heavily with fillers to yield glues which are suitable for softboard laminating, paper overlay gluing, aggregate binding, box shook manufacture and other less stringent adhesive applications. A typical dry glue composition and mix for adhesives of this type are listed below:

Dry glue composition:

	(lb)
Soybean flour	38
Wyoming bentonite	38
Vinsol resin (Hercules Powder Co.)	15
Potato starch	5
Powdered dimethylol urea (Du Pont Arboneeld A)	1
Borax	1
Pine oil or equivalent defoamer	2
Total	100

Mixing directions:

	(lb)
Water at 60–70°F	200
Dry glue	100
Mix 3 min or until smooth	
Water at 60–70°F	150
Hydrated lime in	7
Water	25
50% Sodium hydroxide solution	6
Mix 2 min	
"N" Brand sodium silicate	15
50% Sodium hydroxide solution	6
Mix 1 min	
Carbon disulfide in	1¼
Carbon tetrachloride	½
Mix 10 min	

The working properties of this glue are generally similar to those of a straight soybean plywood glue. It is suitable for both hot- and cold-press applications.

It is possible to include alkaline dispersing agents in the composition of soybean dry glues, thereby eliminating part or all of the normal alkaline mixing steps. Solid sodium and potassium hydroxide are not usually blended into a dry glue because they are excessively hygroscopic and will absorb atmospheric moisture, after which they will dissolve in it and destroy the glue. Moderately strong bases such as trisodium phosphate and sodium carbonate may be blended into dry soybean adhesives, however, yielding glues that disperse fairly well in their own alkali when simply mixed with water.

An alternative technique is the use of salts such as sodium fluoride, disodium phosphate or sodium carbonate in a dry glue, together with calcium hydroxide.[25] The salts dissolve in aqueous solution, then undergo immediate double decomposition with lime, yielding sodium hydroxide and insoluble calcium salts. In this way, a separate sodium hydroxide dispersing step is eliminated and the dry glue is essentially a stable "one-package" adhesive. The soybean-casein blend glue in the next column is an excellent example of this type of dispersion.

A nonstaining soybean adhesive of moderate bond strength can be made with soybean flour and several per cent of hydrated lime blended together into a single dry glue requiring only water. Adhesives of this type are suitable for paper and softboard laminating where staining is a problem, briquet binding and other low-strength applications.[26] These particular glues also have an unusual "non-wicking" property since water does not travel by absorption along the cured glue lines as it does with soybean glues dispersed at higher levels of pH. In such glues, the lime may also be added separately as shown below:

	(lb)
Water at 60–70°F	225
Soybean flour	100
Pine oil or equivalent defoamer	3
Mix until smooth	
Water at 60–70°F	150
Mix until smooth	
Hydrated lime in	30
Water	50
Mix 5 min	

Soybean flour may be combined with other proteins to yield glue properties unobtainable with soybean alone. The addition of casein to soybean glue, for instance, imparts extra tack and assembly time tolerance. Glues of this type are suitable for many normal casein as well as soybean glue applications such as lumber laminating, flush door gluing and furniture assembly, and offer a considerable cost saving over straight casein glues.[27] The following example is typical of these glues:

Dry glue composition:

	(lb)
Soybean flour	57
Lactic acid casein	15
Hydrated lime	12
Wood flour	5
Sodium carbonate	5
Sodium fluoride	3
Pine oil or equivalent defoamer	3
Total	100

Mixing directions:

	(lb)
Water at 60–70°F	20
Dry glue	10
Mix until smooth	
Let stand 15 min	
Mix briefly and add:	
Water at 60–70°F	5
Mix until smooth	

The second water addition may be reduced if a heavier glue is desired. Working life is about 6 to 8 hr at room temperature. For average softwood or hardwood laminates, glue spreads should range from about 50 to 70 lb of glue per 1000 sq ft of single glue line; assembly time is from about 3 to 25 min; clamping pressure is from 100 to 200 psi based on contact area; and clamping time is from 4 to 6 hr.[28] Under favorable conditions, soybean-casein glues can be utilized with the "No-Clamp" process, described later in the chapter, to bond softwood structures.

Soybean flour can also be combined with spray-dried or vacuum pan-dried soluble animal blood to yield glues of improved water resistance and hot-press curing speed.[29] In fact, straight soybean glues are seldom used for bonding hot press plywood at the present time. Instead, blood substitutions ranging from a few per cent to half or more of the soybean content are now preferred. Glues of this type are covered in detail in Chapter 11 on blood adhesives. It is sufficient to mention here that the mixing and handling instructions for these glues are similar to those for straight soybean glues, differing mainly in water content which increases with the blood concentration. Most blood-soybean glues may be used according to both the hot- and cold-press gluing schedules listed for soybean glues.

The insoluble or fertilizer grades of blood find little use in high-strength soybean adhesives except possibly as slightly active organic fillers.[30] Partially insolublized bloods with an alkaline dispersed consistency similar to soybean flour itself (half granular, half gelatinous) are compatible with soybean flour in all proportions, yielding cold-press ("No-Clamp") glues of excellent quality.[31] Again, the mixing techniques and working properties of these glues are generally the same as with straight soybean glues except for water content, which is substantially higher.

Animal glues are occasionally used as protein modifiers for soybean glues, primarily to impart tack and flow properties to the granular soybean consistency.[23, 32] As additives, however, these gelatin glues have the disadvantage of hydrolyzing quite rapidly in the alkaline solution normally used to disperse soybean flour. They also tend to reduce the water resistance of soybean glues in approximate proportion to the amount added, although dry bond strength is excellent.

The protein from soybean flour is available in a variety of isolated forms as an adhesive-base material. This extracted protein is generally similar to casein in cost and performance and has been used in large quantities for paper sizes, emulsifiers, water paints, and paper-coating adhesives.[33, 34] As a wood-glue base, it does not offer sufficient advantage over soybean flour to offset the cost of extraction and is seldom used except as an additive or minor constituent. The following example shows its use as a paper overlay glue:

		(lb)
Water at 70–75°F		385
Alpha protein (Glidden Co.)		100
China clay		100
Sodium sulfite		1
Pine oil		1
Mix 15 min		
50% Sodium hydroxide solution		16
Mix 15 min		
Hexamethylene tetramine in		3
Water		5
Mix 5 min		

This glue may be cured hot or cold and has a working life of 24 hr or more.

A new class of soybean specialty glues has been developed over the last several years involving the addition of certain latex emulsions to conventional soybean and soybean-casein adhesives.[35] The resulting glues have excellent water resistance, tack, flexibility and adhesion and are used primarily for short pressing cycle ("No-Clamp" process), gluing of flush doors, specialty plywood, high-density overlays and millwork at this time.[36] Butadiene-styrene and butadiene-acrylonitrile latices such as Dow's Latex 630, Monsanto's L-650 and Borden's Polyco 2419 appear especially suitable for this purpose. They are added at the end of a normal protein glue mix in amounts ranging from approximately 15 to 150 per cent of the dry glue weight. The straight soybean and soybean-casein glues listed as examples in this chapter both work well with latex additions.

Soybean flour is combined occasionally with phenolic adhesive resins at various levels yielding hot-press interior plywood glues which derive quick-setting properties from the soybean protein and permanency from the resin solids.[37, 38] Glues of this type are moderately successful although somewhat less reactive and more sensitive to stock moisture content than equivalent glues made with soluble blood. An example is shown below to illustrate the alkali-resin type of dispersion:

Dry glue composition:

	(lb)
Soybean flour	50
China clay	30
Walnut shell flour	20

Mixing directions:

	(lb)
40% Solids phenolic adhesive resin*	500
Dry glue	100
Pine oil or equivalent defoamer	3
Mix 5 min	
Water at 60–70°F	400
Mix 2 min	
"N" Brand sodium silicate solution	40
Mix 5 min	

This glue is ready for immediate use and has a working life of about 24 hr. Commercial pressing times are about 30 per cent longer than the soybean hot-press schedule shown below. Glue spreads are about 30 per cent lower.[36]

APPLICATION AND PRESSING

Soybean glues can be mixed in a bucket with a stick, but this is hardly a workable production technique. A combination of scraping and counter-rotating mixer blades provides ideal agitation for handling the heavy stages of mixing on a small or large scale. This action requires specialized glue mixing equipment, however. Laboratory or small production size glue batches can be made with a kitchen food mixer, a small Hobart dough mixer, or a propeller mixer of moderate speed. Production glue mixers are generally large-scale versions of the basic mixer designs such as counter-rotating, propeller, and egg-beater. Regardless of design, the mixer should be fast enough to reduce lumps with reasonable efficiency yet minimize the

* Monsanto PF520, Reichhold "Plyophen" P398, Borden "Cascophen" W1156, etc.

amount of air worked into the glue, and be free of stagnant zones where unmixed glue can accumulate.

Soybean glues may be applied to various adherends by almost any of the conventional methods or equipment. Among these are all forms of direct and indirect roll applicators, knife and comb applicators, curtain coaters and extruders, sprays (with proper viscosity adjustment), dips, screens and wet films. Soybean glues are even occasionally applied as dry powders, drawing their aqueous phase from the adherends under heat and pressure.[39]

The following are typical hot- and cold-pressing schedules for soybean adhesives showing recommended ranges of time, temperature, pressure and glue spread. These schedules apply to all of the adhesive compositions discussed unless otherwise specified.

For many years, all cold-press plywood was clamped after gluing in massive loads with steel beams and turnbuckles for curing periods of

GLUE SPREAD

Core Thickness	Lb Wet Spread per MDGL*
$\frac{1}{16}$ in.	80
$\frac{1}{10}$, $\frac{1}{9}$	85
$\frac{1}{8}$	90
$\frac{1}{7}$, $\frac{1}{6}$, $\frac{3}{16}$, $\frac{1}{4}$	95
Rough core	Add 5 lb

Panels thicker than $\frac{13}{16}$ in. use 100 lb

* Thousand square feet of *double* glue line.

several hours or more; then the loads were broken down and machined into finished plywood. The short clamping cycle "No-Clamp" process for cold-press plywood was developed by Galber and Golick in 1946 and was universally adopted by the softwood plywood industry within a very few years.[40] This process is based on the fact that alkaline dispersed protein adhesives, especially soybean and certain blood glues, lose water rapidly in contact with dry wood veneers to the point where the protein gel remaining on the glue line has sufficient strength in a matter of minutes to hold the veneers in close contact after clamping pressure is released.

Using this process, a load of plywood can be clamped for 15 min or less and then removed from the press with a minimum of handling and

SOYBEAN GLUE
HOT-PRESSING SCHEDULE
For Interior Type Douglas Fir Plywood

Rough Panel Thickness	No. of Plies	Panels per Opening	Platen Temp. (°F)	Pressing Time in Minutes (full pressure)
$\frac{3}{16}$	3	2	230	3
$\frac{1}{4}$	3	2	240	3
$\frac{5}{16}$	3	2	250	$3\frac{1}{2}$
$\frac{5}{16}$	3	3	260	5
$\frac{3}{8}$	3	2	260	4
$\frac{7}{16}$	3	1	240	3
$\frac{7}{16}$	3	2	270	$4\frac{3}{4}$
$\frac{1}{2}$	5	1	230	$3\frac{1}{2}$
$\frac{1}{2}$	5	2	250	6
$\frac{9}{16}$	5	1	230	$3\frac{3}{4}$
$\frac{9}{16}$	5	2	250	6
$\frac{5}{8}$	5	1	240	4
$\frac{11}{16}$	5	1	250	4
$\frac{3}{4}$	5	1	260	$4\frac{1}{4}$
$\frac{13}{16}$	5	1	270	$4\frac{1}{2}$
$\frac{13}{16}$	7	1	260	5
$\frac{15}{16}$	7 and 9	1	270	$5\frac{1}{2}$
$1\frac{1}{16}$	7 and 9	1	270	6
$1\frac{3}{16}$	7 and 9	1	270	7
$1\frac{5}{16}$	9	1	270	$7\frac{1}{2}$
$1\frac{7}{16}$	9	1	270	8
$1\frac{9}{16}$	9 and 11	1	270	9

Total time assembly not to exceed 15 min
Hydraulic pressure not less than 200 lb/sq in

SOYBEAN GLUE
COLD-PRESSING SCHEDULE
("No-Clamp" Process)
For Interior Type Douglas Fir Plywood

Use following wet glue spreads according to core thickness:

(in.)	(lb)
$\frac{1}{10}$ core	125–130
$\frac{1}{9}$	128–132
$\frac{1}{8}$	130–135
$\frac{1}{7}$	133–138
$\frac{1}{6}$	135–140
$\frac{3}{16}$	135–140
All 5 ply $\frac{13}{16}$ in. constructions	150

For rough core, add an extra 8 lb over these spreads.

Special Pressing Instructions:

Hold load 5 min before applying pressure.

Load must be under pressure within 25 min after the first panel is laid.

Pressing time to be measured after pressure gauge reaches full pressure.

Use 175–200 psi hydraulic pressure.

Pressure to be retained for 15 min.

Do not use hot stock.

Spread test piece, $12\frac{3}{4}$ in. by 25 in.

set aside to develop full strength without further pressure, leaving the press free for other loads of plywood. A 4 to 6 hr curing period is usually specified before breaking the load and finishing the plywood. The glue lines actually continue to harden for several days, however, through additional dehydration and insolublizing of the protein. Manual clamping is completely eliminated by the "No-Clamp" process, and the entire output of one or two glue spreader crews is efficiently handled by a single hydraulic cold press and its auxiliary equipment. The soybean cold-press schedule shown earlier is based on the "Noclamp" process and illustrates the cold clamping method in general use today for interior plywood and box shook manufacture.

With variations, this process is also being used for hardboard and softboard laminating, prefabricating wall sections, paper overlaying, door gluing and many other specialized applications where dehydration of a soybean adhesive by absorptive adherends is possible.[26, 41, 42] The keys to its use are low moisture content stock (less than half of the fiber saturation level) and a consistency of protein glue that yields its water phase quite readily.[43, 44] Very tacky or colloidal glues require excessive clamping times to lose water to the adherends and develop a strong gel. Very granular glues lose water too quickly to the adherends and limit assembly (lay-up) times severely. On wet or nonabsorptive adherends, a protein glue simply will not harden at all. Among the protein adhesives in general use, soybean glues exhibit the best balance of properties for successful "No-Clamp" operation at this time, although certain types of modified animal blood glues are beginning to challenge this position.

Practically all soybean adhesives will harden by cold pressing to yield satisfactory cured bonds in wood laminates. As indicated above, some glues can be used in the "No-Clamp" process while others require clamping cycles of at least several hours. Laminates involving paper generally dehydrate and cure in seconds, either hot or cold press, using soybean adhesives at an appropriate spread.[45]

Roll pressure (as opposed to fixed or moving platen pressure) may be used with moderate success either hot or cold to clamp protein-bonded laminates involving paper products, but not wood.[45] The pressure cycle in any given area of wood laminate is too short and too intense, resulting in under-cure or overpenetration or both. For continuous paper gluing operations, however, a soft roll or brush roll type pressure application is well worth considering.

Because of their necessarily high salt content, soybean glues are difficult to cure successfully with radio frequency energy.[46] The presence of this electrolyte severely limits the RF load which can be applied, thus slowing the rate of cure. Also, any excess glue deposited in core joints, defects or on overhangs may cause serious arcing problems.

Viscosity

Viscosity is an important property which largely governs the adhesive behavior of protein glues for many applications, and much of the technology discussed in this chapter is related to its control. The operating limits of soybean glue viscosity are remarkably broad, ranging from watery briquet binding or paper laminating formulations at one extreme to mastic viscosity hot-press plywood glues at the other, or from about 500 to 75,000 cps. Preferred viscosity limits for different soybean glue applications can be roughly divided as follows: 500 to 5000 cps for gluing highly absorptive adherends such as paper, softboard and dried wood aggregates; 5000 to 25,000 cps for most wood laminating purposes, both hot and cold press; over 50,000 cps for mastic consistency wood laminating operations (special mixing and glue spreading equipment is required).[47] The short cycle "No-Clamp" cold-press technique is somewhat more critical in its glue viscosity requirements for successful operation, and a viscosity range of about 8000 to 20,000 is generally specified.[40]

All protein glues exhibit non-Newtonian flow behavior, the viscosity decreasing with increasing rate of shear.[48] Therefore, viscosity-measuring devices for use with protein glues should respond to a wide range of viscosities without change in shear rate. Among the more suitable conventional systems are MacMichael, Stormer and Brookfield viscosimeters, of which the last two are used at a single speed only. Since many protein glues are quite thixotropic, it is usually desirable to determine the viscosity after a fixed period of rotation such as 30 sec to ensure a steady reading.

For a discussion of soybean plywood glue costs, reference should be made to the chapter on blood adhesives. Under average market conditions, these costs generally range from about $1.00 to $2.00 per thousand sq ft of single glue line (MSGL) for both hot- and cold-press soybean glues. Some of the heavily extended paper glues applied at light spreads can cost 50¢ or even less per MSGL; whereas casein-fortified soybean glues may reach $4.00 to $6.00 per MSGL at typical lumber laminating spreads, depending on casein content.[28, 45, 49] As with all other adhesive systems, the rate of application has an overriding effect on actual glue line costs. Expensive glues become cheap at a light spread rate; also the converse is true.

SUPPLEMENTARY
SEED AND NUT MEAL FLOURS

This chapter has drawn heavily on the softwood plywood industry for information and examples because this industry, by consuming the major proportion of all soybean glues for wood, has stimulated the greatest research effort on these adhesive products. The adhesive technology outlined for soybean flour applies equally well to certain other seed and nut meal flours, principally cottonseed, linseed, tepary bean, peanut and Alaska pea;[50, 51] however the market for vegetable protein glues is almost completely dominated by soybean adhesive products.

References

1. *Pen Ts' ao Kong Mu,* the records of Chinese Emperor Sheng-Nung, 2838 B.C.
2. Johnson, O., U. S. Patent 1,460,757 (July 3, 1923).
3. Laucks, I. F., and Davidson, G. (to I. F. Laucks, Inc.), U. S. Patents 1,689,732 (Oct. 30, 1928) and 1,691,661 (Nov. 13, 1928).
4. U. S. Department of Commerce, *Census of Manufactures,* 1942 through preliminary 1958; U. S. Tariff Commission Reports of 1948.
5. Technical Bull., *Prosoy,* Central Soya Co., 1948.
6. Davidson, G. (to I. F. Laucks, Inc.), U. S. Patent 1,724,695 (Aug. 13,1929).
7. Senti, F. R., Copley, M. J., and Nutting, G. C., *J. Phys. Chem.,* **49,** 192–211 (1945).
8. Fontaine, T. D., and Burnett, R. S., *Ind. Eng. Chem.,* **36,** 164–167 (1944).
9. Burnett, R. S., and Eichenberger, W. R., *Paper Trade J.,* **126,** (7), 51 and 52 (1948).
10. Brother, G. H., Smith, A. K., and Circle, J. J., *Soybean Protein,* U. S. Department of Agriculture, Bureau of Agricultural Chemistry, 1940.
11. Davidson, G., and Laucks, I. F., U. S. Patent 1,813,387 (July 7, 1931).
12. Laucks, I. F., and Davidson, G. (to I. F. Laucks, Inc.), U. S. Patent 2,150,175 (Mar. 14, 1939).
13. Bjorksten, J., "Cross Linkages in Protein Chemistry," in *Advances in Protein Chem.,* **6,** 353–358, New York, Academic Press, 1951.
14. Laucks, I. F., and Davidson, G. (to I. F. Laucks, Inc.), U. S. Patent 1,805,773 (May 19, 1931).
15. Laucks, I. F., and Davidson, Glenn (to I. F. Laucks, Inc.), U. S. Patent 1,786,209 (Dec. 23, 1930); Wood, D. M., U. S. Patents 2,297,340 and 341 (Sept. 29, 1942).
16. Laucks, I. F., and Cone, C. N. (to I. F. Laucks, Inc.), U. S. Patent 1,757,805 (May 6, 1930).
17. Lambuth, A. L., U. S. Application 108,305 (May 8, 1961); Fraenkl-Conrat, J. L., *J. Biol. Chem.,* 154, 227–238 (1944).
18. French, D., and Edsall, J. T., *Advances in Protein Chem.,* **2,** 278–327, New York, Academic Press (1945); Satow, T., U. S. Patent 1,994,050 (Mar. 12, 1935); Osgood, G. H., U. S. Patent 1,950,060 (Mar. 6, 1934); Bradshaw, L., U. S. Patent 1,895,433 (Jan. 24, 1933).
19. Izume, S., and Yoshimaru, Y., *J. Agr. Chem. Soc. Japan,* **7,** 87–96 (1931).
20. Circle, S. J., "Soybeans and Soybean Products," Ist Ed., pp. 277–283, New York, Interscience Press, 1950; Volkov, E. N., and Dvinyaninova, I. L., *J. Appl. Chem. (U.S.S.R.),* **13,** 267–274 (1940).
21. Bowen, A. H. (to I. F. Laucks, Inc.), U. S. Patent 2,014,167 (Sept. 10, 1935).
22. Laucks, I. F., *Chemurgic Digest,* **2,** 173–188 (1943).
23. Norris, C. B., and Laucks, I. F., "The Technique of Plywood," pp. 227–249, Seattle, I. F. Laucks, Inc., 1942.
24. Technical Bull. SC-3, *Pentachlorophenol* and SC-4, *Santobrite for Microorganism Control in the Pulp and Paper Industry,* Organic Chemicals Division, Monsanto Chemical Company; Technical Report, *Mold Resistance of Plywood Made with Protein Adhesives,* Douglas Fir Plywood Association, Feb. 15, 1952.
25. Davidson, G., and Laucks, I. F., U. S. Patent 1,813,387 (July 7, 1931).
26. Sheeran, N. J. (to American-Marietta Co.), U. S. Patent 2,788,305 (Apr. 9, 1957).
27. Banks, H. P., and Davidson, G. (to I. F., Laucks, Inc.), U. S. Patent 1,835,689 (Dec. 8, 1931); Cone, C. N., and Brown, E. D. (to I. F. Laucks, Inc.), U. S. Patent 1,962,808 (June 24, 1934); Sutermeister, E., and Browne, F. L., "Casein and Its Industrial Applications," pp. 281–285, New York, Reinhold Publishing Corp., 1939.
28. Perry, T. D., "Modern Wood Adhesives," pp. 104–109, New York, Pitman Publishers Corp., 1944.
29. Cone, C. N., and Galber, H. (to I. F. Laucks, Inc.), U. S. Patent 1,976,435 (Oct. 9, 1934); Dunham, H. V., U. S. Patent 1,892,486 (Dec. 27, 1932).
30. Fawthrop, W. D. (to Adhesive Products Co.), U. S. Patent 2,292,624 (Aug. 11, 1942).
31. Gossett, J. M., Estep, M. H. Jr., and Perrine, M. J. (to American-Marietta Co.), U. S. Patent 2,874,-134 (Feb. 17, 1959).
32. Dike, T. W., and Galber, H. (to I. F. Laucks, Inc.), U. S. Patent 2,178,566 (Nov. 7, 1939); Technical Bull., *M-155 Glue,* I. F. Laucks, Inc., 1942.
33. Bain, W. M., Newbauer, A. W., and Olson, R. A., *Alpha Protein and Protein Adhesives for Coated Papers,* Technical Bull., The Glidden Company.
34. Brother, G. H., Smith, A. K., and Circle, S. J., *Soybean Protein-Resumé* and Bibliography, U. S. Department of Agriculture, ACE-62, 1940.
35. Monsanto Chemical Company, British Patent 832,-227 (Apr. 6, 1960); Kinney, W. B. (to the Borden Co.), U. S. Patent 2,754,240 (July 10, 1956); Biddle, A. (to United Products Corp. of America), U. S. Patents, 1,777,157–162 (Sept. 30, 1930).

36. Technical Service Bull. No. 206, *Protein-Resin Adhesive Combinations for Hollow Core Door Manufacture,* Plastics Division, Monsanto Chemical Company, June, 1955.

37. Satow, T., U. S. Patent 1,877,202 (Sept. 13, 1922).

38. Babcock, G. E., and Smith, A. K., *Ind. Eng. Chem.,* **38,** 85–88 (1947).

39. Dike, T. W. (to I. F. Laucks, Inc.), U. S. Patents 1,851,950–955 (Mar. 29, 1932).

40. Galber, H., and Golick, A. J. (to I. F. Laucks, Inc.), U. S. Patent 2,402,492 (June 18, 1946).

41. U. S. Dept. of Agriculture, Forest Products Laboratory Reports, *Hollow Core Flush Doors,* No. 1983, June, 1954, and *Glues and Gluing in Prefabricated House Construction,* G. N. Arneson, 1946.

42. Technical Bull. No. CG-1-745, *Speedbond Gluing Process,* I. F. Laucks, Inc., July 11, 1945; Technical Bull., *Glued Prefabricated Houses,* Casein Co. of America, Jan. 1947.

43. U. S. Dept. of Agriculture, Forest Products Laboratory Report No. 1534, Olson, W. Z., May 1945.

44. *Ibid.,* **28,** 161–168.

45. "Production of Plyveneer," *Timberman,* (Jan. 1955); Stillinger, J. R., and Williams, W. Jr., *Strength Properties of Paper-Covered Veneer from True Fir and White-speck Douglas Fir,* Report No. T-8, Oregon Forest Products Laboratory, June 1954.

46. Russell, G. F., and Mann, J. W., *Wood Drying and Laminating by Radio Frequency,* SPE-DFPA Joint Conference Report, July 13, 1944; "Albany-Plylock, Pioneer Thermal Heat Plywood Unit," *Timberman,* **42,** 35–39 (July 1941).

47. Dike, T. W., and Galber, H. (to I. F. Laucks, Inc.), U. S. Patent 2,282,177 (May 5, 1942).

48. Burnett, R. S., *Soybeans and Soybean Products,* 1005–1010 and 1024, New York, Interscience Publishers, Inc., 1951.

49. *Ibid.,* **44,** 104–109.

50. Laucks, I. F., and Davidson, G. (to I. F. Laucks, Inc.), U. S. Patent 1,845,427 (Feb. 16, 1932); Laucks, I. F. (to I. F. Laucks, Inc.), U. S. Patent 1,942,109 (Jan. 2, 1934); White, D. J. (to the Borden Co.), U. S. Patent 2,312,056 (Feb. 23, 1943).

51. Smith, A. K., Circle, S. J., and Brother, G. H., *J. Am. Chem. Soc.,* **60,** 1316–1320 (1938); Smith, A. K., and Circle, S. J., *Ind. Eng. Chem.,* **30,** 1414–1418 (1938); Dammer, E., German Patent 274,974 (1913).

—11—

Blood Glues

Alan L. Lambuth
Monsanto Chemical Co.
Seattle, Washington

The use of animal blood as an adhesive reaches backward into antiquity. Aztec Indians allegedly mixed animal blood with cement in their mortar, making possible the flat or eliptical plastered arch design that characterized their buildings. Some of these arches survive to this day, more as a monument to the adhesive strength of blood than the structural soundness of the arch itself. There are indications that the ancient peoples of the Mediterranean were also acquainted with the adhesive properties of blood although the Egyptians, the world's first experts on wood veneering, apparently favored animal glues.[1] Throughout European history the occasional use of blood glues appears to have persisted, although shrouded in the secrecy of proprietary knowledge. The Baltic countries in particular developed considerable skill in using blood glues and remain to the present time among the world's largest consumers of blood for adhesive products.[2, 3]

Two developments spurred a rapid growth in blood glue consumption in the United States during the period 1910 to 1925. One was the discovery that blood could be dried and yet remain soluble by removing the fibrin and subsequently dehydrating at a temperature below the coagulation point of blood protein.[4] The other was an urgent need for water-resistant plywood to be used in aircraft construction during World War I.[5] Heat-cured blood glues were the most water-resistant plywood adhesives available at that time and remained so until phenol-formaldehyde resin film glues were developed in Europe about 1931. These synthetic resin film adhesives rapidly displaced blood glues from all types of weatherproof plywood by setting a new standard for durability

which blood glues were simply unable to match. During the 10 years that followed, blood glues were little used in this country, although the European consumption continued to increase. With the advent of World War II and a growing demand for water-resistant "interior" grades of plywood, blood glues again assumed a place of prominence which they retain to date, assisted by substantial improvements in protein glue materials and technology.

The adhesive uses of blood have been limited primarily to veneering and plywood. The heat curing requirement of blood albumin glues has generally precluded their use in furniture, millwork, lumber laminates and other traditional areas of wood glue application.[6] Because the technology of blood adhesives has changed so markedly in the last two decades, this chapter will emphasize those developments occurring since World War II.

The annual domestic consumption of soluble dried blood in adhesives for the wood industry remained fairly constant at about 15 million pounds from 1945 to about 1955.[7] Partly due to the rapid expansion of the plywood industry and to the excellent cost-performance record of blood glues themselves, this figure has now grown to an estimated 30 million pounds for 1960 and will probably continue to increase steadily. Only a general shift to synthetic resin adhesives for interior grades of plywood is likely to reverse this trend.

SOLUBILITY CATEGORIES

There are three categories of dried blood based on the severity of the drying treatment: soluble, partially soluble, and insoluble. The preliminary steps before drying are the same in each case. Fresh liquid blood is collected in packing plants over a period of hours or even days. The fibrin or clotting substance is removed by mechanical agitation or acid precipitation, and preservative is generally added. The blood, now consisting of serum albumin and hemoglobin in colloidal suspension is relatively stable and ready to be dried.[8]

The first and most important category of dried blood for adhesives is "soluble" blood, which includes bloods of about 85 to 100 per cent cold-water solubility by a standard test; however very few commercially dried bloods are more than 95 per cent soluble. This water-solubility value acts as a rough index for other properties of the dried blood, such as water requirement, soluble nitrogen content, and gel time, all of which are important to its over-all adhesive behavior. Soluble bloods are carefully spray-dried or vacuum-dried at temperatures below the heat denaturing point of the blood protein.[2] As with soybean protein, the adhesive properties are closely related to solubility after processing.[9]

The second category of dried blood is partially insoluble or denatured blood, which is understood to include water solubilities from about 15 to 80 per cent and covers a broad range of actual adhesive behavior. Fifteen per cent soluble blood has a distinctly granular consistency in water and actually requires the presence of some alkali to develop any appreciable degree of water solubility. Eighty per cent soluble blood by comparison closely resembles the soluble grades of blood except for a somewhat higher water requirement. As with soluble bloods, the drying operation is conducted in vacuum or spray dryers, using carefully controlled temperatures at or slightly above the protein denaturing point.[2, 11] Stable, uniform dried bloods of intermediate solubility are the newest and probably the most important blood products to appear on the market since the development of soluble blood itself. The adhesive properties inherent in these products will undoubtedly be responsible for a steady increase in their scope of application and volume used within the wood industry.

The third category of dried blood is totally insoluble, completely denatured blood. This material is generally intended for fertilizer rather than adhesives uses, and is seldom prepared in any way for drying. It is evaporated to dryness and ground to a coarse powder the quickest way possible, using high temperatures and strong agitation. The finished product is, as expected, totally insoluble in water. It may be gelatinized or dissolved (with chemical breakdown) only by using hot water and strong alkali.[12] Considerable ammonia is evolved in the process, giving a rough indication of the extent of actual hydrolysis. At best, insoluble blood is a relatively poor adhesive base and is seldom utilized at present except as an organic filler contributing slightly to the adhesive properties of other active materials.[13]

COMPOSITION, PROPERTIES, FORMULATION

The source of animal blood has a large influence on its behavior and adhesive properties.[14] Bloods differ considerably from one species of animal to another, and also from one animal to another within a given species due to variations in age, condition, feed, etc. The commercial answer to this problem has been to dry blood stocks from different species of animals separately, and to blend large quantities of blood from a single species to yield bulk stocks of average properties.

The principal dried bloods of commerce are beef and hog, which are available separately and in specified blends. Assuming normal levels of solubility, beef blood produces glues of higher viscosity and more positive response to denaturing additives than hog blood.[14] Both bloods can be partially insolubilized during or after the drying operation to yield products of widely varying yet reproducible behavior. Sheep blood is seldom available as a soluble product due to its relatively limited supply; nevertheless it is occasionally combined with the other two bloods into a commercial blend of generally lower viscosity.

All the soluble dried bloods are free-flowing medium density powders ranging in color from dark red to almost black. As the degree of insolubility increases, the color becomes more brown and the bulk density drops considerably. Most particles have become dried bubbles instead of solid droplets. All dried bloods are hygroscopic and should be protected from moisture. A word of caution is in order concerning the handling of dried bloods. A stream of this material moving rapidly through pipes or equipment develops a potentially lethal static charge. All processing equipment, including air lifts, conveyors and vacuum cleaners should be thoroughly grounded if blood products are involved.

As with soybean flour, the primary adhesive constituent in soluble dried blood is its protein, serum albumin.[15] Blood actually contains other protein constituents such as clotting compounds (fibrin) and red cells (hemoglobin), but the fibrin is removed by necessity prior to drying and the hemoglobin is heavily complexed with metal ions, leaving primarily albumin available for adhesive purposes. A typical analysis for soluble dried beef blood is given below:[16]

	%
Mesh size	95.6 through 100 mesh
Water soluble protein	90.5
Total nitrogen	14.7
pH	7.8
Moisture content	6.4

Blood albumin molecules are highly polar and complex but heavily coiled or globular in form;[13] consequently their many reactive groups are largely unavailable due to internal hydrogen bonding. Carefully dried albumin dissolves readily in water to yield a moderately adhesive colloidal solution, but the full adhesive potential of its complex structure is developed only through alkaline dispersion.[17] Acid dispersions of albumin are also possible, but they are extremely unstable and appear to have little practical value for adhesives.[18] As with other animal and vegetable proteins, blood albumin is subject to destruction by hydrolysis in alkaline solution. The rate of hydrolysis is often rapid enough to interfere seriously with the working life of blood glues unless the solution is buffered or the albumin is chemically modified by crosslinking or denaturing.[19]

Almost any alkaline material will disperse soluble dried blood to some degree. Blood protein appears to become strongly adhesive at a lower level of pH than vegetable protein, but several per cent of a strong base such as sodium, potassium or lithium hydroxide are usually necessary to develop its full adhesive potential.[19, 20] In alkaline dispersed form, soluble blood solutions are livery or slimy. Partially soluble blood dispersions are sticky and granular. All blood dispersions are dark in color and tend to stain cellulosic adherends deeply.[21]

Blood albumin reacts with a number of metal ions to form insoluble proteinates.[19, 22] Calcium and magnesium salts are frequently added to blood glues for the purpose of forming these products— both to increase the granular character of the glues and to improve water resistance if they are to be cured cold. Soluble silicates are excellent dispersing agents for blood glues that also act to level their viscosity and prolong their working life, primarily by buffering.[11, 20] In combination with denaturing agents, they increase the water requirement of blood glues without altering other desirable properties. Both calcium compounds and soluble silicates are frequently added to blood glues with a strong base to yield balanced dispersing systems of optimum effect on the blood albumin.[21] Many of the sample formulations shown later in the Chapter contain dispersing systems of this type. For a more detailed discussion of protein dispersions and special systems, refer to the chapter on soybean adhesives.

Alkaline dispersed blood albumin is extremely sensitive to physical and chemical denaturants, far more so than soybean protein, for instance.[23] Consequently the use of denaturants for the modification of working properties must be handled with great care. Among the physical denaturing forces, wet or dry heat is probably the most common and the most useful. Controlled applications of heat can be employed to thicken a blood glue, alter its consistency, lengthen its working life, improve its cold bonding properties, or cure it irreversibly.[24] This effect is mainly responsible for the present popularity of blood glues, by causing them to hot press rapidly with a high degree of water resistance. Listed below is a glue based on soluble blood showing the use of hot water to coagulate the protein into a granular, high water content plywood adhesive.

	(lb)
Water at 145°F	200
Soluble dried beef blood	80
Fir wood flour	18
Pine oil or equivalent defoamer	2
Mix 10 min	
Cold water	350
Pine oil or equivalent defoamer	2
Mix 2 min	
Hydrated lime in	7
Water at 65–70°F	14
Mix 2 min	
50% Sodium hydroxide solution	15
Mix 2 min	
"N" Brand sodium silicate solution	35
(Philadelphia Quartz Co.)	
Mix 5 min	

This glue is ready for use when mixed and has a working life of about 4 to 8 hr depending on storage temperature. Other forms of physical energy such as agitation rate influence the blood coagulation step; therefore individual adjustments for mixing equipment and good control of water temperature are necessary to yield consistent final glue viscosities. The uses and pressing conditions for this glue are discussed later in the Chapter.

The following blood glue which is listed for comparison is also based on soluble blood; however in this case the blood has been denatured with dry heat to a low level of solubility (10 to 20 per cent) prior to its use in the glue mix.[11]

	(lb)
Water at 60–70° F	300
Low solubility dried beef blood	75
Fir wood flour	21
Pine oil or equivalent defoamer	4
Mix 3 min or until smooth	
Water at 60–70° F	330
Mix 2 min	
Hydrated lime in	10
Water at 65–70° F	20
50% Sodium hydroxide solution	16
Mix 10 min	
"N" Brand sodium silicate solution	35
Mix 5 min	

This glue is ready for immediate use and has a working life of about 6 to 12 hr depending on storage temperature. It is simpler to prepare and more reproducible than the hot-water blood glue, but it is still subject to viscosity variation due to mixer speed and efficiency.

An indication of the larger water-holding capacity (water requirement) of heat-denatured blood glues can be seen by comparing the water-to-dry glue ratios for these two examples, 5.7 and 6.6, respectively, with that of a typical soybean glue, about 3.5. This increased water content helps to offset the higher cost of dried soluble blood as an adhesive-base material, yielding glue line costs almost equivalent to straight soybean adhesives for definitely superior performance.

Other forms of physical energy beside heat and mechanical agitation also cause denaturing of blood protein, but these are not often encountered in normal adhesive preparation and use. Examples are grinding in any form, pressure, irradiation, freezing, subsonic or supersonic vibration, and radio frequency energy.[25] It is quite possible that one or more of these physical energy sources could be used to denature and at least partially cure a blood glue while in place in a laminate.

Although the subject of protein denaturing by chemical means is covered in considerable detail in the Chapter on soybean adhesives, a few of the more important groups of chemical denaturing compounds for blood glues will be discussed here.

While blood glues are very susceptible to denaturing by certain classes of chemical compounds and most forms of energy, several of the traditional protein denaturants have less effect on blood albumin than on vegetable proteins. Organic sulfur compounds such as carbon disulfide and thiourea, the mainstay of soybean glue modification, act to stabilize blood glues somewhat against hydrolysis and prolong their useful life, but cause little change in viscosity or water resistance.[26, 27] Complexing

salts such as soluble cobalt, copper and chromium compounds appear to have little effect on blood dispersions.[28] Actually, blood glues are sufficiently more water-resistant than soybean glues that further improvement with many of the conventional additives is simply precluded.

Most of the lower alcohols and ketones, even those only slightly soluble in water, actively denature blood albumin.[25] In general, their effect is to granulate the smooth consistency of an alkaline blood dispersion and cause a slight to moderate reduction in its water requirement. This effect is useful for modification of blood glue working properties and as a means for counteracting the gross effects of other denaturants.[29] Particular application of this reaction was made using aromatic alcohols, phenol and cresol, with alkaline blood dispersions to yield a protein plywood glue of truly exterior quality about 1945.[30] Only the inherent variability of dried blood as a raw material at that time prevented the widespread use of this glue for weatherproof plywood.

Formaldehyde donors are as important a class of denaturants for blood glues as for soybean adhesives. Large additions of formaldehyde and relatively mild alkaline-dispersing agents characterized the aircraft plywood blood glues of World War I, [31] but small additions of formaldehyde and strongly alkaline dispersing agents generally characterize the blood adhesives of today. Aldehyde-acting compounds are useful for increasing the water resistance, viscosity, working life and water requirement of blood glues, while modifying the consistency to any degree from gelatinous to completely granular. Compounds frequently used for this purpose are paraformaldehyde, formalin, dimethylol urea, sodium formaldehyde bisulfite, hexamethylenetetramine, tris (hydroxymethyl) nitromethane, monomethylol dimethylhydantoin, and urea resins. Only small quantities ($\frac{1}{10}$ to 1 per cent) of these materials are required with sodium hydroxide dispersions of blood albumin to yield gross modifications. As the dispersing pH is reduced from approximately 13 to 10, proportionately larger quantities of aldehydes are needed to yield corresponding effects.[31, 32] They are usually added after the blood is in solution, and most frequently after alkaline dispersion.

Specific chemical reactions which alter the basic structure of blood albumin by acetylation and cyanoethylation, for instance, generally destroy the adhesive and water-holding properties of blood glues quite completely.[33] They add little or nothing to blood glue performance, even at low levels of conversion.

Phenol-formaldehyde resin solids are a class of protein denaturants with widely varying effects on blood albumin. These effects are apparently related both to structural complexity and to free formaldehyde or phenol remaining in the system. Resins of simple structure behave much the same as aromatic alcohols, causing a change in blood glue consistency from gelatinous to granular and often a reduction in viscosity.[30] Alkaline phenolic resins of moderate complexity are almost passive to dispersed blood protein. Highly complex and reactive phenolic resins cause gelation of blood glues, thus posing a major problem to their combination at any level.[18, 35] In spite of these limitations, however, there is a growing trend toward the development of hybrid glues based on alkaline blood dispersions and phenolic resins yielding new and useful performance properties.

All phenolic resins seem to impart semipermanent mold resistance to blood glues when added in quantities of 10 per cent or more resin solids based on the weight of dry glue. The mold protection provided by these resins has created a new grade of sheathing plywood for which the mold resistance (and adhesion) are literally guaranteed for the structural life of the panel. Blood glues must be hot pressed to gain the full measure of protection from phenolic resin additives, however.

The following glues illustrate the combination of liquid phenolic resins with alkaline dispersed blood at three different levels for three separate purposes. The first is primarily a protein adhesive containing sufficient phenolic resin to impart mold resistance and is typical of many commercial interior plywood glues. It is used according to the blood glue hot-pressing schedule shown later.

	(lb)
Water at 60–70°F	175
Low solubility dried beef blood	50
Soluble dried beef blood	25
Fir wood flour	22
Pine oil or equivalent defoamer	3
Mix 3 min or until smooth	
Water at 60–70°F	400
Mix 2 min	
Hydrated lime in	6
Water	12
Mix 1 min	
"N" brand sodium silicate solution	45
Mix 1 min	
50% sodium hydroxide solution	16
Mix 5 min	
50% solids phenolic adhesive	27
Resin*	
Mix 3 min	

The second glue contains approximately equal weights of protein and phenolic adhesive resin solids, and is truly a hybrid glue. The protein constituent provides rapid cure under heat and pressure. The resin constituent is cured by latent heat in the laminate after removal from the press to provide a weatherproof, moldproof bond.

	(lb)
Water at 100°F	75
Soluble dried beef blood	75
Fir wood flour	12
Wheat flour	10
Diesel oil	3
Mix 5 min	
Water at 100°F	250
Pine oil	6
Mix 2 min	
"N" brand sodium silicate solution	150
Mix 10 min	
Cold water	150
40% solids phenolic adhesive resin†	200
50% sodium hydroxide solution	50
Mix 5 min	

This glue is ready for immediate use, and it has a viscosity range of about 1500 to 3000 centipoises and a working life of about 24 hr. It can be used to produce plywood, flush doors, or other wood laminates of near-exterior quality at pressing times substantially shorter than the resin constituent would otherwise permit. Its pressing schedule is very similar to the blood glue hot-press schedule shown later in this chapter.

The third blood-resin adhesive is a conventional exterior plywood glue containing primarily alkaline phenolic resin with some soluble blood as its adhesive constituents. This general type of glue was made possible by a recent ruling of the Douglas Fir Plywood Association (for the FHA and Commercial Standard CS45–60) permitting up to 10 per cent proteinaceous or amylaceous materials, based on resin solids, in approved exterior plywood adhesives. Exterior glues, prior to this ruling, were required to be 100 per cent synthetic resin with inert or cellulosic fillers. Adding blood in the amount specified permits a 20 to 25 per cent reduction in the pressing time of phenolic resin adhesives. For glues of this type to operate, the blood and resin solids together must develop sufficient cure or "green bond" in the press to resist internal steam pressure and moderately rough

* Monsanto PF542, American Marietta "Amres" 4565, Reichhold "Plyophen" 1770.

† Monsanto PF520, Reichhold "Plyophen" P398.

handling of the laminate during removal from the press. The resin then completes a latent (and satisfactory) cure in the hot stacked panels. A typical glue mix is given below:

	(lb)
Water at 70°F	190
"Furafil" 100S Extender	70
(Quaker Oats Co.)	
Mix 2 min	
50% sodium hydroxide solution	40
Mix 1 min	
Sodium carbonate	18
Mix 15 min	
Diesel oil	3
Mix 1 min	
Dried soluble blood	20
Mix 5 min	
40% solids phenolic adhesive resin*	500
Mix 5 min	

This glue is ready to use when mixed. It has a working life of about 12 to 24 hr, depending on temperature. Recommended glue spreads are approximately 20 per cent less, and pressing times are about 50 per cent longer than those shown in the blood glue hot-press schedule on page 167. Since this glue is primarily a resin adhesive, it operates at a considerably lower viscosity than regular blood protein glues, on the order of 1500 cps at 70°F. While developed primarily for plywood, it is a suitable weatherproof adhesive for other wood laminates to which penetrating heat and pressure can be readily applied.

Soluble dried blood is also added in moderate quantities to urea-formaldehyde hot-press resin glues, usually with other extenders such as wheat flour for improved water resistance.[38] Unlike similar phenolic adhesives, the blood does not permit a reduction in pressing time. This is apparently related to the type of blood dispersion, which in urea resin glues is neutral or slightly acid rather than strongly alkaline, causing the formation of discrete particles instead of a gelatinous colloid.[39] Blood additions are especially useful for improving the bond strength and water resistance of heavily extended urea resin glues. Assuming the darker color imparted by the blood is not a problem, these glues are excellent adhesives for hardwood plywood, solid- and hollow-core flush doors, prefabricated structural units, lumber overlaying and other uses where a strong, heat-cured water-resistant bond is required, especially involving hardwoods.[40] A typical glue mix is given below.

	(lb)
Water at 70°F	120
Urea resin hot press catalyst	10
Mix 1 min	
Soluble dried beef blood	10
Hard wheat flour	100
Pine oil	1
Mix 5 min	
65% solids urea bonding resin†	100
Mix 5 min.	

This glue is ready to use when mixed and has a working life of about 8 to 16 hr, depending on temperature. Its viscosity is suitable for almost any method of application except spray. The wheat flour extension of the urea resin may be varied from about 25 to 150 per cent depending on the cost-performance level desired, but the blood content with respect to resin should remain about the same.[40] Conventional urea resin hot-press glue spreads and curing times should be used.

Dried soluble blood has found little use in melamine and melamine-urea formaldehyde, or resorcinol and phenol-resorcinol-formaldehyde adhesive resins up to the present. The chemistry of these resins does not favor the development of useful blood dispersions; moreover their cured properties already exceed the levels of water resistance and reactivity which blood can impart.

Blood-Soybean Flour Combinations

Certainly the largest individual use for dried soluble blood during recent years has been as the active constituent in water-resistant hot-press plywood glues, alone or in combination with other proteinaceous materials such as soybean flour.[37] Glues of this type have become the mainstay of water-resistant softwood plywood production since World War II. Soluble blood and soybean flour make a particularly useful combination since each contributes properties in which the other is basically deficient.[11, 21, 41] Dispersed blood, although highly heat-reactive and water-retaining, lacks good working properties and assembly time tolerance. Dispersed soybean flour has excellent working properties and assembly time tolerance but lacks hot-press curing speed and water resistance. Together, these materials make an extremely useful series of low-cost water-resistant fast-curing hot-press adhesives suitable for many wood laminating

* Borden "Cascophen" W156, Monsanto PF535, American Marietta "Amres" 5582.

† Monsanto UF111, Reichhold "Plyamine" SW1740, Borden "Casco" 5H.

operations such as plywood bonding, stored heat lumber laminating, softwood and hardboard laminating, flush door gluing, box shook manufacturing, chipboard and treated paper overlay bonding.[9, 42] Examples of low and high blood content glues are given below.

Low blood content dry glue composition:

	(lb)
Soybean flour	72
Soluble dried beef blood	15
Fir wood flour	10
Pine oil or equivalent defoamer	3
Total	100

Mixing Directions:

	(lb)
Water at 60–70°F	200
Low-blood content dry glue	100
Mix 2 min or until smooth	
Water at 60–70°F	220
Mix 2 min	
Hydrated lime in	8
Water at 60–70°F	16
Mix 1 min	
"N" brand sodium silicate solution	40
Mix 1 min	
50% sodium hydroxide solution	10
Mix 5 min	

High-blood content dry-glue composition:

	(lb)
Soluble dried-beef blood	70
Soybean flour	17
Fir wood flour	10
Pine oil or equivalent defoamer	3
Total	100

Mixing Directions:

	(lb)
Water at 60–70°F	160
High blood content dry glue	100
Mix 2 min or until smooth	
Water at 60–70°F	390
Mix 2 min	
Hydrated lime in	8
Water at 60–70°F	16
Mix 1 min	
"N" brand sodium silicate solution	45
Mix 1 min	
50% sodium hydroxide solution	16
Mix 5 min	
Hexamethylenetetramine	2
Mix 3 min	

Both glues are ready to use when mixed and have a working life of about 4 to 8 hr, depending on temperature. Both glues meet the fast press times, wet spreads, and assembly time limits shown in the hot-pressing schedule on page 167. Under certain conditions, these glues may be used cold press; however their cost is higher and performance generally poorer than blood glues developed specifically for the purpose, which are discussed later.

Other hot press glues may be formulated with blood-soybean flour ratios between 15:85 and 80:20. They all provide satisfactory dry adhesion, but water resistance increases from a moderate level for lower blood ratios to excellent for the higher ratios. Because of the larger water requirement of blood compared with soybean flour, glue costs increase only about 25 per cent over this range of blood contents.

Costs

It is difficult to list comparative blood glue costs which have meaning except on a very short-term basis. Raw material prices change drastically, industrial performance and use requirements change, and technical progress continues to the point where actual cost figures are only valid at the time of quotation. A few generalizations are possible, however, which help to put blood glues as a group in perspective with other adhesive systems.

Except in periods of heavily depressed prices, hot-press blood and soybean glues tend to fall in a glue line cost range of about $1.00 to $2.00 per thousand feet of *single* glue line (MSGL), including a nominal wastage factor. This range is based on the rate of glue application for plywood manufacture, or about 40 to 50 lb/MSGL. The $1.00 to $2.00 range holds for phenolic resin fortification of protein glues about to the point of equivalent resin solids and protein content, and includes most other additives such as mold inhibitors and denaturants. Protein cold-press glues also fall in this general cost range. The higher glue spreads required for cold-press operation, 60 to 80 lb/MSGL, are largely offset by a deliberate increase in water content, primarily through the use of denaturants.

Other Blood-Protein Combinations

A number of animal and vegetable protein materials other than soybean flour may be combined with blood albumin to yield useful wood adhesives. Casein, animal glue, dried whole egg, fish meal, corn zein, peanut flour and cottonseed meal are examples. Some contribute additional tack and flow properties, whereas others contribute a particulate consistency similar to soybean flour. Except for casein, which has been used with soluble blood as a hot-press plywood glue in Europe for many years,[44] none of these materials seem to offer any advantage over straight blood or blood-soybean adhesives in cost or performance. An interesting protein additive for soluble blood is blood itself in the form of totally insoluble (fertilizer grade) dried blood.[12, 13] As indicated earlier, this material, when finely powdered, swells and gelatinizes slightly under normal alkaline dispersion, and is capable of contributing desirable consistency properties to otherwise slimy soluble blood glues.

Fillers

Fillers are important to blood glue technology for the same reason. Since alkaline dispersions of blood are for the most part heavily water-containing and gelatinous in character, an absorptive granular constituent is usually required to lower the effective water content of the adhesive and provide solid substance to prevent excessive glue migration under heat and/or pressure.[24, 41, 45] It will be noted that almost every glue example in this chapter made with straight blood contains wood flour for this purpose. Many other absorptive fillers, both inorganic and cellulosic, perform this function in blood glues, including bentonites, corn cob flour, diatomaceous earth, bark flours, and "Furafil" 100S, a form of hydrolyzed cellulose (Quaker Oats Company). Nonabsorbent fillers such as clays and nut shell flours can also be added to blood glues for a particulate consistency without altering the water requirement of the glues more than slightly.[34, 36] In general, however, the absorptive fillers impart better working properties and frequently yield lower costs with no loss in adhesive quality.

Mold Resistance

The mold resistance of heat-cured protein glues ranges from poor to good, depending on blood content.[46] For example, glues containing primarily soybean flour with a limited amount of blood have no mold resistance;[47] whereas those containing more than half blood in some soluble form have frequently passed mold screening tests of considerable severity.[48] This fact is generally attributed to the high protein content of dried soluble blood compared with other natural protein sources, and the degree to which it reacts irreversibly in the presence of heat and alkali. Without this heat conversion, as in cold-pressed plywood, blood glues are subject to

mold and bacterial attack of almost the same order as other unprotected protein or starch adhesives. Where extreme mold exposure is anticipated, almost any conventional mold inhibitor can be added to a blood protein adhesive in amounts ranging from about 1 to 5 per cent, usually as a final step in the glue preparation. Suitable mold inhibitors include the various chlorinated phenols and phenylphenols, copper naphthenate, tributyltin oxide, copper-8-quinolinoleate and others. Unlike soybean adhesives, these reactive inhibiting compounds should not be blended into dry glues containing blood since they tend to act unfavorably on its protein during prolonged dry storage.

As indicated earlier in the chapter, phenolic adhesive resins also impart excellent mold resistance to blood hot-press glues when added at the rate of about 10 per cent resin solids, based on the weight of dry protein glue.[34, 36] This form of mold protection has the advantage of being very resistant to leaching from the cured glue film under wet service conditions since the resin itself becomes thermoset in place.

APPLICATION AND PRESSING

As a result of fairly recent developments in protein adhesive technology, blood glues are emerging as superior cold-press plywood adhesives, even to the point of challenging soybean glues for their traditional "No-Clamp" cold-press markets on a strictly cost-performance basis. Most of these new glues derive their unusual cold-press properties from partially soluble dried bloods.[11] A few have gained their partial solubility from wet-heat or chemical modifications of soluble blood.[24] The end result is the same in each case; namely, the slippery, gelatinous consistency of alkaline dispersed blood is altered to a granular consistency by converting a portion of the blood into discrete sticky particles. By interrupting the continuous colloidal state of the dispersed soluble blood, these particles help the water phase of the glue to migrate quickly into adjacent dry adherends, thus developing gel strength with sufficient speed to permit successful short cycle cold-press operation. These sticky particles of dispersed blood also help the cold-press glue film resist total absorption into the adherends under pressure, as well as migration from areas of extreme pressure, both of which cause loss of bond strength through overpenetration resulting in starved glue joints.[49]

Both the hot water coagulated blood glue and the low solubility blood glue listed earlier (Examples 1 and 2) are excellent cold-press adhesives.

Between the two, the low solubility blood glue is the more satisfactory for general use since equipment requirements are simpler, the denaturing step is under normal production control, and a generally better balance of particulate and colloidal forms of blood is obtained. An example of the chemically modified type of blood cold-press glue is given below:

	(lb)
Water at 60–70°F	150
Dried soluble beef blood	75
Fir wood flour	22
Pine oil or equivalent defoamer	3
Mix 2 min or until smooth	
Water at 60–70°F	370
Mix 2 min	
Hydrated lime in	7
Water at 60–70°F	21
Mix 1 min	
"N" brand sodium silicate	50
Mix 1 min	
50% sodium hydroxide solution	16
Mix 5 min	
Water at 60–70°F	135
37% formalin	2
Mix 3 min	
40% solids phenolic adhesive resin	10
Mix 3 min	

This glue is ready to use when mixed and has a working life of 4 to 8 hr, depending on temperature. It derives its high water requirement (6.84) and cold-press consistency from the combined denaturing effects of formaldehyde and phenolic resin solids on a normal alkaline dispersion of soluble blood. Both denaturants contribute to water resistance, and the resin adds moderate mold resistance. (It is precipitated in place rather than thermoset as the glue line cures.)

All the cold-press blood glues are excellent adhesives for plywood, flush doors, hardboard and softboard laminating, treated paper overlaying, common lumber laminating, box shook manufacture, and similar applications where a quick-setting, highly water-resistant cold-press bond is required. Glue line costs are almost competitive with soybean adhesives. For most wood laminating, these blood glues are used according to the "No-Clamp" cold-press schedule below.[50, 51] For paper gluing, substantially lower spreads and pressing times in seconds are adequate.[9]

For hot-press purposes, the granular consistency of blood cold-press adhesives is a moderate disadvantage. Since hot-press glue spreads are about 50 per cent lower, this consistency permits rapid loss of water phase from the glue line causing

PRESSING SCHEDULE
COLD-PRESS BLOOD GLUE
"NO-CLAMP" PROCESS
For Interior Type Douglas Fir Plywood

Use following wet glue spreads per MDGL,* according to core thickness:

	(lb)
1/10 core	125–130
1/9	129–134
1/8	133–138
1/7	135–140
1/6	138–143
3/16	140–145
All 5 ply 13/16 constructions	140–145

Glue Spreading Instructions:

(1) Rough or warm core and sub-species, add 5 lb extra spread over maximum spreads listed.
(2) Maximum stock moisture content, 8%.
(3) Do not use hot stock (over 110°F)
(4) Spread test piece, 12¾ in. by 25 in.

Pressing Instructions:

(1) Hold load 5 min before applying pressure.
(2) Load must be under full pressure within 25 min after first panel is laid.
(3) Pressure to be retained for 15 min.
(4) Pressing time is measured after gauge reaches full pressure.
(5) Use 175–200 psi hydraulic pressure.

* Thousand square feet of double glue line.

shortened assembly time limits. A smoother consistency such as that obtained with unmodified soluble blood glues is generally more suitable for hot pressing.

A typical plywood hot-press schedule for protein glues appears below.[52] This schedule can be used with almost any alkaline blood glue outlined in this chapter as long as it contains a minimum of 15 per cent blood and not more than approximately equal weights of blood and phenolic resin solids.

A few special curing techniques are occasionally applied to blood glues, e.g., short cycle cold pressing followed by a kiln heating cycle;[11] rapid glue spreading and a short pressing cycle on preheated stock; and radio frequency curing.[53] The first technique operates well but is cumbersome and largely outmoded in view of the efficiency of present cold- and hot-press blood glues. The second technique is especially useful in conjunction with blood glues due to their unusual reactivity on exposure to heat, their permanence of bond and relatively low cost. The third technique is limited by a problem common to all alkaline protein adhesives—excessive conductivity. Satisfactory RF cures have been obtained with blood glues, however, using reduced energy loads, clean glue spreads, and an insulating air gap.[54]

Viscosity

This important property largely governs the successful operation of most protein adhesives, and much of the technology discussed here is related to its control.

Viscosity of hot-press blood glues varies from 2500 to 25,000 cps. At the lower end of this range the glues are almost too thin to resist overpenetration into many adherends, while at the upper end they are approaching gelation. The practical range is approximately 5000 to 15,000 cps, and all the hot-press glue formulations shown were intended for this range unless otherwise specified. Cold-press blood glues definitely require a heavier, as well as more granular, consistency for successful

Blood Glue
Hot-Pressing Schedule
For Interior Type Douglas Fir Plywood

Rough Panel Thick. (in.)	No. of Plies	Panels per Opening	Lb Wet Spread Per MDGL	Minimum** Stand Time	Pressing Time in Minutes (full pressure)			
					230°F	240°F	260°F	280°F*
1/4	3	2	70	3	3	2¾	—	—
5/16	3	1	75	3	1¾	1½	1¼	1
5/16	3	2	75	3	3½	3	2¾	2¼
5/16	3	3	80	3	—	7	6	5¼
3/8	3	1	80	3	1¾	1¾	1½	1¼
3/8	3	2	80	3	—	4¼	3¾	3
7/16	3	1	85	3	2	1¾	1¾	1½
7/16	3	2	85	3	—	4½	4¼	4
7/16	5	1	70	3	3	—	—	—
7/16	5	2	70	3	—	6	—	—
1/2	5	1	75	3	2¾	2¼	2	1¾
1/2	5	2	80	3	—	6	5½	5
9/16	5	1	80	3	2¾	2½	2¼	2
9/16	5	2	85	3	—	7	6	5¼
5/8	5	1	80	3	3½	3	2½	2¼
5/8	5	2	85	3	—	7½	6½	5½
11/16	5	1	85	3	4	3½	3	2½
11/16	7	1	85	3	4¼	4	3¾	3¼
3/4	5	1	85	3	—	4¼	3¾	3
3/4	7	1	85	3	—	5	4¼	3¾
13/16	5	1	85	3	—	4½	3¾	3¼
13/16	7	1	85	3	—	6	4¼	4
7/8	7	1	85	3	—	—	5	4¼
15/16	7 and 9	1	90	4	—	—	6	5
1	7 and 9	1	90	4	—	—	7	5½
1 1/16	7 and 9	1	95	4	—	—	7	6
1 1/8	7 and 9	1	95	4	—	—	7½	6¼
1 3/16	7 and 9	1	95	4	—	—	8	6½
1 5/16	9	1	100	5	—	—	9	7
1 7/16	9	1	100	5	—	—	10	8
1 9/16	9 and 11	1	100	5	—	—	12	9

Total time assembly limit, 16 min.
5 lb extra spread, as minimum, on rough or warm core.
Core not to exceed 110°F.
Veneer moisture content not to exceed 5%.

Not less than 175 lb hydraulic pressure.
* Veneer moisture content not to exceed 3% at 280°F.
** Time before loading.

"No-Clamp" operation, i.e., about 7000 to 20,000 cps.[51] Since all protein glues exhibit non-Newtonian viscosity, the viscosimeters should operate at constant shear rate. Since most blood glues are quite thixotropic, it is usually desirable to determine the viscosity after at least 30 sec of rotation to ensure a steady reading. The difference between maximum and steady readings can even be used as an informal index of thixotropy in cases where this property is important. Among the more suitable devices are the MacMichael, Stormer and Brookfield viscometers, the last two at one speed only.

Glue mixing and spreading equipment as well as certain facets of pressing are covered in the Chapter on soybean glues.

RECENT DEVELOPMENTS

The technology of blood protein adhesives continues to expand, with the incorporation of new developments and refinement of older ones. For example, a recently issued patent describes the addition of polyvinyl acetate emulsions to blood and other protein adhesives in amounts up to several times the weight of dry protein for the purpose of increasing their tack, curing speed, water resistance and ability to bond green veneer.[14] These glues are intended primarily for paper overlaying wood veneer and box shook, but will undoubtedly find other uses. Calcium hydroxide is used to disperse the protein constituents, with other alkaline agents, and also to insolubilize the polyvinyl acetate. Another patent describes the use of styrene-acrylonitrile copolymer latices in protein adhesive systems.[55] Among the older developments, casein-blood adhesives are again assuming importance, currently as one-package glues for lumber laminating.[44, 56] Alkaline agents of the "double-decomposition" type are blended with the dry glue. Blood-silicate glues are finding occasional use as paper laminating and corrugating adhesives, but as wood glues they have been more or less completely supplanted by conventional sodium hydroxide-dispersed blood adhesives containing denaturants for specific property control.[20, 57]

Blood glues contribute to the over-all scheme of wood utilization in such a variety of unique and important ways that their future seems closely related to that of the forest products industry itself.

References

1. Lucas, A., "Ancient Egyptian Materials," *Analyst,* **51,** 435–450 (1926); Shrewsbury, H. S., "Sources of Albumin in Ancient Egypt," *Analyst,* **51,** 624–625; Pliny's "Natural History," Book XVI, Ch. 83, Bostock and Riley's Translation, London, Bohn, 1855.

2. Knight, E. V., and Wulpi, M., "Veneers and Plywood," pp. 261–263, New York, Ronald Press, 1927; Luther, A., German Patent 198,182 (Aug. 13, 1905).

3. U. S. Tariff Commission Reports of 1948; U. S. Dept. of Commerce, Census of Manufactures, 1942 through Preliminary 1958.

4. Eichholz, W., German Patent 199,903 (Aug. 16, 1907); Buhl, G. A., British Patent 112,965 (Dec. 29, 1916); Terwen, A. J. L., and Hoogenhuyze, C. J. C., British Patent 123,971 (Aug. 13, 1918); Lux, F. (to Firm Luftfahrzeugbau Schutte-Lanz), U. S. Patent 1,468,313 (Sept. 18, 1923).

5. "Aircraft Plywood, Blood Glue Solves the Problem," *Western Flying,* **3,** 84 (Oct. 1927); U. S. D. A. Forest Products Laboratory Report No. 66, "Glues Used in Airplane Parts, 1920."

6. Sutermeister, E., and Browne, F. L., "Casein and Its Industrial Applications," p. 281, New York, Reinhold Publishing Corp., 1939.

7. Douglas Fir Plywood Association, Quality Control, Production Estimate, Apr. 1961; Lane, L. B., Frendreis, J. J., "How Blood Adhesives Are Used," *Adhesives Age,* 20–24 (May 1961).

8. Nafilyan, G. Z., and Winckel, Max, British Patent 221,598 (June 30, 1923) "The Manufacture and Drying of Blood and Slaughterhouse Byproducts," *Chem-Zeitung,* **49,** 957–58 (1925).

9. Sheeran, N. J. (to American-Marietta Co.), U. S. Patent 2,870,034 (Jan. 20, 1959).

10. Cone, C. N. (to M and M Wood Working Co.), U. S. Patent 2,400,541 (May 21, 1946).

11. Cone, C. N. (to I. F. Laucks, Inc.), U. S. Patent 1,976,436 (Oct. 9, 1934).

12. Bradshaw, L., and Stachel, C. L. (to the Borden Co.), U. S. Patent 2,391,387 (Dec. 25, 1945).

13. Fawthrop, W. D. (to Adhesive Products Co.), U. S. Patent 2,292,624 (Aug. 11, 1942).

14. Drugge, C. E., and Hine, John M. (to the Borden Co.), U. S. Patent 2,963,454 (Dec. 6, 1960).

15. Meyer, K. H., "Natural and Synthetic High Polymers," pp. 572–584, New York, Interscience Press, 1950; Takashima, T., and Ariga, K., *Mokuzai Gaikkaishi,* **3,** 71–74, 1957.

16. Soluble Grade Dried Beef Blood Specifications, Wilbur-Ellis Co., Oct. 29, 1959.

17. Bogue, R. H., "The Chemistry and Technology of Gelatin and Glue," pp. 344–348, New York, McGraw-Hill Book Company, Inc., 1922.

18. Cone, C. N. (to American-Manetta Co.), U. S. Patent 2,895,928 (July 21, 1959).

19. Bjorksten, J., "Cross Linkages in Protein Chemistry" in *Advances in Protein Chem.,* **6,** 353–358, New York, Academic Press, 1951.

20. Cleveland, T., and Stericker, W. (to Philadelphia Quartz Co.), U. S. Patent 2,044,466 (June 16, 1936); U. S. Dept. of Agriculture, Forest Products Laboratory Report No. 281–282, *Blood Albumin Glues—Their Manufacture, Preparation and Application,* Revised July, 1938 and Mar. 1955.

21. Cone, C. N., and Galber, H. (to I. F. Laucks, Inc.), U. S. Patent 1,976,435 (Oct. 9, 1934).

22. Biddle, A. (to United Products Corp. of America), U. S. Patent 1,777,160 (Sept. 30, 1930).

23. Lloyd, D. J., "The Chemistry of the Proteins and Its Economic Applications," 44–49, Philadelphia, Blakiston, 1926.

24. Gossett, J. M., Estep, M. H., Jr., and Perrine, M. J. (to American-Marietta Co.), U. S. Patent 2,874,-134 (Feb. 17, 1959).

25. Putnam, F. W. in the "Proteins: Chemistry, Biological Activity and Methods," 1, Part B, pp. 814–826, New York, Academic Press, Inc., 1953.

26. Rippey, H. F., Cone, C. N., Davidson, G., Laucks, I. F., Banks, H. P., U. S. Patent 1,814,768 (July 14, 1931).

27. Jarvi, R. A. (to Monsanto Chemical Co.), U. S. Patent 2,705,680 (Apr. 5, 1955).

28. Cohen, A., British Patent 366,889 (Oct. 24, 1930); Cohen, A. (to General Electric Co.), U. S. Patent 1,935,434 (Nov. 14, 1933).

29. Bowen, A. H. (to I. F. Laucks, Inc.), U. S. Patent 2,014,167 (Sept. 10, 1935).

30. Golick, A. J., and Dike, T. W. (to I. F. Laucks, Inc.), U. S. Patent 2,368,466 (Jan. 30, 1945); Carmichael, O. C. (to I. F. Laucks, Inc.), U. S. Patent 2,375,195 (May 8, 1945).

31. Lindauer, A. C., U. S. Patent 1,459,541 (June 19, 1923).

32. Shelton, F. J., and Chervenka, C. H. (to Reichhold Chemicals, Inc.), U. S. Patent 2,872,421 (Feb. 3, 1959).

33. Ibid., 26, 908–956.

34. Arnot, R., U. S. Patent 1,771,553 (July 29, 1930); Cone, C. N., (to M and M Wood Working Co.), U. S. Patent 2,389,183 (Nov. 20, 1945).

35. Ash, J. R., and Lambuth A. L. (Monsanto Chemical Co.), U. S. Patent 2,817,639 (Dec. 24, 1957).

36. Rozema, C. E., and Tiglaar, J. H. (to Reconstruction Finance Corp.), U. S. Patent 2,066,857 (Jan. 5, 1937).

37. U. S. Plywood Corp. Sales Bulletin, Weldwood L1-R Plywood, AIA File No. 19-F, Feb. 1952.

38. I. G. Farbenindustrie A. G., French Patent 796,389 (Apr. 6, 1936); Menger, A. (to Plaskon Co.), U. S. Patent 2,203,501 (June 4, 1940).

39. Leonardson, C. S., and White, D. J. (to The Borden Co.), U. S. Patent 2,332,802 (Oct. 26, 1943).

40. Technical Service Bull. 211R and 216, UF 5112–5116 Glue Series, Plastics Division, Monsanto Chemical Co., Jan. 1956.

41. Dunham, H. V., U. S. Patent 1,892,486 (Dec. 27, 1932).

42. White, D. J. (to the Borden Co.), U. S. Patent 2,312,-056 (Feb. 23, 1943).

43. General Electric Co., British Patent 202,404 (May 18, 1922).

44. Perry, T. D., "Modern Wood Adhesives," pp. 88–89, New York, Pitman, 1944.

45. Wakita, M., Mokuzai Kenkyu (Wood Research), Japan, 4, 45–49, (1951).

46. Norris, C. B., and Laucks, I. F., "The Technique of Plywood," pp. 229–248, Seattle, I. F. Laucks, Inc., 1942; Brouse, D., "Casein and Blood Glue Joints Under Exposure," Wood Products, 12, 8–10 (Oct. 1934).

47. U. S. Dept. of Agriculture, Forest Products Laboratory Report, Forest Pathology Special Report No. 25, June 1945.

48. Douglas Fir Plywood Association, Approved Mold-Resistant Interior Hot Press Plywood Glues, Apr. 1961.

49. Ibid., 46, 234–249.

50. Schedule No. PG 908, No. 1177 Glue, Feb. 24, 1959, Plastics Division, Monsanto Chemical Co.

51. Galber, H., and Golick, A. J. (to I. F. Laucks, Inc.), U. S. Patent 2,402,492 (June 18, 1946).

52. Schedule No. PG 753, No. 1033 Glue, Dec. 2, 1957, Plastics Division, Monsanto Chemical Co.

53. Russell, G. F., and Mann, J. W., Wood Drying and Laminating by Radio Frequency, SPE-DFPA Joint Conference Report, July 13, 1944.

54. Albany-Plylock, Pioneer Thermal Heat Plywood Unit," The Timberman, 4, 35–39, July, 1941.

55. Dede, J. B., and Watson, D. A. (to Monsanto Chemical Co.), U. S. Patent 2,862,896 (Dec. 2, 1958).

56. Hadert, H., Gelatine, Leim Klebstoffe, 5, 154 and 179, 1937; Kustner, P., Gelatine, Leim Klebstoffe, 2, 254, 1934.

57. Drushel, W. A. (to Haskelite Mfg. Corp.), U. S. Patent 1,476,805 (Dec. 11, 1923); Haskell, H. L. (to Haskelite Mfg. Corp.), U. S. Patent 1,516,566 (Nov. 24, 1924).

— 12 —

Starch and its Derivatives

George V. Caesar

Starch Consultant
Harbor Beach, Michigan

Starch is the principal water-dispersible natural polymer used industrially as an adhesive. Starch-based adhesives are abundant, cheap and stable in price, widely effective, unique in their versatility, and simple in application.

The starch supply of the United States increased from approximately 800 million pounds in 1922 to 2,258 million in 1954.[1] Of this, about 95 per cent was domestically produced. In this enormous aggregate, corn starch was predominant. In 1954 it amounted to slightly less than 2,000 million pounds,[1] and in 1957 it was approximately 2,250 million, including dextrins and other modifications.[2] Approximately 75 per cent of the starch and practically all of the dextrin went into industrial uses,[3] of which the greater part may be classified as adhesives. Potato and wheat, respectively,[1] are the next most important domestic starches. Of the imports potato starch and tapioca flour rank high.

The chemical structure of starch is more intricate and controversial than that of its cousin, cellulose. Starch is a polymer of glucose. Approximately three-fourths of this carbohydrate is a treelike branched structure commonly known as *amylopectin*; the unbranched one-fourth is called *amylose*. Recently a small proportion of another type of branching has been found present. Figure 1[2] is a sketch* of the predominant treelike form and its structural chemical skeleton, stripped, for simplicity, of the bristling hydroxyl groups which impart to starch its very polar water-attracting properties. The complexity of this branched polymer is indicated in the photograph (Fig. 2) of an atomic model of a small segment of amylopectin.

* Courtesy Corn Industries Research Foundation

The structure of one variety of corn starch, waxy maize, is completely branched. Developed by a unique combination of cooperative research in biochemistry, agriculture, and industry, it is produced commercially in relatively minor tonnage. Similarly, effort is under way to produce a high amylose corn starch.

It is the amylose or unbranched component of starches which imparts the property of gelling or setting-back, which is a physical property especially characteristic of the cereal starches. By comparison, the aqueous dispersions or solutions of waxy maize starch remain relatively stable in viscosity. Dried films of the branched polymer are relatively brittle, but films from the unbranched component, amylose, are tougher; hence more nearly like those from cellulose. These properties are also true for derivatives such as esters and ethers of starch.

The two main polymer components of ordinary starches can be separated. Commercial amylose and amylopectin from potato starch and corn starch are available in this country.

Botanically there is a great variety of starches. As previously indicated, the principal commercial starches are corn, potato, tapioca, and wheat. They are marketed as fine white or pearly grained powders of characteristic size, size range, form, and marking. The tiny granules may vary in diameter from approximately 90 microns (potato starch) to less than 5 microns (.005 mm). The two main polymers, amylose and amylopectin, are separable by chemical techniques but only after appreciable degradation, since the oxygen-bridge linking the glucose units is chemically fragile. Under the microscope, we can see the granules absorb hot water and swell rapidly within a comparatively

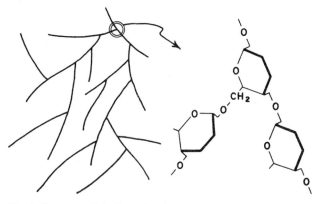

Fig. 1. Structure of the branched fraction of starch. Chemical configuration of the circled branch point is shown at right. (Reproduced from "CORN STARCH" by permission Corn Industries Research Foundation)

narrow temperature range. The temperature varies considerably for different starches; nevertheless any commercial type of untreated starch will be pasted in water between 140 and 170°F. Time, attrition by collision, and increasing temperature cause the swollen granules to burst and more or less disperse. A simple cooking with live steam at a solids concentration of 10 per cent, with only a slight amount of stirring, will produce a very heterogeneous paste of swollen granules in all stages of disintegration and film-forming character. If this crude cooking is followed by homogenizing, a fluid solution of superior filming properties is readily formed. The quality of aqueous dispersions of starches is very dependent on how they are made.

The viscosity of starches is affected by many factors. At low concentrations, particularly, ions in the water may have a pronounced effect. Variations may also result from commercial drying techniques, a factor which is currently appreciated more than in the past. Perhaps the marked differences in physical character between the pastes of cereal starches and those of root starches, such as tapioca and potato, result from (1) the higher moisture in the root than in the cereal kernel, and (2) the differences in handling the two groups of materials. Starch from the root is dried only once, but cereal starch undergoes two dryings, once by sun and again by man after wet-milling of the kernel. Pastes of cereal starches look as if they have suffered some retrogradation of amylose—a uniting of the polymer chains with exclusion of water. When a small proportion of a polar or water-attracting chemical grouping is substituted, as in some of the specialty starches, clarity and rootlike character are increased and even surpassed, pre-

sumably as a result of the opening up or wedging apart of the amylose chains.

Such is the natural compromise polymer, starch, in its unaltered state. Its physical properties in aqueous dispersions are a compromise between those of the amylopectin in its special botanical variety, waxy maize, and of its minor component, amylose, the film-former, which might be called a first cousin of cellulose. In fact, amylose seems almost as insoluble as cellulose, once it has fully retrograded.

If starch could not be readily broken down into a great variety of degradation products, all of

Fig. 2. Scale model (1 Angstrom = 1 cm.) of a segment of a starch amylopectin molecule. Molecule weight of segment is 13600.

them hydrophilic and adhesive, it, like cellulose derivatives, would be useful primarily in a high-viscosity, low-solids state. Fortunately, though, starch can be degraded inexpensively in a number of ways, i.e., by enzymes, acids, oxidizing agents, and heat, into adhesives having a wide range of aqueous viscosity and solids concentration. They are adaptable to machine application over a large range of uses.

The industrial degradation products of starch may be classified into three main groups: (1) thin-boiling starches, (2) oxidized starches, and (3) dextrins.

The latter may further be divided into: (1) white dextrins, (2) canary or yellow dextrins, and (3) British gums.

Degradation of starch reduces viscosity and yields higher solids concentrations with quicker tack or grab and faster drying or setting. A schematic outline[2] of what takes place in a general way, structurally, in degradation processes is indicated in Fig. 3. *Acid hydrolysis* is the primary reaction in making thin-boiling starches and the "starchier" types of white dextrins; *polymerization* takes place in making the canary dextrins and British gums, and to some extent also in the white dextrins. This complex chemical picture is currently under long-range basic investigation by carbohydrate chemists on university fellowships sponsored by the Corn Industries Research Foundation.

Thin-Boiling or "Fluidity" Starches

These are the oldest and cheapest types of modified starches. The low fluidity starches are made by wet-processing in acid slurries. To save serious loss in solubles, the high fluidity starches are usually made by drying-in the acid. These modified starches, selling for only 60¢ per cwt over pearl corn starch, find large-volume use in a number of fields as will subsequently be described.

Oxidized Starch

This type of starch is utilized in quality adhesives for surface sizing of high-grade paper and for paper coating. The whiteness of its solutions and its comparatively high viscous stability are desirable attributes. Oxidized starch is often called "chlorinated" because it is made by wet treatment with sodium hypochlorite.

The Dextrins

White, canary, and British gum are made by heating starch in the dry state. For white and canary types, starch is sprayed with acids and heated; for British gums, heat is the principal factor, although relatively small proportions of acid may be used to shorten conversion times. It is said that the first British gum resulted from a fire in a British starch factory. Although dextrinization is still much of an art, it should become more of a science as a result of fundamental studies now under way. A distinction between some of the highly soluble whites and a canary dextrin may be arbitrary, but generally, the latter will have a more stable viscosity at high solids than the former. The whites are characterized not only by their lighter color but by their pasting tendencies. The gummy, filmy colloids of relatively stable body, at comparatively low solids concentrations as formed from solutions of the British gums, are probably the strongest of the dextrin adhesives but are the slowest to make properly.

Figures 4 and 5, prepared from absolute viscosity data obtained by Cannon-Fenske Ostwald-

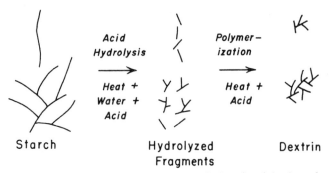

Fig. 3. Hydrolysis and repolymerization during dextrinization of starch. (Reproduced from "CORN STARCH" by permission Corn Industries Research Foundation)

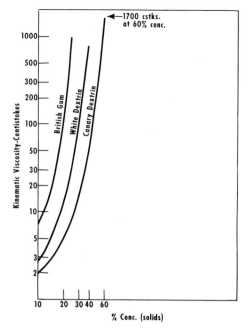

Fig. 4. Viscosity-concentration relationship of corn dextrins at 80°F.

type viscometers, show the rheological properties of these three broad classifications of corn dextrins. Figure 4 gives viscosity-concentration relationships after rapid cooling of the dextrins at room temperature; Fig. 5 gives viscosity-temperature relationship at 25 per cent concentration.

A log-log plot is used in Fig. 4 to emphasize the dependence of viscosity on solids content. For British gum, a 25 per cent solution is getting close to a paste in body, which is equally true for white dextrin at 40 per cent; but the canary dextrin is a fluid 1,700 centistokes at as high as 60 per cent solids!

In Fig. 5 the temperature in reciprocal of degrees Kelvin is plotted against log viscosity. With these coordinates, an ideal or Newtonian solution gives a straight line (cf. Eyring[4]). The 25 per cent solution of the canary dextrin approaches linearity, but the white dextrin shows a pronounced upward trend at room temperature (80°F). The curve for the medium-soluble British gum forms an elongated S, like unhomogenized starch at a much lower concentration.

Thus a wide range of viscosities is available for industrial applications of dextrins. Further variations of viscosity are available from alkaline additives such as borax and metaborate, soda ash, meta-silicates, and caustic soda. Of these agents, borax and metaborate are by far the most impor-

tant since they contribute remarkable increase in wet tack or grab, body, and stability.

INDUSTRIAL USES OF STARCH AND STARCH-BASED ADHESIVES

Of the major industries in which starch and its modifications are used, paper and paper products rank first.

Paper Making

The role of raw unmodified starch in the actual formation of a sheet of paper has been large. There is some controversy regarding the best way to get results from starch as a beater additive. Starch substitutes for beating time through its adhesive fiber-binding properties and effect on sheet formation. It may be added in dry form, both ungelatinized and in a pre-gelatinized state, and after cooking. The newer specialty starches, in which some of the hydroxyl hydrogen has been substituted, are becoming increasingly important in sheet formation. Starch is hard-pressed by other beater additives but is saving itself by research.

Surface Sizing. Surface sizing with starch both on and off the machine is becoming increasingly important. Oxidized starches are highly regarded,

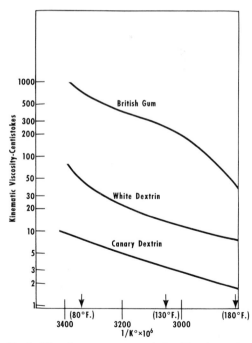

Fig. 5. Viscosity-temperature relationship of corn dextrins at 25% solids

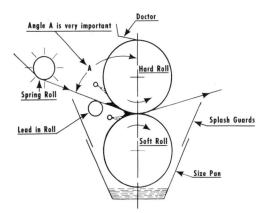

Fig. 6. Conventional size press.

but starch converted by enzymes at the paper mill is the big factor in tonnage (see Fig. 6).

To make a surface size for book paper, potato starch was converted by enzymes in water brought to pH 6.5 to 7.0 with lime. Solids concentration was approximately 8 per cent; viscosity was very low, well under 10 centistokes at 100°F. By comparison, a 9 per cent *unmodified* corn-starch solution, well homogenized, may have a viscosity of approximately 100 centistokes at 200°F.

Coating. The great increase recently of on-the-machine coating, at higher speeds and coating "color" solids than possible in "off-the-machine" coating, has contributed to the use of highly modified starches such as the dextrins. At high total solids—55 to 70 per cent—a pigment binder of lower adhesive strength is more permissible than in a color of low solids. The lighter varieties of compromise British gums (acid modified) and certain types of white dextrins are excellent in machine coating. Enzyme-converted starch leads in tonnage, although conversion at high solids requires special equipment and experience, and the product is necessarily less homogeneous in structure than a dextrin or other factory-modified product.

A formula for a coating color of 60 per cent solids[5] is as follows:

Water	70 gal
Sodium metaphosphate	8 lb
Soda ash	2 lb
Calcium carbonate	400 lb
Clay	1600 lb
Oxidized starch	320 lb
(cooked in 960 lb water)	
Pine oil	1 qt
10% Soap solution	10 gal

One method of preparing a high-solids coating color is first to make up the pigments at 70 per cent

and then work in the cooked starch solution; another is to prepare the starch in all of the water required for the finished color and then work in the dry pigments. Very powerful and efficient mixing equipment must be used. See Fig. 7.

So much for starch-based adhesives in the *making* of paper. In the products made *from* paper, in the bonding of paper *surfaces,* starch-based adhesives also find large and varied usage.

Corrugated Boxboard

Originality of technical thinking was strikingly demonstrated in the conception and development of a practical and efficient process for bonding corrugated board with a starch adhesive.[6] This, the "Stein-Hall Process," has become the largest single new outlet for starch in the last quarter century.

This process makes starch competitive with silicate of soda and its high solids. It takes advantage of the natural property of starch to gelatinize rapidly and with maximum viscosity within a limited temperature range. A concentrated suspension of starch granules—a fluid "milk"—is applied to the flutes of corrugated board to be swollen and burst there by the heat of the machine, *in situ,* in contact with the paper liner. A difficult initial problem was the development of a practicable carrier to keep the starch granules in suspension. The answer was found in gelatinizing a

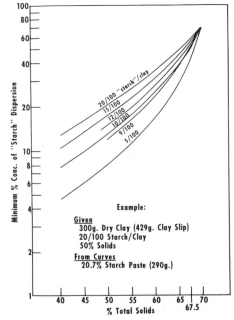

Fig. 7. Relation of "starch"-water concentration to total solids at 70% clay-water.

fraction of the total starch by caustic soda. Other improvements included lowering the gelatinization temperature of the slurry with caustic; increasing the rate of gelatinization with borax; maintaining optimum viscosity of the "milk" and its stability in the paste pans; and providing adequate heating, since the use of starch required more heat than for silicate, as well as the design and construction of special mixing equipment.

The following is a typical formula and directions for preparing a non-weatherproof paste:[7]

"Two-Tank System—Henry Pratt Mixers—333 gal
  Starch: corn

Upper Mixer (No. 1):
(1) Add 400 lb water which will bring the level to about 25 in. from top.
(2) Add 80 lb starch and mix for 3 min.
(3) Dissolve 17 lb caustic soda in 3 gal water in suitable container; stop agitator and add this solution; start agitator and mix thoroughly.
(4) Heat with live steam to 160°F and agitate for 15 min.
(5) Add 500 lb cold water and agitate which should bring the level to about 6 in. from top.
(6) This diluted mixture is the completed carrier and is ready for use in the lower mixing tank (No. 2).

Lower Mixer (No. 2):
(7) Fill with 1520 lb water, i.e., about 18 in. from top.
(8) Add 10 lb bentonite and mix thoroughly.
(9) Add 17 lb borax and mix until dissolved (2 to 3 min).
(10) Add 505 lb starch and mix well until thoroughly dispersed.
(11) Drop contents of upper tank (No. 1) slowly into lower tank (No. 2) and agitate until viscosity reaches about 35 sec. This is on the standard Stein-Hall viscosity tube.
(12) Add 1 qt of formaldehyde or 1 lb of "Dowicide."
(13) Pump to storage tank.

Note: If heavier paste is desired, increase the quantity of starch in Step No. 2 (5 lb should be ample). If thinner paste is desired, decrease quantity of starch in Step No. 2 (5 lb should be sufficient)."

Frequently the entire mixing is done in tank No. 2.

The vast corrugated board industry uses unmodified starch. The corn-starch producers supplying this industry have been active in meeting its needs for ever-increasing rates of production and a demand for weatherproof board.

In other paper-gluing fields, adhesive requirements are met principally by modified starches, i.e., thin-boiling, oxidized, and dextrin, in addition to that indispensable and ubiquitous additive,

borax. Some of the most important of these fields will be discussed.

Paper Bags

One of the large consumers of starch-based adhesives is the paper bag industry. Of the many types of bags, grocery and multi-wall consume the most adhesive.

Adhesives for grocery bags may be divided into two types: *seam* and *bottom*.

A seam adhesive must be fluid, tacky, non-foaming (the *sine qua non* for any adhesive, be it starch or otherwise) and fairly stable in viscosity. It may derive from a thin-boiling starch, an oxidized starch, or from a dextrin, plus borax, meta-borate, soda ash, metasilicate, etc., blended in by the manufacturer. The bag maker may add other chemicals such as caustic, clay, or preservative to help him achieve his purpose which is to get the maximum efficiency for the particular type of machine applying the adhesive. A formula working well on one machine will fail on another. Here, as in all other fields of gluing, there is no substitute for practical experience. Fortunately much information is available from the leading producers and distributors of starch-based adhesives.

For grocery bags, seam adhesives are generally prepared at 20 to 30 per cent solids. A concentration of 22 to 24 per cent and a final viscosity of 1000 to 2000 cps may be suitable for lighter weight small bags, while for heavier weight paper and sack-type bags the adhesive concentration may be 26 to 28 per cent and the viscosity 3000 to 5000 cps. Local conditions and plant set-ups determine the best and cheapest formulations.

Seam adhesives are mechanically applied by: (1) a free-running wheel turned by the paper passing through the bag machine; (2) a small metering pump geared to the machine speed to deliver the proper amount of adhesive, depending on the speed of passage of the paper; (3) a power-driven wheel turning at the paper speed. Methods (1) and (2) require fairly close viscosity tolerance. In the former method the adhesive will drag the wheel if it is too heavy, thereby making it turn slower than the paper speed and causing skips or, at best, uneven gum application; whereas the latter method will deliver excessive gum if it is too thin resulting in loss of wet tack, spreading of the seam line, and sticking together of bags. On the other hand, if the adhesive is too heavy, the metering pump cannot deliver enough of it. Relatively complicated and requiring careful adjustments, method (3) can handle a much wider range of viscosity.

Bottom pastes for grocery and sack bags have a number of requirements: (1) they should be sufficiently thixotropic to keep the paste roll covered, yet not so thixotropic as to break down appreciably under the roll action; (2) they should be short enough not to throw-off from the stencil applying the paste; (3) they should have enough wet tack to hold the bottoms closed until the bags are bundled or wrapped or weighted; and (4) they must form a good dry bond. Either they may be derived from starch *and* dextrin, or from thin-boiling or oxidized starch. Depending on the conditions, bottom pastes may be prepared at from 15 to 25 per cent solids with caustic, clay, soap, tallow, sulfonated oils, etc., added at the point of use. Since formulations are legion, the expert has to look carefully into the particular needs before making a recommendation.

Multi-Wall Bag Adhesives. Ordinarily the term multi-wall refers to large kraft bags having from two to six walls. They may have sewn tops and bottoms, sewn bottoms and open mouths, pasted tops and bottoms, or pasted bottoms and open mouths. Three types of adhesives are required: seam, cross or ply-pasting, bottoming.

For seam and bottom operations the adhesives are further divided into non-water resistant and water-resistant types.

The non-water resistant-starch based adhesives may be compounded by the starch producer from thin-boiling, oxidized starch, or dextrins, separately or in combination to which is added borax. An excellent early multi-wall bag seam gum was made from a British gum, metasilicate, and borax. Present seam adhesives have a normal range of 20 to 33 per cent solids and viscosities of 2000 to 3000 cps. For water-resistant seam and bottom adhesives, the bag manufacturers may buy thin-boiling starches or white dextrins. Subsequently, to a desired combination they may add an urea-formaldehyde resin in a water-soluble stage of polymerization in addition to catalysts to get further polymerization of the resin *after* gumming. The resin reacts with the starch thereby preventing it from softening in water, after the resin has undergone further polymerization to an insoluble state.

Following are two formulas for water-resistant seam gums:

Thin-boiling starches	700	lb
Soap	3¾	lb
Urea-formaldehyde resin	105	lb
Water	196	gal
Trisodium phosphate	10	lb

(added after cooking and cooling)

In this formulation, water resistance developed very slowly over several months of bag storage.

Water	170	gal
White dextrin	700	lb
Soap	2	lb
Urea-formaldehyde resin	70	lb
Cooked by live steam to about 200°F and cooled with water to about 260 gal volume, then:		
Ammonium chloride	14	lb

In this formula, a pH of around 6 causes a much quicker polymerization and development of water resistance in the seams. On the other hand, it is easy to run into trouble because of premature setting of the adhesive in these lower pH formulas.

Multi-wall adhesives for seams must be free-flowing (2000 to 3000 cps), non-staining, and have good wet tack; furthermore, they must not be pressed into the paper and "killed."

Bottom pastes should not string or foam. They should have enough wet tack to hold the flaps down until put under pressure. They should not dry to hard and brittle films.

For sewn top and bottom bags the adhesive is on the seams only. It should set rapidly enough to allow the tubes to go directly from the conveyor to sewing, a period as short as 3 min from application of the seam gum.

For sewn bottom open-mouth bags, a second application of adhesive is needed; this is called ply or cross-pasting. Adhesive is applied in spots to all of the plies so that the top of the bag acts as one wall of paper rather than as separate plies. The inner may not be pasted and can thus be folded in before the sewing of the remaining plies to complete the closure. Ply paste is usually thinned seam gum. The main problems in cross-pasting are foaming and throwing.

For pasted top and bottom multi-wall bags, seam needs are similar, but the tube must have all its plies, both at top and bottom, ply or cross-pasted. Then, in the pasting operation of putting in top and bottom, the tubes act as one ply.

For pasted bottom open-mouth bags the operation proceeds as in pasted top and bottom except that the inner top ply may not be pasted, as may similarly hold true in the case of sewn bottoms.

In bottoming operations—both single and double ender—the multi-wall tubes which have been seamed and cross-pasted are usually aged for at least 24 hr before bottoming. The tubes enter a hopper and are fed automatically into the folding mechanism where a rotating paste pad takes bottom paste from a roll turning in the paste pan and transfers it to the bottoms or the tops of the bags after they have been creased or folded.

From these sketchy descriptions it is evident that the properties of the adhesives for modern bag manufacture must meet exacting specifications. specifications.

Paper Boxes

Large amounts of dextrins, mostly borated, are used in making paper boxes. The operations are classified as: (1) ending; (2) stripping; (3) tight wrap; and (4) loose wrap.

Ending. This operation involves the formation of the box body. After the board is cut and creased, three edges are turned in to form a base for the end to be glued. After the adhesive is applied in dots, the board end is put in position under heavy pressure. Adhesion must be complete when pressure is released. The adhesive must be thin-bodied at high solids and not gummy or stringy; futhermore, it must wet the board, but not disappear into it under pressure. Ending demands very close tolerances in an adhesive.

Stripping. In this operation the sides and covers of the boxes are wrapped with paper. A slow operation, it involves much skilled handwork. An appreciable time lapse exists between the gumming of the wrap and its application to the box where it is rubbed smooth and the edges turned in by hand. Cold water-soluble adhesives composed of 85 to 90 per cent dextrin and 10 to 15 per cent borax are used to a considerable extent, adding 3 to 4 parts of water per part solids, to the desired viscosity. In some instances where difficult high-quality wrap papers are used, gums from high-soluble thin dextrins are employed at only 2 parts of water. Automatic stripping at higher speeds takes less than 2 parts.

Tight Wrap. Die-cut papers—wrap—of the exact size and shape for the boxes to be covered are automatically fed one at a time over a glue roll applying the proper amount of adhesive. Then the wraps pass along a suction belt which keeps the papers from curling until they reach the operator who controls the number of wraps on the belt so that they will have the correct tack and temper when he puts the boxes or covers on them. At this point they must stick to the boxes or covers. A plunger then presses the boxes through rollers and brushes, completing the operation.

Starch-based adhesives are usually high-soluble low-viscosity types blended with borax (10 to 15

per cent) and high in solids (40 to 55 per cent). They must have good grab, and lingering, be pleasant smelling, non-foaming, and impart minimum warping as a result of the wetting of the wrap and its dimensional changes. Running temperatures may be as high as 120°F, thus permitting higher solids and less warping.

Loose Wrap. This operation is similar to tight wrap except that the adhesive is applied only to the border of the wrap.

Carton Sealing

In this operation the adhesives must seal the top and bottom flaps of small knockdown paper boxes coming from the folding-box manufacturer to the packer. A variety of adhesives are used. Bottom gluing is the first station. Adhesive is applied by roller to the two long flaps, and the small flaps are turned in. One long gummed flap is turned in and stuck to the small flaps, then the other long flap is folded in and stuck to the first one. Lastly, the carton is placed on a conveyor and sent to the filling station where the weight of the filling helps to seal the bottom. Although top sealing is more complicated, the principle is similar. The only pressure applied comes from the conveyor belts with none coming from the inside. Here again it is apparent that adhesives specifications are exacting. They should be free-flowing, stable in viscosity, and give good closure. An experienced packer may concoct his own pet glue, or he may buy it in liquid form and have only to dilute it for use.

Case Sealing

This consists of the gluing of both top and bottom flaps of corrugated or solid fiber cases by hand or by machine. In machine-sealing the adhesive is applied to top and bottom flaps simultaneously in 2 to 5 in. widths from rolls set horizontally or vertically. The chief factor in the selection of the proper case-sealing adhesive is in the length of the compression unit controlling time under pressure. In one type of case, designed for easy opening, adhesive is applied only to the corners of the flap by cam operation of the gum rolls.

Frequently a case-sealing adhesive based on starch modifications will run high in caustic soda content; furthermore caustic is the great "sticker" for hard-to-stick papers wherever staining is of little consequence. Liquid starch-based adhesives are favored in this trade, at a price of approximately 4¢ per lb, for both carton and case sealing.

Tube Winding

This field is a large consumer of liquid starch-based adhesives i.e., thin-boiling starches, dextrins, borax, and caustic. There are two main classifications of tubes: convolute and spiral.

A convolute tube is made similar to the rolling-up of a window shade with the adhesive applied to one or both sides of the paper or board before winding on a mandrel. One winding is automatic; another is by hand. In the former, the "chip" is fed from continuous rolls with one end-edge of the chip sanded or feathered. Then adhesive is applied to both sides. It is turned on a mandrel, layer on layer for three to six wraps. The last wrap has the feathered edge and forms a tube with no sharp break. After the tubes are pushed off the mandrel, they are stacked to dry.

Quite a different type of convolute tube is used for product containers. Here the adhesive is applied to one side only, while a mandrel grips the board and spins the desired number of wraps. The inner surface, in contact with the mandrel, is ungummed. After winding, the tube is given a revolving pressing operation, at which point it may be labeled by bringing labels in contact with the gummed outer surface and spinning.

Spiral tubes are wound spirally on a mandrel and may vary from a soda straw to a huge tube for holding concrete, the number of plies being almost unlimited. Generally, the innermost ply has no adhesive; succeeding plies may have one or both sides gummed; and the outermost can have adhesive only on its underside since the top-side must contact the belt keeping the tube moving spirally.

Adhesives specifications include free-flow and the correct tack for the speed of running and length of cutoff. Before recommending a spiral tube adhesive, one must have a complete understanding of all the facts.

Laminated Paper Board

Once a large consumer of thin-boiling starch and borax adhesive, the laminating of paper has been seriously invaded by synthetic adhesives and clay extender owing to the unusually favorable spreads obtained.

Gummed Tape (Water re-moistening)

In recent years, special starch-based adhesives, the profitable fruit of research, have successfully invaded the field of paper-sealing tape adhesives, a field once as completely dominated by animal glue as corrugating was by silicate of soda. The adhesives are of a specially modified dextrinous type and well plasticized. The severe specifications for tape especially require quick and strong initial tack and high permanent strength of bond, together with high gloss and flexibility of film.

Tape adhesives based on potato starch, similarly to products from waxy maize and tapioca have been notably successful in this field. Plasticizers principally used in the formulations have been urea and sodium nitrate. The patent literature is fairly extensive.[8]

Vegetable-type tape adhesives are applied hot at high solids (about 50 per cent) to the kraft paper forming the tape rolls.

Various forms of the McLauren tester are used to determine rate of retack after moistening in cold water; a kraft test paper is expected to tear within 3 sec after moistening the tape.

Gummed Paper (Water re-moistening)

Starch-based high-soluble adhesives such as dextrins and starch converted to dextrin viscosities by means of enzymes find considerable use in gumming paper for labels, postage stamps, etc. Film color, shine, and re-moistening properties play important industrial roles, along with viscosity and viscous stability. The *sine qua non* is workable viscosity at extremely high solids so as to provide sufficient weight of dry gum film per ream without excessive wetting and dimensional changes in the paper base.

Probably the most familiar and certainly an extensive use of gummed paper made with dextrins is in the manufacture of envelopes. Envelope seals are applied from aqueous solutions of high-soluble dextrins varying from 55 to 65 per cent solids at viscosities of a few thousand centipoises and composed of a corn or tapioca base, or of a blend of the two. They will also contain plasticizers or stabilizers of a polar character, in amount and kind dependent on the envelope paper to be gummed and type as well as speed and drying time of machine applicator. A seal gum should have high gloss or shine and preferably a little color—on the light-brown side—although various other tints are sometimes requested so as to be visible to the user. It should be clean-running on the machines, that is, without excessive throwing or cottoning, give minimum curl, and its seals should not tend to block or stick together in the boxes in humid weather. In this latter respect a non-humectant plasticizer is important; a hydrophilic plasticizer which might work well in a dry climate could have a calamitous effect in a humid climate. In recent years, greatly increased rates of production and lighter and stronger papers are making a "witches brew" of formulations for sealing envelopes. Whatever properties are obtained, a moistened seal must stick.

Parenthetically, the back seams, which form the envelope, require a different type of dextrin as well as plasticizer. A much slower drying adhesive is needed, with some wet-tack and no color or show-through. Usually these are white dextrin high-soluble types with plasticizers such as urea or dicyandiamide.

So much for the larger uses of starch-based adhesives in paper and paper products—fields in which they are of major importance and have maximum tonnage. The consumption of corn starch and corn starch-based adhesives by the paper and paper products industry is well over half a billion pounds.[9] There are numerous minor fields in this industry, such as paper-cup forming, cigarette sealing, etc., which cannot be covered here.

Textiles

Second to the paper industry in the consumption of starch is the textile industry. Considered strictly as an adhesive the role of starch and starch-based products is here akin to that in paper making wherein fibers are bound together or coated and surface films are promoted.

Cotton warp sizing is still a very large field for heavy-boiling and thin-boiling starch. The sizing of warp fibers has but one purpose: to improve weaving efficiency by formation of a tough and readily removable film on the warp. The low cost of starch has more than counterbalanced its natural deficiencies as a film-former in comparison to many of the synthetics. However, starch is under increasingly severe competition, and research on starch in warp sizing has been relatively unproductive. This is true to an even greater degree in other fields in textiles such as finishing, once a large consumer of modified and dextrinous starch products. In textiles, the use of starch in large tonnage has narrowed to the sizing of cotton warps. For the most part, synthetic fiber warps are incompatible with starch.

In recent years homogenization of heavy-boiling corn-starch solutions by mechanical means through conversion of high-pressure energy to kinetic energy[10] has been successfully applied in many textile mills. The following are typical warp size formulations used in southern mills:

Denims

80 lb of pearl starch to 106 gal finished size
15 lb softener—tallow, sulfonated oil, calcium chloride
 2 pt kerosene
Cooked to 190° F and homogenized at 2000 psi

Sateen

160 lb of starch to 225 gal
 5 lb of a special softener
 1 pt kerosene
Cooked to 200°F and homogenized at 4000 psi

The laundry industry is another substantial consumer of starch—specifically heavy-boiling starch—in which its adhesive properties combine it to the textile fibers, adding stiffening and soil protection, effectively, attractively, and inexpensively. Wheat starch has been pre-eminent in the laundering of men's shirts. Numerous special laundry starches are produced for this purpose, used both in liquid state and in cold-water dispersible form.

This chapter cannot attempt even a listing of the many fields of industry in which the adhesive properties of starch-based products play a relatively minor role. There are industrial fields in which starch is more important for its colloidal properties, such as in oil-well drilling, ore treatment, etc. This chapter is limited to starch as an adhesive, and more specifically to its major applications.

Prices

Car-lot prices for regular starch products were in the following range, fob Chicago, during 1961:

	cwt
Pearl corn starch	$5.60
Thin-boiling starches	6.20
Oxidized corn starches	7.60
British gum	8.30
White dextrin	7.80
Yellow (canary) dextrin	8.00
Borated dextrins—variable but no lower than base dextrin	

Acknowledgments

The author is particularly indebted to a former co-worker, E. E. Moore of Stein-Hall & Co., for technical data on paper bags, boxes, carton and case sealing, and tube winding.

Other individuals and organizations to whom he is grateful for assistance and for the use of their literature are: Dr. John T. Goodwin and the Corn Industries Research Foundation, Max Goldfrank and the Stein-Hall organization, and R. C. Charron, formerly of United States Envelope Co.

References

1. Kennedy, N. F., "Starch: Raw Material Sources and Economics," Corn Industries Research Foundation, Washington, D. C., *Ind. Eng. Chem.,* **47,** 1405 (1955).
2. "Corn Starch," Corn Industries Research Foundation, Washington, D. C.
3. Personal communication, *ibid.*
4. Kerr, R. W., "Chemistry and Industry of Starch," p. 254, New York, Academic Press, 1950.
5. Compiled by the author.
6. Bauer, J. V. (to Stein Hall Mfg. Co.), U. S. Patent 2,051,025 (1936); U. S. Patent 2,102,937 (1937); and U. S. Patent 2,212,557 (1940) on "Corrugating."
7. Brochure: The Stein Hall Process, Stein Hall & Co., New York, N. Y.
8. Bauer, H. F., Bauer, Jordan V., and Hawley, Don M. (to Stein Hall Mfg. Co., Chicago), U. S. Patent 2,144,610 (1939); U. S. Patent 2,145,195 (1939); U. S. Patent 2,167,629 (1939); and U. S. Patent 2,188,329 (1940). Also Bauer, Hans F., U. S. Patent 2,215,847 (1940); Bauer, Hans F., Bauer, Jordan V., and Hawley, Don M., U. S. Patents 2,220,987 and 2,220,988 (1940); and U. S. Patent 2,238,767 (1941).
9. Caesar, George V., and Thompson, Thomas D. (to Stein Hall & Co., New York), U. S. Patent 2,417,969 (1947); Rees, Lancelot H. (to Manton Gaulin Mfg. Co.), U. S. Patent 2,635,068 (1953).

— 13 —

Cellulosics

Walter D. Paist

Celanese Polymer Company
A Division of Celanese Corporation of America
Clark Township, New Jersey

The origin of cellulose, the "backbone" of many important industrial adhesives, is in the structural elements of plants. Cotton linters, the most familiar form, yields about 82 per cent of purified cellulose; whereas wood pulp—spruce, pine, and hemlock—yields about 60 per cent of useful cellulose.

Cellulose is a long-chain polymer made by nature with the structure shown in Fig. 1. It is seen to be a series of glucosidic rings joined by oxygen bridges. The repeating monomer unit, bracketed in Fig. 1, consists of a ring which carries three hydroxyl groups, one primary and two secondary. All adhesives based on cellulose are derivatives formed by reacting one or more of these three hydroxyl groups. Complete reaction of all three hydroxyl groups is generally neither necessary nor desirable for good adhesives. Some residual percentage of free OH groups generally improves solubility and adhesive qualities. Thus, the best cellulose nitrate adhesives are made with only 11.2 to 11.6 per cent nitrogen; whereas if nitration were carried to completion, the nitrogen content would be about 14.8 per cent. Esters of both organic and inorganic acids, as well as ethers, are used for adhesives and binders. The ethers such as methyl cellulose are generally made by reacting

"soda" cellulose, prepared by the action of aqueous sodium hydroxide on cellulose, with an alkyl halide such as methyl chloride. Some ethers are made, however, by reacting an ethylene oxide with soda cellulose, in which case the hydroxylethyl ether is formed.

A further classification of adhesive cellulose derivatives can be made by virtue of their solubility characteristics. Some, such as cellulose nitrate and ethyl cellulose, are soluble in organic solvents; whereas others are water soluble, e.g., methyl cellulose, hydroxyethyl cellulose, and carboxymethyl cellulose. Where maximum water resistance is needed, the latter types cannot be used. Conversely, where paper is to be printed with an organic soluble ink, a water-soluble binder may be preferred to surface the paper, hold the fibers together, and prevent penetration of the soluble ink.

A summary of bonding classification, solubility and performance characteristics of the cellulosic adhesives is given in Table 1.

Where contact with foods is expected and materials acceptable to the Food and Drug Administration of the United States Department of Agriculture are needed, the cellulosic derivatives are widely

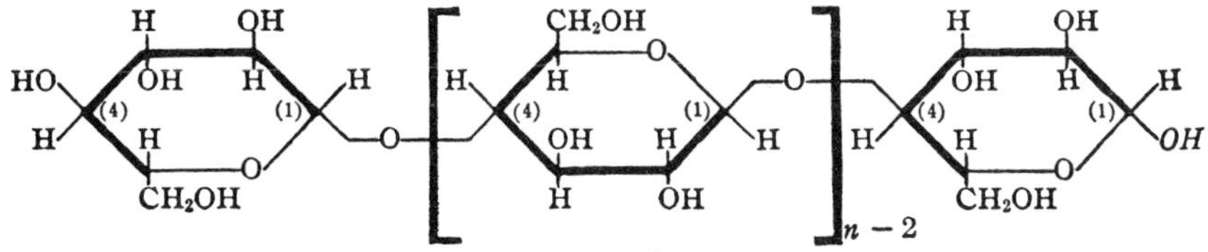

Fig. 1.

B • ADHESIVE MATERIALS

TABLE 1.

Type of Plastic Base	Bonding Classification[a]	Solvents[b]	Resistance Rating[c]					Effectiveness[c] of Bond With:							
			Water	Solvents	Heat	Cold	Fungus	Wood	Metals	Rubber	Glass	Leather	Paper	Textiles	Ceramics
Cellulose acetate	SR, F	Cl, E, K	F	M	G	F	E	M	P	P	P	G	E	G	F
Cellulose acetate butyrate	SR, F	A + H, Cl, E, N, K	G	F	F	F	E	M	F	F	F	G	E	E	F
Cellulose nitrate	SR	E, K (+A, H)	F	F	M	F	E	G	F	P	M	E	E	E	M
Ethyl cellulose	SR, F	A, E, H, K	G	P	F	E	E	F	M	G	P	M	E	G	P
Hydroxyethyl cellulose	SR, F	W	P	E	G	G	M	—	—	F	—	G	E	E	G
Methyl cellulose	SR	W	P	E	M	G	E	M	P	F	P	M	E	M	P
Sodium carboxymethyl cellulose	SR	W	P	E	M	G	F	—	—	—	—	—	—	—	—

[a] Code for bonding classification: SR = Solvent released from solution or emulsion); F = Fused by heating.

[b] Code for solvents: A = Alcohols; Cl = Chlorinated hydrocarbons; E = Esters; H = Aromatic hydrocarbons; K = Ketones; N = Nitrohydrocarbons; W = Water (solution or emulsion).

[c] Code for rating: E = Excellent; G = Good; M = Moderate; F = Fair; P = Poor.

Source: Modern Plastics Encyclopedia, New York (1960).

used. All the following derivatives, for instance, are acceptable to the Food and Drug Administration:

Organic Soluble	Water Soluble
Cellulose nitrate	Methyl cellulose
Cellulose acetate	Carboxymethyl cellulose
Cellulose propionate	Hydroxypropyl methyl cellulose

If these cellulosics are considered for use in applications involving internal consumption, approval should be obtained from the proper Government agency prior to commercialization.

APPLICATIONS

Applications for the use of cellulosic adhesives and binders are numerous. For purpose of classification, we shall consider as "adhesives" those materials which hold together relatively large continuous surfaces or areas such as one piece of wood to another or a piece of paper to the wall; the word "binders" will be used as a classification for those materials which hold together relatively small particles of matter, such as fibers in paper or pigment particles in ceramic materials. Adhesives as used in this classification are available in three different types: solvent type, hot-melt type and dry-powder type. Each type has its own specific area of application which will be covered in the following sections. In some areas especially among the binders, more than one cellulosic has been used with success in the same application.

Adhesives

General-Purpose Adhesive. A general-purpose adhesive and that used in the greatest variety of applications is cellulose nitrate dissolved in suitable solvents. It is a waterproof, clear, flexible adhesive for use with china, wood, metal, glass, paper and leather. On nonporous surfaces such as glass, a thin coat is spread over each surface and then the two pieces are held or clamped together until the cement is dried. On porous surfaces such as wood, a thin coat is first applied and allowed to dry. A second coat is then applied and the two surfaces brought together and clamped until the adhesive has dried.

For adhesive applications, a medium or high viscosity type nitrocellulose is generally used with solvents which are fairly rapid in evaporation rate. A plasticizer is used to give flexibility. A representative composition is as follows:

GENERAL PURPOSE NITROCELLULOSE CEMENT

	parts by wt.
Nitrocellulose (11.4% N) (dry basis)	100.
Camphor	40.
Acetone	75.
Ethyl alcohol (denatured "2B")	300.
Amyl acetate	165.

Nitrocellulose adhesives are used in shoe manufacturing for attaching the soles to the body of the shoe. They are also used in cementing together the splice in leather power-transmission belts.

Other nitrocellulose adhesives have been devel-

182

oped for application to the cardboard used for backing vacuum-formed packages. Upon the application of heat and pressure, the vacuum-formed sheet is sealed to the cardboard. This is often done as the last step of the vacuum-forming operation. The cardboards, often printed, are appropriately perforated to permit vacuum to be pulled through them.

Paper-to-Paper, Plastic and Paperboard Adhesives. Although nitrocellulose adhesives work well when used on paper, in many cases it is desirable to use a less flammable adhesive. Special formulations have been developed by Eastman Chemical Products Co. based on their ½ sec cellulose acetate butyrate which perform well in this field. Three such formulations are presented in Table 2.

TABLE 2. CELLULOSE ACETATE BUTYRATE ADHESIVE.

	A	B	C
	(all given in parts by wt.)		
½ sec Cellulose acetate butyrate	100	100	100
"Santolite" MHP	100	100	—
Polyvinyl acetate, AYAC	—	—	12.5
"Petrex" 7-75T (dry)	—	—	37.5
"Dow 276-V9"	—	—	50
Tricresyl phosphate	—	—	10
"Tecsol" (95% denatured alcohol)	—	—	60
Isobutyl acetate	100	100	—
Toluene	300	300	215
"Solvesso" 100	100	100	—
Nitropropane-1 (Commercial Solvents)	—	—	15

Formulation A will heat-seal paper, cellulose acetate butyrate or paperboard to paper at 250°F under 60 psi for 1 sec. Formulation B will seal cellulose acetate to paper under similar conditions. Formulation C can be heat-sealed at 300°F and is also a high gloss decorative coating for paper.

Glassine Paper. Special "SS" type nitrocellulose as supplied by Hercules finds widespread use in heat-seal lacquers for glassine paper. A representative starting formulation is given in Table 3.

TABLE 3

	parts by wt.
SS Nitrocellulose, ½ sec	100
"Petrex" resin T7RT (dry)	72
Tricresyl phosphate	28
Acetone	400
Denatured alcohol	100

Low-Temperature Adhesives. Where toughness at low temperatures is desired in an adhesive, the use of ethyl cellulose is suggested by Hercules. Adhesives based on ethyl cellulose are water-resistant, free from discoloration in sunlight, also have re-

sistance to deterioration by heat when properly stabilized, are resistant to alkalies, and exhibit low flammability. Such adhesives may be of the solvent type or of the hot-melt type. Typical formulations are presented in Table 4.

TABLE 4. ADHESIVES SUITABLE FOR USE AT LOW TEMPERATURES.

	Solvent Type	Hot Melt
Ethyl cellulose (T-100)	100	—
Ethyl cellulose (N-10)	—	100
"Aroclor" 5460	80	—
"Dow 276 V-9"	20	—
Octyl phenol	4	10
"Staybelite" ester No. 10	—	300
Baker's castor oil No. 10	—	100
Toluene	300	—
Denatured ethyl alcohol	100	—

Leather Pastes. When leather is dried by simply hanging in an oven there is considerable loss of area of the skins because of shrinkage. To avoid this and to provide a flatter skin, it is common practice to apply an adhesive on the back of the skins and to paste them on large glass plates or boards prior to drying. The adhesive should have high strength at elevated temperatures to avoid "drop offs." Because methyl cellulose is the only gum, synthetic or natural, which gels upon heating, it makes an ideal base for leather-pasting adhesives. Such pastes form excellent wet adhesive bonds between the leather and the pasting plate, whether it be porcelain, glass, stainless steel, aluminum or fiber board. The methyl cellulose films have excellent wet tack and are clean, strong and flexible, and since methyl cellulose is impervious to greases, the fat liquor remains unaltered. A starting formulation suggested by Dow is:

	Leather Paste (parts by wt.)
Methyl cellulose (4,000 cp.)	2.0
N-Acetyl ethanolamine	0.2
Casein	0.3
Water	97.5

To prepare this paste add 2½ to 3 oz of 4,000 cp methyl cellulose, 2 oz of 15 per cent casein solution and 0.3 oz of N-octyl ethanolamine to 6 lb of water at 200°F. Stir until cooled to room temperature or allow to stand overnight. To preserve the casein from biological attack, add about 0.02 per cent of a good bactericide such as "Dowicide A."

Carboxymethyl cellulose is also used in adhesives in leather pasting operations where its ready water solubility allows quick removal.

Wallpaper Pastes. One of the youngest members of the cellulosic family, methyl cellulose, is the major ingredient in the "Peel Paste" used for applying wallpaper to movie studio flats. Previously, wallpaper had been applied to the scenery flats using starch or flour paste. After the shooting was over the wallpaper had to be removed by vigorous and lengthy techniques, involving live steam, blow torches, and strong alkaline solutions. The wear and tear on the plywood flats were so great that the flats had to be refinished after every appearance, and this greatly shortened their life. Then methyl cellulose ("Methocel") mixed with glycerin and water was found to be an ideal wallpaper adhesive, which held the paper securely to the flats when required, but permitted the paper to be peeled off without damaging the flat and with a minimum of effort. This development is said to have saved some $200,000 a year.

Another member of the cellulosic family, carboxymethyl cellulose, is used in Sears Roebuck's Workmaster CME cellulose wallpaper paste for do-it-yourselfers. It imparts excellent slip, stays moist, is nonstaining, and will not sour even if left standing for days.

Adhesive Additive. Methyl cellulose is used in some adhesives as an additive to control viscosity, especially in the "hot-set" phenolformaldehyde glues and other hot-pressing adhesives. A small amount present in such a glue makes it gel when heated; thus it prevents excessive penetration of paper or cardboard stock. It is also used in certain cold-setting glues as a means of viscosity control. The good stability of "Methocel" solutions over a fairly broad acidity range makes it useful in polyvinyl acetate emulsions which are widely used as adhesives. For the modification of starch adhesives, "Methocel" HG can be added to starch solutions at 130 to 150°F without precipitation.

One of the principal uses for hydroxyethylcellulose is as an ingredient in polyvinyl acetate emulsions, where it acts as a thickener and protective colloid. Many water-based adhesives are based on polyvinyl acetate emulsions. In these applications the polyvinyl acetate resin is the true adhesive, and the cellulose derivative is an important additive agent.

Oxidized cellulose acetate is occasionally added to cellulose acetate coatings to improve adhesion. Improved adhesion to metal, paper, cardboard and other surfaces can be obtained by the use of 1:4 to 2:1 parts by weight of oxidized cellulose acetate to cellulose acetate in a lacquer or adhesive. It is especially effective when used in very small amounts, up to 1 per cent, in active solvent adhesives for adhering cellulose acetate film and sheeting to highly calendered bristol board.

Corneal Adhesives. Even the extremely delicate job of adhering a glass or plastic contact lens to the cornea of the eye is done with a cellulosic. Contact lens solutions use "Methocel" (N.F. Grade). This material has been extensively tested on laboratory animals, and wide practical experience with humans has shown that methyl cellulose is not a skin irritant.

Powder Adhesive. An adhesive powder using ½ sec cellulose acetate butyrate has been introduced by Eastman Chemical Products, Inc., for heat-sealing applications. The material works well with paper, wood, cloth and similar porous or semiporous materials. It is comprised of 80 per cent ½ sec cellulose acetate butyrate and 20 per cent triphenyl phosphate and seals at 325°F under 40 to 60 psi.

Cellophane Heat-Seal Coatings

Cellophane, as it comes off the casting machine, has relatively little commercial value because it cannot be heat-sealed and has a very high rate of moisture-vapor permeability. Both these shortcomings are overcome by the application of nitrocellulose-based heat-seal lacquers developed originally by the duPont chemists Charch and Prindle. A typical, modern example of such a coating composition is taken from the recent patent literature (U.S. 2,864,724, Dec. 16, 1958, to Hercules).

CELLOPHANE HEAT-SEAL LACQUER

	parts by wt.
Cellulose nitrate (11.4% nitrogen)	43.3
Ester gum	30.4
Dicyclohexyl phthalate	29.3
Hydrogenated castor oil phthalate	10.5
Crystalline paraffin wax (60°C melting point)	3.5
Ethyl acetate	574.0
Ethyl alcohol	20.0
Toluene	289.0

Cigar Wrappers

A recent development makes use of pulverized tobacco leaves, which are bonded together using hydroxyethyl cellulose as an adhesive agent. This continuous sheet of "tobacco paper" is utilized as an outside wrapper for cigars and replaces the extremely fragile, expensive, difficult-to-get, perfect leaves previously required.

Lens Cements

A search was conducted for an improved lens cement to replace Canadian balsam. It was found that cellulose caprylate served the purpose well and did not discolor, as does Canadian balsam, with time. It also had somewhat better heat resistance and remained thermoplastic, so that the lens could be dismantled and reassembled, if necessary.

Decalcomonias

Decalcomanias are decorative emblems or patterns used for decorating childrens' rooms, kitchens, etc. They are purchased as reverse printed designs on specially coated paper. Upon soaking in water, the adhesive layer on one side of the printing is activated, while at the same time a water-soluble layer joining the printing to the backing paper is softened. When the adhesive-coated side is brought in contact with the wall, or other suitable surface, the printing and its carrier adheres and the paper backing is easily stripped or slid off because of the softened temporary adhesive holding it to the printed surface. The water-soluble temporary adhesive for decalcomanias is often hydroxyethyl cellulose.

Binders

Paper Making. To improve fiber bonding in paper and to give better strength and scuff resistance, carboxymethyl cellulose is used. Water solutions are generally applied to the paper at the size press or calender stack, both being located near or at the dry end of a conventional paper machine. When applied at this point, better "mileage" is realized, since the carboxymethyl cellulose stays on the surface, where it does the most good. In addition to acting as a binder for the paper fibers, several other advantages are realized by using carboxymethyl cellulose. It improves printability, since papers treated with carboxymethyl cellulose print more clearly and the ink appears darker and sharper because it stays on the surface. This ability to "hold out" surface coatings is especially important when lacquers or waxes are applied to provide a high surface finish. These coatings are more effective, and less is required than with papers which have not been treated with carboxymethyl cellulose. Paper from lightly beaten pulp is ordinarily quite weak, but is strengthened by the addition of carboxymethylcellulose at the beater.

Hydroxyethyl cellulose ("Cellosize") can also be used with glyoxal as a binder for improving the initial wet strength of paper stocks used in toilet and cleansing tissue, toweling, etc. It is applied either by spraying or tub sizing to a final pickup of about 0.7 per cent by weight of the stock. This use, as covered in U. S. Patent 2,285,490 (A. E. Broderick to Carbide and Carbon) has been found to increase initial wet strength to 30 per cent of dry strength.

Methyl cellulose, because of its high binding power, has also been found particularly useful in the paper and paperboard industry in a broad range of sizing and coating applications. Light surface applications are especially effective in resisting the penetration of gloss ink vehicles, varnishes, lacquers and waxes. In the case of waxed boards, some mills have reported that savings in wax costs alone more than pay for the treatment in addition to producing a level of whiteness not otherwise obtainable.

Pigments. Methyl cellulose has been used very successfully for over 14 years as the binder for the pigment and fillers in noncalcined colored pencil leads. Carboxymethyl hydroxyethyl cellulose is also suggested as a binder for colored pencil leads.

The pigment binding properties of methyl cellulose have proved valuable in many commercial water-based paints of either the emulsion or the dry type. Because of its thickening, protective colloid action, and emulsifying properties, it contributes to the application qualities of paint. Due to its protective colloid action it helps to eliminate caking caused by settling of the pigments. As a good starting point it is suggested that approximately 2 per cent of methyl cellulose (400 cp type) based on the paint solids be used. Methyl cellulose has also proved useful in the formulation of textile printing pastes where its good pigment binding process and high thickening efficiency are found very useful.

Hydroxyethyl cellulose and methyl cellulose are excellent binders, thickeners, and stabilizers for heavily pigmented lotions and make-up preparations.

Carboxymethyl cellulose in its free acid form can also be used as a pigment suspending agent in water-based compositions such as inks and shoe polishes where the free acid acts as a water-soluble binding agent when the product is applied and the water base evaporates.

The special "SS" grade nitrocellulose is useful as a tough pliable binder for inks, especially of the aniline type. Its ethanol solubility makes possible the production of odor-free printed material for food packaging.

Ceramics. Carboxymethyl cellulose has found use in the ceramics industry where its ability to bind and suspend materials during various stages of manufacture are important. This binder is subsequently completely burned out in the kiln. Current applications of carboxymethyl cellulose cover its use in glazes for both colored and white sanitary ware, in glazes for structural tile, in refractories and refractory mortars, as a glaze binder and as a jiggerbody additive in the production of dinnerware, as a temporary binder in low tension electrical porcelains, and in patching plastics and cements. Carboxymethyl cellulose, because of its greater resistance to precipitation by many ions, is suggested as a binder in various ceramic glazes and such other applications where this property is important.

Hydroxyethyl cellulose also finds extensive use in the ceramics industry. It serves as a useful binder and water-retaining agent in dry molding where it produces powders which have sufficient water present to exhibit plasticity under pressure. Luminescent pigments, coatings for instrument dials and various other ceramic colors can be conveniently dispersed by this suspending and binding agent. It also serves as a dispersant and binder for the pigment-glass flock suspension used in the production of opal glassware. This suspension is sprayed on the surface and subsequently fired which completely burns out the organic phase. It is also used as a binder for the refractory materials in the rims of cups when they are fired one upon the other (upside down). It possesses sufficient binding power to hold the cup firmly in place yet is readily burned out during the firing. It is also suggested for trial as a binder in clay slips for flatware manufacture, in steatite compositions, and in various colored glaze formulations.

Methyl cellulose is being used in ceramic glazes by many large manufacturers of dinnerware, sanitary ware and tile. Its major function is that of a binder with excellent uniformity in its suspending action. Approximately ½ per cent of the 15 cp type on the weight of the dry glaze is the maximum amount required for most applications. It is conveniently added as a dry powder to the ball mill when it is charged. Wet milling for several hours is sufficient to obtain complete water solution of the particles. An antifoam agent such as "Polyglycol" P-1200 (2 parts per 1 part "Methocel") should be added at this point to produce foam-free glaze slip. The glaze slip is then ready for application and firing. Methyl cellulose is a useful component as a binder in refractory mortars and cements. It imparts superior green, dried and fired strength. Approximately 0.1 to 0.3 per cent of 4000 cp on the weight of the mix is required.

Pharmaceuticals and Foods. Hydroxyethyl, carboxymethyl and methyl cellulose are useful as binders in tabletting for the pharmaceutical industry. These water-soluble derivatives are innocuous when taken internally in the amounts used for these applications. "Methocel" is a binding agent for ion exchange resin coatings of acid-sensitive drugs.

Oxidized cellulose, having the ability of strongly absorbing cations from aqueous solutions, serves as an excellent binder (chemical) for the isolation and precipitation of ACTH, an important hormone, from crude animal pituitary extracts. This is of particular importance because separation of such materials is very difficult.

"Cellosize" has been suggested as a binder, stabilizer, and bodying agent for foods.

Agricultural Industry. Because of its ready moisture-absorbing properties and its good binding characteristics, methyl cellulose is extremely practical for several important agricultural applications: As a slurry seed binder, 15 cp is used to coat seeds uniformly with a seed protectant, giving smooth, free-flowing seed with firmly bound protectants and other additives. The use of about 25 to 50 per cent by weight of dry protectant is suggested. As a spray spreader and binder, 2 to 4 oz of 4000 cp methyl cellulose per 100 gal of water provide wetting action and acts as a spreader and binder. A film is also formed which resists run off and retards leaching-out by rainfall. As a dust binder, 1 to 2 oz of high-viscosity 4000 cp methyl cellulose to each pound of an agricultural dust makes the dust adhere to foliage; that which remains in the dust is quickly dissolved by moisture present as dew and binds the toxicants to the foliage.

Carboxymethyl cellulose and hydroxyethyl cellulose can also be used as binders for sticking agricultural chemicals to seeds, leaves and other parts of plants.

Textile Industry. When suitably modified with glyoxal, hydroxyethyl cellulose serves as a binder and sizing agent for basic aluminum acetate in a spot-resistant warp size composition for viscose rayon taffeta. Used with minor proportions of urea and formaldehyde it gives a permanent, hard finish which serves as a good wash-resistant binder for pile woven rugs and other pile fabrics. As a binder for nonwoven absorbent fabrics, carboxymethylcellulose contributes to the hydrophilic nature of these fabrics, even when the carboxymethyl cellulose is insolubilized by an inorganic acid (by ion exchange) or by a metal salt.

Metallurgical Industry. Carboxymethyl cellulose has many advantages as a core binder: the small amount required, low drying temperatures, good hot strength (excellent knockout characteristics), low decomposition temperatures and low gas evolution. Hercules Powder Co. used as little as 0.25 per cent carboxymethyl cellulose dissolved in 4 per cent water (sand basis) and obtained cores having as high as 0.55 psi green strength and as high as 68 psi baked strength, and a hardness of approximately No. 57.

A small amount of calcium oxide in the core mix is desirable since it reduces sensitivity to high humidity of baked cores in storage.

"Cellosize" has also been used as a temporary binder to give green strength to tungsten carbide.

Explosives. In 1867 the Swedish inventor Alfred Nobel discovered dynamite—a relatively "safe" mixture of nitroglycerin with kieselguhr, the naturally occurring remains of tiny fossil diatoms. Shortly after, he patented ballistite, a mixture of nitroglycerin bound with nitrocellulose. It was considerably more efficient than dynamite since there was no inactive ingredient. It was the first so-called "smokeless" powder. His formula was 100 parts of nitroglycerin, 50 parts of nitrocellulose, and 200 parts of benzene with 10 parts of camphor. Cordite, later invented by Dr. Fredric Abel and Professor James Dewar, was composed by nitrocellulose dissolved in acetone and then colloided with nitroglycerin. Sometime later Nobel invented another somewhat similar mixture called blasting gelatin, the most powerful industrial explosive, a colloid of nitroglycerin with from .7 to .8 per cent soluble nitrocellulose.

The above examples illustrate the use of nitrocellulose as a sort of chemical binder for nitroglycerin. Smokeless powder is found in "sporting" powders and as propellant for various rockets. During World War II, production reached over 3,000,000 pounds of smokeless powder per day.

14

Introduction to Rubber-Based Adhesives

Frank H. Wetzel

Research Center
Hercules Powder Company
Wilmington, Delaware

Rubber-based adhesives offer the greatest variety of properties of any generic class of adhesives. Relatively low-strength systems such as rubber cement, pressure-sensitive tapes, and self-seal envelopes, all of which are based on rubber, are household items. Recent developments have led to high-strength usage of rubber-based adhesives for structural bonding of aircraft.[2, 26] The unusually wide spectrum of properties available in adhesives based on elastomers is due in part to (a) the variety of properties obtainable in natural and synthetic rubbers, and (b) the many materials such as tackifiers, resins, fillers, plasticizers, and curing agents, which may be physically or chemically incorporated into the elastomers. The many modifications possible in rubber-based adhesives have played a major part in their spectacular market growth in the last 20 years.

The categories of rubber-based adhesives listed in Table 1 are discussed in this and subsequent sections. Examples listed are not all inclusive, and serve only to identify a few of the many fine formulations available.

Historical Background

The adhesive properties of raw natural rubber were recognized as long ago as 1791[56, 118], when naphtha solutions of rubber were used for waterproofing and textile laminations. Later, such adhesives were also vulcanized after application. Latex rubber adhesives were first disclosed in the middle of the 19th century.[56] Adhesives based on cyclized rubber made their appearance about 1925.[68, 69] Until the 1930's, rubber-based systems were used chiefly for rubber-to-metal and rubber-to-textile applications.[56] Strength requirements were, for the most part, relatively low.

With the outbreak of hostilities in 1939, attention was given to the development of synthetic elastomers: butadiene–styrene copolymers and butadiene–acrylonitrile copolymers. Adhesive properties of elastomeric butadiene copolymers had been recognized before,[66, 67] and now, considerable interest developed in the use of these copolymers in adhesives. There were also significant concurrent developments in adhesives based on chlorinated rubber,[111] polychloroprene (neoprene),[15, 97, 101, 127] rubber hydrochloride,[86, 152] and polysulfide rubber.[110] Development* of carboxylic elastomers,[33, 71, 72] silicones,[31, 103] and isocyanates[46, 104] followed. Pressure-sensitive tapes became a well-known commodity, and indeed, were to prove one of the major innovations in the use of adhesives.[62] Improvement of curing systems during World War II led to applications to more substrates and use at higher temperatures. The introduction between 1942 and 1947 of a number of elastomer-thermosetting resin blends[80] completed the framework upon which rubber-based adhesives have grown. The majority of these blends were phenolic resins

---

* The recently introduced fluorocarbon and sulfochlorinated polyethylene elastomers are not yet used in adhesives.[131]

TABLE 1. TYPES OF ADHESIVES BY BASE.

Base Elastomer	Examples of Adhesives (26, 34, 56, 103, 104B, 129)**	Adhesive Manufacturer
Natural rubber	"Armstrong" R-508	Armstrong Cork Co.
	"Bondmaster"* P-595	Rubber and Asbestos Corp.
Cyclized rubber		
by sulfuric acid	"Vulcalock"*	B. F. Goodrich Industrial Products Co.
by stannic chloride	"Pliobond"*	Goodyear Tire and Rubber Co.
Butadiene-styrene copolymer	"Bondmaster"* G-218	Rubber and Asbestos Corp.
(SBR, formerly GR-S)	"Armstrong" G-386	Armstrong Cork Co.
Butadiene-acrylonitrile copolymer	"Bondmaster"* L-379	Rubber and Asbestos Corp.
(buna N or nitrile rubber)	"EC-847"	Minnesota Mining and Mfg. Co.
Chlorinated rubber	"Chemlok" 228	Lord Manufacturing Co.
	"Bostik" 1007	B. B. Chemical Co.
Polychloroprene (neoprene)	"Ray-Bond" R-82002	Raybestos-Manhattan, Inc.
	"EC-1357"	Minnesota Mining and Mfg. Co.
Rubber hydrochloride	"Ty-Ply"*	Marbon Chemical Division, Borg-Warner Corp.
Polysulfide rubber	"Thioment"	Atlas Mineral Products Co.
	"Polybond"	Polymer Industries, Inc.
Carboxcylic elastomers	"A-916-B"	B. F. Goodrich Industrial Products Co.
Silicone rubber	"DC-271"	Dow-Corning Corp.
	"Casco"*	Borden Chemical Co.
Isocyanate rubber	"Bostik" 7070A and B	B. B. Chemical Co.
Phenolic resins blended with:		
buna N	"Armstrong" N-199	Armstrong Cork Co.
	"Cycleweld"* H-2S	Chrysler Corp.
neoprene	"Cycleweld"* C-3	Chrysler Corp.
	"K-25"	Miracle Adhesives Corp.
neoprene-nylon	"Metlbond"*	Narmco Resins and Coating Co.
Reclaim rubber	"Armstrong" K-1	Armstrong Cork Co.
	"EC-226"	Minnesota Mining and Mfg. Co.
Butyl rubber	"Midland"	Midland Adhesive and Chemical Corp.
	"Pliastic"*	Morningstar-Paisley Corp.

*Registered Trade-marks.
**References at end of Chapter.

with neoprene or nitrile rubber. The properties of high strength and low creep of these systems led to many structural applications.

Compositions

Rubber-based adhesives may contain some or all of the materials listed in Table 2.

Elastomers are exemplified by those polymers listed as base elastomers in Table 1. An elastomer may be defined as a polymeric material possessing rubberlike properties. More specifically,[102] an elastomer is a natural or synthetic material which can be or is already vulcanized to have high extensibility and forceful, quick recovery. *Tackifiers* are exemplified by rosin and rosin derivatives, poly-

terpene resins, coumarone-indene resins, and certain types of thermoplastic phenolic resins. They are used extensively in pressure-sensitive and solvent cement adhesives to develop tack, and most commonly with natural rubber and styrene-butadiene rubber (SBR). Tackifiers are discussed in detail subsequently. *Resins* are exemplified by phenolic and resorcinol resins that may be used as thermoplastics or subsequently crosslinked. Application is usually with polar elastomers. *Fillers* are materials such as carbon black, zinc oxide, and various clays. Kieselguhr whitings, acid-treated whitings, barite, French chalk, and calcium silicate are also employed.[34] *Plasticizers* and *softenerss* such as stearic acid, zinc laurate, mineral oil, and lanolin are used. *Antioxidants* are materials such as the

TABLE 2. GENERAL COMPOSITION OF RUBBER-BASED
ADHESIVES.

Material	Composition Range (%)
Elastomer	30–50
Tackifier or resin	30–50
Filler	10–40
Plasticizers and softeners	1–6
Antioxidants	0.2–3
Curing agents	0.5–5
Sequestering agents	0.2–1.5

aromatic amines and substituted phenols or qui-nones. They are similar to the antioxidants used in rubber compounding for tire applications. *Curing agents* are best exemplified by sulfur, which is probably the most common vulcanizing agent. In recent years, other curing agents such as peroxides, metal salts, and organic halides have come into limited use with synthetic rubbers. Accelerators may be used also. *Sequestering agents* are added largely for the capture of traces of manganese and copper. The presence of these metals accelerates the deterioration of many rubbers.

In addition to the components cited above, latex cements also employ a wide variety of other materials, such as protective colloids, emulsifiers, emulsion stabilizers, etc. The primary function of these is to stabilize polymer dispersion or emulsion. They do not necessarily enhance the finished adhesive properties. In fact, a careful compromise must be reached between latex and adhesive properties. For example, emulsifiers necessary to latex stability may reduce tack or migrate into the substrate after application and cause serious staining or water sensitivity.

General Characteristics

The physical characteristics of rubber-based adhesives may be varied by formulation.[124] Rheologically, adhesives may range from extremely viscous liquids, to highly elastic systems, to hard, tightly cured materials of low elongation. Thus, many unvulcanized rubbers such as natural or SBR are tacky, plastic, and flexible, even in the region of −60°C. Characteristic bonds formed by such low modulus, high elongation materials are, however, low in tensile and shear strength. They have a definite sensitivity to increases in temperature. This combination of properties furnishes a marked resistance to impact and vibration load, but is responsible for a decided tendency to creep or cold flow. Other unvulcanized elastomers such as neoprene or rubber hydrochloride are almost as flexible, but are less tacky and much tougher, i.e., have lower

elongation and higher modulus. While the latter elastomers may not retain good impact resistance and flexibility at low temperatures, their creep properties and temperature sensitivity are better than elastomers such as natural rubber and SBR. Thus, much variation in properties can be obtained by changing from one elastomer to another or from one molecular weight distribution to another.

More variations in properties of elastomeric adhesives can be obtained through the use of either fillers or vulcanization, or both. The reinforcing properties of fillers such as a variety of carbon blacks and pigments are well known.[34, 46] Where colored fillers are objectionable, as in surgical adhesives, light-colored materials, such as zinc oxide, are used. Fillers increase the modulus but the effect is usually limited. However, in the case of carbon black compounded into the rubber on a mill, the carbon in some way interacts with free radicals created during mastication.[70] The theoretical aspects of filler reinforcement are not well understood, although an interesting hypothesis on the use of fillers in adhesives has been advanced by Jamieson.[87]

While the majority of rubber-based adhesives are uncured,[100] adhesives that cure are becoming increasingly important. *Curing* is the term applied to the crosslinking of the elastomer or the resin. Theoretical and practical considerations of vulcanization of elastomers have been discussed in detail elsewhere.[34, 47, 131] Curing of rubber considerably improves resistance to creep and deformation. It also increases the modulus of elasticity and the rate of elastic recovery. Ultimate elongation is decreased. Crosslinked elastomers are also much less sensitive to solvents.

Maximum strength is obtained in elastomer-based adhesives in the form of the phenolic blends. In these adhesives, the resin is crosslinked. The elastomer is not intentionally crosslinked, but may well react with the phenol-formaldehyde during cure of the latter.[104A, 132A] These systems are virtually as strong and as creep resistant as systems comprised of thermosetting resins. However, the elastomer contributes resiliency and vibration-damping properties. Elastomer-phenolic blends which cure, are widely used in bonding metals for structural applications.[46] The elastic contribution of the rubber is important. Stresses at the adhesive-substrate interface occur, subsequent to curing, because of differences in thermal coefficients of expansion between metals or metals and adhesives. The rubber component can relax and relieve such stress.

Representative applications of rubber-based adhesives illustrate their versatility. Rubber-based systems exhibit fair to excellent adhesion to practically all substrates. In the automotive industry, one of the oldest and largest consumers of rubber-based adhesives, rubber weatherstrip, metal and plastic trim, silencer pads, flocks, brake bands, clutch facings, rubber motor mounts and body sealers are adhered to metal.[27, 30, 100, 108, 114, 125] Marine applications include polysulfide-based sealers for aircraft carriers and pleasure craft.[100] Aircraft manufacturers assemble nonstructural components, such as floor assemblies, interior trim, engine components, and fuselage sealers.[2] Structural applications in aircraft have already been cited.

Many more uses could be listed in the leather,[27] appliance,[109] building, [36, 27, 126], tire,[28] and textile industries.[78]

TYPES AND APPLICATIONS

Rubber-based adhesives are applied in a number of different forms such as latex cements, solvent cements, pressure-sensitive tapes, and mastics. We shall consider both the theoretical and practical aspects of the preparation, application, and properties obtainable from these systems.

Latex

Natural rubber is obtained from a variety of wild and cultivated trees of the *Hevea brasiliensis*[69] species as a water-dispersed colloid. Globule diameters range from 1 to 3 microns. The protective colloid appears to be of a proteinaceous type. Ammonia is added to prevent fermentation. Rubber solids of approximately 40 per cent occur naturally; then the latex is usually concentrated to 60 per cent.[46] The polymer itself is the *cis* form of polyisoprene[69] with a molecular weight range of approximately 250,000 to 2,500,000.[25] Almost as soon as the rubber latex leaves the tree, oxidative degradation begins and some crosslinking may also occur. The rubber at this point appears to be soluble in aromatic solvents, but in reality such solutions contain a large amount of gel. This has complicated structural investigations considerably.[25]

Most synthetic rubbers which are used in latex adhesives to any extent, are prepared by emulsion polymerization. They are, therefore, available in latex form. The elastomers of interest are butadiene-styrene copolymers, butadiene-acrylonitrile copolymers, and neoprene. The materials are all available in several types, the types varying in molecular weight, molecular weight distribution, rate of crystallization (neoprene), and particle size.

Reclaim rubber has assumed increasing importance in adhesives because of its many property advantages and attractive price. Reclaim is 10 to 11¢/lb, as contrasted to SBR at 19 to 24¢/lb, and

natural rubber at 26 to 34¢/lb.[131] Reclaim is obtained principally from tires and is available in latex form.

A 40 per cent latex is only one hundredth as viscous as a 15 per cent "solution" of milled rubber in toluene. Latex systems therefore have many advantages, i.e., the ease of handling low viscosity materials, high deposition of solids, no loss of an expensive solvent, and minimum fire hazard. Latex systems may be applied by brush, spray, doctor knife, or reverse roll coater. Film formation is usually done at or near room temperature, forming very slowly at high humidities. The major applications are to porous substrates such as textiles, paper, and leather.

Film strength or cohesion of films from unmodified latices is high, while adhesion is low. Natural rubber films never completely coalesce.[45] The film appears to be a closely packed mass of discrete particles which were formerly dispersed in water. These particles elongate when the gross film is elongated, and particle-to-particle adhesion apparently resides in the external sheath of protective colloid of each particle. When a film is cast on a substrate, the sheath of protective colloid probably contacts the surface. Little wonder then that the adhesion obtained with either natural or unmodified synthetic rubber latices to nonporous solids and to many porous substrates is low.

An effective way of improving tack and adhesiveness of an elastomer in latex form is by the addition of water-dispersed nonpolymeric tackifiers such as rosin derivatives. Diffusion of tackifiers into the rubber particles occurs causing particles to soften and coalesce more rapidly and to a greater degree. The mass also contacts and "wets" the substrate much better. Over-all internal strength or cohesion is usually less than in a film from unmodified latex.

Further improvement in adhesion of latices is obtained by means of primers or two-coat systems. The most common primers are based on cyclized rubber cements or a mixture of natural rubber latex and water-soluble materials such as casein or albumen.[29] These systems exhibit high adhesion to metals and glass, and also offer a readily bondable surface for other rubber adhesives.

Low adhesion may also be partially overcome by the use of heat and/or pressure to hasten and improve coalescence and contact. Porous substrates allow rapid diffusion of water and provide a large area of contact. The adhesion of latices may be further improved by coating both substrates to be joined with the same adhesive. When the films are dry, a "contact" bond may be made. This takes advantage of the tack that most elastomers have for themselves.

Although latex-applied adhesives can be cured, the major improvement obtained by curing is in internal strength and not where the major weakness lies, i.e., in adhesion. Except in tire cord adhesives, discussed below, curing latices are not widely used. In contrast to solvent cements, they incorporate all curing ingredients in one system which is quite stable at room temperature. Such systems are used in the manufacture of hoses, as well as in tire cord adhesives.

While solvent cements provide greater ultimate strength, latex systems are often necessary. An adhesive solution is "carried" into a porous substrate. Multiple applications are then required to put enough adhesive on the surface to form a bond. However, latex systems penetrate much less and one coat often suffices for bonding.

Latex adhesives furnish adequate strength for a large number of applications.[57] Probably over three-quarters of the shoes manufactured employ latex adhesives at some step of the process.[27, 128] Latex adhesives are used on paper for labels, laminations, bags, and books, and on textiles for laminations, impregnations, and seam bindings.

A major latex adhesive use, where high strengths are obtained, is for tire cord.[28] These cords are dipped in adhesive and subsequently run through squeeze rolls. The cords are in a parallel array with little, if any, mechanical cross threads to hold them together. Drying is done by oven or tunnel. Subsequently, the parallel arrays are laid on as plies in the tire carcass. A natural latex, sometimes modified with casein and reclaim, or an SBR latex was satisfactory for cotton tire cord. The introduction of rayon cord necessitated a change to a latex formulation containing 85 per cent SBR and 15 per cent resorcinol-formaldehyde copolymer (resol). Today rayon cord is adhered with a latex adhesive containing 65 per cent SBR, 20 per cent terpolymer of butadiene-styrene-vinylpyridine, and 15 per cent resorcinol-formaldehyde. For nylon cord, a latex containing 85 per cent butadiene-styrene-vinylpyridine terpolymer and 15 per cent resol is used. In all probability, the resol reacts chemically with both rayon and nylon cord.[104A] The polarity of both resol and vinylpyridine also contribute substantially to adhesion and internal strength. The butadiene-styrene content lends flexibility and resilience.

Milling

Preparation of almost all solvent cements, mastics, and pressure-sensitive adhesives involves milling or mastication of the elastomer. Milling or mastication is a mechanical "working" of the elastomer previously obtained by coagulation of latex. The rubber is usually kneaded by passing it between two steel rolls, moving at different speeds. The temperature of these rolls may vary from room temperature to 150°C. The polymer is subjected to compression followed by strong shearing forces. A Banbury mixer accomplishes much the same thing. The net effect is a substantial decrease in molecular weight of the polymer. Whereas the rubber was essentially elastic and would undergo permanent deformation only under extreme loads, it is now soft, readily deformable, and soluble in a number of petroleum solvents.

The chief degrading force in milling up to 75°C is mechanical,[70, 98, 139-146] but some chemical changes also occur. The extremely high shearing force, to which the rubber is subjected in its highly viscous state, actually ruptures molecular chains. The free radicals formed in this homolytic cleavage may recombine, add to other chains as side chains, or add to any other materials present. Milling in air also allows reaction of the free radicals with oxygen to form peroxides. These peroxides undoubtedly contribute polarity to the rubber and also subsequently cause oxidative degradation. There is little difference, however, in gross effect of peroxides between milling in an atmosphere of pure oxygen or one containing as little as 0.1 per cent of oxygen. They do not have much degrading effect during milling between room temperature and approximately 100°C. If peroxides contributed to chain scission during milling, such scission should be random along the chain. However, scission occurs primarily in those chains whose molecular weight is greater than 70,000 to 100,000, and probably occurs about the middle of the chain.

Further, if rubber is milled under nitrogen with benzoquinone, its molecular weight is lowered. Benzoquinone is almost as active a free-radical acceptor as oxygen. This compound reacts with free radicals on hydrocarbon chains, formed by shear; because of the relatively low reactivity of the resulting quinhydrone free radical, recombination is minimized. Copolymers of unusual properties have been formed by anaerobic milling of natural rubber and active monomers such as methyl methacrylate. Carbon black, under both hot and cold conditions, appears to form a network through reaction with hydrocarbon free radicals. The network formed is much like that obtained by vulcanization.[123]

The effect of mastication decreases as temperature increases and beyond 115°C its effect on degradation is negligible. On the other hand peroxides produce increasing effects above 75°C and above 115°C become the chief degrading force.

Mastication leads to a narrowing of molecular weight, so that the ratio of weight-average molecular weight to number-average molecular weight approaches two. The theoretical limit is unity. Chains formed are not linear, and some three-dimensional network probably accounts for the presence of gels, even in highly milled rubber. The presence of gels has hampered fractional precipitation of rubber solutions and molecular characterization.

In practice it is difficult to define conditions precisely. Rubber for use in adhesives is not milled as severely as in the work described above. The concentration and type of natural products in raw natural rubber varies as does the amount and type of materials such as emulsifiers contained in synthetic rubber. These variations influence the results of mastication. The milling operation itself is one of art and skill. The carefully controlled conditions of Watson[139-146] are a far cry from those common in the milling operation. Temperature and speed of the rolls, surrounding atmosphere, clearance between the rolls, and size of the "nip" are all variables which are virtually impossible to reproduce quantitatively from milling to milling. Moreover, measurement of these effects on molecular structure are time consuming. Viscosity can be measured by means of a Mooney rotating disk viscometer,[105] a classical means of following the effect of mill time and conditions. Although this instrument was designed for fundamental rheological work, adhesive formulators have correlated Mooney viscosity to end-use properties. A similar situation exists in the use of the parallel plate plastometer.[60] However, data from these instruments do not give much of a hint as to the structure or definitive rheological properties unless used in conjunction with a number of other measurements.[145]

Thus, at present we lack much quantitative or even qualitative knowledge of the majority of milled rubbers.

Solvent Cements

Probably 75 per cent or more of all rubber-based adhesives are used in the form of solvent cements. In general, solvent cements have considerably greater intrinsic adhesion for all substrates and greater film strength than those provided by latex systems.

Solvent cements are prepared by one of two general processes. The freshly milled elastomer may be removed from the mill and dissolved in solvent. This is known as "cutting" the rubber into a solvent because of the cutting action of many high-speed, heavy-duty mixers. For natural rubber and

SBR, solvents such as benzene, toluene, naphtha, or gasoline may be used. For buna N, neoprene, and other polar materials, more polar solvents such as methyl ethyl ketone, methyl isobutyl ketone, or ethylene dichloride may be used. The latter are also often blended with nonpolar solvents. The rubber in solvent may then be blended with solutions of additives, such as tackifiers, to form the cement. Alternatively, addition of the dry materials such as tackifiers may be made to the rubber solution.

A second means of preparing a solvent cement is by milling elastomer and additives together and then "cutting" the whole mass into solvent.

The literature is inadequate regarding the advantages of either technique. Choice seems to be determined by that which is most convenient for any particular formulator. Theoretical considerations, however, favor preparation of the solutions of rubber and of additive, and then blending. As is discussed subsequently, it appears that additives, especially tackifiers, should be chemically separate from the rubber molecules. This may not always be the condition if tackifiers and elastomers are milled together. Furthermore, when adding tackifiers to the elastomer on the mill, care must be taken not to add the tackifier until suitable mechanical degradation has occurred. Once the tackifier is added, viscosity decreases and little further molecular weight lowering occurs.

Solvent cements are usually supplied at concentrations of 10 to 25 per cent solids with viscosities in the range of 1,000 to 30,000 cps. Solvent cements may be applied by spray, doctor knife, reverse roll coater, roller, spatula, or trowel. Solvent may be removed by room-temperature drying or forced drying in ovens or tunnels.

Adhesives applied to nonporous substrates are allowed to dry ("breathe") before final assembly is made. Care must be taken to rid the coating of all solvent. Once the bond is made, residual solvent can escape only slowly, through the edges. Also, the solvent in the adhesive bond softens and considerably weakens it. Many solvent cements, especially when dried in tunnels, tend to "skin," or form a dry layer of adhesive on the top of the film, because of rapid solvent evaporation. Further evaporation of the internally held solvent is deterred, and diffusion of solvent is slow. In extreme cases, a film may appear to be dry and yet have 30 to 40 per cent of the original solvent present.

Where the dry adhesive film has little inherent tack, both substrates are often coated. Tack or instantaneous adhesion of the dry cement film for itself is usually considerably higher than for another surface. Many coated surfaces retain their ability to bond each other for days or months. Considerable use is made of this property in the automotive and flooring industries.

Formulation and application of solvent cements vary greatly. Natural rubber from solvent has good tack and moderate adhesion, but is rather low in internal strength. Adhesion is considerably enhanced by use of tackifiers such as modified-rosin derivatives and polyterpene resins. These types of tackifiers possess good color characteristics and compatibility, and contribute greatly to tack and adhesion. Usual concentrations are equal parts of tackifier and elastomer. The reaction product of acetylene and *tert*-butylphenol, "Koresin," has been reported as useful with SBR.[35, 48] However, other information indicated it to have limited compatibility with SBR.[32] Blends of natural rubber, SBR, and tackifier are often used. Such blends incorporate the good tack and moderate adhesion of natural rubber and the internal strength and stiffness of SBR. Vulcanization of natural rubber or SBR greatly increases internal strength but may substantially lower adhesion. Primers based on cyclized rubber are often used.[29]

The solvent cements based on nitrile rubbers and neoprene are high in internal strength, offer excellent resistance to oil and many solvents, and are quite resistant to oxidation. The inherent adhesion of these elastomers to most substrates is not high. Addition of tackifiers such as phenolic or modified phenolic or coumarone-indene resins considerably enhances adhesion. Moreover, use of a number of primer systems has been reported.[121] Primers so improve over-all adhesion that these systems can then be cured and still provide adequate adhesion.

Many neoprene cements crystallize and perform as if they were vulcanized.[15] Moreover, the magnesia (MgO) present as a stabilizer in all neoprene cements, has been pictured[15, 121] as reacting with the phenolic resins used in these cements. The resulting crosslinked resin has no melting point but decomposes at 450°F. Many nitriles are vulcanized, but many are used with curing resins.[121]

Many grades of reclaim rubber are used in blends of natural and synthetic rubbers in solvent cements. Most reclaim is obtained from auto tires. The carbon black usually present restricts reclaim from use where another color is desired.

Vulcanization of solvent cements after application is growing in importance, but data on the extent of its use are not available.[100] In view of the variety of elastomers used and application techniques recommended for solvent cements, it is difficult to ascertain from trade literature which systems are of the vulcanizing type.

Rubber-to-metal bonds were, at one time,

accomplished chiefly by vulcanizing rubber to a brass-plated metal. Evidence exists that a sulfur to brass bond was formed.[34] However, expensive equipment and careful control of the brass-plating process were required. This practice has now been largely replaced by adhesive bonding. For rubber-to-metal bonds, solvent cements are utilized,[76, 86] in combination with different primers.[29, 34, 132]

The automotive industry has been and continues to be the largest consumer of solvent cements. However, virtually every industry uses solvent cements in one way or another. Reference to the "General Characteristics" section of this chapter will suggest the wide utility of these systems. Subsequent sections will concern themselves with more specific applications.

Mastics

Mastics are a special type of adhesive and may be either latex- or solvent-based. The unique quality of mastics is their extremely high viscosity. Most mastics contain natural rubber, SBR, or reclaim, or blends of these. Often some proportion of asphalt or bitumen is included. Tackifiers and fillers are used widely, though in lower concentrations than in solvent cements. Application is generally by means of spatula, knife, trowel, or pressure gun. Mastics are usually applied to both surfaces to be bonded. Coatings are dried, then a contact bond made. Mastics are used in volume, though chiefly in low-strength applications. They are usually relatively inexpensive, and are employed in adhering floor and wall tile, floor coverings, and automobile silencer and lining pads.

Pressure-sensitive Adhesives

Pressure-sensitive adhesives represent about 10 per cent of the total consumption of rubber-based adhesives. The most common example of this type of system consists of a flexible tape coated with a permanently tacky or sticky mass. The tack, or instantaneous adhesiveness, must not exceed the internal strength or cohesion of the adhesive. These adhesives lack high-strength because they must be soft to be tacky. They are also temperature-sensitive and highly susceptible to creep or cold flow. Tape is generally available in rolls which unwind easily. Usually, the adhesive is required to show quick adhesion to, and yet strip cleanly from, substrates.

The first commercial applications of "pressure-sensitive" tapes were in surgical tape and the electrician's friction tape. These were cloth-backed and did not strip cleanly from the contacted surface. Drew's disclosure[63] in 1925 overcame the latter difficulty. The initial development therefrom was a masking tape for use in painting automobiles. This consisted of a layer of natural rubber-coumarone-indene matrix, applied on a crepe-paper backing.

A typical pressure-sensitive tape consists of the adhesive mass, a "keying" coat, the backing, and a release coat. The *adhesive mass* is usually composed of either synthetic or natural rubber and tackifier[64, 70, 78] in roughly equal amounts. Acrylate polymers are also used, with and without additives.[65] Most of the adhesives are tacky at room temperature, though many are heat-activated.[82, 113] A variety of softeners, antioxidants, plasticizers, and curing agents may also be added.[92] The *"keying"* coat is used between the adhesive and backing to ensure good adhesion between the two. This may be based either on natural or synthetic elastomers[41] and may contain some tackifier. A curing agent may also be used to vulcanize the "keying" coat to the backing or mass.[92] The *backing* may be crepe paper, foil, fabric, cellophane, cellulose acetate, plasticized poly (vinyl chloride), or a number of other flexible materials. The backing may also be reinforced with glass or other fibers. A *release coat* is applied to the side of the backing away from the adhesive mass. This coat may be based on any one of several polymers, such as acrylate,[82] vinyl,[44] or derivatives of cellulose. The function of a release coat is to facilitate unwinding and prevent delamination during unwinding. Delamination occurs when the adhesive mass sticks more tenaciously to the backing upon which it is wound, than to the backing upon which it was applied. In some cases, a removable release sheet is used in lieu of, or in addition to, a release coat.[44]

Surgical tapes are a special class of pressure-sensitive tapes. These were traditionally natural rubber-based with a tackifier and a relatively high percentage of zinc oxide. Applied on cloth, they were faced with crinoline. Recent modifications in surgical plasters such as "Band-Aid"* and "Curad"* utilize a variety of synthetic elastomers and resins, highly plasticized vinyl backings, and paper or polyethylene release sheets.

Pressure-sensitive materials may be applied to a backing in one of three ways. A solution of an adhesive mass, not unlike a solvent cement, may be sprayed, doctor-knifed, or roller-coated on a properly prepared backing up to 6 ft wide. The solvent is then evaporated and the backing slit into desired widths and rolled on paper or plastic cores.

A second method of application involves calendering. As shown in Fig. 1, the warm mass is fed

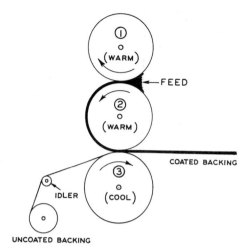

Fig. 1. Stacked calendar. Rolls 1 and 2 usually operate at different speeds, rolls 2 and 3, at the same speed.

into a "stacked calender" between the top roll and the middle or transfer roll, which are both heated. The backing is fed between the transfer roll and bottom roll, which is cooled. The mass may or may not have been previously mixed on another two-roll mill or in a Banbury mixer.

A third method, coating from latex, is not as popular because the tack of latex-applied coatings is considerably less than that of solvent- or calender-applied systems. Polyisobutylene is often added to enhance tack of latex-applied systems. Also, higher proportions of tackifier are used than would be used in solvent- or calender-applied systems.

Applications of pressure-sensitive adhesives vary.[39, 40] Over 200 varieties of pressure-sensitive tape are available. The chief outlet for pressure-sensitive tapes was and continues to be masking tape, primarily for use in the automotive and appliance industries. Masking tapes must adhere to a number of different substrates, such as enamel, chrome-plated steel, steel, aluminum, glass, and rubber. They must hold heavy paper aprons in place and withstand temperatures of 140 to 250°F. Yet, the tape should strip off cleanly and not discolor the substrates. Other masking applications, with two extremes of requirements, are in surgical masking and in stone work.

Tapes are used in holding applications, such as keeping protective wrappings in place, for picture hooks, for binding packages, for bundling pipe and wire, and for holding rivets in place prior to bucking. Reinforced and two-faced tapes are used in packaging and palletizing freight in cars. Nonstructural building uses involve sealing and moistureproofing of insulation,[79] seam sealing, and insulation of wire and windows. Structural building applications such as binding prefabricated

---

* Registered Trade-marks, Johnson and Johnson, and the Bauer and Black Div. of the Kendall Co., respectively.

panels together, are increasing.[151] Tapes are used in protection of polished surfaces during manufacturing and shipping, and as corrosion-resistant coatings. Paper and plastic films are spliced with pressure-sensitive tape. Colored and write-on stock are used for labeling. Pressure-sensitive tape and sheet, indeed, have become a tool of home and industry.

THEORETICAL CONCEPTS

Another section of this book concerns the theoretical aspects of adhesion. We shall discuss here only those facets of theoretical adhesion that are specific to rubber-based systems.

To effect adhesion between an adhesive and a substrate or an adherend, the adhesive must be brought into intimate contact, on a molecular scale, with the substrate. A necessary requirement for such behavior is proper flow and wetting characteristics.[49-51, 53, 115] Poor wetting and flow properties are easily observed on a macroscale. The effect of these deficiencies on a microscale is incomplete contact between adhesive and every fissure and pore of the substrate. Incomplete bonding decreases the area available to bear the load. Moreover, the voids act as points of stress concentration and failure appears to propagate from void to void.[19, 91, 94, 95, 99] Rubber-based adhesives may decrease this effect by relaxation, but it is nonetheless an important one.

Polarity is generally regarded as a necessity for adhesion.[53, 58, 115] Moreover, polar surfaces cannot be joined with nonpolar adhesives.[52] The adhesion of polar elastomers, such as nitriles, acrylates, and polychloroprenes, is due to strong polar effects[1] such as dipole to dipole and dipole-induced dipole interactions. These form the basis for the well-recognized importance of specific adhesion.[53, 58] Tackifiers and resins used in polar systems are probably important in softening these relatively stiff elastomers so that the necessary degree of contact between adhesive and substrate can be achieved. The last traces of solvent also help. Natural rubber, SBR, and butyl rubber are much less polar. Although some polarity is induced in the nonpolar elastomers during milling, the amount is low. In such instances, the contribution of London or dispersion forces to adhesion must be recognized.[94, 115] These forces, often called "van der Waals," are weak. Since natural rubber, butyl rubber and SBR are relatively soft, many points of contact are made with a polar or nonpolar substrate through which such forces can operate. Indeed, as discussed below, adhesion of a nonpolar adhesive to a polar surface appears to be greater than the cohesion of the adhesive itself.

Tackifiers considerably enhance adhesion of nonpolar elastomers through an increase in the amount of polarity of the mass. Wettability also is improved. An important contribution of the tackifier to overall adhesion strength involves decreasing elastic recovery. In an adhesive mass sufficiently deformable to contact a substrate intimately, molecules may diffuse and rearrange into an optimum configuration relative to a surface. In all probability, rubber molecules can and do move up to, and in some cases across, an interface.[59, 135-137] This is a relatively slow process but may account for increase in strength of some adhesive systems minutes or even seconds after application.

On the other hand, the elastomers in adhesives generally will retain some elastic recovery. The mass can therefore "withdraw" from contact with the substrate when bonding pressure is removed. Thus, the resiliency of a rubber-based system is a "two-edged sword." Rubber adhesives are noted for their ability to absorb energy and to elongate before rupture occurs. These properties that are so important for cohesion may account for low adhesive strengths. Obviously, a balance between adhesiveness and cohesiveness must be realized. An approach to achieving a balance of properties is by use of proper tackifiers and resins.

Unfortunately, the commonly used adhesive tests provide little information about the interfacial forces operating in an adhesive bond. There is much evidence to indicate that failure of a bond is seldom, if ever, at the adhesive-substrate interface. One or two monomolecular layers of adhesive always seem to be left on the substrate.[19, 91, 94-95, 99, 115] This effect is qualitatively illustrated in Fig. 2. Pictured are electron micrographs of a tip of a brass probe. The probe was examined when freshly cleaned and metallographically polished (a), and after it had been in contact with a pressure-sensitive adhesive mass for 1 sec under very low load (b).[84] The adhesive strength of the pressure-sensitive mass was low, yet the probe definitely has removed material from the film. Subsequent use of this same probe for measurements did not cause an increase in tack, nor did the surface of the film appear to change.

Such cohesional failure appears to be caused by one or more of several factors. High degrees of adsorption and/or orientation are believed to exist at the interface. This implies that the two or three molecular layers nearest the interface have a different configuration and are in a force field different from the internal molecules. This disrupts the continuity of the adhesive and of those forces regarded as basic for cohesion. On the other hand, the bond may fail in a weakly bound layer on the surface because the latter was not cleaned properly.

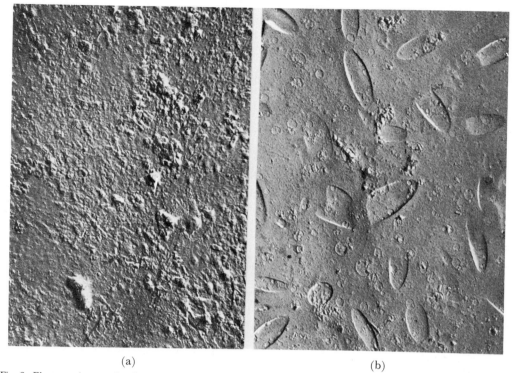

(a)   (b)

Fig. 2. Electronmicrographs of (a) polished probe and (b) probe which had been in contact once with pressure-sensitive adhesive. (Mag. 8,825X)

Pressure-sensitive adhesives require a unique set of properties. No solvent is present to make the adhesive sufficiently fluid when applied to a substrate to effect intimate contact between the adhesive and adherend. The adhesive mass itself must both wet the substrate and deform at the interface to contact the adherend intimately. This requires a relatively low modulus of elasticity, as well as short relaxation times to relieve internal stress. The instantaneous adhesiveness of these systems is largely rheological, but a certain, even though low, degree of adhesion is absolutely essential.

Tack

"Tack" is a widely used term, whose origin is shadowy and meaning seldom clear. Much of the difficulty in defining it resides in the fact that tack is a combination of many physical properties. Personnel active in the adhesive industry demonstrate tack by what a system possessing it does. This usually involves measurement of tack by use of the thumb, forefinger, or both. Quantitatively this leaves much to be desired.

For use in adhesives technology, tack may be defined as the property of a material which enables it to form a bond of measurable strength immediately upon contact with another surface,[14, 74, 148-50] usually with low applied pressure.

Tack is thus "instantaneous" adhesion and differs from ultimate strength. The time required for development of strength by means of tack is very short compared to the time allowed for development of maximum strength. "Measurable" is a function of instrumentation and is not necessarily synonymous with "useful."

Theory. Within broad limits, tack appears to be a rheological property. Making a bond by means of tack relies on either viscous flow or deformability for adequate wetting and contact. The strength developed is undoubtedly due to "van der Waals" forces and, to a lesser extent, diffusion and chain entanglement. Failure of a bond made by tack is cohesive (Fig. 2). Tack is sensitive to variations in temperature, pressure, rate of application and removal, and time of contact. Above a certain modicum of adhesiveness, tack varies as the rheological properties of the system. This is, tack is a direct function of rheological properties such as viscous flow, tensile strength or cohesion, yield value, modulus of elasticity, rate of elastic recovery, and deformability.

Earliest tack measurements were made on Newtonian liquids.[122] Hoekstra and Fritzius[85] have discussed this work excellently in detail. The contributions of Reynolds,[116] Stefan,[122] Beck,[17] Askew,[4] and Bikerman[22] must be recognized. These studies show that a high degree of tackiness is obtained in an adhesive possessing a high yield value and high viscosity. Much of the analysis was based on separating two parallel plates which had liquids or soft materials between them. The rheology in this operation simulates that of an adhesive bond failure.

Figure 3 illustrates the destruction of a bond under tension by flow or deformation of the adhesive. The adhesive must undergo laminar flow in the direction "L" (Fig. 3a). This is necessary for the substrates to move apart. The higher the viscosity and yield value, the greater will be the resistance to separation. Once flow in direction "L" has been initiated, flow in the direction "N", normal to the bond, can occur (Fig. 3b). It is axiomatic that the initial stress required for movement is placed on a cross section considerably larger than that observed after flow in direction "N" has taken place.

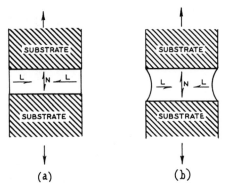

(a)   (b)

Fig. 3. Adhesive (a) prior to, and (b) subsequent to, being placed under tensile stress.

The rate of separation is important in any consideration of adhesion and tack is no exception. If the rate of application of stress is sufficiently high, no flow or yield can occur. The system behaves purely elastically and the film ruptures. At lower rates the adhesive can flow or yield forming "Strings" or "legs" of adhesive. Such phenomena have been observed with printing inks and discussed in detail.[17, 22, 77, 133] Though adhesives are considerably higher in strengths and probably more viscoelastic than printing inks, the same considerations apply.

Thus, failure of an adhesive in bond stress normal to the adhesive-substrate interface can be visualized. However, many considerations of tack are based on peel measurements. These involve tests pictured in Fig. 4. Bikerman[20-24] has considered tack and peel as much a rheological phenomenon as that discussed for tensile failure. His treatments were on idealized situations involving Newtonian liquids or Hookean solids. His conclusions have, however, been borne out by the work of others on practical systems.[35, 81, 117] The entire load in peel

is a "line" load. The stress is supported at a "line" across the peeling material. Nominally low applied loads, therefore, result in quite high loads per bearing area. The removal of a flexible substrate from an adhesive bond by peel must be preceded by deformation of the adhesive. This deformation will usually be by flow, forming "strings" or "legs" in the adhesive. These "legs" are most logically formed by the same mechanism of flow pictured for tensile application. The formation of the "legs," shown by Chang,[37, 38] can be observed by slowly peeling adhesive tape or a piece of tacky rubber off a solid substrate. Bright[32] has resolved peel adhesion into three rate processes: (1) flow of the rubber adhesive with activation energy of 22 kcal, (2) adsorption of adhesive with activation energy of 5 to 10 kcal, and (3) chemisorption of polar parts of an adhesive with activation energy of 50 kcal. Thus, the principal mechanism of peel involves flow of the adhesive and some desorption from the interface. In all probability, chemisorbed material is left on the substrate. The failure is thus largely rheological, like that for tensile faliure.

A similar peel mechanism exists in rolling ball or rolling cylinder tests such as those used at Douglas Aircraft,[37] or by Voet, et al.[133] Peel is inherent also in the approach used by Busse[35] and subsequent work based on his apparatus.[16, 18, 96, 119]

A word of practical caution is in order regarding use and interpretation of peel tests for rubbery materials. It has been stated[37] that in the process of peeling, a slight depression appears on the surface of the backing material. This is near the peeling face but on the side toward the "unpeeled" adhesive. Similar observations were made by Kaelble.[90] His analysis of the peeling system indicates that the composite of rubber adhesive and backing, if present, acts as a lever arm. In peel, this operates across the peeling interface to a line just behind this interface. The interface between adhesive and adherend acts as a fulcrum. The adhesive is thus under tension at the interface and under compression just behind it. Tensile stress placed on the adhesive is, therefore, a function of the modulus or stiffness of the backing plus adhesive. Thickness must also be considered. Moreover, even if the adhesive, rubber, etc., are applied to a substrate under very low pressure, considerably more pressure may be exerted on the bond during the peeling test. This would in turn enhance contact and increase adhesion. The compressive load appears greatest at 180° peel between flexible and rigid adherends, less at 90° peel under the same circumstances, and lowest in peel between two flexible adherends (see Fig. 4a, b, and c).

The foregoing interpretation of tack assumes the existence of a finite adhesion at the adhesive-

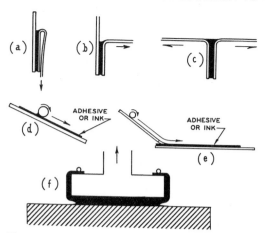

Fig. 4. Representation of peel test:
(a) 180° peel—one flexible and one rigid adherend
(b) 90° peel—one flexible and one rigid adherend
(c) peel between two flexible adherends
(d) inclined plane—rolling cylinder
(e) curved track—rolling ball
(f) tensile pull on adhesive sheet or tape

Josefowitz and Mark[89] indicate that tack is observed for polymers in the viscosity range of 100 to 10,000 poises, or with relaxation times between 10^{-7} and 10^{-4} sec. The phenomenon of tack seems related to an ability of chain segments to slip easily. Optimum chain length is in the range of 50 to 300 monomer units and, more specifically, of approximately 100 monomer units. Voet[133] correlated tack with a modulus of 10^6 to 10^8 dynes/sq cm, and reports relaxation times of the same range as Mark.

Voyutski et al.[134-6] have reported on the self-adhesion or auto-adhesion of polymers. They have defined this property as "tack." Auto-adhesion is a diffusion process. With time, the interface between two surfaces of the same material disappears. Short side chains in the elastomer molecule have little effect on this "tack." However, as side chain length or incidence of polarity increases, "tack" decreases considerably. Polar groups such as nitrile or chlorine were specifically noted. The latter do, however, increase the activation energy of this "tack." The data reported are roughly in the same range as that of Bright,[32] cited earlier. Vulcanization and crystallization, as expected, decrease auto-adhesion.

Function of Tackifiers. Although natural rubber has tack, the strength developed is inadequate for many uses. Most of the commercially available forms of synthetic elastomers have little tack either for themselves or other surfaces. Tackifiers are added to these systems to increase tack. A number of solvent and latex systems, especially those used for contact cements, utilize tackifiers. However, the most common application of tackifiers is in pressure-sensitive adhesives.

The origin of the word "tackifier" is obscure; it probably came from the rubber industry. Examples of the most commonly used tackifiers are listed in Table 3. The materials are thermoplastic, and usually form amorphous glasses at room tempera-

adherend interface. The importance of *adhesion* cannot be overemphasized in the *forming* of a bond by tack. The *failure* of an adhesive bond appears to be largely *cohesive* even on a molecular scale, and therefore a rheological phenomenon. From a practical standpoint, the prime concern with most adhesive bonds is the overall strength of the bond and not where failure occurs. However, in pressure-sensitive adhesives, failure should be very near the interface between adhesive and solid substrate because of the requirement that pressure-sensitive adhesives strip "cleanly" from a surface.

Various authors have discussed the structure and physical properties necessary to furnish tack in polymer systems. Most of these systems consisted of only one polymer, either in bulk or in solution.

TABLE 3. EXAMPLES OF TACKIFIERS.

Base	Trade Names	Manufacturer
Modified wood rosins	"Staybelite"* "Poly-pale"*	Hercules Powder Co.
Derivatives of wood rosin and modified rosin	"Staybelite Ester"* 10 "Pentalyn"* H	Hercules Powder Co.
Polyterpene resins	"Piccolyte"*	Pennsylvania Industrial Chemical Corp.
Coumarone-indene resins	"Piccoumaron"*	Pennsylvania Industrial Chemical Corp.
	"Nevindene"*	The Neville Co.
Phenolic-modified coumarone-indene resins	"Nevillac"*	The Neville Co.

*Registered trade-marks

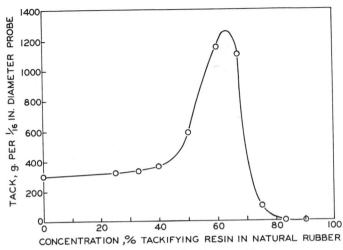

Fig. 5. Variation of tack with composition.

ture. They are available in softening point ranges from room temperature to 150°C, and are usually quite soluble in aromatic solvents. The common features of tackifiers as pictured by deBruyne,[46] are molecular weights from 200 to 1,500 and a structure that is large and rigid. Contrary to deBruyne, however, they need not possess polarity or hydrogen-bonding groups. For example, the polyterpene resins which are β-pinene polymers, are excellent tackifiers, and contain no polarity.

Some quantitative data are available on the action of tackifiers in pressure-sensitive adhesive systems.[148-9] Tack was studied as a function of concentration of tackifiers of various softening points in natural, unvulcanized rubber. Tack versus concentration of a tackifying resin is shown in Fig. 5. The concentration of tackifier in natural rubber at which maximum tack was obtained, varied from 50 to about 80 per cent resin in rubber. Maximum tack obtainable correlated inversely with softening point or viscosity of the resin. The higher the softening point, the lower per cent resin at which maximum tack was obtained. Moreover, resins of lower softening point provided greater obtainable tack but at a higher concentration. Cohesive strengths decreased almost linearly with increasing concentration of tackifier.[148]

The increase of tack over that of natural rubber alone is coincident with the formation of a second phase at the surface.[83] Such a phenomenon is consistent with Busse.[35] The concentration of this phase increases with increasing tack. Comparison of Figs. 5 and 6 will illustrate this. Tack presumably is more responsive to the disperse or second phase (mostly resin plus low molecular weight rubber) than to the original continuous phase (rubber saturated with resin). Increasing the concentration of

resin increases the amount of disperse phase. This will result in an increase in tack only as long as some rubber continues to dissolve in this phase, causing ease of deformation. The resins of lower softening point dissolve to a greater extent in rubber in the continuous phase than do the higher softening resins. By the same token, low molecular weight ends of rubber (fractions of low molecular cut) will continue to dissolve in the lower softening resins in the disperse phase as resin concentration increases. This makes the latter phase more deformable at higher resin concentrations than when harder resins are used. Softer resins will ultimately contribute more deformability, and therefore, more tack, than a hard resin.

At maximum tack, presumably the maximum amount of low ends of rubber have dissolved in the disperse resin phase. Further increase in resin concentration results in a sharp reduction in tack. Perhaps a phase inversion occurs and the continuous phase assumes the characteristics of the brittle, hard tackifier. In any event, the gross adhesive mass becomes considerably less deformable and tack decreases.

Assuming the necessity of a two-phase system for tack, aging presumably causes changes that lead back to a one-phase system. Once tacky films, when aged to zero tack, were found to be one phase.[124]

Thus, the large, rigid structure of tackifying resins appears to be specific. The tackifiers possess a cohesive energy density sufficiently close to that of natural rubber, for example, to be partially miscible. Miscibility is limited, however. The molecular weight of tackifiers is substantially higher than completely miscible materials such as toluene. In general, as the molecular weight of additives to polymeric systems increases, compatibility de-

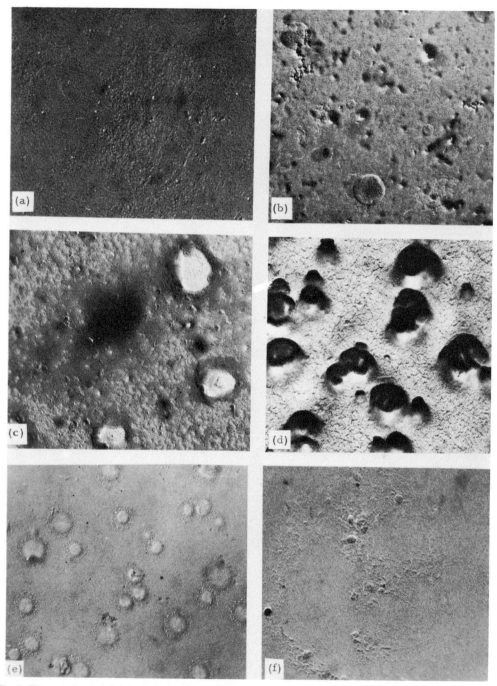

Fig. 6. Electronmicrographs of replicas of pressure-sensitive adhesive films of "Pentalyn" H (pentaerythritol ester of hydrogenated rosin)-natural rubber. (Mag. 11,000X) (833,149)

    (a) natural rubber, tack value 200 to 300
    (b) 1:3 Pentalyn H-rubber, tack value—320
    (c) 1:1 Pentalyn H-rubber, tack value—590
    (d) 3:2 Pentalyn H-rubber, tack value—1100 to 1200
    (e) 5:1 Pentalyn H-rubber, tack value—0
    (f) 9:1 Pentalyn H-rubber, tack value—0

creases. The limited miscibility of tackifier in rubber may well account for the formation of the disperse phase, consisting of mostly tackifier and some rubber. This phase must be deformable but high in viscosity. The large tackifier molecules possess the necessary rheological requirements. Oils will also form a disperse phase or surface layer, but the viscosity of this layer is so low that tack is destroyed and the surface appears to be oily. Many fatty acids or esters also migrate and form a surface layer. They, however, crystallize and so stiffen the surface that tack is zero. On the other hand, tackifiers are amorphous glasses and do not crystallize.

Tack, as determined in the work discussed above, in all probability is a measure of deformability or a modulus of elasticity at low loads for short times. Such rheological measurements have been done in a unique way by Dahlquist[42] and a correlation between tack and modulus or deformability suggested.[43]

TEST METHODS

Methods of testing rubber-based adhesives vary widely. Those methods used most for rubber-based adhesives are outlined briefly and a reasonably complete bibliography is included.

Three rather different approaches are inherent in testing. The first two, evaluation and quality control, concern "end-use testing." Such tests are designed to simulate the rates and kinds of loading to which a fabrication will be subjected in ultimate use. Any given bond can be tested under only one condition of failure. The results of several tests are, therefore, required to assess fully the utility of an adhesive. A relatively large number of tests must be carried out to achieve reproducibility and reliability. For quality control, selection of one or several tests that are most critical must be made. Since most testing is destructive, all finished fabrications cannot be tested. Use of nondestructive, ultrasonic testing has relieved this problem,[3, 61] but destructive test data are still necessary for correlation. Data from production experience are necessary to determine what percentage of the finished parts must be tested before one can say all items produced are satisfactory. All the foregoing are a necessary part of a good testing program and require considerable experience in order to correlate the data.

A third approach in testing is determination of some fundamental physical property such as viscosity. This is then correlated with end-use experience. Property tests are more reproducible and easier to accomplish than end-use testing. Unfortunately, useful correlations between property data and end-use results are not always obtained easily.

Adhesive manufacturers have, therefore, been rather reluctant to follow this path.

In what follows, the rheological response to tensile or peel load should be kept in mind. Rate of testing is of widely recognized importance in plastics and elastomers. Using the same procedures but with varying rates, an adhesive can change progressively from a viscous liquid to a brittle solid.

Peel

Peel testing is widely used because of the peel load to which many fabrications are subjected. The ASTM test[6] has been used extensively. One of the adherends is usually flexible. A common one is canvas duck, varying in weight from 10 to 30 oz/sq yd. The flexible adherend is peeled at $180°$[6] (Fig. 4a), or $90°$[37, 73] (Fig. 4b) from a rigid substrate such as metal. If both adherends are flexible, the angle of peel is difficult to define (Fig. 4c). Rate of loading, defined in speed of peel, varies from 2 to 12 in./min. Strength is obtained in lb/in. width of peeling member.

Specimens are prepared by bonding a sheet of material to a substrate. One-inch strips are then "scored" from the flexible sheet. This is done to avoid edge effects. Koehn[93] has noted interesting effects of adhesive film thickness and discussed the mechanism of failure. Geer and Westcott[75] carefully controlled preparation of specimens and testing by peel and report excellent reproducibility.

A climbing drum peel involves peel of bonds where both adherends are fairly rigid.[147] Developed for use on metal honeycomb structures, nominal angle of peel is dictated by the radius of the drum.

Tensile

The tensile test involves stress applied normal (perpendicular) to the bond between two tensile "buttons"[7] (Fig. 7a). The specimen is loaded by means of U-shaped collars which fit over the angular boss at the end of the specimen. Koehn[93] has shown that often the "buttons" tilt slightly at the moment of rupture. The resultant peel or cleavage loading leads to considerably lower strengths.

The rheological response to tensile loading was discussed earlier and the work of Stefan and others cited. The effect of film thickness has also been discussed.[93, 95] In general, the thinner the film, the stronger the bond. However, use of very thin adhesive films often results in low strength because of "starved joints," that is, incomplete coverage by adhesive. The maximum strength then becomes a matter of surface preparation.

Measurement of adhesion of vulcanized rubber

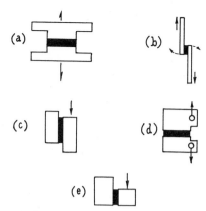

Fig. 7. Representation of various adhesive test:
    (a) tensile
    (b) shear by tension
    (c) shear by compression
    (d) cleavage
    (e) impact

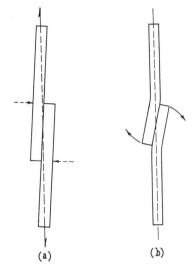

Fig. 8. Schematic explanation of stresses and deformation of a bond under shear stress by tensile loading:
    (a) joint before loading
    (b) joint after loading

to metal utilizes the same tensile "buttons" and type of loading.[4] The rubber is, however, considerably thicker (³⁄₁₆ in.) than in adhesive testing.

Wake and co-workers[78, 138] have studied rubber-to-textile bonds quite extensively by means of a tensile-type test.

Shear by Tension

Testing of adhesives in shear by tension[12] is a popular test, largely because of the ease of sample preparation. The adhesive is loaded in shear to assess its ability to distribute load. Specimens overlap (see Fig. 7b) with direction of loading parallel to the bond. Usually, the specimens are 1 in. wide and the lap is ½ in. Interpretation of data obtained from such "lap shear" testing is difficult.[93] The eccentricity of stress during loading joints in shear by tension is illustrated in Fig. 8. The adherends are subjected to a bending stress at the ends of the bond (indicated by broken arrows). Similarly, stress on the adhesive is concentrated at the same two points. If the adherends are brittle and inflexible, breaks often occur at the end of the bond. Conversely, if the adherends are very flexible, a peeling load results. Strength varies considerably with depth of lap.[93]

The static problems encountered on such a joint have been considered at length by Mylonas and deBruyne.[54, 106-7] While lap shear continues to be a popular test, more and more use is being made of tapered lap or "scarfed" joints (Fig. 9) in fabricating for service.

Twiss[130] has recently reported use of a disk shear test. This avoids many of the hazards of lap shear in tension. Strengths obtained are considerably higher than those in shear by tension.

Shear by Compression

Shear by compression[10] (Fig. 7c), like shear by tension, is used to study the ability of an adhesive to distribute load. It depends on the flexibility of the adhesive to a degree. It has much the same stress concentrations as shear by tension; but use of thicker adherends avoids the stress eccentricity. Shear by compression has been studied in some detail,[93] especially for wood by Yavorsky.[155-6]

Impact

Adhesive tests for bond strengths are sensitive to the rate at which loading is applied. Impact testing[11] is essentially a special case of shear loading (Fig. 7e), where the load is applied by a pendulum tester.

Cleavage

Cleavage testing,[13] like shear, is difficult to interpret (Fig. 7d). The edge of the bond line nearest the applied force is subjected to tension. The opposite edge is subjected to compression. A fulcrum for

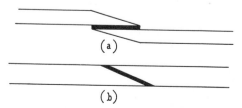

Fig. 9. (a) tapered lap joint and
    (b) scarfed joint

a lever arm probably exists near the back edge of the bond. The mechanism of peel discussed earlier, therefore, applies. Yavorsky[154] has analyzed cleavage tests in the same manner in which he analyzed shear by compression.

Tack

Tack is generally measured as the stress required to break bonds between two surfaces in contact for a relatively short time. To reiterate, adhesives, in general, may fail "grossly" in either cohesion or adhesion, whereas pressure-sensitive adhesives usually are required to strip "cleanly."

In addition to the bibliography already cited, attention is also called to the survey of tack measurements by Yang.[153]

Many commonly used tack tests are based on ASTM tests for peel,[6] shear[12] or tensile[7] strengths or a combination of them.[8] These tests involve making the bond and then testing it at some short time afterwards. A principal shortcoming is that the manual manipulations required in the test often make it difficult to test the bond shortly after assembly.

Perry and Hills[9, 112] have studied liquid or thermoplastic, tacky adhesives by means of a modified Interchemical Tackmeter.[77] It involves the separation of two metal "fingers." While the measurement cannot always be made immediately after application, the data, in poises, have been correlated with end use. The analysis of data for these Tackmeter studies is similar to that originally used by Scott[120] for parallel plate plastometer studies.

Tack of printing inks has been studied by Voet.[133] The method of measurement involves rolling a cylinder down an inclined plane (Fig. 4d & e). During a portion of the travel down the plane, the cylinder rolls over a film of ink. The distance which the cylinder rolls up an opposing and inclined plane is analyzed in terms of tack. While this appears to have yielded much worthwhile data on printing inks, it has certain limitations in the testing of adhesives. Foremost among these is the fact that once the cylinder has made one complete revolution in or on the liquid, the liquid is subsequently contacting itself and not a fresh surface. Acceleration and geometric analyses are also complex.

Rubber-to-rubber tack has been the subject of much work because of its importance in tire manufacture. The test of Busse et al.[35] involves fastening a sheet of rubber to the pan of the balance. Another sheet of rubber is wound around a circular mandrel. This is brought into contact with the sheet on the balance under a predetermined load. Tack is measured as the resistance to separation. Schmitt[119]

utilized the same principle in the use of a pendulum tester. This technique has the major advantage of allowing two surfaces to be in contact for only a short period of time. Flexing of the film on the balance pan and/or around the mandrel unfortunately has not been considered. The energy required to do the flexing is indivisible from that required to overcome the adhesion. Area of contact is also difficult to ascertain. Subsequently, a number of workers[16, 18, 96] utilized modifications of the Busse apparatus.

Chang's method[37] for determining the tack of pressure-sensitive tapes has provided very precise data which correlate with end-use experience. Tape and substrate are brought into contact under the load of the tape itself. Tack is determined as force of separation in 90° peel. Application of Busse's principle[35] to tape is of doubtful significance because of the inability to prevent flexing of the tape backing during separation. As already discussed, Wetzel[149] used a polished probe for the determination of pressure-sensitive tack of glass-supported films of adhesive.

Use of the Douglas curved track, rolling ball tests has been reported.[37] The test involves rolling a ball down a track and onto a pressure-sensitive film. The angle of incidence of the ball onto the tape is carefully controlled. Tack is measured as the distance the ball rolls across the film. Like the rolling cylinder tests for inks, the ball, after one revolution, does not have a fresh surface. Moreover, while the ball is moving relatively rapidly during the initial part of its roll, it does not sink in as far as when it decelerates. Thus, the geometry of the test leaves much to be desired.

Aging and Stability

No one aging test has gained widespread application. Adhesive bonds are prepared in such a way that they can be tested in peel, tensile, shear, impact, etc. The bonds may then be exposed to a variety of temperatures and humidities such as are furnished by Fade-Ometers, Weather-Ometers, humidity cabinets, ultraviolet and infrared lamps, or use conditions. The change in strength when subjected to a test appropriate to the sample is then used as a monitor. Specific reference is made to McClellan[100] and deBruyne.[55]

References

1. Alstadt, D. M., *Rubber World*, **133,** 221 (1955).
2. Anon., *Materials in Design Engineering*, **48,** (7), 9 (Dec. 1958).
3. Arnold, J. S., Wright Air Dev. Command, Tech. Rept. 54–231; WADC-Univ. of Dayton Joint

Symposium, Dayton, Ohio, June 12–3, 1957, WADC–TR 57–513.

4. Askew, F. A., *Paint Technol.,* **9,** 217 (1944).

5. ASTM D429–56T, "Adhesion of Vulcanized Rubber to Metal," ASTM Standards on Adhesives, Philadelphia, Am. Soc. for Testing Materials, Dec. 1957.

6. ASTM D903–49, "Test for Peel or Stripping Strength of Adhesives," ASTM Standards on Adhesives, Philadelphia, Am. Soc. for Testing Materials, Dec. 1957.

7. ASTM D897–49, "Test for Tensile Properties of Adhesives," ASTM Standards on Adhesives, Philadelphia, Am. Soc. for Testing Materials, Dec. 1957.

8. ASTM D816–55, "Rubber Cements," ASTM Standards on Adhesives, Philadelphia, Am. Soc. for Testing Materials, Dec. 1957.

9. ASTM "Suggested Method for Measurement of Tack of Adhesives," ASTM Standards on Adhesives, Philadelphia, Am. Soc. for Testing Materials, Dec. 1957.

10. ASTM D905–49, "Strength Properties of Adhesives in Shear by Compressive Loading," ASTM Standards on Adhesives, Philadelphia, Am. Soc. for Testing Materials, Dec. 1957.

11. ASTM D950–54, "Test for Impact Strength of Adhesives," ASTM Standards on Adhesives, Philadelphia, Am. Soc. for Testing Materials, Dec. 1957.

12. ASTM D1002–53T, "Strength Properties of Adhesives in Shear by Tensile Loading (Metal-to-Metal)," ASTM Standards on Adhesives, Philadelphia, Am. Soc. for Testing Materials, Dec. 1957.

13. ASTM D1062–51, "Tests for Cleavage Strength of Metal-to-Metal Adhesives," ASTM Standards for Adhesives, Philadelphia, Am. Soc. for Testing Materials, Dec. 1957.

14. ASTM D907–58, "Definition of Terms Relating to Adhesives," ASTM Standards for Adhesives, Philadelphia, Am. Soc. for Testing Materials, 1959, in press.

15. Bake, L. S., *Rubber Age,* **76,** 253 (1954).

16. Beaven, R. K., Croft-White, P. G., Garner, P. J., and Rooney, G., Proc. Second Rubber Technol. Conf., London, June 23–25, 1948, p. 224; printed in *Rubber Chem. and Technol.,* **23,** 719 (1950).

17. Beck, J., *Deut. Druck,* **44,** 450 (1938).

18. Beckwith, R. K., Welch, L. M., Nelson, J. F., Cheney, A. L., and McCracken, E. A., *Ind. Eng. Chem.,* **41,** 2247 (1949); reprinted in *Rubber Chem. and Technol.,* **23,** 933 (1950).

19. Bikerman, J. J., "The Mechanism of Adhesion," pp. 72–3, in Clark, Rutzler, and Savage (Editors), "Adhesion and Adhesives, Fundamentals and Practice," New York, J. Wiley & Sons, Inc., 1954.

20. Bikerman, J. J., in Eirich, F. R. (Editor), "Rheology, Theory and Practice," Vol. III, New York, Academic Press, Inc., (1960).

21. Bikerman, J. J., *J. Appl. Phys.,* **28,** 1484 (1957).

22. Bikerman, J. J., *J. Colloid Sci.,* **2,** 163 (1947).

23. Bikerman, J. J., "The Fundamental Study of Adhesion," 13th Annual Conf., Reinforced Plastics Div., Soc. of Plastics Ind., Chicago, Feb. 1958.

24. Bikerman, J. J., "The Rheology of Peeling in a Newtonian Liquid," "The Rheology of Peeling through a Hookean Solid," Abstracts, Society of Rheology, Meeting, Nov. 7–9, 1957, Princeton, N. J.; to be published in *Trans. Soc. Rheol.,* **2.**

25. Bloomfield, G. F., *Rubber Chem. and Technol.,* **24,** 737 (1951).

26. Blomquist, R. F., *Modern Plastics,* **36,** No. 1A, 177 (1958).

27. Blyler, L. L., *Rubber World,* **137,** 883 (1958).

28. Borg, E. L., *Rubber World,* **137,** 723 (1958).

29. Bramley, A., *Rubber Age and Synthetics,* **33,** (3), 160 (1952).

30. Brams, S. L., *Rubber World,* **137,** 888 (1958).

31. Bramwyche, P. L., "A Review of Synthetic Adhesives," pp. 158–64, in Clark, Rutzler, and Savage (Editors), "Adhesion and Adhesives, Fundamentals and Practice," New York, J. Wiley & Sons, Inc., 1954.

32. Bright, W. M., "The Adhesion of Elastomeric Pressure-Sensitive Adhesives: Rate Processes," pp. 130–138, in Clark, Rutzler, and Savage (Editors), "Adhesives and Adhesion, Fundamentals and Practice," New York, J. Wiley & Sons, Inc., 1954.

33. Brown, H. P., *Rubber Chem. and Technol.,* **30,** 1347 (1957).

34. Buchan, S., "Rubber-to-Metal Bonding," London, Crosby, Lockwood, and Son, Ltd., 1948.

35. Busse, W. F., Lambert, J. M., and Verdery, R. B., p. 294, in Robinson, H. A. (Editor), "High Polymer Physics," New York, Remsen Press Div., Chemical Publishing Co., 1948.

36. Building Research Institute, "Adhesives and Sealants in Building," Division of Engineering and Industrial Research, 2101 Constitution Avenue, Washington 25, D. C., 1958.

37. Chang, F. S. C., *Adhesives Age,* **1,** 32 (1958).

38. Chang, F. S. C., *Rubber Chem. and Technol.* **30,** 847 (1957).

39. Clauser, H. R., "Pressure-Sensitive Tapes," *Materials and Methods,* Manual No. 125 (March 1956).

40. Corbin, J. E., "Practical Applications of Pressure-Sensitive Tapes," pp. 139–41, in Clark, Rutzler, and Savage (Editors), "Adhesives and Adhesion, Fundamentals and Practice," New York, J. Wiley & Sons, Inc., 1954.

41. Coulter, R. I. (to Minnesota Mining and Manufacturing Co.), U. S. Patent 2,328,057 (Aug. 12, 1943).

42. Dahlquist, C. A., Hendricks, J. O., and Taylor, N. W., *Ind. Eng. Chem.,* **43,** 1404 (1951).

43. Dahlquist, C. A., Private communication.

44. Dahlquist, C. A. (to Minnesota Mining and Manufacturing Co.), U. S. Patent 2,532,011 (Sept. 21, 1946).

45. Davis, C. C., and Blake, J. T., "The Chemistry and

Technology of Rubber," pp. 150–156, New York, Reinhold Publishing Corp., 1937.

46. deBruyne, N. A., and Houwink, R., "Adhesion and Adhesives," pp. 391–392, New York, Elsevier Publishing Co., 1951.

47. deBruyne, N. A., and Houwink, R., "Adhesion and Adhesives," pp. 399–405, New York, Elsevier Publishing Co., 1951.

48. deBruyne, N. A., and Houwink, R., "Adhesion and Adhesives," p. 404, New York, Elsevier Publishing Co., 1951.

49. deBruyne, N. A., *Plastics (London)*, **16,** 308 (1951).

50. deBruyne, N. A., *Aero Res. Technical Notes, Bulletin 168,* Dec. 1956, Aero Research, Ltd., Duxford, Cambridge, England.

51. deBruyne, N. A., *Aero Res. Technical Notes, Bulletin 179,* Nov. 1957, Aero Research, Ltd., Duxford, Cambridge, England.

52. deBruyne, N. A., *Aircraft Eng.,* **18,** 51 (1939).

53. deBruyne, N. A., and Houwink, R., "Adhesion and Adhesives," pp. 3–88, New York, Elsevier Publishing Co., 1951.

54. deBruyne, N. A., "Some Investigations into the Fundamentals and Applications of Synthetic Adhesives," pp. 137–52, in Morgan, P. (Editor), "Plastics Progress," New York, Philosophical Library, 1951.

55. deBruyne, N. A., and Houwink, R., "Adhesion and Adhesives," pp. 485–88, New York, Elsevier Publishing Co., 1951.

56. Delmonte, J., "Technology of Adhesives," pp. 178–228, New York, Reinhold Publishing Corp., 1947.

57. Delmonte, J., "Technology of Adhesives," pp. 179–85, New York, Reinhold Publishing Corp., 1947.

58. Delmonte, J., "Technology of Adhesives," pp. 322–51, New York, Reinhold Publishing Corp., 1947.

59. Deryagin, B. V., Zherbkov, S. K., and Medbedeva, A. M., *Colloid J. (U. S. S. R.),* **18,** 404 (1956); printed in English in *Rubber Chem. and Technol.,* **30,** 837 (1957).

60. Dienes, G. J., and Klemm, H. F., *J. Appl. Phys.,* **17,** 458 (1946).

61. Dietz, A. G. H., "Nondestructive Testing of Adhesives by Ultrasonic Waves," pp. 218–21, in Clark, Rutzler, and Savage (Editors), "Adhesion and Adhesives, Fundamentals and Practice," New York, J. Wiley & Sons, Inc., 1954.

62. Drew, R. G. (to Minnesota Mining and Manufacturing Co.), U. S. Patents 1,760,820 (May 2, 1930), reissue 19,128 (Apr. 4, 1934); 1,856,986 (May 16, 1932), reissue 21,762 (Apr. 12, 1941); 2,236,567 (Apr. 24, 1941).

63. Drew, R. G. (to Minnesota Mining and Manufacturing Co.), U. S. Patent 1,760,820 (May 16, 1930).

64. Drew, R. G. (to Minnesota Mining and Manufacturing Co.), U. S. Patent 2,410,053 (Oct. 27, 1946).

65. Ebell, C. J. (to Minnesota Mining and Manufacturing Co.), U. S. Patent 2,553,816 (May 22, 1951).

66. Ebert, G., Fries, A. F., and Garbsch, P. (to I. G. Farbenindustrie A.-G.), German Patent 524,668 (Oct. 13, 1929).

67. Farbrach, D. V., *India Rubber World,* **108,** 249 (1943).

68. Fisher, H. L., *Ind. Eng. Chem.,* **19,** 1325 (1927).

69. Fisher, H. L., "The Chemistry of Natural and Synthetic Rubber," p. 166, New York, Reinhold Publishing Corp., 1957.

70. Fisher, H. L., "The Chemistry of Natural and Synthetic Rubber," pp. 79–81, New York, Reinhold Publishing Corp., 1957.

71. Frank, C. E., Kraus, G., and Hefner, A. J., *Ind. Eng. Chem.,* **44,** 1600 (1952).

72. Frank, C. E., and Kraus, G. (to General Motors Corp.), U. S. Patent 2,692,841 (Oct. 1, 1954).

73. Freedman, D. M., U. S. Patent 2,473,517 (June 21, 1949).

74. Gainsly, M., and Dow, J., "Pressure-Sensitive Adhesion," p. 127–30, in Clark, Rutzler, and Savage (Editors), "Adhesion and Adhesives, Fundamentals and Practice," New York, J. Wiley & Sons, Inc., 1954.

75. Geer, W. C., and Wescott, W. B., *Rugger Age,* **49,** 241 (1941).

76. Gerstenmaier, J. H., *Rubber Age,* **73,** 495 (1953).

77. Green, H., *Ind. Eng. Chem., Anal. Ed.,* **13,** 632 (1941).

78. Hammond, G. L., and Moakes, R. C. W.; Borroff, G. M., and Wake, W. C., *Trans. Inst. Rubber Ind.,* **25,** 172 (1949); reprinted in *Rubber Chem. and Technol.,* **23,** 467 (1950).

79. Hann, G. E., "Sealing Compounds and Tapes," pp. 14–18 "Adhesives and Sealants in Building," Building Research Institute, 2101 Constitution Avenue, Washington 25, D. C., 1958.

80. Havens, G. G., and Ford, R. D., *Plastics,* **1,** (4), 51 (1944).

81. Hendricks, J. O., Lindner, G. F., and Wehmer, F., *Rubber Age,* **63,** 327 (1948).

82. Hendricks, J. O. (to Minnesota Mining and Manufacturing Co.), U. S. Patent 2,607,711 (Aug. 9, 1952).

83. Hock, C. W., and Abbott, A. N., *Rubber Age,* **82,** 471 (1957).

84. Hock, C. W., unpublished data from this laboratory.

85. Hoekstra, J. and Fritzius, C. P., "Rheology of Adhesives," pp. 55–82, in deBruyne, N. A., and Houwink, R. (Editors) "Adhesion and Adhesives," New York, Elsevier Publishing Co., 1951.

86. Irvin, M. H., and Cornell, W. H., *Rubber World,* **77,** No. 1, 55 (1955).

87. Jamieson, A. M., *Plastics Institute (London) Trans. and J.,* **17,** 20 (1949).

88. Joesting, E. O. (to Minnesota Mining and Manufacturing Co.), U. S. Patent 2,567,671 (Sept. 11, 1951).

89. Josefowitz, D., and Mark, H., *Indian Rubber World,* **106,** 33 (1942).

90. Kaelble, D. H., "Theory and Analysis of Peel Adhesion," Abstracts, Society of Rheology, Meeting, Nov. 5–7, 1958, Philadelphia, to be published in *Trans. Soc. Rheol.,* **3.**

91. Kemball, C., "Intermolecular Forces and the Strength of Adhesive Joints," pp. 69–71, in Clark, Rutzler, and Savage (Editors), "Adhesion and Adhesives, Fundamentals and Practice," New York, J. Wiley & Sons, Inc., 1954.

92. Kellgrin, W. (to Minnesota Mining and Manufacturing Co.), U. S. Patent 2,410,079 (Sept. 22, 1941).

93. Koehn, G. W., "Behavior of Adhesives in Strength Testing," pp. 120–126, in Clark, Rutzler, and Savage (Editors), "Adhesion and Adhesives, Fundamentals and Practice," New York, J. Wiley & Sons, Inc., 1954.

94. Kraus, G., "Energy of Adhesion, Molecular Forces and Adhesive Rupture," pp. 45–50, in Clark, Rutzler, and Savage (Editors), "Adhesives and Adhesion, Fundamentals and Practice," New York, J. Wiley & Sons, Inc., 1954.

95. Kraus, G., and Manson, J. E., *J. Polymer Sci.,* **18,** 359 (1955).

96. Lambert, J. M., and McDonald, R. A., *Rev. Sci. Inst.,* **19,** 119 (1948).

97. Lanning, W. H., *Adhesives & Resins,* **1,** 188 (1953).

98. Larfen, H. A., and Drickamer, H. G., *J. Phys. Chem.,* **61,** 1643 (1957).

99. Lasoski, S. W., and Kraus, G., *J. Polymer Sci.,* **18,** 359 (1955).

100. McClellan, J. M., *Rubber Age,* **77,** 385 (1955).

101. McDonald, A. (to B. B. Chemical Co.), U. S. Patent 2,067,854 (Jan. 14, 1937).

102. McPherson, A. T., and Klemin, A., "Engineering Uses of Rubber," p. 2, New York, Reinhold Publishing Corp., 1957.

103. McRegor, R. R., "Silicones and their Uses," p. 145, New York, McGraw-Hill Publishing Co., 1954.

104. Merrill, J. A., *Rubber Age,* **59,** 313 (1946); see also Roquemore, G. D. (to Wingfoot Corp.), U. S. Patent 2,381,186 (Aug. 8, 1945).

104A. Miller, A. L., and Robison, S. B., *Rubber World,* **137,** 397 (1957).

104B. Monsanto Tech. Bulls., P-125, P-145, and P-151; St. Louis, Mo.; Monsanto Chemical Co., Phosphate Div., 1953.

105. Mooney, M., *Ind. Eng. Chem., Anal. Ed.,* **6,** 147 (1934).

106. Mylonas, C., Aero Research Tech. Bull. No. 161, "Experiments on Composite Models with Application to Cemented Joints," Duxford, Cambridge, England, Aero Research, Ltd., 1956.

107. Mylonas, C., and deBruyne, N. A., "Static Problems," pp. 91–142, in deBruyne, N. A., and Houwink, R., "Adhesion and Adhesives," New York, Elsevier Publishing Co., 1951.

108. Panel Discussion, "Automotive Adhesives," Detroit Rubber and Plastics Group, Feb. 13, 1953; see *Rubber Age,* **73,** 209 (1953).

109. Panel Discussion, "Rubber-to-Metal Adhesion," Akron Rubber Group, Oct. 25, 1957; see *Rubber Age,* **82,** 478 (1957), and **82,** 672 (1957).

110. Patrick, J. C. (to Thiokol Corp.), U. S. Patents 2,206,641–3 (July 7, 1940).

111. Peachey, S. J., U. S. Patent 1,234,381 (July 14, 1917); see also Hercules Powder Company, "Parlon, Hercules Chlorinated Rubber," Form No. 579-C.

112. Perry, L., and Hills, H., Presented before ASTM Committee D-14 on Adhesives, Washington, D. C., Oct. 1958, unpublished.

113. Perry, L. (to Nashua Gum and Coated Paper Co.), U. S. Patent 2,462,029 (Feb. 13, 1949).

114. Piper, R. S., *Product Engineering,* Feb. 1952.

115. Reinhart, F. W., "Survey of Adhesion and Types of Bonds Involved," pp. 9–15, in Clark, Rutzler, and Savage (Editors), "Adhesion and Adhesives, Fundamentals and Practice," New York, J. Wiley & Sons, Inc., 1954.

116. Reynolds, O., *Phil. Trans. Roy. Soc. (London),* **177,** 157 (1886).

117. Rivlin, R. S., *Paint Technol.,* **9,** 215 (1944).

118. Rossman, J., *India Rubber World,* **91,** No. 4, 37 (1935).

119. Schmitt, E., *J. Rubber Research,* **17,** 195 (1948).

120. Scott, J. R., *Trans. Inst. Rubber Ind.,* **7,** 169 (1931).

121. Smith, D. A., *Rubber and Plastics Age,* **38,** No. 3, 231 (1957).

122. Stefan, J., *Sitzber. Akad. Wiss., Wien, Math. naturw. Kl.,* **69,** 713 (1874).

123. Sweitzer, C. W., Goodrich, W. C., and Burgess, K. A., *Rubber Age,* **65,** 651 (1945).

124. Swire, W. H., *Adhesives & Resins,* **1,** 186 (1953).

125. Swire, W. H., and Walton, E. H., *Adhesives & Resins,* **2,** 3 (1954).

126. Swire, W. H., *Adhesives & Resins,* **2,** 57 (1954).

127. Swire, W. H., *Adhesives & Resins,* **2,** 277 (1954).

128. Swire, W. H., *Adhesives & Resins,* **1,** 268 (1953).

129. Thielsch, H., "Adhesive Bonding," *Materials and Methods,* Manual No. 110, New York, Reinhold Publishing Corp., Nov. 1954.

130. Twiss, S. B., and Clougerty, L. B., *Adhesives Age,* **1,** 39 (1958).

131. "Vanderbilt Rubber Handbook," p. 200, New York, R. T. Vanderbilt Co., Inc., 1958.

132. "Vanderbilt Rubber Handbook," pp. 508–11, New York, R. T. Vanderbilt Co., Inc., 1958.

132A. Van der Meer, S., *Rec. trav. chim.,* **63,** 147, 157 (1944).

133. Voet, A., and Giffkin, C. F., *Ind. Eng. Chem.,* **43,** 1614 (1951).

134. Voyutski, S. S., and Margolina, Yu. L., *Uspekhi Khim.* **18,** 449 (1949); printed in English in *Rubber Chem. and Technol.,* **30,** 531 (1957).

135. Voyutski, S. S., and Zamazy, B. M., *Colloid J. (U. S. S. R.),* **15,** 421 (1953); printed in English in *Rubber Chem. and Technol.,* **30,** 544 (1957).

136. Voyutski, S. S., and Shtarkh, B. V., *Colloid J. (U. S. S. R.),* **16,** 1 (1954); printed in English in *Rubber Chem. and Technol.,* **30,** 548 (1957).

137. Voyutski, S. S., Shapovolava, A. I., and Pisarenko, A. P., *Colloid J. (U. S. S. R.),* **18,** 485 (1956); **19,** 274 (1957).

138. Wake, W. C., "The Adhesion of Rubber and Textiles," pp. 185–189, in Clark, Rutzler, and Savage (Editors), "Adhesion and Adhesives, Fundamen-

tals and Practice," New York, J. Wiley & Sons, Inc., 1954.

139. Watson, W. F., *Ind. Eng. Chem.,* **47,** 1281 (1955).

140. Watson, W. F., *Trans, Faraday Soc.,* **49,** 1369 (1953).

141. Watson, W. F., and Angier, D. J., *J. Polymer Sci.,* **18,** 129 (1955).

142. Watson, W. F., and Angier, D. J., *J. Polymer Sci.,* **25,** 1 (1957).

143. Watson, W. F., Angier, D. J., and Chambers, W. T., *J. Polymer Sci.,* **25,** 129 (1957).

144. Watson, W. F., Ayrey, G., and Moore, C. G., *J. Polymer Sci.,* **19,** 1 (1956).

145. Watson, W. F., and Pike, M. J., *J. Polymer Sci.,* **9,** 229 (1951).

146. Watson, W. F., and Wilson, J., *J. Sci. Inst.,* **31,** 98 (1954).

147. Werner, F., and Eickner, H. W., *Modern Plastics,* **34** (4), 187 (1956).

148. Wetzel, F. H., *ASTM Bull.,* **221,** TP72 (1957).

149. Wetzel, F. H., *Rubber Age,* **82,** 291 (1957).

150. Wetzel, F. H., and Reynolds, A. E., presented before ASTM Committee D-14 on Adhesives, New York, Apr. 1, 1955, unpublished.

151. Wilson, P. H., "Tapes for Building Panels," pp. 140–143, "Adhesives and Sealants in Building," Building Research Institute, 2101 Constitution Avenue, Washington 25, D. C., 1958.

152. Winkelmann, H. A. (to Marbon Corp.), U. S. Patents 2,096,660–2 (Oct. 19, 1937).

153. Yank, C., *Tappi,* **40,** No. 6, 167A (1957).

154. Yavorsky, J. M., presented before ASTM Committee D-14 on Adhesives, Washington, D. C., Oct. 1954, unpublished.

155. Yavorsky, J. M., Cunningham, J. H., and Hundley, N. G., *Forest Products J.,* **5,** (5), 306 (1955).

156. Yavorsky, J. M., and Cunningham, J. H., *Forest Products J.,* **5,** (1), 80 (1955).

— 15 —

Natural and Reclaimed Rubber Adhesives

Stephen Palinchak and W. J. Yurgen

Battelle Memorial Institute

Columbus, Ohio

Natural and reclaimed rubber adhesives were used extensively prior to World War II. Since then the emphasis has been on adhesives and cements based on synthetic elastomers. Although the natural and reclaimed products have been used successfully for a long time in industry, little technical data excluding patents have been published. In 1941, Adenoff[1] pointed out this lack of information and indicated that remedial steps should be taken to correct the situation. Today, this dearth still exists, and most of the data published are on synthetic rubber adhesives of varying complexity.

Therefore, it is hoped that the information presented in this chapter on natural and reclaim adhesives and cements will be useful to adhesive technologists. A brief historical development of natural and reclaimed rubber cements and adhesives together with information on their characteristics, present applications, and methods of preparation is included.

HISTORY AND ECONOMICS

It is not known who first discovered that crude rubber could be dissolved in solvents to form sticky solutions capable of bonding different materials together. Records show that Herrisant and Macquer in 1761–1763[2] found that natural rubber would swell and finally dissolve in turpentine, ether, and volatile oils. In 1823, Charles Macintosh[2] discovered tar naphtha developed by the coal gas industry to be an excellent solvent for natural rubber. These discoveries led to the investigation of the use of other solvents, and by 1900[2] a number of them were used including turpentine, "Dipentene," petroleum spirits, carbon disulfide, benzene and its homologs, and chloroform.

The first commercial application of a natural rubber solution, which was initiated by Macintosh in 1823,[3] involved the use of natural rubber solutions as coatings for waterproofing and joining of cloth. Beginning with a patent issued to Jeffrey in 1843[4] on the preparation of a natural rubber adhesive, a large number and variety of similar patents appeared in the United States and England. Ross,[4] in 1940, prepared a survey by abstracting 105 U. S. patents dealing with natural rubber cements issued from 1843 to 1935, of which the majority were for adhesives for the manufacture and repair of boots and shoes, various rubber goods, books, and metal and leather goods.

The public first became aware of natural rubber cements with the advent of the pneumatic automobile tire where they were used to repair punctures. Typical cement for repairing tires contained 10 to 12 per cent masticated Para rubber in gasoline or benzene with 1 to 2 per cent rosin added for improved adhesion.[5] Similar cements are currently used to repair natural rubber tubes, and adhesives based on the above recipe are employed in the household and office for bonding paper and other porous products.

After the vulcanization of natural rubber was discovered, numerous attempts were made to devulcanize or regenerate cured rubber products to their original plastic state. Subsequently, it was noted that devulcanized rubber could be dissolved in benzene or naphtha to form a cement having excellent adhesive qualities and properties unattainable with crude natural rubber.

Originally, boots and shoes represented the primary source of vulcanized rubber for reclaiming. With the invention of the automobile, the source of scrap rubber gradually changed to tire scrap. In the ensuing years, a vast amount of tire scrap has been made available to the reclaim industry and tires continue to be the main source of reclaimed rubber. The average yearly consumption of reclaimed rubber in the United States during the period from 1940 to 1959 has been approximately 265,000 tons, i.e., about 20 per cent of the total quantity of rubber consumed in the United States.[6] Of this amount, approximately 5 per cent was used for cements and dispersions.

Prior to 1935, the amount of reclaimed rubber used for cements was negligible. It soon was discovered that with fast-setting reclaim adhesives, it was possible to secure automobile trim to foundation boards faster than with other adhesives and still maintain good appearance. Moreover, the use of reclaim adhesive reduced costs. Prior to the use of such adhesives, the trim was attached by means of mechanical fasteners and dextrin paste. The pastes set slowly; hence much valuable floor space was used for storage. The use of reclaim adhesives in automotive fabrication gradually increased, and by 1940 approximately 3,250,000 gal of the cement were consumed by the automotive industry—an average of 0.8 gal per automobile.[7] The estimated annual consumption of adhesives and sealers by the automotive industry is 110 million lb, of which reclaimed rubber-based materials are most widely used because of low cost, ease of application, and their ability to attain maximum bonding strength rapidly.

It is estimated that about 5 per cent of all the rubber consumed in the world is utilized as adhesives;[8] furthermore approximately 50 per cent of this world consumption of rubber for adhesives is still based on natural and reclaimed rubber. This percentage may be somewhat lower in the United States, but a substantial quantity is being consumed. Although synthetic rubber adhesives have in certain applications replaced natural and reclaim adhesives, the over-all use of adhesives has increased to such an extent that the weight consumption of natural and reclaimed rubber has remained relatively constant throughout the years.

RECENT APPLICATIONS

Today, natural and reclaimed rubber-based adhesives are still used extensively to bond paper, rubber, plastic films, leather, wood, ceramic and plastic tile, plasterboard, metals, etc., to each other

and to other materials; also, these rubbers are used as base materials for many pressure-sensitive tapes, e.g., surgical, masking, cellophane, and cloth types. The major applications are in the automotive, building, shoe, and sundry-drug industries. It is estimated that the automotive industry utilizes 40 million lb of dry natural rubber and rubber latex as well as 70 million lb of reclaim-asphalt mixtures annually. The reclaim-asphalt mixtures are employed for adhering nonmetallic trim, for sound insulation, and as body sealers. Specifically they are used in the formation of flocked surfaces for trim.

In the building industry, there are three primary uses for natural and reclaimed rubber cements,[9, 10] i.e., weatherproofing, attachment of interior finishes, and construction. For weatherproofing, the reclaim cement is available as a stiff paste or an extruded ribbon. The compound seals brick, wood, metal, and concrete. In modernizing old buildings, improvement is made by sealing chinks and holes in poor-fitting window frames where no mastic had been used. Improvement of living areas is made possible by the bonding of thermal and acoustical insulation to walls and ceilings. Frequently, tiles are attached to wood battens by means of staples; however, natural rubber or reclaim mastic may be used to fasten sections directly to a flat surface. The cement is applied in nodules at each corner and in the middle of each tile before it is pressed onto the ceiling.

Ceramic tile, plastic sheeting, and resin-bonded decorative veneers can be attached to plaster, brick, wood, and steel. Rubber flooring or linoleum or plastic tile can be applied to wood subflooring or concrete. A reclaim solvent-type mastic is generally preferred for this purpose. The adhesive is applied by troweling; lumps should be avoided since they retain solvent. The floor covering is laid when the solvent is completely evaporated; thus, the mastic must have good inherent tack. Approximately 3 to 4 million gallons of natural and reclaimed rubber adhesives are allegedly consumed annually in this area.

Reclaim cements are also used in the construction of prefabricated panels, which are usually constructed from fibrous soft boards, hardboard, or plasterboard. They may be made up from two or three thicknesses of board by applying cement by roller or spraying. An example of unusual interest is the manufacture of decorative tile-face, nonload-bearing panels used in curtain-wall construction.[11] The use of sandwiched-panel construction provides more interior floor space and simultaneously permits a corresponding reduction in weight. Two types of adhesives are available, i.e., a solvent type, where precautions are necessary because of the flammability hazard, and an aqueous type which is both nonflammable and nontoxic, but requires longer assembly time.

A reclaim mastic adhesive of trowelable viscosity has been used successfully for a variety of requirements in addition to cost reduction, among which are efficient, low-cost, quick, simple production techniques, elimination of pressure or heating, ease of application, quick drying, high bond strength during service, and high moisture resistance. This same cement has also been used successfully in the manufacture of interior panels for radomes to bond magnesium skins to a foamed polystyrene core.

The shoe industry consumes about 5 million lb of dry natural rubber and 5 million lb of latex yearly. Latex cements find extensive use in the manufacture of boots and shoes where a water-resistant highly flexible adhesive is required. These adhesives are employed for bonding leather and canvas felt to themselves or to other materials such as rubber or crepe soles. In the latter case, the latex is usually applied to the leather or fabric and a solvent-based adhesive to the rubber sole.

In addition to the above industries, natural and reclaimed rubber are utilized in medical, metallurgical, and military applications. In the medical and sundry-drug field, natural rubber adhesive tape is the primary product. Although there are no figures for the quantity of rubber used for this application, it is estimated at millions of pounds annually. In the metallurgical industry,[12] reclaim adhesives of the solvent-curable types are used to bond certain materials to a mold. Water-dispersion type adhesives are not suitable since they often attack ferrous metals or aluminum causing rust or corrosion. In military packaging, reclaimed rubber adhesives are utilized because of their rapid gain in strength and good water resistance. Natural and reclaim rubbers are not used in food packaging because of the odor they impart to the food.

Typical cement recipes for various broad applications, which are listed in the appendix at the end of the chapter, represent basic formulations which may be changed or modified for specific end uses.

CHARACTERISTIC PROPERTIES

Natural and reclaimed rubber adhesives have unique specific properties, of which the most important is "dry tack," i.e., the ability of two fresh, nonsticky film surfaces of rubber which are deposited from a dough, solvent solution, latex, or dispersion, to adhere strongly to each other or to other surfaces after they are thoroughly dried and free of solvent. Tack is frequently used as a substitute for pressure in the bonding operation, particularly in contact pressure applications. The relative tack of

natural rubber as compared to butadiene-styrene type synthetic is shown in Table 1.

TABLE 1. TACK PROPERTIES OF NATURAL AND BUTADIENE-STYRENE RUBBERS.[13]

	Rubber			
	Natural		Synthetic	
Filler	None	Carbon black	None	Carbon black
Relative tack	1.0	0.8	0.3	0.3

The relative difference in properties for natural and reclaimed rubber as compared to synthetic rubbers is shown in Table 2. Although both natural and reclaim adhesives have excellent tack qualities, a reclaim adhesive has the better aging qualities and is more resistant to heat flow.[15] The tacky adhesiveness and cohesiveness of natural and reclaimed rubbers cannot be readily attained with other elastomers. The natural and reclaim products have thus become important rubbers for pressure-sensitive tapes.

Because of their tack properties, these adhesives are quite versatile. They may be applied from solvent solution, water dispersion, or from a semisolid state as in the case of sealers, pastes, or putties. Application can be accomplished by calendering, spraying, knife coating, rolling, brushing, or dipping.

In many applications, reclaim adhesives are more prevalent than natural rubber because of their low cost, ease of application, rapid gain in strength, and long open time. Furthermore reclaim adhesives show a high level of stability in solution and have the most suitable sprayability of all rubber-based adhesives.

ADHESIVE TYPES

Natural and reclaimed rubber adhesives may be classified as (1) solvent solutions, (2) latex, (3) dispersions, and (4) semisolids. The compositions for each are similar, i.e., usually similar materials are utilized to obtain a specific property such as tack. Moreover, although the method for applying the adhesive to a surface may differ, the final dried film from each class has similar properties if similar components are used in the manufacture.

There are a variety of natural rubbers that may be used in adhesives, of which the most common are pale crepe, smoked sheet, and Para rubber. Some adhesives are made from balata or gutta-percha types; however, these have found more use abroad than in the United States. Pale crepe and smoked sheet are prepared from rubber obtained from cultivated plantation trees in the East India areas. Para, a South American rubber, is not ex-

TABLE 2. RELATIVE PROPERTIES OF NATURAL, RECLAIM, AND SYNTHETIC RUBBER ADHESIVES.[14]

Properties	Resilience	Strength	Tack	Adhesion to Metals	Plastic Flow	Oxidation	Heat	Resistance to Water	Resistance to Solvent	Common Solvents
Natural	Best	Good	Excellent	Poor	Fair	Fair	Fair	Good	Poor	Petroleum
Reclaimed	Good	Good	Excellent	Good	Fair	Fair	Fair	Good	Poor	Petroleum
Butadiene-styrene (SBR)	Fair	Fair	Poor	Poor	Fair	Fair	Fair	Best	Poor	Petroleum
Butyl	Fair	Fair	Fair	Poor	Poor	Excellent	Poor	Good	Poor	Petroleum
Polybutylene	Fair	Fair	Fair	Fair	Poor	Excellent	Poor	Good	Poor	Petroleum
Neoprene	Good	Best	Fair	Fair	Best	Good	Excellent	Good	Good	Toluene, methylethyl ketone, ethyl acetate
Buna-N	Fair	Good	Poor	Best	Good	Good	Best	Good	Excellent	Methylethyl ketone
"Thiokol"	Poor	Fair	Poor	Best	Poor	Excellent	Poor	Excellent	Best	Ethylene dichloride

tensively used in adhesives presently because of its high cost. However, this rubber produces high quality adhesives which have greater strength and better aging qualities than those prepared from plantation rubbers. Balata and gutta-percha, which are *trans* forms of natural rubber, are used primarily to obtain stiffer film qualities in natural rubber adhesives. In the United States, these materials have largely been replaced by synthetics such as the high-styrene resinous copolymers.

In preparation of a solvent or semi-paste adhe--sive, natural rubber must be milled since unmilled natural crude rubber behaves in solvents similarly to vulcanized rubber, i.e., it swells. When masticated sufficiently, it will dissolve to form a viscous solution, the viscosity of which is determined by the degree of mastication.[16] The effect of milling on viscosity is shown in Table 3.

Although milling is commonly used to reduce viscosity, other methods are also effective, e.g., exposing the solutions to light in the presence of air or adding traces of certain acids, bases, or oxidizing chemicals to the solution. Chemicals frequently used are piperidine, diethylamine, aniline, pyri-

dine, acridine, α-iodobenzoic acid, acetic acid, aminoazobenzene, diphenylguanidine, and piperidine pentamethylene dithiocarbamate. Milling time may be reduced by the addition of chemical peptizing agents to the rubber during milling; also mercaptans are effective materials.

The solution viscosity of natural rubber cements varies with the type of solvents,[16] e.g., solutions with chlorinated solvents ordinarily have a comparatively high viscosity; hydrocarbons produce solutions of medium viscosity; and oxygen-containing compounds give low viscosity. Addition of a small proportion of an alcohol-type solvent will tend to reduce viscosity.

Natural rubber tends to oxidize readily in the presence of air, sunlight, and humidity. To improve aging, antioxidants such as diphenyl-beta-naphthylamines are added. If staining is undesirable, a number of phenol-type antioxidants are available. Typical reclaims used for adhesives are described in Table 4.

To improve tack and adhesion, a variety of thermoplastic and thermosetting resins are used in natural and reclaim adhesives. The thermoplastic or heat-softening resins are usually natural rosins, rosin derivatives, polyterpenes and terpene phenolics. The thermosetting resin types used are chiefly oil-soluble, heat-reactive phenolics. Combinations of thermoplastic rosins or resins may be used. Thermosetting resins are generally used in conjunction with thermoplastic resins.

The choice of resin determines the qualities of the adhesive from the standpoint of tack, tensile strength, color retention, and resistance to embrit-

TABLE 3. EFFECT OF MILLING ON CEMENT VISCOSITY.

Number of Passes Through Cold Mill	Approximate Viscosity (cps)
0	28.0
7	16.0
15	10.0
37	3.5
100	1.5

TABLE 4. ALKALINE RECLAIMS FOR ADHESIVES.[17]

Type	Color	Specific Gravity	Acetone Extraction	Ash	Carbon Black	RHC*	Tensile Strength	Elongation (%)
Carcass	Gray	1.22–13.2	8	28–34	None	60–56	1200–800	450–300
	Black	1.18	12	17	12	58	800	300
Inner tube (natural)	Black	1.9	8	20	12	58	1200	400
	Red	1.2–1.3	7–12	26–36	None	65–54	750	350

* Rubber hydrocarbon.

tlement by oxidation. Esters of rosin are generally chosen as tackifiers. Unmodified gum or wood rosin yields esters that exhibit fair tack properties initially but which have poor aging characteristics in finished adhesive applications. Esters of rosin types, that have been stabilized against oxygen attack by hydrogenation or polymerization, possess the best combination of characteristics for adhesive use. Examples of these are a glycerol ester of hydrogenated rosin, a pentaerythritol ester of hydrogenated rosin, and a glycerol ester of polymerized rosin.

In cements, terpene phenolic heat-softening resins impart excellent initial strength but will not maintain it for long periods of time. Therefore, they are recommended for pressure-sensitive applications. Although the polyterpenes act similarly, they provide better aging quality; consequently they are usually given primary consideration in the development of pressure-sensitive cements. Because the thermosetting heat-reactive phenolics have limited compatibility with natural and reclaimed rubber, they are used in lesser amounts in combination with the terpene phenolics and polyterpene resins. They control the thermal softening point and both the adhesive and cohesive bonding forces in the cement.

Other materials, notably extenders, reinforcing agents, softeners, antioxidants, colorants, waxes, accelerating agents, etc., are added to reduce the cost of the cement or to impart some desired property, which will be discussed under specific types.

SOLVENT SOLUTIONS

Solvent types of natural and reclaim adhesives are prepared generally by dissolving milled and compounded rubber stocks in suitable solvents, e.g., benzene or gasoline. Such adhesives are quick drying, flammable, and may contain toxic solvents, of which benzene is an example. These cements can be adapted to high-speed production operations because of their ease of application, fast tack, rapid drying, high green strength, good film resiliency, and impact resistance. The cements can be made in a wide range of viscosities from thin solutions to viscous paste.

There are several methods of preparing natural or reclaim solvent cements. In one procedure, the rubber or reclaim is first softened by working on a mill or in a Banbury. Fillers, pigments, and processing agents are blended in, and subsequently the softened compounded stock is placed in an internal mixer of Baker-Perkins or Werner-Pfeiderer type and worked into a fairly smooth mass. Pulverized rosin or resin is added slowly to avoid breaking up the rubber into separate particles, at which point slaked lime is added if specified in the recipe; then the batch is heated to approximately 270°F and maintained there for 5 to 10 min or until the desired viscosity, tack, and cohesive characteristics are obtained. The batch is then cooled to approximately 150°F before the addition of solvent. (Cooling is accomplished by passing cold water through a water jacket surrounding the mixer.) Solvent is added slowly in increments at first making certain that each portion is completely dispersed before adding more. If addition is too rapid, the cement will break up into large segments which take a considerably longer time to dissolve. Usually, when somewhat more than half of the solvent is thoroughly mixed, the remainder can be added rapidly to complete the mix. Some solvent may evaporate during the mixing; consequently, additional solvent must be added to compensate for the loss and to restore the viscosity to the proper level. Hence, it is good practice to check the viscosity of the final mix.

There are three other methods of preparing adhesives, all of which utilize either a mill or Banbury. The technique selected will depend somewhat on the type of product being made. In the first method, following mill or Banbury compounding, all components including resins, the natural or reclaimed rubber, fillers, etc., the mass is added to an internal sigma blade mixer and solvent is added to obtain the desired viscosity and solids content. Heat is employed to improve processibility and reduce the time of mixing.

In the second method, where a high thermal softening cement containing curing agents is required, the pigments, processing and curing agents, and other required ingredients except resin are worked in during the compounding stage. The stock is then transferred to an internal mixer, and the resin and solvent are blended in until a homogeneous dispersion of rubber in solvent is obtained. No heat is involved in this method except that generated by shearing of the rubber.

In a third method, the rubber or reclaim and all the components except the resin are worked in on a rubber mill or in a Banbury. The resin is dissolved separately in a churn containing the solvent. The compounded reclaim, in strips, is placed in the churn and thoroughly agitated to the desired cement viscosity. The churn method of mixing cement usually requires 6 to 12 hr to complete the dispersion of rubber in solvent, as compared to ½ to 2 hr when the sigma blade method is used.

In the preceding methods, the mixing equipment used most commonly is the internal sigma blade-type mixer, a two-bladed mixer which performs a kneading rather than a cutting action. The type most commonly used in the cement industry is a 100-gal capacity mixer which can produce a full batch of reclaim cement in 30 to 60 min. However, because of maintenance and original equipment costs, this machine is being replaced by less expensive, larger capacity, single- and double-shaft propeller-type churns and mixers[18] designed specifically for rubber cements. A battery of large capacity mixing churns can be set up to produce any gallonage of rubber or reclaim cement desired at a nominal processing cost.

Latex

Natural rubber latex adhesives[19] consist of a colloidal suspension of rubber particles, usually with dispersions of various resins and fillers. Solvent cements contain only about 12 to 20 per cent rubber; whereas a latex cement contains a minimum of 35 per cent. The rubber in latex is not masticated as in solvent cements; hence films formed are tougher, stronger, and have better aging properties. However, the tack qualities are not as good as for solvent-type cements.

Latex adhesives can be modified to produce specific properties similar to those of solvent types. However, since oils, resins, or fillers added directly to latex cause coagulation of the rubber, these must be added in the form of an emulsion. Emulsions of tack-producing resins such as rosin and its derivatives may be added to improve the tack of latex films. The bonding quality of films of this type may be improved by heating the latex for several hours.

Solvents may be added directly in concentrations of 10 to 20 per cent to latex under strong agitation.

A sticky, adhesive mass, which is somewhat similar to that obtained with solvent adhesives, results. Latex may also be added to solvent cements in approximately 20 per cent concentrations to improve their strength.

Sodium silicate and colloidal silica are frequently added to latex cements to promote adhesion on nonporous surfaces such as tiles or glass. Wetting agents improve wetting and consequently adhesion on nonporous surfaces. Ammonia is added to latex for stabilization although excessive ammonia decelerates drying.

Reclaimed Rubber Dispersions

A rubber dispersion is a solid-in-liquid system, in which the rubber is the dispersed phase and the water the continuous phase. The art of redispersing rubber in an aqueous solution was investigated early in the nineteenth century.[20] Although many patents were obtained, they were of no commercial value. A process discovered by Pratt[21] and further developed by Dispersions Process, Inc. and the Naugatuck Chemical Company laid the foundation for reclaimed rubber dispersions as known today.

In the short period following the discovery of making dispersions, the use of these products has enjoyed a healthy growth, principally because of their favorable price. Reclaimed rubber is less expensive than natural or synthetic rubber; therefore these dispersions have a definite economic advantage. Currently, there are about six producers of reclaimed rubber-water dispersions,[22] and many manufacturers produce dispersions for their own use. Dispersions are used in large volume with latices in impregnation of tire cord fabric; consequently their volume is regulated to the price of the latex and fluctuates with its cost. There are many other types of applications for dispersions, notably impregnating and saturating compounds; treatment for carpet and rug backings; spreading compounds; sound insulating; and corrosion-insulating materials. Reclaim dispersions are useful for blending with natural or synthetic rubber latices where the reclaimed rubber imparts different and desirable properties to the rubber film.

In preparing dispersions, reclaimed rubber is plasticized on a rubber mill or Banbury, at which point the desired fillers, softeners, sulfur, and accelerating agents are added. The compounded reclaim is next placed in an internal sigma-blade type mixer ranging in capacity from 100 to 500 gal. When the rubber mass is uniformly mixed, the resin or rosin (if required) is incorporated slowly to avoid dispersing the rubber into separate particles.

Water is subsequently added in small portions until approximately 10 per cent of the total water has been taken up by the reclaim. At this time, the dispersing agent in paste, fluid, or solid form is added in portions or all at once and kneading is continued. When the additive has been thoroughly worked into a smooth batch, more water is added until the rubber contains approximately 20 to 30 per cent water. With continued working, a dispersion of the rubber in water is formed as the water in the rubber dispersion inverts. This inversion can be hastened by adding a small amount of hot water or by heating the mass; also the remaining water is added to dilute the dispersion to the desired viscosity.

Another method commonly employed for dispersing rubber in water is the attrition technique.[23] In this process, a heavy paste of clay, whiting, or starch is loaded into the mixer, the temperature is increased, and the plasticized reclaim, with modifiers, is added with continued mixing. Formation of a rubber in water dispersion by this system which is immediate is assisted by various emulsifiers.

Quick-drying rubber dispersions have been prepared by Brams[24] from alcohol dispersion of rubber wherein the alcohol is the main vehicle. The rubber is dispersed by the action of shellac or other alcohol-soluble gums. Any alcohol that is not a solvent for rubber may be used. The method of dispersing is similar to the one previously described for reclaimed rubber in water. Various compounding and curing agents may be added to make the dispersions suitable for specific applications.

Curable reclaim dispersions can be made by incorporating vulcanizing agents into the rubber on mill rolls or in a Banbury according to standard practice or by adding these agents to the reclaim in a dough mixer prior to the addition of the water.

Where large volumes of dispersions are manufactured, multiple batches are blended and stored in large capacity storage tanks. Preservatives, stabilizers, and occasionally thickeners are added to preserve quality. Dispersions are preserved with suitable antioxidants such as phenyl-beta-naphthylamine, which is used in casein-dispersed rubbers. Clay and soap dispersions are preserved with a chloroform and toluene mixture.

Reclaimed rubber dispersions in black, gray, or red are available from various manufacturers; furthermore the reclaim for preparing dispersions should be well refined to obtain a fine particle size.

The types of reclaim dispersions are characterized by determining solids content, viscosity in centerpoises, pH (electrometric), particle size, weight per gallon, per cent ash, tensile strength of dried film, and rate of development of adhesion.

Important compounding ingredients in preparing dispersions are emulsifiers, fillers and extenders, softeners and plasticizers, tackifiers, sulfur, accelerators, antioxidants, stabilizers, preservatives, deodorants, and thickeners.

One of the more important types of products from the standpoint of volume is the reclaimed rubber-asphalt dispersion. The good tack and setting properties of these cements make them valuable for many uses, e.g., soundproofing automobiles; joining fabric or felt to metal; attaching glass fiber to metal; attaching floor mats to metal floors in automobile bodies; attaching jute to the trunk compartment; etc. These cements adapt themselves to the assembly lines of automobile plants. Usually of a sprayable type, they have other properties which permit them to be used in place of flammable gasoline-solvent cements.

When the water evaporates from reclaim-asphalt dispersions, these adhesives yield a highly tacky, pressure-sensitive film. Upon application of slight pressure, these films will adhere tenaciously to smooth metal surfaces; moreover they are highly resistant to redispersion in water.

In making a reclaimed rubber-asphalt dispersion, the reclaim is initially worked on a mill to increase its plasticity, which may be accomplished on an ordinary rubber mill in about 10 to 15 min. The softened reclaim is then placed in an internal mixer of the Baker-Perkins or Werner-Pfeiderer type. The rubber is worked in the mixer to a fairly smooth mass, and resin is added slowly. Each increment of resin should be thoroughly incorporated before a subsequent addition is made. During the operation, the mass is heated so that the mix is kept sufficiently mobile and smooth. After the resin melts, it is distributed uniformly throughout the rubber, at which time the emulsifier is added, all at once, if desired.

Following this addition, the rubber mix should be reduced to a temperature below 155°F by adding cold water and ice if necessary. Best dispersions are obtained at temperatures between 140 and 150°F, and the proportion of water and ice should be adjusted to reach this temperature reduction without neither adding excessive water nor exceeding the maximum optimum water content prior to inversion. If this method is not closely followed, the batch of cement may be ruined.

After the cold water is thoroughly incorporated within the rubber mix, an alkali solution is slowly added, dispersed in the reclaim mass; then additional water is added fairly rapidly.

Prior to the addition of the alkali, the rubber is in the continuous phase and the water is in the dispersed phase. After the addition of alkali, an inversion takes place with the water forming the continuous phase of the emulsion. Subsequently the asphalt called for in the recipe can be added fairly rapidly until the ingredients are well mixed. The clay slurry may now be added rapidly. Following this, the remainder of the water may be added to bring the emulsion to the specified solids content or desired viscosity. When the batch has been diluted to a viscosity at which it can be pumped, it is dumped from the mixer, screened, and pumped directly into shipping containers or into a storage tank. Here, multiple batches are accumulated, and stabilizer and thickener added if necessary to obtain the final solids and viscosity required.

Higher proportions of asphalt may be employed, and the resin content may be decreased while still maintaining adequate tack in the final dried film of cement. By juggling the ratios of asphalt, rubber, clay, and resin, the amount of the latter may be reduced considerably and possibly omitted while maintaining favorable adhesiveness.

The ratio of asphalt to rubber may be varied; however if the ratio of asphalt to rubber is greatly increased, the resulting product might be inferior as a cement for many uses because the final dried film would have less cohesive strength and poorer heat resistance. The control of tack time can be regulated by the type and amount of reclaim and resin used.

Semisolid Products

There are two types of semisolid adhesive materials involving natural and reclaimed rubbers: some adhesive tapes and all sealers or putties.

Tapes. A tape consists of two parts:[25] (1) the backing material, cloth, plastic film, etc., and (2) the adhesive mass, rubber, resin, and filler. There are two principal methods for preparing adhesive masses for application to tapes:[26] (1) the dispersion of the rubber and other ingredients in a suitable solvent, and (2) intimate mixing of all components in the dry state by means of a Banbury or a rubber mill. The first type is applied by a coating procedure (spread from solution), and the second is calendered at elevated temperatures on a backing material.

In preparation of the solution type masses, sigma-blade type mixers are commonly used. The mixing procedure varies depending on the manufacturer. Usually, the rubber is allowed to gel in a solvent to form a viscous mass; then compounding ingredients are added such as resins, fillers, antioxidants, softeners, etc. In one specific method, the rubber and a portion of the solvent are kneaded together for

1 to 2 hr until homogeneous. Following this, plasticizers, fillers, resins, antioxidants, and medicaments (if used) are added in a dry state. To ensure complete dispersion, it is good practice to mix the fillers with a softener, e.g., lanolin, before adding them to the rubber; then the batch is diluted to the desired viscosity. In another method, the various ingredients are added first and mixed, after which rubber and solvent are added.

Many surgical adhesives are prepared and applied in a dry state without solvent. The rubber is placed in a rubber mill, and the various ingredients gradually added and mixed in. The order of mixing is: rubber, antioxidant, resin, softener, and filler. In this case, high temperatures are needed to soften rubber and resin for good mixing; consequently, some oxidation and breakdown of rubber occurs. The antioxidant is therefore added first to prevent undue oxidation. The general opinion of adhesive manufacturers is that better aging properties may be obtained by the solution method. In either case, the rubber must be masticated first, and control of this step is important. In the dry process, a higher degree of mastication occurs; consequently control of original breakdown is more critical. The amount of milling needed will depend on the properties required, the quality and type of rubber used, and the processing temperature.

A tape mass consists principally of rubber, resin, a wax, filler, lubricant, and antioxidant. A typical composition is as follows:

Ingredients	Parts per 100
Rubber	100
Resin	50–150
Filler	50–150
Lubricant	5–20
Wax	5–10
Antioxidant	1–3

Starch, which some manufacturers add to the mass, will adsorb water from the ingredients and often prevent coloring of the fillers; furthermore it tends to counteract the slippery properties of the lubricant. It is commonly used in surgical tapes where the most common lubricant is lanolin.

The resin most commonly used for surgical purposes is a modified rosin such as "Stabelite" or "Galex." Some terpenes may be used for industrial applications. The filler is usually calcium carbonate or zinc oxide. The latter was used in surgical tapes originally because it allegedly had antiseptic qualities. Zinc oxide also tends to combine in some way with the resin to produce a higher strength adhesive.

Sealers and Putties. Sealers and putties are available as high-viscosity liquids and in bulk form as extruded ribbons of specified shapes. Primarily they are dispersions of reclaim and extenders in aliphatic solvents such as nonleaded gasoline and petroleum naphtha; nevertheless some of them are dispersions of rubber and asphalt in a nonsolvent such as water and alcohol. In sealers and putties, the ratio of solvent or water to rubber may be of the order of 1 to 3 or 1 to 4. Unlike cements, sealers contribute no strength to a joint, but they seal openings and gaps as well as reduce noise and vibration.

The procedure for making reclaimed rubber solvent-type sealers or putties is the same as that described for reclaim solvent cements; however, the amount of solvent is limited to obtain appropriate viscosities and solids content for these semisolid compounds. If desired, the adhesive mass may be removed from the mixer before the addition of the solvent and applied by friction coating on backing. Bulk sealers may be similarly prepared by removing the compounded rubber mass from the mixer before adding solvent and extruding it into ribbon form of specified shape.

Sealers and putties can also be made from aqueous dispersions of reclaimed rubber or latex by following the procedures outlined for aqueous reclaim dispersions. Sealers and putties can be compounded with the same ingredients as those required in cements. The filler content, however, is usually quite high, as indicated by an ash content of approximately 30 to 40 per cent. If a tighter setting product is desired, curing agents may be added. As mentioned previously, the dispersion process does not alter the possibility of curing the product by any hot or cold method of vulcanization.

Reclaim base sealers and putties serve in various useful applications. Their function is twofold: (1) they close openings and gaps against penetration of dust, water, and fumes; (2) they provide a vibration and shock-resistant barrier between similar or dissimilar surfaces. Made to perform under extremes of temperature, humidity, and corrosive environments, they can be applied by spraying, troweling, or brushing. Sealers and putties have been recommended for:[27]

(1) Sealing seams in auto bodies.
(2) Bonding rubber mats.
(3) Sealing linoleum to wood, steel, or concrete floors.
(4) Glazing railroad cars, trucks, and buses.
(5) Sealing window frames.
(6) Sealing joints in stone cornices.
(7) Sealing between enameled metal tiles.
(8) Sealing built-in bathtubs.
(9) Waterproofing, caulking.

(10) Providing protective and acoustical coating on metal sheets.
(11) Bonding "Styrofoam" and similar materials.
(12) Bonding to rigid, porous and nonporous surfaces.
(13) Bonding metal to wood, concrete, metal, and other dry rigid surfaces.

Advantages of reclaim putty[25] are:

(1) Dries more rapidly than ordinary putty.
(2) Becomes firm, shrinks slightly, but becomes neither brittle nor hard.
(3) Withstands vibration effects of expansion and contraction.
(4) Resists corrosive fumes and salt spray, but is affected by strong oxidizing acids.
(5) Maintains airtight joints.
(6) Shows excellent adhesion to wood, glass, or steel.
(7) Can be painted over sooner than ordinary oil-whiting type putties.
(8) Is available in several colors.

References

1. Adenoff, S., *Rubber Age*, **49,** 171 (1941).
2. Davis, C. A., and Blake, John T., "Chemistry and Technology of Rubber," pp. 183–184, New York, Reinhold Publishing Corp., 1937.
3. Delmonte, J., "Technology of Adhesives," p. 178, New York, Reinhold Publishing Corp., 1947.
4. *Ibid*, p. 186.
5. *Ibid*, p. 189.
6. Whitby, G. S., "Synthetic Rubber," p. 593, New York, John Wiley & Sons, Inc., 1954.
7. Wheeler, R. L., *Rubber Age*, **49,** 169 (1941).
8. Round, A. A., *Trans. Inst. Rubber Ind.,* **1,** 72–80 (1954).
9. Swire, W. H., *Adhesives and Resins,* **2,** (3), 57–62 (1954).
10. McClellan, J. M., *Rubber Age,* **77,** (3), 386 (June 1955).
11. *Adhesives Age,* **2,** (9), 20 (1959).
12. Wehmer, F., *Die Castings,* **6,** (9), 46–49, 70–77 (1948).
13. Puddefoot, L. E., *Rubber Developments,* "Rubber Adhesives in Industry," **1,** (6), 30 (Dec. 1948).
14. McClellan, J. M., *Rubber Age,* **77,** (3), 385–90 (June 1955).
15. Kilbourne, F. L., in Whitby, G. S., "Synthetic Rubber," p. 954, New York, John Wiley & Sons, Inc., 1954.
16. Davis, C. C., and Blake, John T., "Chemistry and Technology of Rubber," p. 201, New York, Reinhold Publishing Corp., 1937.
17. "Manual of Reclaimed Rubber," pp. 18–19, Rubber Reclaimers Association, Inc., Ed. J. M. Ball.
18. Seaman, R. G., and Merril, A. M., "Machinery and Equipment for Rubber and Plastics," *India Rubber World,* **1,** 86 (1952).

19. Noble, R. J., "Latex in Industry," 2nd Ed., pp. 642–643, New York, Rubber Age, 1953.

20. Alexander, British Patent 14,681 (1905); 25,735 (1906).

21. Noble, R. J., "Latex in Industry," 2nd Ed., p. 165, New York, Rubber Age, 1953.

22. "Rubber Red Book," p. 994, New York, Rubber Age, 1957–58.

23. Cubberly, R. H., "The Vanderbilt Latex Handbook,"

p. 75, New York, R. T. Vanderbilt Publishing Company, Inc., 1954.

24. Brams, S. L. (to General Motors Corp.), U.S. Patent 2,501,654 (Mar. 28, 1950).

25. Clauser, H. R., "Pressure Sensitive Tapes," *Materials and Methods,* 124–125 (Mar. 1956).

26. Dow, J., "Manufacture of Adhesive Tapes," *Trans. Inst. Rubber, Ind.,* **1,** (4), 105–114 (Aug. 1954).

27. Trade Literature, B. F. Goodrich Plastikon Putty.

Appendix

TYPICAL RECIPES FOR NATURAL AND RECLAIMED RUBBER ADHESIVES

Pressure-Sensitive Adhesive

Ingredients	Parts per 100
Smoked sheets	100
Calcium carbonate or zinc oxide	30–150
Coumarone-indene, 35°	30–150
Rosin esters or other forms of modified rosin	
Antioxidants	1.5
Toluene gasoline mixture	*

Shoe Adhesive

Smoked sheets	100
Calcium carbonate	50–100
Stearic acid	1
Zinc oxide	5–15
Antioxidant	1–2.5
Soft clay	25–75
Coumarone-indene, 25°	5–20
Rubber solvent	*

Curable adhesive may be made by adding the following:

MBTS	0.5–1
MBT	0.5–1
Sulfur	1.5–2.5

Photo Gum Cement

Smoked sheets	100
Rosin	20–35
Gasoline	*

* To viscosity.

Floor-Tile Adhesive

Ingredients	Parts per 100
Smoked sheets	45
Calcium carbonate	15–40
Soft clay	75–150
Coumarone-indene, 110°	50–100
Antioxidant	0.5–1.5
Mineral spirits	*

Cloth Adhesive

Smoked sheets	100
Zinc oxide	3–5
Stearic acid	1
Antioxidant	1
Coumarone-indene, 150°	20–50
Toluene	*

Curable adhesive may be made by adding the following:

Sulfur	3–5
Accelerator	10–15

Wall-Tile Adhesive

Smoked sheets	20–30
Calcium carbonate	40–60
Titanium dioxide	40–60
Antioxidant	0.3–0.5
Coumarone-indene, 35°	40–50
Mineral spirits	70–80
Soap	3–6
Water	25–35

Seating Adhesive

Ingredients	Parts per 100
Black reclaim	100
Rosin	75–100
Softener	3–5
Magnesia	3–5
Gasoline	*

Black Industrial Cement

Black reclaim	100
Rosin	75–125
Lime	4
Water	approx. 6
Gasoline	*

Brown Industrial Cement

Red reclaim	100
Black reclaim	10–15
Plasticizer	5–8
Rosin	100–120
Lime	4
Water	6
Gasoline	*

Heat-Resistant Cement

Black reclaim	70
Red reclaim	30
Plasticizer	2–6
Rosin derivative	30–40
Zinc resinate	65–75
Hexane	*
Methanol	approx. 1–17 ratio based on Hexane

Heat-Resistant Cement

Gray reclaim	100
Polyterpene resin	70–90
Heat-reactive phenolic resin	10–30
Clay	5–15
Pigment	5–15
Petroleum naphtha	*

Friction Tape Cement

Black reclaim	100
Brown crepe	290
Carbon black	40–50
Barytes	30–40
Whiting	205–215
Rosin oil	5–15
Coumarone-indene resin	135–145
Toluene	*

Pressure-Sensitive Cement

Black reclaim	100
Smoked sheets	61
Rosin	30–40
Zinc oxide	40–50
Coumarone-indene resin	10–20
Toluene	*

Upholstery Cement

Ingredients	Parts per 100
Black reclaim	100
Red reclaim	10–15
Processing oil	5–8
Plasticizer	2–4
Rosin	75–125
Magnesia	2–4
Pigment	5–10
Clay	5–10
Gasoline	*

Upholstery Cement

Pale crepe	100
Rosin derivative	75–125
Gasoline	*

Reclaim-Asphalt Dispersion Cement

Black reclaim	100
Emulsifier	2–5
Clay	30–40
Caustic potash	1–2
Ester gum	20–30
Asphalt emulsion	175–185
Water	70–80

General-Purpose Reclaim Dispersion Cement

Black reclaim	100
Casein (swollen)	35–40
Caustic soda	0.5–1
Preservative	0.01
Water	45–55

Curable adhesive may be made by adding the following:

Sulfur	3–8
Zinc oxide	5–10
"Accelerator"	0.2–1

General-Purpose Sealer

Black reclaim	100
Asphalt emulsion	165–175
Clay	30–40
Emulsifier	2–4
Ester gum	15–25
Caustic potash	1–3
Water	65–75

Heat-Resistant Putty

Black reclaim	100
Red reclaim	10–20
Plasticizer	2–4
Rosin	115–125
Shellac	35–40
Pigment	10–15
Magnesia	20–30
Sulfur	1–4
Ethylene dichloride	*

Pressure-Sensitive Cement

Ingredients	Parts per 100
Gray reclaim	100
Hydrocarbon resin	15–25
Hydrocarbon plasticizer	15–25
Pigment	15–25
Zinc oxide	20–30
Petroleum naphtha	*

High-Tack Reclaim-Asphalt Dispersion Cement

Ingredients	Parts per 100
Tube reclaim	100
Asphalt	140–160
Rosin	20–30
Calcium carbonate	3–8
Caustic potash	1–4
Water	125–135

—— 16 ——

Butyl Rubber and Polyisobutylene

Kurt F. Richards

Enjay Chemical Company
New York, N. Y.

Butyl rubber and polyisobutylene are elastomeric polymers widely used as the binder or elastomer in cements and adhesives. The principal difference between them is that butyl is a copolymer of isobutylene with a minor amount of isoprene, whereas polyisobutylene is a homopolymer.

Both butyl rubber and polyisobutylene are highly paraffinic and therefore resistant to environmental attack. Both have good resistance to aging, ozone, vegetable and animal oils, and chemicals other than hydrocarbon solvents; both have low permeability to moisture, vapors, and gases, and have essentially no odor or taste. Physical, chemical, and compounding properties vary with degree of unsaturation, molecular weight, and minor constituents in the polymer. The range of properties of commercial polymers is illustrated by reference to "Enjay"* butyl rubber and "Vistanex"* polyisobutylene in the following discussion.

Grades of "Enjay" butyl and "Vistanex" polyisobutylene currently available in commercial quantities are listed in Table 1. Butyls are synthetic rubbers that can be vulcanized or cured; polyisobutylene cannot be cured. The molecular weight range covered by grades of "Vistanex" polyisobutylene straddles that of "Enjay" butyl. With proper allowance for gross differences in molecular weights, butyl and polyisobutylene can be used interchangeably in cement and adhesive compositions that will not be cured.

"Enjay" Butyl

All grades of "Enjay" butyl are tacky rubbery amber-colored solids, manufactured by copolymer-

* Enjay Chemical Co.

izing isobutylene with less than 3 per cent isoprene. Double bonds introduced into the macromolecule by isoprene permit the polymer to be crosslinked or vulcanized like other rubbers. The various grades differ in mole per cent unsaturation (number of isoprene units per hundred monomer units in the polymer chain), molecular weight, and nature of the stabilizer incorporated during manufacture to prevent degradation when processing at elevated temperatures. Commercial grades contain about 0.1 to 0.25 wt. per cent of stabilizer, as well as a minor amount of zinc stearate added to prevent agglomeration of polymer particles at one stage of the manufacturing process.

Commercial grades are available in 55-lb blocks or bales wrapped in polyethylene film which disperses completely during mixing operations conducted above 250 to 260°F; most grades are also available in coated cartons, without the film.

The stabilizer in "regular" grades of "Enjay" butyl (035, 150, 215, 217, 218, 325) is phenyl-beta-naphthylamine; that in the three "nonstaining" grades (165, 268, 365) is *n*-lauroyl *p*-amino phenol.

Two new grades of butyl rubber, one a latex, the other a chlorine-containing elastomer, are now available in commercial quantities. "Enjay" butyl latex 80-21 was developed for tire-cord and fabric dips and coatings, and is of considerable interest for water-based adhesive systems. The chlorine-containing elastomer, butyl HT 10-66, can be cured through both double bonds and chlorine atoms in the molecule, and therefore cures faster and can be cured with nontoxic systems such as zinc oxide. This is an important advantage in food-packaging applications.

TABLE 1. COMMERCIAL GRADES OF "VISTANEX" POLYISOBUTYLENE AND "ENJAY" BUTYL.

Specific Gravity (all grades): 0.92

Grade	Approx. Viscosity Average Molecular Weight	Isoprene Units/100 Monomer Units (Mole % Unsaturation)
"Vistanex" LM-MS	36,000– 45,000	0
LM-MH	45,000– 58,000	0
"Enjay" butyl 035	300,000– 360,000	0.6–1.0
150 and 165	300,000– 360,000	1.0–1.5
215	300,000– 360,000	1.5–2.0
217	360,000– 450,000	1.5–2.0
218 and 268	450,000– 520,000	1.5–2.0
325 and 365	300,000– 360,000	2.0–2.5
HT 10–66*	350,000– 400,000	1–2
Latex 80–21**	300,000– 400,000	1–2
"Vistanex" MM L-80	800,000–1,150,000	0
MM L-100	1,150,000–1,600,000	0
MM L-120	1,600,000–2,000,000	0
MM L-140	2,000,000–2,600,000	0

* Contains 1.1 to 1.3 wt. % chlorine.
** Total solids 53 wt. %, pH 5.0, specific gravity 0.96.

"Vistanex" Polyisobutylene

Polyisobutylenes have the inertness characteristic of paraffinic hydrocarbons, and cannot be cured or vulcanized. The LM grades of "Vistanex" are permanently tacky, clear white to light yellow semi-solids, and contain no stabilizer; the MM grades are light yellow rubberlike solids inhibited with less than 0.3 per cent "Parabar" 441,* a butylated hydroxytoluene of the type widely used as a preservative in frying fats, oils, and other foodstuffs. Tolerance limits for this stabilizer have been established by the Food and Drug Administration. The MM grades also contain trace amounts of sodium stearate remaining from one step in their manufacture.

Polyisobutylene of higher molecular weight than the grades shown in Table 1 is available in market-development quantities. Continued availability will depend on demand.

Choice of Polymer

Where the cement or adhesive, or the finished fabricated article, is to be cured or vulcanized, butyl rubber must be used since polyisobutylene cannot be cured. Polyisobutylene can be included in butyl compositions that are to be cured, to contribute tack or green strength, and acts as an inert diluent during the curing process. Other, more unsaturated rubbers such as natural rubber, SBR, etc., must not be included in butyl compositions as they rob the butyl of curatives.

* Enjay Chemical Co.

Ozone and acid resistance of butyl rubber decrease with increasing mole per cent unsaturation, while rate of cure, solvent, fat, and heat resistance increase. This behaviour is largely related to the degree of crosslinking achieved during cure; all grades of butyl rubber are of such low unsaturation that they are, for practical purposes, equivalent in uncured compositions.

Choice of grade of polyisobutylene will depend on the processing equipment available and on the desired balance between tack and cohesive strength. As with other rubberlike materials, the lower molecular weight fractions contribute tack and quick grab, while the higher fractions contribute body and cohesive strength.

Both butyl rubber and polyisobutylene have long been used as ingredients of chewing gum and in adhesives, jar sealants, and wrappings used for food packaging. Addition of butyl rubber or polyisobutylene to wax and polyethylene used for coating paper increases flexibility, particularly at low temperatures, and sealing strength, and decreases moisture and gas permeability—properties that are important in food packaging. The non-staining grades are preferred over regular grades of butyl for such applications.

Compounding

Butyl latex and the lower molecular weight grades of polyisobutylene can be compounded in conventional heavy-duty dough mixers or churns. Equipment suitable for dry rubber such as two-roll mills or Banbury mixers is needed to compound dry butyl and the higher molecular weight grades of polyisobutylene. Pigments, fillers, tackifiers and resins are best incorporated on a mill or Banbury, preferably at temperatures of 280 to 320°F, and curatives are added last, on a cold mill. The compound is then dissolved in solvent in a rubber churn or heavy-duty mixer. To facilitate solution, the surface area of the compounded polymer should be increased as much as possible, either by sheeting out on a mill or by shredding. Polyisobutylene of high molecular weight is particularly slow to dissolve, and should either be shredded or combined with the first increments of solvent on a cold mill. Attempts to dissolve high molecular weight polyisobutylene by dropping chunks of polymer into a large volume of solvent are usually not successful. A masterbatch technique, or some method for working the solvent into the polymer, is recommended. Vigorous churning of butyl rubber or polyisobutylene cements will usually entrap air, which may result in films that are porous when dried or cured. Because of their molecular structure, the polyisobutylenes are relatively slow to release solvent or trapped air, just as they are relatively impermeable to gases. Mild heating will reduce the viscosity of butyl and polyisobutylene cements, and facilitate the escape of entrapped air.

Pigments and Fillers

The same pigments and fillers commonly used with other rubbers can be compounded with butyl rubber and polyisobutylene, and the general principles of selection are the same. Very fine pigments increase cohesive strength and stiffness, and reduce cold flow, but also reduce tack. Platy pigments such as mica, graphite and talc increase acid and chemical resistance and gas impermeability. Some of the coarser pigments increase tack.

Zinc oxide increases tack and cohesive strength, and also plays an important chemical role in the vulcanization of butyl. Aluminum hydrate, lithopone, whiting, and the coarser carbon blacks such as thermal blacks also increase tack with moderate increase in cohesivity. Clays, hydrated silicas, calcium silicates, silico-aluminates, and the fine furnace and thermal blacks increase cohesive strength and stiffness. Stiffness can also be increased by use of very fine silica pigment and magnesium oxide or carbonate.

Tackifiers and Plasticizers

Butyl and polyisobutylene have excellent tack strength in comparison with other elastomers of comparable molecular weight. The LM grades of "Vistanex" can be included as tackifiers in formulations based on "Vistanex" MM or butyl rubber. Other tackifiers frequently used include relatively nonpolar resins and esters such as "Amberol"* ST-137X (a nonreactive substituted phenolformaldehyde resin), "Pentalyn"** pentaerythritol esters of rosin and modified rosin, "Staybelite"** esters of hydrogenated rosin, "Piccolyte"***S-115 terpene resin, rosin, and others. The combination of "Amberol" ST-137X and "Pentalyn" K or "Pentalyn" X in the ratio 7 to 3 has been found particularly effective.

Paraffinic process oils will both tackify and plasticize butyl and polyisobutylene compositions. They are sometimes incorporated to do just what the name implies: act as internal lubricants to facilitate processing during compounding. U. S. P. white oils should be used in compositions for surgical tapes or where lack of odor, color, or toxicity is important.

Butyl compositions can be strongly bonded to metal by use of commercial bonding agents (usually halogenated rubber derivatives or polymeric resins), and then vulcanizing under pressure. The metal must first be carefully prepared as recommended by the supplier of the bonding agent. Usually this involves degreasing, sandblasting with fine sand, and finally chemical cleaning or activation by such agents as phosphoric or chromic acid. Adhesion is by chemical bonding and does not depend on surface roughness; cleaning with coarse abrasives is usually not recommended.

Most of the bonding systems for butyl involve two compositions: a primer for the bare metal surface, and a cover cement to be applied over the primer. Among primer/cover combinations that have been found satisfactory for bonding butyl to steel are "Ty-Ply"† UP/Ty-Ply BC; "Thixon"†† P3/Thixon XN 756; and "Braze"††† P/Braze C.

Solvents and Solutions

Butyl rubber and polyisobutylenes are soluble in hydrocarbon and chlorinated solvents, but not in the common alcohols, esters, ketones, and other low molecular weight oxygenated solvents. Volatile paraffinic solvents such as hexane, heptane, naphtha, and carbon tetrachloride are commonly

* Rohm & Haas Co.
** Hercules Powder Co.
*** Pennsylvania Industrial Chemicals Corp.

† Marbon Chemical Division, Borg-Warner Corp.
†† Dayton Chemical Products Laboratories, Inc.
††† R. T. Vanderbilt Co.

used in cement and adhesive work. Cyclohexane and the chlorinated solvents give solutions of higher viscosity (at the same solids level) than the common paraffinic and aromatic solvents.

The presence of minor amounts of stabilizer and metal stearate in "Enjay" butyl and "Vistanex" MM has already been mentioned. Under certain circumstances, these will slowly settle out of low-viscosity solutions of the polymers. Pure gum cements thus may appear to layer or be slightly cloudy even though the polymer is completely dissolved. The only deficiency is in appearance, and the settling can be avoided or retarded by working with higher viscosity solutions such as those given by carbon tetrachloride.

Extraneous polyethylene from the film around film-wrapped grades of polymer will similarly give cloudy cements, and unless thoroughly dispersed on Banbury or hotmilling equipment may cause seams to be porous and inhomogeneous after cure. Clarity and cure problems can be avoided either by carefully unwrapping bales of polymer and discarding the film or by purchasing polymer boxed in coated cartons.

Carbon tetrachloride solutions of regular grades of butyl will sometimes develop a green-brown color on exposure to light, because of formation of colored complexes with the stabilizer in the polymer. Color formation can be avoided by either using the non-staining grades, or by avoiding exposure to light by packaging cement in cans or in brown glass.

To facilitate solvent release and avoid porosity, gum cements should be applied in thin coats, with adequate drying between coats when multiple applications are needed to build up thickness. Cements containing appreciable volumes of filler are much less critical in this respect.

The optimum solids level of cements to be applied by various methods is, of course, subject to broad variation depending on the viscosity given by various solvents, filler content, etc. In general, butyl rubber and polyisobutylene cements for application by spraying contain 5 to 10 per cent solids, for dipping 10 to 30 per cent, for spreading 25 to 55 per cent, and for application by finger or spatula, 50 to 70 per cent.

Curing Systems

Two general classes of crosslinking systems are of interest for butyl cements: those based on sulfur and sulfur compounds ("sulfur cures," "vulcanization"), and those based on polynitroso compounds ("quinoid cures").

Sulfur curing systems for butyl generally include elemental sulfur, thiuram or dithiocarbamate accelerators, thiazole or thiazyldisulfide activators, and zinc oxide. Zinc or other metallic oxide improves the physical properties of the resulting vulcanizate.

These sulfur curing systems are similar to those now used to cure natural rubber and SBR. Though butyl rubber is "unsaturated" relative to polyisobutylene, its 0.5 to 2.5 per cent unsaturation is still far less than the 100 per cent unsaturation of natural rubber or the 60 to 80 per cent unsaturation of SBR. This purposely limited functionality of butyl rubber accounts for its excellent resistance to environmental attack. The relatively minor differences in unsaturation between grades of butyl are significant in regard to sulfur cures. Rate of cure and number of attainable crosslinks increase with increasing polymer unsaturation, while chemical and ozone resistance decrease. For maximum heat resistance a highly crosslinked system is desirable. With sulfur cures, maximum heat resistance is achieved by using the most unsaturated grade of butyl, limiting the amount of sulfur to minimize excess that does not contribute to the crosslink network, and including substantial amounts of zinc oxide to combine with hydrogen sulfide formed in the vulcanization reaction.

Quinoid cures depend on crosslinking through the nitroso groups of aromatic nitroso compounds. A commonly used system employs p-quinone dioxime ("G-M-F"*) and an oxidizing agent such as lead dioxide, red lead oxide (Pb_3O_4), or benzothiazyl disulfide. The actual crosslinking agent is believed to be the oxidation product of quinone dioxime, p-dinitroso benzene. The benzoic acid ester of p-quinone dioxime, dibenzoyl-p-quinone dioxime ("Dibenzo G-M-F"*), is less active and therefore easier to control when curing at elevated temperatures. Needless to say, dinitroso compounds introduced as such rather than formed by oxidation of quinone dioxime are also active crosslinking agents for butyl. Commercially available compounds include p-dinitrosobenzene on a clay base ("Polyac"**), and N-methyl-N, 4-dinitrosoaniline on a clay base ("Elastopar"***).

Quinoid cures are very rapid, and produce a tightly crosslinked structure highly resistant to ozone, heat, chemicals, and other environmental attack. Dark color bodies are formed during the reaction, hence these cures cannot be used to make white or light-colored products. Differences in

* Naugatuck Chemical Division of United States Rubber Co.

** E. I. duPont de Nemours & Co.

*** Monsanto Chemical Co.

polymer unsaturation among the grades of butyl have little effect on the speed of cure with quinoids.

Quinoid cures are of interest to formulators of cements and adhesives largely because the necessary combination of dioxime and oxidizing agent permits formulation of split batch two-part cements that cure at room temperatures or slightly above. One part of the cement contains the dioxime, the other the oxidizer (usually a lead oxide), and the parts are mixed just before use.

Dinitroso compounds can be used to increase the green strength and body of butyl cements and adhesives. This is done by pre-curing to give a lightly crosslinked structure, which increases effective molecular weight. "Polyac" is the dinitroso compound commonly used; it is dispersed into the butyl on a cold mill, then the reaction is carried out by milling or working in a Banbury at temperatures above about 275°F. Too much dinitroso compound or too high a temperature may result in lumpy gelled cement. The amount of active dinitroso compound should not exceed about 0.4 parts per hundred of butyl in pure gum cements, and about 0.8 parts in highly filled compounds. Milling or working 15 min at 280°F or 5 min at 300°F is enough to complete the desired reaction. Use of "Polyac" and similar dinitroso compounds results in an amber color and may reduce tack.

The purpose of "Polyac" is to increase strength and body of butyl compounds in the uncured state, in presence or absence of fillers. Another use of "Polyac" and related products is to improve the dynamic, electrical, and other properties of filled butyl vulcanizates. "Polyac" and, to an even greater extent, "Elastopar" promote dispersion of fine active carbon blacks such as channel blacks, and certain mineral fillers such as hard clays and fine particle silicas, in butyl rubber. The process is variously spoken of as "heat treatment" or "thermal interaction" to produce "pigment-polymer bonding." Heat treatment can be carried out without a promoter, although at present promoters are almost invariably used. Vulcanizates prepared from heat-treated stocks have increased resilience, moduli, abrasion resistance, electrical resistivity, acid resistance, and other improved properties. Compounders of cements and adhesives will be interested in heat treatment only when formulating vulcanizable compositions for highly critical applications, and will then need more detailed instructions than can be given here.

Formulations

Butyl rubber and polyisobutylene can be formulated to satisfy widely diverse applications of cements and adhesives. Great latitude is possible in formulating noncuring compositions, and formulators familiar with other tacky rubbery elastomers will have no difficulty. In formulating curing compositions to join either cured or uncured butyl structures, it is obviously wise to pattern the adhesive formulation after the parent compound. In most cases the only modification needed will be additional tackifier to increase the tack, and solvent to permit application of the adhesive.

The eleven formulations that follow have been chosen to suggest various applications and to illustrate some of the compounding suggestions previously given. Certain compounding ingredients used in working out the formulations are identified by trade name; suppliers are listed in Table 2. Equivalent products from other suppliers would presumably work as well.

Formulation 1 is the simplest possible composition: polymer plus solvent to permit application of the polymer to a substrate. Neither grade of polymer nor nature and amount of solvent are critical. Tack can be increased by adding tackifying resins or "Vistanex" LM; snap can be reduced by adding oil.

Formulations 2A and 2B are for pressure-sensitive adhesives such as are used on paper masking tapes, friction tapes, etc. Formulation 2A is essentially Formulation 1 with tackifiers and plasticizer added. Formulation 2B illustrates the technique of bodying butyl with "Polyac," and then compounding with fillers.

FORMULATION 1

PAPER CEMENT

(*For home, office, school use*)

"Vistanex" MM L-100 or "Enjay" butyl 268	100
Solvent (naphtha or chlorinated solvent)	900

Tack of this cement can be increased by adding tackifying resins; the cement can be softened by adding paraffinic oils.

Formulation 3 is an old recipe for adhesive tape, similar to Formulation 2B except that it is based on polyisobutylene rather than butyl 268. The polyisobutylene, of higher molecular weight, gives about the same degree of body as butyl reacted with "Polyac". Dinitroso compounds such as "Polyac" are not believed to be desirable in compounds that will be in extended contact with the human body.

Formulation 4 is a black composition to be calendered onto vinyl film for use as industrial pressure-sensitive tape. This particular tape was to be used for wrapping pipes buried in the ground, and therefore contains copper oxide as a fungicide.

FORMULATION 2

PRESSURE-SENSITIVE ADHESIVES
(For masking and friction tapes, etc.)

A

"Vistanex" MM L-100	100
"Amberol" ST-137X	45
"Pentalyn" K	45
Paraffinic process oil	50

Make up to 15% solids in naphtha.

B

"Enjay" butyl 268	100
"Polyac"	0.7
Zinc oxide	50
Hydrated alumina	50
"Piccolyte" S-115	70
Paraffinic process oil	40

Make up to 20–40% solids in naphtha.

Add "Polyac" to butyl in a Banbury, mix at 300°F for 5 min. Then add zinc oxide and aluminum hydrate, and dump. Dissolve resin and process oil in the solvent, and add to the rubber batch in a churn or dough mixer.

FORMULATION 3

SOLVENT ADHESIVE FOR SURGICAL TAPE

"Vistanex" MM L-100	100
Zinc oxide	50
Hydrated alumina	50
U.S.P. white oil	50
"Amberol" ST-137X or	
"Piccolyte" S-115	70
Solvent naphtha or heptane	600

FORMULATION 4

MASTIC FOR PRESSURE-SENSITIVE VINYL TAPE
(For calendering onto untreated vinyl backing film)

"Enjay" butyl 215	100
FT black	90
Whiting	20
"Pentalyn" K	3
"Amberol" ST-137X	7
Cuprous oxide (Cu_2O)	2
Paraffinic process oil	5

Formulation 5 was developed for seaming adjacent widths of proofed cotton fabric to fabricate large sheets. It is representative of vulcanizable compositions used to join butyl vulcanizates, and mixing and application details are included. In this instance color of the seams was important, therefore some of the color used in the fabric proofing was incorporated. The butyl was first reacted with "Polyac" to give green strength, so the seamed sheets would not come apart in handling before cure. This and the heavy loading of clay then required considerable resin to bring up the tack; formulations with less tackifier performed almost as well. The combination of zinc oxide,

sulfur, thiazole, and thiuram is a typical curing system for butyl. The seams were cured by festooning in an oven; shorter cure at higher temperature would have been possible had there been some way of keeping the seams under pressure.

Formulation 6 is a typical split batch self-curing cement. Though this illustrates the "sulfurless" quinoid cure, it has been found that inclusion of 1 to 2 parts of sulfur gives better physical properties in the cured compound. A cement very similar to this was used to field-fabricate butyl-coated glass fabric into irrigation canal liners in Utah. Ten years later the canals were abandoned and the liners taken up. Seams and patches adhered with this cement were still strong and in excellent condition.

Sealers, putties, caulking compounds, etc., are often considered part of the adhesives field. Formulation 7 represents a simple mastic or putty-like composition that can be widely modified to suit individual requirements and utilize available fillers. It is based on "Vistanex" LM, and can therefore be prepared in a dough or putty mixer. As given, the formulation was suggested for use as an automobile undercoat.

Formulation 8 is for a gun-grade caulking compound said to be easy to apply, to give good adhe-

FORMULATION 5

BUTYL SEAMING CEMENT
(For lap-seaming cured butyl fabric)

"Enjay" butyl 217	100
"Polyac"	0.6
Hydrated calcium silicate	50
Soft clay	100
"Amberol" ST-137X	40
Zinc oxide	5
Stearic acid	0.5
Sulfur	2
Mercaptobenzothiazole	0.5
Tetramethylthiuram disulfide	1
Color masterbatch	3

Dissolve to 40% solids in toluene.

Banbury Mixing Cycle

Time, Mins.	Ingredients
0	Add "Polyac" to butyl in a Banbury.
2 to 9	Mix at 300°F for at least 5 min.
9	Half the fillers, all "Amberol," zinc oxide, color, and stearic acid.
11	Remainder of fillers.
13	Dump at 200 to 250°F.

Add curatives on a cool two-roll mill. Dissolve in toluene in a churn or mixer.

Give surfaces to be joined one brush coat of cement; oven-dry 5 to 10 min. at 200°F, then ply up and roll seams. Cure 2 hr at 240°F in an oven.

FORMULATION 6

BUTYL SELF-CURING CEMENT

*(For adhering fabric, cured or uncured butyl, and
butyl to other elastomers)*

	Part 1	Part 2
"Enjay" butyl 218	100	100
Zinc oxide	5	5
Stearic acid	3	3
SRF black	—	80
"Staybelite" ester gum No. 10	40	—
Sulfur	1.5	1.5
p-Quinone dioxime	4	—
PbO_2	—	8

Per Gallon of Cement

Stock	400 g	540 g
Naphtha (boiling range 140–215°F)	1950 g	1950 g
Isopropyl alcohol, 91%	24 ml	24 ml

Stir well and mix equal volumes of Parts 1 and 2 just before use. Gel time, unmixed, is over 1 yr; after mixing is about 6 hr. This cement gives strong bond after curing several days at room temperature, or after 40 to 60 min. oven-cure at 270 to 320°F. Green strength can be improved by first hot-mixing the butyl in Part 1 with 0.4 parts "Polyac."

FORMULATION 7

GENERAL-PURPOSE SEALER OR PUTTY

"Vistanex" LM-MH	80
Whiting	40
Short-fibered asbestos	15
Graphite	15
Blanc Fixe	105
Kerosene	85

Mix in a kneader to give a stiff putty. Can be softened to any desired plasticity by adding more kerosene.

sion to a variety of mineral and metal surfaces, and to form a permanently rubbery tack-free seal. To permit compounding on mixers available to caulk manufacturers, the butyl is introduced as a solution in mineral spirits. As it stands, the caulk is formulated with titanium dioxide to be white; if an aluminum color is desired aluminum paste can be substituted for titanium dioxide.

Formulation 9 illustrates the application of butyl latex to water-based systems such as fabric dips. Development of the latex, and subsequently this formulation, were key points in making the modern all-butyl tire possible. Butyl tires were made years ago by calendering butyl directly onto cotton fabric to be used in the carcass. By the time the technique was reasonably perfected, highway speeds and automotive horsepower had sharply increased, and rayon and nylon fabrics had replaced cotton. Adhesion requirements in tires are unusually severe, and butyl carcass stocks do not

FORMULATION 8

WHITE GUN-GRADE CAULKING COMPOUND

*(Formulation developed by Research Laboratory of
Thompson, Weinman and Co., suppliers of "Atomite")*

	Pound	Gallon
50% "Enjay" butyl 035 in mineral spirits	388	55.0
60% Piccopale 100 in mineral spirits	74	10.0
"Hercolyn"	8.5	1.0
Denatured alcohol	1.3	0.2
"Bentone" 38	25	1.7
"Atomite"	400	17.8
International fiber (Regular)	100	4.2
"TiPure" R-510	50	1.4
Mineral spirits	57	8.7
	1103.8	100.0

Mix in a heavy-duty sigma-bladed dough mixer. Mix "Piccopale" 100, "Hercolyn," "Bentone" 38, and alcohol until they form a uniform heavy paste. Add about half the butyl solution, then titanium dioxide, "Atomite," and talc. Keep the mix stiff to get good dispersion. Add remainder of butyl solution, followed by mineral spirits in small increments.

FORMULATION 9

LATEX TIRE-CORD DIP

(For rayon or nylon fabric)

"Enjay" butyl latex 80–21 (55% solids)	29.6 wt. %
Resorcinol	2.4
Formaldehyde (37% solution)	3.9
Zinc oxide (50% dispersion)	0.3
Water	63.8
Solids content	20–21 wt. %
Density	8.2–8.3 lb/gal.

Preparation

1. Weigh water, dissolve resorcinol, then add formaldehyde.
2. Weigh latex, add zinc oxide dispersion before mixing with resorcinol-formaldehyde.
3. Add latex to resorcinol-formaldehyde solution with constant agitation.
4. Adjust pH of the mix to 8.4 with 10 to 20% NaOH.
5. Store in closed containers to avoid skinning on exposure to open air. The dip can be stored a month or more without deteriorating.
6. Age the dip at least 48 hr, preferably 72 hr, before use.

bond well enough to bare rayon or nylon to be satisfactory at high speeds. Formulation 9 acts as a tie system, giving good mechanical anchorage by penetration into the fabric, and also a chemical bond, possibly by reaction of the resorcinol-formaldehyde with active centers on the rayon or nylon fibers. The zinc oxide serves only as a stabilizer, to keep the dip from thickening on standing.

Formulations 10 and 11 display high points of adhesive formulator's skill. Tires are built up layer by layer from flat sheets and strips. A "built" but unvulcanized tire looks like a 55-gal. drum without heads. The cylindrical tire does not become a doughnut until it is bagged and cured, days or even weeks after it is built.

Adhesives used in building tires must be tacky enough to allow production speeds, strong enough to keep the assembly together during factory handling, storage, and deformation in forming, and must then cure with the rest of the tire to make a dynamically homogeneous whole. Any zone of weakness introduced by an improperly formulated building adhesive causes premature failure of the finished tire.

Formulation 10 is a building cement used to glue white sidewall stock onto butyl tires: the last step in building. It demonstrates the use of "Vistanex" LM and "Amberol" resin to give tack, high molecular weight "Vistanex" to give cohesive strength, and the most unsaturated "Enjay" butyl

FORMULATION 10

WHITE SIDEWALL CEMENT
(Used in building all-butyl tires)

"Enjay" butyl 365	60
"Vistanex" LM-MS	20
"Vistanex MM L-100	20
Titanium dioxide	30
Hydrated silica	10
Zinc oxide	5
"Amberol" ST-137X	10
Light process oil	8
Sulfur	1.5
Tetramethylthiuram disulfide	3
Benzothiazyl disulfide	1

Dissolve to 10 to 25% solids in hexane.

FORMULATION 11

TIRE TREAD CEMENT
(For adhering tread to carcass in building all-butyl tires)

"Enjay" butyl 325	100
"Vistanex" MM L-100	10
"Elastopar"	1
MPC black	40
Zinc oxide	5
"Amberol" ST-137X	5
Pentalyn X	2
Sulfur	2
Tellurium diethyldithiocarbamate	2
Benzothiazyl disulfide	1

Dissolve to 15 to 20%solids in hexane.

to give rapid cure. The sulfur-thiuramthiazole cure system is chosen to be compatible with both the white sidewall and the fourth-ply stocks.

Formulation 11 is used to cement tread to carcass and tread splices in building all-butyl tires. The formulation is basically patterned after the tread compound, but contains the highest unsaturation butyl for rapid cure, "Vistanex" MM to give green strength, and two resins in combination to give tack. The sulfur-dithiocarbamate-thiazole cure system is again a typical one for butyl. This is the only formulation given here that includes "Elastopar," to promote heat treatment. The dynamic (flexing, resilient) properties of the cured cement compound are as important as the dynamic properties of the tread itself, and this adhesive has to meet many stringent requirements.

TABLE 2. SUPPLIERS OF TRADE-MARKED INGREDIENTS LISTED IN FORMULATIONS 1 TO 11

"Amberol" ST-137X	Rohm & Haas Co.
"Piccolyte" S-115 "Piccopale" 100	Pennsylvania Industrial Chemical Corp.
"Hercolyn" "Pentalyn" K and X "Staybelite" ester 10	Hercules Powder Co.
"Polyac" "TiPure" R-510	E. I. duPont de Nemours & Co.
"Elastopar"	Monsanto Chemical Co.
"Atomite"	Thompson, Weinman and Co.
"International Fiber"	International Talc Co.
"Bentone" 38	National Lead Co.

Acknowledgment

Most of the information in this chapter was developed by people at Enjay Laboratories and the Chemicals Research Division of Esso Research and Engineering Company. The author has freely consulted the chapter by Thomas and Sparks (the inventors of butyl rubber) in Whitby's "Synthetic Rubber" (Wiley, 1954), the chapter by Wernersbach in Winspear's "The Vanderbilt Rubber Handbook" (R. T. Vanderbilt Co., 1958), the chapter by Dunkel, Neu, and Zapp in Morton's "Introduction to Rubber Technology" (Reinhold 1959), Buckley's monumental review paper, "Elastomeric Properties of Butyl Rubber," in Volume XXXII, No. 5 of *Rubber Chemistry and Technology* (Division of Rubber Chemistry, American Chemical Society, 1959), and numerous Enjay Laboratories reports.

——— 17 ———

Nitrile Rubber Adhesives

H. P. Brown and J. F. Anderson
Research Center
The B. F. Goodrich Company
Brecksville, Ohio

Nitrile rubbers are rubberlike copolymers of unsaturated nitriles with dienes. The commercial nitrile rubbers are predominantly copolymers of butadiene and acrylonitrile. The oil resistance and adhesive properties of these copolymers increase with an increase in nitrile content. The nitrile rubbers are compatible with phenol-formaldehyde resins, resorcinol-formaldehyde resins, vinyl-chloride resins, alkyd resins, coumarone-indene resins, chlorinated rubber, hydrogenated rosins, coal-tar resins, epoxies and other resins, forming compositions which can be cured and which can provide excellent adhesives of high strength, oil resistance and good resilience. They are superior to polychloroprene in compatibility with resins. The nitrile-rubber adhesives are applied in the form of latexes, cements, mastics and tapes. They have outstanding shelf-stability and high-temperature properties. The nitrile rubbers have been used to bond cured and uncured nitrile rubbers to themselves, to vinyls, to polychloroprene and to other elastomers. They have been used for coating fabrics to provide oil resistance and wear resistance and to adhere vinyls and elastomers to fabrics.

Blended with phenolic resins, they have been used to

(1) laminate aluminum and stainless steel;
(2) fabricate many airplane structures;
(3) bond abrasives to metal;
(4) bond brake linings to brake shoes;
(5) fabricate panels for curtain-wall constructions;
(6) bond metal to nitrile-rubber stocks, polyvinyl chloride films, leather, wood and other surfaces;
(7) laminate leather;
(8) attach soles in shoe manufacturing;
(9) bond cork, cardboard, leatherboard, fiberboard, paper, masonite, nitrocellulose, cellulose acetate, nylon, and other polymeric films to themselves and to each other.

However, the nitrile rubber-phenolic resin blends are poor adhesives for natural rubber, butyl rubber and polyethylene unless these surfaces are treated to make them reactive, for example by cyclization, etc. The nitrile rubbers have excellent compatibility as adhesives with polar adherends such as protein fibers, textiles, paper and wood. Thus nitrile rubber cements may be employed for adhering a wide variety of surfaces and types of material.

HISTORY

A nitrile rubber, buna N, was described and became commercially available during 1936 and 1937 in Germany.[2] In 1937 the name "Perbunan" was assigned to a grade of buna N containing about 25 per cent acrylonitrile which was commercialized in Germany.[2] Preparation of copolymers of this type was covered by the German patent 658,172 (March 25, 1938) and related earlier patents of other countries.[3] Nitrile rubber probably was developed as early as 1930. Importation of buna N to the United States began in March, 1937.[1] In the United States, plants for the production of nitrile rubbers were put into operation by The B. F. Goodrich Company in January, 1939, Goodyear Tire & Rubber Company in 1940, Firestone Tire & Rubber Company in 1940, and Standard Oil Company in March, 1941.[1]

COMMERCIAL PROCESSES AND APPLICATIONS

Preparation and Properties of Nitrile Rubbers

The nitrile rubbers are commonly prepared by emulsion polymerization, although they may be prepared in bulk or in solvent. Preparation by emulsion copolymerization yields a rubber of greater uniformity and more consistent properties than the other methods. For a typical polymerization recipe and related details refer to an excellent review of nitrile rubber by W. L. Semon.[1]

The diene commonly employed is butadiene. Use of isoprene, 2-ethyl butadiene, 2,3-dimethyl butadiene, piperylene or other substituted dienes has been investigated, but these monomers tend to yield less useful, somewhat more leathery products. The nitrile commonly employed is acrylonitrile. Methacrylonitrile, ethacrylonitrile and other unsaturated nitriles have been used also. Partial replacement of acrylonitrile by methacrylonitrile or ethacrylonitrile has given improved cement-making properties.[1] The oil resistance of the copolymers is directly dependent on their nitrile content, while the cement forming and adhesive properties of the copolymers are influenced by the choice of monomers. Small proportions of other comonomers may also be used in conjunction with the two principal components. Ethyl acrylate, methyl methacrylate, styrene, vinylidene chloride, acrylic acid, methacrylic acid, N-vinyl-2-pyrrolidone, vinyl acetate and similar monomers have been employed in varying amounts to adjust the adhesive and elastomeric properties.

The influence of small amounts of acrylonitrile on the properties of polybutadiene is readily recognized by oil solubility, compatibility and adhesion characteristics. Copolymers of butadiene containing 5 per cent acrylonitrile are still high-swelling in oil. Those containing 15 per cent acrylonitrile are fairly oil resistant. With 25 per cent acrylonitrile, they develop medium oil resistance. When the acrylonitrile content reaches 40 per cent, the copolymer becomes highly resistant to oil and has a significant resistance to aromatics. Nitrile rubbers of less than 25 per cent acrylonitrile content, or its equivalent, are seldom employed in cements.[4]

The conditions as well as the constituents of the polymerization process profoundly influence polymer and adhesive properties. The proportion of acrylonitrile entering the butadiene copolymer usually differs from that in the charge for batchwise polymerizations. However, certain commercial copolymers have essentially the same composition as that of the comonomer charge. Solubility of the copolymers formed is dependent on their ultimate conversion and molecular weight. At conversions in excess of 75 per cent, branching and crosslinking occur to degrees which may interfere with easy formation of gel-free or clear cements of 25 to 50 per cent total solids content. Molecular weight control is achieved by the use of modifying agents such as alkyl mercaptan, bis(xanthogen disulfides), and haloalkanes. The choice of modifying agent can significantly influence adhesive properties of nitrile rubbers. For some adhesive and sealant applications where soft, near liquid polymers are preferred, the amount of modifying agent added becomes so large that the amount incorporated approaches the order of a comonomer. Liquid nitrile rubbers are used as tackifier agents. "Hycar"* 1312 is such a polymer.

In the preparation of nitrile rubbers by emulsion polymerization, some of the emulsifier, the initiator, modifier, the shortstopping agent, and coagulating agents remain in the copolymer. To minimize self-adhesion and sticking to packaging containers, nitrile rubbers are dusted with soapstone, talc, resins, powdered polymers or other materials. Some formulators of adhesives desire completely soluble polymers, even polymer crumbs, requiring no milling prior to cement preparation. Such polymers require even greater levels of dusting powders to prevent undue aggregation. These materials, included in the nitrile rubbers, may significantly influence their adhesive properties. To prevent deterioration of the nitrile rubbers owing to their unsaturation, antioxidants, antiozonants, and other additives are incorporated during the polymerization and coagulation processes, and may influence adhesive properties.

Since the conditions of polymerization and the additives incorporated may be varied widely as well as the comonomer composition, it is not surprising that manufacturers offer several varieties of nitrile rubbers which provide a range of adhesive characteristics. In general, the higher the Mooney viscosity of the raw nitrile rubber, the greater the strength of the adhesive formulated from it. Conversion, modification, and nitrile content all influence the Mooney viscosity.

It has been reported that nitrile rubbers prepared by emulsion polymerization and converted into cements without drying,[39] have given cements superior to analogous conventionally dried polymers. However, such a procedure is seldom convenient.

Nitrilic rubbers, prepared by over-polymerization of acrylonitrile onto elastomeric polymers, may

* Registered trade-mark.

be used in the preparation of adhesives, but have not been used extensively. As early as 1947, an acrylonitrile derivative of natural rubber[36] admixed with chlorinated rubber was described as a useful laminating and impregnating adhesive.

Nitrile rubbers exhibit reactivities characteristic of both their unsaturation and their nitrile contents. They may be vulcanized by the standard rubber curing agents, and are usually vulcanized with sulfur. For the same Mooney viscosity, the more nitrile present in the polymer, the less sulfur required. The lower the Mooney, the more sulfur required. Organic compounds which yield sulfur, such as tetramethyl thiuram disulfide may be used instead of free sulfur. Commonly 1 to 3 parts of sulfur are required while 3 phr* of tetramethyl thiuram disulfide usually suffice. Cement compounds are usually adjusted to cure faster and at lower temperatures than corresponding stocks for normal molded products. An extra quarter part each of sulfur and accelerator is usually ample.

Almost any accelerator employed with natural rubber, SBR or polybutadiene may be used with nitrile rubbers. Preferably the cement accelerator should be of the same type used in the rubber stocks to be adhered. Generally, about 5 phr of zinc oxide is employed for activation, but certain cements sometimes use higher loadings advantageously. Zinc salts of thiuram disulfides, and accelerators which are activated by aldehyde amines, are commonly employed for low-temperature-curing type cements. Usually, best adhesions are obtained when the accelerator is added to the cement just prior to use.

The nitrile groups contribute stiffening effects and enhance inter- and intramolecular bonding. The hydrogen on the carbon bearing the nitrile group is activated and may be a point of crosslinkage by oxidizing agents, by addition to the nitrile group in the presence of alkaline agents, or by heat. The incorporation of increasing amounts of nitrile in polybutadiene elevates the elasticity range, enhances film-forming properties, increases resistance to hydrocarbon solvents, increases hardness and abrasion resistance, and increases adhesion to many surfaces. For the development of adhesives of high structural strength and high oil resistance,[4] an acrylonitrile content of 25 per cent or more is preferred.

The Commercial Nitrile Rubbers Employed as Adhesives

For the adhesive applications of nitrile rubbers, formulations based on "Hycar" rubbers, produced

* phr—parts per hundred parts of rubber, by weight.

by the B. F. Goodrich Chemical Company, have been employed predominantly in this chapter. In order that the properties of the polymers referred to may be defined, the "Hycar" rubbers commonly employed in adhesives[4] are tabulated in Table 1. Similar polymers offered by other manufacturers are indicated in Table 2.

Nitrile-Rubber Cement Adhesives

Polymer Selection and Solubilization. The commercial nitrile rubbers employed in cement preparation fall into two major classes, those which require milling prior to cement preparation and those which do not. Details concerning the milling and processing of nitrile rubbers are available in literature reviews[1] and suppliers' bulletins.[4, 18, 19, 33, 55] Milling on tight cold-mill rolls is probably the most efficient method of breaking down nitrile rubbers and rendering them soluble. Nitrile rubbers and their compounded stocks, prepared for cement use by milling, should be put into solution as soon after milling as possible since solubility is progressively lost with time. Nitrile rubbers, which are directly soluble and do not require milling for cement preparation, will yield cements of lower viscosity if they are milled. The effect of milling on the viscosity and shelf stability of an insoluble ("Hycar" 1041) and a soluble nitrile ("Hycar" 1042) rubber[4] is shown in Tables 3 and 4.

A good indication of the potential bond strengths obtainable from nitrile rubbers is given by the Mooney viscosity of the raw polymer. In general, the higher the Mooney viscosity, the higher the strength of the cement adhesive.

From a series of solubility tests on crude unvulcanized nitrile rubber of about 38 per cent nitrile content in eighty typical solvents, Sarbach and Garvey[5] concluded that such rubbers are soluble in aromatic hydrocarbons, chlorinated hydrocarbons, ketones, esters, and nitroparaffin[7] compounds, and are insoluble in aliphatic hydrocarbons, hydroxyl compounds and acids. Solvents that swell nitrile rubber and dissolve it rapidly are useful in making cements. Among the solvents commonly employed with nitrile rubbers, where rapid evaporation is desired, are acetone, methylethyl ketone, chloroform, ethylene dichloride, ethyl acetate, and trichloroethylene. Slower evaporating solvents include nitromethane, nitroethane, the nitropropanes, dichloropentenes, chlorobenzene, chlorotoluene, dioxane, methyl isobutyl ketone, butyl acetate and methyl chloroform.

The higher the nitrile content, the more difficult the solubility of nitrile rubbers of comparable Mooney viscosity. The most effective solvents are

TABLE 1. PROPERTIES OF "HYCAR" RUBBERS.

Type of "Hycar"	Description	Physical Form	Specific Gravity	Mooney Viscosity	Cement Viscosity (cps)[c]	Antioxidant	Oil Resistance	Remarks
1001	High-acrylonitrile copolymer	1 in. thick slabs	1.00	85–115	(1001 x 225) 2,500 max (1001 x 245) 2,500–5,000	"AgeRite"** Stalite	Excellent	The original nitrile rubber; best fuel and oil resistance; high-strength cements, adhesives.
1041		Slabs	1.00	70–95	5,000 max	"AgeRite" Stalite	Excellent	Low-temperature polymerized easy processing types of "Hycar" 1001.
1051		Slabs	1.00	70–95	5,000 max	"AgeRite" Stalite	Excellent	
1002		Slabs	0.98	75–110	12,000 max	"AgeRite" Stalite	Very good	Excellent water resistance. General-purpose cements.
1042		Slabs	0.98	70–95	20,000 max[d]	"AgeRite" Stalite	Very good	High strength, high elongation, low-temperature polymerized rubber otherwise similar to "Hycar" 1002. Excellent solubility both milled and unmilled.
1052	Medium-high	Slabs	0.98	45–70	10,000 max[d]	Non-staining	Very good	A low-Mooney viscosity, easier processing polymer, otherwise similar to "Hycar" 1042.
1022	high	Slabs	0.98	45–70	12,000 max[d]	Non-staining	Very good	Directly soluble low-Mooney viscosity, cement-grade polymer.
1072[a]	acrylonitrile copolymer	Slabs	1.00	42–62	8,500 max[d]	Non-staining	Very good	Hycar "1042" modified to contain carboxyl groups. Can be cured with zinc oxide alone or with conventional curatives. Product has higher hardness, and better high-temperature properties. High strength cements.
1312		Liquid	0.98	. . . .	. . . .	Non-staining	Very good	Liquid "Hycar" 1002 type polymer, vulcanizable to hard rubber stage. Tackifying agent for cements.
1432 1442[b]		Crumbs	0.98	70–95	15,000 max[d]	Non-staining	Very good	Cold-polymerized, directly soluble polymers in crumb form; contain a good grade; non-staining, non-discoloring antioxidant.

* Registered trade-mark.
[a] Refer to Chapter on Carboxylic Elastomers for adhesive uses of this polymer.
[b] Soapstone dusted.
[c] At 20% total solids in methylethyl ketone.
[d] Unmilled cement.

TABLE 2. COMMERCIAL NITRILE RUBBERS FOR ADHESIVES APPLICATIONS.

Manufacturer	Firestone Tire & Rubber Co.		B. F. Goodrich Chem. Co		Goodyear Tire & Rubber Co.		Naugatuck Chem. Co.		Polymer Corp. Ltd.
Trade Name	"Butaprene"		"Hycar"		"Chemigum"		"Paracril"		"Polysar Krynac"
	Type	Mooney Viscosity[a]	Type	Mooney Viscosity[a]	Type	Mooney Viscosity[a]	Type	Mooney Viscosity[b]	Type
High acrylonitrile copolymers	NXM	80–100	1001	85–115	N3NS	50–60	D	80–90	801
			1041	70–95	N5	87–112			
			1051	70–95					
	NAA		1002	75–110	N6	40–65	C	80–90	
							CV	80–90[b]	
							CS	80–90[a]	
Medium acrylonitrile copolymers			1022	45–70	N6B	40–65[c]	CLT	80–90	800
			1042	70–95	N600	40–65			803
			1052	45–70	N7	77–102[c]			
			1072	42–62	N1NS	25–35	BV		803 (crumb)
			1432[e]	70–95					
			1442[d]	70–95					

[a] ML-4′-212°F.
[b] ML-2′-212°F.
[c] Only partial MEK solubility.
[d] Soapstone-dusted crumb.
[e] Vinyl-dusted crumb.

TABLE 3. EFFECTS OF MILLING ON VISCOSITY AND SHELF STABILITY OF NITRILE-RUBBER CEMENTS.

Recipe No.	1	2	3	4
"Hycar" 1041	20.0	20.0	—	—
"Hycar" 1042	—	—	20.0	20.0
Methylethyl ketone	80.0	80.0	80.0	80.0
Total	100.0	100.0	100.0	100.0
Treatment	Milled	Unmilled	Milled	Unmilled
LVF Brookfield Viscosity, 30 rpm, No. 4 spindle (cps)				
Initial	1,200	Gel	940	2,380
24 hr	1,200	—	940	2,380
48 hr	1,200	—	1,080	2,800
72 hr	1,200	—	1,080	2,940
144 hr	1,200	—	1,080	3,300

TABLE 4. EFFECT OF VARIATIONS IN MILLING PROCEDURE.

A. *"Hycar" 1001—20% total solids in methylethyl ketone*

LVF Brookfield Viscosity (cps)	Unmilled	Standard Milling	Hot-Milled at 250°F
Initial	Gel	2,700	15,000
4-wk aging	—	2,900	30,800

B. *"Hycar" 1022—20% total solids in methylethyl ketone*

LVF Brookfield Viscosity (cps)	Unmilled	Standard Milling (7 min)	Milled 14 min
Initial	4,700	1,700	1,400
4-wk aging	5,000	1,900	2,000

the ketones, nitroparaffins and the chlorinated hydrocarbon solvents. The nitroparaffins[7] tend to retard gelation in solvent mixtures. 1-Chloro-1-nitropropane has likewise been found effective as a stabilizer.[6] Final selection of a solvent for a nitrile-rubber cement will be determined, in addition to effective solvent action, by such factors as availability, cost, toxicity, odor, flammability, and desirability of the rate of evaporation. A compromise of desired conditions is usually necessary. Some solvent mixtures which have been recommended for use with nitrile rubbers to achieve desired balance of cost, evaporation rate and good solvent action are given in Table 5.

Cements of 20 to 35 per cent total solids of nitrile rubbers are easily obtainable in methylethyl ketone and chlorinated solvents. Total solids as high as 50 per cent have been obtained in nitroparaffin solvents.[7] In general, the nitrile-rubber cements are quite stable. This is true even of compounded cements as long as the accelerator is omitted. Nitrile-rubber cements have much better shelf sta-

bility than many other synthetic rubber cements.

For brushing and dipping applications, nitrile-rubber cements of 15 to 25 per cent solids are usually employed. For spreading applications with nitrile-rubber cements, total solids contents of 25 to 35 per cent are commonly employed. In general, the more concentrated the nitrile-rubber cement, the poorer its stability.

Thickening agents are sometimes added to nitrile-rubber cements to give them desired pseudoplasticity wherein apparent viscosity or consistency decreases rapidly with increase in rate of shear. This property, together with a high yield value, is very desirable for cements to be employed in spread-coating operations. Such properties also tend to prevent excessive strike-through during spread coating. Low total solids, low-viscosity solvent cements can be thickened to usable viscosities. Such thickening agents are also employed to improve the properties of spray-type cements, especially where thick coatings are desired. A carboxylic vinyl polymer, "Carbopol" 934,* has been very effective for thickening nitrile-rubber cements[4, 17] based on methylethyl ketone. The use of 0.5 to 2 per cent of "Carbopol" 934 is usually ample. Organic compounds of hydrous silicate minerals (e.g., "Bentone" 27) have also been used.[56]

The viscosity of a 5 per cent solution of a medium high nitrile-content rubber was approximately trebled, to 16,000 cps, by inclusion of "Carbopol" 934 in the following recipe:

	parts by wt.
"Hycar" 1042	54
Methylethyl ketone	877
"Carbopol" 934	22
Di(2-ethylhexyl)amine	22
Water	105

(For detailed instructions on the use of "Carbopol" 934 in a recipe of this type, consult Refs. 4 and 17.)

An illustrative recipe[4] for a spraying-cement of a nitrile rubber, which has been thickened with "Carbopol" 934, is given in Table 6 and contrasted with an unthickened analogous recipe.

Compounding Nitrile-Rubber Cements. Nitrile rubbers may be compounded for many cement applications and are preferable where oil resistance is of prime importance. For details concerning the milling and processing of the polymers, reference should be made to nitrile rubber suppliers' manuals.[4, 18, 19, 33, 55]

For the self-adhesion of nitrile-rubber stocks, the use of a cement solution of the rubber stock itself is an

_____
* Manufactured by B. F. Goodrich Chemical Company.

TABLE 5. SOLVENT MIXTURES FOR NITRILE-RUBBER CEMENTS.

Two-Component Mixtures	(%)	Three-Component Mixtures	(%)
1. Nitroethane or nitromethane	10–30[a]	1. Chlorotoluene	10–20
Benzene, toluene, or xylene	90–70	Nitroethane	10–20
		Benzene	80–60
2. Ethylene dichloride	10–30	2. Ethylene dichloride	10–20
Benzene, toluene, or xylene	90–70	Chlorobenzene	10–20
		Methylethyl ketone	80–60
3. Chlorotoluene or chlorobenzene	10–30	3. Butyl acetate	33⅓
Benzene, toluene, or xylene	90–70	Chlorobenzene	33⅓
		Acetone	33⅓
4. Chlorobenzene	10–30	4. Ethylene dichloride	10
Methylethyl ketone	90–70	Toluene	10
		Benzene	80
5. Nitroethane	10–30	5. 1-Nitropropane	25
Methylethyl ketone	90–70	Acetone	50
		Benzene	25
6. Chlorotoluene	10–30		
Diisopropyl ketone	90–70		

[a] All units are per cent by volume.

excellent and usually preferred adhesive. Additional tackifiers and accelerator are often added. Preferably, the accelerator should be the same as that employed in the stock to be adhered. Soft or even liquid nitrile rubbers such as "Hycar" 1312, or liquid carboxylic nitrile rubbers such as "Hycar" 1300X2, are illustrative tackifiers. Many resins, especially the phenolic resins such as "Durez" 12686, are employed to improve tack of uncured nitrile-rubber cements. The higher the nitrile content of the nitrile rubber, the greater its compatibility with phenolic resins.

High-strength, oil-resistant, resilient adhesives are prepared from nitrile rubbers by modification with resins and other rubbers. The phenolic resins are extensively employed for this purpose. (Those recommended include "Durez" 12687, "G-E" resins 12316 and 12393, CKRA 1977, BKR 2620, "Synco" 721, "Schenectady" varnish resins SP 8014 and SP-12, and "Bendix" R-114). Resorcinol-formaldehyde resins, polyvinyl-chloride resins and alkyd resins have also been employed. "Vinsol" resin, hydrogenated rosin, and its derivatives, coal-tar resins, and coumarone-indene resins are useful tackifying agents. Soft, near-solid or liquid nitrile rubbers like "Hycar" 1312 are similarly employed. Chlorinated rubber has been used to improve tack, stability and adhesion to a variety of materials, including metals.

Curing agents are used with nitrile rubbers when high strength, and especially strength at elevated temperatures, is a requisite of the adhesive. Vulcanizing systems employed with nitrile rubbers for molded products may be used. Sulfur (2) with benzothiazyl disulfide (1.5) and zinc oxide (5) is a common system. When low-temperature curing cements are desired, ultra-accelerators such as the zinc salts of the thiuram disulfides or accelerators activated by aldehyde-amine complexes, may be used. Preferably, these are incorporated just before use of the cement.

TABLE 6. RECIPE FOR SPRAYING APPLICATIONS.

Recipe No.	(Unthickened) 1	(Thickened) 2
"Hycar" 1042	10.0	10.0
Methylethyl ketone	79.0	79.0
Water	11.0	11.0
"Carbopol" 934	—	0.5
Di(2-ethylhexyl)amine	—	0.5
Total	100.0	101.0
Webbing	None up to 3 ft	
Sagging	Severe on thick coats None on thin coats	None
Leveling	Fair	Excellent
Atomization	Very good	Very good
Orange-peel	Some	Very little
Can pressure (psi)	12	17
Atomization pressure (psi)	72	72
Needle-tip	Fx	Fx
Cap	#704	#704

LVF Brookfield Viscosity, 30 rpm, No. 4 spindle (cps)

	Very thin	3000

Softeners are sometimes employed with nitrile rubbers to improve tack and adhesive properties. They are added to high nitrile content rubbers to aid processability. Commonly employed in cement applications are esters (e.g., dibutyl phthalate, dioctyl phthalate, tricresyl phosphate, tributoxy ethyl phosphate, dibenzyl sebacate), ester gums, alkyd resins, coumarone-indene resins, liquid nitrile rubbers, coal-tar resins, etc. Tack and adhesive properties of nitrile rubbers have been improved for some applications by the inclusion of chlorinated alkyl carbonates[34] such as chlorinated dibutyl carbonate.

Pigments are included in nitrile-rubber cements for a variety of purposes. These include improvement of adhesive strength, promotion of tack, extension of storage life, improvement of heat resistance, and reduction of costs. Carbon blacks enhance the strength of cured nitrile-rubber films. The best black for cements is channel black, usually used in amounts of 40 to 60 parts. Softer blacks give lower tensile properties, but provide longer shelf life and somewhat lower costs. Among the nonblack pigments, iron oxide, zinc oxide, hydrated silica, titanium dioxide and clays are the most commonly employed. Iron oxide is commonly used at levels of 75 to 100 parts. It yields smooth cements of relatively high tensile strength, improved tack and storage life, but lacking good abrasion resistance. Zinc oxide (25 to 50 parts) improves tack but not film strength. Hydrated silica (20 to 100 parts) is used to improve tensile strength where blacks are objectionable, and is especially useful in fabric adhesions, but excessive loadings tend to reduce adhesion. Titanium dioxide (5 to 25 parts) is used to impart whiteness, promote tack and extend storage life. Clays are employed to reduce cement costs at the expense of tensile strength and adhesion. Antioxidants are employed to improve heat resistance. They may also contribute stability and tack. The antioxidants are those commonly used in nitrile rubbers.

A typical black curing-cement[4] recipe for nitrile rubber is the following:

RECIPE A

Nitrile rubber	100
Zinc oxide	5
Sulfur[a]	3
EPC Black[b]	50
"AgeRite" Resin D	5
Coumarone-indene resin[c]	25
Refined coal tar	25

[a] Blackbird
[b] "Wyex"
[c] "Picco" 10

The following is a typical nonblack curing-cement[4] recipe for nitrile rubber:

RECIPE B

Nitrile rubber	100
Stearic acid	0.5
Zinc oxide	10
Sulfur[a]	2
Calcium silicate[b]	100
Titanium dioxide	25
Coumarone-indene resin[c]	10
Dibutyl phthalate	10
Accelerator "808"[d]	1.5

[a] "Spider"
[b] "Silene" EF
[c] "Picco" 10
[d] Du Pont Trade-mark

Table 7 shows the effect of three different nitrile rubbers on the viscosities of solutions of Recipe A with various solvents. Note that all solutions contain 35 per cent total solids.

Table 8 shows the comparative viscosities of solutions of Recipes A and B in the same solvents at 10, 20, and 30 per cent total solids. Note here that all solutions contain the high-nitrile rubber.

Applications of Nitrile-Rubber Adhesives

Laminating Adhesives. *Heat-Activated Adhesives for Lamination.* Adhesives which are essentially tack-free toward other surfaces at room temperature, but which become adhesive at some prescribed elevated temperatures, are of interest in many applications. In the shoe industry, for the adhesion of leather-to-rubber resin shoe-sole compositions, activation must occur at 120 to 130°F. For leather-to-vinyl adhesions, activation must occur below 175°F. A medium-high nitrile-content rubber (e.g., "Hycar" 1432) with half as much by weight of a phenolic resin (e.g., "Schenectady" SP-12), or this same rubber with half as much or an equal weight of a polyvinyl chloride resin (e.g., "Geon" 400X110)* is an effective adhesive for heat activation at the lower temperature range. For the higher temperature range, the use of twice as much of a polyvinyl chloride resin (e.g., "Geon" 400X110) as nitrile rubber ("Hycar" 1432) is effective. Various solvent systems may be used to apply such formulations. Some suggested combinations[4] which yielded adhesive bonds of 25 to 40 lb/in. for leather-to-leather, composition soling or vinyl, are given in Table 9.

Cements containing heat-hardening resins can be used to bond metal-to-nitrile rubber, polyvinyl chloride resins, leather, wood and fibrous mate-

* Manufactured by B. F. Goodrich Chemical Company.

rials. Cements have been prepared which satisfactorily bond the following materials to themselves or to other materials: cork, cardboard, leatherboard, fiberboard, paper, wood, masonite, nitrile rubbers, polyvinyl chloride, copolymers of vinyl chloride, nitrocellulose, cellulose acetate, phenolic resins, nylon, polyvinyl alcohol, "Mylar", iron, steel, aluminum, brass, tin, copper, lead and glass. They are poor adhesives for natural rubber, butyl rubber, and polyethylene, unless surfaces are made reactive.[37] Adhesive properties may be improved in many cases by the use of carboxylic nitrile rubbers of the "Hycar" 1072 type as replacements for the nitrile rubbers.

Low-Temperature-Curing Laminating Adhesives. Nitrile rubbers, blended with various epoxy resins activated by suitable amines and/or acidic agents, have been employed to bond elastomers, plastics, fabrics, wood and metals to themselves and to each other at or near room temperature. Formulations adapted to the particular surfaces to be adhered, must also be designed for the applications concerned. The recipe given in Table 10 may be adapted to many applications by choice of constituents and varying their amounts. Such a cement will cure in 4 to 24 hrs at room temperature or in less than 30 min at 150°F.

A cold-setting liquid adhesive particularly

TABLE 7. COMPARISON OF VISCOSITIES OF SOLUTIONS OF THREE NITRILE RUBBERS IN RECIPE (A)[a] IN VARIOUS SOLVENTS.

Recipe A Containing	Solvent	Brookfield Viscosity (cps) at 35% T.S.[e] of Solution of Recipe A of Solvent	
		Initial	Aged 1 Month
"Hycar" 1001[b]	Methylethyl ketone	1,900	4,300
	Chlorobenzene	5,500	12,000
	Nitropropane	5,600	8,800
"Hycar" 1432[c]	Methylethyl ketone	920	1,200
	Chlorobenzene	5,200	8,200
	Nitropropane	3,600	4,900
"Hycar" 1022[d]	Methylethyl ketone	1,400	2,500
	Chlorobenzene	8,600	21,500
	Nitropropane	4,200	6,100

[a] Black curing-cement recipe (A).
[b] "Hycar" 1001, a high nitrile rubber, slab form.
[c] "Hycar" 1432, a medium-high nitrile rubber, crumb form.
[d] "Hycar" 1022, a medium-high nitrile rubber, slab form.
[e] T.S. = total solids.

TABLE 8. COMPARISON OF VISCOSITIES OF SOLUTIONS OF A HIGH NITRILE RUBBER[a] IN RECIPIES A AND B IN VARIOUS SOLVENTS.

Solvent	% T.S.[d]	Recipe A[b]		Recipe B[c]	
		Brookfield Viscosity (cps)			
		Initial	Aged 1 Month	Initial	Aged 1 Month
Methylethyl ketone	10	10	17	13	14
	20	160	440	79	160
	30	1,900	4,300	1,360	4,500
Chlorobenzene	10	38	42	39	50
	20	620	900	1,680	1,820
	30	5,500	12,000	42,400	78,000
Nitropropane	10	33	33	27	25
	20	490	530	680	400
	30	5,600	8,800	6,000	9,000

[a] Containing "Hycar" 1001, a high nitrile rubber, slab form.
[b] Black curing-cement recipe (A).
[c] Nonblack curing-cement recipe (B).
[d] T.S. = total solids.

TABLE 9. ADHESIVES FOR LEATHER-TO-LEATHER OR LEATHER-TO-COMPOSITION SOLING.

Recipe No.	1	2	3	4
"Hycar" 1432	20.0	10.0	20.0	10.0
"Geon" 400X110	—	10.0	—	5.0
Phenolic resin[a]	10.0	5.0	10.0	5.0
Triphenyl phosphate	—	—	—	2.0
Monochlorobenzene	—	—	90.0	40.0
Methylethyl ketone	100.0	75.0	30.0	40.0
Totals	130.0	100.0	150.0	102.0

ADHESIVES FOR LEATHER-TO-VINYL OR LEATHER-TO-LEATHER

Recipe No.	5	6	7	8
"Hycar" 1432	9.0	9.0	9.0	9.0
"Geon" 400X110	18.0	18.0	18.0	18.0
Triphenyl phosphate	2.0	2.0	2.0	—
Phenolic resin[b]	—	—	—	2.0
Tetrahydrofuran	—	58.0	—	—
Methylethyl ketone	73.0	—	20.0	73.0
Toluene	—	—	48.0	—
Cyclohexanol	—	25.0	25.0	—
Totals	102.0	112.0	122.0	102.0

[a] "Schenectady" SP-12.

[b] "Catalin" 8369.

suited for leather-to-leather adhesion has been described in the patent literature[26] as consisting of nitrile rubber with an arylamine modified resin in ratios of 60:40 to 67:33, together with sulfur and accelerators.

Miscellaneous Laminations. Cellophane has been adhered to cotton by nitrile rubber[13] in benzene cement. Adhesion was promoted by heat.

Polyvinyl chloride, polyvinyl acetate and other polymeric films have been laminated to aluminum, brass and other metals by coating the polymeric film and the metal with an adhesive consisting of:

Nitrile rubber (e.g., "Hycar" 1002)	150
Vinyl chloride-vinylidene chloride copolymer	50
Dioctyl phthalate	20
"Paraplex" G-30	10
A barium stabilizer (e.g., "Staflex" QMXA)	6
Sulfur	1
Benzothiazolyl disulfide	1

The laminates are subsequently pressed together under 200 psi. pressure at 300 to 300°F for 15 min.[16]

Nitrile rubber in solvent treated with 10 to 20 parts of phosphoric acid at 50 to 100°C and subsequently neutralized has been recommended[38] as especially suited to laminating nitrile rubbers and linear polyamides.

Blends of nitrile rubber with "Vinsol" ester gum[42] in ethylene dichloride or similar solvent have been recommended as adhesive cements and surface coatings.

Blends of nitrile rubbers with pyroxylin[44,45] and other ingredients such as sulfur, zinc oxide, and calcium silicate have been used as adhesive cements for leather and shoe fabrication.

Cellulose acetate flock has been adhered to textile materials to make a pile surface[46] by the use of the following cement:

Nitrile rubber (e.g., "Hycar" 1002)	100
Sulfur	3
Mercaptobenzothiazole	2.4
Phenyl guanidine	0.6
Zinc oxide	7.5
Coumarone resin	37.5
Dimethyl phthalate	300
bis(2-ethylhexyl)phthalate	45
Methylethyl ketone	378
Methyl isobutyl ketone	256

TABLE 10. LOW-TEMPERATURE-CURING ADHESIVE.[a]

"Hycar" 1042	10–50
"Epon" 820	90–50
Methylethyl ketone	80
Triethylenetetramine[b]	2–20

[a] Mixed cement stable 4 to 24 hr.

[b] Added as 50% solution in methylethyl ketone just prior to use.

TABLE 11. BOND STRENGTHS OF NITRILE RUBBER-PHENOLIC CEMENT IN VARIOUS APPLICATIONS.

Recipe No.	1	2	3
"Hycar" 1001	100	100	—
"Durez" 12687	50	100	100
"Hycar" 1022	—	—	100
Totals	150	200	200
	Adhesion (Pounds per inch)		
Cotton duck to cotton duck (No. 633)	20	5	5
Cotton duck to cotton duck (No. 674)	5	5	4
Nylon to nylon (No. 936)	5	2	2
Nylon to nylon (No. 937)	6	6	5
Cotton duck No. 633 to wood	20	18	15
Cotton duck No. 674 to wood	18	15	25
Nylon No. 936 to wood	9	7	9
Nylon No. 937 to wood	7	10	10
Wood to wood (yellow pine)	387	619	641
Wood to cured "Hycar" 1022	35	12	23
Wood to cured "Hycar" 4021	25	12	10
Wood to cured natural rubber	15	25	20
Wood to cured SBR	10	5	6
Wood to steel	1,400	1,245	1,360
Wood to brass	1,000	930	1,230
Wood to aluminum	860	758	883
"Hycar" to "Hycar" 1022 (cured)	33	28	30
SBR to SBR (cured)	6	18	25
Uncured "Hycar" 1022 compound to:			
Aluminum	5	4	3
Brass	28	23	18
Steel	5	5	3
Uncured "Hycar" 4021 compound to:			
Aluminum	8	10	4
Brass	23	20	21
Steel	17	18	20
Uncured natural rubber compound to:			
Aluminum	9	7	6
Brass	21	25	18
Steel	12	20	20
Uncured SBR compound to:			
Aluminum	1	0	0
Brass	1	0	0
Steel	1	0	1

General-Purpose Adhesive Cements. *Heat-Activated.* Nitrile-rubber cements, without added curing agents, may be used to bond a wide variety of materials. Equal parts by weight of a nitrile rubber and a phenolic resin (e.g., "Durez" 12687, "G-E" resins 12316 and 12393, "CKRA" 1977, "BKR" 2620, "Synco" 721, "Schenectady" varnish resins SP 8014 and SP-12, or "Bendix" R-114) in a suitable solvent (e.g., methylethyl ketone) at a total solids level of 20 to 30 per cent is suitable for many adhesive purposes. For some purposes, less phenolic resin is preferable, but commonly 30 to 100 parts per 100 parts of rubber are employed.

Some indication of the applicability of such cements is given by bond strength data[4] on three formulations of this type in Table 11. The cements were prepared as 20 per cent total solids solutions in methylethyl ketone. The adhesive was applied as a single-brush coating, and subsequently air-dried. Leather samples were pressed 5 min at 200°F. The other assemblies were press-cured 30 min at 310°F. All samples were 1 in. by 6 in. strips. Rigid samples were assembled with a 1 in.

TABLE 12. INFLUENCE OF RESIN CONTENT ON ADHESION TO STEEL.

Rubber[a] to Resin Ratio	Resin A[b] lb/in. (width)[d]	Resin B[c] lb/in. (width)[d]
10:1	8.3	8.1
4:1	15.6	14.1
1:1	18.3	15.8

[a] "Hycar" 1002.

[b] Monsanto Resin 378 (conditioned 16 hr at 122°F).

[c] "Durez" Resin 11078 (conditioned 2 hr at 212°F).

[d] Test specimen 1 in. by 8 in. white drill cloth stripped from steel at angle of 180°.

overlap and the cured assemblies tested by determining the force required to pull them apart. Assemblies involving one or more flexible parts were overlapped 5 in. on the cemented surfaces and the cured assembly was tested by using a standard peel test.

The more phenolic resin employed, the greater the bond strength and the more brittle the adhesive. The increase of bond strength with resin content for nitrile rubber-phenolic resin cements is illustrated by the data of Lindner, Schmelzle and Wehmer[14] given in Table 12. The rubber and resin were dissolved separately in methyl isobutyl ketone as 20 per cent total solids solutions and then blended. The adhesive was coated on the steel and the cloth was bonded after tack developed.

Nitrile rubber-phenolic resin blend cements have been used to laminate aluminum foil to paper and then to wood.[27]

Low-Temperature-Curing Adhesives. The recipe[4] in Table 13 is illustrative of a low-temperature curing two-part cement possessing a fair degree of tack and giving good adhesion of various materials to cured or uncured nitrile rubbers. Cure cycles of 10 min at 175°F to 2 hrs at 100°F are effective.

Adhesive systems of the type described in the Laminating Adhesives Section (pp. 236–238) also are effective as low-temperature curing general-purpose adhesives.

Adhesives based on nitrile rubbers and "Vinsol" resins[53] cured under pressure for 5 min at 200°F or equivalent, have been used to adhere canvas, leather, natural rubber, wood and steel to themselves. Resin to elastomer ratios of 2:3 to 1:1 by weight are preferred.

The inclusion of bivalent metal (zinc or magnesium) salts of an hydroxy benzoic acid (salicylic) in nitrile rubber cements, which may also contain resins (e.g., soft coumarone-indene, phenol-aldehyde, pine wood rosin or other tackifier resins), has been reported[54] to give stable viscous adhesives. They are effective at room temperature or slightly elevated temperatures for sealing metal-to-metal joints, bonding plasticized materials to themselves, coating fabrics, and for adhering adhesive grits to provide antislip floor coatings.

Adhesion of Nitrile Rubber to Various Surfaces: Polyvinyl Chloride, Leather, Wood, Metal, Glass, etc. The nitrile rubbers can bond a wide range of materials to metal, wood, porcelain and even glass if the hard surface is first coated with a chlorinated rubber cement. Inclusion of chlorinated rubber in nitrile-rubber cements achieves this same purpose in some instances, and also assists the adhesion of surfaces pretreated with chlorinated rubber. Pigmentation of the primer coat of chlorinated rubber with chromium or iron oxide is beneficial for use on metals.

The following recipe[4] is illustrative of a nitrile-rubber cement containing chlorinated rubber.

	parts by vol.
Compound A of Table 13 20% in methylethyl ketone	25
Compound B of Table 13 20% in methylethyl ketone	25
Chlorinated rubber ("Parlon") 12% in toluene	50

Some of the best and most oil-resistant adhesives for bonding nitrile rubbers to metal are blends of nitrile rubber and resole-type phenolic resin in which the resin content is very high, often over 80 per cent.

TABLE 13. LOW-TEMPERATURE-CURING CEMENT.

Recipe	A	B
"Hycar" 1001	100.0	100.0
Zinc oxide	5.0	5.0
Sulfur	6.0	—
Channel black	50.0	50.0
Coumarone-indene resin[a] (m.p. 25°C)	25.0	25.0
"AgeRite" Resin	5.0	5.0
Coal-tar hydrocarbon[b]	25.0	25.0
Mercaptobenzothiazole[c]	—	6.0
Total	216.0	216.0

Break down "Hycar" rubber 15 min on a cool mill. Mix each batch separately on the mill.

Make each recipe as 20% total solids solution in chlorobenzene or methylethyl ketone.

Add to Recipe B before use, 2.5 parts butyraldehyde aniline condensation product mixed with equal parts of solvent.

Mix equal volumes of A and B just before using.

[a] "Cumar" P-25.

[b] "Nevoll."

[c] "Captax."

Nitrile-Rubber Splicing Cement. Blends of nitrile rubbers with phenolic resins (e.g., "Durez" 12687, "G-E" resins 12316 and 12393, CKRA 1977, BKR 2620, "Synco" 721, "Schenectady" varnish resins SP 8014 and SP-12 or "Bendix" R-114) may be used to give good splicing cements which are useful in laminating and general-purpose applications. In addition to related formulations mentioned elsewhere, the two recipes of Table 14 are illustrative of nitrile rubber-phenolic blends.[4] Carboxylic-nitrile rubbers may be used effectively in such formulations.

Similar compositions have been reported in the patent literature as effective adhesives for vinyl resins to wood and metal,[29] and for nitrile rubbers to metal surfaces.[30]

Curing Cements for Nitrile-Rubber Adhesion. For self-adhesion of a nitrile-rubber stock, a cement of the rubber stock with some accelerator added is usually preferable. Such systems are often effective with other surfaces to which the nitrile rubber is to be adhered.

Special-Purpose Cements. *Cements of High Tack.* The tackiness of nitrile-rubber cements may be enhanced by tackifying and plasticizing agents combined with large amounts of zinc oxide. An illustrative recipe of this type[4] is given in Table 15. Liquid nitrile (e.g., "Hycar" 1312) or liquid carboxylic nitrile rubbers (e.g., "Hycar" 1300X2) may also be employed to enhance tack. Liquid carboxylic rubbers should not be used in recipes containing metal oxides such as zinc oxide.

Spreading and Coating Formulations. Nitrile-rubber spreading compounds suitable for coating and impregnation of fabrics to provide resistance to gasoline and oils require spreadable, adhering curing compositions. Oil resistance is dependent on nitrile content of the rubber employed. Some typical spreading recipes[4] are given in Table 16. Cure times of approximately 2 hrs at 250°F should be adequate.

TABLE 14. NITRILE RUBBER-PHENOLIC SPLICING CEMENTS.

	1	2
"Hycar" 1001	75.0	—
"Hycar" 1002	—	50.0
Phenolic resin[a]	25.0	50.0
MPC black	2.0	—
Sulfur[b]	1.25	—
Tetramethylthiuram monosulfide[c]	0.04	—
Total	103.29	100.0

Make up to 30% total solids in methylethyl ketone.

a Any of the recommended phenolic resins may be used.
b "Spider" brand.
c "Unads."

TABLE 15. HIGH-TACK CEMENT.

	Part A	Part B
"Hycar" 1001	100.0	100.0
EPC black[a]	10.0	10.0
Zinc oxide	150.0	150.0
"AgeRite" Resin D	5.0	5.0
Refined coal tar[b]	35.0	35.0
Benzyl alcohol	18.0	15.0
Dibutyl metacresol	35.0	35.0
Sulfur	5.0	—
Butyraldehyde aniline[c]	—	8.0
Total	358.0	358.0

Dissolve 1,400 g of A in ½ gal chlorotoluene and make up to 1 gal with chlorobenzene.
Dissolve 1,400 g of B in ½ gal chlorotoluene and make up to 1 gal with chlorobenzene.
Mix equal proportions by volume just before using.

a "Wyex."   b "BRT" 7.   c Accelerator "808."

Paper coating cements to impart resistance to ASTM Oils No. 1 and No. 3 may be prepared similarly.[4] A typical recipe is given in Table 17.

The gas permeability of nitrile rubbers is less

TABLE 16. NITRILE-RUBBER SPREADING CEMENTS.

Recipe No.	1	2	3	4
"Hycar" 1001	100	100		
"Hycar" 1042			100	100
Zinc oxide	5	5	5	5
Sulfur[a]	2	2	1.5	1.5
SRF black[b]	75	60	75	75
Benzothiazyl disulfide[c]	1.5	—	1.5	1.5
Stearic acid	—	—	1.0	1.0
Triacetin	35	—	—	—
"Flexricin" P-4	—	—	10	10
Synthetic resin extender[d]	—	—	—	20
Litharge	—	10	—	—
"AgeRite" Resin D	—	2	—	—
Diocytyl phthalate[e]	—	25	—	—
Total	218.5	204.0	194.0	214.0

Cement preparation:

Recipe No. 1. Dissolve 675 g in 1 qt of nitroethane and make up to 1 gal with "Solvesso" No. 1.

Recipe No. 2. Make up as 45% total solids in ethylene dichloride and then dilute to 25% total solids with methylethyl ketone.

Recipe No. 3. Make up to 20% total solids in methyl-ethyl ketone.

Recipe No. 4. Make up to 25% total solids in methyl-ethyl ketone.

a "Spider."   c "Altax."   e "GP-261."
b "Sterling" S.   d "Turpol" 1093.

TABLE 17. COATING CEMENT FOR PAPER RESISTANT
TO ASTM OILS No. 1 AND No. 3.

The recipe below is for a fast-curing cement for paper
coating that retains good adhesion after hot-oil aging.
Samples were immersed in ASTM Oils No. 1 and No. 3
for 72 hr at 212°F without significant loss of adhesion.

"Hycar" 1001	100.0
Zinc oxide	5.0
Sulfur[a]	1.5
SRF black[b]	20.0
Clay[c]	75.0
Whiting[d]	75.0
Phenolic resin[e]	40.0
Plasticizer[f]	10.0
"AgeRite" Resin D	1.0
Benzothiazyl disulfide[g]	1.0

Add hexamethylene tetramine in solvent.

Make up as a 35% total solids cement in 95% methylethyl ketone 5% isopropyl alcohol. Just before coating,
add 4 parts of "Butyl" 8[h] as a 5 to 10% solution
in methylethyl ketone. After coating, the cement is
cured 2 min at 212°F. The cement can be refrigerated
to prolong working life if it cannot be used immediately.

Since "Durez" 12686 contains no "hexa" (hexamethylene
tetramine), 3 parts should be added along with the
"Butyl" 8. Adding the hexa to the finished cement
will retard gelation.

[a] "Spider."	[d] "Atomite."	[g] "Altax."
[b] "Sterling" S.	[e] "Durez" 12686.	[h] R. T. Vanderbilt.
[c] "Dixie."	[f] "Paraplex" G-25.	

than that of either natural or SBR and comparable to that of polychloroprene.[1] Hence, fabrics
coated with nitrile rubbers have been used effectively in the manufacture of inflatable products.

White Cement Formulations. Nitrile-rubber cements
in which white pigmentation is required may be
prepared with titanium dioxide, silica and similar
materials. Such a recipe[4] is given in Table 18.

A similar nonblack cement suggested[18] for the
adhesion of cotton, wood, paper compositions,
leather, nuclear shoe soling, blown closed-cell
soling or microcellular soling is given in Table 19.

Leather adhesives[47, 48] have been formulated
from nitrile rubbers using the following composition:

Nitrile rubber	100
Vinyl chloride-vinyl acetate copolymer	100
Zinc oxide	5
Stearic acid	1.5
Calcium silicate	2
Solvent	600:800

Vinyl-to-Fabric Adhesives. Nitrile-rubber adhesives
suitable for use in bonding vinyl films to fabrics
may be made by the inclusion of chlorinated-
rubber resins. Such a recipe[4] is given in Table 20.

Similar adhesives based on nitrile-rubber compounds with zinc resinate and chlorinated rubber[49] have been mentioned in the patent literature.

Pressure-Sensitive Adhesives. Copolymers of butadiene with 25 parts of acrylonitrile or methacrylonitrile modified with 4 to 5 per cent dodecyl
mercaptan have been described as pressure-
sensitive adhesives.[12]

Structural Adhesives. *Nitrile Rubbers with Phenolic
Resin.* Nitrile rubbers blended with phenolic
resins may be used to bond a wide variety of construction materials to themselves and to each
other.[4, 50, 51, 52] These include, iron, wood, glass,
masonite, fiberboard, cardboard, cork, phenolic
resins, vinyl chloride polymers and copolymers,
paper, and many porous materials.

The adhesive bonding of metal and plastic parts
has become a reliable and economical method, assuming a position of considerable importance.
Blends of nitrile rubbers with phenolic resin have
been widely used. In the aircraft industry, adhesive
fabrications have offered the advantages of weight

TABLE 18. TYPICAL WHITE CEMENT FORMULATION.

"Hycar" 1022	100.0
Zinc oxide	5.0
Sulfur	1.5
Titanium dioxide[a]	15.0
Hydrated silica[b]	25.0
Chlorinated paraffin wax[c]	10.0
Tetramethylthiuram monosulfide[d]	0.4
Stearic acid	1.0
Total	157.9

Methylethyl ketone to make 15% total solids.

Four parts of "Butyl" 8 are added to the cement just before use. The "Butyl" 8 is made up as a 5 to 10%
solution in methylethyl ketone before addition.

[a] "Titanox."	[c] "Chlorowax" 40.
[b] "Hi-Sil."	[d] "Unads."

TABLE 19. NONBLACK CEMENT FORMULATION.

Masterbatch:		
Nitrile rubber	100	
Stearic acid	1	
Zinc oxide	5	
Calcium silicate	10	
Cement solution:	(1)	(2)
Masterbatch	103	103
Sulfur	2	—
Dibenzylamine	2	—
Zinc diethyldithiocarbamate	—	2
Zinc butyl xanthate	—	2
Methylethyl ketone	600	600

Mix equal parts of cements (1) and (2) prior to use.

reduction, fatigue resistance, and simultaneous fastening and sealing of joints. Military Specifications MIL-A-5090B and MIL-A-8431 (U. S. A. F.) are commonly accepted standards for adhesives for bonding aircraft structures.

Films of nitrile rubber-phenolic resins (i.e., tapes), both supported and unsupported, are employed extensively in the aircraft industry for bonding metal-to-metal surfaces in both plain and honeycomb sandwich constructions. In honeycomb constructions, a fabric-supported film minimizes the tendency for the thin metal edges of the honeycomb to cut through the adhesive film and enhances film strength. A supporting fabric also facilitates the preparation of tapes consisting of two different adhesives, one on top for bonding to a regular planar metal surface and one below possessing filleting properties for bonding to honeycomb. Many fabrics (cotton, rayon, nylon) of varied weave and mesh size have been employed as carriers. Aluminum foil has also been employed. The adhesive films may be dipped, sprayed, spread or calendered onto the supporting member. For some bonding of honeycomb and metal-to-metal panels, liquid or cement nitrile-phenolic resin adhesives are useful. For details on the use of nitrile rubber-phenolic resin tapes in metal laminates and honeycomb sandwich constructions, reference should be made to suppliers' manuals and literature[15] and to publications of the Wright Air Development Center.[23, 24]

Illustrative commercial tapes of this type include "Scotchwelds" AF-6 and AF-31 made by Minnesota Mining & Manufacturing Company, "Metlbond" 4021 made by Narmco, Inc., "Bloomingdale" PA-101, and "Plastilocks" 601, 608, 620, 637, 638, and 650 of the B. F. Goodrich Company. Typical liquid nitrile rubber-phenolic resin adhesives are "H2P" made by Cycleweld and "Plasti-

TABLE 20. ADHESIVE FOR BONDING VINYL TO FABRIC.

"Hycar" 1001	100
Calcium silicate[a]	40
Titanium dioxide[b]	10
Refined coal tar	25
Coumarone-indene resin[c]	25
Chlorinated rubber (128 cps)[d]	100

Use regular breakdown procedure and add all ingredients except chlorinated rubber. Make 20% solution in methylethyl ketone, and a separate 20% solution of chlorinated rubber in toluene. Then blend 200 parts of the "Hycar" solution with 100 parts of chlorinated rubber solution.

[a] "Silene" EF.   [c] "Cumar" P-25.
[b] "Titanox."   [d] "Parlon."

TABLE 21. NITRILE RUBBER-PHENOLIC RESIN TAPE FORMULATIONS.

Nitrile rubber[a]	100
Phenolic resin[b]	75 to 200
Zinc oxide	5
Sulfur	1 to 3
Accelerator	0.5 to 1
Age resister	0 to 5
Stearic acid	0 to 1
Carbon black	0 to 20
Filler	0 to 100
Plasticizer	0 to 10

Bonding metals to themselves requires heat (20 min to 120 min at 300° to 400°F) and pressure (50 to 150 psi).

[a] Nitrile content is usually in excess of 30%.
[b] Novolac type is suitable.

TABLE 22. NITRILE RUBBER-PHENOLIC RESIN HIGH-TEMPERATURE LIQUID ADHESIVE.

Nitrile rubber[a]	100
Phenolic resin A[b]	0 to 200
Phenolic resin B[c]	0 to 200
Zinc oxide	5
Sulfur	1 to 3
Accelerator	0.5 to 1
Age resister	0 to 5
Stearic acid	0 to 1
Carbon black	0 to 50
Filler	0 to 100
Solvent	for 20 to 50% solids

[a] Nitrile content is usually in excess of 30%.
[b] Novolac type.
[c] Resole type.

locks" 605 and 618 made by The B. F. Goodrich Company. Details of the compositions of such products are not revealed by manufacturers, but a generalized formula for tape-type adhesives is given in Table 21. A formulation for a high-temperature liquid phenolic-resin adhesive suitable for structural fabrication is given in Table 22. Much of the effectiveness of a nitrile-rubber tape depends on the techniques of preparation. A Wright Air Development Center report by Smith, Imholz and Elliott[20] describes in detail the preparation of a nitrile rubber-phenolic resin tape using the recipe in Table 23. As emphasized by these authors, properties depend largely on mixing conditions. The method of preparation of metal surfaces is critical. An excellent description of metal surface preparation methods is contained in Wright Air Development Center reports by Thelen[21, 22] and others from the Franklin Institute Laboratories. The consistency of metal bonds can be enhanced by the use of certain agents such as B. F. Goodrich's A934B.[25c]

TABLE 23. A NITRILE RUBBER-PHENOLIC RESIN
TAPE RECIPE.[20]

"Hycar" 1001	100
"Durez" 7031A	150
"Pelletex"	20
Zinc oxide	5
2-Mercaptobenzothiazole	1
Sulfur	1
Stearic acid	0.5

A cure cycle of 20 min at 325°F and 118 psi gave satisfactory results.

For methods of evaluating structural adhesives of
this type, reference should be made to Wright Air
Development Center reports[23, 24] by H. R. Merriman and others of the Glenn L. Martin Company.

A tape made from the formulation given in
Table 21 and employed with 2024-T3 clad
aluminum alloy will show lap shear strengths of
the following order when tested according to
MIL-A-8431:

°F	psi
−67	2000 to 4000
76	3000 to 6000
260	1000 to 3000
300	500 to 2500

On 17-7PH stainless steel lap shear strengths of
the following order are obtained:

°F	psi
−67	4000 to 6000
76	3000 to 6000
300	2000 to 3000
500	1000 to 2000

In addition to aircraft applications, adhesives of
this type are employed in the bonding of friction
materials (e.g., grinding wheels), brake lining to
brake shoes, clutch facings, automotive transmission parts, structural assemblies for home appliances (e.g., evaporator tube assemblies in refrigerators), building assemblies (e.g., honeycomb
sandwich curtain walls), in the fabrication of jet
fuel filters, for attaching plastic fixtures to safety
glass, etc.

The liquid nitrile rubber-phenolic resin adhesives are used in the bonding of friction materials,
brake bonding, in binders for friction materials,
primers for aircraft and other metal-to-metal structural assemblies, seam sealants for steel or tin plate,
container sealants, sealants for oil or gasoline filters,
adhesives for fabrication of printed circuits, the
adhesion of synthetic fibers to vinyl compounds or
coatings, the binding of abrasives to polyurethanes,
in primers for adhesion of vinyl plastisols to metals,
the bonding of paper honeycomb to metal for various structural applications, etc.

Liquid nitrile rubber-phenolic resins containing
polyvinyl alcohol[32] have been recommended for
both metallic and nonmetallic bonding.

Nitrile rubber-phenol formaldehyde resin films
activated by hexamethylenetetramine may be used
to bond plywood.[28]

Aluminum flakes[35] have been included in nitrile
rubber-phenolic resin tapes to improve processability, uniformity and consistency of cure.

Nitrile Rubbers with Other Resins. A product[31] resulting from the treatment of a mixture of nitrile
rubber and resorcinol in solvent with dry hydrogen chloride has been used in sheet form as an
adhesive.

Phenol-ketone condensation products and their
subsequent condensations with nitrile rubbers[43]
have been used in sheet form as adhesives.

Nitrile-Rubber Latex Adhesives

The principal advantages in employing nitrile-
rubber latex adhesives, rather than solvent-cement
adhesives of the same nitrile rubbers, are the freedom from fire and toxicity hazards associated with
certain solvents, and the ease of application. Disadvantages include the relatively slow drying rate
and the fact that high strengths obtained with solvent cements by curing with resins canont be
matched in latex formulations.

The blending of nitrile-rubber latexes with materials such as casein, phenolic resins and "Vinsol"
resin produces materials useful for the lamination
of a variety of materials.

A 1959 review in the *Vanderbilt News*[10] lists eleven
latexes made by International Latex Corporation
(none specified for adhesive use), eight made by
the Chemical Division of Goodyear Tire & Rubber Company (two specified for adhesive use), one
made by the Heresite & Chemical Company (adhesive use specified), and six made by the B. F.
Goodrich Chemical Company (adhesive use specified for four). Naugatuck Chemical Company also
manufactures nitrile rubber latexes (six or more).
A list of latexes which have been designated for
adhesive use by the various suppliers is given in
Table 24. A latex that has not been designated for
adhesive uses does not preclude such applications,
but only those which have been specifically recommended by the manufacturer for this use have
been included in Table 24.

Blends of Casein with Nitrile-Rubber Latex. Blends
of nitrile-rubber latex with casein have been used
to adhere vinyl sheeting and vinyl plastisol coatings to paper, nylon and rayon. Casein in fairly
large amounts is miscible with nitrile-rubber latices.
Carboxylic nitrile-rubber latexes have been simi-

TABLE 24. NITRILE-RUBBER LATICES RECOMMENDED FOR ADHESIVE APPLICATIONS.

Trade Name	Supplier	Acrylonitrile (% Monomer Charge)	Third Monomer	% Total Solids	Particle Size Å	pH, Initial
"Chemigum" 248	A	33	—	55	2500	9.0
"Chemigum" 200	A	30	—	55	4000	10.5
"Herecol" N-33	B	33	—	50	—	9.0
"Hycar" 1551	C	High	—	52	1800	9.5
"Hycar" 1571	C	High	Methacrylic acid	40	1200	8.5
"Hycar" 1552	C	Medium	—	52	1800	9.5
"Hycar" 1562	C	Medium	—	40	500	9.5

A—Chemical Div., Goodyear Tire & Rubber Co.
B—Heresite & Chemical Co.
C—B. F. Goodrich Chemical Co.

larly employed and are outstandingly effective. For details on the methods of using such mixtures of casein with nitrile-rubber latexes, reference should be made to manufacturers' bulletins.[9, 10, 55] The following is an illustrative recipe:[9]

"Hycar" 1571	80
Borated casein	20

To prepare the borated casein, use casein with 20 parts per 100 by weight of borax and of "Dowicide" A, made up to 12% total solids.

To laminate vinyl sheeting to nylon, coat the fabric with latex-casein blend. Cure 1.5 min at 325°F under pressure of 7.4 psi.

For formulations using ammonia-solubilized casein and a wetting agent, consult Ref. 40.

Blends of Phenolic Resin with Nitrile-Rubber Latex. Phenolic resins (e.g., "G-E" resin 12353, "Durez" 14136, "Durez" 14798, "Synco" 550, "Synco" 721, and "Catovar" 170) may be blended with nitrile-rubber latexes to give adhesives useful for bonding and impregnation of many surfaces. Such blending can be achieved without coagulation by employing precautions, such as proper adjustment of total solids, adding resin to the latex, stirring the latex during the addition of the resin, and following manufacturers' recommendations regarding choice of latex and amount of resins.[9]

Blends of "Vinsol" Resin with Nitrile-Rubber Latex. Blends of nitrile-rubber latexes with "Vinsol" resin emulsions yield adhesives suitable for bonding many types of materials.[9, 11] Thus aluminum foil has been bonded to itself, asbestos board, wood, cardboard, kraft paper and saran film. Other bondings have included canvas to itself, cotton to natural rubber, felt base to polyvinyl chloride sheet, leather to itself or to masking tape, natural rubber to wool or steel, wood to itself, steel to itself or aluminum, etc. Equal weight blends of nitrile rubber and "Vinsol" resin represent an effective composition at or near which maximum bond strength

results for many applications. Bond strengths of laminates prepared with nitrile-rubber latexes are often increased 50 to 200 per cent by the inclusion of an equal weight of "Vinsol" resin.

The initial tack of nitrile-rubber latex blends with "Vinsol" resin may be increased by the addition of plasticizers and/or solvents. The stability of the latex-adhesive blend may be improved by the addition of emulsifying agents. Thickening agents may be employed to increase viscosity, if necessary. "Carbopol" 934 and similar resins[17] have been used for this purpose. They are especially useful where the total solids are below 30 per cent, where a nonpourable, easily spread formulation is desired, or where a high yield value at low viscosity is important.

Miscellaneous Nitrile Rubber-Latex Adhesives. A pressure-sensitive, air-drying coating adhesive[41] for waxed paper, metallic foil, glassine, cellophane or similar materials may be formed from a low-molecular-weight nitrile-rubber latex containing an emulsified rosin alcohol. When spread on a suitable backing, it shows minimum tack toward other surfaces, but it forms a bond that can be repeatedly opened and closed with similarly coated surfaces.

References

1. Semon, W. L., Chapter 23, "Synthetic Rubber," New York, John Wiley & Sons, Inc., 1954.
2. Roelig, H., *Kautschuk,* **13,** 179–80 (1937); Koch, A., *Z. Ver. deut. Ing.* (*VDI*), **80,** 963–8 (1936).
3. Konrad, E., and Tschunkur, E., British Patent 360,821 (May 30, 1930); U. S. Patent 1,973,000 (to I. G. Farben. Akt.), (Sept. 11, 1934); French Patent 710,901 (Feb. 4, 1931); German Patent 658,172 (Mar. 25, 1938); German Patent 654,989 (Jan. 6, 1938).
4. Hycar Manual HM-4, "Making Cements with Hycar Rubber," B. F. Goodrich Chemical Co. (June 1959).

5. Sarbach, D. V., and Garvey, B. S., *India Rubber World,* **115,** 798–801 (1947); *Rubber Chem. and Technol.,* **20,** 990–7 (1947).

6. Campbell, A. W., and Burns, J. W., *India Rubber World,* **107,** 169–170 (1942).

7. Garvey, B. S. (to The B. F. Goodrich Co.), U.S. Patent 2,360,867 (Oct. 24, 1944).

8. Marsden, C., "Solvents and Allied Substances Manual," Cleaver-Hume Press, 1954.

9. "Hycar Latex Manual," B. F. Goodrich Chemical Co. (1956).

10. "Information on Latices," *Vanderbilt News,* **25,** (5), 24–5 (Oct. 1959).

11. "Vinsol Resin for Adhesives," Naval Stores Department of Hercules Powder Co. (1954).

12. Deanin, R. D. (to Allied Chemical & Dye Corp.), U.S. Patent 2,783,166 (Feb. 26, 1957).

13. Shapovalova, A. I., Voyutskii, S. S., and Pisarenko, A. P., *Kolloid Zhur.,* **18,** 485–93 (1956).

14. Lindner, G. F., Schmelzle, A. F., and Wehmer, F., *Rubber Age,* **56,** 424 (July 1949).

15. Minnesota Mining & Manufacturing Co. Bull. No. 4 (1957).

16. Hussey, H. A., and Wright, D. D. (to The B. F. Goodrich Co.), U.S. Patent 2,653,884 (Sept. 29, 1953).

17. "Carbopol 934" Bull., B. F. Goodrich Chemical Co. (1957).
    (*a*) Supplement No. 1, "Using Carbopol Polymers in Emulsions" (Mar. 1959).
    (*b*) Supplement No. 2, "How to Thicken Latices with Carbopol 934" (May 1959).
    (*c*) Supplement No. 3, "Forming Cosmetic Gels with Carbopol 934" (July 1959).
    (*d*) Supplement No. 4, "Dispersing Carbopol Polymers" (July 1959).

18. "Polysar Krynac," A Bulletin of the Polymer Corp., Ltd. (1954).

19. "Paracril Cements," Tech. Bull. No. 9, Naugatuck Chemical Co.
    (*a*) "Nitrile Rubbers," Tech. Bull. No. 1.
    (*b*) "Paracril CLT," Bull. No. 211 (Nov. 26, 1956).
    (*c*) "Paracril D," Bull. No. 199 (Sept. 13, 1954).

20. Smith, A. E., Imholz, W. C., and Elliott, P. M., "High Temperature Metal to Metal Adhesives," A. F. Tech. Rept No. 5896, Part 2, by U. S. Rubber Co. (July 1951).

21. Thelen, E., Hollinger, R., Haigh, T. I., Drew, J. B., Varker, C. J., and Wallace, E. F., "Treatment of Metal Surfaces for Adhesive Bonding," W.A.D.C. Tech. Rept 55–87, Part V (Feb. 1958) from The Franklin Institute Laboratories.

22. Thelen, E., "Preparation of Metal Surfaces for Adhesive Bonding," W.A.D.C. Tech. Rept 57–513 (June 1957).

23. Merriman, H. R., "Research on Structural Adhesive Properties Over a Wide Temperature Range," W.A.D.C. Tech. Rept 56–320 (April 1957) from the Glenn L. Martin Co.

24. Merriman, H. R., and Goplen, H., "Research on Structural Adhesive Properties Over a Wide Temperature Range," W.A.D.C. Tech. Rept 57–513 (June 1957).

25. Manual IPC-95, "Adhesives and Sealants," B. F. Goodrich Industrial Products Co.
    (*a*) "Duolock System for Bonding Rubber to Metal" Bull.
    (*b*) "Adhesives, Coatings, Sealants for the Aircraft Industry" Bull.
    (*c*) "A-934-B Metal Primer," Product Information Sheet (Mar. 1959).

26. Gleim, C. E. (to Wingfoot Corp.), U. S. Patent 2,630,420 (Mar. 3, 1953).

27. Pintell, M. H. (to Reynolds Metals Co.), U. S. Patent 2,711,380 (June 21, 1955).

28. Williams, G. M. (to United States Rubber Co.), U.S. Patent 2,724,675 (Nov. 22, 1955).

29. Wada, S. (to Nippon Dustkeeper Co.), Japan Patent 8,039 (Dec. 7, 1954); *C.A.* **50,** 8254c.

30. Dogliotti, L., and Maurizio, B. (to FIAT Soc. per Azioni), Italian Patent 473,355 (July 24, 1952); *C.A.* **48,** 3059c.

31. Sear, D. W. (to Dunlop Rubber Co., Ltd.), British Patent 743,587 (Jan. 18, 1956).

32. Union Quimica del Norte de Espana, Spanish Patent 215,887 (May 20, 1955); *C.A.* **50,** 6100h.

33. "Butaprene N," Firestone Tire & Rubber Co.; "Loxite Adhesives" (1959).

34. Sarbach, D. V. (to The B. F. Goodrich Co.), U.S. Patent 2,395,070 (Feb. 19, 1946) and U. S. Patent 2,395,071 (to The B. F. Goodrich Co.), (Feb. 19, 1946).

35. Fiedler, L. F., and Leakey, P. J. (to The B. F. Goodrich Co.), U. S. Patent 2,575,265 (Nov. 13, 1951).

36. Jarrijohn, A., and Gossot, J., *Inds. Plastiques,* **3,** 121–3 (1947).

37. Bascom, R. C., *Modern Plastics,* **27,** 84–6 (1949).

38. DiMasi, A. T. (United States Navy), U. S. Patent 2,510,090 (June 6, 1950).

39. Reid, R. J. (to The Firestone Tire & Rubber Co.), U. S. Patent 2,514,222 (July 4, 1950).

40. Morris, T. C., and Johnson, E. C. (to B. B. Chemical Co., Boston, Mass.), U. S. Patent 2,572,877 (Oct. 30, 1951) and U. S. Patent 2,572,879 (Oct. 30, 1951).

41. Hatfield, A. L., and Owen, H. P. (to The B. F. Goodrich Co.), U. S. Patent 2,535,852 (Dec. 26, 1950).

42. Chmiel, E. M. (to Minnesota Mining & Manufacturing Co.), U.S. Patent 2,491,477 (Dec. 20, 1949).

43. Sear, D. W. (to Dunlop Rubber Co., Ltd.), British Patent 743,587 (Jan. 18, 1956).

44. Teppema, J., and Manning, J. F. (to B. B. Chemical Co., Boston, Mass.), U. S. Patent 2,379,552 (July 3, 1945).

45. Teppema, J., and Manning, J. F. (to B. B. Chemical Co. of Canada, Ltd.), Canadian Patent 431,615 (Dec. 4, 1945).

46. Ewing, H., and Blackmore, J. S. (to Celanese Corporation of America), U. S. Patent 2,681,292 (June 15, 1954).

47. Teppema, J., and Manning, J. F. (to B. B. Chemical Co. of Canada, Ltd.), Canadian Patent 431,616 (Dec. 4, 1945).

48. Teppema, J., and Manning, J. F. (to B. B. Chemical Co., Boston, Mass.), U. S. Patent 2,367,629 (Jan. 16, 1945).

49. Puddefoot, L. E., and Swire, W. H. (to B. B. Chemical Co., Ltd.), British Patent 569,666 (June 4, 1945).

50. Groten, F. J., and Reid, R. J. (to The Firestone Tire & Rubber Co.), U. S. Patent 2,581,926 (Jan. 8, 1952).

51. Groten, F. J., and Reid, R. J. (to The Firestone Tire & Rubber Co.), U. S. Patent 2,459,739 (Jan. 18, 1949).

52. Torii, T. (to Fujikura Electric Wire & Cable Co.), Japan Patent 4,340 (Oct. 22, 1952); *C.A.* **47,** 10902f.

53. Mayfield, E. E. (to Hercules Powder Co.), U. S. Patent 2,606,884 (Aug. 12, 1952).

54. Finn, A. L. (to Minnesota Mining & Manufacturing Co.), U. S. Patent 2,537,982 (Jan. 16, 1951).

55. "Chemigum, Tech. Book Facts," Chemical Div., Goodyear Tire & Rubber Co.

56. "Bentone 27," Bull. National Lead Co.

Styrene-Butadiene Rubber Adhesives

J. F. Anderson and H. P. Brown
Research Center
The B. F. Goodrich Company
Brecksville, Ohio

SBR (styrene-butadiene rubber) has relatively low polarity compared to other synthetic rubbers, and conforms generally to the theory that it should not be an effective adhesive copolymer. In the manufacture of synthetic tires, belting and many other items using SBR, it is necessary to add natural rubber or special resins. More resins are required in the above synthetics than in similar natural rubber products, in order to obtain sufficiently adhesive surfaces to hold the component plies or parts together prior to vulcanization.

Of the many elastomers used in the rubber industry, SBR is probably the least often employed in the manufacture of adhesives. The main reason it is used at all is its resistance to atmospheric conditions and heat.

Juve and Schoch,[1] in a study of "The Effect of Temperature on Air Aging of Rubber Vulcanizates," showed that upon exposure to elevated temperatures for prolonged periods, SBR actually improved in modulus and suffered less loss in tensile strength than did natural rubber. Although this work was conducted with tire-tread-type recipes, the relationship would probably be similar for other compounding recipes. This work thus confirms and substantiates the superior aging properties of SBR adhesives compared to natural rubber, for which it is frequently a replacement in adhesive applications.

HISTORY

For economic and other practical reasons, styrene-butadiene rubber was promoted by the United States Government and industry as a replacement for tree rubbers when World War II deprived this country of natural rubber resources. For many years industry operated styrene-butadiene polymerization plants for the Government. During this period, from 1941 to 1958, styrene-butadiene copolymer rubber was known as GR-S. The name was eventually changed to SBR, styrene-butadiene rubber, after the plants were sold by the Government to industry. Under the standardization program supported by The American Society for Testing Materials, uniformity of classifications for various types of SBR has been achieved.

In 1951, the Synthetic Rubber Section, Office of Rubber Reserve, Reconstruction Finance Corporation,[2] listed 31 GR-S copolymers made by fatty acid soap emulsification process, 25 made by rosin acid soap emulsification, 6 crosslinked copolymers made with fatty acid soap, and 28 masterbatches incorporating various types and brands of carbon black.

Included also in the published list were 19 non-staining varieties and 9 slightly staining types. Thirteen copolymers were listed as having low water absorption properties. This report also accounted for 27 copolymers whose monomer ratios varied from the standard GR-S (71-29 butadiene-styrene). There were 19 copolymers varying in viscosity from standard Mooney (ML-4'-212°F) of 50 for GR-S and 54 for GR-S-10 (made with Dresinate instead of fatty acid soap). Low temperature copolymers were assigned a Mooney value of 52. The special viscosities ranged from 25 to 115 in Mooney viscosity. Seventeen GR-S latexes were also listed in this report. It should be noted that some items occur in more than one classification, and some special experimental copolymers are not mentioned here.

The R. T. Vanderbilt Handbook for 1948 listed 55 GR-S solid and 25 GR-S latex copolymers.

None of these copolymers were made especially for adhesive purposes, though an effort was made to prepare special polymers for use in coating fabrics for garments, etc. By contrast, certain polychloroprenes and butadiene-acrylonitrile rubbers were prepared especially for making adhesives and cements, almost from the start. The chapter on carboxylic rubbers emphasizes the special adhesive properties of carboxylic butadiene-styrene copolymers.

Today there are about 200 available SBR copolymers. Some of the copolymers are prepared in such a manner that they are more suitable for adhesive formulations. Special SBR copolymers produced in crumb form* are particularly adaptable to the manufacture of adhesives and cements because of their solubility characteristics.

Generally speaking, the so-called "hot" rubbers, copolymerized at 120 to 130°F, are better suited for use as cements or adhesives than are the "cold" rubbers copolymerized at 40 to 43°F. SBR 1011 is particularly suited for use in making pressure-sensitive adhesive tapes.

The early discovery of some adaptability of SBR copolymers to adhesives manufacture is evident from at least one general patent issued in England in 1945.[13] The problems involved in the use of this general purpose synthetic rubber as an adhesive polymer may serve to explain why it took five or six years to arouse much patent activity.

COMMERCIAL PROCESSES AND APPLICATIONS OF SBR

Preparation and Properties of SBR

SBR is made by emulsion copolymerization of butadiene and styrene (usually in a 71-29 butadiene-styrene ratio). Monomers are emulsified in the presence of a suitable agent, e.g., fatty acid soap, rosin acid soap, etc. Copolymerization is effected by means of a peroxide or persulfate catalyst to a specific conversion and plasticity at prescribed temperatures.

Hot polymerization, 120 to 130°F, and low temperature polymerization, 40 to 43°F, have both been used to obtain selected physical properties.

* Such copolymers are SBR 1006 and 1012, both manufactured by Goodrich-Gulf Chemicals, Inc., Cleveland, Ohio.

Recently, cold rubber has grown in preference because of superior properties imparted to items other than adhesives. Control of molecular weight by addition of a modifier, such as dodecyl mercaptan, is essential and is especially critical in making soluble polymers. An inhibitor, such as hydroquinone, is used to stop conversion at a desirable point, and thus is also important in controlling processing properties. Stabilizers or antioxidants, such as phenyl-beta-naphthylamine or BLE (acetone-diphenylamine reaction product), are added in dispersed form. Unreacted monomers are removed in "blow-down" tanks by elevating the temperatures or by steam distillation. The emulsion, or latex, is then coagulated with salt-acid, glue-acid, alum, or similar agents. The coagulum is then washed and dried. Continuous polymerization techniques are usually employed.

It should be kept in mind that variations in polymerization procedures are apt to affect the behavior of polymers adapted to adhesives applications. The possible influence of residues of additives and foreign materials from the polymerization process, as well as dusting powders on adhesive properties, is worth consideration in selection and control of materials and methods used for producing adhesives. These potential variables probably account for the difference in behavior between supposedly identical butadiene-styrene copolymers produced by different manufacturers.

It is possible to polymerize SBR in solution.[10] Monomer ratios may be varied to yield selected properties, such as film toughness, solution viscosity, etc. Solution polymerization generally results in lower viscosity polymers, useful as adhesives and as plasticizers for other styrene-butadiene rubbers.

The styrene-butadiene rubbers are tougher and more difficult to process than natural rubber.[23] It is often necessary to soften styrene-butadiene rubbers by adding plasticizers[25] and mechanical working. This is sometimes a satisfactory substitute for the natural or developed tackiness of tree rubbers. SBR copolymers are characterized by low tensile and film strength in pure gum and vulcanizates. This is a deterrent to their acceptance as an adhesive base.

In spite of their negative qualities, the SBR copolymers have these advantages to qualify them for use in making adhesives.

1. Reinforced compounds retain their strength better than natural rubber equivalents.
2. SBR compounds possess good abrasion resistance. This is important in making coatings.
3. SBR compounds absorb less water than natural rubber compounds.

4. SBR compounds, vulcanizing and nonvulcanizing, possess atmospheric and heat-aging properties superior to those of natural rubber, and comparable with those of polychloroprene and nitrile rubbers.

5. One of the principal advantages of SBR copolymers is that they can be processed on rubber machinery and handled in practically the same manner as natural rubbers from warehousing through mill or Banbury mixing, and through the churning operation.

6. Economically, SBR is favorably competitive with other rubbers.

SELECTION AND COMPOUNDING OF SBR

Since industry took over the manufacture of SBR, standards have been established for the various numbered rubbers.

The manufacturers of the different types of polymers should be consulted for their help in selection of the SBR for a specific use. Some SBR copolymers are more easily processed than others, particularly in the manufacture of adhesives. Generally speaking, the hot rubbers are more useful than cold rubbers in making cements and adhesives.

Where milling facilities are not available, SBR 1006 having a Mooney viscosity of 50–58, and SBR 1012 having a Mooney viscosity of 95–115 (both ML-4'-212°F), are produced in crumb form, which is directly soluble in conventional rubber solvents.

SBR is compounded in much the same manner as natural rubber, except that tackifying resins are used more frequently and more liberally to compensate for the deficiency in SBR copolymers. Curing agents are generally the same as those used in compounding natural rubber adhesives.

As is true with natural rubbers, curing systems should be compatible with systems used in rubber adherents. Two part curing systems may be employed in applications where heat and pressure are not both available.

Typical Formulations and Applications of SBR Adhesives

Spreading and Laminating Adhesives. A typical spreading compound, using "Butyl" 8 for low temperature vulcanization, is one suggested in *The Vanderbilt News.*[3]

SBR	100
"Bondogen"*	2
"Reogen"*	5
"AgeRite Alba"*	1

Zinc oxide	5
Titanium dioxide	50
Clay	100
Sulfur	3
†"Butyl 8"*	6

† Added separately to the dissolved mass.
* Trade names of R. T. Vanderbilt Co. chemicals.

The compounded stock is run through a warm-up mill and dispersed in rubber solvent (e.g., lead-free naphtha, boiling range 100 to 285°F). Concentration depends on the type of equipment used for application. This type of compound is used for doubling, laminating and impregnating.

A moisture vapor resistant laminated film material is obtained when films of regenerated cellulose and of a rubber hydrochloride are bonded together by means of an adhesive[11] comprised of:

SBR	9–15
Coumarone-indene resin	37–54
Mixture of microcrystalline wax and paraffin wax	37–53
Compounded to a total of 100 parts	

The mass is dissolved in a solvent and applied to one of the surface adherends and doubled to the other.

Another example of a laminating adhesive is based on a partially cured copolymer of butadiene-styrene. In this patented adhesive formulation,[12] the following procedure is employed:

SBR	100
Sulfur and accelerator	1–20
Wood rosin, hardened wood rosin or coumarone-indene resin	150–200
Mix at 275–325°F	

The milling effects a partial cure. When the mass is sufficiently cooled, solvent is added to produce the desired consistency. This preparation possesses good adhesive qualities, combined with resilience and heat resistance.

A typical coating[24] based on SBR, including well selected tack producing resins, is illustrated by the following formulation:

Butadiene-styrene copolymer	100
Zinc oxide	5
Titanium dioxide	10
Yellow pigment	0.3
Oil-soluble heat-reactive phenol-aldehyde resin	12
Ester gum	40
Paraffin oil	25
Soft coumarone-indene resin	40
Heptane	300
Alcohol	10

Tire-Tread Splicing Cements. SBR is suitable for making tire-tread splicing cements, especially when used with oil extended SBR tread stocks. Patents issued to one manufacturer[4] cover, among other items, the use of high Mooney viscosity (ML-4'-212°F of ca. 150) SBR, suitable resins and preparation, as exemplified by the following recipe:

High Mooney SBR	100
Koresin*	40
Softener—"Sundex" 53	10
HAF black ("Philblack" O)	60
Zinc oxide	5
Sulfur	2.2
BLE	1.0
"Santocure"	1.2
Diphenyl guanidine	0.3

* Koresin (an acetylene-*t*-butyl phenol condensation product).

One hundred parts of the above recipe are dissolved in 900 parts of benzene or petroleum naphtha. Benzene is usually a more effective solvent, but in some places its use is prohibited because of toxicity.

A similar adhesive for building tire carcass plies substitutes SRF or FRF for HAF black. A smaller quantity of carbon black may be used.

Container Coatings and Adhesives. The uses of adhesives in container industries are many and varied. Laminating adhesives, such as have already been cited, are used to make foil laminates with films and/or papers for food packaging, etc.

Adhesive formulations for can end coating or sealing have been based on SBR copolymers because of their superior aging properties. Adhesives for this use may be either vulcanizing or nonvulcanizing compounds.

Pressure-Sensitive Adhesives. Many pressure-sensitive adhesives have been made with SBR copolymers as a base. The following example[5] is typical:

SBR (originally GR-S-85)	12
Rosin	10
Graphite	6
Lanolin	2
"AgeRite" Resin	0.5
Benzene	29.5

Another pressure-sensitive adhesive[6] is made from high Mooney viscosity SBR copolymer (ML-4'-212°F of *ca.* 145). In this case a 50 per cent benzene solution of a pentaerythritol ester of rosin is added to a 10 per cent benzene solution of SBR. High adhesive strength, compared to natural rubber, was obtained. Emulsion cements may also be prepared from similar high Mooney viscosity copolymers, by blending equal amounts of copolymer

and a resin emulsion of a methyl ester of hydrogenated rosin. An emulsion cement may also be prepared by using an aqueous ammonia dispersion of a pale rosin as the blending resin.

Joesting and Ethier prepared a pressure-sensitive tape adhesive[7] which remains firm and tacky at temperatures of 250 to 400°F without softening to a point of delamination or offsetting. This adhesive was prepared by causing a mixture of vulcanizable rubbery copolymer (butadiene-styrene) and a compatible heat advancing phenol-formaldehyde resin to completely react at an elevated temperature without concurrent mixing, then physically working and mixing the cured mass. In this application, the following recipe was cited:

SBR (warmed on mill)	100
Zinc oxide	20
Lecithin	2.5
"Pentalyn" H	10
"Bakelite" Resin BR 14634	5.0

"This mass was taken from the mill and cured in an autoclave for 3 hr at 30 lb of steam, cooled, and returned to the mill for about 6 min. The mass was then dispersed in 400 parts of heptane and 10 parts of alcohol." An additional 37 parts of "Pentalyn" H were blended and the adhesive solution coated on the desired backing.

Joesting[8] also prepared a pressure-sensitive and tacky tape adhesive consisting of a blend of 25 to 75 parts of natural rubber and corresponding amounts of butadiene-styrene copolymer (i.e., 75 to 25), and 40 to 90 parts of a thermoplastic terpene resin of zero acid number, whose melting point exceeded 80°C. For example:

Latex crepe rubber	50
SBR	50
Antioxidant (alkylated polyhydroxy phenol)	1
Resin—"Piccolyte" S-85	50
Heptane	600

This recipe illustrates the good compatibility of natural rubber with SBR as utilized quite frequently in the adhesive industry.

Pike and Bemmels[9] produced an improved pressure-sensitive tape adhesive by dissolving undercured butadiene-styrene copolymers. An example is as follows:

SBR (50 Mooney viscosity ML-4'-212°F)	100
Glyco ester gum	75
Zinc oxide	80
Sulfur	0.3
Diethyl thiuram disulfide	0.3
Zinc butyl dithiocarbamate	0.3

This was cured for one hour at 212°F, then dissolved in benzene or petroleum naphtha. This technique produces a tough, durable, yet permanently tacky tape adhesive.

Metal-to-Metal and Rubber-to-Metal Adhesives. SBR has been successfully employed in the manufacture of metal bonding adhesives, where the second adherend may be metal,[14] rubber[15] or other materials comprising structural components. A typical metal to metal adhesive disclosed in the reference patent[14] was prepared as follows.

Sixty to 90 parts of 1,3-butadiene and 10 to 40 parts of styrene were copolymerized at 20 to 100°C. The catalyst in this copolymerization was finely divided sodium. Reaction diluents were xylene, benzene, toluene, cyclohexane or the like. Films produced were used as metal to metal adhesives and cured from 0.5 to 5 min at 550 to 650°F.

An example given in the patent literature[15] for rubber to metal bonding points out the importance of the degree of flocculation of carbon black in the adhesive formulation. The variety of functional groups on the carbon black surfaces probably accounts for adhesion between the substrate and rubber. Acidic carbon blacks gave the strongest bonds. Adhesion is ascribed to covalent bonds or hydrogen bonds. The base recipe is:

SBR	100.0
Carbon black	Variable
Zinc oxide	3.2
Sulfur	8.0
Accelerator (2,2'-benzothiazyl disulfide)	3.2
Antioxidant (phenyl-β-naphthylamine)	3.2
Plasticizer (dibutyl phthalate)	32.0
Solvent (xylene)	1000.0

The effect of mixing or degree of flocculation is illustrated by data in the following tabulation of bond strengths in tension between a natural rubber compound and steel, treated or primed, as indicated.

Miscellaneous Applications of Solvent-Base SBR Adhesives. Other applications of SBR adhesives include bonding of wood[16] by means of hot-setting adhesives, joining vinylidene-chloride polymer to cork or paper,[17] etc.

Latexes and Dispersions of SBR as Adhesives. As is the case with other rubbers, latexes and dispersions of SBR are often preferred for use as adhesives when toxicity, flammability or cost prohibits the use of organic solvents.

A fabric-to-metal[5] adhesive has been formulated as follows:

SBR latex (23–25 per cent total solids)	15.0
Asphalt	44.3
Rosin soap	1.4
Methyl cellulose	0.1
Carbon black	6.0
Water	33.2

Aqueous dispersions are prepared by methods usually employed in making natural rubber dispersions. Special equipment, manufactured for this purpose, is required. Dispersion machines of the original Werner-Pfleiderer type are available in a range of sizes from a number of American manufacturers, including the Struthers-Wells Company, Baker-Perkins Company, The J. H. Day Company, and others. SBR dispersion was mentioned in the patent literature as early as 1946.[18]

A technique and type of recipe used in making latex adhesive dispersions is illustrated by the following formulation:

Zinc oxide	3.00
Sulfur	2.00

TABLE 1. ADHESION RESULTS WITH SBR-CHANNEL BLACK CEMENTS.[a]

		Primer Films		
	On Brass Plate	On Chlorinated Rubber[b]	On Chlorinated Polyisoprene[b]	On Butadiene Methacrylic Acid Copolymers[c]
Ball-milled carbon black cement	1225 psi	1180 psi	1220 psi	1350 psi
Dough-mixed carbon black cement	950	645	700	—
Without carbon black cement	850	320	290	935

[a] All evaluations are against a standard natural rubber tread stock of 52 hardness. Cure 30 min at 298°F.

[b] 60 per cent chlorine in polymer which is used as primer film.

[c] 22 per cent methacrylic acid. The copolymerization of dienes with unsaturated acids and use of resulting copolymers as adhesives for rubber-to-metal are described in other publications, including the chapter on "Carboxylic Elastomers as Adhesives." Uncured carboxylic polybutadiene is used here as primer.

"AgeRite White"*	1.00
Butyl zimate	2.00
"Darvan" No. 1*	0.32
Casein	0.24
Caustic soda	0.10
Water	7.34

* R. T. Vanderbilt Co.

The above dispersion is prepared separately and then added to SBR latex. This recipe (in pounds) is added to 100 lb of latex containing approximately 25 per cent solids. Such a formulation is a general-purpose adhesive.

Similarly, a pressure-sensitive or laminating adhesive may be prepared by adding the following recipe (in lb) to 100 lb of SBR latex:

Zinc oxide	5.00
Sulfur	4.00
"AgeRite White"	1.00
"Darvan" No. 1	0.40
Casein	0.30
Caustic soda	0.10
Water	9.20

SBR latexes are used extensively as adhesives for bonding fibrous materials.[19] Resorcinol-formaldehyde resins are compounded with SBR latexes, similar to the way they are compounded with natural rubber latex, for bonding rubber to tire cords.

SBR latexes are useful in preparing low-cost carpet backing, and in making back-sizing for upholstery fabrics for furniture and automobiles.

Vulcanizing agents, predispersed, may be added to SBR latexes, rendering them more resistant to heat and oxidation. Since they contain no proteinaceous material, they are less apt to develop unpleasant odors often experienced with natural rubber latex.

Generally speaking, the physical properties, wet strength, dry film strength, etc., are low in SBR latexes when compared to natural rubber counterparts.

Sometimes the real advantage in using latex base adhesives lies in the fact that high percentage total solids may be achieved by one means[21] or another. This affords heavy and oftentimes strong films for bonding and coating purposes.

The relatively low cost of monomers and of polymerization processes make SBR copolymers attractive for many solvent and water based adhesive applications.

Although SBR is lacking in tack and strength compared to natural rubber, proper compounding makes it a fair substitute for rubber adhesives. Where aging properties are of paramount importance, it is an established material in the cement field. Thus for can sealing cements, coatings, and sealants, SBR is a preferred material.[22]

BRAND NAMES AND SUPPLIERS OF SBR

Following is a list of brand names and manufacturers of SBR copolymers. Suppliers of these materials are also listed in the Rubber Red Book. Each supplier furnishes several types of SBR.

"Ameripol." Goodrich-Gulf Chemicals, Inc., East Ohio Bldg., 1717 E. 9th St., Cleveland, Ohio.

"ASRC" Polymers. American Synthetic Rubber Corp., P. O. Box 360, Louisville, Ky.

"Baytown" Masterbatches. United Rubber & Chemical Co., Baytown, Tex.

"Carbomix" "Copo" Polymers. Copolymer Rubber & Chemical Corp., P. O. Box 2591, Baton Rouge 1, La.

"Darex" Latices. Dewey & Almy Chemical Div., W. R. Grace & Co., 62 Whittemore Ave., Cambridge 40, Mass.

"FR-S." Firestone Synthetic Rubber & Latex Company, Div. of Firestone Tire & Rubber Co., Akron, Ohio.

"Gentro." Chemical Div., General Tire & Rubber Co., Akron 9, Ohio.

"Hycar" 2001 (OS-10). B. F. Goodrich Chemical Co., 3135 Euclid Ave., Cleveland 15, Ohio.

"Naugapol." Naugatuck Chemical Div., U. S. Rubber Co., Naugatuck, Conn.

"Naugatex." Naugatuck Chemical Div., U. S. Rubber Co., Naugatuck, Conn.

"Philprene." Rubber Chemicals Div., Phillips Chemical Co., 318 Water St., Akron 8, Ohio.

"Plioflex." Chemical Div., Goodyear Tire & Rubber Co., Akron 16, Ohio.

"Pliolite" Rubber Latices. Chemical Div., Goodyear Tire & Rubber Co., Akron 16, Ohio.

"Polyco." Borden Chemical Co., 350 Madison Ave., New York 17, N. Y.

"Polysar Kryflex" 200, "S-X371"; "SS-250" and "Kryflex" 252. Polymer Corp., Ltd., Sarnia, Ontario, Canada.

"Polysar" Latices. Polymer Corp., Ltd., Sarnia, Ontario, Canada.

"Polysar" S and S-630. Polymer Corp., Ltd., Sarnia, Ontario, Canada.

"S-Polymers." Synthetic Rubber Div., Shell Chemical Corp., P. O. Box 216, Torrance, Calif.

"Synpol." Texas-U. S. Chemical Co., P. O. Box 1597, Port Neches, Tex.

References

1. Juve, A. E., and Schoch, M. G., Jr., ASTM Bull. No. 195, Jan. 1954.
2. "Classified List of Currently Produced GR-S Polymers and Latices," Synthetic Rubber Section, Office of Rubber Reserve, R.F.C., July 30, 1951.
3. *Vanderbilt News*, Sept.–Oct. 1958.

4. General Tire & Rubber Co., Italian Patent 492,409 (Mar. 26, 1954).
5. Bennett, H., "Chemical Formulary," Vol. X, New York, Chemical Publishing Co.
6. Hulse, G. E. (to Hercules Powder Co.), U.S. Patent 2,649,425 (Aug. 18, 1953).
7. Joesting, E. O., and Ethier, D. O. (to Minnesota Mining & Manufacturing Co.), U.S. Patent 2,708,192 (May 10, 1955).
8. Joesting, E. O. (to Minnesota Mining & Manufacturing Co.), U.S. Patent 2,567,671 (Sept. 11, 1951).
9. Pike, C. O., and Bemmels, C. W. (to Industrial Tape Corp.), U.S. Patent 2,576,968 (Dec. 4, 1951).
10. Crouch, W. W. (to Phillips Petroleum Co.), U.S. Patent 2,577,677 (Dec. 4, 1951).
11. Carson, C. M. (to Wingfoot Corp.), U.S. Patent 2,541,689 (Feb. 13, 1951).
12. Brams, S. L. (to General Motors Corp.), U.S. Patent 2,643,235 (June 23, 1953).
13. Puddefoot, L. E., and Swire, W. H. (to B. B. Chemical Co., Ltd.), British Patent 567,096 (Jan. 29, 1945).
14. Nelson, J. F., McKay, J. F., Jr., Welch, L. M., and Koenecke, D. F. (to Standard Oil Development Co.), U.S. Patent 2,701,780 (Feb. 8, 1955).
15. Sheehan, G. M., Kraus, G., and Conciatori, A. B., *Ind. Eng. Chem.,* **44,** 580–2 (1952).
16. Cottle, D. F., Young, D. W., and Franklin, H. J. (to Esso Research & Engineering Co.), U.S. Patent 2,758,953 (Aug. 14, 1956).
17. Nairkas, V. A. (to Armstrong Cork Co.), U.S. Patent 2,601,318 (June 24, 1952).
18. Wingfoot Corp., British Patent 576,665 (Apr. 15, 1946).
19. "Vanderbilt Handbook," pp. 40–41, New York, R. T. Vanderbilt Co., Inc., 1954.
20. 1959 Rubber Red Book, 12th Ed., pp. 566, 575, New York, Palmerton Publishing Co.
21. Fryling, C. F. (to Phillips Petroleum Co.), U.S. Patent 2,739,954 (Mar. 27, 1956).
22. Crawford, R. A., "Synthetic Rubber," Chapter 14, New York, John Wiley & Sons, Inc., 1954.
23. "The Vanderbilt Rubber Handbook," p. 37, New York, R. T. Vanderbilt Co., 1948.
24. Oace, R. J., Snell, R. B., Eastwold, E. E. (to Minnesota Mining & Manufacturing Co.), U.S. Patent 2,559,990 (July 10, 1951).
25. "Vanderbilt Handbook," 272, New York, R. T. Vanderbilt Co., Inc., 1958.

— 19 —

Carboxylic Elastomers as Adhesives

H. P. Brown and J. F. Anderson

Research Center
The B. F. Goodrich Company
Brecksville, Ohio

Carboxylic elastomers are polymers containing carboxyl groups and possessing a recognizable degree of elasticity. For use as adhesives, the degree of elasticity may vary widely, from truly rubbery to virtually resinous, depending on the nature of the application for which they are made. The inclusion of carboxyl groups in elastomer molecules increases interchain and intrachain forces, thereby imparting increased strength to the polymer at the expense of elasticity.

In general, the inclusion of increasing numbers of carboxyl groups in an elastomer results in elevation of the elasticity range, enhancement of film-forming tendencies, increased hardness and abrasion resistance, and improved adhesion to many surfaces, especially those capable of reaction with carboxyl groups. These include many metal surfaces. The carboxyl groups may be used as centers for chemical reaction to effect inter- and intrachain crosslinkages of the elastomer as well as linkages to the fillers, pigments and adherends. The carboxyl groups, and salts thereof, can confer the same adhesion-enhancing effects on an elastomer that are often achieved by fillers, pigments or resins. Thus, carboxylic elastomers frequently are effective adhesives with a minimum of additives, and often with no additives. The ability of polymers to penetrate cellulosic materials is increased by the presence of carboxyl groups, e.g., adhesion to cellulose, rayon, cellophane and similar materials is enhanced by the incorporation of carboxyl groups into elastomers.

HISTORY

Preparation of a carboxylic elastomer was first reported in a French patent[1] published in June, 1933. Acrylic acid was copolymerized with butadiene to give an elastomeric product. Use of the polymer as an adhesive was not suggested.

Anhydride rubbers, prepared by the treatment of rubber and other unsaturated elastomers with maleic anhydride, are readily converted by moisture and other hydrolyzing agents into carboxylic elastomers. The anhydride rubbers were described by Bacon, Farmer[2,3,4] and others beginning in 1938, and by Compagnon, LeBras and co-workers[5,6,7] starting in 1941. Use of an anhydride rubber prepared from natural rubber as an adhesive agent[8] for rubber to artificial silk was mentioned in 1944.

A patent[9] issued in 1952 described the use of copolymers of higher acrylate or methacrylate esters with acrylic acid or methacrylic acid in the preparation of improved pressure-sensitive tapes and liners for adherent rubber surfaces. The carboxyl content of these copolymers was so high, they probably should be regarded as plasticized polyacrylic acids rather than carboxylic elastomers.

The preparation of copolymers of butadiene and of isoprene with methacrylic acid and with acrylic acid, described by Frank, Kraus and Haefner[10,11] in 1952, for use in rubber-to-metal bonding, is probably the first preparation of carboxylic elastomers made specifically for use as adhesives. They indicated that their consideration of the carboxyl group as a means of enhancing adhesion was stimulated by the observations of Doolittle and Powell[12] in 1944. These included the effectiveness of small proportions of maleic anhydride (0.1 to 1 per cent), when copolymerized into copolymers of vinyl chloride with vinyl acetate, in improving the adhesion of such films to metal surfaces. McLaren has described the increase of adhesion with increasing carboxyl content of vinylite copolymers to unmodified cellulose.[33]

The enhancement of the adhesive properties of several elastomers by the incorporation of carboxyl groups has subsequently been mentioned several times in the literature. Included have been carboxylic analogs of butadiene-styrene copolymers, butadiene-acrylonitrile copolymers, butadiene-methacrylonitrile copolymers, butadiene-acrylate ester copolymers, polychloroprene, butadiene-vinylidene chloride copolymers, and the polyacrylates.[13, 14] The potentials of such materials as adhesives are just beginning to be utilized.

COMMERCIAL PROCESSES

Preparation and Properties of Carboxylic Elastomers

Carboxylic elastomers have been prepared principally by the copolymerization of olefins and diolefins with acrylic acid-type monomers. Many carboxylic monomers have been employed. References and details concerning such preparations are available in the literature and have been summarized in a review[13] by Brown. Commonly, the carboxylic elastomers employed as adhesives contain between 0.1 and 25 per cent of the carboxylic comonomers, although polymers containing higher levels of carboxylic comonomers have occasionally been used. Factors influencing the adhesive properties of the carboxylic elastomers are method of polymerization, molecular weight, molecular weight distribution, carboxyl level, distribution of the carboxyl groups, source of the carboxyl groups, the degree of neutralization or sequestering of the carboxyl groups, and the nature of the elastomer.

The adhesive characteristics of an elastomer are recognizably altered by the inclusion of as little as 0.01 equivalent of carboxyl per hundred grams of rubber (ephr) although larger amounts, even in excess of 0.1 ephr, are often preferable. The optimum carboxyl content, molecular weight and the particular elastomeric polymer selected for use as an adhesive depend on the nature of the surfaces to be adhered and the requirements of the adhesive bond.

Carboxylic elastomers have also been prepared[13] by the addition of a carboxyl-bearing molecule such as thioglycollic acid, maleic anhydride, or acrylic acid to rubber in solvent, on the mill or in latex. The preparation of a carboxylic polymer from a butadiene-acrylonitrile copolymer in an internal- or Banbury-mixer has been mentioned in the adhesives patent[22] literature. The carboxylation of vulcanized natural rubber and of butadiene-styrene copolymers, including reclaimed stocks of these elastomers, by treatment with maleic anhydride in an extruder plasticator[24] has been described. Elastomeric copolymers containing groups convertible to carboxylic groups have been used[15, 25] to prepare carboxylic elastomers. Adducts of fumaric and itaconic esters[26] to unsaturated polymers such as liquid polybutadiene and copolymers of butadiene subsequently hydrolyzed to carboxylic elastomers have also been described as adhesives.

The carboxylic elastomers may be employed as adhesives in solutions of suitable solvents, as latexes, or, as aqueous solutions or dispersions in alkaline or ammoniacal media when the carboxyl content and molecular weight are suitably selected.

The carboxylic polyacrylates are effective laminating adhesives[14] for both flexible and rigid surfaces. The particular carboxylic acrylate used for a given laminating application is determined by the characteristics of the surfaces to be adhered, whether adhesive or cohesive bond failure is desired, the bond strength required of the adhesive, and many other factors desired. These may include stiffness, friability, extensibility, clarity, cold flow, moisture resistance, solvent or chemical resistance, heat and light insensitivity, radiation resistance, compatibility with resins and other polymeric materials or pigments, and vulcanizability. The carboxylic polyacrylates may be varied to meet the adhesive requirements of a specific application by

1. carboxylic content,
2. the acrylate or acrylates constituting the polymer chain,
3. molecular weight,
4. molecular weight distribution,
5. state of crosslinkage,
6. degree of inter- and intrachain reactivity induced by the inclusion of other functional groups in addition to carboxyl,
7. degree of solubility or dispersibility in solvents of application, and
8. by copolymerization or superimposed polymerization.

While a given carboxylic elastomer may approximate the requirements of many applications and permit a rather wide variety of uses, the maximum performance for a given pair of surfaces to be adhered is best achieved by tailor-making the polymer for the selected application. Some degrees of adaptation can be achieved by the incorporation of foreign polymers and reagents such as resins, pigments, elastomers, thickening agents, crosslinking reagents, and the like.

For the preparation of adhesive cements the solubility criteria for the carboxylic elastomers can be predicted from those of analogous noncarboxylic elastomers. Literature[30, 32] on the solubility and ease of solution of raw polar elastomers in various solvents, allowing for the influence of the carboxyl level, suggests the solvents most suitable for given carboxylic elastomers. As the carboxyl content increases in a given elastomer type, solubility in hydrocarbon solvents decreases, and solubility in alcohols, amines, pyridines, and similar solvents increases. Milling procedures are similar to those for analogous noncarboxylic elastomers, except that carboxyl groups tend to make the milling somewhat more difficult. In some instances, carboxylic elastomers in solvent for adhesive application is advantageous. Such a procedure avoids emulsifiers and certain other additives of emulsifier polymerization, as well as the necessity of milling. However, it has the disadvantage of yielding lower molecular weight materials. For carboxylic butadiene-acrylonitrile elastomers, methylethyl ketone, nitroparaffins and chlorinated hydrocarbons are useful cement media. For the carboxylic polyacrylates, acetone, methylethyl ketone, methyl isobutyl ketone, and toluene are preferred. For carboxylic polybutadiene or copolymers of butadiene, benzene, toluene, or methylethyl ketone are usually employed.

Carboxylic Elastomers as Metal-to-Rubber Adhesives

From studies of copolymers of butadiene with methacrylic acid, Frank and co-workers[10, 11] concluded that, in order to achieve maximum adhesion of rubber to steel, the copolymer should be of as high a molecular weight as possible and still remain soluble in the solvents of application. It should also possess sufficient diene groups for vulcanization to rubber, and a sufficient number of carboxyl groups to secure high adhesion to steel. They concluded that the optimum level of methacrylic acid was 15 to 24 per cent. Their data were based on the adhesion to steel of a diphenyl guanidine accelerated natural rubber compound containing 38 per cent zinc oxide and having a 52 Shore A hardness. For their tests, they used a single coat of unmodified, unformulated butadiene-methacrylic acid copolymer cement applied to grit-blasted steel inserts and vulcanized 30 min at 298°F against the rubber stock, following ASTM D429-39 procedures. Copolymers of acrylic acid and butadiene or isoprene were less effective as adhesives. Methacrylic acid-isoprene copolymers were less effective than the analogous butadiene

copolymers. A butadiene-methacrylic acid copolymer of 70 per cent conversion containing 22 to 24 per cent methacrylic acid, when used with cumene hydroperoxide accelerators, was reported to give adhesion of rubber-to-steel having shear strengths of approximately 1100 psi.

The high zinc oxide loading of the natural rubber stock was favorable to adhesion of the carboxylic polybutadiene. In our experience with steel-to-rubber bonding by means of a carboxylic elastomer cement, best results are obtained when the rubber is rather heavily loaded with zinc oxide (over 20 per cent). Perhaps adhesion depends on reaction of the carboxylic groups of the cement with the zinc oxide which may itself be bound by the rubber to be adhered. The presence of carboxyl groups in the rubber molecule favors even tighter binding.

In the bonding of rubber to metal with unsaturated carboxylic elastomers in the presence of vulcanizing or other agents not reactive with carboxyl groups, the bond to rubber is accomplished by crosslinkages dependent on the unsaturation, while the bond to the metal arises from interaction of polar groups with the metal. This requires fairly simultaneous cures of the cement, the rubber stock and the metal-to-cement interface. When curing agents for the carboxyl groups are also present, the several vulcanizing mechanisms undoubtedly proceed simultaneously and are competitive.

We have employed carboxylic polybutadienes and carboxylic butadiene-styrene copolymers, both in latex formulations and in solvent cements for the adhesion of rubber-to-steel. The presence of carboxyl groups enhances the adhesion of the rubber to the steel.[14]

Carboxylic polystyrene resins[18] have been used in SBR cements to promote the adhesion of rubber to steel. This is a carboxylation of SBR by mechanical admixture. The adhesion obtained resembles the results obtained by using carboxylic SBR polymers.

Cements prepared from carboxylic butadiene-acrylonitrile copolymers blended with phenolic resins,[16, 17] like the analogous cements prepared with noncarboxylic butadiene-acrylonitrile copolymers, are adhesive agents for steel to rubber. Employed without curative agents, the carboxylic copolymers give better steel-to-rubber adhesion than the analogous noncarboxylic copolymers (Table 1). The carboxylic copolymer cements show greater bond strength as well as a desired cohesive failure within the rubber, whereas the analogous noncarboxylic copolymers show failure at the steel surface. Thus carboxyl groups enhance the adhesion of the rubber to the metal surface and improve

TABLE 1. ADHESION OF RUBBER TO STEEL WITH CARBOXYLIC AND NONCARBOXYLIC RUBBER AND PHENOLIC RESIN.[a]

Polymer	Carboxylic[b]	Carboxylic[b]	Non-Carboxylic[c]
Polymer (parts)	6	6	6
Phenolic resin[d]	24	24	24
Coumarone-indene resin[e]	0	1.5	1.5
Methylethyl ketone	70	68.5	68.5
Cement Viscosity[f] (Cps)			
Original		70	130
Shelf-aged 1 wk		60	120
2 wk		60	120
6 wk		60	120
3 months		100	140
Adhesion—Steel to "Hycar" * 1042*[g]			
Stripping force (lb/in.)[h]	69	90	40
Type of adhesion failure	stock	stock	at steel

[a] Data from Ref. 19.
[b] "Hycar" 1072, a carboxylic polymer.
[c] "Hycar" 1042, a noncarboxylic "Hycar" 1072.
[d] "Durez" 12687.
[e] "Cumar" P-10.
[f] Brookfield.
[g] Canvas backing used. Vulcanizate recipe was:

"Hycar" 1042	100
NBS zinc oxide	5
Sulfur	1.5
NBS stearic acid	1.0
SRF black	65.0
TMTM	0.4
"Good-rite" * GP261	15.0

[h] In this test "Plastilock" 604 showed 70 lb/in. and stock failure. Rate of peel was 2 in./min.
* Trade name product B. F. Goodrich Chemical Co.

the cohesive strength of the bonding agent. Inclusion of carboxyl groups in butadiene-acrylonitrile copolymers widens their range of compatibility with phenolic resins and increases the strength and hardness of the resultant adhesive.

A commercially available carboxylic butadiene-acrylonitrile copolymer is "Hycar"* 1072. This is a medium-high acrylonitrile copolymer comparable in nitrile content to "Hycar" 1042, but including carboxylic groups attached to the polymer chain. "Hycar" 1432 is a crumb-type directly soluble copolymer of comparable nitrile content to

* Registered trade name.

"Hycar" 1042. Noncuring cements of "Hycar" 1072 have excellent viscosity stability and may be stored for long periods of time comparable to those for cements made from the noncarboxylic analogue polymers[17] (Table 2). A type of "Hycar" 1072 made specifically for cement applications readily dissolves without milling in methylethyl ketone to give excellent clear cements of 40 per cent or more total solids.

Carboxylic Elastomers as Metal-to-Metal Adhesives

Carboxylic butadiene-acrylonitrile copolymers have been employed in phenolic-resin-blend cements as metal-to-metal adhesives. In both curing and noncuring cement systems, comparable recipes[17] have given similar bonding of steel-to-steel by carboxylic and noncarboxylic polymers. More rapid bonding can be achieved with carboxylic polymers. Sulfur vulcanization is not required with carboxylic polymers (Table 3).

Curative systems which include di- and polyvalent metal compounds such as zinc oxide yield cements with carboxylic polymers which have poor shelf stability. The stability may be improved by the inclusion of ammonia or of an amine which volatizes from the cement when applied [13] (Table 4). The improved stability is obtained at some sacrifice of color and texture of the cement and with considerably higher cement viscosities. Ammonium hydroxide is similarly effective as a stabilizing agent in cements containing phenolic resins[17] (Table 5).

The use of maleic anhydride elastomer adducts in adhesives for metals has been mentioned[24, 28] in the literature.

The inclusion of carboxyl groups in polyethyl acrylate improves the adhesion to steel. Thus, for a series of comparable polyethyl acrylates the inclusion of 4, 8 and 12 parts of acrylic acid increased the bond strength in tension between two steel block surfaces from 100 to 300 psi, 600 and 900 psi, respectively.[14] These values were obtained with uncompounded polymers. Larger amounts of carboxyl and reinforcing resins may be used to achieve greater bond strengths.

Terpolymers of ethyl acrylate, acrylonitrile and acrylic acid have been cited as thermosetting adhesives[27] for "Duralumin." The thermosetting has been ascribed to the formation of

$$-CO-NH-CO-$$

crosslinks. Curing cycles of 10 min at 180°F under 1000 psi were effective.

TABLE 2. EFFECT OF AGING ON "HYCAR" 1072 AND RELATED CEMENTS.

Polymer-"Hycar"	1072[c]	1432[e]	1072[c]	1042[d]
Polymer (parts)	100	100	6.0	6.0
Methylethyl ketone	400	400	68.5	68.5
Phenolic resin[a]	—	—	24.0	24.0
Coumarone-indene resin[b]	—	—	1.5	1.5
Original Properties				
Brookfield viscosity (cps)	2,000	3,100	70	130
Color	Yellow	Yellow	Dark brown	Dark brown
Shelf-aged 2 Wk				
Brookfield viscosity (cps)	2,200	3,360	60	120
Color change	None	None	None	None
Shelf-aged 3 Wk				
Brookfield viscosity (cps)	2,300	3,500	100	140
Color change	None	Slight	None	None

[a] "Durez" 12687.
[b] "Cumar" P-10.
[c] "Hycar" 1072, a medium high carboxylic butadiene-acrylonitrile copolymer.
[d] "Hycar" 1042, a noncarboxylic "Hycar" 1072.
[e] "Hycar" 1432, crumb type, directly soluble type "Hycar" 1042.

TABLE 3. STEEL-TO-STEEL ADHESION WITH "HYCAR" AND PHENOLIC RESIN BLEND CEMENTS.

Polymer-"Hycar"	1072[e]	1042[f]	1072[e]	1042[f]
Polymer (parts)	6	6	20	20
Methylethyl ketone	68.5	68.5	208.4[a]	207.7[a]
Phenolic resin[b]	24.0	24.0	80.0	80.0
Coumarone-indene resin[c]	1.5	1.5	2.0	2.0
Zinc oxide	—	—	2.0	1.0
Stearic acid	—	—	0.2	0.2
Sulfur[d]	—	—	—	0.3
Benzothiazyl disulfide	—	—	—	0.35
Steel-to-Steel Adhesion				
(One-inch square overlap)				
Shearing force (lb)	930	910	1040	1000
Type failure	Cohesive	Cohesive	{ ½ Cohesive { ½ Adhesive	Cohesive

[a] Milled compound prepared as 30 per cent solution.
[b] "Durez" 12687.
[c] "Cumar" P-10.
[d] "Spider."
[e] "Hycar" 1072, a medium-high carboxylic butadiene-acrylonitrile copolymer.
[f] "Hycar" 1042, a noncarboxylic "Hycar" 1072.

Carboxylic Elastomers as Bonding Agents for Non-Metallic Surfaces

Carboxylic elastomers adhere well to glass surfaces and may be used to coat or laminate glass surfaces. They adhere[14] so well that sampling of polymerization preparations of carboxylic elastomers with glass syringes is difficult due to bonding of the moving glass parts. Carboxylic polyacrylates have refractive indices so nearly identical with glass that the presence of such bonding agents between glass surfaces causes almost no deviation of traversing light beams.

Dispersions of copolymers of butadiene with acrylic acid or methacrylic acid in aqueous potassium hydroxide have been mentioned in the patent

TABLE 4. STABILIZATION OF AIR-CURING CARBOXYLIC BUTADIENE-ACRYLONITRILE CEMENTS.[a]

Carboxylic copolymer[b]	20	20	20
Methylethyl ketone	80	80	80
Zinc oxide	2	2	2
Ammonium hydroxide (28%)	4	2	0
Cement Viscosity[c] (cps)			
Original	13,300	26,800	6,500
Shelf-aged 1 wk	13,900	34,100	28,700
2 wk	13,700	43,000	>100,000
3 wk	13,600	63,000	gelled
16 wk	13,400	>100,000	
Strength of cast Film			
Age of cement	24 wk	New	New
Tensile (psi)	3860	3700	1370

[a] Data from Ref. 14, by the authors.

[b] Carboxylic butadiene acrylonitrile copolymer containing 0.075 equivalents of carboxyl per hundred grams of polymer.

[c] Brookfield viscosity.

literature[19] as a dip for adhering rayon tire cord to rubber. An "exceptionally strong rubber-to-fabric bond" was claimed, but no data were quoted.

Carboxyl groups can improve the adhesion of rubber stocks to rayon cords.[14] The effect is most evident when carboxyl groups are present in the adhesive, the tie cement and the cover stocks. The adhesive may be applied as latex, aqueous dispersion or cement. Illustrative data based on applications of carboxylic butadiene-acrylonitrile copolymers from latex are given in Table 6. Such adhesives should be useful in hose, belting and other applications requiring oil resistance. Similar observations have been made with carboxylic

TABLE 5. STABILIZATION OF AIR-CURING CARBOXYLIC BUTADIENE-ACRYLONITRILE AND PHENOLIC RESIN-BLEND CEMENTS.

"Hycar" 1072	100
Phenolic resin[a]	30
Zinc oxide	8
Ammonium hydroxide[b]	20
Methylethyl ketone	552
Cement Viscosity[c] (cps)	
Original	2,800
Shelf-aged 1 wk	2,600
2 wk	5,200
3 wk	5,300
4 wk	5,300

[a] "Bakelite" CKR-1634.

[b] 28% concentration.

[c] Brookfield LVF.

butadiene-styrene copolymers applied as latex adhesives (Table 7). Such adhesives may find use in carcass and tire fabrication and similar applications. The carboxyl groups appear to improve interpenetration of the latex adhesive, tie cement, and cover-stock polymers. Probably zinc oxide in the cover stock and tie cement forms bonds between carboxylic groups in the latex adhesive, tie cement and cover stock. Presumably, the carboxyl groups also would form bonds with hydrogen and hydroxyl groups of the rayon cord. Carboxylic copolymer cements are used most effectively with tie stocks based on carboxylic rubbers.

The bonding of fibers of paper, fabric or similar materials by rubber latexes or cements[21] may be enhanced by the inclusion of carboxyl groups[20] in the adhesive or binder copolymer molecules. For example, in the bonding of semi-bleached kraft crepe paper with polyethyl acrylate latex, the inclusion of 0.045 ephr of carboxyl gave approximately a 50 per cent further improvement in internal bond strength. Similarly, while a butadiene-acrylonitrile copolymer improved the internal bond strength of semi-bleached kraft crepe paper, a latex of a copolymer having the same butadiene content but including 0.09 ephr of carboxyl, showed a 15 per cent or more additional improvement in the internal bond strength. The beneficial action of the carboxyl group is probably due to improvement in copolymer-adhesive penetration and subsequently greater hydrogen bonding with the paper cellulose (Table 8).

Maleic anhydride rubbers have been cited as adhesive agents[29] for artificial silk.

TABLE 6. INFLUENCE OF CARBOXYL LEVEL (IN BUTADIENE-ACRYLONITRILE COPOLYMERS) ON ADHESION OF RUBBER TO RAYON.[a]

RFL (COOH ephr)	Tie Cement	Cover Stock	H-Test (lb)	Separation
0.026[b]	VP	SBR	26	From RF
0.075	VP	SBR	27	From RF
0.103	VP	SBR	29	From RF
0.157	VP	SBR	27	From RF
0.026	VP	0.075[b]	5	From RF
0.075	VP	0.075	11	From RF
0.103	VP	0.075	10	From RF
0.157	VP	0.075	12	From RF
0.026	0.103[c]	0.075	37	From RF
0.075	0.103	0.075	42	From RF
0.103	0.103	0.075	55	From RF
0.157	0.103	0.075	54	From RF
0.24[d]	0.0[c]	0.0	21	From RF
0.24	0.0	0.0		
0.24	0.15	0.025	26	From tie
0.24	0.15	0.075	47	From tie
0.24	0.075	0.075	88	From tie
0.24	0.103	0.075	110	Broke cord

RF = resorcinol-formaldehyde rubber layer. VP = vinyl pyridine-styrene-butadiene rubber.
RFL = resorcinol-formaldehyde latex. SBR = butadiene-styrene rubber.

[a] From Ref. 14.

[b] Butadiene-acrylonitrile-methacrylic acid copolymers derived by replacement of acrylonitrile by methacrylic acid in the butadiene-acrylonitrile 67-33 system. Carboxyl content expressed in chemical equivalents per hundred grams of rubber. Copolymers applied from resorcinol-formaldehyde latex (RFL) systems.

[c] A butadiene-acrylonitrile 55-45 charged ratio system in which acrylonitrile has been replaced by methacrylic acid.

[d] A butadiene-acrylonitrile 55-45 type polymer wherein methacrylic acid has been substituted for butadiene.

Two pieces of fabric, or unwoven fibers, may be adhered with carboxylic latexes such as "Hycar" 1571. Bond strength may be enhanced when necessary by cure with a crosslinking agent such as sodium aluminate.

A carboxylic butadiene-acrylonitrile copolymer (e.g., "Hycar" 1072) employed as a 30 per cent cement in methylethyl ketone with zinc oxide (10 phr) and stearic acid (5 phr) has been used to bond nylon to plastisol constructions.[16] Good bonds[20] between nylon and rubber have also been obtained with this cement.

Carboxylic Elastomers as Permanently Tacky Laminating Adhesives for Flexible Surfaces

Metal Foil-to-Polymeric Film Laminates. The influence of carboxylic groups on the laminating power of permanently tacky adhesive copolymers used in nonload bearing applications is well illustrated by the performance of polyacrylates[14] in the lamination of "Mylar"* films to aluminum foils, each 1 mil thick.

* Registered trade mark.

Noncarboxylic polyacrylate polymers are weak laminating adhesives for "Mylar" to aluminum bonding. The adhesion varies with the polyacrylate used. In a series of comparable poly-n-alkyl acrylates, ranging from polymethyl through polytridecyl acrylate, applied from methylethyl ketone cements, the strongest bond (180° peel strength) between "Mylar" and aluminum was obtained with polyethyl acrylate. A value of 80 oz/in. for a separation rate of 12 in./min. was typical for polyethyl acrylate (Fig. 1). Dilute solution viscosity data (DSV), in deciliters per gram, and other polymer data are also included. Carboxyl contents are expressed as equivalents per 100 of rubber (ephr).

The introduction of carboxylic groups into a given poly-n-alkyl acrylate improves or develops laminating adhesive properties[14] for the "Mylar"-to-aluminum system (Fig. 1). The nature of the comonomer employed to introduce the carboxyl groups influences the adhesion obtained. Different surfaces require different compositions of the adhesive copolymer for development of optimum bond strength. It is possible to "tailor-make" adhesives

TABLE 7. INFLUENCE OF CARBOXYL LEVEL (FOR BUTADIENE-STYRENE COPOLYMERS) ON ADHESION OF RUBBER TO RAYON.[a]

COOH (ephr)[b]	Styrene (phm)[c]	Tie Cement	Cover Stock	H-Test (lb)	Separation
0.22	5	VP	SBR	38	From RF
0.23	20	VP	SBR	40	From RF
0.22	30	VP	SBR	37	From RF
0.20	40	VP	SBR	29	From RF
0.22	5	VP	0.075[d]	19	Cover from tie
0.23	20	VP	0.075	10	Cover from tie
0.22	30	VP	0.075	18	Cover from tie
0.20	40	VP	0.075	10	Cover from tie
0.22	5	0.103[e]	0.075	74	From cord
0.23	20	0.103	0.075	61	From cord
0.22	30	0.103	0.075	60	From cord
0.20	40	0.103	0.075	46	From cord

RF = resorcinol-formaldehyde rubber layer. VP = vinyl pyridine-styrene-butadiene rubber.
RFL = resorcinol-formaldehyde latex. SBR = butadiene-styrene rubber.

[a] From Ref. 14.

[b] Carboxyl content of butadiene-styrene-methacrylic acid latex employed wherein 20 parts per hundred parts monomer (phm) of methacrylic acid was charged. Copolymers applied from resorcinol-formaldehyde latex (RFL) systems.

[c] Parts per hundred of monomer charged in butadiene-styrene-methacrylic acid system wherein 20 phm of methacrylic acid was charged.

[d] Butadiene-acrylonitrile-methacrylic acid copolymer derived by replacement of acrylonitrile by methacrylic acid in the butadiene-acrylonitrile 67-33 system.

[e] A butadiene-acrylonitrile 55-45 copolymer system wherein acrylonitrile has been replaced by methacrylic acid.

to develop maximum cohesive bond strength between any pair of selected surfaces. For example, in the adhesion of "Mylar" to aluminum, the use

TABLE 8. CARBOXYLIC RUBBERS AS PAPER[a] BONDING AGENTS.[b]

Latex	COOH (ephr)	Internal Bond[f] Uncured[c] (oz/in.)	Internal Bond[f] Cured[d] (oz/in.)
Polyethyl acrylate	0	35.2	38.4
Carboxylic polyethyl acrylate	0.045	48.0	54.0
Butadiene-acrylonitrile	0	39.2	45.6
Carboxylic butadiene-acrylonitrile[e]	0.09	46.4	51.2
None		(4–6)	(4–6)

[a] Semi-bleached kraft crepe paper 6 mil.

[b] B. F. Goodrich Chemical Company data.

[c] Dried at room temperature.

[d] Dried 3 min x 325°F.

[e] Same butadiene content as the butadiene-acrylonitrile copolymer.

[f] Failure of the paper in a peel test at 12 in./min separation rate using a test procedure similar to that described by I. R. Dunlap in Technical Association of the Pulp and Paper Industry papers, **40**, 676–680 (Aug. 1957).

of appropriate carboxylic comonomers and polymerizing conditions has a significant influence on bond strengths obtained (Fig. 2). The introduction of increasing amounts of carboxyl groups into polyacrylates results in increased bond strengths until a maximum value is reached. Thereafter, further introduction of carboxyl groups causes loss of bond strength. The variation of bond strength with increasing carboxyl content derived from three carboxylic-ethyl acrylate comonomer combinations is illustrated in Fig. 2.

For a given pair of adherends, the best laminating bond strengths obtainable with carboxylic polyacrylates varies not only with the carboxyl content, but also with the particular acrylate ester employed as the polymer backbone. The optimum carboxyl level, as indicated by bond strengths of the laminates, is different for each polyacrylate. When optimal carboxyl level, molecular weight, and molecular configuration have been achieved, bond strength is not improved and usually is lowered by addition of resins, fillers, or other additives.[14] However, such additives may be used to improve inferior laminating adhesives. Such additives frequently destroy the excellent clarity and transparency of the carboxylic polyacrylates. By the use of such additives, carboxylic polyacrylates

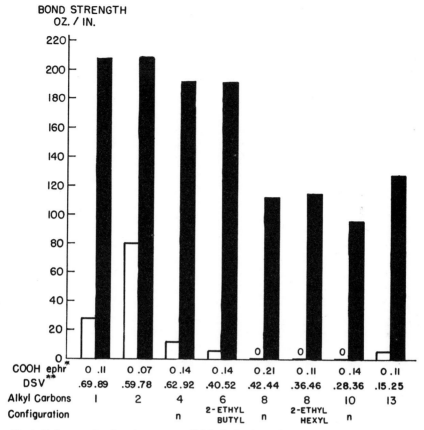

BOND STRENGTH OZ./IN.							
COOH ephr*	0 .11	0 .07	0 .14	0 .14	0 .21	0 .11	0 .14	0 .11
DSV**	.69 .89	.59 .78	.62 .92	.40 .52	.42 .44	.36 .46	.28 .36	.15 .25
Alkyl Carbons	1	2	4	6	8	8	10	13
Configuration			n	2-ETHYL BUTYL	n	2-ETHYL HEXYL	n	

Fig. 1. Influence of carboxyl content on "Mylar" aluminum laminate adhesive bond strength of polyacrylates.

* Carboxyl contents expressed as equivalents per 100 grams of rubber (ephr.).
** Dilute solution viscosity data in deciliters per gram.

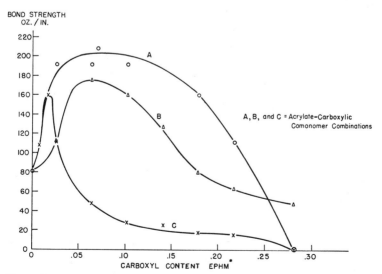

Fig. 2. Influence of carboxyl level and source upon bond strength of carboxylic polyethyl acrylates in Mylar-to-aluminum foil laminates.

* Equivalents per 100 of Manomer.

designed for use with one pair of adherends may be adapted for satisfactory performance with several adherends.

A carboxylic polyacrylate known as A916B[31] is available commercially as a 50 per cent solution in methylethyl ketone. It was developed primarily for permanently tacky bonds for the adhesion of "Mylar" to aluminum, but may readily be adapted for use with many other surfaces. It is also valuable for imparting permanent tack to other adhesive formulations. Variations of this material for lamination of other adherends are also available. Agents of this type have been supplied in a variety of solvents for various applications.

Excellent adhesion of many polymeric films to metal foils has been made with carboxylic polyacrylates.[14] Thus "Pliofilm," kraft paper, polystyrene, cellophane, cellulose acetate, polyvinyl chloride, "Videne," nylon, saran and polyethylene are some of the polymeric films which have been bonded to aluminum, tin and other metal foils with A916B and related carboxylic polyacrylates (Fig. 3).

Carboxylic polybutadienes and carboxylic copolymers of butadiene are also laminating adhesives for polymeric films to metal foils.[14] The inclusion of carboxyl groups in diolefin polymers enhances their adhesive properties in "Mylar" film to aluminum foil laminates. Noncarboxylic elastomers such as polybutadiene, butadiene-styrene, butadiene-acrylonitrile and polychloroprene without additive resins or fillers are not effective as "Mylar"-to-aluminum laminating adhesives since they exhibit bond strengths of less than 6 oz/in. for a 12-in./min separation rate. The inclusion of

0.3 ephr of carboxyl in polybutadiene gave a laminate bond strength of 56 oz/in. The incorporation of 0.07 ephr of carboxyl into a butadiene-styrene copolymer gave a bond strength of 47 oz/in. in peel. A butadiene copolymer containing 36 per cent acrylonitrile and 0.076 ephr of carboxyl gave a laminate bond strength of 128 oz/in. for a 12-in./min separation rate. Incorporation of carboxylic groups into polychloroprene converted it from a weak laminating adhesive to an effective agent. Inclusion of 0.08 ephr of carboxyl gave a bond strength of 56 oz/in. compared with 5 oz for an analogous noncarboxylic polychloroprene. All data were obtained without use of additives with the carboxylic copolymers.

A carboxylic anhydride butadiene-acrylonitrile copolymer prepared by treating a butadiene-acrylonitrile copolymer with maleic anhydride has been cited in the patent literature[22] as a component of an adhesive composition for bonding polyperfluorovinyl chloride to metal. The adhesive composition also contained polychloroprene and a rosin acid.

Paper has been bonded to aluminum foil with carboxylic polyacrylates deposited from aqueous solutions.[14] When the carboxyl level and molecular weight of carboxylic polyacrylates are properly adjusted, aqueous alkaline solutions of 20 to 50 per cent solids may be prepared. Ammoniacal dispersions are preferable in such adhesive applications. In adhesion of kraft paper to aluminum foil, such an aqueous ammoniacal dispersion has given bonds stronger than the paper at room temperature. To achieve bonds stable at elevated temperatures, a mild degree of crosslinking of the polyacrylate by

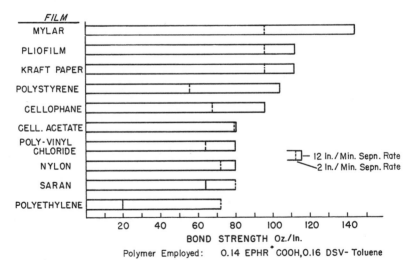

Fig. 3. Bond strength of carboxylic polyacrylate A-916-B in laminates of aluminum foil to polymer films

* Equivalent per 100 grams of rubber.

a suitable water-soluble reagent such as sodium aluminate is necessary. Ammoniacal polyacrylates, such as A-926-B, are commercially available.[31]

A carboxylic butadiene-acrylonitrile copolymer[16] (e.g., "Hycar" 1072) employed as a 30 per cent cement in methylethyl ketone containing zinc oxide (10 phr) and stearic acid (5 phr) has also given a bond between aluminum foil and kraft paper which was stronger than the paper. Similar results have been obtained without the zinc oxide and stearic acid; a permanently tacky bond was made which was stronger than the paper at room temperature, but for elevated temperatures, crosslinking is desirable. Crosslinking reduces or may eliminate tackiness of the adhesive.

Pressure-sensitive tapes have been constructed with the carboxylic polyacrylates.[14, 34] They are unique in that essentially no compounding is required provided that proper balance of creep, peel, shear and tack properties are built into the elastomer during its preparation.

Metal Foil Laminates. Permanently tacky laminations of metal foils to each other are readily prepared with carboxylic polyacrylates. Thus 0.002-in. foils of aluminum laminated to aluminum, lead, tin and copper foils of the same thickness with A916B showed permanently tacky cohesive bond failures of approximately 80 to 100 oz/in. for a separation rate of 12 in./min (Fig. 4). Similar laminates of copper-to-copper, tin-to-tin, lead-to-lead, lead-to-tin, lead-to-copper, and copper-to-

tin showed cohesive bond strengths of 80 to 100 oz/in. With analogous noncarboxylic polyacrylate polymers such metal laminates showed only 5 to 8 oz/in. bond strengths (Fig. 5).

Superior bond strengths for metal-foil laminates have been obtained with other carboxylic elastomers by preparing polymers specifically adapted to the surfaces and by cement formulation with selected additives. Carboxylic butadienes and butadiene copolymers such as "Hycar" 1072 may be thus employed.

Polymeric Film Laminates. The carboxylic polyacrylates have been effectively employed to laminate polymeric films. Pliofilm to kraft paper laminates have been prepared wherein the paper tore before the adhesive bond was broken (60 to 70 oz/in. for separation rates of 12 in./min). "Mylar"-to-"Mylar" permanently tacky laminates have shown cohesive failures with bond strengths of as much as 96 oz/in. for one mil films. Similarly, "Mylar" may be laminated to metallized "Mylar" with carboxylic polyacrylates, with bond strengths of 130 oz/in. being obtained easily. Polyvinyl fluoride films have been laminated with carboxylic polyacrylates.

Aqueous dispersions of carboxylic polyacrylates, such as A926B, have been used to prepare paper laminates. These laminates may be strengthened, especially for service above room temperature, by crosslinking with agents such as sodium aluminate.

Elastomer Laminates. The permanently tacky

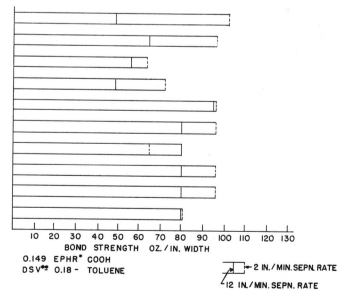

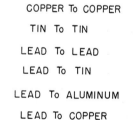

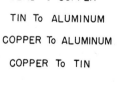

Fig. 4. Lamination of metal foil using carboxylic polyacrylate A916B.

* Equivalent per 100 grams of rubber.
** Dilute solution viscosity data.

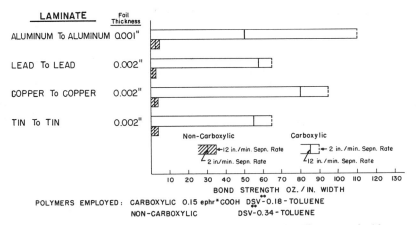

Fig. 5. Lamination of metal foils by carboxylic polyacrylate A916B compared with non-carboxylic polyacrylate.

* Equivalent per 100 grams of rubber.
** Dilute solution viscosity.

lamination of elastomers to themselves, to other elastomers, and especially to carboxylic elastomers may be enhanced by the use of carboxylic elastomer adhesives. Such bonds are not of as much interest as permanent bonds, but can be achieved with uncrosslinked carboxylic elastomers. Thus carboxylic butadiene-acrylonitrile (e.g., "Hycar" 1072) has been used to laminate films of vulcanized "Hycar" 1042 and "Hycar" 1072. Similarly A916B has been used to laminate films of cured polyethyl acrylate ("Hycar" 4021). These adhesives are of especial interest where temporary nonload bearing laminations are required.

Carboxylic Elastomers as Compounding Ingredients for Adhesive Formulations

The carboxylic elastomers function effectively as adhesive materials without additives. They can be tailor-made to function optimally with given adherend pairs. When not tailor-made for a given adherend system, they can be used to enhance the properties of other adhesive systems.

Carboxylic elastomers, especially the carboxylic polyacrylates, are useful for imparting permanent tack to systems with which they are not chemically reactive. For example, the inclusion of 5 to 20 per cent of a carboxylic polybutyl acrylate or carboxylic polyethyl acrylate to a "Hycar" 1042 noncuring rubber cement imparts quick grab and permanent tackiness. A carboxylic "Hycar" 1072 may be similarly employed.

Carboxylic groups tend to stiffen elastomers. More or less highly carboxylated elastomers may replace resins used to stiffen rubber cements or may replace portions of both resins and elastomers in typical formulations. This stiffening tendency

may be augmented by salt formation[15] with either mono- or divalent or polyvalent radicals or metals. Carboxylic elastomers are reactive with amines, diamines, polyamines, amine resins, and their carbonates.

Carboxylic elastomers may be used to impart elongation, elasticity and resilience to epoxy resin formulations. The carboxyl groups of the carboxylic elastomers react with the epoxy groups of the epoxy resins. Dependent on the relative quantities of the reactants involved, the reaction is probably as a crosslinking of the carboxylic elastomers[13, 15, 23] or of the epoxy resins.

An adhesive based on a carboxylic butadiene-acrylonitrile copolymer, such as "Hycar" 1072, in conjunction with epoxy resins and selected catalysts, may be used to bond various types of rubbers to themselves, metals, polymer films and other surfaces.

In noncuring butadiene-acrylonitrile, polybutadiene, SBR or polychloroprene-based cements, analogous carboxylic elastomers may frequently be substituted to enhance tack, reactivity toward metal surfaces, penetration of, and adhesion to, cellulosic or other hydrogen bonding surfaces. Some soft near-liquid and even liquid carboxylic elastomers have been used as cement tackifiers. The liquid carboxylic butadiene-acrylonitrile copolymer, "Hycar" 1300X2, is a commercial material of this type.

References

1. I. G. Farbenindustrie, Aktiengesellschaft, addition to French Patent 701,102 (June 21, 1933).
2. Bacon, R. G. R., and Farmer, E. H., *Rubber Chem. and Technol.,* **12,** 200–209 (1939).

3. Bacon, R. G. R., Farmer, E. H., Morrison-Jones, C. R., and Errington, K. D., Rubber Technol. Conf., London Reprint No. 56, May, 1938; *C.A.*, **32**, 8201.

4. Farmer, E. H., *Rubber Chem. and Technol.*, **15**, 765 (1942).

5. Compagnon, P., and LeBras, J., *Compt. rend.*, **212**, 616 (1941); *Rev. gen. Caoutchouc*, **18**, 89 (1941).

6. Compagnon, P., and Delalande, A., *Rev. gen. Caoutchouc*, **20**, 133–5 (1943).

7. Compagnon, P., and LeBras, J. N. L., U. S. Patent 2,388,905 (vested in the Alien Property Custodian), (Nov. 13, 1945).

8. Kambara, S., Mizushima, H., and Saito, K., *J. Soc. Chem. Ind. Japan*, **45**, 141–3 (1944); *C.A.*, **43**, 1595 (1949).

9. Hendricks, J. O. (to Minnesota Mining & Manufacturing Co.), U. S. Patent 2,607,711 (Aug. 19, 1952).

10. Frank, C. E., Kraus, G., and Haefner, A. J., *Ind. Eng. Chem.*, **44**, 1600–1603 (1952); *J. Polymer Sci.*, **10**, 441 (1953).

11. Frank, C. E., and Kraus, G. (to General Motors Corp.), U. S. Patent 2,692,841 (Oct. 26, 1954).

12. Doolittle, A. K., and Powell, G. M., *Paint, Oil, Chem. Rev.*, **107**, (7), 9–11, 40–2 (1944).

13. Brown, H. P., *Rubber Chem. and Technol.*, **30**, 1347–1399 (1957).

14. Brown, H. P., and Anderson, J. F., "Adhesive Properties of Carboxylic Rubbers," unpublished paper presented at Gordon Research Conference on Adhesives, Aug. 1958.
Boguslavskii, D. B., Tikhomirov, B. P., Epshtein, V. G., *Soviet Rubber Technology*, p. 47 (Jan. 1960).
Uzina, R. V. and Basin, V. E., *Soviet Rubber Technology* p. 27 (Feb. 1960).
Boguslavskii, D. B., Dostyan, M. S. and Uzina, R. V., *Soviet Rubber Technology*, p. 25 (Mar. 1960).

15. Brown, H. P., and Gibbs, C. F., *Ind. Eng. Chem.*, **47**, 1006–1012 (1955).

16. Hycar Service Bulletin H-21, "Hycar 1072X3, A Carboxylic Elastomer," B. F. Goodrich Chemical Co., June 1956.

17. Hycar Manual HM-4, "Making Cements with Hycar Rubber," B. F. Goodrich Chemical Co., June 1959.

18. Kraus, G. (to Phillips Petroleum Co.), U. S. Patent 2,901,448 (Aug. 25, 1959).

19. Reynolds, W. B. (to Phillips Petroleum Co.), U. S. Patent 2,774,703 (Dec. 18, 1956).

20. B. F. Goodrich Chemical Co. data.

21. "Hycar Latex Manual," B. F. Goodrich Chemical Co., Mar. 1956.

22. Fischer, W. K. (to United States Rubber Co.), U. S. Patent 2,710,821 (June 14, 1955).

23. Mika, T. K., *J. Appl. Chem.*, **6**, 365 (1956).

24. Green, J., and Sverdrup, E. F., *Ind. Eng. Chem.*, **48**, 2138 (1956).

25. Brown, H. P. (to The B. F. Goodrich Co.), U. S. Patent 2,671,074 (Mar. 2, 1954); (to The B. F. Goodrich Co.), U. S. Patent 2,710,292 (June 7, 1955).

26. Dazzi, J. (to Monsanto Chemical Co.), U. S. Patents 2,782,228 and 2,782,229 (Feb. 19, 1957).

27. Milne, J. N., and Crick, R. G. D. (to The Distillers Co., Ltd., Edinburgh, Scotland), U. S. Patent 2,759,910 (Aug. 21, 1956).

28. Jarrijon, A., and Louia, P., *Rev. gen. Caoutchouc*, **22**, 3 (1945).

29. Kambara, S., Mizushima, H., and Saito, K., *J. Soc. Chem. Ind. Japan*, **47**, 141 (1944); *C.A.*, **43**, (1949).

30. Sarbach, D. V., and Garvey, B. S., *India Rubber World*, **115**, 798–801 (1947); *Rubber Chem. and Technol.*, **20**, 990–7 (1947).

31. "Adhesive Specification Sheet, A916B, A926B," Adhesives Div., B. F. Goodrich Industrial Products Co., 1958.

32. Marsden, C., "Solvents and Allied Substances Manual," Cleaver-Hume Press, 1954.

33. McLaren, A. D., "Adhesion and Adhesives," pp. 57–59, New York, John Wiley & Sons, Inc., 1954.

34. Ulrich, E. W. (to Minnesota Mining & Manufacturing Co.), U. S. Patent 2,884,126 (Apr. 28, 1959).

20

Neoprene Cements

Louis S. Bake

E. I. du Pont de Nemours & Co., Inc.
Elastomer Dept.
Wilmington, Delaware

This chapter describes the adhesive cements made from neoprene which are being used widely in the shoe, automotive, aircraft, ship, furniture and other industrial fields. The properties of the various types of neoprene and the adhesives made from them as well as their methods of manufacture will be described in detail.

HISTORY

Neoprene

Neoprene was the first synthetic elastomer developed which had many of the properties of natural rubber. Since the first commercial production in 1931, many types of neoprene polymers have been developed, and hundreds of reports on them and their uses have been published.

The early history of neoprene development has considerable interest. In the early 1920's, Dr. Nieuwland of Notre Dame University discovered that acetylene could be polymerized by passing it through a catalyst based on cuprous chloride. The main product of this reaction was divinyl acetylene. Many unsuccessful attempts were made to prepare a synthetic rubber from this compound.

In 1930, a team of Du Pont chemists studying the polymerization of acetylene found that by varying the conditions of polymerization, monovinyl acetylene could be prepared in abundance while the divinyl acetylene produced was present only as an impurity. It was further found that monovinyl acetylene could be reacted with hydrochloric acid to form chloroprene which could be polymerized under certain conditions to yield a rubberlike polymer. This rubberlike polymer was first called "DuPrene" and later neoprene, the name by which it is known today.

The chemical equations given below illustrate the reactions required for the preparation of neoprene:

The reaction takes place in a water emulsion. The resultant polymer can be used in this form as latex, or the neoprene can be coagulated and used in the solid form. Both the solid form and the latex are used as adhesive bases.

$$C(coal) + CaCO_3(limestone) \rightarrow CaC_2(calcium\ carbide)$$

$$CaC_2 + H_2O \rightarrow CH{\equiv}CH(acetylene)$$

$$CH{\equiv}CH + catalyst \rightarrow C{-}CH{=}CH_2(MVA)$$

$$C{-}CH{=}CH_2 + HCl \rightarrow CH_2{=}\overset{\underset{\textstyle |}{Cl}}{C}{-}CH{=}CH_2(chloroprene)$$

$$CH_2{=}\overset{\underset{\textstyle |}{Cl}}{C}{-}CH{=}CH_2 + polymerizer \rightarrow (-CH_2{-}\overset{\underset{\textstyle |}{Cl}}{C}{=}C{=}CH_2{-})_n\ (neoprene)$$

Neoprene Cements

Prior to the introduction of neoprene, the only elastomer available for the manufacture of solvent adhesives was natural rubber, but rubber cements were limited in use by several adverse properties:

(1) Solutions of unmilled or slightly milled rubber were very viscous even at low percentage solids, so that it was difficult to apply a sufficient quantity to give a satisfactory thickness of dried film.

(2) Rubber films had poor resistance to oils, weather, ozone and oxidation; hence they would deteriorate after a comparatively short service life.

(3) The low cohesive strength of uncured natural rubber films could be increased by the use of room temperature accelerators; however these accelerators tended to overcure the rubber, resulting in early deterioration. This deterioration could be decreased by less active accelerators but these accelerators would not react readily at room temperature, at which the majority of adhesives was used.

In spite of these limitations of rubber, large volumes were manufactured before World War II for application in the shoe, automotive and other industrial fields. At that time if a combining operation could not be accomplished with a natural rubber adhesive, it had to be realized by nailing, screwing, sewing, or by some other fastening method.

Although neoprene had been developed some years before, little thought was given to it as an adhesive base for the following reasons:

(1) It was expensive, costing from 3 to 5 times as much as natural rubber.

(2) A comparatively expensive solvent such as toluene was required to dissolve it while natural rubber was soluble in low-cost petroleum naphtha.

(3) To obtain a given viscosity considerably more neoprene was required than natural rubber.

Because of these differences, the adhesive user would have had to pay $3 to 4 for a gallon of neoprene adhesive against 40 to 50¢ per gallon for a natural rubber cement; consequently there was little incentive for the user to specify a neoprene cement.

This situation changed soon after the advent of World War II when the use of natural rubber in adhesives was prohibited. At that time neoprene was the only synthetic rubber available for use in adhesives, and the manufacturers who were dependent on adhesives to fabricate their products had to utilize it. They soon found that neoprene adhesives were as efficient as natural rubber adhesives in most cases and frequently were much superior.

Any type of neoprene which can be dissolved can be used as a cement base. Adhesives made from the different types of neoprene however will vary in properties. In this discussion, emphasis will be on the use of neoprene Type AC (AD).

Neoprene Type KNR is noted for its ability to become plasticized, either chemically or by milling, to a greater extent than any other type generally used in adhesives. Its uncured films have comparatively low cohesive strength; consequently it is not used extensively in adhesive formulations.

Neoprene Type GN and GNA crystallize slowly and are used where long tack retention is desired and high cohesive strength is not required. The dried films may be cured readily at room or elevated temperature.

Type GNA differs from GN in that it contains a staining antioxidant and cannot be used in contact with any material which must not discolor when exposed to light.

Neoprene Type GRT is similar to Type GN in most of its properties; however it differs in its slower rate of freeze, resulting in somewhat longer tack retention time and lower ultimate cohesive strength.

Neoprene Type W will crystallize or freeze somewhat more rapidly and to a greater extent than will Type GN; hence it will have higher original and ultimate cohesive strength.

The tack retention of neoprene Type W films is excellent and only slightly less than can be obtained with those from Type GN. Neoprene Type W cements are appreciably more stable than are Type GN with respect to both viscosity increase and decrease during aging; moreover neoprene Type W films can be cured at room temperature, but not as rapidly as Type GN or GNA films.

Neoprene Type WRT is similar in its properties to Type W but differs in that it does not crystallize to any appreciable extent. Due to this lack of freeze, the ultimate cohesive strength of its film is lower.

Neoprene Type WHV is similar to Type W but differs in that it has a much higher plasticity value; consequently Type WHV cements are much higher in viscosity, and their films have considerably higher cohesive strength. Although it is useful in the preparation of cements requiring high viscosity such as those for tile and wall board laying, it is particularly useful in blends with other polymers to control the cement viscosity.

Neoprene Type CG was the first of a series of quick-freezing polymers to be developed especially for use in solvent adhesive cements. It was used extensively during World War II for seaming barrage balloons. After the war it was first used for permanent attachment of shoe soles and for adhering sponge weather strip to automobile doors.

Because of the quick-freezing characteristics of neoprene Type CG and the extent of freeze, its films develop high original and ultimate cohesive strength. Even though neoprene Type CG makes excellent adhesive cements, it has several disadvantages which tend to limit its use:

(1) The raw polymer discolors during aging and in several months may change from a light yellow color to green and finally to black.

(2) The plasticity value of the raw polymer decreases on aging; thus the ratio of solution viscosity to the solids content varies as the polymer ages.

(3) Cements made from Type CG become lower in viscosity as they age and have a limited storage life when they contain magnesium and zinc oxides.

Neoprene Type AC was developed to lessen the disadvantages of Type CG and was a decided improvement. For example, Type CG will become almost black if aged for a long period of time at room temperature while AC will undergo a minimal change in color. Occasionally it will develop a light green color due to contamination with traces of iron salts. Its cements will discolor in certain metal containers, but not as extensively as cements made from Type CG. Type AC is more stable than Type CG although its plasticity value will decrease somewhat during aging and its cements will decrease slowly in viscosity.

Neoprene Type AD represents the latest development in quick-freezing polymers for adhesives and is similar in performance to Type AC, except that the raw polymer stability is appreciably superior in both color and plasticity value. The cement stability is also superior with respect to color change as well as stability of viscosity on aging.

Neoprene Type AD can be exposed to a temperature as high as 70°C for several weeks without any appreciable change in color whereas Type AC will become almost black in 7 days at the same temperature. The same difference is noted between gum cements of the two polymers aged at elevated temperatures.

One of the chief advantages of Type AD is that its gum cements (simple solutions in solvents) may be packaged in metal containers without discoloration. Although these gum cements without anti-acids are not generally recommended, they are made by some manufacturers. For such cements neoprene Type AD is indispensable.

Films of neoprene Type AD which contain magnesia and zinc oxide are considerably more stable than similar films of Type AC; however if NA-22 is added, the neoprene Type AD film will cure noticeably faster as illustrated by data on press-cured samples listed in Table 1.

The stress-strain properties in Table 1 were obtained on dumbbell samples which had been heated to remove the room temperature freeze; then they were aged at 75°F for 30 min to reach temperature equilibrium. Had the properties been determined on samples which had been allowed to freeze, high and misleading values would have been obtained.

The results in Table 1 indicate that neoprene Type AD compounded only with magnesia and zinc oxide cures considerably more slowly than similarly compounded Type AC; furthermore it is less scorchy. The neoprene Type AD compound containing 0.5 part of NA-22 cured more rapidly than the Type AC compound and was more scorchy. The results also show that by decreasing the amount of magnesia in the neoprene Type AC compound from four parts to two parts, the rate of cure is substantially increased without apparent effect on the Mooney scorch. A similar reduction of magnesia in the Type AD compound produces no significant change either in the rate of cure or the Mooney scorch.

TYPES OF NEOPRENE CEMENTS

Neoprene cements may be classified broadly into two types—curing and non-curing. Curing cements are employed where service is at a temperature high enough to soften an uncured film and cause bond failure. They may be cured at room temperature by the use of ultra-accelerators or by the application of heat using less active ones.

For service at room or somewhat elevated temperatures, it is usually unnecessary to cure a neoprene film, since it has excellent uncured cohesive strength. By certain resins discussed later, it is possible to prepare uncured films which have high cohesive strength at moderately high temperatures.

TABLE 1. CURE RATE OF NEOPRENE TYPE AD VS. TYPE AC.

Compound No.	1	2	3	4	5	6
Neoprene Type AC	100	—	100	—	100	—
Neoprene Type AD	—	100	—	100	—	100
Magnesia	4	4	2	2	4	4
Zinc oxide	5	5	5	5	5	5
NA-22	—	—	—	—	.5	.5
Mooney scorch—minutes to						
5 Pt. rise at 250°F	28	43	25	42	15	10
Stress-strain (press cured at 307°F)						
Tensile Strength at Break (psi)						
5 min	400	350	2100	450	1700	3050
10 min	1750	740	2700	750	3200	3300
20 min	3300	1160	2850	1360	3400	3300
Elongation at Break (%)						
5 min	*	*	*	*	*	910
10 min	*	*	980	*	940	800
20 min	*	*	960	*	880	710
Hardness (Shore A)						
5 min	37	38	39	35	39	37
10 min	39	38	42	39	42	47
20 min	44	39	43	39	44	47

*No break at 1500% elongation.

Neoprene solvent adhesives may be classified arbitrarily as shoe adhesives and industrial adhesives. Shoe adhesives may be divided into two general types, temporary and permanent. An example of a temporary adhesive is one used in sole laying, where the sole is held in place by the adhesive only until it is nailed or sewn on; whereas a permanent adhesive is one used to attach shoe soles where nails or thread are not used.

Industrial adhesive cements may be used either cured or uncured. Uncured cement is used to attach sponge weather strips to automobile doors; cured cement is used to adhere the seams of barrage balloons. If this cement were uncured, failure of the seams might occur when the balloon is in service, during which a temperature as high as 170°F may be reached.

SOLVENTS USED IN NEOPRENE CEMENTS

Neoprene is soluble in aromatic hydrocarbons such as toluene; chlorinated compounds such as carbon tetrachloride; and certain ketones such as methylethyl ketone. It is insoluble in aliphatic hydrocarbons, acetone or ethyl alcohol. Neoprene may be dissolved in mixtures of aromatic and aliphatic hydrocarbons, and such mixtures are widely utilized in the cement industry. Neoprene is partially soluble in certain esters such as ethyl acetate but is readily soluble in mixtures of ethyl acetate and hydrocarbons, including aliphatics in which neoprene is insoluble alone. A mixture of cyclohexane and toluene containing 85 per cent cyclohexane and 15 per cent toluene dissolves neoprene quite easily although neoprene is insoluble in cyclohexane alone. It is an interesting fact that neoprene, although not soluble in certain solvents alone, will dissolve quite readily in a blend of two of them. Two solvents which illustrate this are acetone and hexane. In Table 2 are listed several two-component blends and their approximate solubility ranges with respect to amounts of each component.

The above solubility ranges were determined on unmilled neoprene Type GN and Type CG; however it is possible that the range will be increased somewhat if the polymer has been broken down by milling.

All of the acetone blend cements of neoprene Type GN and Type CG are unstable, some of them gelling after overnight storage at 82°F, and all of them gelling after 24 hr at 121°F. Cements made in blends with methylethyl or higher ketones, methyl acetate or ethyl acetate as the A component are all stable. Cements of neoprene Types AC, AD, W, WRT and WHV in solvents containing acetone all appear to be stable.

TABLE 2. Two-Component Solvent Blends
for Neoprene.

Compound A	Compound B	Minimum to Maximum Range of Compound A to Give Smooth Solution % by vol
Acetone	Cyclohexane	30–60
Acetone	Hexane	30–60
Acetone	Heptane	30–60
Acetone	Kerosene	30–60
Methylethyl ketone	Hexane	30–100
Methyl isobutyl ketone	Hexane	30–100
Methyl acetate	Hexane	30–60
Ethyl acetate	Hexane	40–80
Benzene	Hexane	40–100
Toluene	Hexane	40–100

Cements made in blends of nonaromatic solvents or in mixtures of aromatic and nonaromatic solvents are somewhat less viscous than those made in aromatics and exhibit less decrease in viscosity on aging.

Selection of Solvent

By selecting the various solvent components, cements differing in physical characteristics may be obtained. For example, a neoprene GN cement made in a blend of methyl acetate, 30 vol and hexane, 70 vol, contains methyl acetate as the more rapid evaporating component. Films of this cement lose their methyl acetate first, leaving a film of neoprene and hexane in which neoprene is insoluble. Because neoprene is not soluble in the residual liquid and comparatively little of the hexane is absorbed by the neoprene, the total liquid evaporates rapidly and high initial bond strength is obtained. Due to the rapid loss of methyl acetate and consequent speedy transfer of the blend from a solvent to a non-solvent, this cement has the disadvantage, that the applied film is apt to be rough and lumps of neoprene may collect in the brush. Consequently, this type may not always be practicable.

If methylethyl ketone is substituted for methyl acetate in the above cement, the hexane non-solvent portion becomes the lower boiling component and evaporates at a faster rate than does the methylethyl ketone. Consequently, the ratio of methylethyl ketone to hexane becomes greater as the applied film loses solvent. Inasmuch as neoprene is soluble in blends of methylethyl ketone

and hexane containing from 30 to 100 per cent (by volume) of methylethyl ketone, the residual blend at all times is a neoprene solvent; therefore the cement will spread smoothly and will not exhibit stringiness.

The choice of solvent to be used with an adhesive cement depends on the rate of evaporation desired. If bonds are to be made within a few minutes' time, a rapid evaporating solvent blend must be employed. An example of such a mixture is one-third each of toluene, hexane, an ethyl acetate. If rate of evaporation is relatively unimportant, a solvent such as toluene, which has a medium rate of evaporation, may be used alone. In foreign countries the amount of aromatic solvent permitted is limited in some cases to 10 to 20 per cent of the total blend. Here the selection of the solvent blend becomes quite important.

The tack retention of an applied film may also be varied, within narrow limits, by the use of various solvents. Cements with xylene, for example, will retain their tack for a longer period of time than will those made in toluene.

The solvent used for dissolving neoprene also affects the viscosity of the cement, as illustrated by the data in Table 3:

Generally blends of solvents will give lower viscosity cements than will hydrocarbons alone; an exception is an 80/20 blend of cyclohexane and toluene.

TABLE 3. Effect of Solvent on Viscosity
of Neoprene Cements.

Base Compound				
Neoprene				100
Magnesium oxide				4
Zinc oxide				5
Cement				
Base				1.5 lb
Solvent				to 1 gal
Neoprene Type	AC	W	CG	GN
Solvent:				
Toluene	2700	1600	2200	1100
Toluene 20 Cyclohexane 80	3000	1700	3900	1000
Toluene 20 ethyl acetate 80	1500	1200	500	300
Toluene 20 M.E.K. 80	1500	1100	400	300
Toluene 30 methyl acetate	1500	1100	500	400
Acetone 40 hexane 60	1200	800	400	300

The manufacturer is cautioned against the use of a solvent blend containing insufficient aromatic solvent in cements which are to be exposed to abnormally low temperature. If the solvent blend is too lean in aromatics, coagulation of the neoprene from the solvent may occur. A mixture containing one-third each by volume of toluene, ethyl acetate, and gasoline is satisfactory for temperatures as low as approximately −40°F.

SOLUBILITY OF NEOPRENE

The solubility of a particular type of neoprene depends on the amount of gel present. If the gel structure predominates, the neoprene may merely swell when placed in solvent. As the ratio of gel to sol decreases, the polymer becomes more soluble and the swollen gel particles become smaller, until finally a smooth solution is obtained.

In all types of neoprene-containing gel, the gel content may be decreased by milling. The time required to transform all the gel content to sol depends on the type of neoprene and the amount of gel present; thus it may vary from a few passes through the mill for neoprene Type AC to as much as 2 hr for neoprene Type S.

Neoprene Types AD, W, and WRT are low in gel content. These polymers, in the normal plasticity range of 50 to 60 Mooney, dissolve readily without mill breakdown resulting in smooth, easily brushable cements. Neoprene Type WHV, despite a Mooney plasticity of 125, is also low in gel content and furthermore will dissolve without milling to form smooth solutions.

Neoprene Types CG and GN contain large amounts of gel when freshly prepared unless the plasticities are abnormally low; therefore when they are placed in solvent, they will swell but not dissolve. The gel in these types will decrease comparatively rapidly in storage and the aged sample will eventually become completely soluble. Decomposition of the gel will occur rapidly also in solvent; moreover continued stirring for a relatively short time will convert a gelled cement into one which is perfectly smooth, providing the gel is not caused by partial cure due to compounding ingredients or excessive total heat history.

Neoprene Type AC in the soft plasticity range will dissolve without breakdown. The gel in the higher plasticity range material may be readily changed to sol by milling but the change will not take place to any great extent on aging as with neoprene Types GN and CG. Neoprene Type AD is essentially gel-free and may be dissolved without milling to form smooth solutions.

COMPOUNDING NEOPRENE FOR ADHESIVES

Basic Compound

Neoprene compositions for adhesive cements, as for all other applications, should contain magnesium oxide, zinc oxide, and a suitable antioxidant. This applies to the so-called gum stocks as well as loaded compounds and is necessary to ensure excellent aging properties in the neoprene film. The metal oxides act as acid acceptors and minimize any deterioration of fabric with which the film may be in contact. A suitable adhesive cement which may serve as a basis for further compounding is as follows:

	parts by wt.
Neoprene	100
Light calcined magnesia	4
Neozone D*	2
Zinc oxide	5
Solvent	As desired

A cement thus formulated has good to excellent storage stability depending on the type of neoprene used; furthermore it may be used uncured. The film deposited will slowly vulcanize at room temperature. The choice of neoprene to be used in adhesive cements depends on its intended application.

In adhesive cements, Type AC or AD is most often preferred because of its quick grab and the high bonding strength attained soon after the joining of the cemented surfaces. This is the result of the high degree of freeze or crystallization in these types of neoprene.

When longer tack retention is required, Types W and WRT may be used either alone or in blends with Type AC or AD.

Modifications of the base compound, to obtain certain properties will now be discussed.

Fillers

Conventional fillers such as clay, whiting and carbon black may be added to the base compound to reduce the cost of the finished adhesive; however this will diminish the cohesive strength of the film. They may also be added to a cement for reinforcement; but they are not recommended for such purposes because other fillers such as hydrated calcium silicate and precipitated silica are much more effective. The effect of calcium silicate

* If discoloration cannot be tolerated, a non-discoloring antioxidant should be used.

TABLE 4. THE EFFECT OF HYDRATED CALCIUM SILICATE ON STRENGTH OF NEOPRENE TYPE GN FILM.

Compound No.	7	8	9	10
Neoprene Type GN	100	100	100	100
Magnesia	4	4	4	4
Neozone D	2	2	2	2
Zinc oxide	5	5	5	5
Calcium silicate*	—	10	20	—
Clay	—	—	—	20
Toluene		25% solids		
Cohesive strength (canvas-to-canvas) lb/in.	9	26	33	7
Cement stability at 158°F glass days to gelation	5	9	11	7

* Silene EF used.

on the cohesive strength of a neoprene film as compared to that of clay is shown in Table 4.

Calcium silicate improves greatly both the cohesive strength of the film and stability of the cement. The presence of clay results in a slight increase of the cement stability at 158°F but a decrease of film strength. Calcium silicate increases the cohesive strength of other types of neoprene as well as of Type GN; nevertheless if used in Types W, WRT, AC, AD or WHV cements, it causes thixotropy with as little as two parts based on 100 parts of neoprene. The thixotropy may be eliminated by the addition of approximately 10 parts of a phenolic resin—either thermoplastic or heat-reactive.

Antioxidants

As previously stated, all neoprene cements should contain a good antioxidant. Where discoloration is not a problem, the use of "Neozone" A or D is recommended. In applications requiring nonstaining and nondiscoloration, the use of a nonstaining antioxidant such as "Zalba" is advised. Generally 2 parts of antioxidant per 100 parts of polymer is sufficient. The efficiency of "Zalba" as a nondiscoloring antioxidant is shown in Table 5.

The canvas-to-canvas bonds were made with uncured cement film. The adhesion of all samples except the control increased during aging because of the cure which occurred in the bomb. The film of the cement containing no antioxidant was so severely deteriorated at the end of 10 days that it could not be tested.

Resins

Various resins are often added to neoprene cements to obtain longer tack retention, greater cohesive strengths or adhesion to specific surfaces. Some of the resins are low-melting thermoplastics; whereas others react with oxides to give modified resins having high heat resistance. In the trade, the former are termed "thermoplastics;" the latter are referred to as "heat-reactive resins."

The former group includes certain phenolic resins, e.g., those modified with terpene, coumarone-indene resins, hydrogenated rosins etc. All these extend the tack life of a neoprene cement, but only the phenolics show specific adhesion properties to metal, glass and other rigid surfaces. The use of any of these thermoplastic resins will result in decreased heat resistance of the dried film but may have insignificant effect on the cohesive strength at room temperature.

Certain phenolic resins* such as those based on butyl phenol are low-melting thermoplastics in their original form; however they have the ability to react with certain oxides such as magnesia to form modified resins with high melting points, occasionally in excess of 500°F. Neoprene adhesive films, containing such a modified resin, release their solvent very rapidly and have high cohesive strength, both at room and elevated temperatures. The modified resin is soluble in the solvents generally used in neoprene solutions and is compatible with the neoprene itself.

The magnesium oxide will react with the resin at room temperature either in a slurry of magnesia in solvent or in the cement itself containing the magnesia. The resin and oxide will not react in the absence of water. In the presence of one part water per hundred parts neoprene, the reaction takes place in 30 min or less. To illustrate the reaction of the resin and magnesia, several slurries containing various ratios of resin to magnesia were

* Most of our work with heat-reactive resins was done with Union Carbide CKR-1634 (formerly BR 14634), but the following resins have been tested and found to give results similar to those obtained with CKR-1634:

CKR-1282 (formerly BR-10282) Union Carbide Plastics Co., Bound Brook, N. J.

Varcum 875 and 921, Varcum Chemical Co., Niagara Falls, N. Y.

Phenorin 55, A Honig's, Kunstharsinindustrie, Zaandam, Holland.

SP-126, Schenectady Varnish Co., Schenectady, N. Y.

SP-134, Schenectady Varnish Co., Schenectady, N. Y.

"Catalin" 8743, 8732, and 9672, Catalyn Corp. of America, New York, N. Y.

TABLE 5. THE EFFECT OF "ZALBA" AS AN ANTIOXIDANT IN NEOPRENE CEMENTS.

Compound No.	11	12	13	14	15
Neoprene Type AC	100	100	100	100	100
Magnesium oxide	4	4	4	4	4
Zinc oxide	5	5	5	5	5
Terpene phenolic resin	10	10	10	10	10
N. S. Antioxidant No. 1	—	2	—	—	—
"Zalba"	—	—	2	—	—
Neozone A	—	—	—	2	—
N. S. Antioxidant No. 2	—	—	—	—	2
Toluene		To make 20% solution			
Staining of pyroxylin (8 hr in direct sunlight)	None	Trace	None	Bad	Trace
Adhesion (canvas-to-canvas) (lb per in.)					
Original	19	35	28	21	20
After 10 days in O_2 bomb	Brittle	45	48	49	47

agitated for 72 hr. The excess magnesia was filtered off, and the solvent in the filtrate was evaporated at room temperature. The melting point and per cent ash were determined on the resultant resin. Results obtained are listed in Table 6:

The results indicate that the optimum amount of magnesia is approximately 10 per cent of the weight of the resin; this ratio is recommended as the minimum to use in neoprene cements. This is equivalent to the normal amount of four parts of magnesia in a cement containing 100 parts of neoprene and 45 parts of resin which is the maximum amount recommended. The reaction between resin and magnesium oxide at room temperature in toluene is essentially complete in 1 hr.

The magnesia-resin reaction takes place readily in blends of equal amounts of toluene and hexane or toluene, ethyl acetate and hexane. The reaction does not occur readily in ketones, esters or blends of an ester with toluene. This slow speed of reaction probably explains why cements made in some solvent blends do not have the heat resistance of those made in toluene and petroleum naphtha. The heat resistance of all cements improves as the cement ages.

The beneficial effect of a heat-reactive resin on the strength of a neoprene Type AC cement film is shown in Table 7.

Note the high cohesive strength of the film containing the resin at both room and elevated temperature.

As previously stated, the type of solvent used in the cement will influence the heat-resistance of a neoprene film containing a modified heat-resistant resin. The differences appear to be related to the rate at which the magnesia and resin react in

TABLE 6. EFFECT OF VARYING AMOUNTS OF MAGNESIA ON HEAT REACTIVE PHENOLIC RESIN.

Heat-reactive resin		45
Benzene		450
Magnesia		X

Magnesium Oxide	Ash (%)	M. P. (°C)
0	0.05	85
0.5	1.25	111.6
1.0	2.17	147.4
1.5	3.1	153
2.0	4.0	156
2.5	4.8	Decomposed 196
4.0	7.2	Decomposed 265
8.0	7.0	Decomposed 260

TABLE 7. EFFECT OF HEAT-REACTIVE RESIN ON TYPE AC FILMS.

Compound No.	16	17
Neoprene Type AC	100	100
Magnesium oxide	4	4
Zinc oxide	5	5
Heat-Reactive resin	—	45
Toluene	To 25% Solids	
Adhesion (canvas-to-canvas), lb per in.		
At 75°F (frozen)	55A	57A
At 75°F (unfrozen)	14C	51A
At 140° F	1C	20C

A = Failure at canvas surface.
C = Failure within cement film.

TABLE 8. EFFECT OF SOLVENTS ON HEAT RESISTANCE OF NEOPRENE FILMS.

Compound No.	18	19	20	21	22
Neoprene Type AC	100	100	100	100	100
Magnesium oxide	4	4	4	4	4
Zinc oxide	5	5	5	5	5
Heat-reactive resin	45	45	45	45	45
Toluene	600	—	120	—	120
Ethyl Acetate	—	—	—	300	—
Methylethyl ketone	—	300	240	—	300
Petroleum naphtha	—	300	240	300	300
Adhesion (canvas-to-canvas), lb per in.					
140°, Original cement	20	7	5	6	9
Aged cement (30 days at 75°F)	24	18	16	17	18

various solvents, as formerly discussed. This is depicted by the lower heat resistance of a film deposited from a freshly made cement which increases to practically normal as the cement ages as shown in Table 8. These results show that with solvents other than straight aromatics, improved heat resistance of the film will be obtained if the cements have aged prior to use. The difference in the age of the cement was observed only when tested at 140°F. No difference was obtained at 75°F.

The *amount* of heat-reactive resin present in a cement affects the heat-resistance of the film as illustrated by results in Table 9.

Recently, it has been found that in some applications requiring high heat-resistant adhesive films, the adhesion results obtained at 140°F may be misleading. Cements have been encountered which gave similar results at 140°F but differed widely when tested at 176°F. This difference is illustrated by data in Table 10, obtained on a cement differing only in its age at the time of testing:

These results show that at 140°F, the aged cement was only slightly superior to the fresh sample; however at 176°F the aged cement shows a fivefold improvement.

The improvement in cohesive strength of the film at 176°F can be attained by several methods. One method is to allow the cement to age at room temperature as indicated by results listed above or hot-mill the compound excessively, however not to the extent that it will not dissolve into a smooth solution.

Similar good results will be obtained if the cement is aged at an elevated temperature for a comparatively short period of time. A freshly prepared neoprene Type AC or AD solution containing a heat-reactive resin will remain stable at 158°F for 17 to 20 days. If, for example, by aging the polymer or the solution the stability can be decreased from 5 to 7 days, good results at 176°F will usually be achieved.

Occasionally, neoprene cements containing heat-reactive resins and magnesia and zinc oxide will separate into two phases. The separated cement consists of a clear supernatant liquid with flocculated zinc oxide and other fillers settling to the bottom. In the conventional method of preparing a neoprene cement, the base compound is dissolved in the solvent first; however if the resin and magnesia are added to the solvent and allowed to react before the milled compound is dissolved, little or no separation occurs in toluene or mixtures of toluene and gasoline.

Neoprene Type W cements separate to a greater extent than do cements made from Type AC or AD; furthermore those made from unmilled Type

TABLE 9. EFFECT OF VARYING AMOUNTS OF RESIN ON THE HEAT RESISTANCE OF NEOPRENE TYPE AC CEMENT FILMS.

Compound No.	23	24	25	26
Neoprene Type AC	100	100	100	100
Magnesium oxide	4	4	4	4
Zinc oxide	5	5	5	5
Heat-reactive phenolic resin	—	10	20	40
Toluene		To 20% Solids		
Adhesion (canvas-to-canvas, lb. per linear in.)				
Original	3	7	9	17

TABLE 10. EFFECT OF AGE OF CEMENT ON HEAT RESISTANCE.

Formula:

Neoprene Type AC	100
Magnesium oxide	4
Zinc oxide	5
Heat-reactive resin	45
Toluene	462

	Age of Cement	
Adhesion, lb per In.	24 Hr	6 Wk
at 75°F	52	51
140°F	18	22
176°F	3	15

TABLE 11. VULCANIZATION OF NEOPRENE TYPE AC WITH THIOCARBANILIDE.

	Cohesive Strength at 140°F (lb per in.)	
Conditions of Cure	Control	Control plus 2% Thiocarbanilide
1 day at 82°F	4.0	4.0
2 days at 82°F	4.0	10.0
4 days at 82°F	4.0	10.0
6 days at 82°F	4.0	12.0
1 hr at 158°F	3.5	3.5
2 hr at 158°F	3.5	22.0*
15 min at 212°F	5.0	12.0
30 min at 212°F	5.5	23.0*

* These values represent adhesion of the film to the fabric. The cohesive strength of the film itself was greater than the adhesion shown above.

W are the worst offenders. If unmilled neoprene Type W is added to the solvent with the magnesia, zinc oxide and resin and stirred until the solution is smooth, approximately 70 per cent of settling will occur in 1 hr; if, however, the unmilled neoprene Type W and zinc oxide are added to the solvent slurry which contains the pre-reacted magnesium oxide and resin, no separation occurs in 30 days.

In order to minimize phasing out of neoprene solutions, therefore, the resin and magnesium oxide should be allowed to react in the solvent before the base compound is added.* If the compound is a milled one containing zinc oxide, it should also contain the usual four parts of magnesia to prevent scorching which may occur in the absence of this stabilizing ingredient. In other words, a neoprene cement containing a heat-reactive resin will contain eight parts of magnesia rather than the conventional four parts. This increase in magnesia does no harm, but rather tends to increase the cohesive strength of the cement film. The length of time required for this reaction will vary from 1 hr or less to 72 hr or more depending on the solvent or solvent blend used. The more practical solvent appears to be toluene alone or a 50–50 blend of toluene and a petroleum naphtha such as hexane.

Curing Agents

All the neoprenes used in cements may be compounded to cure at room temperature. The choice of curing system and the amounts required depend on the type of neoprene and conditions under which the cement will be employed.

The amounts of magnesium oxide and zinc oxide recommended for use in neoprene cements will effect a slow room temperature cure. This cure is accelerated at elevated temperatures.

The W Types of neoprene are slower curing and are aided in elevated temperature cures by the addition of an accelerator such as NA-22. Although this accelerator hastens the curing of G Type neoprenes, it contributes to instability of the cements.

Thiocarbanilide is an effective heat-curing accelerator for Type AC cements. Generally it is added as a solution in methylethyl ketone. The curing effect of this accelerator is illustrated in Table 11.

The excellent stability of the cement containing thiocarbanilide is evidenced by the fact that the viscosity of this cement after being stored 6 wk at 82°F increased only to 3600 cps from an original value of 2000.

Mixtures of litharge and "Accelerator" 808 or "Accelerator" 833 are used in room temperature curing systems for neoprene Types CG, GN and KNR. These mixtures are also effective in curing neoprene Types AC and AD, but the rate of cure is somewhat slower. If 2 to 4 parts of sulfur are added to the Types AC or AD cements, comparatively rapid room temperature cures are obtained. The litharge is generally added as a ball-mill slurry. Since "Accelerator" 808 or "Accelerator" 833 is the more active part, it is usually added separately. Any curing system which is accelerated for rapid cure will decrease the pot life of the cement; therefore the accelerated cements must be prepared just prior to use.

The room temperature curing effect of litharge and "Accelerator" 808 on neoprene Type GN is shown in Table 12.

Triethyl trimethylene triamine** alone and in

* British Patent 790803, Armstrong Cork Co.; United States Patent 2918442, Minnesota Mining and Manufacturing Co.

** Trimene Base (Naugatuck Chemical Co.)

TABLE 12. ROOM TEMPERATURE CURE OF NEOPRENE TYPE GN BY LITHARGE AND "ACCELERATOR" 808.

Base Compound:

Neoprene Type GN	100
Magnesium oxide	4
Zinc oxide	5
Toluene	327
	436

Compound No.	27	28	29	30
Cements:				
Base compound	436	436	436	436
Litharge				
(50% in toluene)	—	20	20	20
"Accelerator" 808	—	2	4	8
Adhesion (canvas-to-canvas), lb per in.				
Tested at 140°F				
Aged at 75°F for:				
1 day	0	2	3	7
2 days	0	3	7	12
4 days	0	6	11	21
8 days	0	10	18	30

TABLE 13. CURING EFFECT OF TRIETHYL TRIMETHYLENE TRIAMINE ON NEOPRENE TYPE AC CEMENT.

Compound No.	31	32	33
Neoprene Type AC	100	100	100
XLC magnesium oxide	4	4	4
Zinc oxide	5	5	5
Neozone D	2	2	2
Sulfur*	—	—	2
Litharge*	—	20	20
T.T.T.	4	4	4
Toluene	400	400	400
Cohesive strength at 140°F, lb per linear in.			
Aged at 82°F			
1 day	8.0	11.00	15.0
2 days	15.0	17.0	17.0
4 days	20.0	24.0**	24.0**

* Compounds which contain both litharge and sulfur may be black due to the lead sulfide which is formed.

** Values represent adhesive strength since film separated from canvas.

combination with litharge will cure neoprene Types AC, AD or Type W films as illustrated in Table 13.

The addition of litharge, "Accelerator" 808, sulfur and "Trimene Base" to neoprene adhesives should be made just prior to use since the pot-life of the mixed cement is limited.

EQUIPMENT FOR MANUFACTURING OF NEOPRENE CEMENTS

Neoprene cements may be made by one of two methods. The first and most widely used procedure involves mill mixing the neoprene and the compounding ingredients and subsequently dissolving the resultant compound in the solvent in a cement churn. The second method consists of adding a solvent slurry (preferably ball-milled) of the dry ingredients to the churn with the milled or unmilled neoprene and solvent. Both methods will be discussed in detail later.

Examples of the types of churns and mixers used in manufacturing neoprene cements are discussed below.

Vertical Churns

These consist of vessels (usually jacketed) equipped with paddles mounted on a vertical shaft; also there are usually stationary arms or baffles mounted on the sides of the churn and positioned so as to create turbulence in the churn

during mixing. These churns may be used for all types of cements—especially for high viscosity solutions.

Horizontal Churns

These churns are positioned in the manner indicated by their name and are agitated by arms mounted on a horizontal shaft. There may be stationary arms or baffles mounted on the inner wall of the churn. Although especially suited for low viscosity cements, they are unsuited for heavy cements such as those used for spreading applications. Generally they are easier to clean than vertical churns.

High-Speed Churns

The new high-speed churns such as those manufactured by the Struthers Wells Corp. and the "Velofin" mixer made by H. E. Serner of Oakland, New Jersey, are designed to permit preparation of smooth cements in less time than previously possible. The manufacturers assert that the high-speed agitation coupled with the shearing action of the blades results in a smooth cement in a comparatively short period of time.

Heavy-Duty Mixers

These are especially adapted to the manufacture of heavy doughs or troweling compounds which have viscosities that are too high for practical processing in the previously mentioned churns. The technique employed with heavy-duty mixers requires adding the solvent slowly to the previously mill-mixed compound as mixing continues. By careful addition of solvent a smooth cement can be prepared in 1 or 2 hr. Too rapid addition of solvent will cause the compound to "liver," consequently an unusually long time will be required for solution.

TESTING NEOPRENE CEMENTS

The data presented here are based on tests conducted by the following methods:

Cohesive Strength

Method A. The cohesion or internal strength of neoprene adhesive films is determined by measuring the force required to separate, in peel, two 1 in. strips of canvas which have been bonded together with the cement. Unsized No. 10 canvas duck is employed using a sufficient number of coats of cement to give a continuous film over the surface. With a 20 to 25 per cent solids content, three brush coats are usually sufficient. All except 1 in. of each canvas strip is coated. The uncoated ends are matched in bonding to permit attaching the assembly in the jaws of the testing machine. Drying approximately 30 min between coats is considered average; however bonds should be made while the last coat is still tacky. The assemblies are firmly rolled with a steel hand roller to ensure good contact of the cement films. The bonded assemblies are allowed to rest for a minimum of 48 hr at room temperature before testing.

If the film being tested is of the slow-freezing type such as Type W or WRT, the adhesion to the canvas will exceed the cohesive strength; thus the film will separate during testing. Values obtained represent cohesive strength. With fast freezing or crystallizing types such as CG, AC or AD the cohesive strength is usually greater than the adhesive strength which will be measured. The nearest approach to the cohesive strength of such a film is obtained by splitting the film with a safety razor blade as the sample is being tested, thereby allowing separation to begin in the film. Generally higher values will be obtained which are in excess of the adhesive strength. The ultimate cohesive strength is not measured because the film soon begins stripping from the canvas. The film cutting procedure is repeated several times, and the maximum value obtained is recorded. Values obtained in this fashion are recorded as "frozen" cohesive strength.

The "unfrozen" values are obtained by warming the bonded assemblies for 10 min at 158°F to remove the crystallization. After they are conditioned at 75°F for 30 min to reach temperature equilibrium, they are tested. However to obtain the comparative strength of the film at elevated temperatures, the assemblies are conditioned for 10 min at the desired temperatures and tested at that temperature. A tensile testing machine modified with a jacket for temperature control is used. Head speed is 2 in. per min. The values are reported in pounds per linear inch.

Method B. Most of the data listed here were obtained by the use of Method A. Recently, it has been found that occasionally the 48 hr drying period allowed for the bonded assembly was insufficient to allow all the solvent to evaporate. By allowing additional time for solvent evaporation, excessively high results at elevated temperatures were obtained allegedly due to a continued action of the resin. These objections have been eliminated by the adoption of a new procedure described in detail as follows:

The canvas strips are coated as described under Method A; then they are suspended in a manner that allows the air to circulate freely around all surfaces of the assembly. After 24 hr, the strips are laid together in their proper positions on a piece of cardboard, the cement is activated, and the bonds are provided by pressure of a hot electric iron maintained at a temperature of 100 to 120°C. The strips are immediately rolled by hand pressure, using a steel roller to ensure good contact of the tacky cement surface; then the strips are allowed to age at 75°F to reach temperature equilibrium and tested as described in Method A. By this procedure, the "unfrozen" adhesion may be obtained on separate test pieces if desired, or those which were tested at elevated temperature may be tested the following morning when the films have become "frozen."

Method B is usually preferred over Method A for the reasons stated above; however there may be cases where Method B is unsatisfactory because the film will fail to become activated at 100 to 120°C. Here, the temperature may be increased or in extreme cases, Method A used.

Adhesive Strength

The adhesion to various nonporous surfaces such as metals, glass and plastics is determined by adhering a strip of unsized canvas to the surface using the candidate cement.

A strip of canvas is coated with the cement as

previously described. When the last coat is relatively dry but still tacky, one coat is applied to the nonporous surface. When both cement surfaces are fairly dry but still tacky, the bond is made and rolled down. Adhesion is determined by tensile testing at 2 in. per min head speed each day until maximum adhesion is obtained.

Tack Retention

Many methods for the determination of tack retention or open tack time have been used, of which the most satisfactory is based on the use of pre-coated canvas.

Unsized canvas is pre-coated with three coats of a 20 per cent solids solution in toluene of a compound containing 100 parts of neoprene Type AD, four parts of magnesia, and five parts of zinc oxide. The coated canvas is allowed to dry several days before use. A 0.040-in. wet film of the cement to be tested is spread onto the pre-coated canvas. At various intervals of time, two strips 3 by 1 in. are cut from the canvas and rolled together after placing a 1 in. piece of cellophane between them at one end to prevent adhesion at that spot.

The assemblies thus made are tested on the following day rather than just after bonding because the freeze of the films influence tack retention. A cement film which is unfrozen may appear to have satisfactory initial tack but upon freezing, failure at an abnormally low strength value will occur. As an example, assemblies made using a Type AC cement and bonded after drying 1, 2, and 3 hr may all show adhesion values of 30 lb per in. when tested the same day. If the assemblies are allowed to rest overnight before testing, the values might be 30 lb per in. for the one-hour sample, 20 lb per in. for the two-hour sample, and 5 lb per in. for the three-hour sample. One hour would then be considered the limit of tack retention; thus the immediate "grab" or bond is not necessarily an indication of effective tack retention.

Freeze Rate

The freeze rate of a neoprene polymer is established by determining the rate of development of the cohesive strength of a film-adhering canvas to itself.

Canvas-to-canvas assemblies are prepared in the determination of cohesive strength. After the bonded samples are heated for 15 min at 158°F to remove crystallization, they are placed immediately in the Scott Tester at 75°F. The cohesive strength is then determined at various intervals of time.

Room-Temperature Cure Rate

Canvas-to-canvas assemblies are prepared as previously described and aged at 75°F. At different time intervals the adhesion at 140°F is determined. This temperature is chosen because it is well above that which is required to remove room temperature freeze from the film; thus any progression in cure will be reflected by the 140°F adhesion and is unaffected by room temperature "freeze."

Viscosity

Neoprene solution viscosities are determined at 75°F with an LVF model Brookfield Viscosimeter. Results are reported in centipoises.

PROPERTIES OF NEOPRENE CEMENTS

Tack Retention

Tack retention of a cement film is the maximum time two cemented surfaces may be allowed to dry before bonding to provide satisfactory adhesion. The length of tack retention required depends on the specific application.

Sole laying and sole attaching are examples of two extremes. In sole laying, during which soles are held in place by cement only until they can be sewed or nailed on, a tack retention of only 15 to 30 min may be all that is required; whereas in permanent sole attaching, a tack retention period of 24 to 72 hr may be necessary.

No difficulty is experienced in compounding a neoprene cement for a short-tack retention period; however where extensive tack retention periods are desired, the compounder may have difficulty.

The type of polymer as well as the compounding ingredients used has a pronounced effect on the tack retention of a cement; for example, a simple solution of neoprene Type GN, W or WRT will deposit a film which will hold its tack for several days while films of quick-freezing neoprene such as neoprene Types CG, AC and AD will lose their tack in 1 hr or less.

A gum cement of neoprene Type AC containing 50 parts of a terpene phenolic resin and 100 parts of neoprene will retain its tack for as long as 72 hr at room temperature. If either more or less than 50 parts of resin is used, the tack retention time will be decreased.

Although pure gum cement containing 50 parts of resin retains its tack for an exceptionally long time, such cement is impractical when in contact with fabrics since it contains no acid acceptors. When magnesia and zinc oxide are added as acid acceptors, the extended tack retention time is only obtained on freshly made cements. If the cement is allowed to stand for several days at room temperature before testing, only the nominal several hours' tack is obtained. If 10 parts of basic zinc carbonate is used as an acid acceptor to replace the magnesium oxide and zinc oxide, from 24 to 48 hr tack is obtained either on cements which are freshly made or which are allowed to age for several months. One disadvantage of the use of basic zinc carbonate is that the material generally available has a considerably larger prticle size than magnesium oxide or zinc oxide; consequently settling out of solution will occur more rapidly. This settling out will not be nearly so noticeable, however, in cements of high viscosity; moreover it can be improved by ball milling the carbonate with solvent and adding it as a slurry. Basic zinc carbonate tends to scorch Type AC neoprene on the mill, and if used, care should be taken to use a cold mill or possibly to add 10 parts of terpene phenolic resin to the mill batch prior to adding the zinc carbonate.

The use of neoprene Types W or WRT to secure long tack retention will result in loss of cohesive strength because of their inability to freeze as rapidly or to as extensively as neoprene Type AC. Nevertheless by heat-reactive phenolic resins, cements are obtained which have comparatively long tack retention combined with high cohesive strength both at ordinary and elevated temperatures. Results obtained by the use of such cements are shown in Table 14.

The addition of 30 parts of resin not only improves the tack retention but also significantly increases the cohesive strength of the films at room temperature and at 141°F.

The resin used in the above experiments was ineffective in increasing the heat resistance when magnesium oxide and zinc oxide were omitted from the cement formula. Tack retention of neoprene Type AC (or AD) cements may be increased also by blending either neoprene Type W or WRT with the Type AC (or Type AD). Results obtained with such blends are shown in Table 15.

These results show that the tack retention may be lengthened considerably without considerably affecting the cohesive strength of the film, for example, a neoprene Type AC film alone had a tack period of only ½ hr with the cohesive strength of at least 56 lb per in. By blending 75 parts of neoprene Type W with 25 parts of neoprene Type AC, the tack retention was extended to 24 hr while the cohesive strength still remained high at 55 lb per in.

Adhesion of Neoprene to Various Materials

Cements made from any type of neoprene will adhere to most porous materials such as cotton fabric, leather, etc. In order to enable neoprene to adhere to fabrics made from materials such as nylon and "Dacron" polyester fiber or to nonporous materials such as metals and glass, a phenolic resin must be incorporated into the cement.

The resins normally used with neoprene are oil-soluble modified phenolics, either thermoplastic or heat-reactive. Thermosetting resins containing

TABLE 14. HIGH STRENGTH CEMENTS POSSESSING LONG TACK RETENTION.

Compound No.	34	35	36	37	38	39
Neoprene Type AC	100	100	—	—	—	—
Neoprene Type W	—	—	100	100	—	—
Neoprene Type WRT	—	—	—	—	100	100
Magnesium oxide	4	4	4	4	4	4
Zinc oxide	5	5	5	5	5	5
Heat-Reactive resin	—	30	—	30	—	30
Toluene	400	400	400	400	400	400
Adhesion (canvas-to-canvas), lb per in.						
75°F Frozen	49A	50A	23C	32A	24C	40A
75°F (Freeze removed)	25	38	14	24	20	30
141°F Original	2	10	1	5	1	3
141°F After 2 hr at 121°C	22	34	12	22	4	25
Tack Retention						
Hours	0.5	4	24	72	120	120

C = Cohesive Failure
A = Adhesive Failure at Canvas

TABLE 15. EFFECT OF NEOPRENE TYPES W AND WRT BLENDS WITH TYPE AC ON TACK RETENTION.

Compound No.	40	41	42	43	44	45	46	47	48
Neoprene Type AC	100	—	—	25	50	75	25	50	75
Neoprene Type W	—	100	—	75	50	25	—	—	—
Neoprene Type WRT	—	—	100	—	—	—	75	50	25
Magnesium oxide	4	4	4	4	4	4	4	4	4
Zinc oxide	5	5	5	5	5	5	5	5	5
Base	168	168	168	168	168	168	168	168	168
Toluene	504	504	504	504	504	504	504	504	504
Adhesion (canvas-to-canvas), lb per in. 75°F (frozen)	56A	18C	17C	55A	58A	60A	26C	45A	55A
Tack Retention Hours	0.5	48	48	25	5	2	48	24	3

A = Adhesive Failure
C = Cohesive Failure

hexamethylene tetramine are not generally used because of their limited compatibility with neoprene.

The amount of resin to use will depend on the particular application involved. If the adhesion is to metal, larger amounts of resin may be required than if the adhesion is to rubber. The adhesion to metal increases proportionately to the amount of resin; however the reverse is true with adhesion to elastomeric materials. Therefore, to obtain optimum adhesion between these two materials, it is necessary to choose the amount of resin which will allow good adhesion to the elastomer without decreasing the metal adhesion below the required amount.

To obtain optimum adhesion to metal, as much as 100 to 200 parts of resin on the neoprene may be required; however films containing such large quantities of resin tend to become brittle on aging. Thus ultimate adhesion may be poor. It is recommended in most cases to use smaller amounts of resin, e.g., 40 to 45 parts, which despite the initial lower adhesion will have better ultimate strength because the films containing these lesser amounts of resin will not become brittle. Another reason for preferring smaller quantities is that cements containing larger amounts have limited tack retention; thus bonding is sometimes difficult unless the surfaces are put together while the cement is unusually wet.

Results showing the adhesion of neoprene Type AC films with and without resin to various materials are listed in Table 16.

The build-up of adhesion to the various materials is slower with 45 parts of resin than with larger amounts; nevertheless the lesser amount is preferred because of greater ultimate strength. To illustrate the effect of amount of resin on ultimate bond strength, two canvas-to-steel bonds were made, one with a Type AC cement containing 45 parts of a heat-reactive resin, and one with 100 parts. The assemblies were tested after aging at 75°F for 9 months. The assembly bonded with the cement containing 45 parts of resin had an adhesion of 72 lb per in., failure being at the metal surface; whereas the one bonded with the cement containing 100 parts of resin failed at 10 lb per in. Failure was at the canvas, and adhesion to the metal was still excellent. The failure at the canvas was due to the brittleness of the resin and not due to the deterioration of the fabric as shown by the tensile strength of the canvas being 245 lb per in. prior to the test and 255 lb per in. after the test.

TABLE 16. EFFECT OF RESIN ON ADHESION OF NEOPRENE CEMENTS TO VARIOUS MATERIALS.

Compound No.	49	50
Neoprene Type AC	100	100
Magnesium oxide	4	4
Zinc oxide	5	5
Resin (heat-reactive)	—	45
Toluene	436	616
Adhesions (Peel), lb per In. at 75°F		
Assemblies aged 7 days at 75°F		
Canvas-to-steel	5	58
Canvas-to-aluminum	6	57
Canvas-to-glass	5	45
Canvas-to-"Lucite"	17	62
Nylon-to-nylon	3	45
Rayon-to-rayon	4	38

Stability of Dried Neoprene Films

There are often applications of adhesives requiring the deposition of a film of cement which is dried and the article stored for future bonding. Neoprene cements lend themselves to reactivation of tack by heat or solvent when properly compounded.

If the cement film contains curing ingredients which cure the polymer slowly at room temperature, it is apparent that storage will progressively decrease the tack that can be obtained by reactivation. For these applications the conventional cement containing only 4 parts of magnesia and 5 parts of zinc oxide is not recommended. While the cement is relatively stable, the dried films will soon become partially cured.

The recommended formulation in Table 17 incorporates calcium silicate and a heat-reactive phenolic resin for increased stability.

A terpene phenolic may be substituted for the heat-reactive resin for somewhat greater stability and better heat-reactive properties, but cohesive strength at elevated temperatures will be somewhat lower. For most applications, however, the listed formula is satisfactory as the dried film will remain stable and capable of being heat-or-solvent-activated for at least 4 wk of storage at 75°F.

Viscosity Control of Neoprene Cements

The viscosity of a neoprene cement may be controlled by several methods described as follows:

(1) *Varying the Solvent Blend.* This method, as previously pointed out, has only a limited effect on the viscosity; hence it is not used to any great extent.

(2) *Varying the Time of Mill Breakdown.* Varying the time of milling has a pronounced effect on the cement viscosity. The effect on the G Type polymers is considerably greater than on W Types or on Type AC and AD; thus the method is limited.

(3) *Blending with Neoprene Type WHV.* Probably the most practical method of controlling the viscosity of neoprene cements is to add varying amounts of neoprene Type WHV, either milled or unmilled, to increase the viscosity as shown in Table 18.

The characteristic freeze of the neoprene Type AC cements and blends containing this polymer is noted by the high strengths and adhesion failures of the frozen films. In all blends, even the one which contained only 25 per cent neoprene Type AC, the cohesion was greater than the adhesion to the canvas. The lower degree of freeze of neoprene Type WHV can be seen in the results on the cement containing only this polymer. In all cases, the films containing blends of neoprene Type AC and neoprene Type WHV decreased approximately 60 per cent in cohesive strength by warming to remove the freeze. The viscosities of neoprene Type AC cements can be increased even more markedly by the addition of unmilled neoprene Type WHV.

The cements shown were all very smooth solutions because Type WHV is a sol polymer. Ratios

TABLE 17.

Compound No.	51
Neoprene Type W	100
Antioxidant	2
Silene EF	10
XLC magnesium oxide	4
Zinc oxide	5
Heat-reactive resin	20
Solvent	As needed

TABLE 18. EFFECT OF MILLED NEOPRENE TYPE WHV ON VISCOSITY OF TYPE AC CEMENTS.

Compound No.	52	53	54	55	56
Neoprene Type AC (milled)	100	75	50	25	0
Neoprene Type WHV (milled)	0	25	50	75	100
Magnesium oxide	4	4	4	4	4
Zinc oxide	5	5	5	5	5
Toluene	433	433	433	433	433
Viscosity, cps	2400	2600	3400	4000	4800
Adhesion (canvas-to-canvas) lb per In.					
75°F (frozen)	52A	50A	50A	57A	20C
75°F (unfrozen)	15C	15C	18C	19C	17C

A = Adhesive failure—cohesion greater than adhesion
C = Cohesive failure

TABLE 19. EFFECT OF UNMILLED NEOPRENE TYPE WHV ON VISCOSITY OF TYPE AC CEMENTS.

Compound No.	57	58	59	60
Neoprene Type AG (milled)	100	95	75	50
Neoprene Type WHV (unmilled)	—	5	25	50
Magnesium oxide	4	4	4	4
Zinc oxide	5	5	5	5
Toluene	433	—	—	—
Viscosity, cps	2400	4000	6000	8000
Adhesion (canvas-to-canvas)—lb. per In.				
75°F Frozen	52A	45A	45A	46A
75°F Unfrozen	15C	20C	18C	16C

A = Adhesive failure.
C = Cohesive failure.

of WHV to AC greater than 1:1 were not tested because it was believed that for most applications greater ratios would result in cements too viscous to be practical for most applications. The adhesions of all cements were approximately the same irrespective of the amount of WHV added.

Milled vs. Unmilled Neoprene

It was stated earlier that milled or unmilled neoprene could be used in the slurry method of compounding. Cements made from unmilled neoprene differ from those made from milled neoprene in the following important properties. Cements made from a milled compound are smoother in texture and the dry ingredients are usually dispersed better. Milled neoprene cements contain less gel, with smaller particle size; consequently they will penetrate porous surfaces such as fabric or leather to a greater extent than will cements made from un-

milled polymer. As a result they will have greater adhesion to these surfaces. Dried films from cements made from milled polymer will freeze more rapidly and extensively, giving greater ultimate cohesive strength. Cements made from unmilled polymers will, however, have greater original cohesive strength and greater strength at elevated temperatures.

Unmilled neoprene is preferred for cements which require highest strength at elevated temperatures. One disadvantage of a cement made without milling is that dispersion of the dry ingredients may be poor. Another disadvantage is that not all types of neoprene or all plasticities of a given type are soluble without first milling. If neoprene is to be used without milling, it is better to add the dry compounding ingredients as a ball-milled slurry in solvent, because better dispersion will be obtained than when the dry ingredients are added as such to the churn containing the solvent and neoprene.

Neoprene Types W, WRT, WHV and AD are very low in gel content; these types are recommended if unmilled polymer cements are desired.

The question has often been asked about the effect of mill breakdown on various hardness grades of neoprene Type AC. In order to determine this, the Mooney viscosities, the solution viscosities, and the cohesive strengths at 75°F (unfrozen) of soft, medium and hard neoprene Type AC were determined after 0, 5, 10 and 20 min milling on a laboratory mill. The results obtained are given in Table 20.

These results indicate that irrespective of the grade of neoprene used, if milled to the same point with respect to solution viscosity, the performance measured by cohesive strength will be the same. The high cohesive strengths of the films from the unmilled polymer solutions are noteworthy.

TABLE 20. EFFECT OF MILLING ON SOFT, MEDIUM AND HARD TYPE AC.

Milling Time (min)	SOFT				MEDIUM				HARD			
	A	B	C	D	A	B	C	D	A	B	C	D
0	42	8800	18	10	50	16800	20	11	60	—	28	13
1	34	2800	16	4	45	8000	19	8	56	18600	20	12
5	24	1200	11	2	27	1600	12	2	38	3000	19	5
10	20	800	8	1½	22	1200	11	1.5	28	1600	12	2
20	16	400	4	1	16	800	7	1	22	800	8	1

A = Mooney viscosity of milled polymer (small rotor).
B = Solution viscosity, in cps, of 20% solution in toluene-hexane (1-1).
C = Cohesive strength in pounds per inch of unfrozen film.
D = Cohesive strength at 140°F.

EFFECT OF CONTAINER MATERIALS ON NEOPRENE CEMENTS

The effect of containers in which neoprene cements are stored or shipped depends on the type of neoprene as well as the compounding ingredients used, both of which will be discussed separately.

Iron

The greater volume of cements are stored or shipped in iron or steel containers. Simple solutions of neoprene except those made from neoprene Types W, WHV, WRT, and AD will darken in iron and tend to gel prematurely. To prevent this, it is necessary to add an acid acceptor such as magnesia and zinc oxide to the cement.

Solutions of neoprene Type W, AD, WRT, or WHV do not discolor to any great extent when in contact with iron, and solutions in toluene discolored only slightly after storing for 30 days at 158°F in contact with steel wool. A neoprene Type GN or CG cement stored under the same conditions will become black to reflected light in 1 or 2 days.

Brass

A solution of neoprene made from any type of neoprene except Type W, AD, WHV, and WRT will start to discolor within a few minutes upon exposure to brass. Within 1 hr the solution will become an almost opaque dark red. Magnesia and zinc oxide will greatly though not entirely decrease the rate and extent of discoloration.

Glass

Although it is generally believed that glass is inactive with respect to the stability of neoprene cements, this is not necessarily true. On numerous occasions neoprene cements stored in glass at 158°F have gelled in less time than when stored in aluminum or even lead. It was originally thought that the alkali in the glass possibly caused premature gelation; however rinsing the glass with the acid and drying had no effect on the stability. Still it is not known if the glass has a destabilizing effect on the cement or if the aluminum acts in some way to stabilize it.

Lead

Lead or terne-plate containers are not, as a rule, recommended for neoprene cements because it causes the premature gelation of certain cements. The premature gelation in lead containers has been observed only with gum cements of the G-type polymers, and it is believed that compounded cements containing magnesia and zinc oxide may be stored satisfactorily in this type of container.

Aluminum

This metal is the most satisfactory container material of those tested. Compounded cements stored in aluminum are more stable than those stored in glass.

Tin

Although this metal appears to be satisfactory, data indicate that it is not quite as good as aluminum.

The most generally used material for storage and shipment of neoprene cements in quantities greater than 10 gal is iron. Containers lined with certain baked-on epoxy and phenolic resins have been successfully utilized by the trade for the packaging of neoprene cements.

ADVERSE EFFECTS OF NEOPRENE CEMENTS

As neoprene ages, traces of hydrochloric acid are formed by a slight decomposition of the chloroprene molecule which tends to deteriorate cotton, rayon and other cellulosic materials with which the neoprene may come in contact. The formation of hydrochloric acid takes place very slowly at room temperature but is catalyzed by heat or exposure to direct sunlight. The deteriorating effect of neoprene cements in fabrics is inhibited by the presence of certain compounding ingredients such as magnesia and zinc oxide, which act as antacids by neutralizing the acid, as well as particular phenolic resins and antioxidants which tend to inhibit the formation of the acid. Magnesia and zinc oxide are effective in reducing the amount of deterioration at elevated temperatures but have less beneficial effect in direct sunlight. Antioxidants and phenolic resins have little effect in gum solutions of neoprene but improve markedly those cements containing magnesium and zinc oxides.

Neoprene adhesive films used in contact with pyroxylin or lacquer finishes will not stain them if appropriate nonstaining compounding ingredients are employed. Certain good antioxidants such as "Neozone" A or D unfortunately stain.

—21—

Polysulfide Sealants
and Adhesives

Julian R. Panek
Thiokol Chemical Corporation
Trenton, New Jersey

POLYSULFIDE SEALANTS

Sealants based on polysulfide liquid polymers have found wide acceptance in a number of applications requiring a flexible, adhering, chemically resistant composition of matter. Specifically formulated sealants are used as void fillers to seal electrical components from the effects of moisture, while protecting the various components from severe vibration. Other sealants are required to seal joints in aircraft made of riveted sections and to maintain a flexible adherent barrier that will withstand chemical attack. The modern curtain wall requires flexible sealants which will adhere to a variety of building surfaces while keeping out the wind, rain, and dust. In the modern curtain wall, the wide movement at the joints is a result of gravity, heat, light, and wind, and only elastomeric sealants based on polysulfide liquid polymers have been found to perform satisfactorily over the entire gamut of environmental conditions. Satisfactory sealants have been developed for caulking wooden aircraft flight decks, for sealing aircraft cabins, sealing fuse caps, and many other specialty applications requiring superior performance.

Many of the sealants have been prepared using "Thiokol" LP-2, LP-32, or LP-31 as the base polysulfide liquid polymer; the chemistry, cure mechanisms, reinforcement, and applications will thus be restricted to these polymers. The chemistry and applications of polysulfide polymers, crudes, water dispersions, and various liquid polymers are covered completely in an extensive bibliography by Berenbaum and Panek.[1]

General Chemistry

The general preparation of polysulfide liquid polymers, as discussed by Patrick and Ferguson,[2] involves first the reaction of bis-chloroethyl-formal with a sodium polysulfide solution containing specific emulsifying and nucleating agents as shown below:

$$nClC_2H_4OCH_2OC_2H_4Cl + nNa_2S_{2.25} \longrightarrow$$
$$(-C_2H_4OCH_2OC_2H_4S_{2.25})_n + 2nNaCl$$

In the next step, the high molecular weight polymer is split into segments which are simultaneously terminated by mercaptan groups as shown below:

$$RSSR + NaSH + NaHSO_3 \longrightarrow$$
$$2RSH + Na_2S_2O_3$$

The concentration of splitting salts controls the average molecular weight of the LP-2 and LP-32, which has the following general formula:

$$HS(-C_2H_4OCH_2OC_2H_4SS-)_{23}$$
$$- C_2H_4OCH_2OC_2H_4SH$$

Both polymers are prepared at an average molecular weight of 4000, and they only differ in the mole percentage of crosslinking agent (trichloropropane) used in the initial reaction. LP-2 is made using 2 mole per cent of trichloropropane; whereas LP-32 is prepared with 0.5 per cent.

Decreasing the crosslinking agent gives lower modulus and higher elongation desirable in applications involving greater movement. In some instances LP-31 is used in sealant applications and differs from LP-32 in that it has a higher molecular weight and viscosity. The physical properties of the three polymers used in sealant applications are compared in Table 1.

The mercaptan terminated liquid polymers are readily polymerized to cured elastomeric solids by the use of active oxidizing agents. A large number of curing agents have been evaluated, among which lead dioxide has been the most widely used in sealant applications. Other curing agents which have found merit in specific sealant formulations include tellurium dioxide, managanese dioxide, zinc peroxide, the various alkaline chromates, antimony trioxide, etc.

The general reactions involving lead dioxide appear below:

$$2\text{-RSH} + PbO_2 \longrightarrow -RSSR- + PbO + H_2O$$
$$2\text{-RSH} + PbO \longrightarrow -RSPbSR + H_2O$$
$$RSPbSR + S \xrightarrow{heat} -RSSR- + PbS$$
$$RSPbSR + \longrightarrow RSR + PbS$$
$$RSPbSR + PbO_2 \longrightarrow RSSR + 2PbO$$

Compounding

In order to obtain the optimum properties, a polysulfide sealant has to be specifically formulated to best meet the requirements at hand. Working life has to be adjusted to fall within the desired range; the catalyst and the compound adjusted to the average temperature; and humidity conditions have to prevail at a specific season. Reinforcing fillers are properly dispersed, and selected adhesion additives are used to enable the cured sealant to adhere to a variety of surfaces under various conditions. Specific thixotropic additives are used to enable the compound to be placed into vertical seams without flow. The various elements of compounding such as curing agent, retardation, acceleration, reinforcement, and adhesion methods will be covered separately.

Curing Agents. Although a number of curing agents have been found for the polysulfide liquid polymers, lead dioxide has been the most widely used for sealants. This is due in part to its high reactivity, availability, and reasonable cost. Other systems have been found, which give good cure properties, but which are less tolerant to changes in pH, ambient temperature, relative humidity, and the various ingredients that are required to make up a finished sealant.

Technical grade lead dioxide is generally more satisfactory than the C.P. grade, which is purer but much slower in cure rate activity. It is believed that some of the impurities such as lead oxide and zinc oxide are catalytic and, therefore, desirable for faster cures. The only practical specification for lead dioxide is that it must react with the liquid polymer in a standard formulation to meet a performance requirement. This technique has been employed to test polymer batches against standard batches of catalyst pastes; to check the performance of the various ingredients; and generally to test any component against a component with known performances.

In many known cases of variation in sealants, indiscriminate substitution of one ingredient was found to be at fault. The experienced processors are aware that control testing of all ingredients prior to factory processing is necessary.

Formulations for lead dioxide pastes are shown in Table 2. The C-2 paste is used when no extractable plasticizer is permissible in the resultant compound; the toluene usually volatizes very readily. C-5 is safer to use, since it has no volatile solvent and disperses more readily. C-10 is used where very rapid cures are desired since the retarder, stearic acid, is omitted.

For most sealant formulations, C-5 or a similar accelerator has been used extensively. Numerous studies in the past have determined the sensitivity

TABLE 1. THE PHYSICAL PROPERTIES OF POLYSULFIDE LIQUID POLYMERS.

	LP-31	LP-2	LP-32
Viscosity at 25°F, poises	800–1400	350–450	350–450
Average molecular weight	7500	4000	4000
Specific gravity	1.31	1.27	1.27
Refractive index	1.570	1.5689	1.5689
Pour point, °F	45–50	45–50	45
Flash point, (open cup)°F	455	450	455
Fire point, (open cup)°F	475	475	485
Crosslinking agent, %	0.5	2.0	0.5

TABLE 2. LEAD DIOXIDE ACCELERATOR PASTE.

	C-2	C-5	C-10
	(%)	(%)	(%)
Lead dioxide	55	50	50
Stearic acid	7	5	—
Dibutyl phthalate	—	45	50
Toluene	38	—	—
Recommended Ratios			
Parts per 100 of LP-2 and LP-32			
	14	15	15

of the lead dioxide cure to relative humidity and moisture content in the polymer. Both high relative humidity and high moisture content accelerate cure. While ambient humidity cannot be controlled, the moisture content of all polymer batches is adjusted to a very small range, i.e., 0.1 to 0.2 per cent for proper control. Other variables that might affect cure are adjusted by varying the retarder to make batches conform to a performance specification.

Retarders. The oxidation and reaction of thiol groups is accelerated in an alkaline environment and retarded in an acidic environment; consequently, pH plays an important part in cure-rate studies. A number of acidic retarders have been evaluated for lead peroxides, the three most effective being stearic acid, lead stearate, and aluminum distearate. The effectiveness of stearic acid as a retarder is shown in Table 3. In this study, the stearic acid is incorporated into the base compound. The retarder can be just as readily incorporated into the paste. Aluminum distearate and lead stearate are less sensitive to changes in relative humidity.

Reinforcement. Most uses for liquid polymers require reinforcing fillers which both strengthen and reduce the cost of the compound; furthermore, fillers are used to impart thixotropy and color to sealant compounds. Indiscriminate choice of the filler can ruin the performance of a polysulfide sealant. There is an optimum filler loading which will vary with the different fillers depending on their particle size and their effect on thixotropy. The electrical properties of the sealant, color, possible effects on the aging properties, as well as package stability are other factors to consider. The choice of filler should depend on its performance in a polysulfide polymer. Too frequently, fillers and filler loadings have been selected on the basis of their performance characteristics in synthetic elastomers or in other binder systems.

Table 4 lists a number of fillers that are used with polysulfide polymers, together with the physical properties at the various loadings given. Although the list is not a recommendation of specific types, it is an example of the types of fillers. In most cases, sealants are prepared using a combination of fillers to obtain a desired effect. Where thixotropy is de-

TABLE 3. THE EFFECT OF VARIABLE STEARIC ACID ON THE WORKING LIFE OF LP-2.

	1	2	3	4	5
LP-2	100	100	100	100	100
"SRF" carbon black	30	30	30	30	30
Stearic acid	—	0.5	1.0	1.5	3.0
C-10 "Accelerator"	15	15	15	15	15
Working life, hr	<0.25	1.0	2.0	3.0	3.5

TABLE 4. THE EFFECT OF FILLER ON THE PROPERTIES[b] of LP-32[a].

Filler	Loading	Description	Original			Heat Aged 1 WK at 250°F		
			T	E	H	T	E	H
None	0		125	350	25	285	300	40
"Thermax"	60	thermal black	550	740	53	625	450	61
"SRF" No. 3	30	furnace black	600	800	52	800	600	65
"Calcene" TM	20	calcium carbonate	225	650	45	265	590	50
"Witcarb" RC	40	calcium carbonate	525	880	44	450	575	54
"Cab-O-Sil"	15	silicate	475	820	46	575	500	60
"Zeolex 23"	15	silicate	280	820	40	430	460	48
"ASP" No. 1200	40	clay	340	550	45	520	500	55
Lithopone	40	ZnS-BaSO4	275	760	40	300	350	51
"Blanc Fixe"	40	BaSO4	220	620	40	280	500	45
ZS-800	40	zinc sulfide	425	830	38	275	350	50
"Titanox" AMO	40	titanium dioxide	350	860	40	400	700	50
"Reynolds" 5XD	40	aluminum powder	150	170	46	300	150	65

[a] The base formula is:

LP-32	100 parts
Sulfur	0.1 part
"Accelerator" C-5	15 parts
Filler	As shown above, all parts by weight

sired, either "Cab-O-Sil," or "Calcene TM" is used in conjunction with other fillers to impart this property. When aluminum powder is used, then a small quantity of scavenger such as "Syloid AL-1" is suggested to absorb any moisture present in the compound, thereby preventing the formation of hydrogen gas. This agent is satisfactory when used at a volume loading of 4 to 5 parts per 100 of polymer.

While aluminum powder has been used alone to impart luster to a sealant, this is not recommended practice since little reinforcement is imparted by this filler; and other reinforcing fillers should be used in conjunction with it.

Some fillers such as the clays have an inherent acidic effect and should be used with caution; other fillers, e.g., silicate fillers, have a high pH which can cause package instability. These factors must be carefully considered in formulating sealant compositions.

Adhesion Methods. Polysulfide polymers when cured against solid surfaces do not exhibit any appreciable adhesion, unless specific steps are taken. Adhesion is absolutely necessary in sealant applications and built-in adhesion greatly simplifies applicability. Adhesion can be obtained with polysulfide sealants by the use of specific additives, primers, or a combination of these methods.

Adhesion Additives. A number of adhesion additives have been evaluated, none of which is universally satisfactory for all surfaces; moreover, these additives may perform differently when the sealants are in contact with various wet and dry surfaces. Consequently, evaluation of various additives is usually directed toward obtaining adhesion to the most commonly used building materials. Generally it is concluded that adhesion to glass, aluminum and steel in the presence of water, cold, and heat would cover the predominant needs. An example of the improved adhesion obtained by the use of a specific phenolic resin additive, "Durez" 10694, is given in Table 5. Other phenolic resins that perform as well are: "Bakelite" Resin BRL-2741, "Catalin" 633, and "Rexinox" 468. Where other cure systems were used such as tellurium dioxide, it was found that these phenolic resins retarded the cure; but another additive, a liquid epoxy resin having an epoxy equivalent in the range 170 to 210 in combination with polyvinyl acetate, performed satisfactorily with this cure system and improved water resistance. Ironically enough, the epoxy resin does not impart adhesion in a lead dioxide cure.

One limiting factor involving sealants containing certain phenolic resins is that these sealants may cause staining of marble under certain conditions. Where this problem is contemplated, one recom-

TABLE 5. LP-32 ADHESION COMPOUNDS

	1	2	3
LP-32	100	100	100
"SRF" black	30	30	30
Stearic acid	1	1	1
Sulfur	0.1	0.1	0.1
PVA[1]	—	—	1
"Durez" 10694	—	5	4
C-5 paste	15	15	15

Adhesion Peel Test
(ASTM D-903-49T)

	After 7 Days Room-Temperature Aging		
Aluminum (lb/in.)	0	16C	35C
Steel (lb/in.)	0	15C	25C
Glass (lb/in.)	0	16C	39C
	After 7 Days Aging and 7 Days Water Immersion		
Aluminum (lb/in.)	0	24C	26C
Steel (lb/in.)	0	24C	23C
Glass (lb/in.)	0	0	33C

C = Cohesive failure

[1] Polyvinyl acetate—"Vinac" RP-250, Colton Chemical Co. When used with "Durez" 10694 (Durez Resin & Plastics). it is first soaked in the phenolic resin to effect partial solution before incorporation into LP-32.

mended practice is to resort to the use of a primer to obtain adhesion, while eliminating the troublesome component from the sealant. The tellurium dioxide cured sealant, using an epoxy resin, will not stain marble and could be used in this instance.

Primers. The use of adhesion additives may be undesirable from certain standpoints; therefore, in these cases, primers are required to achieve the desired performance. Table 6 gives data on the adhesion values obtained using a non-adhering base compound in conjunction with various primers. The data illustrate that "Polyclad" 932, PR-1099, and "Ty-Ply" S are good primers for stone and masonry; whereas PR-1422 and N-15 are good primers for steel, aluminum, and glass.

The combined effect of primers used in conjunction with an adhesion additive gives better adhesion peel values as shown in Table 7. The best over-all results in this series are shown by "Chemlock" 220 although N-15 is satisfactory against all surfaces except concrete.

Compounding for Improved Heat Resistance. Where maximum retention of physical properties after heat aging is desired, selection of the curing agent becomes a prime factor after selection of the proper reinforcing agent. The oxidizing agents which react to form mercaptides are less desirable. The formation of mercaptides can be expected when zinc oxide, zinc peroxide, lead peroxide (in certain formulations), barium peroxide, etc., are used. On the other hand, manganese dioxide, tellurium di-

TABLE 6. ADHESION PRIMERS FOR USE WITH A NON-ADHESIVE LP-2 COMPOUND.[a]

Original Peel Adhesion* (ASTM-903-49T) After 7 Days Room Temperature Cure

Primer	Description	Aluminum	Steel	Glass	Concrete
"Polyclad" 932[b]	vinyl	9	15	13	10
PR-1099[c]	furan resin	15	12	16	12
PR-1422[d]	polysulfide	15	15	18	poor
"Ty-Ply" S[e]	chlorinated rubber	10	9	12	10
"Chemlock"-200[f]	chlorinated rubber	14	9	22	poor
N-15[g]	neoprene	14	16	19	poor

*values in lb per in. width

After 7 Days Aging and 7 Days Water Immersion

Primer	Description	Aluminum	Steel	Glass	Concrete
"Polyclad" 932		poor	poor	poor	10
PR-1099		poor	poor	poor	11
PR-1422		10	13	16	poor
"Ty-Ply" S		poor	11	poor	12
"Chemlock" 220		12	16	21	poor

[a] LP-2 100 parts, "SRF" black 30 parts, stearic acid 1 part, "Accelerator" C-5 15 parts
[b] "Polyclad" 932: Carboline Co.
[c] PR-1099: Products Research Co.
[d] PR-1422: Products Research Co.
[e] "Ty-Ply" S: Marbon Chemical Co.
[f] "Chemlock" 220: Lord Manufacturing Co.
[g] N-15: Gates Engineering Co.

TABLE 7. ADHESION PRIMERS USED IN CONJUNCTION WITH AN ADHESIVE LP-2 COMPOUND.[a]

Original Peel Adhesion* (ASTM D-903-49T) After 7 Days Room Temperature Cure

Primer	Description	Aluminum	Steel	Glass	Concrete
"Polyclad" 932	vinyl	10	10	9	12
PR-1099	furan resin	28	30	32	11
PR-1422	polysulfide	20	12	16	poor
TPT[b]	organic titanate	29	30	31	poor
"Chemlock" 220	chlorinated rubber	37	33	40	11
N-15	neoprene	34	36	40	29

*value in lb per in. width

After 7 Days Aging and 7 Days Water Immersion

Primer	Description	Aluminum	Steel	Glass	Concrete
"Polyclad"		poor	15	poor	15
PR-1099		10	20	10	poor
PR-1422		19	28	17	poor
TPT		21	25	10	poor
"Chemlock" 220		27	30	15	10
N-15		22	22	20	poor

[a] LP-2 100 parts, "SRF" black 30 parts, stearic acid 1 part, "Durez" 10694 5 parts, "Accelerator" C-5 15 parts
[b] TPT (tetraisopropyl titanate): duPont Co.

oxide, and ammonium dichromate, as well as a specifically formulated compound based on cumene hydroperoxide, give cured sealants having improved heat resistance.

The resultant by-products of the oxidizing agents used also have a considerable effect on heat-aging properties. The reactive by-product using para-quinone dioxime is paraphenylene diamine. The by-products from various organic peroxides are either acids or tertiary alcohols which are mildly acidic. Both reaction products can cause chain scission at elevated temperatures.

Typical formulations which exhibit improved heat resistance are given in Table 8.

Liquid polymers with other backbones have been prepared and compared in high temperature resistance. The use of dichlorobutyl ether and dichlorobutyl formal in place of dichlorodiethyl formal has given polymers with slightly improved high temperature properties as well as improved flexibility at lower temperatures.

Other Properties. The use of nonblack reinforcing agents with polysulfide polymers gives compositions having very satisfactory electrical resistant

TABLE 8. FORMULATIONS EXHIBITING IMPROVED
HEAT RESISTANCE.

	1	2	3	4
LP-32	100	100	100	100
TiO$_2$	—	50	50	—
Sulfur	0.1	—	—	—
(NH$_4$)$_2$Cr$_2$O$_7$	6	—	—	—
DMF	14	—	—	—
"SRF" black	40	—	—	—
Stearic acid	1	—	—	—
"Durez" 10694	5	—	—	—
Sodium stearate	—	10	—	—
Tellurium dioxide	—	3	—	—
Manganese dioxide	—	—	2	—
Dinitro-benzene	—	—	0.5	—
"Cab-O-Sil"	—	—	—	20
"DMP"-30	—	—	—	1.2
MgO	—	—	—	4
Cumene hydroperoxide	—	—	—	6.5
Maleic anhydride	—	—	—	0.5

properties. Values for surface resistivity for non-black fillers fall into the range of 10^{10} to 10^{14} ohms over a temperature of 70 to 212°F. For this same temperature, the values for volume resistivity vary from 10^{10} to 10^{12} ohm-cm. Values for dielectric constant vary from 6 to 9. A combination of 50 parts of lithopone and 15 parts of "Kenflex" A resin in LP-2 cured with C-5 exhibits better electrical resistance.

Where optimum solvent resistance properties are desired, LP-2 is generally used in preference to LP-32 or LP-31. Volume swell values on a carbon black-reinforced LP-2 compound are given in per cent volume swell after one month's immersion in the following solvents: toluene 95, carbon tetrachloride 55, ethyl acetate 40, butyl acetate 30, methyl isobutyl ketone 24, acetone 19, methylethyl ketone 56, water 2, alcohol 0, and SR-6 8. Low solvent swell is desired where these sealants are used to seal wing integral fuel tanks.

Applications

Several of the major applications involving the use of polysulfide sealants will be discussed in this section. These applications will be approached by first defining the problem; second, by describing the simulated tests covered in specifications; and

third, by recommending compounding formulations to meet the requirements.

Sealants for the Aircraft Industry. Five military specifications are in existence that require polysulfide sealants, of which three require a heat-resistant, high-adhesion sealing compound for integral fuel tanks which differ slightly in their high temperature requirements. A fourth specification is for pressure-cabin sealing; the fifth calls for a low adhesion sealing compound for fuel-cell cavities.

(1) MIL-S-7502B. This specification covers a polysulfide sealant for sealing and repairing integral fuel tanks and fuel-cell cavities. This sealant requires a protective coating of buna-N sealing topcoat conforming to MIL-S-4383. This specification requires high adhesion and fuel resistance. The problem was to obtain a polysulfide joint which would not leak fuel in spite of temperature variations from −65 to 140°F in contact with the Type III Reference Fuel. The sealant was further required to maintain good adhesion under these conditions, be nonvolatile, remain flexible, and have low extractibility.

Simulated test conditions required measuring the change in elastic properties on cast sheets (overcoated with the sealing topcoat after immersion in the test media for 1 and 2 months at 140°F). The adhesion was determined on adhesion peel tests using a 180° strip-back of a sealant layer reinforced with fabric. Low temperature flexibility was measured by bending a coated panel over a mandrel having a 2 in. radius. Coated aluminum surfaces were also tested for possible corrosion by the sealant by immersing the assembly in a two-layer salt water-hydrocarbon mixture for 10 days. Lastly, a test assembly is immersed in test fluid and vibrated with no resultant failure.

All of the conditions in the test procedures are extrapolations of the real environment on an airplane wing. While there is no guarantee that performance in the specified test program will result in satisfactory performance on aircraft, subsequent use has established that the sealants do perform adequately and that the tests are realistic.

The sealants for this specification are not designed for high speed aircraft; therefore high temperature performance requirements are not necessary. They have been based on the use of lead dioxide as the curing agent. Adhesion was obtained by incorporating minimum amounts of adhesion additives to get satisfactory adhesion while maintaining low extraction. The use of the buna-N cover coat minimized the adsorption of fuel and extraction and ensured the proper functioning of the system. This cover coat did not peel off, and the combination results in a very adequately performing system. The usual filler is a semi-reinforcing carbon black, and the sealant is adjusted for viscosity and flow by varying the filler.

(2) MIL-S-8802A. In essence, this specification is a more rigorous treatment of MIL-S-7502B. Another requirement has been added to the physical property requirements after solvent aging, and a heat cycle of 7 days at 275°F has been included. An additional reference fluid containing traces of butyl mercaptan is included in the specification to simulate the greatest permissible limits in jet fuels. Unless some stabilizing agents are used with the lead dioxide cure, such sealants do not exhibit the necessary solvent resistance to the mercaptan containing test fluid; moreover, this system is more difficult to control in heat aging. It is permissible to use a protective overcoat in this specification also, which may be the means by which a lead dioxide cured sealant meets the requirements of the specification.

Conversely, the more exotic cure systems based on tellurium dioxide, manganese dioxide, and ammonium dichromate exhibit sufficient resistance to the mercaptan containing test fluid, and, when properly formulated, exhibit better heat resistance. It is also possible that LP-31 has merit since it lowers the incidence for terminal contamination or side reaction due to its significantly higher molecular weight and fewer reactive sites.

(3) MIL-S-8784A. This specification covers a sealing compound having low adhesion for use as void fillers in integral fuel tanks and fuel-cell cavities. Its over-all requirements are mild compared to the above specifications. The general test methods are similar to those in the above specification. Essentially, the compounds should strip and the maximum adhesion should not exceed 2 lb. The sealant is dyed red so that it is never confused with other sealants.

This compound does not require any adhesion additive; it is made using some white filler, added to a red dye. There are no problems expected in meeting performance requirements with a lead dioxide cure.

(4) MIL-S-7124 (Bu-Aer-52310). This specification covers a pressure-cabin sealant to be applied over seams, rivets, and faying surfaces for the purpose of making pressurized areas airtight. The general requirements are that the compound adhere to aluminum, remain flexible down to −65°F, and protect aluminum against attack by salt water. Simulated tests call for sealing a test panel in an assembly that is subjected to pressure and vibration. No specific problems are envisioned using lead dioxide with adhesion additives together with

standard fillers and a retarder to adjust for viscosity and cure rate.

(5) MIL-S-5817A. This specification covers the requirements for a solvent-based polysulfide sealant used to seal integral fuel tanks. This system was desirable in that it could be used to seal small, irregularly shaped fuel tanks after complete assembly of the wing by the fill-drain method; furthermore it would permit the penetration of the solvent-based polysulfide paint into any thin void areas between riveted sections, would cover all rivets, and would coat the entire inner surface with a film of 3 mil minimum thickness. The film was subsequently cured by subjecting the film to an environment of ammonia gas for approximately 12 hr at ambient temperatures at a pressure of 2 psi. Requirements for the films are quite similar to those for MIL-S-7502B. The cure system for this sealant is based on zinc peroxide. The solvent-based sealer compound formulated with carbon black is stable unless exposed to an ammonia atmosphere, thereby permitting the re-use of drained compounds in the fill-drain operations.

Bolted Steel Tanks:

(1) MIL-S-14231 B. This important specification is written around a polysulfide sealant for use on bolted steel and aluminum storage tanks which are made from sections of panels that are bolted together. The overlapping sections and joints are subsequently sealed with a suitable sealant which will adhere, resist the various aviation fuels, neither extract nor contaminate the fuel, and remain flexible down to −65°F. No dynamic tests are involved, and the usual adhesion tests, extraction test, bend test around a mandrel for low temperature, and solvent swell are employed. For a polysulfide compound, no real problems are posed in order to meet these requirements. The usual adhesion additives are used normally in conjunction with any of several black or nonblack fillers and cured with lead dioxide.

Sealants for Electrical Potting. Polysulfide sealants formulated with proper reinforcing fillers have good electrically resistant properties which have the additional property of remaining flexible over wide temperature ranges. These sealants are thus being used to pot electrical connectors and assemblies where they absorb considerable mechanical vibration. Their low water adsorption properties prevent any possible shorting, which is another advantage. Several specifications call for polysulfide sealants.

(1) MIL-S-8516B and MIL-I-16923C. Both of these specifications require several classes of dielectric properties. With polysulfide compounds several classes can be met by very carefully balancing the

formulation ingredients to obtain the minimum properties required. Emphasis should be placed on the use of nonmoisture-absorbing electrically resistant reinforcing fillers. It has also been found that higher states of cure further improve these properties. For this reason, traces of sulfur are used to obtain better resistance. The lead dioxide cure did not corrode copper and silver, which was not generally the case with other cure systems. Several electrical-grade resins such as "Kenflex" A also imparted improved resistance. Good adhesion is generally essential. Simulated tests are not generally used in electrical testing, and the approach is straightforward.

Flight Decks. Polysulfide sealants have given very satisfactory performance on wooden flight decks where the functions of the sealant are to maintain flexibility and adhesion to the wooden planking; keep water from seeping between planks to the lower decks; and prevent rotting of the deck.

(1) MIL-C-18255. The basic requirement in this specification is that the compound adhere to the various woods that have been used in decks, including Douglas Fir and Teak. Because of the high extensibility required in this specification and the need to maintain adhesion to the various woods, primers were evaluated and found necessary to obtain the desired properties. Their use becomes more obvious in simulated water-immersion tests. Another reason for using primer is that it keeps water away from the interface. An additional problem which became apparent during initial test trials was that certain formulations bubbled due to the nature of their ultimate cure. The bubbling, which was due to air being forced through the compound by a bellows action of the flight deck, was eliminated by proper formulation. For the future, a bubble test was added to the specification. Proper formulation requires small quantities of a thermal black in order to obtain a flowable compound that exhibits high elongation and low modulus after cure. A properly formulated sealant will exhibit these properties; nevertheless it will have a high state of cure that will resist bubbling. This is not a paradox, since research studies show wide differences in the state of cure which are not apparent by superficial physical property tests. Tests are made in simulated environments on standard sample assemblies in conjunction with the so-called "bubble test." Sealants that meet this specification have given satisfactory performance.

Sealer Compounds:

(1) MIL-S-7126A. This specification covers the requirements of a sealant in sealing methyl methacrylate sheets into aluminum window assemblies for use on aircraft. The requirements are adhesion of the sealant to the acrylate sheet and the aluminum frame under various exposure environments and the property of non-crazing. The sealant must remain flexible over a wide temperature range and perform over a pressure gradient. No unusual problems are contemplated in formulating a sealant to perform under these conditions.

(2) MIL-C-15705A. This specification covers a polysulfide-based sealant for use in seams, joints, and dams between metal surfaces to provide watertight and airtight seals. The sealant was developed primarily for sealing the cocoon structures on board deactivated ships. This is one of the few existing specifications that defines the exact formulation to be used. (See Table 9.) The compound covered in this specification is not intended for caulking seams of wooden decks, or hulls of ships, nor is it recommended for any working expansion joint since it has poor adhesion to most surfaces.

Hose Repair Compounds:

(1) MIL-S-2869A. This specification gives the requirements of a polysulfide-based sealant for repairing large oil suction and discharge hose covers. Many large hoses receive considerable abuse due to their large size, weight, and the fact that they are dragged and lifted by means of chains. The tough neoprene covers are sometimes torn and abraded, thus exposing the reinforcing fabric of the hose. Unless the exposed area is quickly patched, water is readily absorbed into the hose and rapid deterioration results. A polysulfide sealant was developed which adheres to fabric, has sufficient toughness to withstand rough handling, and resists the oils and fuels with which it may come in contact.

Building-Trade Sealants:

(1) ASA Specification A116.1–1960. This specification covers minimum performance requirements for sealants in applications where a reasonable degree of expansion and contraction may occur. The modern curtain wall with its large expanse of aluminum, glass, steel, stone, and other construction materials has emphasized the need for an elastomeric sealant. In this specification, the sealant is required to maintain a minimum tensile adhesion of 10 psi to a wide variety of surfaces with minimum elongations of 100 to 150 per cent over various test environments, including accelerated aging, water immersion, low temperature cycling, and ultraviolet exposure. These tests have been designed to test the elastomeric sealants in simulated joints under any outdoor conditions that may exist from Alaska to the Equator. Because of possible discoloration of marble under specific conditions, the

TABLE 9. RECOMMENDED STARTING FORMULATIONS FOR POLYSULFIDE SEALANTS.

	a	b	c	d	e	f	g
PART A							
LP-2	100	100	100	100	100	—	100
LP-32	—	—	—	—	—	100	—
"SRF" No. 3 black	30	30	—	—	—	10	—
Stearic acid	1.0	1.0	1.0	1.0	—	1.0	1.0
"Durez" 10694	5.0	—	5.0	—	—	—	—
"Calcene" TM	—	—	25.0	25.0	—	—	—
"Titanox" AMO	—	—	10.0	10.0	—	—	—
Lithopone	—	—	—	—	50	—	—
"Kenflex" A	—	—	—	—	15	—	—
"Sterling" MT	—	—	—	—	—	10	—
Sulfur	—	—	—	—	—	0.15	—
"Thermax"	—	—	—	—	—	—	100
"Santicizer" E-15	—	—	—	—	—	—	50
PART B							
C-5 "Accelerator"	15	15	15	15	15	—	—
C-9 "Accelerator"	—	—	—	—	—	13.8	—
PbO$_2$	—	—	—	—	—	—	75
Dibutyl phthalate	—	—	—	—	—	—	60 } 25
Stearic acid	—	—	—	—	—	—	3
	Black thixo- tropic	Black thixo- tropic	Tan thixo- tropic	Tan thixo- tropic	Tan elec- trical	Black self leveling sealant primer required	
Recommended use:	Adhesive	Nonadhesive	Adhesive	Nonadhesive	Potting compound	(Deck seal)	For MIL-C-15705A

specification also includes a discoloration test which applies when the sealant is to be used against marble. The specification has been developed by a committee consisting of all the major suppliers, who have correlated performance of their sealants with the performance required in the specification resulting in a high-level performance specification.

Basic Formulations. Each of the specifications described above requires very exact formulations which will meet all the test conditions prescribed.

In order to depict the difference between compounds for these various applications, a number of suggested starting formulations are given in Table 9 to show the importance of various compounding ingredients.

ADHESIVES FROM POLYSULFIDE LIQUID POLYMER-EPOXY RESIN REACTIONS

The first reactions of polysulfide liquid polymers with epoxy resins were studied by Fettes and Gannon.[3] It immediately became apparent that the reaction between these two classes of polymeric compounds gave reaction products which could be considered in compositions for applications involving castings, coatings, laminates, potting, adhesives, etc. The complete treatment of this extremely versatile class of reaction compounds is given by Berenbaum and Panek.[1]

This discussion will be limited to adhesive compounds. In formulations developed for adhesives, the epoxy resin is the major component. However, modification of the epoxy resin with polysulfide liquid polymers gives compositions which in many cases have unique physical and chemical properties.

General Chemistry

Of the several polysulfide liquid polymers (LP-3, LP-33, and LP-8) which have been studied, LP-3 has been used most extensively. The formula for this polymer is:

$$HS(C_2H_4OCH_2OC_2H_4 \ SS)_8— $$
$$C_2H_4OCH_2OC_2H_4SH$$

This polymer has an average molecular weight of 1000 and a viscosity of 7 to 12 poises. It is prepared using 2 mole per cent of trichloropropane which gives a measurable amount of crosslinking when cured alone; this however is not readily apparent when cured with epoxy resins.

A number of liquid epoxy resins as well as blends of liquid and solid epoxy resins have been studied. The most widely used resins are found in the viscosity range of 80 to 200 poises and have an epoxy equivalent of 175 to 210.

Examples of epoxy resins within this classification are "Epon" 820 and "Epon" 828 (Shell Chemical Co.), ERL-3794 (Union Carbide), Araldite 6020 (Ciba Co.), "Epi-Rez" 510 (Jones-Dabney Company), DER-331 (Dow Chemical Co.), and Polytool 6140 (Reichhold Chemical Corporation).

The epoxy resins which are described as reaction products of "Bis-Phenol-A" and epichlorohydrin have the following formulas:

$$CH_2\!-\!CH\!-\!-\!CH_2\!-\!(O\!\!\bigcirc\!\!\overset{\overset{\displaystyle CH_3}{|}}{\underset{\underset{\displaystyle CH_3}{|}}{C}}\!\bigcirc\!\!-\!O\!-$$

$$CH_2\!-\!CH\!-\!CH_2)_n\!-\!\\ \qquad\quad \underset{OH}{|}$$

$$-\!O\!\bigcirc\!\overset{\overset{\displaystyle CH_3}{|}}{\underset{\underset{\displaystyle CH_3}{|}}{C}}\!\bigcirc\!-\!OCH_2\!-\!CH\!-\!CH_2$$

This reaction between polysulfide liquid polymers and epoxy resins is catalyzed or promoted by organic amine compounds. Although a considerable number have been evaluated, final selection has narrowed the list down to a few practical catalysts among which are: "DMP"-10 (dimethylaminomethyl phenol), "DMP"-30 (tri-dimethylaminomethyl phenol, Rohm & Haas), DET (diethylenetriamine), and BDA (benzyldimethylamine). The amine catalysts are used in a fairly high ratio, in most cases 10 per cent based on the weight of the epoxy resin. Because of this co-reaction, they are more properly classified as reactive hardeners. The

general reaction of a polysulfide liquid polymer, an epoxy resin, and a primary amine hardener is:

$$-RSH + \overset{\displaystyle C\!-\!C}{\underset{\displaystyle O}{\diagdown\!\diagup}}\!-\!R'\!-\!\overset{\displaystyle C\!-\!C}{\underset{\displaystyle O}{\diagdown\!\diagup}} + -R''\,NH_2 \longrightarrow$$

$$-RS\!-\!\overset{\displaystyle C}{\underset{\displaystyle H}{\overset{|}{|}}}\!-\!\overset{\displaystyle C}{\underset{\displaystyle OH}{\overset{|}{|}}}\!-\!R'\!-\!\overset{\displaystyle C}{\underset{\displaystyle OH}{\overset{|}{|}}}\!-\!\overset{\displaystyle CN}{\underset{\displaystyle H}{\overset{|}{|}}}\!-\!R''\!-$$

Physical Properties

LP-3, when used to modify a liquid epoxy resin cured with "DMP"-30 accelerates the cure and increases the maximum temperature due to reaction exotherm. The use of LP-3 with epoxy resins gives compositions which have higher elongation, greater impact resistance, and less brittleness. The effect of increasing amounts of LP-3 on the physical properties of a liquid polymer epoxy resin is given in Table 10.

It is interesting to note the increase in tensile properties of the epoxy resin by adding up to 50 per cent LP-3. The straight epoxy-resin cured compound theoretically has higher tensile, but due to its low elongation, breaks before its ultimate tensile may be realized. The effect of increased flexibility, tensile strength, and elongation is very desirable in adhesives.

The data in Table 10 show the effect of LP-3 on the coefficient of linear expansion of the same epoxy resin. Increased amounts of LP-3 causes an increase in the coefficient; however this effect is more than compensated for by the greatly increased flexibility of these compositions which has been demonstrated by the fact that they have withstood many freeze-thaw cycles.

The improved impact resistance of compositions containing LP-3 is apparent as well as very desirable in certain adhesive formulations.

Other properties affected by the addition of LP-3 are moisture vapor transmission, which is reduced by as much as 90 per cent when the LP-3 is

TABLE 10. THE EFFECT OF LP-3 ON THE PHYSICAL PROPERTIES OF LIQUID EPOXY RESIN.

Epoxy resin[a]	100	100	100	100	100	100	100
LP-3	—	25	33	50	75	100	200
"DMP"-30	10	10	10	10	10	10	10
Physical Properties on Sheets Cured for 7 Days at 77° F							
Tensile (psi)	3500	5500	6500	7200	3075	2350	150
Elongation (%)	0	1	2	5	7	10	300
Shore D hardness	80	80	80	80	76	76	15
Coefficient of linear expansion							
in./in./°C x 10^5	4.5	5.5	6.0	7.5	10.0	13.5	15.0
Impact resistance (ft-lb)	2	1	3	5	27	70	>100

[a] Liquid epoxy resin, epoxy equivalent 175 to 210

increased to a 1:1 ratio, and water absorption which may increase slightly when approaching the same ratio with epoxy resin.

The heat distortion temperature is only slightly affected by the incorporation of 20 per cent LP-3, but at 1:1 ratio may become significant. This is illustrated by the fact that a straight epoxy resin cured with DET has a heat distortion temperature of 55°C which is reduced to 54°C when the LP-3/epoxy resin ratio is 1:4; to 50°C at a 1:2 ratio; and to 40°C at a 1:1 ratio. These specific properties prevent the use of such compositions as elevated temperature adhesives but do not deter their use when proper temperature limitations are maintained.

The electrical properties of LP-3/epoxy resin

TABLE 11. COMPARISON OF ADHESIVE VALUES ON ALUMINUM.

	Straight Epoxy Control		LP/EP Adhesive	
	A	B	A	B
"Thiokol" LP-3	—	—	100	—
Liquid epoxy resin[a]	—	100	—	100
Calcium carbonate[b]	—	100	71	179
"DMP"-30	15	—	15	—
A/B ratio	1/13.3		1/1.5	
Cure (considered optimum)	1 hr at 250°F		1 hr at 250°F	

Tensile Shear Bond Strengths psi[c] Tested at 0.05 in./min

Tested at room temperature	1700	4500
Tested at 180°F	2000	1500
Tested at −67°F	1400	2500

Peel Strength[d] lb/in.

8	18

Bend Bond Strengths[c] lb

100	140

Shear Bond Strengths After 30 Days Drop Immersion in Various Media[d] at 80°F

Water	1100	1700
Sea water	0	1100
JP-4 Fuel	1800	3200
Isopropyl alcohol	2000	3200
Ethylene gylcol	1600	3700
Engine oil	1700	3200
Methylethyl ketone	1600	500
Dibutyl phthalate	1800	3400

[a] Liquid epoxy resin epoxide equivalent 175 to 210.
[b] Burgess pigment No. 20.
[c] MIL-A-8331 (U.S.A.F.).
[d] deBruyne, N. A., "Redux in Aircraft," pp. 71–73, Ciba Co., Inc., 1953.

TABLE 12. COMPARISON OF CONCRETE ADHESIVE VALUES.

	Straight Epoxy Control		LP/EP Concrete Adhesive	
	A	B	A	B
"Thiokol" LP-3	—	—	100	—
Silica filler[a]	—	50	80	—
"DMP"-30	7.5	—	20	—
Liquid epoxy resin[b]	—	100	—	200
A/B ratio	1/20		1/1	

Tensile Adhesion Values lb/sq in.

Tested at room temperature and after 7 days cure	0–150[d]	345[c]
Tested at room temperature and after 7 days water immersion	0–150[d]	335[c]

Verticle Bond—Flexural Strength lb/sq in.

Tested at room temperature and after 7 days cure	35[d]	335[c]

Note. Values are practically identical whether bonding old-to-old concrete or new-to-old concrete. Concrete was prepared using ASTM Designation C-185. Tensile adhesion assemblies and tests complied to ASTM Designation C-190-49, whereas flexural assemblies and tests complied to ASTM Designation C-348-54T.

COMPARISON OF SHEAR STRENGTH AT VARIOUS TEMPERATURES (PSI).

	Straight Epoxy Control	LP/EP Concrete Adhesive
Tested at Room Temperature and After 7 Days Cure at:		
(°F)		
150	400[d]	4200[c]
212	300[d]	4300[c]
350	100[c, d]	100[c, d]

[a] Mortar white silica HDS-100.
[b] Liquid epoxy resin, epoxide equivalent 175-210.
[c] Concrete failure.
[d] Bond failure.

compounds are only slightly lower than those of unmodified epoxies, even when a 1:1 ratio is used. These compounds thus can be used in electrical potting.

The adhesive properties of LP-3/expoy compounds are better than those of the epoxy alone, as is illustrated in Table 11.

The data compare compositions after an oven cure of 1 hr at 250°F, which is considered optimum. Shear bond strengths of LP-3 modified compositions are appreciably higher than straight epoxy compositions in a number of various environments, involving changes in temperature or immersion media.

Similar improvement is obtained in peel and bend strengths, which are a result of the improved flexural properties of these systems through the use of LP-3.

Applications

One very practical application for the LP-3/ epoxy adhesives is in bonding old-to-old concrete and new-to-old concrete. These adhesives have definite applications in the construction and maintenance of concrete structures such as highways, bridges, buildings, dams, airport runways, sidewalks, driveways, commercial and industrial floors for patching, overlaying, surface sealing, and skid proofing, as well as a number of other operations. Table 12 illustrates the improved adhesive properties obtained using an LP/EP concrete adhesive as compared to a straight epoxy resin compound. The LP/EP compounds show considerably improved bond strengths that, in almost all cases, are limited to the strengths of the concrete. These compositions are unique in applications involving adhering new freshly poured concrete to old concrete. Bonds based on these assemblies exhibit the same adhesive values as when old-to-old concrete is used. Tentative specifications involving LP/EP concrete adhesives are presently being developed by various State Highway Departments and the Corps of Engineers, and industries.

In one of these specific problem areas, an LP/EP adhesive is used to adhere a super-duty spall-resistant refractory of ASTM Designation C-27[a] to Portland cement concrete.

In conclusion, the LP/EP adhesives should not be analyzed as general modified epoxy-resin compounds, since it has been shown that the use of LP-3 in modifying epoxy resins gives unique properties for these compositions of matter.

References

1. Berenbaum, M. B., and Panek, J. R., "The Chemistry and Application of Polysulfide Polymers," ch. to be published in a book on Polysulfides and Polyesters by Interscience Publishers.
2. Patrick, J. C., and Ferguson, H. R. (to Thiokol Chemical Corp.), U. S. Patent 2,466,963 (Apr. 12, 1946).
3. Fettes, E. M., and Gannon, J. A. (to Thiokol Chemical Corp.), U. S. Patent 2,789,958 (Apr. 23, 1957); *Chem. Abs.* **51**, 1723 (1957).

[a] Sept. 1959 Tentative Specification for Refractory Brick for Initial Areas of Aircraft and Missile Facilities.

Phenolic Resin Adhesives

Charles B. Hemming
United States Plywood Corp.
Brewster, New York

HISTORY

A. Baeyer was the first to study the phenol-aldehyde reaction in 1872. Like other organic chemists of his time, he was primarily interested in preparation of pure compounds; hence he avoided the polymeric and resinous materials and concentrated on crystalline products now known as dihydroxydiphenylalkanes. This group, of course, represents only one of the two important phenol-aldehyde reaction products.

The hydroxy methylphenols were first obtained independently by Lederer and Manasse in 1894.

Both of these classes of compounds were studied as possible dye intermediates and drugs. The resinous products, which often formed in spite of every percaution, were discarded as useless. Ironically, it is these "undesirable" products which now occupy the dominant commercial position.

Shortly thereafter, the first patents covering resinous phenol-aldehyde reaction products were issued. DeLair, Lebach and Smith searched unsuccessfully for shellac substitutes. Then, around 1905, Dr. Leo H. Baekeland began his studies of the means of obtaining control over resin preparation.

There are two basic classes of phenolic resins: *resoles* and *novolacs*. Both begin as phenol alcohols regardless of whether the catalyst is acid or alkaline. When phenol and excess formaldehyde are reacted in the presence of alkali, the reaction products contain methylol side or end groups, which are the resoles. They are cured to the final or *C* stage by heat; hence they are commonly called one-stage resins. The cured resin is termed a *resite*. The

so-called water-soluble phenolic resins are actually dispersions of resoles in alkaline solutions.

In contrast, if phenol and formaldehyde are reacted in the presence of an acid and there is less than 1 mole of formaldehyde available per mole of phenol, the products will resemble dihydroxydiphenyl alkanes in structure, that is, the chains are phenol ended. These are the novolacs; moreover they are permanently soluble and fusible and must have added to them a curing agent. Thus they are commonly known as two-step resins. The common curing agents are hexamethylenetetramine and paraformaldehyde.

It was Aylsworth who in 1911 recommended hexamethylenetetramine as a curing agent for the novolacs. This was a major contribution in the technology of phenol-formaldehyde resins for high pressure laminates and moldings. While resins based on novolacs have certain limited and special uses in adhesives, most of our modern phenolic adhesives have been derived from the resoles.

Baekeland suggested in 1912 that phenol-formaldehyde resin could be used as a wood adhesive. Earlier, in British Patent 17,327 (1901), the Societié Derepas Frères claim the use of phenolic resin for bonding plywood. Whether any use was ever made of this revelation has not been determined.

John R. McClain in his U. S. Patent 1,299,747 (1919) described impregnation of a fiber sheet from a solution of phenolic resin to act as an adhesive to bind the plies or layers together. This particular sheet was not suitable as a film adhesive.

Between 1920 and 1930 attempts were made to create dispersions, emulsions or solutions so that these resins might be spread on surfaces of wood to be bonded, but without success. It is thought that the failure was due partly to lack of satisfactory machinery for obtaining uniform glue spread.

L. C. F. Pechin, in French Patent 722,128 (1931), proposed an adhesive by reacting phenol and formaldehyde in the presence of sodium hydroxide, treating with lactic acid and holding for a period at 140°F until syrupy. While Pechin's revelation would not be considered useful now, it was certainly prophetic and soon followed by the disclosure of E. C. Loetscher in U. S. Patent 1,972,307 (1934) of the bonding of layers of paper or wood veneers to metal. Phenolics would hardly be used for this purpose today.

The principal texts on plywood reveal little regarding the history of phenol-formaldehyde resins as a plywood adhesive. The first commercial success appears to have been made by the Germans, who in 1930 made a film adhesive based on phenol-formaldehyde resin. Because of its high cost its use did not increase rapidly, and it was reserved for the manufacture of exotic hardwood plywood decorative panels. Shortly thereafter, emulsions in water and varnishes in alcohol or acetone were successfully developed. While the latter never achieved large commercial success, the emulsions in water were the forerunners of our sols or colloidal solutions in water, made alkaline with sodium hydroxide. Most of this development proceeded between 1930 and 1939 and may well have been given emphasis by the film glue. By 1939 the alkaline water dispersions were in general use in both the United States and Europe.

The effect of World War II on the growth of phenolic adhesives for both plywood and other purposes is well known. Since 1941 they have been adopted widely. Special variants have been developed for specific purposes, or to meet specific manufacturing conditions. Poly-functional adhesives have been developed in which these resins are only one of two or more necessary components.

In the last ten years new resins have appeared, attempted to replace the phenolics as adhesives and then subsided into oblivion like novae or became mere components of complex or special-purpose mixtures.

Early Commercial Forms

Phenol-formaldehyde resin glue film, the German answer to the problem of spreading adhesives, is still important in both the United States and Europe. It has some advantages not easily obtained by other means. The domestic version of this film is a tissuelike paper web or carrier about .001 in. thick which has been saturated with a phenol-formaldehyde resin in solution and dried. The resin-tissue ratio is about 2 to 1 by weight and the over-all thickness averages about 0.003 in. The phenolic resin carried by the web is water-soluble and alkaline. The cure of this film is best accomplished with a glue-line temperature of at least 250°F, and it is common practice to utilize hot presses in which the platens are controlled between 290 and 300°F. The cure time will depend on the distance between the hot plate and the innermost glue line but generally varies between 5½ and 7½ min. Moisture content of the wood at the time of pressing is somewhat critical for if it should be below about 8 per cent, the phenolic resin in the film will not liquefy and flow adequately and therefore will not wet the wood veneer well. Above about 12 per cent there will be excessive moisture which will tend to "wash" the phenolic resin into the wood surface, thereby causing a starved glue line.

Film adhesive has important advantages. There is less bleed-through due to highly porous or highly figured woods, and it permits the bonding of very thin veneers which might be too fragile to withstand spreading with a liquid adhesive. Film adhesive does not lend itself to assembly gluing or secondary gluing. Neither has it been successful in the high volume field of the manufacture of softwood plywood, partly because of economics and partly because of the relatively rougher surfaces that softwood species veneers exhibit.

In the early days of softwood plywood manufacture, a great deal of bonding was done with protein solutions requiring no heat beyond room temperature. Unfortunately, plywood made this way had no water resistance and no outdoor durability. The few phenol-formaldehyde resins available required such long times and high temperatures for cure that they were used only where absolutely necessary. They complicated the manufacturing process because the heat tended to aggravate checking and caused blows. An early alternative was an adhesive composed mainly of blood albumin in alkaline solution. This material could be spread and then hot-pressed to "cook" the albumin forming a water-resistant bond. But it did not have the outdoor durability hoped for, and its water resistance was undependable because of biological sensitivity. These weaknesses gave rise to phenol-formaldehyde resin-blood solutions as adhesives, which were in vogue around 1940. This compromise was a considerable improvement. The blood albumin content allowed shorter press cycles, and the phenolic resin enhanced the durability and resistance to biological deterioration. However, such combinations have never been successfully formulated to have full outdoor durability, and for a time they fell into disuse. More recently they have been used successfully in the bonding of softwood plywood requiring intermediate degrees of durability, as in severe interior use and temporary storage out-of-doors. However, the newer formulas are not at all identical with the older ones. The blood albumin must be especially processed before formulation into the adhesive, and the phenolic resin: blood albumin ratio has been considerably decreased since these modern versions do not claim outdoor durability. The phenolic resin is also specially formulated to impart toxic properties which will retard organisms of decay, an effect not known or discovered until 1950. It is thought that certain low molecular weight components of phenolic resins are fungicidal. The effect is not noticed in novolacs or thoroughly cured resites.

Cresol-formaldehyde resins, commonly called *cresylics,* have had limited use as adhesives in the bonding of plywood. The high temperature required for their cure and the higher material costs have tended to prevent serious exploitation. Attempts to isolate lower cost cresol bodies from petroleum products have not been entirely successful.

During World War II, phenol-formaldehyde resins of the so-called casting-resin type, actually acid catalyzed single-stage resins, were used to a limited extent as adhesives. These were among the first phenolic adhesives developed for secondary or assembly bonding. They could be conveniently formulated to set or cure at summer room temperatures. Unfortunately, the very low pH required has been found to be somewhat damaging to the strength of wood fibers, particularly where severe usage such as outdoor exposure is involved, and they have been replaced by the equally convenient resorcinol-formaldehyde resin adhesives mentioned elsewhere in this text.

The novolacs, already described, gave rise during World War II to certain adhesives used in the molding of plywood to compound curvatures. They were variously known as lump resins or varnish resins because they were dissolved in alcohol or mixtures of alcohols and ketones. A considerable number of plywood boat hulls were molded with these resins as adhesives because they remained in the B stage longer for a given complete cure time than the simpler adhesives made with single-stage resins. This in turn permitted the plies to slip into place during the molding operation, a requirement not so exacting in flatwork; furthermore these resins could be temporarily plasticized further to enhance the slip by adding reactive solvents such as furfural and furfuryl alcohol. In more recent times very little molded plywood is made by these processes, and the lump resins and varnishes have been largely abandoned as adhesives.

MODERN USAGE

By far the largest use of phenol-formaldehyde resin adhesives is in the manufacture of exterior grade Douglas fir plywood. Some hardwood plywood for special purposes is also made with these adhesives, such as for example, in the manufacture of hardwood plywood for use out-of-doors, fire-resistant plywood, and certain types of composite fire doors involving wood veneers. Doors for exterior openings also make use of phenolic resin adhesives.

Assembly gluing is not a big factor in the modern uses of phenol-formaldehyde resin adhesives. The principal reason, of course, is the successful development and adaptation of resorcinol formaldehyde resins which cure at temperatures as low as 70°F. While resorcinol resin adhesives are closely related chemically to phenol-formaldehyde resins, they are generally treated separately because the technology differs and their behavior as resins when formulated into adhesives does not overlap.

The newest use for phenol-formaldehyde resins, and one predicted to grow the fastest in the near future, is as a binder for wood particles in the infant particle board industry. Until now, urea-formaldehyde resins have been used almost exclusively in the manufacture of particle boards. More recently, however, in order to gain more durability, somewhat better stability and certain desirable properties necessary for severe indoor use, phenol-formaldehyde resins have been adopted, and boards using them are already on the market. While either the resole or the novolac-type of resin could be used for this purpose, the resole is generally chosen because of somewhat lower cost and faster cure.

Adhesives are applied in a variety of ways. With one exception, techniques learned in the use of urea-formaldehyde in particle boards have been carried over into the newer phenol-formaldehyde bound particle boards. The exception is the dry application of powdered phenolic resins, often followed by a sintering process to make the resin particles adhere to the wood particles. Pressing and curing follow as usual. Obviously, the use of substantially dry material throughout reduces the chance of blows from moisture and allows a faster rise to the curing temperature than could be obtained if it were necessary to pass through the boiling point of water and eliminate substantial amounts of moisture. It is to be remembered that, unlike urea-formaldehyde resins, phenolic resins cannot generally be made to cure substantially below the boiling point of water without resorting to expensive modification with resorcinol or questionable use of acid catalysts. Where the phenolic resin is applied from solution, the wood particles and the solution are mixed in some form of ribbon mixer during which the solution is uniformly distributed. By the rubbing of the wood particles on each other, the necessary thin films and partial evaporation of the solvent are accomplished. The formation of the mat then proceeds similarly to the technique used with the dry resin powder, except that the sintering stage is, of course, not necessary.

A somewhat older use related to the manufacture of particle boards is the tempering of fiber boards. The rapid growth of the fiber board industry, also known as hardboard, has brought about demands for tempering other than with drying oils and for intermediate degrees of tempering. In these fields, the phenol-formaldehyde resins are eminently suited. In the wet process, the phenol-formaldehyde resins can be successfully precipitated on the fiber and recovered quantitatively, thus overcoming the biggest hurdle to resin tempering. Of course, partly dried water webs can be saturated with resin solutions; the choice is likely to depend on the equipment available as much as on the relative merits of the two processes. In the dry process fiber board, techniques similar to those used for making wood particle boards as described above are used.

The bonding of glass-fiber mats, particularly for insulation work, is another important use of phenolic resins. Here the cleaned glass fiber is formed into mats, and the phenolic resin solutions are applied by spray, after which the mats are passed between rollers for the necessary degree of compression and heated for cure of the resin. This technology is not to be confused with the older technology of high pressure laminates using glass-fiber fabrics or glass-fiber mats with novolac-type resins, for in this case the product is an extremely dense and strong laminate for structural purposes rather than soft, fluffy mats for insulation and sound absorption. A closely related reinforcing substance is asbestos fiber, which is used in both of these fields and handled in a similar manner for each type. Sisal fiber mats are treated similarly, but almost always a dense finished product is the goal. This may be accomplished at upward of 1200 psi for very dense plastics or as low as 50 psi for molding of large compound curved shapes using low-pressure techniques. Choice of resin largely governs the pressure to be used.

A somewhat older use which is still important is the bonding of abrasive grits in the manufacture of grinding wheels. Until the mid 1930's good grinding wheels were bonded with vitrified ceramic. This required firing in a kiln at high temperatures for a long time, and production was low; furthermore because of the brittle nature of the bond, such wheels could only be operated at relatively low peripheral speeds. The use of phenol-formaldehyde resins has allowed speeds in excess of 9000 ft/min for most grinding wheels and up to 16,000 ft/min for thin cut-off wheels. There has been one important modification, that is, some cut-off wheels, where resistance to shock is at a premium, are bonded with mixtures of elastomer and phenolic resin. The process of manufacture of these grinding wheels is not greatly different from the process of manufacture of phenolic resin-bonded particle board. The abrasive grits are usually first blended with a small amount of liquid resin to ensure wetting of the surface of the grit. This is followed by addition of the remaining quantity of powder resin and thorough mixing with the grit. The quantity of resin employed is from 7 to 15 per cent of the wheel; this is also the range customarily used in particle boards. After thorough mixing, the mixture is compressed and cured under pressure in a mold.

Foundry molds made of sand bound with phenolic resins have proved to be a limited use for phenolic resins because of the equal suitability of other binders or adhesive materials of lower cost. Procedures for the manufacture of such molds or cores are more or less obvious from the above discussion, except that the acid catalyzed room temperature-setting resins can be used satisfactorily without concern for pH.

A border-line case between true laminating as is accomplished in high-pressure processes and adhesive bonding is represented by low-pressure laminating, which utilized phenolic resins in very large quantity during World War II but to a lesser degree since that time. It is mentioned here for the purpose of completeness. Paper or fabric webs of suitable uniformity were saturated with phenolic resin solutions and dried. They were then laid up in blankets using techniques similar to the manufacture of plywood and were similarly pressed, the pressures being in the range of 150 to 300 psi as opposed to upward of 1200 psi for high-pressure laminating. Cures were effected at 300°F or less depending on the resin.

Laminates so made tend to be somewhat more expensive than equivalent high-pressure laminates and are not necessarily better for many uses. They do have less strains and are likely to be substantially more stable. Much greater precision in thickness can be accomplished; this is the principal justification for the manufacture of this type of laminate.

Very porous surfaces frequently cannot be bonded satisfactorily with phenol-formaldehyde resin adhesives. This may be due to either excessive absorption of the adhesive during the period when it is liquid and able to flow under pressure, or it may be because the dry, porous surface does not wet well under the bonding conditions and a strong anchorage to the porous surface by the adhesive line is not obtained. The remedy is to prime or surface-size the porous surface with a relatively dilute solution of phenolic resin adhesive, preferably of the same type that will be used to form the final bond. Any fillers or extenders that may be included in the adhesive itself should not be used in the primer or sizing material since they may filter out and lie on the surface. In some instances it is desirable to pre-cure the primed surface; whereas in others it makes no difference. However the end result is a very superior bond where one or both materials tend to be relatively weak, very porous and exhibit dry or weak surface layers. There is a pronounced reinforcing action of the surface layers of the adherend in addition to the establishment of a more suitable surface for adhesive bonding.

RESIN CHEMISTRY

As mentioned under "History," the two types of phenolic resins are the resole or one-stage and the novolacs or two-stage resins.

Resoles are always made using alkaline catalysts, with the ratio of phenol to formaldehyde in the range of 1:1 to 1:1.5. A decrease of the phenol:formaldehyde ratio yields an increased rate of gelation because of the higher percentage of cross-links formed; but there is also danger of loss of the batch in the kettle and poor keeping qualities of the finished resin. Ammonia is the favorite catalyst for resole formation; however the "solution" for adhesive purposes is a dispersion in aqueous sodium hydroxide. After the resin dispersion has been spread on the work and the water evaporated,

the sodium hydroxide in the presence of heat completes the cure or resite formation, thereby setting the bond.

Novolacs may be formed either with acid or alkaline catalysts although acid is preferred. A common one is oxalic acid. The phenol to formaldehyde ratio is in the range of 1:0.8 to 1:1. Since these resins are "incomplete," they keep indefinitely either in the dry form or as solutions in organic solvents. Cure is effected by adding 10 to 15 per cent of hexamethylenetetramine ("hexa") and furnishing heat in the range, 250 to 300°F.

For a complete description of the chemistry of phenolic resins and the probable structure formula, the reader should study some of the excellent texts devoted to the subject and listed in the bibliography at the end of this chapter.

SURFACE CHEMISTRY

Modern adhesive bonding techniques have brought with them a new awareness of the matter of cleanliness and the need for a better understanding of surfaces.

Surfaces of solids as they normally exist are almost never what they seem. At the very least they have an absorbed layer of moisture on them. Very probably they will also be coated with an oily film and some dust not at all related to the composition of the solid. Generally the surface will also contain oxidation products in some degree and an adsorbed gas layer. Treatments preparatory to bonding must correct for these conditions, or at least those which interfere with bonding. An interesting example may be cited. If veneers are heated for a substantial period of time, above 300°F, the surface tends to become nonpolar and will be wet by solvents like toluene, but not wet by water. If these surfaces are glued with water dispersions or water-borne adhesives, there is likely to be limited wetting of this changed surface and inferior bonds will result. The change is not visible and can only be detected by some form of testing. The point to be made here is that when the nature of the surface or its cleanliness are in doubt, a fresh surface should be exposed before spreading the adhesive.

The simplest procedure, generally used on wood and some plastics, is to expose a fresh surface by means of some type of cutting operation which of itself does not contaminate the new surface, and coat the fresh surface with adhesive promptly. More suitable for metals, glass and other mineral surfaces are detergent or chemical cleaning procedures. The important point to be remembered is that, no matter what the treatment, the surface must be put in a condition so that it "accepts" the adhesive. Otherwise, a superficial and perhaps solely a mechanical attachment will result.

Surface chemistry is involved in another way. While phenol-formaldehyde resins make some of the world's best adhesives, it is well-known that they will by no means adhere to all surfaces. They are particularly lacking in adhesion to metals and glass and since they are highly polar in nature will generally not adhere to any nonpolar surface. The reasons for this are complex and involve both the physics and the chemistry of the bond, for example, phenolic resins can be made to bond temporarily to steel freshly cleaned by adding certain fillers to them. However, thermal expansion and contraction of the metal will shear the bond loose, and it has no permanent value.

Two courses are open to the technician. He can change the surface chemistry by priming with some substance which will adhere to the surface involved and which will in turn exhibit a surface satisfactory to the phenolic resin adhesive. Alternately, he can modify the phenolic resin by adding another resin which is capable of adhering to the surface resistant to the phenolic resin. However, the point often overlooked is that in either method the modification involved must also solve the mechanical problem and prevent the generation of high local "glue-line" stresses due to thermal, humidity or vibratory changes. The shear rigidity of cured phenol-formaldehyde resins is extremely high, and unless the specific adhesion of the resin for the surface is very high or the adherend can take up the stresses within itself, the unmodified resin will almost certainly not form a useful bond.

TECHNOLOGY OF UTILIZATION

The first duty of the adhesives technician is to specify the type of phenolic resin adhesive he needs, which rarely means choice between a resole and a novolac. Rather, it means specifying consistency in solution at the necessary solids content, pot life of the mixture, assembly time of the spread adhesive, degree of extension necessary or desirable, bonding time and temperature to be met, type of surface to be bonded and durability of the bond to be expected. True, the resin manufacturer cannot meet utopian demands with regard to all of these required properties, but he can effectively compromise most of them and make known to the user the conditions to be met to satisfy the ones he cannot compromise. It would serve no good purpose to detail how these properties are compromised, for plant conditions, equipment requirements and material to be adhered vary widely from plant to plant and the best results are most efficiently achieved by working closely with the resin manufacturer.

After the specifications have been agreed upon, it is the responsibility of the resin manufacturer to adhere to them; moreover the customer owes it to himself to set up quality control procedures to ensure that he gets the resin that has proved successful in the original trials. Too often the brunt of this responsibility is shifted back to the resin manufacturer; and when the inevitable off-batch occurs, it is not discovered until it has produced a sub-standard finished product. Since accidents of this type are not frequent, quality control usually serves the more useful purpose of detecting trends in quality away from the optimum.

Handling and storage procedures are wisely based on the resin manufacturer's recommendations for he more than anyone should be aware of the limitations of his resin. Generally, it must be borne in mind that a phenol-formaldehyde resin for adhesive purposes is a highly reactive chemical. To preserve this desirable reactivity, purchases must be scheduled so that its storage life is not exceeded. Contamination must be avoided. Since heat is the principal factor in affecting cure, storage must be at reasonably cool temperatures. Inadequate protection against unreasonable temperatures in transportation and storage can upset the curing conditions and even render it impossible to obtain adequate bonds because of undesirable advancement of the resin reaction during such storage.

The make-up of the "glue mix" may be worked out either by the user or by his supplier. To the resin dispersion or solution is added the desired filler which also acts as a reinforcing agent. A moderate amount will not affect durability and in fact may improve it slightly. It helps control excessive penetration and in the case of coarse, porous surfaces, leads to more reliable bonding through bulking action and reinforcement of excessively thick glue lines. Of course, fillers are often used to lower cost; herein lies a source of abuse and the adulteration of quality. Fillers used for this purpose must be carefully related to the service required of the resulting adhesive bond. Resins vary in their ability to withstand extension, so no hard and fast rules can be laid down; but for top outdoor durability, filler contents vary from 15 to 50 per cent of the neat resin content. For lesser durability requirements, extension may be as high as twice the resin content. Fillers generally used are bark flour, nut-shell flour and wood flour. Since some of these are acidic, their effect on the pH of the resin solution must be watched or the batch of adhesive may be spoiled by gelation or curdling.

Extenders are not to be confused with fillers. Extenders generally have some adhesive action in their own right, or at least act as adhesives in the presence of adhesive resins. Some which are in use include "Vinsol," rosin, lignin, blood albumin, and water-soluble synthetic gums such as methyl cellulose. They help keep cost down and are particularly effective in controlling penetration; however they too can be done excessively if top durability of bond is the requirement.

Modifiers of the glue mix occasionally used in minor quantities include surface-active or wetting agents and antifoaming agents. Except for control of pH, this generally completes the list of ingredients other than any additional water that may be required.

Pot life is generally set by choice of resin and glue mix. Its limits must be observed for if an attempt is made to spread an adhesive which has exceeded its pot life, the spreader may be fouled badly; or worse, a product with inadequate bonds may result. The effect is similar to that resulting from "pre-cure."

Spreading is efficiently done on equipment designed for the purpose, the roller coater being most common. Control of the spread-rate to meet the strength requirement of the bond is maintained by the depth of grooving on the applicator rolls and the pressure with which they bear on the surface to be coated, coupled with the consistency of the "glue-mix."

The allowable assembly time is also set by the resin used and the nature of the "glue-mix." Rarely, a formula will have a minimum time limit below which blows or steam explosions will result upon release of bonding pressure. Most formulas have a maximum time limit beyond which the product will have weak or "pasted" bonds and in severe cases will suffer a type of failure similar to that resulting from pre-cure.

Resoles can be formulated to give adhesives with very long assembly times, but they are apt to be more expensive and slow curing. Novolacs can be formulated into adhesives with assembly times of over a year, but these too are relatively expensive and slow curing and are seldom used at present except in laminating, which is not strictly an adhesive application. Prolonged assembly life resoles are presently used as adhesives in overlay work and in the production of dry-film type adhesives.

With the single exception of acid catalysis of resoles, not presently used as adhesives, heat is the means of setting phenolic resin adhesives. Pressure is also necessary to maintain contact of the faying surfaces, to prevent slippage of one surface relative to the other as the resin passes through the irreversible soft gel stage, and to furnish back pressure to prevent steam and gas induced bubbling or frothing of the "glue line." Phenolic resin adhesives generally are cured at temperatures in the range of 250 to 300°F. Pressures will vary from 50 to 300 psi depending on rigidity of the adherends, type of pressure producing device, and the flow properties of the resin chosen. Temperatures in excess of 300°F are to be avoided where cellulose and particularly wood is involved, or ketonization of the wood surface will occur, encouraging subsequent checking and causing finishing and assembly adhesive problems.

The curing reaction is simply one of completing the crosslinking of the side chain and terminal methylol groups in the case of the resoles, and of reacting the phenol ended chains of the novolacs with the added hexamethylenetetramine. In either case the curing action may be said to complete the resin formation until substantially all ability to react is destroyed. The end product in either case is insoluble and infusible and can only be altered by chemical or thermal destruction of the resin; consequently phenolic resin adhesives exhibit outstanding durability.

There are no completely reliable accelerated tests for cure of bonds based on resoles, but cold-water soak followed by measurement of loss of bond strength, if any, is perhaps the best. Boil tests should not be regarded as final because the heat of boiling water generally completes the cure giving misleading, favorable results. Some newer, cyclic tests which begin with a cold-water step under pressure are promising but these procedures do not differentiate between undercured bonds which are otherwise good and faulty bonds caused by other procedural errors mentioned above.

The novolacs are more amenable to test, and the acetone extraction test is simple and adequate for most purposes. The suspected glue line is cut into tiny pieces and soaked overnight in cold CP acetone. About ½ g in 10 ml of acetone will suffice. The supernatant liquid is poured off and mixed with an equal volume of distilled water. Any haze or turbidity is an indication of incomplete cure.

Release of pressure at the end of the cure calls for a little good judgment. Some adherends such as plywood and some types of particle boards will develop steam blisters or rupture of areas of the "glue line" if press pressure is released too fast. Slow release costs but a few seconds of time and helps prevent this type of defect from occurring.

Cellulosic materials bonded at temperatures upward of 250°F should be reconditioned so that they regain their normal moisture of condition before inspection and shipment. Means for accomplishing this hardly need be discussed here, but importance of the step must not be minimized.

Inspection needs little discussion. It is designed to see that the product with visible defects does not get shipped to the customer if the defects exceed those allowable under the agreed-to-specification.

Quality tests are more of a problem. Since there are no adequate nondestructive tests for glue line integrity or durability, the only alternative is statistical sampling followed by destructive tests. These are chosen with regard to the durability expected. Generally the bond strength must be greater than the strength of the adherend material, maintaining this relationship throughout a set of accelerated deteriorating tests related in nature to the most severe service use likely to be encountered. This subject is very adequately covered in the various publications of the American Society for Testing and Materials.

DURABILITY

Durability is measured in terms of the resistance of the bond to the deteriorating influences encountered in service. Desirably the bond strength should be unchanged for the life of the adherends in the most severe service for which the assembly is intended.

Durability is a composite of strength maintenance and fatigue and creep resistance. Deteriorating influences depend on the service exposure but in the extreme will include heat, biological factors, weathering and cyclic stresses. Phenol-formaldehyde resins of the proper type, suitably formulated into adhesive mixtures are outstanding in resistance to all these factors. If we may exclude mineral adherends, no adherend that can be well bonded with phenolic resins will have more resistance to heat deterioration than the bonds made with these resins. Even in a fire, the adherend frequently is destroyed ahead of the bond.

Biological factors seem to be without effect. Fungi will grow superficially if moisture conditions are correct, but live only on dust which has accumulated on the surface. One exception to this is excessive or improper use of fillers or extenders; but even in these cases the resin itself is not attacked. Bacteria will attack proteins sometimes used as extenders if conditions of exposure are very severe; but singularly enough, the phenolic resin has a positive and readily proven protective action, actually retarding biological deterioration of protein extenders.

The resistance to deterioration due to weathering of phenolic-resin adhesive bonds is superior to that of practically all adherends which can be readily bonded with these adhesives. Mineral adherends are perhaps the lone exception, and even these are often damaged by water absorption and freezing before the bond itself weakens. Certain extremely durable woods are equal in durability out-of-doors to good phenolic resin adhesive bonds.

One of the most damaging natural effects on bonded assemblies is alternating stresses set up by thermal expansion and contraction, or by expansion and contraction due to moisture content changes. Sometimes both effects are involved. In severe exposures involving these stresses, only the best phenol-formaldehyde resin adhesives should be used with careful control of pH and no more than optimum filler content. Extenders should not be used. An example of such a service is marine work such as marine plywood, laminated wood keels and other bonded boat parts. It is in this field that phenol-formaldehyde resin adhesives, including the sister resin, resorcinol-formaldehyde, reach their peak of usefulness and it is in this service that they are without peer.

References

Ellis, Carleton, "Synthetic Resins and Their Plastics," New York, Chemical Catalog Company, 1923.

Ellis, Carleton, "Chemistry of Synthetic Resins," New York, Reinhold Publishing Corp., 1935.

Fleck, Ronald, "Plastics—Scientific and Technological," Brooklyn, Chemical Publishing Company, 1945.

Carswell, T. S., "Phenoplasts—Their Structure, Properties, and Chemical Technology," New York, Interscience Publishers, Inc., 1947.

Robitsek, P., and Lewin, A., "Phenolic Resins—Their Chemistry and Technology," London, Iliffe and Sons, 1950.

DeBruyne and Houwink, "Adhesion and Adhesives," New York, Elsevier Publishing Company, 1951.

Martin, R. W., "Chemistry of Phenolic Resins," New York, John Wiley & Sons, 1956.

Megson, N. J. L., "Phenolic Resin Chemistry," New York, Academic Press, 1958.

Society of the Plastics Industry, "Plastics Engineering Handbook," New York, Reinhold Publishing Corp., 1960.

Resorcinol Resin Adhesives

Charles B. Hemming
United States Plywood Corp.
Brewster, New York

HISTORY

Although he was not the earliest worker in the field by about thirty years, Novotny appears to have been the first to work out a controllable method for producing a condensate of resorcinol and formaldehyde suitable for hardening with paraformaldehyde in a later step and capable of being used as an adhesive.

The very early investigators were plagued by rapid transformation into insoluble products. Indeed, some workers did not recognize the resulting materials as being a resin. Even today, little is known about the exact structure as it is so difficult to isolate intermediate products, because of the speed of the reaction.

Commercial introduction occurred in 1943 in time to serve some of the pressing war-time needs for a highly durable, room-temperature setting adhesive. Growth has been slow but steady since then.

USES OF RESORCINOL-FORMALDEHYDE RESIN ADHESIVES

Resorcinol is relatively high in cost and limited in availability. The dark brown-to-purple color of the adhesive is a disadvantage where stain or color would be objectionable. Consequently, resorcinol adhesives have been used only where their unique properties are necessary.

Phenolic adhesives cannot be made room-temperature curing without resorting to strong acid catalysts which tend to weaken wood fiber adjacent to the glue line. Furthermore, no other convenient, moderate-cost resin was available which could cure at room temperature to give bonds adequate for exterior exposure. Thus the resorcinol resins from the beginning filled a definite need in spite of their limitations. Here was an adhesive capable of being cured at room temperatures, substantially neutral and harmless to wood fiber, yielding bonds of highest durability, equal in performance to the well established heat-cured phenolic resin adhesive. These adhesives naturally found substantial outlets in boats and other marine structures, and in assembly gluing where exterior exposure of the structure is expected. During World War II, they were also used in wooden aircraft assembly.

Renewed interest is now being shown in these adhesives for special uses, alone and in combination with other adhesives.

(1) Veneer plugging or patching in the manufacture of top-grade exterior plywood and particularly marine plywood. Here the heat resistance as well as the durability are significant.

(2) Splicing of plywood panels to make larger panels. For exterior or marine service the scarf-joint must have durability at least equal to that of the plywood itself.

(3) Lamination of lumber to form built-up timbers, arches, boat keels and other heavy members which will be heavily loaded or exposed in otherwise severe service.

(4) Bonding of certain plastics to each other and to wood where durability and strength are required, or where a water-borne adhe-

sive may interfere by failing to wet one surface or may cause "photographing" of wood grain structure through the plastic.

(5) Bonding of metal-to-wood and plastics where room temperature cure is necessary. In these cases the metal surface is first primed with an elastomer-phenolic adhesive and baked to cure the primer. While the resorcinol adhesive will not bond even to clean metal it will bond easily and strongly to a properly cured primer suitable for this work. Cure of the primer must be controlled carefully. Over cure reduces the ability of the resorcinol to bond to the primer; under cure may permit the resorcinol to strip the primer by solvent action.

(6) Bonding of metal and wood to foamed plastics in the manufacture of sandwich constructions. Wood does not need a primer.

(7) Bonding of metal, wood, and certain plastics to mineral cores or masonry work. As before, the metal will require priming, the plastic may or may not. The wood will not.

Each of these applications calls for at least one of the three advantages of resorcinol adhesives: room temperature curing, high durability of bond, or specific adhesion of the resorcinol resin for one or both adherends.

RESIN CHEMISTRY

Two principal types of resorcinol adhesives are presently popular: straight resorcinol and phenol resorcinol. Phenol resorcinol adhesive generally contains about 15 per cent phenolic resin, is slower curing, has a higher minimum curing temperature, is a little lower in cost, has shorter shelf life in the uncatalyzed state and tends to craze less if inadvertently heated too soon in the cure cycle for the purpose of hastening set. Crazing is not a problem of either type at 75 to 80°F cure temperature.

The ability of resorcinol resins to cure at room temperature results from the additional hydroxyl groups in the phenol nucleus, which cause an increase in the rate of condensation with formaldehyde. The syrup is prepared by first condensing 1 mole of resorcinol with 0.6–0.65 mole of formaldehyde in the absence of a catalyst but at 100 to 150°C, followed by cooling to prevent continued reaction. The condensate is diluted with ethyl alcohol which helps further to stabilize the syrup and give it good consistency for handling and mixing. A 65 per cent nonvolatile content is convenient. The adhesive is readied for use by mixing

with additional formaldehyde or paraformaldehyde as the hardener. Paraformaldehyde is almost universally used because it has less odor and is more pleasant for the user to mix. Paraformaldehyde is usually furnished premixed with nut-shell flour which is a desirable reinforcing agent. Thus, the user automatically adds both ingredients at once when he adds the so-called "hardener" to the resin syrup.

The pot life of the mixture varies between 1½ and 4 hr depending to a certain extent on the temperature of the batch at the time of mixing and the ambient temperature. Best results are obtained by cooling during mixing in a jacketed kettle and maintaining the mixture during use at 70 to 75°F.

The assembly time has a minimum as well as a maximum limit. The minimum time will depend on the nature of the assembly, but it is wise to allow most of the alcohol to evaporate off (5 to 10 min) before assembly so that the hardening will be started sooner. The maximum limit is set by ambient temperatures and varies from about 15 to 45 min. Of course, in all these matters the manufacturer's instructions should govern since each proprietary adhesive varies slightly in its requirements.

The reinforcing agent does not enter directly into the reaction but the paraformaldehyde, of course, furnishes the necessary formaldehyde to complete the condensation and form the infusible resite which becomes the cured glue line.

SURFACE CHEMISTRY

The problems in surface chemistry do not differ greatly from those involved in phenolic resin bonding. It is important that the surfaces to be adhered be clean and that their nature be known at least nominally or from experience, and, of course, it is fundamental that the adhesive wet both faying surfaces, preferably at the time of spreading. In the bonding of wood there is evidence of some chemical reaction between adhesive and adherend.

The resorcinol glue line is hard, glasslike and extremely rigid. Since the sole reason for using such an adhesive is its durability, it is important that this be taken into account in considering appropriate adherends. If the adherends expand and contract appreciably with changes in ambient conditions, the bond may fail in shear either at the interface or if the bond is unusually strong, within the glue line itself. It is partly for this reason that the nut-shell flour is added.

Wood has strong resilient fibers which can absorb these stresses. Many plastics will yield sufficiently to absorb the stresses. Metal cannot be bonded permanently without first coating with a tough resilient primer which of itself has good adhesion to the metal and which in turn will permit the resorcinol resin to make good bonds with it. A few popular and effective primers are: phenol formaldehyde-butadiene acrylonitrile rubber; phenol formaldehyde-polyvinyl acetal; phenol-formaldehyde-neoprene rubber and casein-neoprene latex mixtures.

Glass and porcelain or other glasslike bodies must also be especially primed. In addition, the glass surface must be chemically treated to assure primer adhesion in the presence of moisture such as will occur on outdoor exposure.

Porous mineral or masonry surfaces bond well with resorcinol-formaldehyde resin adhesives, but for best results the nut-shell flour must often be omitted as it tends to prevent wetting in these cases.

Most plastics which bond well with resorcinol-resin adhesives must first be sanded rather thoroughly. This not only cleans by removing parting agent, but may also uncover substantial areas of reinforcing agent which furnish even better surfaces for adhesion than the plastic itself. Finally, the interior composition of the plastic may be more suited chemically for bonding than the surface layers.

TECHNOLOGY OF UTILIZATION

For all practical purposes there are only two types of resorcinol-containing adhesives on the market: straight resorcinol and phenol-resorcinol. They are generally so identified and may be so specified. Custom compositions can be made higher in phenol than normal, but the minimum cure temperature becomes increasingly higher with little advantage for general work.

Quality control of incoming shipments should include visual inspection, but not too much attention should be given to color variations as shades of brown to deep maroon will be encountered. Consistency (viscosity) is significant, particularly of the phenol resorcinols, as improperly stored or over-aged material could be unuseable. Solids content of the liquid portion is significant within reasonable limits as it is related to the amount of hardener required as well as to the spread rate. Since both of these values are set by the manufacturer, it is well to establish an agreement as to acceptable variations. Obvious contamination or incompatibility is cause for rejection. The solid or hardener portion should not be heated alone, as loss by sublimation of the paraformaldehyde will occur. A simple check can be made by extracting with alcohol, weighing the dried residue and determining by difference the true hardener content, the rest being filler or reinforcing agent.

The best quality control method is, of course, to prepare some compression shear blocks according to one of the well known methods and to determine the bond strength after curing for the recommended time, making sure that the minimum specified cure temperature is not violated.

Because these resins are "incomplete" until the hardener is added, storage temperature in tight containers is not particularly critical. Nevertheless high temperatures are to be avoided for prolonged storage. Low temperatures are harmless but the container must be warmed and remixed if there is any separation, before sampling. The shelf-life of the separate components varies with the source, so the manufacturer's recommendations should be followed.

Pot life, spread rate, assembly time and time and temperature of curing of the mixed adhesive will also depend on the exact composition furnished and are, therefore, matters to be discussed with the supplier except that variations in handling and mixing have some effect as discussed earlier in the chapter.

There is no precise test for cure except to measure the strength of the bond developed; but the hardness of the glue line in the early stages of cure is a rough indication. A cured line is glass hard and rather brittle.

DURABILITY

This family of adhesives is capable of producing the most durable bonds known, especially in wood-to-wood. The only application that requires special attention is the bonding of oak-to-oak for exposure to salt water, particularly where high stresses are involved. Should specification work be attempted in this application, it will be well to know that the adhesive is acceptable for such service and that mixing and curing requirements are rigorously met. The straight resorcinol types are generally the only ones used in this work.

All the other deteriorating factors met in exterior exposure have no more effect on the bonds formed by these adhesives than they do on the better known phenol-formaldehyde resin adhesives cured under heat and pressure.

Creep and fatigue are no more problems with

these adhesives than they are with phenol-formaldehyde bonds, and if they occur at all they are likely to be found in the adherends involved.

There is one problem quite unique with these adhesives; they are bad stainers. The staining may take two forms. The least troublesome is the simple direct stain which occurs when the adhesive is accidentally spread on an area where it was not intended. If not immediately removed with an appropriate solvent, it can only be removed by sanding, planing or cutting, and the cut must be deep enough to remove any absorbed material. The more serious stain is the latent image that may be deposited on the accidentally coated surface. This latent image can persist in spite of prompt solvent removal. Later on, due to time

and actinic light, a form of dye coupling occurs and the latent image becomes a visible and often bad stain. The best way to remove it is by discharge with a chemical dye stripping agent, being careful to choose one that will not damage the surface which has been stained.

References

1. Megson, N. J. L., "Phenolic Resin Chemistry," Chapter X, New York Academic Press, 1958.
2. DeBruyne and Houwink, "Adhesion and Adhesives," Chapter 5C, New York, Elsevier Publishing Company, 1951.
3. Carswell, T. S., "Phenoplasts," Chapter IV, New York Interscience Publishers, Inc., 1947.

— 24 —

Amino Resin Adhesives

John F. Blais

Consultant

Norwalk, Connecticut

The principal amino resins used for adhesive applications are urea formaldehyde, urea formaldehyde modified with furfuryl alcohol, melamine formaldehyde, melamine-urea formaldehyde copolymers, and mixtures. The urea resins are available in solutions containing 45 to 67 per cent resin solids, and also in powder form as 100 per cent neat resin, resin-filler combinations, and resin-filler-catalyst combinations. Urea resin modified with furfuryl alcohol is available in liquid form only. Melamine and melamine-urea resins are usually available only in powder form, as neat resins or in combination with wood or shell-flour fillers.

Amino resin adhesives find a wide range of application for the bonding of plywood, furniture, flush doors, boats, laminates, fiber boards, bag seam pastes, particle boards, and general assembly gluing. Urea resins are the most economical and versatile of the group, providing moderately moisture-resistant bonds. Where greater resistance to moisture is desired, the use of a melamine-urea adhesive is recommended. For even greater boil resistance and outside durability, a straight melamine resin is the most desirable of the amino resins.

The more expensive melamine resin is mixed or co-reacted with urea resins to increase the moisture resistance of the cured glue line. Even 10 per cent substitution of the urea by melamine produces a noticeable improvement. With a 50 per cent substitution, the moisture resistance of the glue line is about 90 per cent of that obtained with an all melamine adhesive.

AMINO RESIN CHEMISTRY

The basic primary reaction between an aldehyde, as represented by formaldehyde, and urea, melamine, substituted urea or substituted melamine is similar for all. Under proper conditions the primary reaction results in a combining of the aldehyde with the nitrogen of an amino group, splitting out water. Further reaction between the initial materials and polymerization of the intermediate condensates is quite complex and is influenced by a number of variables:

(1) Mole ratio of the reactants.
(2) Number of reactive amino groups.
(3) Size or complexity of nonreactive N-substituents.
(4) Degree of reactivity of the amino group as influenced by the other components in the molecule.
(5) Reaction pH and pH buffers.
(6) Time and temperature of reaction.
(7) Concentration of reactants.
(8) Presence and proportion of nonaqueous liquids such as alcohol in the reaction mixture.

Urea Resins

The mechanism by which the monomeric derivatives of urea and formaldehyde are converted to an intermediate and fully polymerized or cured state has been studied intensively. References to these investigations are included at the end of this chapter. There appears to be general agreement that, in the first stage of polymerization of the monomers, different mechanisms are possible depending on the reaction conditions and proportion of primary reactants.[9] Analysis of intermediate condensates indicates the presence of two possible structural likages: methylene, $-NH-CH_2-NH-$, and ether, $-NH-CH_2-O-CH_2-NH-$. Terminal groups may exist as amide, $-NH_2$, methylol, $-CH_2OH$, or azomethine, $-N=CH_2$. In the case of alkylated resin, the terminal groups of the intermediate condensates may include the above as well as alkoxy group such as $-NH-CH_2-O-CH_3$ for methylated and $-NH-CH_2-O-C_4H_9$ for the butylated products.

The urea resins manufactured for most industries are essentially monomeric or only slightly advanced in polymerization. The low degree of polymerization is necessary to provide solubility or plasticity of the resin product in the initial stage of application. For example, solubility in water or other solvent is a basic requirement for adhesive, laminating, textile finishing, paper making, coating, etc., and plasticity is a requisite for compression molding. The resins for molding are advanced in polymerization beyond the solubility stage needed for the other applications.

All of the commercial resins contain the reactive terminal groups in varying proportions that enable them to further condense under the influence of heat, catalyst, or both to yield the infusible "cured" product. Water, in the case of unmodified resins, and the corresponding alcohol, in the case of the alkylated resins, are split out in the condensation. In order to obtain optimum properties of the finished product for most applications, polymerization is not carried to the greatest possible degree. Some reactive terminal groups are still present in the "cured" products.

Because the cured urea resins are insoluble and infusible, direct determination of their molecular size by methods applicable to the thermoplastic resins is not possible. Estimates based on analysis of cured products indicate a relatively low degree of polymerization compared to the thermoplastics. The highest value obtained by Walter[8] in his work was 536, and an average of about 400. This molecular weight indicates that the cured polymer could contain as few as 5 to 6 monomeric units. Melamine resins, which are considered to have polymerization mechanisms similar to urea, are estimated by Wohnsiedler[10] to have possible degree of polymerization values above 20 to 30 for cured products.

Adhesive Resins

Urea resins intended for adhesive applications are condensates of urea and formaldehyde that have been advanced in polymerization to a degree that still allows essentially complete dispersion in water at high concentrations. Complete solution or dispersion in water at low concentrations is usually not possible. Mole ratios of approximately two of formaldehyde to one of urea are common for these resins. They are available as solutions or spray-dried powders.

If protected from moisture, the spray dried products are stable in storage with greater leeway in mole ratio, polymer advancement, and pH. These same variables are quite important for stability of the liquid types. The liquid dispersions have an alkaline pH, preferably buffered, to prevent instability by polymer growth on storage. Also they should contain a sufficient amount of intermediate polymers to act as protective colloids that will prevent crystallization of the monomeric constituents.

Curing of the resins is accomplished by the addition of an acid or acid-releasing catalyst just prior to application. Heat may or may not be used to increase the rate of polymerization. Theoretically, the free acids could be added to the resin for curing; but the short working life so obtained is impractical. In common practice, the acid catalyst is introduced in the form of an ammonium salt. Even at room temperature, the ammonium salt of a strong acid will react with any uncombined formaldehyde present in the resin dispersion, as well as with the terminal methylol groups of the monomeric species, to form hexamethylenetetramine and the corresponding free acid.

The liberation of the acid from the salt is usually too rapid for a reasonable working life of the adhesive. It is therefore customary to include a pH buffer such as tricalcium phosphate to slow down the polymerization at room temperature. This buffer further serves to prevent the glue-line pH from dropping so low as to degrade the glued structure.

The acid released from the salt acts as a catalyst to promote condensations of the monomers and intermediate polymers by elimination of water, forming straight or random chains and closed-ring structures. The condensation may take place between two terminal methylol groups, between one methylol and one amide, or by elimination of water from a methylol group to form an unsaturated methine that is capable of ring formation.

The fibrous fillers used in adhesive formulations may have an influence on the rate of polymerization by the introduction of soluble catalytic or inhibitor constituents, but are included primarily for viscosity and film-reinforcement purposes.

Melamine Resins

Reaction between melamine, 2,4,6-triamino-1,3,5 triazine, and formaldehyde is believed to be very similar in mechanism to that of urea. All experimental evidence to date leads to the conclusion that the triazine ring structure in melamine remains intact and that resinification takes place by condensation of the formaldehyde with one or more of the amino side groups.

The discovery and identification of melamine is attributed to Liebig in 1834. Commercial scale production in 1939 by American Cyanamid Co., using dicyandiamide as raw material, was the basis for the first production of melamine resins in the United States. Melamine is a white, crystalline chemical with very low solubility in water, alcohol, or other ordinary solvents. It readily dissolves in warm formalin by reaction to form a variety of methylol melamines. Three reactive amino groups are present which can be reacted with as many as 6 moles of formaldehyde. By reacting 1 mole of melamine with 3 moles of warm formalin until solution is obtained, and quickly cooling, crystalline trimethylol malamine may be obtained:

mercial practice, the reaction is carried only to the water-soluble or water-alcohol soluble stage and then inhibited by increasing the pH to about 10 and cooling.

If the reaction is carried out at pH levels of 6 or below, insoluble polymers are formed very rapidly. The various mechanisms possible for methylol melamine condensation has been reported by Wohnsiedler,[9, 10] Gams and co-workers,[4] and Payne.[6]

Curing of the melamine resins may be accomplished by simply heating. The presence of small amounts of acid will accelerate the heat cure, especially for butylated products. Unlike urea resins, however, melamines do not cure satisfactorily at room temperature even in the presence of an acid catalyst.

Typical Manufacture of Amino Resin Adhesives

Liquid Urea Adhesives. A typical urea-formaldehyde adhesive for use in plywood manufacture is made in a reaction kettle equipped with turbo-agitator and reflux condenser and jacketed or coiled for heating and cooling. As with most amino resins, a variety of products may be made by changing the mole ratio of the reactants, pH and buffer adjustment during reaction, and degree of polymerization attained in the condensation cycle.

Urea is charged to the reactor containing formalin. Preferred mole ratios are 1.5 to 2 of formalde-

$$H_2N-C \quad C-NH_2 \qquad + \ 3 \ HCHO \rightarrow \qquad HOCH_2NH-C \quad C-NHCH_2OH$$

Melamine   *Trimethylol melamine*

The methylol melamines condense to form resinous polymers by heating under mild alkaline conditions. The progressive polymerization of the methylol melamines is dependent on the reaction pH. Small changes in acidity or alkalinity have greater effect on the reaction progress than in the case of the methylol urea. At a pH of 7, water-soluble, hydrophilic polymers are first formed. Under continued heating the resin solution has less tolerance for dilution with water but is readily diluted with water-alcohol mixtures. With still further heating, some resin may be precipitated from solution by alcohol and the solution will separate into two layers on cooling. In com-

hyde to 1 of urea. The urea may be added fully at the start of the reaction or stepwise to obtain variations in polymer distribution and reactivity of the final product. The urea will dissolve readily in the formalin with a small endothermic effect. The pH of the solution is adjusted with sodium hydroxide or other alkali to a level of 7.5 to 8.0 and the mixture heated to reflux. Temperature at reflux is about 98°C. The reaction is continued at reflux until the desired polymerization is reached, as measured by solution viscosity. A total cycle of 4 to 8 hr is typical for plywood-type adhesives. In order to increase the rate of polymer growth without extending the heating period beyond economical limits, the reaction pH is lowered by the addition of formic acid to a level of 5.6 to 6.0. This adjustment of pH is made at a selected time during reflux and after all the urea charge has been added. At the lower pH, the solution viscosity gradually rises to the control value desired for the product. The resin is then adjusted in pH to about 8.0 to inhibit further reaction and cooled for drum or tank shipment. Resin solutions containing 45 to 66 per cent solids are made by this method.

A craze-resistant modification of a liquid urea-formaldehyde resin is obtained by the addition of furfuryl alcohol to the urea resin solution near the end of the reflux period.

The liquid urea adhesive resins exhibit good stability in storage. They are not sufficiently reactive to be used as adhesives as made and shipped. Catalysts and extenders must be added just prior to use as an adhesive to obtain a cured glue line.

Powdered Urea Adhesives. Powdered urea resins are made by spray drying a liquid resin prepared in a similar manner described above. The products are free-flowing powders with excellent shelf life when stored at low temperatures and protected from atmospheric moisture. Again as with the liquid urea resins, catalysts and fillers or extenders must be added prior to application as an adhesive. While the bulk of powdered urea resins for industrial use are shipped without added catalysts, commercial formulations containing the powdered resin blended with filler, catalyst and cure retarders are available. Usually these products are sold in small containers for non-commercial applications and require only mixing with water for activation.

Commonly used for adhesive fillers are wood flour, walnut shell flour and combinations. Catalysts are usually ammonium salts such as ammonium chloride or sulfate. Cure retarders such as tricalcium phosphate are employed to buffer the adhesive mixture and extend the working life of the wet glue mix.

Powdered Melamine and Melamine-Urea Adhesives. Powdered melamine and melamine-urea copolymer resins for adhesive usage are manufactured in the same equipment as spray-dried amino resins. The resins are essentially the same as those prepared for making industrial molding compounds or for use in laminating, but are polymerized to a more advanced stage in the primary liquid stage of manufacture. The products still retain water solubility, but only in highly concentrated solutions.

Melamine resins can be cured to an insoluble glue line without catalyst by application of heat, and therefore are sold as neat resins or mixed with ligneous filler. Copolymers of melamine and urea may or may not require a separate catalyst to achieve complete cure depending on the proportion of melamine to urea in the formulation. When the melamine content is equal or greater than the urea content, no catalyst is used.

Blending of powdered amino resins with filler and other additives is accomplished by physical mixing in the dry state in a cone or ribbon blender. At times anti-caking agents are added to the blender to aid in retaining their free-flowing properties during storage.

APPLICATIONS

Amino resins for adhesives have two major groups of application: curing of the glue line by cold pressing, and curing by hot pressing. Cold pressing requires the presence of a catalyst and is limited to the urea and modified-urea resins. Hot pressing is effective for all the amino resins and can be carried out by the use of steam or electrically heated platens, high-frequency or dielectric heating, and strip heating.

Cold Pressing

Cold-pressing methods are used for the preparation of interior-grade plywood, furniture, interior doors, sporting goods, general assembly gluing and bonding of decorative laminates to substructures such as hard boards and plywood. Both solid and liquid urea resins are available for cold-press gluing. They require an added catalyst and may be used unextended or with varying amounts of cereal flour as extender. Shell flours, walnut or pecan, are usually incorporated to control flow and limit penetration of the glue line.

The equipment required for cold pressing is the simplest and least expensive of the gluing methods and frequently is the most practical means for the smaller fabricator. While the rate of production of materials bonded by cold pressing is very much slower than that of hot pressing, the modest capital investment for this method is often a key advantage.

Pressures required for cold pressing will vary from mere contact to a maximum of about 200 psi depending on the type of adhesive and the nature of the product. Plywood presses for cold-set adhesives operate from 150 to 200 psi. For low-density woods such as poplar, mahogany, or gum, pressure of 150 to 175 psi are desirable. For the denser woods such as maple, oak or birch, pressures from 175 to 200 psi are recommended. Pressures above these values will tend to crush the wood cells and produce a "starved" glue line by too much penetration and "squeeze-out." Unmodified urea resins, when cured in thick films, are hard and brittle and exhibit cracking or crazing which weakens the bond. Adequate gluing pressure is therefore necessary to produce thin glue lines for best bonding strength, and to flatten the stock sufficiently to produce intimate over-all contact.

Urea resins that have been modified with furfuryl alcohol produce cured glue lines that are more resistant to cracking and crazing than the unmodified types. These adhesives contain a ligneous filler but cannot be extended with cereal flour or water for cost reduction of the glue line, hence are not economical for plywood manufacture. They are utilized mainly for assembly wood gluing or for bonding decorative laminates to substructures of plywood, pressed board, or particle board. Since the glue line thickness is relatively unimportant for the craze-resistant urea resins, low clamping pressures are sufficient if they provide intimate contact of the surfaces to be bonded. For perfectly flat and rigid surfaces, this pressure can approach zero, but for practical purposes, pressure of 40 to 60 psi will be needed. The use of hand-operated "C" clamps can produce this pressure.

Assembly gluing of furniture or other nonplanar, shaped structures is accomplished with conventional wood clamps or fixture jigs especially designed for the product. The products must be kept under pressure in the fixture for several hours. This pressure period is usually double the gelation time of the adhesive and may be as long as 24 hours at 70°F. Cold pressing below 70°F is not recommended for urea resin adhesives. Full cure of the glue line is not obtained during the pressure period, but unstressed parts have sufficient strength on removal of pressure to be handled or trimmed. Stressed assemblies should remain under pressure for as much as double the pressure period required for flat work. An aging period of 6 to 12 days is usually needed for the development of maximum water resistance and bond strength.

In the manufacture of lightly stressed products such as plywood or for bonding decorative laminates to substructures in the manufacture of table tops, simple veneer presses or cold platen hydraulic presses are used. A number of assemblies of the plywood, as determined by the maximum opening of the press, are sandwiched between heavy wood or metal caul plates to achieve and maintain a more even pressure distribution. The use of heavy caul plates is especially important with a simple veneer press. Further, in order to increase the productivity of an hydraulic cold press, after pressure has been established, the entire bundle can be rigidly clamped between the caul plates using turnbuckle clamps. The clamped bundle is then removed from the press and stored in the clamped condition of the necessary aging period.

For cold-press bonding of decorative laminates to plywood, hard board, or particle board, the same technique of pressing and clamping may be used. The pressing bundle is laid up with each two assemblies having the decorative surfaces face to face. Precautions should be taken to prevent or remove any dust particles or other foreign matter from the surfaces of the laminates before lay-up. Even though platen pressures as low as 50 psi are used, the inclusion of a small particle of grit between the decorative laminates can produce a permanent indentation of the surfaces. Pressures are kept as low as possible, depending on the flatness of the product and the desired glue line thickness, to avoid a "telegraphing" of the grain of the veneer through the decorative laminate. This surface ripple can be minimized by selection of a uniform substructure or by use of a craze-resistant adhesive that can tolerate the thicker glue lines obtained with low pressures.

Modified Urea-Liquid Resin Adhesives. The adhesives representative of this group are characterized by their ability to produce a craze-resistant, low shrinkage, thick glue line. The term "gap-filling" adhesive is applicable to this group. They are sold as two-component systems, liquid resin and powdered hardener. The liquid component is usually a furfuryl alcohol-modified urea-formaldehyde resin in aqueous medium. It has a readily pourable consistency. When freshly made, the resin solution is clear to slightly turbid; but it becomes milky and more viscous on aging. Storage at cool temperatures is recommended to obtain a useable life of more than three months.

The hardener component contains inorganic curing agents such as ammonium salts and pH buffers such as tricalcium phosphate intimately mixed with ligneous fillers of wood flour and shell flours. If properly protected from heat and moisture, the hardener component has a useable life of more than a year.

While the craze-resistant urea adhesives supplied by the several manufacturers are not identical, they are believed to be similar in composition and general behavior. To avoid repetition, the application instructions for the use of "Urac" 185, supplied by American Cyanamid Co. are presented as representative.

The craze-resistant adhesives of this type are only slightly more expensive than the unmodified

TABLE 1. MANUFACTURERS OF CRAZE-RESISTANT UREA ADHESIVES.

Company	Trade Name
American Cyanamid Co.	Urac 185, Formica Urac 185
Catalin Corp.	Catalin
Borden Chemical Co.	Casco-Resin
National Casein Co.	National Casein
Allied Chemical Corp.	Plaskon 5399
Reichholdt Chemicals, Inc.	Plyamine

urea adhesives as supplied, but since they should not be extended with cereal flours, the cost of the glue spread is appreciably greater. The manufacturers recommend a resin to filler ratio which yields the optimum in craze resistance and other properties of the glue line. Dilution of the glue mix with water or bulk extenders will detract from these properties.

Consistency of Adhesive Mix. The consistency of the adhesive mix is chosen according to the method of application suitable for the job. Flat work is adaptable to the use of a mechanical roll spreader to yield thin glue lines with a thin consistency of mix. Many applications require the use of spatula or brush spreading of a thicker mix. Within the limits suggested by the manufacturer, the strength and craze-resistance of the glue line is not influenced by the consistency of the mix.

TABLE 2. COMPOSITION OF ADHESIVE MIX.*

Consistency	Thin	Medium	Thick
Applicator	Mechanical	Brush	Spatula
Liquid component, parts by wt	100	100	100
Hardener component, parts by wt	10–13	13–16	16–18

* American Cyanamid Co., Instructions for "Urac 185."

Mixing and Working Life. Because of the limited working life of the adhesive mix, the amount to be mixed at one time should be regulated by the rate of application. The hardener is added slowly to the liquid resin under agitation. Hand mixing or a strong, double action mechanical mixer may be used. The final mixture should be smooth and lump-free.

Once the hardener is in contact with the resin, a chemical reaction begins which continues until complete set and cure is obtained. Some exothermic heat is developed during the mixing and will shorten the working life if not controlled. The use of water-cooled containers is therefore recommended

for amounts exceeding a few pounds of mix. The useable life of the adhesive is reduced by one-half for each temperature rise of 10°F, as shown in Table 3. While the number of hours working life at a given temperature may vary with the source of the adhesive, the rate of change is typical of the urea resin polymerization.

TABLE 3. WORKING LIFE OF ADHESIVE MIX.*

Mix temperature, °F	60°	70°	80°	90°
Working life, hr	8.0	4.0	2.0	1.0

* American Cyanamid Co., Instructions for "Urac 185."

Pressing Conditions. The time between spreading and pressing should be kept as short as possible to prevent air-drying at the film surface. At normal operating temperatures, the assembly time should not exceed 10 to 20 min. The glue line should be of minimum thickness for both economy and quality. Even with the craze-resistant adhesives, glue lines should not exceed .020 in. The clamping pressure is maintained until the glue line has developed sufficient strength to allow handling without rupture of the bond.

The rate of polymerization of the urea-formaldehyde resin increases with glue-line temperature. Consequently, as in the liquid mix, the minimum allowable pressing time will be reduced by one-half for each rise of 10°F (see Table 4).

TABLE 4. INFLUENCE OF TEMPERATURE ON MINIMUM CLAMPING TIME.*

Assembly temperature, °F	70	80	90	100
Clamping time, hr	12	6	3	1.5

* American Cyanamid Co., Instructions for "Urac 185."

Pressing time will also vary with the moisture content and species of the wood. Furthermore, unstressed assemblies require a shorter pressing period than stressed parts.

Unmodified Urea-Resin Adhesives. The unmodified or "straight" urea-formaldehyde adhesives are available in liquid or powder varieties. The liquid types commercially available are solutions or dispersions of urea-formaldehyde polymers in water at various concentrations. The resin powders are usually spray-dried polymers which, when supplied without added fillers or catalysts, can be dispersed in water at the desired solids content to be essentially equivalent in properties and behavior to the liquid resins.

The liquid urea resins and the unfilled powder resins require the separate addition of catalysts and fillers before application. These resins are the most economical and versatile of the urea adhesives. They are most often extended with varying amounts of cereal flours to reduce the cost of the glue line. The powdered resins containing catalysts and fillers are generally dispersed in water according to the manufacturer's directions, without further extension.

The manufacture of interior-grade plywood is one of the largest outlets for unmodified urea adhesives. Much of this is made by cold-press methods. The bonding of decorative laminates and "Masonite" to substructures, the manufacture of interior doors, furniture panels, mill work and joint assemblies, sporting goods assemblies and the gluing of lumber cores are examples of urea resin applications by cold-press technique.

Type of Bond. The bonds obtained with unmodified urea adhesives are highly moisture resistant, even with long flour extension. Bonds of equivalent quality are obtained with cold pressing or hot pressing provided the proper catalyst is used and the supplier's instructions are followed. Glue bonds that meet Commercial Standard Specifications CS-35-49 for a type II bond are possible with these adhesives.

Formulations. While the liquid and powdered urea resins supplied by the several manufacturers are similar in composition and behavior, the hardeners vary considerably. Frequently, especially with the liquid urea resins, the resins from two manufacturers are interchanged in adhesive formulation. This practice is not advisable with hardeners, however. Each manufacturer offers a variety of hardeners for different end use or process applications. While the hardeners are based on the same chemical principles, they may vary widely in over-all composition.

An effective hardener contains an activating agent such as an ammonium salt which reacts with free formaldehyde and low molecular weight methylol ureas to form hexamethylenetetramine and the acid corresponding to the ammonium salt. The liberated acid acts as a polymerization catalyst for the urea resin. The proportion of activator to resin is adjusted to provide a practical working life for the adhesive mix while ensuring complete cure of the resin. Approximately 2 per cent of ammonium chloride based on resin solids will furnish enough acid for a cold-press cure of the resin. If the ammonium chloride were used alone, the working life of the spreadable mix would be too short for practical application. Further, the pH of the mix would become too low (acid) for a permanent bond. Wood cellulose degrades and loses fiber strength on aging in contact with an acid film. Consequently the hardener usually contains a pH buffer such as tricalcium phosphate which prevents the pH of the liquid mix from dropping below a value of about 3 and at the same time extends the working life to practical time periods. Tricalcium phosphate concentrations of 2 to 5 per cent based on resin can be used to control the working life.

The hardeners should also contain wood flours to control the viscosity and shell flours to reduce glue-line penetration. Hardeners that do not contain the ligneous fillers should not be added to the adhesive until the time of mixing.

When the adhesive is extended with a cereal flour to reduce the cost of the glue-line spread, increasing amounts of water are necessary to obtain workable viscosities. For example, the following cold-press formulations are suggested for the use of Monsanto "Lauxite" UF-71, a neat powdered urea formaldehyde resin.

The amount of water necessary to provide the proper adhesive consistency for flour-extended mixes will vary with the grade and variety of flour. Adjustments in the water addition may be necessary to obtain a spreadable viscosity.

When the hardener contains catalysts, buffers and ligneous fillers, increasing amounts are required, based on the resin, to obtain the same working life with increased extension of cereal flours. This is shown by the suggested formulations for cold pressing of plywood using American Cyanamid Co. "Urac" 110, a neat powdered urea formaldehyde resin.

Glue-Line Spreads. Cold-press adhesives generally are used with a heavier spread than are hot-press adhesives. The spreads will vary from 40 to 55 lb of adhesive mix per 1000 sq ft of glue line. The density of the wood to be glued is the most important criterion for estimating the proper amount of spread. High density woods like birch, maple,

TABLE 5. FORMULATIONS AND WORKING LIFE, COLD PRESS.*

"Lauxite UF," lb	100	100	100
Shellflour, lb	15	15	15
Wheat flour, lb	—	25	50
Water, lb	80	100–110	130–140
"71 Hardener," lb	5	5	5
Working life, hr			
at 70°F	4	4	4½
80°F	2	2	2½
90°F	1	1	1½

* Monsanto Chemical Co., Instructions for "Lauxite UF-71."

TABLE 6. CEREAL FLOUR-EXTENDED ADHESIVE FORMULATIONS, COLD-PRESS.*

% Extension	9	25	59	100	125	150
"Urac Resin 110," lb	70	70	70	70	70	70
Soft wheat flour, lb	—	17½	35	70	87½	105
Water, lb	45	60	85	120	145	170
"Hardener C-110-S," lb	—	1	2	4	5	6
"Hardener 181," lb	7–10	—	—	—	—	—
"Smoothing Agent WF-61," lb	—	—	—	—	¼	¼
Viscosity—poises	15–27	12–18	15–20	18–27	20–30	20–30
Working life, hr at 80°F	3–4	3–4	3–4	3–4	3–4	3–4
Gelation time, hr at 80°F	5–6	5–6	5–6	5–6	5–6	5–6

* American Cyanamid Co., Instructions for "Urac 110."

or beech will bond with the lower spreads while the low density species like pine and poplar require heavier spreads.

Sources of Urea Resin Adhesives. Most of the many suppliers of unmodified urea resin adhesives offer the liquid form only. A few of the larger suppliers, who have spray-drying facilities, offer both powdered and liquid varieties. The wide acceptance of urea adhesives in the plywood, furniture, and particle board industries has encouraged the growth in the number of suppliers. As a result of the increased sources available, coupled with seasonal fluctuations in demand of the end products, the urea adhesive market has become highly competitive. In recent years many manufacturers, faced with ever diminishing profit margins, have established reactors for making liquid urea adhesives as close as possible to areas of potential markets to minimize shipping costs. Some companies who had been major suppliers of urea adhesives have curtailed manufacture or withdrawn from the market altogether.

Hot Pressing

Formulations. All the urea resins suitable for cold-press application may be hot pressed. For hot pressing, a smaller amount of hardener or a different formulation of catalyst-filler system is used. Melamine resins and melamine-urea combinations are usually hot pressed without the addition of a catalyst. Some adhesive formulations that contain only small amounts of melamine resin still require a catalyst to obtain cures, especially if a rapid cure is desired, even with high glue-line temperature. Typical of the latter are adhesives for tapeless splicing of veneer.

Equipment for Adhesive Application and Hot-Pressing. A mechanical glue spreader is essential for commercial application of adhesives in the manufacture of flat stock. Glue spreaders developed for resin adhesives are necessarily rugged, precision-designed machines. A uniformly thin coating of adhesive is applied by the spreader in closely controlled quantities. The adhesive is transferred to the stock from rubber-coated rolls which have enough resiliency to conform to irregularities in a commercial veneer. The gluing rolls are grooved to control the amount of spread within a given range. One manufacturer of mechanical glue spreaders, The Black Bros., recommends roll grooving .035 inch deep arranged as follows:

For hot-press urea-formaldehyde adhesive in range of 20 to 35 lb per 1000 sq ft, roll grooving of 20 to 22 threads per inch is suggested.

TABLE 7. DOMESTIC SOURCES OF UREA RESIN ADHESIVES

Trade Name	Supplier
Amres	American-Marietta Co.
Bakelite	Bakelite Co., Div. Union Carbide Corp.
Casamite, Casco-Resin	Borden Chemical Co.
Catalin	Catalin Corp.
Foramine, Plyamine	Reichhold Chemicals, Inc.
Fuller, Full-O-Mite	H. B. Fuller Co.
Griptite	Adhesives Products Corp.
Holdbest	C. B. Hewitt and Bros., Inc.
Lauxite	Monsanto Chemical Co.
Lebec	Lebec Chemical Corp.
Loven	Loven Chemical of California
Midland	Midland Adhesive & Chemical Corp.
National Casein	National Casein Co.
Perma weld, Vraform	Polymer Corp. of Pa.
Plaskon	Allied Chemical Corp.
Polybond	Polymer Industries, Inc.
Residex	Paisley Products, Inc.
Synco	Synco Resins, Inc.
Synvarol	Synvar Corp.
Uformite	Resinous Prods. Div. Rohm & Haas Co.
Urac	American Cyanamid Co. Plastics & Resin Div.
Weldwood	U. S. Plywood Corp.

For cold pressing, where the required spread is 35 to 60 lb per 1000 sq ft, the roll grooving has 18 threads per inch.

For heavier spreads in the range of 50 to 75 lb, 16 threads per inch are preferred.

The rubber rolls are adjustable to obtain the desired gap, and are in contact with precision-adjusted metal doctor rolls which provide further control of the glue spread.

The heating of the glue line to accelerate cure is accomplished by specialized equipment designed for the operation at hand. In the manufacture of plywood, for example, two basic types of product are made: all veneer plywood and veneer faced, lumber core plywood.

Veneer plywood is composed of multiple layers of thin veneers made by edge splicing strips of wood usually ⅟16 to ⅛ in. thick and of varying widths. For the bonding of the wood strips to form a panel of the desired width, a tapeless splicer is used, frequently the Diehle tapeless splicer.

The spliced veneers that have been coated with the desired amount of adhesive are assembled in plies and placed between platens in a multiple platen hydraulic press. A single composite of the required number of plies is placed in each opening of the press. Pressures of 150 to 250 psi are applied depending on the wood species. Platen temperature from 240 to 280°F are appropriate for the cure of unmodified urea, melamine-urea, and melamine adhesives. If temperature is too high, steam "blows" or blisters are apt to occur. The platen temperature should not exceed 300°F, and 260°F is the usual value.

Bonding of decorative laminates to plywood or particle boards can be accomplished effectively by hot pressing. If a single laminate surface is to be applied, two assemblies placed back to back are inserted between platens. For structures comprising a laminate on both surface and back, a single assembly is placed between platens. Moderate platen temperatures are desirable for hot pressing decorative laminates to substructures to avoid an overcure, which could result in a lowering of the craze resistance of the surface.

Pressing Schedules for Hot-Press Plywood. Wood is an effective insulator. Since the pressing period is a function of the glue-line temperature and the species of wood, the distance between the heated platen and deepest glue line will control the pressing time for each resin-catalyst system. The pressing or cure time will vary with different formulations and sources of resin-hardener components, but all will be proportionally longer for thicker sections as controlled by the heat transfer of the wood. Typical schedules are shown in Tables 8, 9, and 10 for various adhesives.

Pressing schedules are determined by the time needed for the heat from the press platens to penetrate the wood sections and cure the innermost glue line of the assembly. Hot pressing of lumber sections becomes less practical as the thickness of the stock increases. Also when hot pressing an assembly containing multiple glue lines, the glue lines nearest the platens will be at temperature for longer periods than the deepest glue line. This condition could result in "overcure" of the outer glue lines especially with urea adhesives.

High-Frequency Curing. High-frequency presses

TABLE 8. PRESSING SCHEDULE AT 260°F PLATEN TEMPERATURE UNMODIFIED CATALYZED UREA-LIQUID ADHESIVE*

Glue-Line Depth (In.)	Pressing Time (Min)	
	50% Flour Extended*	100–150% Extended
⅟16	1	3
⅛	3	5
¼	3½	6
⅜	7½	10
½	9	13

* American Cyanamid Co., Instructions for "Urac 180, Hardener WF-101"

TABLE 9. PRESSING SCHEDULE AT 240°–260°F PLATEN TEMPERATURE UNCATALYZED MELAMINE-UREA ADHESIVE.*

Glue-Line Depth (In.)	Pressing Time (Min)	
	Veneer Cores	Lumber Cores
⅟28	1½–3	3½–6
⅟16	2–4½	4–6½
⅛	3–6	5–8
¼	4¾–8½	6¾–10
⅜	6¾–11	8¾–13
½	8½–13½	10¾–16

* Monsanto Chemical Co., Instructions for "Lauxite 326."

TABLE 10. PRESSING SCHEDULE AT 260°F PLATEN TEMPERATURE UNCATALYZED MELAMINE ADHESIVE.*

Glue-Line Depth (In.)	Pressing Time (Min)
⅟16	4
⅟10	5
⅛	6
¼	8

* American Cyanamid Co., Instructions for "Cymel 401."

are commonly used for curing adhesives in plywood and panel assemblies. Edge gluing of lumber cores by high-frequency heating is widespread in the industry.

High-frequency curing may be accomplished by three methods of application of the field energy in relation to the glue line: parallel, perpendicular, and stray field. The choice of heating is decided by the nature of the assembly.

Parallel heating is usually employed for lumber core edge gluing. The electrodes are so placed that the high-frequency energy travels along the glue line, which becomes heated by absorption of the energy. In this method, the distance between the electrodes is small. Since the energy does not have to pass through the wood to reach the glue line, the power consumption per area of glue line is the lowest of the three methods.

Perpendicular heating is used for curing of plywood and other flat panel-type gluing. The energy is directed across the glue line and is consequently absorbed by the wood also. More power is needed for this method than for parallel heating. The power input across the electrodes required to bring the glue line to curing temperature will vary with the wood density, moisture content, and depth of glue line. Power of 1000 volts per inch across the electrodes is usually sufficient for gluing of low density woods, but 2500 volts per inch may be needed for denser species.

Stray-field heating is used for curing assemblies that, because of structure, cannot be cured by the other methods. Bonding of plywood panels to frames in the manufacture of hollow-core doors is an example. The electrodes are placed on the outer surfaces of the assembly to be bonded. Relatively higher power per unit of glue line is required by this method.

The pressing schedule for high-frequency heating will vary with the capacity and efficiency of the heating unit as well as with the type of adhesive, wood species, and structure of the assembly to be glued. The manufacturers of the high-frequency equipment usually make proper recommendations for each type of job.

Melamine Resin Adhesive. Melamine resins and melamine-urea resins are normally used without catalyst and are hot pressed to obtain a cured glue line. The melamine resins are more expensive than the urea resins and are therefore customarily restricted to applications requiring improved water resistance. Waterproof exterior-grade plywood, marine-grade plywood, and heavy timber marine laminations are good examples of melamine adhesive applications. In addition, melamine resins can be used advantageously in wood particle boards, molded wood waste products, sporting goods, and quality applications requiring light-colored, nonstaining glue lines.

Melamine resin is frequently added to urea resin to provide improved water resistance. Because of the beneficial effect of even modest amounts of melamine resin, improved glue lines can be obtained at a moderate increase in cost. Unmodified melamine resin adhesives give bonds comparable in durability to those obtained with phenolic and resorcinol resin adhesives.

The melamine resin adhesives are superior to urea adhesives in the following properties:

> Boil resistant
> Long working life and assembly time
> High bonding strength
> Heat and chemical resistance
> Neutral glue line pH

Sources. Melamine resin adhesives are supplied mostly as dry, stable powders without catalyst or filler. Combinations of urea and melamine which contain fillers or filler catalyst systems are also available for tapeless splicing and boil-resistant plywood. Manufacturers of melamine resin adhesives are few in number compared with urea resin manufacturers.

Formulations. Unmodified melamine resins, listed in Table 11, are used for the production of waterproof plywood, as fortifiers of urea adhesives, and as resin binders for wood particle boards and wood waste molded products.

For plywood adhesive applications, the resin is dispersed in water. Shell flour is added to obtain a spreadable consistency. Catalysts may be added to shorten the cure cycle, but normally the adhesive is hot pressed in the uncatalyzed state. Typical formulations are shown in Table 12 for some commercially available melamine resin adhesives.

Fortification of urea resin adhesive with varying amounts of melamine resin will improve the boil resistance of the glue line and lengthen the maximum allowable assembly time in direct proportion to the amount of added melamine resin. A typical series of formulations is shown in Table 13.

Particle Boards. Particle board or more specifically wood particle board is a general term covering a wide range of products which vary in wood species, particle size and shape, and type of binder. The binders used are various, from inorganic types such as gypsum to thermosetting resins of the amino and phenolic classes. Only the amino resin binders fall within the scope of this discussion.

TABLE 11. DOMESTIC SOURCES OF MELAMINE RESIN ADHESIVES.

Trade Name	Description and Application	Supplier
Catalin 822	Melamine-urea resin plywood adhesive	Catalin Corp.
Catalin 852	Melamine resin powder without filler or catalyst. Plywood adhesive and fortifier of urea adhesives	Catalin Corp.
Cymel 401	Same as above	American Cyanamid Co.
Diaron 3570	General purpose melamine resin powder without filler or catalyst. Plywood adhesive, fortifier of urea adhesives, wood waste binder	Reichhold Chemicals, Inc.
Lauxite MF-300	(Same as Catalin 852)	Monsanto Chemical Co.
Lauxite MF-325	Melamine resin powder without filler or catalyst. Wood waste binder.	Monsanto Chemical Co.
Lauxite 326	Melamine-urea resin powder with added filler, no catalyst. Plywood adhesive	Monsanto Chemical Co.
Melurac 300, 305	Same as above	American Cyanamid Co.
Melurac 304	Melamine-urea resin powder without filler or catalyst. Wood waste binder	American Cyanamid Co.
Melurac 255	Melamine-urea resin powder without catalyst. Veneer splicing adhesive	American Cyanamid Co.
Melurac 259, 260	Melamine-urea resin powder containing catalyst. Veneer splicing adhesive	American Cyanamid Co.

TABLE 12. FORMULATIONS FOR MELAMINE ADHESIVES.
*Uncatalyzed Mix—Long Working Life.**

"Cymel 401," lb	80
Shell flour, lb	20
Water, lb	60
Viscosity, poises	10–12
Working life, hr at 80°F	12–18
Gelation time, hr at 80°F	24

* American Cyanamid Co., Instructions for "Cymel 401."

*Catalyzed Mix—Influence of Catalyst on Working Life.**

"Lauxite MF-300," lb	100	100
Shell flour, lb	20	7.5
Water, lb	55	40–50
"Catalyst Y," lb	0.25	2.5
Working life, hr at 75°F	8	2–3

* Monsanto Chemical Co., Instructions for "Lauxite MF-300."

Particle boards are commonly described as chipboards, flake boards, wood waste boards, wafer boards, and sawdust boards, according to the particle shape or source. The utilization of sawdust and waste machine chips, other than burning, has been of interest to wood-working companies for many years. The use of synthetic resin binders to make a wood waste board is by no means of recent origin.

There are at present over fifty particle board plants in production in the United States. Their total estimated capacity is reportedly from 600 million to one billion square feet annually on a three-quarter inch stock basis. Actual production falls well below these estimates but has been increasing rapidly since 1950 and more especially since 1956. Out-put rose from 200 million square feet in 1957 to almost 300 million in 1959, dipped

TABLE 13. MELAMINE RESIN—FORTIFIED UREA ADHESIVES.*

"Cymel 401" fortifier, lb	0	5	10	15	20
"Urac 180 or 186," lb	150	150	150	150	150
Shell flour, lb	10	10	10	10	10
"Hardener M-325"	2	2	2	2	2
Viscosity, poises	7–10	7–10	7–10	8–12	10–15
Mix life, hr at 80°F	—	8–10	8–10	8–10	8–10
Gelation time, hr at 80°F	—	20–24	20–24	20–24	20–24
Maximum assembly, hr at 80°F	2–3	12–15	15–20	20–24	20–24
Boil resistance, hr	½	1	2	3	4

* American Cyanamid Co., Instructions for "Cymel 401."

in 1960, but resumed its upward trend in 1961. Production of high-density hard boards, which have been available commercially for a much longer time, exceeds two billion square feet per year.

The supply of natural wood waste is inadequate for low-density particle board production. Approximately one-fourth of the present United States production is based on the use of virgin wood. This proportion will undoubtedly increase in the future.

Applications of particle boards are not necessarily based on replacement of plywood. In many end uses, the homogeneous nature of the particle board is advantageous. Current applications include furniture construction, substructure for plastic laminates and flooring, wall panels, and cores for flush doors. Furniture manufacture is the largest outlet with plastic and floor covering underlay in second place.

The particle board industry offers a large present and increasingly large future outlet for synthetic resin binders. An estimated total of 100 to 150 million pounds of synthetic resin solids would be required as binder if present plants were operated at capacity. Of this amount, urea and urea-melamine resins could well exceed 50 per cent of the total.

Two basic types of particle are used for the particle board construction: short, thick "chips" and long, thin "flakes." Except perhaps for special applications, the two types are used separately. The source of the wood waste usually determines the type of particle to be used. Ordinary wood waste from general mill work can produce the "chip"-type and larger pieces such as veneer peeler cores can be reduced to the "flakes."

While there are numerous processes for particle board production, two basic methods are applicable: the wet process and the dry process. The wet process is very similar to paper making and requires a large capital investment. It is best adapted to large-scale production of "hardboards" such as "Masonite." Phenolic resins, waxes, and lignins are used as binders.

The dry process requires a much lower capital investment and is the most commonly used process for making low- and medium-density particle boards. Only mechanical treatment of the waste material is needed without the digesting, defiberizing, and filtering stages of the wet process. The dry process may be further separated into two categories: the batch process and the semi-continuous process. The dry process utilizes urea, melamine-urea, and phenolic resin binders. Urea resins are chosen for light-colored applications. Melamine-urea resins are used for light-colored

applications with improved flexural strength. Phenolic resins yield boards with high flexural strength where the color of the binder is not important. Unmodified or "straight" melamine resins could be used for high flexural strength particle boards, but are at present too expensive.

Details of the various methods for production of particle boards are beyond the scope of this discussion. With the exception of differences in the nature of the wood particles and mechanical handling, all methods using the dry process are basically similar. The selected wood particles are conditioned to a moisture content of 5 to 10 per cent. The particles are then intimately mixed with about 7 per cent resin binder, 1 to 2 per cent petroleum wax, usually in the form of an emulsion, and sufficient water to bring the moisture content of the entire mix to about 12 per cent. Since the resin binder content is small in proportion to the wood, little effect on the water absorption of the final product can be attributed to the resin, regardless of which type resin is used. Water absorption and swelling of the product are minimized by the use of a water-repellant coating on the particle.

The homogeneous mixture of wood and binder is spread in controlled amounts on trays or caul plates approximately the size of the finished products. The mats so formed are then pressed individually between heated platens in a hydraulic press to cure the binder. The dry mix of known weight per square foot is pressed to a predetermined thickness to result in a board of desired density. Pressures up to 600 psi and temperatures from 270 to 300°F are used for production of particle boards with densities below 1.0 g/cc.

The boards are kept in the hot press for about 6 min to set the resin binder, and are removed without cooling. On removal from the press, sufficient flexural strength has been achieved to permit handling and trimming; but full cure as measured by flexural strength is not developed until after an aging and conditioning period of about 3 days.

Flexural strength of the particle board will vary with resin content, type of particle, and moisture content for each density board. Increased resin content and higher moisture content within pressable limits yield higher flexural strengths. Board density exhibits the greatest effect on flexural strength. A board made with a urea resin binder shows a fourfold increase in flexural strength when density is increased from 0.6 to 1.0 g/cc.

Paperboard. Paperboard is available in two basic types: solid fiber and corrugated. Starch and dextrins are used as the adhesive for much of the paperboard manufacture, producing satisfactory dry bonds. In order to obtain bonds capable of withstanding high humidity or prolonged exposure to moisture conditions usually encountered in storage and shipping, these adhesives may be fortified with urea resin adhesives.

Solid Fiber. Solid fiber paperboard is composed of multiple plies, three to five, of kraft or other paper bonded together by the adhesive in a continuous laminating machine. For a three-ply construction, the center ply or core is spread on both sides with adhesive and interleaved continuously between the liners through pressure rolls. The product may be heated between platens or rolls to speed the cure of the glue line.

A typical water-resistant adhesive for use in solid fiber-board manufacture is prepared as follows: a charge of 500 lb of the selected starch is mixed with about 120 gal of water with agitation and heated to 200°F to "cook" the starch. The partially hydrolyzed starch dispersion is then cooled to about 100°F and adjusted to a pH value of 6 with a mild alkali such as sodium carbonate. While the dispersion is under agitation, 100 lb of a powdered urea adhesive or the equivalent of a liquid urea adhesive is added. When solution of the resin is complete, approximately 17 lb of ammonium chloride catalyst, dissolved in water, is added and mixed.

The above adhesive is spread on the inner plies at a coverage of approximately 10 lb of wet mix per 1000 sq ft of single glue line. Optimum water resistance is developed after several days aging of the laminated product. After immersion in water for 24 hr, tearing of the paperboard will show failure in the paper rather than the glue line.

Corrugated. Corrugated paperboard is constructed by bonding together an inner core of fluted paper between two paper liners. Production rates of corrugated paperboards machines are as high as 500 ft/min. The bonding of the liners is carried out in two stages. As the center ply is crimped into flutes, adhesive is roller-applied to the top of the flutes. The top liner is immediately laid on the coated flutes and the combination passed over a festooning bridge to release tensions. The flute gluing and liner application is then repeated for the bottom face and the board is passed over hot plates to cure the glue line.

Corn, potato, and tapioca starch are used as the basic adhesive. In a typical starch paste, only about 15 per cent of the starch is "cooked" or hydrolyzed with heat in the presence of 1.0 to 1.5 per cent sodium carbonate or sodium hydroxide. The remainder of the starch is dispersed in the "raw" state. The starch paste provides an effective dry bond by itself, but its water resistance is improved by addition of approximately 5 per cent of a urea-formaldehyde resin adhesive catalyzed with ammonium chloride or sulfate.

A typical resin-fortified starch adhesive contains the following ingredients:

Hydrolyzed starch	100	lb
Uncooked starch	650	lb
Sodium carbonate	1.5	lb
Urea-formaldehyde, resin solids	40	lb
Ammonium chloride or sulfate	60	lb
Mold preventive	as desired	
Water	250	gal

The paperboards bonded with resin-fortified starch adhesives are sometimes known as V Board; they are intended to pass the water-resistance tests of Government JAN-P-108 specifications for "V" weatherproof boxes.

Multi-wall Paper Bags. As in the production of paperboard urea resin adhesives are used as fortifiers of bag pastes. Many different starch and dextrin formulations are used for seam and bottom pastes in paper bag manufacture. Paste viscosity, gel time, and other handling characteristics are controlled for optimum performance with each of the various automatic machines and types of paper. The incorporation of about 10 per cent urea resin adhesive solids based on the total starch will produce water-resistant bonds. Ammonium chloride of paper-makers' alum may be used as the resin catalyst.

References

1. Allied Chemical Corp., Technical Data U. F. "Concentrate 85."
2. Ellis, C., "The Chemistry of Synthetic Resins," New York, Reinhold Publishing Corp., (1935).
3. H. John, U. S. Patent 1,355,834 (Oct. 19, 1920).
4. Gams, A., Widmer, G., and Fisch., *Helv. Chim. Acta* **24,** 302 (1941).
5. Marvel, C. S., *et al., J. Am. Chem. Soc.,* **68,** 1681 (1946).
6. Payne, H. F., "Organic Coating Technology," Vol. 1., New York, John Wiley & Sons, Inc., 1954.
7. Ripper, K., (to Fritz Pollak, Vienna, Austria), U. S. Patent 1,687,312 (Oct. 9, 1928)
8. Walter, *Trans. Faraday Society,* **32,** 3777 (1936).
9. Wohnsiedler, H. P., *Ind. Eng. Chem.,* **44,** 2679 (1952).
10. Wohnsiedler, H. P., *Ind. Eng. Chem.,* **45,** 2307 (1953).

─── 25 ───

Epoxy Resin Adhesives

Irving Skeist

Skeist Laboratories, Inc.
Newark, New Jersey

The epoxy resins, in commercial use for little more than a decade, have had a marked impact on the technologies of coating, potting, tooling, laminating, and adhesive bonding.[1, 2, 3] Though expensive—$0.62/lb in bulk for the common liquid resins—they find increasing application for the structural bonding of metals, ceramics, glass, plastics, polyesters, phenolics, and other materials. Consumption of epoxy adhesives, body solders, sealing and patching compounds is estimated at 4 to 5 MM lb for 1960, and is expected to double in 5 yr.

High strength and relative ease of application have endeared the epoxies to the aircraft industry. They bond aluminum sheet to itself or to other metals, permit the construction of thin-skinned, honeycombed sandwiches, and are tougher than metal solders for joining many materials. Fiber glass-reinforced polyester fuel tanks are made in sections and then sealed together with epoxies to give a stronger bond than is obtainable from the polyesters themselves. New concrete can be bonded to old with epoxies. They make possible the bonding of "Alnico" magnets to die-cast zinc, polyester film to aluminum, even cementable "Teflon" to stainless steel.[4]

Along with other adhesives, the epoxies offer advantages over fasteners for metal-to-metal bonding. Labor cost is generally reduced. Stress is distributed uniformly over the widest possible surface, making for high strength and resistance to fatigue, and permitting the use of thin metal skins which would distort if riveted or welded. Smooth outside contours, so important in high-speed aircraft, become feasible. Two different metals may be joined without creating corrosion problems.

In addition, epoxies have special advantages over other resins as bonding agents:

(1) *Adhesion.* Because of their epoxide, hydroxyl, amine and other polar groups, the epoxies have high specific adhesion to metals, glass and ceramics. They can be formulated to give mixes of low viscosity with improved wetting, spreading, and penetrating action. The variety of functional groups also provides good affinity between metals and plastics. For example, epoxies are in use for the bonding of copper to phenolic laminate in printed circuits.

(2) *Cohesion.* When the resin is properly cured, the cohesive strength within the glue line is so great, and the adhesion of the epoxy to other materials so good, that failure under stress often occurs in one of the adherends rather than in the epoxy or at the interface. This happens with glass and aluminum as well as with weaker adherends such as concrete and wood.

(3) *100 Per Cent Solids.* Unlike the phenolics and some other resinous adhesives, the epoxies cure without releasing water or other condensation by-products. This makes it possible to bond the epoxies at only contact pressures, or with no pressure at all. Also, since there is no water to remove (as with rubber latices) and no volatile solvent (as with nitrocellulose cements), the epoxies are convenient for the assembly-line bonding of impervious surfaces such as metals and glass.

(4) *Low Shrinkage.* The epoxies cure with only a fraction of the shrinkage of vinyl-type adhesives such as the polyesters and acrylics; consequently less strain is built into the glue line, and the bond is stronger. Also, the epoxies do not pull away

from glass fibers as polyesters do. The shrinkage can be reduced to a fraction of one per cent by incorporation of silica, aluminum, and other inorganic fillers.

(5) *Low Creep.* The cured epoxies, like other thermoset resins, maintain their shape under prolonged stress better than thermoplastics such as polyvinyl acetate, nitrocellulose, and polyvinyl butyral.

(6) *Resistance to Moisture and Solvents.* Unlike proteins, starches, dextrins, gums, and polyvinyl alcohol, the epoxies are insensitive to moisture. Their resistance to solvents is also outstanding and accounts for their rapid advance in the coatings field. They are effective barriers to heat and electric current.

(7) *Can be Modified.* The properties of epoxy adhesives can be changed by (a) selection of base resin and curing agent; (b) alloying the epoxy with another resin; or (c) compounding with fillers.

A few materials are not bonded effectively with ordinary epoxies. These are the crystalline and less polar plastics; untreated polyethylene, most silicones, untreated fluorocarbons, plasticized vinyl, and butyl rubber. The first three, at least, are inherently "abhesive" (nonadhesive) materials.

THE RESIN INTERMEDIATES

The epoxide or ethoxylene group,

$$-\overset{|}{C}-\overset{|}{C}- \atop \diagdown O \diagup \tag{1}$$

is a highly reactive three-membered ring. Both basic and acidic materials cause it to open. With primary or secondary amines, a glycidyl ether reacts to give an amine alcohol.

$$RNH_2 + H_2C{-}CH \cdot CH_2O{-} \longrightarrow \atop \diagdown O \diagup \tag{2}$$

$$RNH \cdot CH_2 \cdot CHOH \cdot CH_2O{-}$$

Under the influence of other bases, anhydrides, and Lewis acids, an external or internal epoxide may polymerize to a short-chain polyether.

$$n(R^1CH{-}CHR^2) \overset{cat.}{\longrightarrow} \atop \diagdown O \diagup \tag{3}$$

$$+CHR^1{-}CHR^2{-}O+_{\overline{n}}$$

In addition to catalyzing the polymerization of epoxides, anhydrides react with epoxides to form ester alcohols. A small amount of water or alcohol is required to initiate the reaction.

If at least some of the epoxy molecules contain more than one epoxide group, the possibility exists for forming a crosslinked network that is insoluble and infusible.

Resins Derived From Epichlorohydrin ("epi")

The most widely used epoxy intermediates are those made by the alkaline condensation of epichlorohydrin and bisphenol-A ("bis") to give resins of the structural formula:

$$(4)$$

The commercial "bis-epi" resins are essentially mixtures of polymers in which the average n varies from zero to approximately 20. Resins in which the average n is 2 or more are solid at room temperature. It is the liquid "bis-epi" resins, however, which are of greatest interest to adhesives formulators.

Each of the polymer molecules has n hydroxyl groups, which increase the rate of cure of the resins with amine hardeners. In addition, they result in increased adhesion of the cured epoxy to metals and other polar substrates. Consequently, the more viscous liquid epoxies are usually preferred to the less viscous members of the series for adhesives applications.

The solid "bis-epi" resins have even greater hydroxyl content, and also give better heat resistance. However, they must be dissolved, and the solvent must be evaporated before cure is completed. This makes their utilization more troublesome.

Table 1 gives the properties of the leading resins derived from epichlorohydrin which are made by United States manufacturers (listed alphabetically). The *aliphatic* resins in this table are made by condensation of epichlorohydrin with aliphatic polyols such as glycerin. The *modified* resins are made by blending or reacting unmodified "bis-epi" resins with aliphatic polyepoxides, monoglycidyl ethers (allyl, butyl, phenyl), or plasticizers such as dibutyl

TABLE 1. COMMERCIAL EPOXY RESINS DERIVED FROM EPICHLOROHYDRIN.*

Types	Ciba "Araldite"	Dow "DER"	Jones-Dabney "Epi-Rez"	Reichhold "Epotuf"	Shell "Epon"	Union Carbide "ERL" and "EKR"	Viscosity (cp) (73°F)	Melting Point (°C)	lb/gal	Epoxide Equivalent Weight	Hydroxyl Equivalent Weight	Average Molecular Weight	Hydroxyl Functionality	Calculated Epoxides per Molecule
Aliphatic			504				90–150		10.2	140–160	65			
Modified	506	334			812		150–210		9.1	170–180				
	502			6130	815	"ERL"-2795	500–700		9.3–9.6	170–200				
							3,000–6,000		9.3–9.6	232–250				
Liquid bis-epi	6005	332					3,600–6,400		9.7	173–179				
	6010	331	510	6140	826	"ERL"-2772	7,000–10,000		9.7	175–190	85			
	6020				828	"ERL"-2774	10,000–20,000		9.7	180–195				
	6030						16,000–20,000		9.7	196–208				
	6040	337	515		834		25,000–32,000		9.7	196–222				
					836		>32,000			230–280				
							A1–B‡	40–45	9.9	280–350	115			
Solid bis-epi	6060		520	6301	1001	"EKR"-2002	C–G‡	60–75	9.9	385–500	145	875	6.0	1.7–1.9
	6071						D–G‡	64–76	9.9	425–550				
	7071		522				D–G‡	65–75	9.9	450–530				
							F–J‡	65–75		550–650	175	1350	7.75	1.3–1.6
		661	530	6304	1002		G–K‡	75–85		475–700				
	6084	664	540	6307	1004	"EKR"-2003	R–V‡	95–105	9.6	870–1025	200	2625	13.0	1.3–1.7
	6097	667	550	6309	1007		Y–Z1‡	120–135	9.6	1500–2000	220	3875	17.5	1.0–1.6
	6099		560		1009		Z2–Z5‡	145–155		2400–4000				
								145–155		3500–5550				

* In order of increasing viscosities.
‡ Viscosity of 40% solution in butyl carbitol (Gardner-Holdt scale).

phthalate. Modified resins on the same horizontal line in Table 1 are of approximately the same viscosity, but may have different modifiers.

Along with the desired diepoxides, the condensation of "bis" and "epi" yields some by-products having less than two epoxide groups. Like the monoglycidyl ethers deliberately added as modifiers, these by-products result in greater flexibility but less heat resistance.

The *epoxy novolac resin,* Dow "DEN" 438, is made by the reaction of epichlorohydrin with a novolac resin to give the following idealized structural formula in which the average value for n is 1.3.

TABLE 2. "EPI" RESINS WITH MORE THAN TWO EPOXIDES.

	Dow "DEN" 438	Shell "Epon" 1031
Viscosity (77°F)	semi-solid	solid
Durran softening point	—	80°C
Specific gravity	1.220	—
Lb/gal	10.2	—
Epoxide equivalent	180	200–220
Average molecular weight	600	703
Hydroxyl functionality	0	0.25
Epoxide functionality	3.3	3.2–3.5

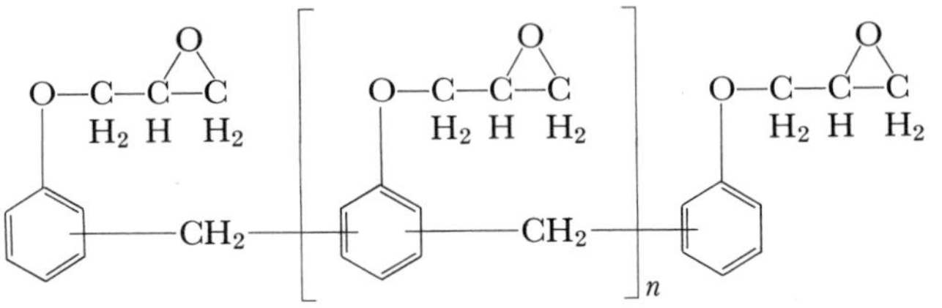

$$(5)$$

Shell's "Epon" 1031 is a solid epoxy resin with high functionality and reactivity. It is a mixture of isomers and homologues having an idealized structure as follows:

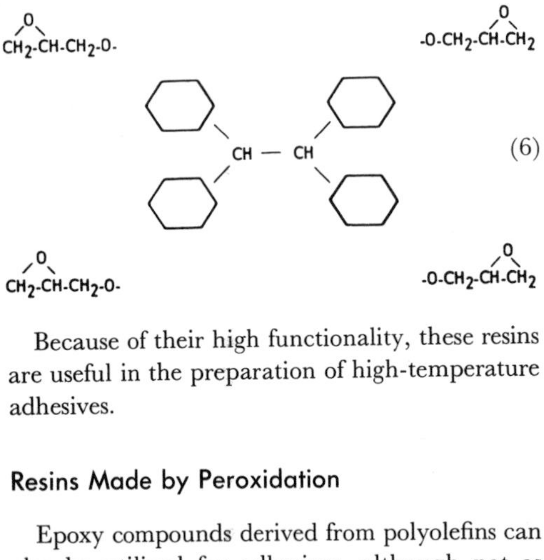

$$(6)$$

Because of their high functionality, these resins are useful in the preparation of high-temperature adhesives.

Resins Made by Peroxidation

Epoxy compounds derived from polyolefins can also be utilized for adhesives, although not as readily as the "epi"-derived glycidyl ethers. Polyolefins are peroxidized with peracetic acid to produce resins such as the "Unox" epoxides of Union Carbide Chemicals Co. and the "Oxirons" of Food Machinery & Chemical Corp. (FMC). "Unox" 201 is a diepoxide with a viscosity of about 1800 cps and an epoxy equivalent of approximately 156.

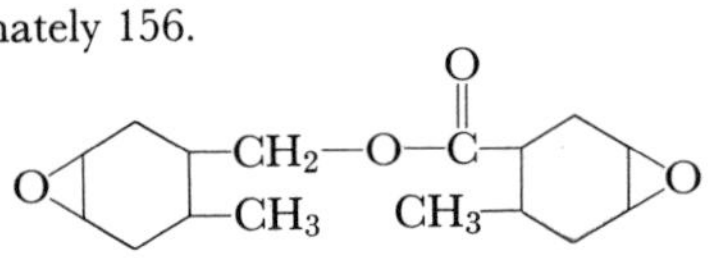

$$(7)$$

When blended with dimer acid or tall oil fatty acid for flexibility, and heat cured with 2 per cent stannous octoate, it yields adhesives and sealants having good resistance to thermal shock and impact.

"Oxiron" 2000, made by the peroxidation of polybutadiene, has the idealized structure shown on p. 327.

It possesses a variety of functional groups: hydroxyl, internal and terminal epoxides, vinylene and vinyl groups. Through the vinyls, it can be cured with peroxide catalysts such as dicumyl peroxide. "Oxiron" 2001 is a lower viscosity version, useful where penetration is required. Table 3 gives their properties.

For best heat resistance, the dicumyl peroxide is supplemented by an anhydride curing agent in a glycol as reactive internal plasticizer. An aromatic amine can also be used to advantage as a

TABLE 3. TYPICAL PROPERTIES OF UNCURED OXIRON RESINS.

	2000	2001
Appearance	Amber Liquid	Light yellow liquid
Viscosity, poise at 25°C	1800	160
Active ingredients, per cent	100	100
Specific gravity	1.010	1.014
Epoxy per cent	9.0	11.0
Epoxide equivalent weight	177	145
Hydroxyl per cent	2.5	2.0
Iodine number	185	154

$$\left[-CH_2-CH-CH-CH_2-CH_2-CH-CH-CH_2-CH_2-CH=CH-CH_2-CH_2-CH-CH_2-CH- \right]_X \quad (8)$$

curing agent in the presence of a catalyst such as phenol or resorcinol, but must be heated to a high temperature to achieve good heat distortion characteristics. For the first two formulations, the anhydride is melted and blended in before adding the peroxide as a glycol solution.

for combination with 100 parts of liquid epoxy resin having an epoxide equivalent of 190. The pot-life is an indication of the stability of the mixed composition at room temperature.

In general, the aromatic amines and cyclic anhydrides result in best heat resistance. A consid-

| | Parts by Weight | | |
	No. 1	No. 2	No. 3
"Oxiron" 2000 resin	100	0	100
"Oxiron" 2001 resin	0	100	—
Maleic anhydride	30.8	35.4	—
Propylene glycol	7.9	9.3	—
Dicumyl peroxide	0.5	0.5	—
Meta-phenylenediamine	—	—	24
Resorcinol	—	—	5
Cure	2 hr/80°C	2 hr/80°C	1 hr/100°C
Post cure	3 hr/120°C	3 hr/155°C	3 hr/155°C
Heat distortion temperature	144°C	186°C	116°C

CURING AGENTS

The uncured epoxy intermediates are either honey-colored liquids or brittle amber solids which become liquid when heated. When cured or hardened, the short polymer molecules are joined to each other to form large crosslinked structures. These final products are *thermoset,* i.e., insoluble and infusible.

Whether the curing agent is a catalyst or *reactive hardener,* the cure results in an *exotherm* or an evolution of heat. In the casting of thick sections, the higher temperatures thus developed result in faster cures. In adhesive bonding, however, the glue line is ordinarily thin and the heat developed by the curing reaction is largely conducted away into the adherends. Consequently, the fastest hardeners are preferred if no heat is to be supplied to the adhesive joint from without.

Table 4, from the literature of Shell Chemical Corp. and other sources, gives the characteristics of some of the more important curing agents for epoxy adhesives, and the proportions recommended

erable body of literature has been accumulated on specific systems.[1, 2, 3]

Ciba researchers, comparing HET anhydride with pyrodimellitic anhydride, MDA, and an aliphatic amine, have found that HET gives the best tensile shear strength at elevated temperatures. They used 140 parts HET with 100 parts "Araldite" 6020. The resin was first heated to 150°C, and the hardener was added and stirred into solution; then the mixture was cooled and formed into a stick. The stick adhesive was applied to hot aluminum panels. Cure was 30 min at 140°C, postcure 16 hr at 160°C. A tensile shear strength of 3000 psi was maintained at a temperature of 175°C. By comparision, the MDA composition weakened at temperatures above 150°C, and the other panels at even lower temperatures.

TOXICITY

Cured epoxies appear nondeleterious to health, when fed to laboratory animals in massive doses over long periods; conversely the uncured resins

TABLE 4. CURING AGENTS FOR LIQUID EPOXY RESINS.

Symbol	Name	Recommended Concentration (phr*)	Pot-life at Room Temp. (min)	Optimum Cure Schedule	
				(min)	(°C)
DETA	Diethylenetriamine	8–10	53	30	115
TETA	Triethylenetetramine	10–12	short	300	room temp.
DEAPA	Diethylaminopropylamine	6	210	60	115
"DMP" 30[a]	tris (dimethylaminomethyl) phenol	6	29	60	80
MPDA	Metaphenylenediamine	14	long	120 +240	85 150
MDA	Methylenedianiline	28.5	long	120	150
Dicy	Dicyandiamide	6	440	30	165
BF$_3$: MEA[b]	BF$_3$: monoethylamine	3	very long	240 +240	120 200
PA	Phthalic anhydride	45	long	300	150
HET	Chlorendic anhydride	120	long	240	150
NMA[d]	"Nadic" methyl anhydride	82	long	960 + 60	120 180
BDMA	benzyl dimethylamine	0.5			

* Parts per hundred parts of resin, by weight
[a] Rohm & Haas Co.
[b] General Chemical Div., Allied Chemical Corp.
[c] Hooker Electrochemical Company
[d] National Aniline Division, Allied Chemical Corp.

and hardeners are reactive chemicals which should not be allowed to come in contact with the skin. Amine hardeners, the worst offenders in common use, may cause dermatitis or asthmatic attacks. Certain aliphatic diepoxides—butadiene dioxide and especially vinyl cyclohexane dioxide—have produced tumors when painted on the skin of mice; consequently these materials are not recommended for adhesives formulations.[2]

Hydroxyethylated aliphatic amines are less irritating than ordinary aliphatic amines. These modified amine hardeners are available from Union Carbide, Shell and other companies.

Dermatitis from epoxy-hardener exposure, like that caused by poison ivy, affects some individuals worse than others. Fair-skinned people, blonds and redheads are more susceptible than brunettes; women are more sensitive than men. Those with allergic histories had best avoid contact with amines.

The danger of skin sensitization can be minimized by following good housekeeping rules and using proper equipment for dispensing two-part adhesives; see Chapter 47.

FILLERS

Fillers are often incorporated in epoxy adhesives to obtain one or more of the following advantages:

(1) Lower cost.

(2) Less shrinkage.
(3) Lower coefficient of thermal expansion.
(4) Greater heat resistance.

Shell Chemical researchers have obtained the tensile shear strengths shown in Table 5 at the indicated filler concentrations, with "Epon" 828 and DETA. All of the fillers listed are seen to impart superior strength at 180°F. At room temperature, however, the unfilled system is stronger than the filled compositions, except for those containing moderate amounts of "Hi-Sil," alumina, or ferric oxide.

FORMULATIONS

Tough, General-Purpose Adhesives

For resilient bonds and good low temperature characteristics, Ciba has investigated blends of liquid epoxy resin and a liquid polysulfide resin cured with a liquid amine hardener, for example:

	Parts by Weight	
	No. 4	No. 5
"Araldite" 6020	100	100
"Thiokol" LP-3[a]	50	50
DMAPA (dimethylaminopropylamine)	10	—
"DMP" 30	—	6

[a] Thiokol Corp.

TABLE 5.

Filler	Amount of Filler Per 100 G Resin	Tensile Shear Strength (psi)		
		(at −70°F)	(at Room Temperature)	(at 180°F)
None	0	—	2710	1350
Titanium dioxide	166.7	1490	1550	2070
	150	1700	1860	2680
	100	2080	2040	2520
	66.7	2330	2730	1760
Nickelic oxide	233.3	2220	1800	2620
	216.7	1800	1930	2330
	166.7	2120	2050	2440
	90	2020	2020	2670
Lead oxide	250	1810	2090	2930
	233.3	2220	2200	3770
	183.3	2160	2390	3150
	150	2530	2720	2760
Ferric oxide	133.3	2200	2460	3680
	108.9	1940	3060	3200
	83.3	2540	2630	2900
	66.7	2390	2880	2760
Alumina	103.3	2050	1920	2490
	86.7	2060	2430	2820
	53.3	2460	2700	2680
	36.7	2020	3070	2160
"Hi-Sil"[a]	23.3	2290	3220	2240
	20	2370	3310	1820
	13.3	2540	2890	1660
	10	2210	2910	1780

[a] Davison Chemical Corp.

After a cure of 1 hr at 100°C, the tensile shear strengths were as follows:

Test Temperature °C	Tensile Shear Strength (psi)	
	No. 4	No. 5
−40	870–1885	2180–2470
20	1740–3200	2470–3200
70	145–290	580–725

The high molecular weight aliphatic polyamines are also widely used as flexibilizing agents. They are reactive hardeners which become internal plasticizers in the cured product. Among those found in many formulations, in order of increasing fluidity, are "Versamids" 115 and 125 (General Mills) and "Lancast A" (Ciba). The "Versamids" are discussed fully in the chapter on Polyamides. They cure slowly at room temperature, but most usually must be heated to reduce their viscosity for easy blending with epoxy. They can be used without addition of other curing agent.

(In the formulations that follow, "epoxy" and "modified epoxy" refer to the corresponding liquid bis-epi resins of epoxide equivalent 175 to 200, listed in Table 1.)

> 100 parts modified epoxy
> 70 parts "Versamid" 115
> filler as desired.

To speed the cure, part of the polyamide may be substituted by "DMP"-30:

> 100 parts modified epoxy
> 35 parts "Versamid" 115
> 5 parts "DMP"-30
> filler as desired.

Lancast A is sufficiently fluid to be mixed and cured at room temperature. It is used in similar proportions to the polyamides, for example:

> 100 parts epoxy
> 70 parts Lancast A
> 50 parts aluminum powder.

The flexibilized epoxies are generally not as heat resistant as other epoxy compositions. On the other hand, they have far greater peel strength than more rigid formulations.

High Temperature Adhesives

Heat resistance is built into the adhesive with aromatic amine reactive hardeners such as meta-phenylenediamine (15 phr), methylenedianiline (26 phr), DADPS (30 phr), or liquid eutectic mixtures of the type of Curing Agent Z[a] and "Sonite 41"[b] (20 phr). Cure is effected in 30 min at 350°F. While the aromatic primary amines give pot-lives of several hours at room temperature, they still require separate packaging of curing agent and resin.

At the U.S. Forest Products Laboratory, Black and Blomquist[13, 14] achieved fairly good shear strengths at temperatures up to 250°F from their FPL-881 formulation, involving an aliphatic tertiary amine catalyst:

> 100 parts "Epon" RN-48
> 4 parts pentamethyl diethylenetriamine[c]

[a] Shell Chemical Co.
[b] Smooth-on Mfg. Co.
[c] Union Carbide Chemicals Corp.

One-component adhesives are based on curing agents that do not react at room temperature but are activated when heated. BF_3:MEA, the adduct of boron trifluoride and monoethylamine, is effective in 1 to 3 per cent concentration. It is a highly acidic material. "Dicy," dicyandiamide, is used in 5 to 10 phr. It is a solid, thus can be ball-milled with resin, with or without filler, to give a dusting powder adhesive. It is activated at temperatures of 350°F and higher.

Phenolic-epoxy alloys are suitable for many extreme temperature applications. Good resistance to 500°F has been obtained with some formulations. The epoxy is a minor component but is essential for good adhesion.

Structural members of jet aircraft have been bonded with a glass tape impregnated with Shell's Adhesive 422:

> 33 parts "Epon" 1001 (solid at room temperature)
> 67 parts "Plyophen" 5023*
> 6 parts dicyandiamide (100 mesh)
> 100 parts aluminum dust (64 per cent through 325 mesh).
> * (Reichhold)

The "Plyophen" is a low molecular weight phenolic made with excess formaldehyde, containing 15 per cent water.

The glass tape acts as a carrier for the adhesive and permits a heavier glue line. The prepreg is stable for several months at room temperature, or indefinitely when refrigerated.

Black and Blomquist have been able to attain high resistance to aging at 550°F with their FPL-878:

> 125 parts "Durez" 16227 (phenolic, 80 per cent solids)[a]
> 33 parts "Bakelite" BV 9700 (phenolic, 60 per cent solids)[b]
> 20 parts Epon 1007 (solid epoxy)
> 20 parts ethyl acetate
> 2.8 parts 1-hydroxy-2-naphthoic acid
> 1.4 parts n-propyl gallate.
> [a] Hooker Electro Chemical Co.
> [b] Union Carbide Plastics Co.

The acid is a cure accelerator; the gallate is an oxidation inhibitor; both are believed to be chelating agents, tying up dissolved iron and other metals which might otherwise promote deterioration of the hot film.

The liquid adhesive was impregnated into glass mat on a "Teflon" film liner and precured—B-staged—at 270°F for 35 min. While it was still hot, another "Teflon" film was placed over it, and air and excess resin were squeezed out. After cooling, the prepreg was stored between sheets of polyethylene film. This tape adhesive has been used to make a composite of glass cloth honeycomb cores and aluminum or stainless steel faces, bonding at 300°F for 1 hr.

A price must be paid for the high hot shear strength: the laminates tend toward brittleness, especially in the cold. However, the phenolic-epoxies have superseded many of the earlier combinations of phenolic with nitrile rubber or vinyl butyral on the basis of over-all better properties at high, "jet-age" temperatures.

Effect of Resin Selection on Temperature Resistance. Research at Shell Development Company has indicated that the dependence of adhesive bond strength on temperature varies greatly with the type of resin. In many tests, "Epon" 828—a liquid resin—out-performed epoxy resins of higher molecular weight as the temperature was raised. When cured with MPDA, "Epon" 828 did not begin to lose its strength until 300°F, compared with 230°F for "Epon" 1001 and 200°F for "Epon" 1007. Similar differences were noted when the curing agent was dicyandiamide or diamino-diphenylsulfone (DADPS).

Apparently, greater weight concentration of epoxide groups in the lower molecular weight resin results in a greater concentration of cross-links in the cured product, hence better heat resistance.

On the other hand, at temperatures appreciably below the softening range, e.g., 180°F and room temperature, the higher molecular weight resins have slightly better tensile shear strength. At these temperatures, the higher hydroxyl content of the higher molecular weight resins appears to give them the advantage.

Novolac Epoxies. Novolacs can be substituted for conventional "bis-epi" resins for both tape-supported and liquid-adhesive systems. The novolacs give better resistance to high temperatures than the "bis-epi" resins, retaining physical properties at temperatures as high as 260°C.

In view of the high functionality of the novolacs (3.3 epoxies/molecule in "DEN" 438), it is unnecessary and undesirable to use highly functional amines such as DETA. Curing can be accomplished with low functionality hardeners, using only 80 per cent of the stoichiometric amount. Tertiary amines are helpful in small quantities.

"Epon" 1031. "Epon" 1031, which has on the average more than 3 epoxide groups per molecule, is a desirable ingredient of high temperature adhesives. Several compositions, cured for ½ hr at 330°F, result in products having appreciable bond strength at 500°F.

Curing Agent	(phr)	Tensile Shear Strength (psi) (at 77°F)	(at 500°F)
2,6-Diaminopyridine	6	1875	1200
2,6-Diaminopyridine	13	1665	425
Benzimidazole guanidine	10	1175	530
Benzimidazole guanidine	20	1425	110
4,4′,4″-Triaminotri-phenylmethane	23.5	865	525
Diaminodiphenylsulfone	30	2300	1090
Dicyandiamide	6	2200+	500+

Furthermore, "Epon" 1031 compositions display good strength retention; thus the DADPS cured samples retained 90 per cent of their strength at 200 hr at 500°F.

The addition of 30 phr of a polyvinyl formal resin to an "Epon" 1031 adhesive cured with "Dicy" results in almost a 100 per cent increase in strength at room temperature but causes a marked loss of strength at 500°F.

All of the above work was carried out with 100 parts of aluminum dust as filler.

Epoxy-Nylon Alloys. At Narmco Industries, Inc.,[12] it has been found that some nylons can be made compatible with some epoxy resins, under special conditions, to give adhesives of extremely high peel strength. The epoxy/nylon blends are prepared in the form of dry films. In a typical process for bonding aluminum skin to a honeycomb sandwich core, the dry adhesive film is interposed, a pressure of 25 psi is applied, and the composite

is cured at 350°F for 1 hr. Thus, a single adhesive takes the place of a pair of materials: a nitrile phenolic film for high peel strength, and an epoxy filleting compound for good wetting of the sandwich.

Patching, Caulking and Sealing Compounds

Every formulator has his own recipes for epoxy patches and sealing compounds, of which these are only a few of the favorites:

Stick Solder (Union Carbide Plastics Co):

100	parts "ERL"-3794
60	parts aluminum powder
5 to 10	parts "Santocel" 54[a]
28½	parts methylenedianiline

[a] Monsanto Co.

The hot-melt mix is cast in ½ in. diameter tubes and allowed to harden at room temperature. The sticks remain usable for more than 5 wk at room temperature, or much longer when refrigerated.

The part to be soldered must first be heated sufficiently to melt the end of the stick under slight pressure; then additional heat is applied cautiously to effect cure.

Caulking and Glazing Compound (Jones-Dabney: Co.)

Part A:

50 parts "Epi-Rez" 510
50 parts "Epi-Rez" 504
20 parts aluminum stearate
80 parts titanium dioxide
65 parts calcium carbonate

Part B:

150 parts "Epi-cure" 85 (viscous flexibilizer-hardener)
20 parts aluminum stearate
225 parts calcium carbonate

Parts A and B are mixed mechanically and applied to clean surfaces with a caulking gun, putty knife or high-pressure gun. This compound is suggested for bonding window sash metal to wood, steel to concrete, steel to wood.

Concrete Floor Patch:

100 parts liquid epoxy
300 parts dry, salt-free sand
70 parts "Lancast" A
5 parts bisphenol-A

The surface to be repaired must be free of loose spaltings, dirt and oil. If the surrounding concrete is weak, it is best to break it up and clean it. After the patch has been troweled on and smoothed over, additional sand may be sprinkled on top to provide a nonskid surface. At ordinary temperatures, gelation occurs in 1 to 2 hr, but it is best to wait overnight before submitting the floor to severe usage.

Boat Patch Compound and Sealer:

100	parts liquid epoxy
80	parts "Lancast" A
10	parts triphenyl phosphite
50	parts calcium carbonate
5	parts "Cab-O-Sil"
	No. 164 Glass cloth as desired

The boat must be thoroughly dry and clean. Rotted wood should be scraped away. The patch will cure overnight at moderate room temperature, or in 1 hr under infrared lamps. Both wooden and polyester boats may be repaired. Unlike other resinous patches, the epoxies function satisfactorily with all the common keel woods.

Bonding of New to Old Concrete (Reichhold Chemicals, Inc.).

Oil and grease should be removed from the concrete by etching with 15 per cent hydrochloric acid solution, then flushing with copious amounts of fresh water.

	Parts
"Epotuf" 6140	100
"Thiokol" LP 3	50
"DMP 10" and "DMP 30"[a]	7.5 total*
"Surfex" (calcium carbonate)[b]	120

* "DMP 10" is slower than "DMP 30", hence more "DMP 10" should be used in the summer time and more "DMP 30" in the winter time.

[a] Rohm & Haas Co.
[b] Diamond Alkali Co.

Organic Body Solder (Ciba Co.).

Epoxy-based solders for repairing automobile bodies have excellent adhesion to the base metal, negligible shrinkage during cure, superior impact resistance, and good machinability.

parts by wt.

Component A:

"Araldite" 6005	65
"Araldite" RD-2[a] (reactive diluent)	8
Glass fibers[b]	7
"Cab-O-Sil"[c]	10
Kaolin[d]	15
Titanium dioxide	2

Component B:

"Lancast" A[a]	35
DMP 30	5
Halo black[e]	0.15
"Cab-O-Sil"	5
Asbestine" 3-X[f]	50
Kaolin	5

[a] Ciba Products Corp.
[b] Ferro Corp. (1/32 in. HC Milled Fibers SO 10606)
[c] Cabot Corp.
[d] Whittaker, Clark & Daniels.
[e] Binney & Smith Co.
[f] International Talc Co.

The ingredients of each component are mixed in numerical sequence at room temperature, then passed through a three-roll mill. The two components are mixed in equal proportions by weight and applied by putty knife. The pot-life is 1 hr at room temperature, but the materials will cure in 20 min at 100°C, e.g., under a heat lamp.

References

1. Lee, H., and Neville, K., "Epoxy Resins," New York, McGraw-Hill Book Co., 1957.
2. Skeist, I., and Somerville, G. R., "Epoxy Resins," New York, Reinhold Publishing Corp., 1958.
3. Paquin, A. M., "Epoxydverbindungen," Berlin, Springer, 1958.
4. Gould, B., from "Everybody Needs Epoxies," New York, Breskin Publications, 1960.
5. Ciba Products Corp., Fairlawn, N. J.
6. Dow Chemical Co., Midland, Mich.
7. Jones-Dabney Co. (Div. Devoe & Reynolds), 1481 South 11th Street, Louisville, Kentucky.
8. Reichhold Chemical Company, 525 North Broadway, White Plains, N. Y.
9. Shell Chemical Company, 50 West 50th Street, New York 20, New York.
10. Union Carbide Corp., 270 Park Avenue, New York, New York.
11. Food Machinery & Chemical Corp., 161 East 42nd Street, New York 17, New York.
12. Riel, F. J., "Adhesive Bonding—A New Concept in Structural Adhesives," Society of Plastics Engineers, Inc., Vol. VII Technical Paper 27–2, Washington, D. C. (Jan. 1961).
13. Black, J. M., and Blomquist, R. F., "Development of Metal-Bonding Adhesive FPL-710," U.S.N.A.C.A. Research Memo 52F19 (1952).
14. Black, J. M., and Blomquist, R. F., "Metal-Bonding Adhesives with Improved Heat Resistance," Modern Plastics, 32, (4), 139–47, 237 (1954).

26

Isocyanate-Based Adhesives

C. S. Schollenberger
The B. F. Goodrich Company
Research Center
Brecksville, Ohio

Urethane materials including foams, coatings, and solid elastomers continue to receive ever-increasing attention and application in industry. The widespread acceptance and use of isocyanate-based adhesives, on the other hand, has been slower to materialize, even though this application of isocyanates is among the earliest of their anticipated and favorably documented uses.

It is possible that the rather sudden exposure of industry to massive amounts of the relatively complicated technology involved in the use of isocyanates in many urethane materials has hindered the widespread trial and general acceptance of adhesives based on isocyanates.

Assuming that this is so, it is to be hoped that the present chapter will serve to aid in simplifying this picture by pointing out the four principle methods of using isocyanates in adhesives that have developed, and by providing examples of each method as well as reviewing the reasons advanced for the superior effectiveness of these materials in adhesive applications.

No comprehensive listing of isocyanate-based adhesive suppliers was attempted in this chapter due to the frequent and natural reluctance of the manufacturers and their chemical suppliers to divulge information concerning proprietary adhesive formulations.

DEVELOPMENT OF THE USE OF ISOCYANATES IN ADHESIVES

Allied interrogation teams, who were assigned the task of studying the state of development of the German plastics and rubber industries at the end of World War II, reported substantial accomplishments in the preparation and use of isocyanates in Germany during the war. Not among the least of these was their use in adhesive systems.

A translation of a portion of a German technical paper appearing in a CIOS Report,[1] the section later appearing in essence in a German scientific publication[2] and referred to in a recent monograph on polyurethanes,[3] indicates that the exceptional and useful adhesive properties of the isocyanates became apparent to investigators of the I. G. Farbenindustrie, A. G., Laboratories about 1940. In the course of attempting to vulcanize hydroxylated buna (butadiene-styrene) rubber and hydroxyl-bearing buna copolymers with diisocyanates (to replace a sulfur cure), they discovered that natural rubber and buna-S themselves both undergo distinct vulcanization effects with diisocyanates. Of greater importance to the present subject was their observation that such stocks adhered strongly to the metal parts of the vulcanization press after the cure. This effect was studied more thoroughly in cooperation with the Central Rubber Laboratory of I. G. Farbenindustrie. Such studies led to "the long-sought adhesive for applying buna to various supports."[1]

Heat-stable bonds of normal buna-sulfur mixtures to iron, light metals, porcelain, etc., with strengths up to 1138 psi (stock failure) were realized using toluene diisocyanate (I)* and hexamethylene diisocyanate (II). Still, some problems in the use

* Roman numerals refer to structural formulas at end of chapter.

of isocyanates in adhesive systems were encountered; thus "Desmodur R (III) had shown outstanding adhesion in bonding rubber tank treads to steel. It still gave erratic performance, however, and needed further development."[4] These studies apparently represented the beginning of the diverse application of isocyanates in adhesive systems in Germany.

One could easily conclude that the above development was related to the use of diisocyanates as coupling agents in the preparation of polyurethane plastics and elastomers, whose intense study was in progress in Germany at about the same time. At any rate, German exploitation of polyisocyanates ("Desmodurs") in adhesive systems centered for the most part about their use in admixture with reactive low-molecular-weight, hydroxyl-bearing polyesters ("Desmophens"). Combinations of certain "Desmodurs" and "Desmophens" comprised the "Polystal" line of adhesives. Concerning these, it is stated: "The Desmodur-Desmophen systems were reported to give some of the best adhesives yet developed. They were said to stick 'anything to anything.' The advantages were: curing at low temperatures, good bond strength, versatility, good water resistance, and good low temperature flexibility."[4]

In somewhat greater detail: "the varieties sold in small amounts as "Polystal" were tough, resistant combinations of a flexible alkyd such as "Desmophen" 1200 (IV) with an isocyanate such as "Desmodur" TH (V) and an auxiliary such as an amine or anything which would change the pH. Cures were immensely speeded by acid, alkali, or a little trimethylamine. For a tough cold-curing wood adhesive to be used where vibration was bad, they proposed 40 parts of a 70 per cent ethyl acetate solution of "Desmophen" 900 (VI) and 100 parts of a 75 per cent ethyl acetate solution of "Desmodur" TH" (V).[1, 4]

German enthusiasm for isocyanate-based adhesives seems to have been justified. In later work Buist and Naunton[8] conclude the following concerning rubber-to-metal adhesion: "On the whole, when tested by a discriminating method (by impact) isocyanate-based cements give higher strength than do other cements. The bonds are fast to heat and solvents, are better able to withstand continued fatigue. The polyisocyanates suffer from the disadvantage that they are highly reactive chemicals and must be treated as such by avoiding their contact with moisture or the skin. For many uses the better results justify the extra care necessary in using them."

REASONS FOR THE EFFECTIVENESS OF THE ISOCYANATE-BASED ADHESIVES

The effectiveness of isocyanate-based adhesives could be due to a combination of several features which are characteristic of the materials:

(1) Isocyanates react readily with a variety of other functional groups.

(2) Di- and polyisocyanates can undergo self polymerization to form three dimensional resins in situ.[1, 2]

(3) Isocyanates are quite soluble in many organic substances, and due to their small molecular size readily permeate insoluble porous structures.[2]

(4) The reaction of di- and polyisocyanates with hydroxyl-bearing polyesters and polyethers, co-reactants in many isocyanate adhesive applications, produces the strong, flexible polar polyurethanes which wet, intimately contact, and show strong attraction for a variety of surfaces.

(5) Isocyanates provide elastomer-metal bonds whose favorable gradation in physical properties between elastomer and metal affords superior fatigue life.[8]

(6) Isocyanates "react even with hydrated oxide layers on metal surfaces, thus producing a *clean* surface and therein most probably allowing the urea groups of the adhesive to form chemical bonds, or at least subsidiary valency bonds, with the residual valencies of the metal lattice."[1, 2]

In the following pages the above features of isocyanates are discussed in detail.

(1) In considering the likelihood of adhering two objects with an adhesive, one is the more inclined to expect strong adhesion if the development of chemical bonds linking the objects to the adhesive is a possibility. The ready reaction of the isocyanate group with a large number of other functional groups would, on this basis, favor the success of isocyanate-based compositions as adhesives.

Organic isocyanates tend to react, in many cases quite readily, with substances containing active hydrogen atoms, that is, such hydrogen atoms as can be replaced in their compounds by alkali metals[2] or by the Zerewitinoff reagent, methyl magnesium iodide.[5]

In the case of ethyl alcohol the hydrogen on the oxygen atom is an active hydrogen atom:

$$CH_3CH_2OH \;+\; CH_3MgI \;\longrightarrow$$

Ethyl alcohol   *Methyl magnesium iodide*

$$CH_4 \;+\; CH_3CH_2OMgI$$

Methane   *Ethoxy magnesioiodide*

Functional groups containing active hydrogen atoms and therefore capable of reacting with isocyanates, include: —OH (hydroxyl), —SH (sulfhydryl), —NH— (imino), —NH$_2$ (amino), —NHR (substituted amino), —CO$_2$H (carboxyl), —CONH$_2$ (carbonamide), —CONHR (substituted carbonamide), —SO$_2$NH$_2$ (sulfonamide), —SO$_2$NHR (substituted sulfonamide), —CSNH$_2$ (thioamide), —SO$_2$OH (sulfonic), etc.

The reaction of isocyanates with some of these groups is illustrated below. For simplicity's sake, monoisocyanates are used in the equations to demonstrate the chemistry. In actual adhesive applications, di- or polyisocyanates are used; therefore the reader must realize that the reactions illustrated here occur simultaneously in more than one position in each isocyanate molecule.

For example, isocyanates react with alcohols to produce urethanes

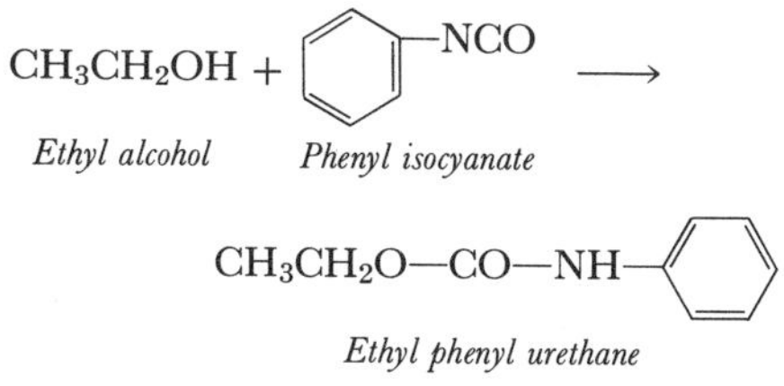

$$CH_3CH_2OH \;+\; \underset{\textit{Phenyl isocyanate}}{\bigcirc\text{—NCO}} \;\longrightarrow$$

Ethyl alcohol

$$CH_3CH_2O\text{—}CO\text{—}NH\text{—}\bigcirc$$

Ethyl phenyl urethane

with amines to produce substituted ureas,

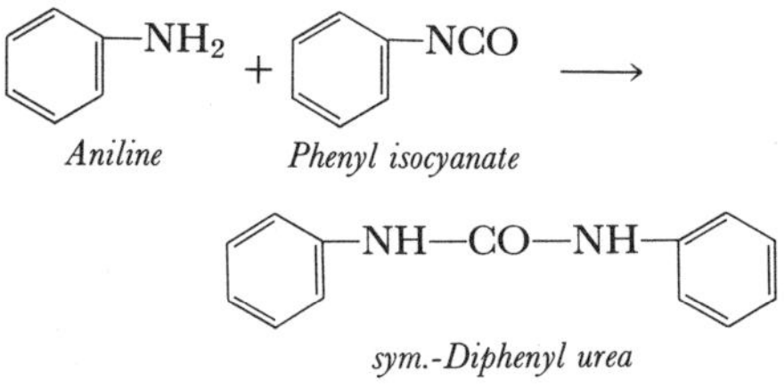

$$\underset{\textit{Aniline}}{\bigcirc\text{—NH}_2} \;+\; \underset{\textit{Phenyl isocyanate}}{\bigcirc\text{—NCO}} \;\longrightarrow$$

$$\bigcirc\text{—NH—CO—NH—}\bigcirc$$

sym.-Diphenyl urea

with carboxyl groups to produce substituted amides and/or substituted ureas and carbon dioxide,

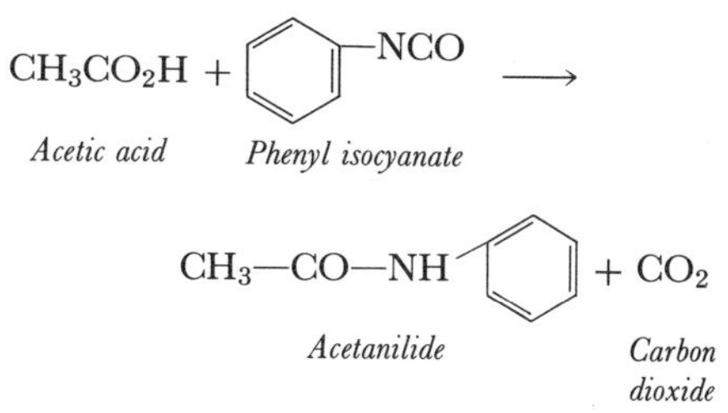

$$CH_3CO_2H \;+\; \underset{\textit{Phenyl isocyanate}}{\bigcirc\text{—NCO}} \;\longrightarrow$$

Acetic acid

$$CH_3\text{—CO—NH}\bigcirc \;+\; CO_2$$

Acetanilide   *Carbon dioxide*

and so on.

One might expect raw cellulose, containing its many hydroxyl groups, to react readily with isocyanates, but surprisingly, it is believed this reaction has never been effected. Although cellulose derivatives (e.g., nitro-, sec. acetyl-, ethyl-, benzyl-, etc. celluloses) react normally with isocyanates, the reaction of unmodified cellulose with isocyanates is considered very problematical, because even the most carefully dried samples of unmodified cellulose still contain about 5 per cent of so-called "crystal water" and will not swell even slightly in any isocyanate. Since isocyanates react more readily with water than with the hydroxyl groups of cellulose, symmetrical disubstituted ureas are formed on the surface of or among the cellulose fibers and, being basic, react relatively easily with more isocyanate; thus the isocyanate is consumed before it is able to react with the cellulose.[2] However, the very process of penetration, then self reaction, apparently entangles the isocyanate reaction product so thoroughly in the raw cellulose fibers as to result in a firm attachment.

A quantitative indication of the readiness with which isocyanates react with certain active hydrogen groups is provided by Morton and Deisz[6] who revealed phenyl isocyanate to react with the following compounds at the indicated relative rates at 80°C:

Active Hydrogen Compound	K x 10⁴ 1/mole sec	Relative Rate
n-Butyl phenyl carbamate	0.06	1
Acetanilide	0.99	16
n-Butyric acid	1.56	26
Diphenyl urea	4.78	80
Water	5.98	98
n-Butanol	27.5	460

Saunders[6] claims that there is evidence to suggest more nearly equal reactivity of water and alcohols with isocyanates in other systems.

(2) Isocyanates can undergo self polymerization to form stable three dimensional resinous structures. This ability appears to be restricted to the aromatic isocyanates[7] and is promoted by traces of iron salts, alkalies, pyridine, light, and oxygen.[2] Strong heating is also believed to promote this change, which can be represented, in the case of phenyl isocyanate, as follows:

Phenyl isocyanate   *Phenyl isocyanate trimer*

A thermally unstable phenyl isocyanate dimer structure is also possible as a consequence of the use of pyridine catalyst.

(3) Bayer,[1, 2] notes the excellent solubility of the isocyanates in practically every organic substance and their small molecular size, which allows ready diffusion. These properties promote adhesion by allowing the isocyanates to penetrate the adherend. There they may undergo the foregoing multiple reactions, all of which enlarge the molecule, presumably entangling it in, or attaching it to, the adherend.

Good strength and flexibility characteristics in the boundary film formed between the adherend members by the isocyanate-based adhesives is also considered to be an important and favorable contribution.

(4) The reaction of di- and polyisocyanates with hydroxyl-bearing polyesters and polyethers, their co-reactants in many adhesive applications, produces the polar polyurethanes which wet, intimately contact, and show strong attraction for a variety of surfaces.

(5) Buist and Naunton[8] state that "polyisocyanate cements not only give a stronger (rubber-metal) bond but produce, possibly by a gradation of physical properties from the immovable rubber in contact with the metal to the soft mass of the rubber, a condition in the rubber capable of withstanding greater fatigue."

(6) To explain the adhesion of isocyanate-based adhesives to impervious, apparently unreactive surfaces such as glass and metals, Bayer[2] suggested: the reaction of the isocyanate groups with the tightly adsorbed molecular film of water always present on such surfaces; the reaction of the isocyanate groups with the oxyhydrate layer on metal surfaces; isocyanate polymerization on (alkaline) glass. All these processes provide intimate contact if not actual chemical bonds between adhesive and adherend.

de Bell, Goggin and Gloor[4] cite a striking example of the adhesion of isocyanates to glass: "One ingenious soul had patented a process for etching designs on glass by cementing on a metal stamping (carried on a mesh), and then tearing the mesh loose, whereby the surface of the glass pulled off."

TYPES AND USE OF ISOCYANATE-BASED ADHESIVE SYSTEMS

Isocyanates have been used in adhesive systems in several ways:

Method A

A di- or polyisocyanate, usually in solution, is applied to the surface of an adherend prior to its contact with other adherend member(s) similarly coated.

Ex. 1. Buna-sulfur mixtures which are to be cemented are brushed with a solution of Desmodur R (III) and then vulcanized; thus bond strengths of up to 1138 psi are realized.[1, 2]

Ex. 2. MDI-50 (VII) affords heat-, fatigue-, impact-, oil- and solvent-resistant bonds between metals and elastomers by press- or hot air-curing the green, freshly milled or calendered stock against the metal which has previously been roughened (light sandblasting), solvent washed thinly coated with MDI-50 and dried.[9] Humidity is an important factor in the degree of adhesion obtained. The following demonstrates the adhesion possible using this system with various elastomers and metals:

	psi
Neoprene W to steel	1100
Neoprene W to brass	1050
Neoprene W to stainless steel	1200
Neoprene W to aluminum	1325

Neoprene W to copper	950
Natural rubber	
(smoked sheet) to steel	1200
Butadiene-acrylonitrile rubber	
to steel	850

Ex. 3. Elastomer coatings may be adhered to synthetic fiber fabrics and other materials by (dipping or spraying) of "Hylene" M (VIII) or "Hylene" M-50 (IX) (as a 2 per cent solution in toluene) to the fabrics, drying, then applying elastomer coating.[10]

Ex. 4. Degreased, sandblasted steel plates are coated by dipping in Leukonat adhesive (X); green-filled stocks of Nairit, SKN-26 (butadiene-acrylonitrile), natural, and SKS-30 (butadiene-styrene) rubbers are freshened with solvent; freshened rubber and coated metal are contacted and heated in a press.[11]

Method B

A di- or polyisocyanate is mixed with di- or polyhydroxy substances and the combination is: (a) partially pre-reacted or (b) allowed to react largely *in situ,* to form polyurethanes which contain free isocyanate groups capable of reacting with the adherend upon application. Dry solvents, free of alcohols, carboxylic acids, etc., are used with these systems.

Ex. 1. Windemuth[7] teaches the practice of (a), a one-part system. An isocyanate-terminated, viscous (in the melt), linear prepolymer is prepared from 2 moles of hexamethylene diisocyanate (II) and 1 mole of hydroxyl-terminated linear polyester prepared from diethylene glycol and adipic acid. Two per cent of hexahydrodimethyl aniline (a basic catalyst) is added to this prepolymer dissolved in dry benzene. The solution is applied to adherend members (e.g., the two ends of a leather drive belt) and dried. Subsequent brief exposure of the coated parts to moist air, followed by their contact under light pressure, results in a tough, flexible, rubbery bond in 2 to 3 hr.

Ex. 2. System (b) is exemplified as follows in a two-part adhesive: one part of "Polystal" U-1 (a 70 per cent solution of "Desmophen" 900 (VI) in ethyl acetate) is mixed with two to two and one half parts of "Polystal" U-II ("Desmodur" HH (XI) in 75 per cent ethyl acetate

solution). At room temperature such a cement has a pot life of 1 to 2 days, and with accelerators 3 hr. The setting time of this cement, containing accelerators, in wood adhesion is 4 to 5 hr at 10°C; 7 hr at 0°C; overnight at less than 0°C.[2]

Ex. 3. The two part "Multranil" 176 Adhesive is presumably of type (b) above and is used by mixing 100 parts of "Multranil" 176 (a 20 per cent solution of the "base resin" in ethyl acetate-acetone) with 8.3 parts of "Mondur" TM (XII) for bonding rubber, or 5.0 parts of "Mondur" CB-75 (a 75 per cent solution of the adduct of excess toluene diisocyanate (I) with a triol in ethyl acetate) for nonrubber bonding applications. Rubber-to-rubber or rubber-to-leather bonds formed by the drying and cure of this adhesive at room temperature are reported to be so strong as to cause laminar failure in the rubber or leather rather than in the bond during peel adhesion test. These bonds are also said to remain intact after several weeks at 122°F under a 2000 g static load. It is not recommended to mix a quantity of this adhesive larger than can be used in a single day's operation.[12]

Ex. 4. The two part M/M* adhesive formulation which cures at room or elevated temperatures is even more like the "Polystal" U-I/U-II system in that the resin portion, "Multron" R-12 (80 per cent in ethyl acetate), is mixed (100 parts) with 120 parts (or 200 parts for a room temperature cure) of "Mondur" CB, the polyisocyanate reaction product of toluene diisocyanate (I) and a triol, making "Mondur" CB the counterpart of the "Desmodur" HH (XI) used in "Polystal" U-II. "The tensile strength of steel bonds formed with this M/M adhesive is approximately 6800 psi for room temperature-cured bonds (realized in 8 days) and 7800 psi when cured at elevated temperatures" (realized in 3 hr at 195°F, 2 hr at 265°F, or 1 hr at 355°F). M/M adhesive gels and cannot be reconstituted 24 hr after mixing.[12]

Ex. 5. "Bostik" 7070 (100 parts) with "Boscodur" No. 1 (5 parts) appears to be another example of a type (b) (two-part)

* "Mondur"/"Multron."

system. It is recommended by the manufacturer as a laundering- and dry cleaning-resistant cement for bonding urethane sponge and urethane rubber. It is also recommended as an adhesive which provides strong elastic bonds with leather, natural and synthetic fabrics, cork, wood, Masonite and a wide variety of porous materials.

The combination of "Bostik" 7070 and "Boscodur" No. 1 is reported to have a working life of about 18 hr. Although a hot bonding method (4 min at 130°F) is optional, the cement will cure at room temperature (maximum adhesion in 6 days at room temperature).[14]

Ex. 6. "Desmocol" G, recommended by the manufacturer for adhering rubber, is made from one part of "Desmocol" Gl and two and one half parts of "Desmodur" R solution (III). The adhesive realizes its ultimate properties as a bond after 24 hr at room temperature. The Desmocol Gl-Desmodur R mixture at room temperature can be used up to 1½ to 2 hours after mixing but solidifies to a gel in 3 to 4 hr.[15]

Method C

A di- or polyisocyanate is mixed with a conventional elastomeric or plastic vehicle, usually in a dry, inert solvent. The combination is spread over the surfaces to be adhered, which are then air-dried and contacted. Curing is at room or elevated temperatures.

Du Pont[9] points out some special advantages in elastomer-to-metal adhesion which result from the use of an elastomeric vehicle with MDI-50 bonding cements. First, the elastomeric vehicle (usually the same as the adherend elastomer) covers the diisocyanate component in applied coatings, protecting it from moisture and allowing longer but not unlimited* useful life of cement-primed parts. Second, the elastomeric vehicle affords greater building tack in assembling the adherend members.

Ex. 1. Natural rubber (pale crepe or smoked sheet), SBR, or neoprene Types GN, GR-M or GR-MIO are broken down in Banbury mixers or on mills. Dry aromatic solvents such as xylene, toluene or chlorobenzene (900 parts) are added and agitated to dissolve 100 parts of elastomer. Forty parts of MDI-50 (VII) are

added to the elastomer solution with agitation. The cements are stored at room temperature: the rubber cement keeps 7 days, the SBR keeps 3 to 4 days, and the neoprene cement keeps 3 days.

The above cements applied at 10 to 15 per cent of the fabric weight are excellent primers for the adhesion of elastomers to fabric. The cements can be applied to fabric by any of the conventional methods, and the primed fabric used after solvent-removal or stored in a dry place until needed. The composite product may be cured by the methods conventionally used for curing rubber (press, oven, air pressure vulcanizers). High pressures are unnessary; moreover good contact between the two surfaces is sufficient to produce a strong bond.[16]

Table 1 demonstrates the degree of adhesion obtained on the platen press curing of rubberized 10 oz cotton duck to square woven fabric samples made from rayon, cotton and nylon. The duck had been skim-coated 90 mils with some typical tire carcass stocks made from neoprene GR-M, SBR, and natural rubber. The other fabrics were pre-coated with 20 per cent by weight of the MDI-50 adhesive primers.[16]

Ex. 2. The adhesion of "Terylene,"** a polyester fiber, to rubber is greatly improved by the addition of "Vulcabond" TX** (XIII) a diisocyanate; thus a natural rubber stock containing all pigments (curing, reinforcing, processing agents) was made into a dough using Pool Rubber Solvent. Twenty-five per cent by weight of "Vulcabond" TX was blended into this dough, and the mixture was spread onto "Terylene" fabric, topped with rubber stock on a calender, doubled, and finally platen press-cured (200 psi) for 30 min at 141°C. Peel tests on 1 in. wide strips of this construction 24 hr later showed adhesions of 30.8 lb/in. (to initiate) and 22.0 lb/in. (average to maintain peeling). The control, minus

---

* MDI-50-elastomer cements slowly increase in viscosity with time, eventually gelling on prolonged storage at room temperature.[9]

** Imperial Chemical Industries, Ltd., Manchester, England.

TABLE 1. THE ADHESION OF FIBERS TO ELASTOMERS VIA MDI-50 PRIMING CEMENT.[16]

| | Neoprene GR-M MDI-50 | | Natural Rubber MDI-50 | | SBR/ MDI-50 | |
	A	B	A	B	A	B
Rayon to natural rubber	35	24	19	—	30	19
Rayon to neoprene GR-M	30	21	39	—	33	12
Rayon to SBR	37	26	28	—	35	17
Cotton to natural rubber	25*	16*	25*	16*	—	—
Cotton to neoprene GR-M	24*	16*	35*	21*	—	—
Cotton to SBR	29*	15*	27*	15*	—	—
Nylon to natural rubber	20*	11*	15*	8*	—	—
Nylon to neoprene GR-M	18*	9*	23*	12*	—	—
Nylon to SBR	22*	10*	20*	11*	—	—

A = adhesion at 28°C (lb pull/in. width) ⎫ Strip adhesion test
B = adhesion at 95°C in water (lb pull/in. width) ⎬ (ASTM D413-39)
* = Greater adhesion realized with more adhesive primer.

"Vulcabond" TX, showed only 3.5 lb/in. adhesion in this test. Triphenylmethane-p,p',p''-triisocyanate (III, X, XII) was similarly effective at the same concentration.[17a]

Ex. 3. Natural, "Hycar," "Paracril," butyl and neoprene rubbers are bonded to seven metals/alloys with an adhesive comprising 50 parts of a chlorinated rubber ("Alloprene" B) and 100 parts of "Vulcabond" TX (XIII) dissolved in 150 parts of ethylene dichloride. Bonds to copper and "Monel" metal were inferior. Information is provided on the effect on bond strength of accelerator, loading types (carbon blacks, white fillers) in the bonded stocks, and the age of the fully formulated adhesive.[17b]

Ex. 4. A 3 per cent rubber solution of a standard tire carcass compound was supplemented with 50 per cent of "Vulcabond" TX (XIII) on the weight of rubber. Rayon cord dried for 1 hr at 100°C was then dipped into this cement, squeezed between glass rods, air-dried overnight, and baked 30 min at 100°C. This pretreated cord, carefully positioned in a metal jig to provide a concentration of 24 cords per in., was cured into a strip of rubber compound, which was then fatigued 4 days/80°C in a modified Roelig machine and finally tested for cord adhesion to the rubber. The following table shows how rayon cord primed with the "Vulcabond" TX-rubber cement outperformed a latex-resorcinol-formal-

dehyde priming cement, ("Vulcabond" T).*[8]

The Relative Effectiveness of "Vulcabond" T and TX in Rayon Cord-to-Natural Rubber Adhesion.[8]

| | Load (lb) to Pull out a Single Cord | |
	Not fatigued	After 4 days fatigue at 80°C
"Vulcabond" TX cement	12.5	11.0
"Vulcabond" T cement	11.3	9.6

Ex. 5. For metal adhesion, polyisocyanates are best mixed into a solution of a synthetic or chlorinated rubber. The following table compares the adhesion of natural rubber tire tread to mild steel using a polyisocyanate priming cement ("Vulcabond" TX) with that obtained using a chlorinated rubber cement.[8]

"Vulcabond" TX Versus Chlorinated Rubber in Natural Rubber-Steel Adhesion.[8]

	Straight Pull (psi)	Impact Strength (ft lb)	Strength after Fatigue (%)
"Vulcabond" TX cement	835	220	90
Chlorinated rubber cement	785	116	20

Ex. 6. A priming cement for the high level adhesion (ca. 28 lb/in.) of vinyl plastisol or film to nylon, "Dacron," rayon or glass fabric is prepared from "Geon" 400 × 110** (100 parts) or certain other polyvinyl chloride resins, dioctyl phthal-

* Imperial Chemical Industries, Ltd., Manchester, England.
** B. F. Goodrich Chemical Co., Cleveland, Ohio.

ate (60 parts), methylethyl ketone (380 parts) and DADI, dianisidine diisocyanate, (XIV) (10 parts). The adhesion is reported to be surprisingly independent of fabric construction and is obtained with a minimal effect on the fabric properties. The bond is reported to have been submitted to one million "S" flexes with no reduction in bond strength. The fabric is coated via normal solution-coating methods to about 0.8 oz per sq yd (dry weight) and is cured against PVC film or plastisol at 300 to 400°F for maximum adhesion (optimum adhesion 2 min/360°F).

The primed fabric is stable for at least 60 days, and probably indefinitely; therefore it need not be laminated to PVC film or coated with plastisol immediately.[18]

Ex. 7. The incorporation of PAPI, a polyisocyanate (XV), in specially compounded rubber-coating compositions has provided improved adhesion of rubber to nylon and polyester cord.[19]

Method D

A stable "blocked" di- or polyisocyanate in suspension (including aqueous suspension) or solution is applied to an adherend member, the coating is dried, the coated members are then assembled, and the assembly is heated to decompose the blocked diisocyanate and regenerate free diisocyanate which proceeds to bond the adherend members. The cleaved blocking agent diffuses into the surrounding matrix or escapes to the air. "Hylene" MP (XVI)[20], in which the blocking agent is phenol, typifies this sort of water-stable compound. Blocked-, masked- or pseudo-diisocyanates date back to German studies of 1949.[21] The stability of blocked isocyanates toward active hydrogen compounds enables their formulation and application even in water media; however such media must be removed by drying before the blocked isocyanate is heated to its cleavage temperature. Otherwise, the generated isocyanate may be neutralized by reaction with the media before it can react with the adherend.

Ex. 1. Vulcanized neoprene and SBR can be adhered strongly to nylon and "Dacron" polyester fiber fabric by means of the following aqueous adhesive system:

	(parts)
"Hylene" MP dispersion (40%)	27.5
Neoprene latex type 635	173.0
Zinc oxide dispersion (50%)	15.0
Zalba emulsion (50%)*	6.0

* A hindered phenolic antioxidant- du Pont Elastomers Dept.

This combination is spread or roller coated onto the fabric which is then allowed to dry. Bonds to sheet rubber stock can be made immediately after the treated fabric is dried or at any time thereafter. When the sheet rubber is applied, it should be held under moderate pressure of about 30 psi to provide intimate contact with the treated fabric and to prevent lifting if any gases are emitted during cure. Press cures of 20 to 40 min at 284°F are sufficient to cure the adhesive and most elastomer compositions being adhered. If a latex film is applied to the treated fabric, the assembly can be cured in a hot-air oven at 250°F. Bond strengths of 50 to 52 lb (nylon to neoprene, SBR) and 30 to 35 lb ("Dacron" to neoprene, SBR) are claimed. A chemical bond allegedly, results between nylon and the diphenylmethane-p,p'-diisocyanate generated on the thermal cleavage of "Hylene" MP.[22]

HANDLING ISOCYANATE-BASED ADHESIVES

Isocyanates unquestionably are highly reactive chemicals, which to a large degree explains their effectiveness in adhesive applications; consequently adhesive formulations containing isocyanates must have reasonable protection from contact with agents which can combine with the isocyanate group, thus neutralizing it before it is able to react with the adherend. This dictates the use of essentially dry solvents which are nonreactive and free of reactive impurities, as well as avoiding the exposure of isocyanate-based adhesives to moisture during storage and excessive moisture during use.[17c]

Reasonable caution in the use of materials containing free isocyanate, including adequate ventilation in use areas and the prompt cleansing of body areas contacted, is recommended by all isocyanate suppliers.

IDENTIFICATION OF ADHESIVE COMPONENTS

(I) Toluene diisocyanate

2,4-isomer   2,6-isomer   *(mixture)*

(II) Hexamethylene diisocyanate $ONC—(CH_2)_6—NCO$

(III) "Desmodur" R—triphenylmethane-p,p',p''-triisocyanate—a 20 per cent solution in methylene chloride[2]

(IV) Desmophen 1200—a polyester prepared from adipic acid (3.00 moles), trimethylol propane or glycerine (1.00 mole) and 1,3-butylene glycol (3.00 moles)[2]

(V) Desmodur TH—adduct from 2,4-toluene diisocyanate (3.00 moles) and 3-methylol pentylene glycol-2,4 (1.00 mole)[2]

(VI) Desmophen 900—a polyester prepared from adipic acid (3.00 moles), trimethylol propane (4.2 moles)[1]

(VII) MDI-50—diphenylmethane-p,p'-diisocyanate—50 parts, orthodichlorobenzene—50 parts[9]

(VIII) "Hylene" M—diphenyl methane-p,p'-diisocyanate[10]

(IX) "Hylene" M-50—"Hylene" M—50 parts, orthodichlorobenzene—50 parts[10]

(X) Leukonat adhesive—triphenylmethane-$p,p'p''$-triisocyanate—a 20 per cent solution in dichloro-ethane[11]

(XI) "Desmodur" HH—adduct from 1,6-hexamethylene diisocyanate (3.00 moles) and 3-methylol pentylene glycol-2,4 (1.00 mole)[2]

$$OCN-(CH_2)_6-NH-CO-O-\underset{\underset{\underset{\underset{\underset{NCO}{|}}{(\overset{}{C}H_2)_6}}{\overset{|}{N}H}}{\overset{|}{C}O}}{\overset{\overset{CH_3}{|}}{C}H}-\underset{\underset{\underset{\underset{O}{|}}{\overset{|}{C}H_2}}{}}{\overset{\overset{CH_3}{|}}{C}H}-\overset{\overset{CH_3}{|}}{C}H-O-CO-NH-(CH_2)_6-NCO$$

(XII) "Mondur" TM—triphenylmethane-p,p',p''-triisocyanate—a 20 per cent solution in methylene chloride[13]

A 50% solution of diphenylmethane-p,p'-diisocyanate in xylene or orthodichlorobenzene[23]

(XIII) "Vulcabond" TX—a polyisocyanate, principally a diisocyanate[17c]

(XIV) DADI—dianisidine diisocyanate[19]

(XV) PAPI—polymethylene polyphenyl isocyanate[19]

(XVI) "Hylene MP"—Methylene-bis-phenyl-(4-phenyl carbamate)[20]

Hylene MP

Phenol   *MDI*

References

1. CIOS Report 29-12 (Appendix, Item 22), PB46961 (Feb. 1946).
2. Bayer, O., Angew. Chem., **59**, (9), 257–272 (Sept., 1947).
3. Dombrow, B. A., "Polyurethanes," New York, Reinhold Publishing Corp., 1957.
4. DeBell, J. M., Goggin, W. C., and Gloor, W. E., "German Plastics Practise," Springfield, Mass., DeBell and Richardson, 1946.
5. Kohler, E. P., Stone, J. F., Jr., and Fuson, R. C., *J. Am. Chem. Soc.*, **49**, 3181 (1927).
6. Morton, M., and Deisz, M. A., "Kinetics of Isocyanate Addition Reactions," Paper 34, Symposium on Isocyanate Polymers, Division of Paint, Plastics and Printing Ink Chemistry, ACS Meeting (Sept. 1956). [See Saunders, J. H., "The Reactions of Isocyanates and Isocyanate Derivatives at Elevated Temperatures," *Rubber Chem. Technol.* **32**, (2), 337–345, (1959)].
7. Windemuth, E., (to Farbenfabriken Bayer, A. G., Leverkusen, Germany), U.S. Patent 2,650,212 (Aug. 25, 1953).
8. Buist, J. M., and Naunton, W. J. S., "Rubber Bonding," *Trans. Inst. Rubber Ind.,* **25**, (6), 378–406 (Apr., 1950); reprinted in *Rubber Chem. Technol.* **23**, (4) (Oct.–Dec. 1950).

9. Bonding Elastomers to Metals with MDI-50, Elastomers Division Bull. BL-241, Wilmington, Del., (Apr. 30, 1951). E. I. du Pont de Nemours & Co.

10. Hylene M, Hylene M50—Organic Isocyanates, Elastomers Division Bull. HR-5, Wilmington, Del., E. I. du Pont de Nemours & Co. (Dec. 1955).

11. Medevdeva, A. M., Deryagin, B. V., and Zherebkov, S. K., *Colloid J. (USSR)*, **19,** 417–423, (1958); reprinted in *Rubber Chem. and Technol.* **32,** (1), 67–76 (1959).

12. "Urethane Adhesives" revision, New Martinsville, W. Va., Mobay Chemical Co., (Jan. 28, 1958).

13. Mondur TM, Data Sheet No. 32, New Martinsville, W. Va., Mobay Chemical Co., (Aug. 15, 1956).

14. Bostik Temporary Data Sheet, Bostik 7070 with Boscodur No. 1, Cambridge, Mass., B. B. Chemical Co., (July 25, 1958).

15. Desmocol, G, Division LK, Chemical Sales, Farbenfabriken Bayer, Leverkusen, Germany.

16. Abernathy, H. H., and Radcliff, R. R., Rubber Chemicals Division, "The Adhesion of Fibers to Elastomers," Report No. 47–4, Wilmington, Del., E. I. du Pont de Nemours & Co., May 1947.

17. Meyrick, T. J., and Watts, J. T., "Polyisocyanates in Bonding:"
    (a) "Terylene Polyester Fibre to Rubber," *India-Rubber J.*, 467–8, (Mar. 22, 1952).
    (b) "Rubber to Metals," *India-Rubber J.*, 505–6, (Mar. 29, 1952).
    (c) *Trans. Inst. Rubber Ind.* **25,** (3) (1949).

18. "Vinyl Adhesion to Synthetic Fabric," Technical Bull. North Haven Conn., The Carwin Chemical Co. (June 1, 1959).

19. Product Catalog, (1957), The Carwin Chemical Co., North Haven, Conn.

20. Owen, G. E., Jr., Hylene MP-Water Stable Diisocyanate Generator, Elastomer Chemicals Department Bull. HR-25, Wilmington, Del., E. I. du Pont de Nemours Co. (July 1957).

21. Petersen, S., *Ann. Chem.*, **562,** 205–229 (1949).

22. Gelbert, C. H., and Owen, G. E., Jr., "An Aqueous Adhesive System for Bonding Elastomers to Synthetic Fibers," Elastomer Chemicals Department Report BL-338.

23. Buchan, S., "Rubber to Metal Bonding," Crosby Lockwood and Son, LTD., London, 1959.

— 27 —

Introduction to Vinyl Polymers for Adhesives

Forrest H. Norris

Shawinigan Resins Corporation
Springfield, Massachusetts

In 1947, J. Delmonte[1] noted the accelerating pace of developments in adhesives during the preceding decade. He linked this progress to the growing selection of synthetic resins available for adhesive formulation. Since then, progress in adhesive technology has continued to parallel progress in the chemistry of synthetic resins or polymers. His predicted *not too distant time,* "when adhesives will be formulated on the basis of chemical and physical structure" rather than empirical methods, is now here. Knowledge of the organic and physical chemistry of synthetic polymers is an indispensible tool in formulating adhesives from modern synthetic resins. Many modern adherends are bonded best by adhesives containing polymers, i.e. resins, because they include surfaces made from polymers, e.g., plastic film.

Historically, polymeric substances have been used as adhesives ever since man decided to stick two surfaces together. Mud, pitch, tar, gums, starches, animal and vegetable glues, rubber latex, casein; in fact, most adhesives of natural origin are indeed polymers. Man has improved early adhesives from nature over the centuries through chemical or physical modification. More recently, in the twentieth century, he has obtained new adhesives by syntheses (often quite by chance in early work) of macromolecules to supplement those available naturally. In the last three decades, we have come to understand the physical nature of polymers and the chemistry of their synthesis or "polymerization."

Vinyl polymers are macromolecular substances formed by (addition) polymerization of those monomolecular organic chemicals containing the unsaturated ethylenic or vinyl double bond. Strictly, a vinyl monomer is

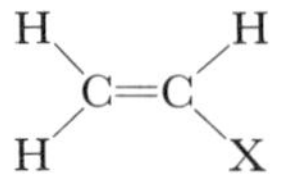

$$\underset{H}{\overset{H}{\diagdown}}C=C\underset{X}{\overset{H}{\diagup}}$$

where X is a hydrogen, halogen, alkyl, aryl, ester or other group. More generally, the term vinyl polymer has been used to include a variety of resins, plastics, elastomers and fibers obtained by polymerizing monomers having one or more unsaturated double or triple bonds, including diolefins such as butadiene, vinylidenes like vinylidene chloride or methyl methacrylate and vinylenes such as maleic anhydride.

The general equation for vinyl polymerization is:

$$n\text{CH}_2{=}\text{CX}^{H} \xrightarrow[\text{or catalyst}]{\text{heat, light}} {-}\left[\text{CH}_2{-}\text{CX}^{H}\right]_n{-}$$

The chemical nature of the substituent group X, the length and configuration of the macromolecular chain, the presence of one (homopolymer) or more than one (copolymer) monomer species, and the physical form (powder, emulsion, solution, beads, etc.) of a vinyl polymer are some of the factors that determine its use as an adhesive.

Table 1 lists several representative vinyl homo-

344

TABLE 1. VINYL POLYMERS.

Monomer Formula	Polymer	Abbreviation
$CH_2=CH$, H	Polyethylene	PE
$CH_2=CCH_3$, H	Polypropylene	PP
$CH_2=CCl$, H	Polyvinyl chloride	PVCl
$CH_2=CCl$, Cl	Polyvinylidene chloride	PVCl$_2$
$CH_2=C$—⬡, H	Polystyrene	PS
$CH_2=C$—⬡ (with Cl, Cl), H	Polydichloro styrene	PDClS
$CH_2=COOCH_3$, H	Polyvinyl acetate / Polyvinyl alcohol / Polyvinyl butyral / Polyvinyl formal	PVAc / PVOH / PVB / PVF
$CH_2=COOCC_2H_5$, H	Polyvinyl propionate	PVPr
$CH_2=COOCC_3H_7$, H	Polyvinyl butyrate	PVBu
$CH_2=COOCC_{17}H_{35}$, H	Polyvinyl stearate	PVSt
$CH_2=COOC$—⬡	Polyvinyl benzoate	PVBz
$CH_2=CH—CH=CH_2$	Polybutadiene	PBD
$CH_2=C—CH=CH_2$, CH$_3$	Polyisoprene	PI
$CH_2=C—C=CH_2$, CH$_3$, CH$_3$	Polydimethyl butadiene	PDMBD
$CH_2=C—CH=CH_2$, Cl	Polychloroprene	PCl
$CH_2=CCOOH$, H	Polyacrylic acid	PAA
$CH_2=CCOOCH_3$, H	Polymethyl acrylate	PMA
$CH_2=CCOOC_2H_5$, H	Polyethyl acrylate	PEA
$CH_2=CCOOC_4H_9$, H	Polybutyl acrylate	PBA
$CH_2=CCOOC_8H_{17}$, H	Polyethyl hexyl acrylate	PEHA
$CH_2=CCOOH$, CH$_3$	Polymethacrylic acid	PMAA
$CH_2=CCOOH_3$, CH$_3$	Polymethyl methacrylate	PMMA
$CH_2=CCOOC_2H_5$, CH$_3$	Polyethyl methacrylate	PEMA
$CH_2=CCN$, H	Polyacrylonitrile	PAN
$CH_2=CCN$, CH$_3$	Polymethacrylonitrile	PMAN
$CH_2=COOCC=CH$, H, H, CH$_3$	Polyvinyl crotonate	PVCr

Monomer Formula	Polymer	Abbreviation
$CH_2=C—COOH$, CH$_2$COOH	Polyitaconic acid	PItA
$CH_2=C—COOCH_3$, CH$_2$COOCH$_3$	Polydimethyl itaconate	PDMeIt
$CH_2=C—COOC_2H_5$, CH$_2$COOC$_2$H$_5$	Polydiethyl itaconate	PDEIt
$CH_2=CCONH_2$, H	Polyacrylamide	PAM
$CH_2=CCONH_2$, CH$_3$	Polymethacrylamide	PMAM
$CClF=CF_2$	Polychlorotrifluoroethylene	PClF$_3$E
$CH_2=CCH_3$, CH$_3$	Polyisobutylene	PIBy
$CH_2=COCH_3$, H	Polyvinylmethyl ether	PVME
$CH_2=COC_2H_5$, H	Polyvinyl ethyl ether	PVEE
$CH_2=CN$ (pyrrolidone ring, H, CH$_2$—CH$_2$, C—CH$_2$, O)	Polyvinylpyrrolidone	PVP
$CH_2=CHCO—CH_3$	Polyvinyl methyl ketone	PVMK
$CH_2=COCH_2CH$, H, CH$_3$, CH$_3$	Polyvinyl isobutyl ether	PVIBI

polymers of possible interest to the adhesives industry.

Other unsaturated compounds, notably the vinylenes, do not polymerize by themselves but readily form copolymers. Among such monomers are:

Monomer Formula	Monomer
CH$_3$, H, C=C, H, COOH	crotonic acid
C$_4$H$_9$OOC, H, C=C, H, COOC$_4$H$_9$	dibutyl fumarate
H, H, C=C, C$_4$H$_9$OOC, COOC$_4$H$_9$	dibutyl maleate
HC=CH, OC CO, O	maleic anhydride

Copolymer combinations available to the adhesive chemist include PS/BD (styrene/butadiene), PVAc/DBM (vinyl acetate/dibutyl maleate), and PVAc/EHA (vinyl acetate/ethylhexyl acrylate). The uninitiated reader will want to become more familiar with the chemistry[2] and technology[3] of the polymers in Table 1. Many textbooks or reference books are available.[4]

Free-Radical Vinyl Polymerization

Vinyl polymers are synthesized by a chain-reaction type of propogation in which an "activated" vinyl group adds to the unsaturated vinyl or ethylenic double bond of a monomer by a primary valence linkage; simultaneously, the double bond of the monomer is activated and can add to more monomer. Thus, hundreds and thousands of monomer molecules are linked together to form macromolecular chains or polymers by the process of addition polymerization.

The vinyl bond is activated initially either thermally, photochemically, by reaction with a free-radical initiator, or by reaction with an ionic catalyst. Industrial addition polymerizations to make adhesives are usually initiated by free radicals obtained from the decomposition of oxidative agents such as benzoyl peroxide. A free radical is a resonance stabilized molecule having an unpaired electron, and it readily forms a covalent link with a carbon atom of a vinyl bond by pairing its odd electron. Simultaneously, the vinyl bond is activated since it now has an unpaired electron at the other carbon atom; thus a free-radical chain reaction ensues.

Activated molecules undergo chain addition reactions with monomer molecules so rapidly that ordinarily only long polymer chains or unreacted monomer can be found in the reaction process. No intermediates are isolated in contrast to the step-wise condensation type polymerization of monomers like phenol and formaldehyde.

The growth of a polymer chain ceases when its activated site becomes deactivated by collision with a similar site on another growing chain, or with a free radical, a catalyst fragment or other component of the polymerization system that is capable of terminating the chain reaction.

The final properties of the polymer depend on many factors operating during the polymerization as well as on the structure (functional groups) of the original monomer. The reactivity of a monomer free radical toward another monomer of its own or a different species; the type and amount of initiator; the presence of chain-transfer, cross-linking or other agents capable of affecting the length and linearity of the chain; environmental conditions such as pH and temperature; and the presence of impurities affect the kinetics of the polymerization and the properties of the final polymer.

Since vinyl polymerizations are chain reactions, they are susceptible to inhibitors and retarders sometimes present either deliberately or as impurities. Chain transfer agents such as carbon tetrachloride regulate the degree of polymerization, i.e., molecular weight, by terminating a growing chain upon collision and simultaneously producing a free radical which will initiate another monomer free radical to start another growing chain. Polymer chains can be tied together into two- and three-dimensional networks by cross-linking agents such as divinylbenzene.

When more than one monomer species is used, they can unite on the one extreme randomly, i.e., copolymerize; on the other extreme, in perfectly regular alternation, i.e., heteropolymerize. Variations in between can be obtained depending on the reactivity and concentration of the respective monomers; thus by manipulating reaction conditions and reagents, the polymer chemist can obtain various sequences of addition of monomer units in a polymer chain. He can also add chains of one monomer to a backbone chain of another, i.e., "graft polymerization;" or he can cause groups of one monomer to add in definite order with groups of another, i.e., "block polymerization."

The termination of a growing chain by pairing the electron at its activated site with that of another growing chain, free radical or other molecule is called termination by combination. In some polymerizations, two growing chains terminate by disproportionation, i.e., abstraction of a hydrogen atom from one growing chain by the other.

Monomers with two or more unsaturations, such as vinyl crotonate or diallyl phthalate, can crosslink to form network structures that are insoluble and infusible.

Ionic Vinyl Polymerization

Vinyl addition polymerization by ionic catalysts is rapidly growing in commercial importance because of the spatially regular structures that it can provide in polymer chains. Ionically catalyzed polymerization is less understood than free-radical initiated polymerization even though it preceded the latter historically. Only in the last decade has it received the attention that previously had been given to free-radical methods. Ionically catalyzed polymerizations also are chain-type additions. The vinyl bond is activated either as a carbonium ion, i.e., by cationic, Friedel-Crafts acid catalysts or as a carbanion, i.e., anionic, basic catalysts.

Ziegler, Natta and others have found that certain heterogeneous catalyst systems, e.g., titanium tetrachloride plus aluminum triethyl are particularly useful for the production of stereo-regular polymers.[7]

Vinyl alkyl ethers, isobutylene, α-methyl styrene, ethylene, propylene and isoprene are some of the monomers that are readily polymerized by cationic catalysts. Acrylonitrile, methacrylonitrile, methyl methacrylate, styrene and butadiene are representative of monomers polymerized by anionic catalysts. Vinyl polymers from ionic poly-

merizations can reasonably be expected to become increasingly important in the adhesives industry—not only as adhesives, but as adherends.

Testing, Characterization and Use In Adhesives

Elaborate equipment and test methods now exist by which the structure and properties of polymers can be determined.[4] Some of the distinctions that are made to help determine the potential of a polymer in adhesives are: chain length (molecular weight); amorphous versus crystalline nature; temperature of transition from rubbery to glassy behavior; cohesive or tensile

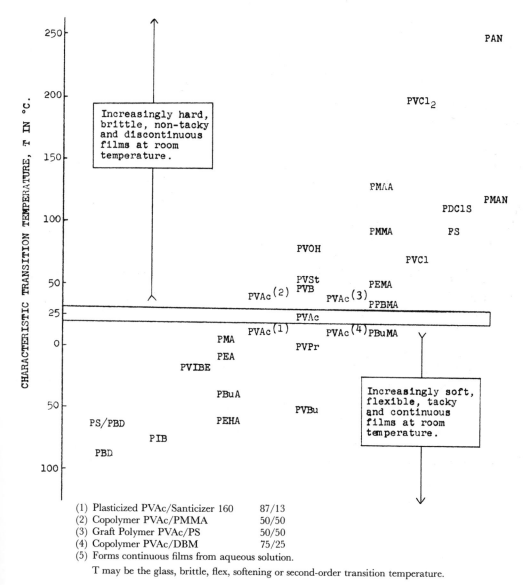

(1) Plasticized PVAc/Santicizer 160   87/13
(2) Copolymer PVAc/PMMA   50/50
(3) Graft Polymer PVAc/PS   50/50
(4) Copolymer PVAc/DBM   75/25
(5) Forms continuous films from aqueous solution.

    T may be the glass, brittle, flex, softening or second-order transition temperature.

Fig. 1. Chart of adhesives polymers in terms of film properties at room temperatures.

strength; compatibility with various chemicals; polarity; electrical properties; dimensional stability; hard, soft, tough, brittle, tacky or waxy nature; ability of the groups attached to the polymer chain to enter into further chemical reaction; and resistance to water, acids, solvents and other chemicals.

Once a polymer has been made, tested and characterized, it still needs to be subjected either unmodified or compounded to adhesive performance tests. Adhesion to specific surfaces; resistance of the bond to aging, temperature extremes and chemicals; proper application characteristics; and economics are a few important considerations.

Figure 1 charts some of the more familiar polymers in terms of properties of films cast from aqueous dispersion at room temperature. In most cases, the polymers are positioned along the temperature scale approximately according to their second-order transition temperature. This intrinsic property depends on the chemical nature and physical structure of a polymer. Above their second-order transition (glass) temperature polymers are rubbery, soft or thermoplastic; below it, they are brittle, hard or inflexible. In a few cases, brittle temperature or some other characteristic temperature that approximates the transition temperature was used. In an extreme case, the softening temperature (*ca.* 210°C) of polyvinylidene chloride (PVCl$_2$) was considered more appropriate than the transition temperature (*ca.* −17°C). Despite the nonrigorous nature of the chart, it does indicate what might be expected of polymer adhesive films at working temperatures. The extremes of the elastomeric or tacky nature of materials on the left and the hard, inflexible nature of those on the right of the figure are obvious from a study of the properties of these polymers. It is also interesting to note.the versatility of those resins located in the center of the figure. For example, polyvinyl acetate emulsions can readily be made to give adhesive films that are harder or softer, tacky or nontacky, continuous or noncontinuous by the methods of copolymerization or graft polymerization mentioned earlier or by compounding with plasticizers, solvents or

other agents.[5] These same principles could be applied, of course, to any of the polymers shown. A study of the change in properties in a homologous series of resins is rewarding. The transition from a resin that can be tough or brittle, hard or soft depending on its molecular weight (polyvinyl acetate), to softer and tackier resins (polyvinyl propionate, polyvinyl butyrate) is a simple example. Polyvinyl valerate is rubbery at room temperature whereas polyvinyl stearate is waxy. Polyvinyl trimethyl acetate on the other hand is harder than polyvinyl acetate. A similar situation exists among the acrylate and methacrylate series of polymers. Among these, the brittle temperature becomes progressively lower as the chain length is increased. A minimum is reached at eight carbon atoms for the acrylates and twelve for the methacrylates.[6] Further increases in chain length result in higher softening or melting points as the polymers become crystalline and waxy.

References

1. Delmonte, J., "The Technology of Adhesives," Ch. 1, New York, Reinhold Publishing Corp., 1947.
2. Flory, P. J., "Principles of Polymer Chemistry," Cornell University Press, 1953.
3. Schildkneckt, C. E., "Vinyl and Related Polymers," New York, John Wiley & Sons, Inc., 1952.
4. (a) "High Polymer Series," Vols. 1–12, New York, Interscience Publishers, Inc., 1940–1959.
   (b) Schmidt, A. X., and Marlies, C. H., "Principles of High Polymer Theory and Practice," New York, McGraw-Hill Book Co., Inc., 1948.
   (c) Billmeyer, F. W., Jr., "Textbook of Polymer Chemistry," New York, Interscience Publishers, Inc., 1957.
   (d) D'Alelio, G. F., "Fundamental Principles of Polymerization," New York, John Wiley & Sons, Inc., 1952.
5. Data at Shawinigan Resins Corporation, Springfield, Massachusetts.
6. Riddle, E. H., "Monomeric Acrylic Esters," New York, Reinhold Publishing Corp., 1954.
7. Gaylord, N., and Mark, H., "Stereoregular Polymerization," New York, Interscience Publishers, Inc., 1959.

— 28 —

Polyvinyl Acetate and Related Polymers for Adhesives

F. H. Norris and P. M. Draghetti

Shawinigan Resins Corporation
Springfield, Massachusetts

POLYVINYL ACETATE AND COPOLYMERS

Polyvinyl acetate has been available commercially in the United States since the 1930's. Growth was slow until the 1940's when polyvinyl acetate dispersions were introduced. The volume of resin consumed has since grown from a negligible amount in 1945 to 40 million pounds (solids) in 1950 and 165 million pounds in 1960.

The adhesives industry is currently the most important outlet for polyvinyl acetate. Approximately 80 million pounds were used in adhesives in 1960 compared to 55 million in paints and coatings and 20 million in textile finishes and binders. Other uses including paper coatings, printing inks, "permanent" starches and chewing gum accounted for 10 million pounds.

Polyvinyl acetate came into widespread use in adhesives in the 1940's as a synthetic resin substitute for hide glue. Superior properties of the synthetic resins offset their higher price. Polyvinyl acetate adhesives were adaptable to new high-speed machinery in the paper converting and packaging fields and were enthusiastically received. They found a place in wood adhesives[53-56] and later were introduced in the familiar household "white glue." Polyvinyl acetate is now used in adhesives for bookbinding, paper bags, milk cartons, drinking straws, envelopes, gummed tapes, convolute tubes, folding boxes, multiwall shipping bags, labels and a host of other common products —foils, film and paperboard, decals, cigarette tips, lagging compounds, wood assembly, padding, automobile upholstery, pencils, leather binding, tile cements, etc.

Because of their relatively low cost, ready availability, wide compatibility and excellent adhesive characteristics, many polyvinyl acetate resins, solutions and emulsions are treated as commodity items by the adhesives industry. Many manufacturers have been attracted by the prospects of polyvinyl acetate as indicated by Table 1. The resulting competition has benefited adhesives manufacturers with low prices, good quality, new improved products and greater technical service from the resin manufacturers. The current bulk selling price of polyvinyl acetate is in the vicinity of 30¢/lb of resin or 16½¢/lb of 55 per cent solids emulsion, delivered.

Mention of polyvinyl acetate for use in the adhesives industry alone gives a rather confining picture of the resin. Its use in other industries actually depends on its adhesive, binding and film properties as much as it does in the adhesives industry. In surface coatings, dynamic growth of polyvinyl acetate has continued since 1950. The early technology produced emulsion paints for exterior masonry and subsequently for interior primer-sealers and flat-wall paints. Recent developments are in gloss and texture interior paints, exterior wood paints and industrial primers and

Adco Chemical Co.
Amalgamated Chemical Corp.
American Alkyd Industries
Borden Chemical Co.
Brooklyn Paint and Varnish Co.
Calvert Chemical Co.
Celanese Chemical Co.
Cellate Co.
Colton Chemical Co.
H. B. Davis Co.
De Soto Chemical Coatings Co.
Dewey and Almy Chemical Co.
E. I. du Pont de Nemours & Co.
Emkay Chemical Co.
Farnow, Inc.
Franklin Glue Co.
H. B. Fuller Co.
B. F. Goodrich Chemical Co.
Hart Products Corp.
Jersey State Chemical Co.
Jones Dabney Co.
McClosky Varnish Co.
Morningstar-Paisley, Inc.
National Starch and Chemical Corp.
Onyx Oil and Chemical Co.
Polymer Industries, Inc.
Polyvinyl Chemicals, Inc.
Quaker Chemical Products Corp.
Reichhold Chemicals, Inc.
Rohm and Haas Co.
Scholler Brothers, Inc.
Seidlitz Paint and Varnish Co.
Shawinigan Resins Corp.
Sherwin-Williams Co.
Specialty Resins Co.
Stein-Hall and Co.
Union Carbide Plastics Co.
U. S. Coatings Co.
T. F. Washburn Co.
Wica Chemicals, Inc.
Yenkin-Majestic Paint Co.

finishes. The textile industry uses polyvinyl acetate, mostly in emulsion form, for finishes that impart durability, strength and "hand" to woven cotton and other fabrics. New uses as binders for "non-woven" or "bonded" fabrics may exceed those on woven fabrics. Paper coating and manufacturing offer an excellent potential for new polyvinyl acetate copolymers. The use of polyvinyl acetate in all fields is estimated to become greater than 225 million pounds per year by 1965. How much greater depends on realization of potential new markets in paints, textiles and paper coatings. It depends also on expansion of relatively new uses such as hot melts, redispersible powders, cement

additives, etc., in the adhesives and building products industries.

This chapter presents polyvinyl acetate and related commercial resins on the basis of information obtained from primary manufacturers and technical publications in the United States. The products are listed as examples of the types available. Other companies make quality grades of polyvinyl acetate. It would be difficult to present the hundreds of grades of products made by all manufacturers. The manufacturers and their literature should be consulted for final details on the use and properties of their products.

Monomer

Vinyl acetate is the most available and widely used member of the vinyl ester family. This colorless flammable liquid was first prepared in 1912.[2] Liquid-phase processes were commercialized early in Germany[3] and Canada,[4] but these have been replaced generally by vapor-phase processes.[5, 6] Both methods are based on calcium carbide in utilizing acetic acid reacted with an excess of acetylene. Newer processes not dependent on calcium carbide are being investigated, and one of these is used commercially.[7]

Vinyl acetate is supplied in the United States by Air Reduction, Celanese, du Pont, Pacific Carbide, Shawinigan Resins and Union Carbide and in Canada by Shawinigan Chemicals. Its properties and reactions are reviewed in trade bulletins of the suppliers,[8-11] and more extensive discussions are presented in technical literature.[12-16]

Commerical grades contain diphenylamine (DPA), copper acetate or hydroquinone (HQ) inhibitors. DPA grades contain 200 to 325 ppm of inhibitor and may be stored indefinitely under recommended conditions. The DPA is readily removed before polymerization by simple distillation through a short packed column. The HQ grades contain 12 to 20 ppm of inhibitor and can be used without removing inhibitor in noncritical commercial polymerizations. Vinyl acetate sells today in bulk at 15.6¢/lb. A brief review of the economics of its conversion into polymer appeared in 1958.[1] The current capacity for production of vinyl acetate in the United States is estimated to be over 310 million pounds per year.[19]

References to the preparation of several other vinyl esters exist;[16] however only a few are receiving attention currently, mostly as comonomers with vinyl acetate. The propionate, butyrate, 2-ethylhexoate, and stearate esters have been available commercially.

Fig. 1 relates types of adhesives to vinyl acetate.

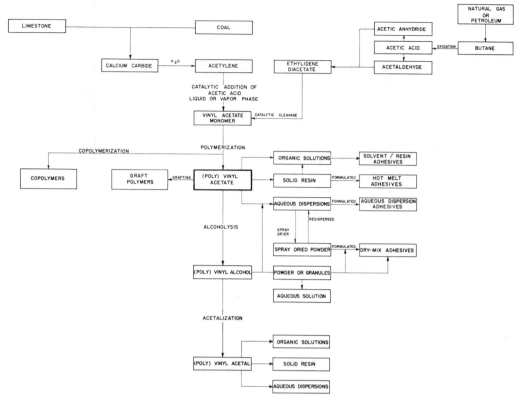

Fig. 1. Adhesives raw materials from (poly) vinyl acetate.

Polymerization

Early studies of the polymerization of vinyl acetate and the structure and properties of the polymer were made during the first quarter of the century.[17, 18] The first patents on polymerization were also issued during that period;[19, 20] the first real commercial development on this continent began in 1925. Commercial polymerization was underway by 1929.[21-23] Since then, numerous technical articles have been published dealing with polyvinyl acetate.[36, 47] All but the last five years of this work is well-reviewed.[12,16]

Vinyl acetate polymerizes by the free-radical addition reaction described in the introduction to this series of chapters. Free radicals generated by the decomposition of organic peroxides such as benzoyl or hydrogen peroxide or of inorganic "per" salts such as potassium or ammonium persulfate are commonly used to initiate polymerization. Conventional methods[24] of bulk, solution, suspension and emulsion polymerization are used. Reactions ordinarily are accomplished at temperatures above room temperature. Recent studies on polymerization at room temperature or below, on irradiation techniques and on the use of ionic catalysts foreshadow the preparation of newer modifications. Longer and straighter molecules, finer particle size in the case of emulsions, and even spatially regulated structures are visualized. Vinyl acetate copolymerizes with various vinyl monomers. Vinyl chloride, vinylidene chloride, dibutyl and other dialkyl maleates and fumarates, crotonic, acrylic, methacrylic and itaconic acids and their esters, vinyl pyrrolidone and ethylene are commercially important comonomers. A monomer that does not combine with vinyl acetate alone can be combined by use of a third monomer that copolymerizes with both. "Grafting" can be used with monomers such as styrene, that do not copolymerize with vinyl acetate.

Laboratory processes for the polymerization of vinyl acetate and some of the other vinyl esters are readily available from monomer suppliers and in the patent literature. Manufacturing processes are also available.[14, 48]

Solid Resins

Solid polyvinyl acetate has been manufactured by three processes: bulk, solution and aqueous suspension or "bead" polymerization. The first two processes were used originally; however they have been supplanted extensively by the aqueous suspension process. The latter affords easier temperature control, dispenses with hazardous solvents, and avoids the dangers inherent in bulk polymerization. Bulk and solution processes are still preferred to produce low-molecular weight and other special-purpose resins.

Polyvinyl acetate is a thermoplastic, odorless, tasteless, nontoxic, essentially clear and colorless resin. It has a noncrystalline and relatively branched rather than linear structure. Most grades of resin have a somewhat broad molecular weight distribution. They do not melt sharply, but soften over a temperature range. The resin is unaffected by sunlight, ultraviolet light and air; furthermore it will adsorb a small amount of water. Polyvinyl acetate is neutral and noncorrosive. The various grades have good heat stability below 100°C, show slight discoloration at approximately 150°C and decompose at 200 to 250°C. They are soft at 50°C, but brittle at 10 to 15°C. Polyvinyl acetate burns slowly. The chemical properties and reactions of polyvinyl acetate are those typical of stable esters. Some of the properties of polyvinyl acetate that are substantially the same for all commercial grades are given in Table 2.

TABLE 2. PHYSICAL PROPERTIES OF POLYVINYL ACETATE.

Density, at 20°C	1.19 g/ml
Refractive index, at 20°C	1.466
Water absorbtion	2%
Thermal coefficient of linear expansion	8.6×10^{-5} per °C
Thermal conductivity	38×10^{-5}
Specific heat	0.39 cal/g/°C
Dipole moment	1.85 Debye units
Dielectric strength at 30°C	1000 v/mil

Some of the properties that differ among the different molecular weight grades available commercially are given in Table 3. The different molecular weight resins are conveniently graded by a V- or viscosity number. The V- number is the viscosity in centipoises of a $1M$ (with respect to the repeating monomer unit) solution of polymer in benzene. Most of the differences in physical properties among polyvinyl acetate grades are primarily a function of molecular weight. Low-molecular weight grades are soft and deformable at room temperature; whereas the high-molecular weight grades are hard and tough. All grades have outstanding adhesion to many surfaces, porous and nonporous. The excellent adhesion is due in part to the highly polar acetate groups in the polymer and partially to the unique combination of vis-

cosity, tack, tensile strength and other properties that exists during application of the adhesive and during formation and aging of the bond. The properties of polyvinyl acetate resins are amply illustrated in the trade literature of the major manufacturers. Representative commercial grades of polyvinyl acetate resin are given in Table 4. Other special grades are offered to fit particular needs. In some cases, the viscosity number varies ±10 per cent from the given value.

Solutions

Polyvinyl acetate resins are also sold in solutions of organic solvents, often those in which they are polymerized. Many users prefer, however, to dissolve the resin in solvents of their own choice and under conditions appropriate to their own particular needs. There is a variety of solvents in which the resin can be dissolved with simple stirring at room temperature. Some good solvents are: acetone, ethanol (95 per cent), isopropanol (90 per cent), cyclohexanone, diacetone alcohol, methylethyl ketone, methanol, n-butanol (90 per cent), butyl acetate, ethyl acetate, methyl acetate, dioxane, carbon tetrachloride, ethylene dichloride, trichloroethylene, acetic acid, acetic anhydride, benzene and toluene. Addition of small amounts of water improves the solubility in many solvents. In certain classes of solvents, e.g., aliphatic alcohols, the solubility of the resin decreases as the molecular weight of the solvent increases.

Polyvinyl acetate is swollen by anhydrous butanol, amyl alcohol, xylene, ethyl benzene, ethylene glycol and other poor solvents. The resin will dissolve in some of these, e.g., anhydrous butanol or xylene, at higher temperatures. Poor solvents may be used as diluents to modify the viscosity, evaporation rate or cost of the solvent system. The resin is not appreciably soluble in aliphatic hydrocarbons, animal fats, gasoline, glycerin, diethyl ether, hexanol, kerosene, linseed oil, naphtha, mineral and vegetable oils, turpentine, waxes and water.

When polyvinyl acetate resin solutions are applied as adhesives or coatings, the last amount of solvent is released slowly. Solvent retention of polyvinyl acetate resins is of practical concern primarily with adhesives between two nonporous surfaces. Forced drying, baking, or inclusion of high boiling solvents to maintain a wet surface assists the release of solvent. Ordinarily, resin applied from solution dries to the touch rapidly and low boiling solvents can be used without causing blushing. Advantages of these solutions

TABLE 3. CHARACTERISTICS OF "GELVA" RESINS.

Grade "Gelva"	Form	Viscosity (cps)[a]	Molecular Weight (wt. avg.)	Softening Point (°C)[b]	Heat Seal Temp. (°C)[c]	Max. Tensile Strength (psi)[d]	% Elongation at Yield	Abrasion Resistance[e]	Second Order Transition Temp. (°C)
V-1.5	Lumps	1.40–1.70	11,000	65	Too brittle	Too brittle	Too brittle	150	16
V-2.5	Lumps	2.25–2.75	18,000	81	Too brittle	Too brittle	Too brittle	126	17
V-7	Granules	6–8	45,000	106	60	4100 (0.2 in. min)	3.3	88	21
V-15	Granules	13–17	90,000	131	70	5500	4.8	77	24
V-25	Granules	22–28	140,000	153	82	5600	4.7	70	26
V-60	Granules	54–66	300,000	196	85	6500	4.8	68	27
V-100	Granules	90–110	500,000	230	87	7200	4.6	64	28
V-800	Granules	700–1000	Ca. 1.5 million	—	90	7300	4.3	59	29

Note: Volatiles of all grades is 2 per cent maximum.

[a] Viscosity is that of a benzene solution containing 86 g of resin per 1000 ml of solution, determined at 20°C, with an Ostwald-Cannon-Fenske viscometer.

[b] Softening point is determined by a modified Kraemer and Sarnow method using 10 g of mercury over a 6.35 mm cylindrical plug of resin in a 7-mm diameter glass tube.

[c] Minimum heat seal temperatures measured on 1.8-mil film cast on Ditto paper conditioned 48 hr at 73°F, 50% relative humidity using "Pack-Rite Robot" at 60 psi, 1.5 sec dwell, 1 in. sq area face to face.

[d] Molded specimen (2% in. gauge × ¼ × .07 in.) conditioned 48 hr at 71°F, 50 per cent relative humidity Instron Tester at 2 in./min crosshead speed.

[e] Taber abrasion in mg loss/1000 revs. on cast film conditioned 48 hr at 73°F, 50 per cent relative humidity C-10 wheels—1000 g load.

TABLE 4. COMMERCIAL POLYVINYL ACETATE RESINS.

Supplier* Grade (V-Number)	(1) "Vinylite"	(2) "Lemac"	(3) "Vinac"	(4) "Gelva"
1½	AYAC	—	—	V-1½
2½	AYAB	—	—	V-2½
7	AYAA	7	B-7	V-7
12	—	12	—	—
15	AYAF	15	B-15	V-15
21	AYAT	—	—	—
25	—	—	B-25	V-25
45	AYAW	—	—	—
100	—	—	B-100	V-100
150	—	150	—	—
800	—	—	B-800	V-800
1000	—	1000	—	—

* *Note:* Key to Product Suppliers in reference to this and other tables.

are the clarity, gloss, rapid drying and relatively good water resistance obtained in the adhesive film. Time-dependent adhesive properties such as wet tack and flow during bond formation may be controlled by formulation at the proper solution viscosity. Solution viscosities depend markedly on the grade and concentration of resin, the solvent system and, of course, the temperature. Some of the regularly available solutions of polyvinyl acetate resins are given in Table 5. Many special solutions are supplied by polyvinyl acetate manufacturers.

Redispersible Powders

Preparation of polymers redispersible in aqueous media was accomplished abroad by 1940. Dispersions of rather hard polymers or copolymers containing acid groups which could be dried without major difficulties and later redispersed in aqueous alkaline media were used. Redispersible 100 per cent polyvinyl acetate powder had also been suggested.[25] Pioneering work on the difficult task of preparing a water-dispersible powder of the comparatively soft polyvinyl acetate resin was underway in the United States in the early 1940's. Several methods including spray- and freeze-drying were investigated. The good adhesive and film-forming properties of polyvinyl acetate were now problems to be overcome in the preparation, storage and eventual redispersion of the powder. By the early 1950's semicommercial development of spray-dried polyvinyl acetate powder had begun, and a U. S. Patent was issued to cover this work.[26] Today at least three domestic products are commercially available, and these are listed in Table 6.

Stable dispersions can be reconstituted by adding the powders uniformly and slowly to water using good agitation. The unique advantage of these powders is their ability to be used as a binder in dry-mix formulations. A list of ingredients that can be dry-mixed with polyvinyl acetate powders includes: polyvinyl alcohol, dextrin (with "Gelva" Powder 702), starch, clay, soybean protein, animal glue ("Gelva" Powder 702), casein, thermosetting resins, Portland cement,[27] plaster of Paris, talc, sand, silica, mica, pigments, wood flour, asbestos fibers, ground cork or leather, natural gums, perlite, vermiculite as well as many inorganic fillers and extenders. Solid plasticizers and, in certain cases, small amounts of liquid plasticizers may be incorporated into the dry blend.

Many attractive uses of spray-dried powders exist, e.g., they can be added to polyvinyl acetate emulsions or other emulsion systems to build solids, increase viscosity, improve tack and decrease drying time. One-package systems of spray-dried polyvinyl acetate, thermosetting resin and curing catalyst are feasible. Dry-mix adhesives containing starch, polyvinyl alcohol, clay and the spray-dried resin have been investigated for paper laminating. The advantages of redispersible polyvinyl acetate are most apparent in adhesive and binding applications in the building products trade. Tile mastics and grouts, caulking compounds, curtain wall sealants, drywall joint cements, texture paints, patching compounds, mortar mixes, cement underlayment compositions and fill coats have been formulated. Most dry mixes are readily prepared in a conical or ribbon-type blender.

The ready redispersibility of these powders is accompanied by lower water resistance of their films, which can be improved in many cases by other ingredients in the dry mix. Some care is necessary in handling and storing these materials to prevent caking.

Emulsions

Polyvinyl acetate is most widely used in the form of a dispersion of solid resin in water. These dispersions are produced by the emulsion polymerization process[49-52] and are more commonly termed "emulsions."

By 1940 polyvinyl acetate emulsions had been introduced commercially in the United States. By 1950 their annual volume had increased to about 45 million pounds (wet basis); in 1960 to about 260 million pounds. A conservative estimate suggests an annual volume greater than 350 million pounds by 1965. Currently almost one-half of the

TABLE 5. COMMERCIAL POLYVINYL ACETATE RESIN SOLUTIONS.

Product	Solvent	Solids (%)	Viscosity (cps)	Supplier	Comments
"Polyco" 346-LV	Methanol	60	2500–4000	2	Low-molecular weight polymer for formulating general-purpose adhesives, polystyrene lamination.
"Polyco" 514W	Acetone	60	15,000–25,000	2	Medium-molecular weight for laminating, saturant, greaseproof coatings, heat seal coatings.
"Gelva" V-55–E29	Ethanol	29	12,000–20,000	4	General adhesives for paper, wood, glass, leather, textiles, ceramics, metal foil and many plastic materials. Also for paper coatings for glass, greaseproofing and heat sealing; fabric and paper sizing; and binder for metallic inks.
"Gelva" V-55–E34	Ethanol	34.5	35,000–77,000	4	
"Gelva" V-7–M50	Methanol	50	1000–4000	4	
"Elvacet" 60–05	Methanol	60	—	7	
"Resyn" 1015	Methylene chloride	35	18,500	12	Fast drying coatings.

volume goes into the adhesives industry and approximately one-third to surface coatings. The remainder is used chiefly in the paper, textile and building products industries. Use in all industries depends not only on the outstanding adhesive properties of the resin, but also on the excellent compatibility of the emulsions with many modifying agents.

The properties, uses and methods of formulating emulsions are graphically and comprehensively described in the trade literature of several manufacturers. This literature is readily available (see key to Product Suppliers). Most manufacturers specify properties of their emulsions, which ordinarily include: per cent solids, emulsion viscosity, pH, acid content, per cent unreacted monomer and density. Other properties generally described are: particle size (sometimes as weight average, occasionally as number average), molecular weight (usually as high, medium or low), film properties such as clarity, water and grease resistance, and tolerance of the emulsions to various organic and inorganic chemicals. Other special tests may be necessary to characterize an emulsion polymer more thoroughly, for example, surface tension; dilution, mechanical, freeze-thaw, heat, storage and compounding stabilities; solubility of the resin in various solvents; compatibility of the emulsion with plasticizers, thickening agents, film coalescing agents, pigments, extenders and other modifiers; bond strengths between various substrates; film heat seal temperatures; flex temperatures; blocking temperatures; tensile strength; hardness and other film properties; and rheological behaviour. Successful performance tests on adhesive formulations in accord with adhesive manufacturers' requirements are the ultimate criteria. For a complete accounting, analytical methods including infrared spectra can be used to identify components.

TABLE 6. REDISPERSIBLE POLYVINYL ACETATE POWDERS.

	"Gelva" Powder 700	"Gelva" Powder 702	"Vinac" RP-250 and RP-251 *
Manufacturer	4	4	3
Particle size of powder	20 microns	15 microns	99% through 100 mesh
Volatile content	1.5%	3.0%	—
Bulk density	32–38 lb/cu ft	32–38 lb/cu ft	0.53g/cm
Viscosity, cps			
at 55% solids in water	1660	200	4500
at 60% solids in water	7800	700	
at 70% solids in water	—	11,000	

* Premium grade of RP-250—added resistance to caking.

It is necessary to state that the classification of emulsions in Table 7 is an illustrative interpretation of the trade literature. Reference to the manufacturers' literature or to the manufacturers' technical staff for their recommendations is again suggested. A more detailed classification is possible based, for example, on resin composition, resin molecular weight, particle size, type and amount of protective colloid/surfactant system and viscosity/shear information. Such a system, augmented with other tests, has been used successfully to classify emulsions and to predict their performance in adhesives. However, the classification used here is broad enough to include conveniently the major types of polyvinyl acetate emulsions currently available.

Class I: General-Purpose Homopolymer Emulsions. This is a specific designation for those emulsions that can be used in a multitude of adhesive formulations. These emulsions are usually made by a continuous or semicontinuous process. They have a heterogeneous particle size and molecular weight. They are outstandingly stable to storage, handling and compounding. Polyvinyl alcohol is the usual protective colloid. Dried films from the unmodified emulsions are redispersible in water; however the emulsions can be modified or the films treated directly to obtain water resistance.

Some manufacturers supply these general-purpose adhesive bases in several emulsion viscosity grades from 500 to 4000 cps. Solids content is generally 55 per cent, and pH is 4 to 5. Probably the most important characteristic of emulsions in this class is their excellent compatibility with plasticizers, wetting agents, solvents, thickeners and other modifying agents; furthermore they can be transformed readily into a variety of adhesives.

Class II: Special-Purpose Homopolymer Emulsions. Emulsions in this class are similar to those in Class I but lack the broad range of compatibility with modifying agents. This has usually been somewhat sacrificed to obtain other special properties. For example, high molecular weight for higher heat-seal temperatures, coarse particle size for better holdout on porous surfaces, or low-molecular weight for quick-tack may be the chief advantage of such an emulsion. These emulsions are mostly made by the batch or semicontinuous processes. Polyvinyl alcohol is the usual protective colloid but often is combined with natural gums or synthetic colloids. Other colloids than polyvinyl alcohol are, of course, occasionally encountered in emulsions in Class I and II. Many emulsions in Class II are sold to adhesives manufacturers already modified with plasticizer, solvents, surfact-

ants, thickeners or other agents to achieve better filming, tackiness, freeze-thaw stability, special viscosity or other effects. The chief characteristic of an emulsion in Class II is the special property imparted to it by the manufacturer, combined with the good adhesion of the polyvinyl acetate/polyvinyl alcohol or other resin/colloid system.

Class III: Free Filming Homopolymer Emulsions. Emulsions in Class III form free films at room temperature that remain continuous in the presence of water without baking the film or adding coalescing agents to the emulsions. These emulsions have a finer and more uniform particle size than those in Class I and II. Most have particles of 0.5 to 1 or 2 microns, whereas Class I and II emulsions range from 0.5 to 10 microns. In Class I especially there is a double distribution with a number average below 1 micron and a weight average of 1 to 3 microns.

Most Class III emulsions are made by the gradual monomer addition process to control particle size and molecular weight. Surfactant is used to get a smaller and more uniform particle. The amount of protective colloid is reduced to less than half that used in making Class I and II products to improve free-film properties.

A further subdivision according to type of protective colloid is useful among emulsions in this class. Class III A emulsions contain polyvinyl alcohol and have the advantages of the adhesion of Classes I and II combined with more water-resistant free-filming properties. Class III B emulsions contain synthetic colloid other than polyvinyl alcohol. Materials such as methyl cellulose, sodium carboxymethyl cellulose and hydroxethyl cellulose are examples. The change in protective colloid alters the compounding characteristics of such emulsions. For example, these products are stable to large additions of borax and other polyvalent salts that coagulate polyvinyl alcohol/acetate dispersions under normal conditions. Class III C emulsions contain natural products as protective colloids. The natural gums, starches and dextrins are examples. These emulsions have excellent stability to further additions of natural products and are noted for excellent tolerance for inorganic pigments, fillers and extenders. These subdivisions are not specified in Table 7.

Class III emulsions because of their finer particle size, lower molecular weight and protective colloid content generally have less tolerance for the more polar organic solvents than Class I emulsions. Excluding that, their compounding stability is good. They are used primarily when improved filming properties are desired. Combinations of

TABLE 7. VINYL ACETATE HOMOPOLYMER AND COPOLYMER EMULSIONS FOR ADHESIVES.

Class I: General-Purpose Homopolymer Emulsions

Product	Supplier	Solids (%)	Emulsion[a] Viscosity (cps)	Particle[b] Size (microns)	Remarks
"Elvacet" 81-900	7	55	800-1000	1-3	General-purpose adhesive base. Excellent stability. Wide compatibility. High bond strength. Excellent solvent tolerance.
"Elvacet" 81-1600	7	55	1500-1700	1-3	
"Elvacet" 81-3000	7	55	3000	1-3	
"Gelva" S-55L	4	55	800-1000	1-3	General-purpose adhesive base. Excellent stability. Wide compatibility. High bond strength. Excellent solvent tolerance. S-55P is lightly plasticized.
"Gelva" S-55	4	55	1100-1300	1-3	
"Gelva" S-55H	4	55	1500-1700	1-3	
"Gelva" S-55VH	4	55	1800-2200	1-3	
"Gelva" S-55P	4	55	1550-1750	1-3	
"Vinac" XX-210	3	55	900-1200	1	General-purpose adhesive base. Excellent stability. Wide compatibility. High bond strength and solvent tolerance.
"Vinac" XX-220	3	55	1500-1700	1	
"Polyco" 117SS	2	55	1150-1400	2-7	General adhesive compounding. Good solvent stability. 117FR is freeze-thaw stable.
"Polyco" 117FR	2	55	1100-1300	2-7	
"Polyco" 561	2	55	850-1100	2-7	
"Polyco" 571	2	55	1400-1600	2-7	
"Plyamul" 9350-LV	5	55	900-1200	2-6	General-purpose adhesive base. Excellent stability. Wide compatibility. High bond strength and solvent tolerance. 9153 is plasticized. 9360 has excellent wet tack, mechanical stability and machinability.
"Plyamul" 9350-HV	5	55	1500-1900	2-6	
"Plyamul" 9153	5	55	1300-2000	2-6	
"Plyamul" 9360	5	55	3200-4200	2-6	
"Darex" 60L	10	55	800-1300	1.5	Good solvent receptivity and machinability for highly compounded adhesives.
"Darex" 17100	10	55	1500-2200	1.5	

Class II: Special-Purpose Homopolymer Emulsions

Product	Supplier	Solids (%)	Emulsion Viscosity (cps)	Particle Size (microns)	Remarks
"Elvacet" 80-900	7	55	800-1000	1-3	Similar to 81-900, but low molecular weight to give tackier and lower heat-sealing adhesives.
"Gelva" TS-10	4	55	1800-2200	1-3	Medium molecular weight adhesive base. Heat-sealing paper adhesives.
"Gelva" S-50	4	55	1050-1450	1-4	High molecular weight adhesive base. Good tack and machinability.
"Gelva" S-51	4	55	3500-4500	1-3	High molecular weight adhesive base. Good tack when formulated. Good machinability.
"Gelva" D-852	4	55	3000-4000	1-4	Medium molecular weight adhesive emulsion. Good tack and machinability.

TABLE 7. VINYL ACETATE HOMOPOLYMER AND COPOLYMER EMULSIONS FOR ADHESIVES. (cont'd.)

Class II: Special-Purpose Homopolymer Emulsions (cont'd.)

Product	Supplier	Solids (%)	Emulsion[a] Viscosity (cps)	Particle[b] Size (microns)	Remarks
"Gelva" D-859	4	37.5	3500–4500	1–5	Special adhesive base for paperboard laminating, wood adhesives.
"Gelva" D-869	4	55	1000–2000	.05–2	Excellent compatibility with fully hydrolyzed polyvinyl alcohols. Excellent compounding and mechanical stability.
"Vinac" HF-300	3	55	3700–4200	1	Easily compounded into high viscosity adhesives for paper and paper bags.
"Vinac" S-700	3	50	3500–5000	4	Plasticized. Nontacky, flexible films. Quick setting, strong bonds to paper, wood, etc. Concrete bond coats.
"Vinac" CE1-P	3	55	700–900	5	Cement additive. Floor toppings. Concrete adhesive. Bonding agent for plaster.
"Vinac" PB-600	3	55	—	5	For padding and bookbinding. Permanently tough and flexible films. For paper, fabrics and leather.
"Vinac" AA-63	3	52	1600–2300	0.5–2.5	Excellent compatibility with fully hydrolyzed polyvinyl alcohols. Excellent compounding and mechanical stability.
"Polyco" 345	2	55	3000–4000	3–8	Compounded wood adhesive. Excellent shear strength, wood failure and speed of set. Non-staining.
'Polyco" 289	2	55	3000–4000	2–8	Base for high viscosity, fast grabbing adhesives. Excellent wet tack. For furniture, fabric and packaging.
"Polyco" 117H	2	55	1000–1500	3–10	For general adhesives, coatings and textile finishes.
"Polyco" 199	2	55	1250–1400	3–8	Compounded wood adhesive. Similar to "Polyco" 345.
"Polyco" 809	2	55	1000–1500	2–8	Compounded adhesive having a flexible water-resistant film.
"Polyco" 692	2	55	800–2000	1–6	Textile adhesives and finishes.
"Polyco" 1360-15	2	55	1200–1400	2–4	Freeze-thaw stable compounded wood adhesive.
"Polyco" 1361-4B	2	43	5000–7000	2–4	Compounded wood adhesive.
"Polyco" 1404-30	2	51	3000–4000	2–4	Compounded packaging adhesive.
"Darex" 65L	10	55	800–1200	<2	Fast grab, residual tack for high-speed adhesives.
"Vinrez" 202A	9	55	1100–1600	2–10	Adhesive and binder uses.
"Vinrez" 202	9	55	800–1800	5–10	Primarily for textile finishes.
"Neovac" V31N	6	55	1000–2000	2–4	Adhesives, finishes and coatings.

CL-101	11	55	800–1200	large	General adhesives, coatings and finishes. High bond strength. F.D.A. accepted.
CL-101-H	11	55	1500	large	
CL-101-E	11	55	3000	large	
CL-101-V	11	55	4000	large	
"Resyn" 1001	12	55	3800	0.8	Adhesive base. Bodies well with plasticizer. Good water resistance. Textile finishing.
"Resyn" 1025	12	55	1200	0.9	High molecular weight. Good heat and water resistance in adhesives. Fast setting.
"Resyn" 1011	12	55	3500	1	Adhesive base with good compounding and mechanical stability. General purpose.
"Resyn" 1021	12	55	2300	1	Adhesive base with superior solvent tolerance. General purpose.

Class III: Free-Filming Homopolymer Emulsions

"Elvacet" 84-1100	7	54	900–1300	1–3	Adhesive base. Water-resistant films.
"Gelva" TS-22	4	55	350–650	1–2	Borax stable. Dextrin compatible. Readily compounded with pigments and extenders.
"Gelva" TS-23	4	55	200–500	1–2	Similar to TS-22. Excellent compatibility with fillers and extenders.
"Gelva" TS-30	4	55	1200–1400	1–2	Borax stable. General adhesive compounding.
"Gelva" TS-31	4	55	500–700	1–2	Similar to TS-30. Excellent compatibility with pigments and extenders.
"Gelva" TS-35	4	55	800–100	1–2	Heat sealing and paper adhesives.
"Gelva" TS-36	4	50	300–500	0.5–1	Similar to TS-30.
"Gelva" TS-63	4	55	900–1200	1–2	Fast filming, low molecular weight resin for special adhesive compounding.
"Vinac" WR-50	3	55	1200–1800	0.5	Fast filming. Water-resistant films. Medium molecular weight. Excellent adhesion. Borax stable. Heat sealing.
"Flexac" FA-5	3	56	800–1200	0.5	High molecular weight Clear, glossy films even at low temperature.
"Polyco" 953	2	55	1250–1800	0.5–2	Borax stable. Low settling rate. Wash-resistant coatings. Heat-seal coatings.
"Polyco" 529	2	55	1200–1800	1–5	Compounds readily into water-resistant adhesives and coatings.
"Polyco" 522	2	55	1200–1800	0.3–1.5	Water-resistant coatings.
"Polyco" 505	2	55	1300–1800	1–5	Beater additive. Water-resistant and heat-seal adhesives and paper coatings.
"Polyco" 612	2	60	800–1400	0.5–2	Borax stable. Good water resistance. Adhesives and textiles.
"Pliamul" 9370	5	55	900–1200	0.5–2	Borax stable. General-purpose adhesive latex.
"Darex" 52L	10	55	300–600	<2	General-purpose adhesive base. Soft polymer. Good film water resistance.
"Darex" 56L	10	55	300–600	1	High film tensile strength. Polymer resistant to cold flow. For textile sizes, bag adhesives and blocking resistance.

TABLE 7. VINYL ACETATE HOMOPOLYMER AND COPOLYMER EMULSIONS FOR ADHESIVES. (cont'd.)

Class III: Free-Filming Homopolymer Emulsions (cont'd.)

Product	Supplier	Solids (%)	Emulsion[a] Viscosity (cps)	Particle[b] Size (microns)	Remarks
"Darex" 61L	10	55	2000–4000	1	Borax compatible. Specific adhesion to metal foil.
"Darex" 62L	10	55	2200–2700	1	Same as "Darex" 56L.
"Darex" 64L	10	55	800–1200	<2	Borax compatible. General-purpose adhesive base. Excellent water resistance.
"Vinrez" 130	9	55	1300–1900	<1	General adhesive, coating and finish applications. Water-resistant film.
"Neovac" V-19N	6	55	1000–2000	—	Borax and dextrin compatible. Water resistant, glossy film.
"Neovac" V-13N	6	55	1200–2200	—	Borax compatible. Clear, glossy water-resistant films. For decals and coatings.
CL-100	11	55	1000–1500	Medium	General textile finishing and adhesives.
WC-130	1	58.5	1500–2500	0.5–2	For coatings and adhesives.
"Resyn" 1004	12	56	600	1	Good compatibility with starches, gums, borax, clay and plasticizers. Primarily textile finishing.
"Resyn" 1035	12	55	900	0.5–1	Adhesive base with high water resistance and film clarity. Nonwoven binder.
Class IV: Homopolymer Latices					
"Elvacet" 1440	7	54	900–1500	<0.5	Films have excellent water resistance.
"Gelva" TS-85	4	55	1400–1700	0.2–0.3	Clear, glossy, water-resistant, flexible films. Low heat-seal temperature.
"Gelva" D-800	4	46.5	30–100	<0.1	Excellent films. Ultra-fine particle size for coatings and adhesives.
"Geon" 970X11	8	53	39–50	0.2	For coatings and finishes. Clay binder. Mechanical and freeze-thaw stability.
"Vinac" D-25	3	36	1000–3000	<0.5	Primarily saturant/binder and size/stiffener for textiles. Non-blocking film. Water dilutable.
"Polyco" 583	2	45	500	0.1	Borax stable. For textile finishes and laundry starches.
"Polyco" 577G	2	55	800–1200	0.5 max.	For compounding borax stable adhesives, industrial coatings, textile finishes.
"Darex" 63M	10	51	100–600	0.1	Borax compatible. Scuff resistant coatings.
CL-102	11	55	1000–1500	0.05–0.3	For coatings, finishes and specialty adhesives.
WC-125	1	55	120–500	0.05–0.3	For coatings, finishes and adhesives.

Product					Description
"Resyn" 1014	12	55	1200	0.3	Good pigment binder. Borax stable. High degree of water resistance—clear and glossy films.
"Resyn" 1032	12	55	35	0.2	Primarily for textile finishing.
"Resyn" 1103	12	46	20	<0.1	Pigment binder. Gloss coating textile finish.

Class V: Vinyl Acetate-Acid Copolymer Emulsions

Product					Description
"Gelva" Emulsion C-3	4	55	700–1000	1–1.5	Alkali redispersible or soluble films. Can be transformed into C-3 resin solutions. Padding, bookbinding and other adhesives and coatings.
"Gelva" Emulsion C-3P	4	55	1000–1700	1–1.5	Plasticized version of 'Gelva" Emulsion C-3.
"Vinac" RS-100	3	55	1000–2000	2–8	Alkali soluble or redispersible. For paper coatings and adhesives. Padding adhesives.
"Polyco" 618A	2	55	1200–3000	2–8	Alkali-dispersible emulsion. Base for padding adhesives and paper adhesives.
"Polyco" 497	2	35	200	0–5	Alkali-soluble copolymer emulsion. Adhesives, paper and textile coatings and sizes. Floor finishes. Water resistant.
"Darex" 2757	10	55	2000–6000	1	Alkali soluble. Specific adhesion to metal. Metal foil adhesive.
"Neovac" V-26N	6	55	1000–2000	—	Water-resistant, alkali-removable films. Metal foil and bottle label adhesives. Synthetic yarn sizes.
"Resyn" 1601	12	55	1900	0.9	Superior adhesion to polar materials. Low heat seal. Alkali-redispersible films.
"Resyn" 1101	12	45	3000	<1	Superior adhesion to glass, foil and wood. Films redispersible in alkali. Slowly thermo-sets on heating.
"Resyn" 1411	12	51	4300	1	Superior adhesion to glass, foil and wood. Films redispersible in alkali.

Class VI: High-Colloid Content Emulsions

Product					Description
"Gelva" S-98	4	60	400–800	1–2	Highly compatible with dextrin and low cost extenders. For remoistenable and other adhesives.
"Gelva" S-99	4	58	2000–2800	1–2	Similar to S-98. Not borax stable.
"Gelva" D-165	4	55	1800–2200	0.5–1	Remoistenable adhesive base. Not dextrin compatible.
"Vinac" WR-20	3	55	600–1200	1	Anionic. Excellent dextrin tolerance. Remoistenable adhesives, paper tapes, decals, carton seals. For textile sizes and finishes. Stiffening properties. Wash resistance.
"Vinac" WR-21	3	55	600–1200	1	Nonionic. Modified emulsion. Uses similar to WR-20.
"Polyco" 694	2	55	3500–5000	0.5–3	Borax stable, dextrin compatible. For remoistenable adhesives, coatings and envelope glues.

TABLE 7. VINYL ACETATE HOMOPOLYMER AND COPOLYMER EMULSIONS FOR ADHESIVES. (*cont'd.*)

Class VI: High-Colloid Content Emulsions (cont'd.)

Product	Supplier	Solids (%)	Emulsion[a] Viscosity (cps)	Particle[b] Size (microns)	Remarks
"Polyco" 684	2	60	300–700	1–6	For envelope adhesives, decals, carton seals, label glues. Dextrin compatible.
"Vinrez" B-166-M	9	55	2200–2800	<1	Highly compatible with high soluble dextrins.
"Neovac" V-29N	6	55	1000–2000	—	Borax and dextrin compatible. For remoistenable adhesives. Glossy films.
"Resyn" 1006	12	60	1400	1	Formulation with dextrins for remoistening gum adhesives.

Class VII: Vinyl Acetate-Alkyl Maleate Copolymer Emulsions

Product	Supplier	Solids (%)	Emulsion[a] Viscosity (cps)	Particle[b] Size (microns)	Remarks
"Elvacet" 1423	7	54	900–1500	<0.5	Adhesive base for difficult surfaces. Very good film properties.
"Gelva" TS-70	4	55	900–1300	0.5–1.5	Adhesive base for difficult surfaces. Excellent solvent tolerance. Very good film properties.
"Gelva" TS-70A	4	55	900–1300	0.5–1.5	Similar to TS-70. Contains hexylene glycol for improved film properties.
"Gelva" TS-71	4	55	1000–1400	0.5–2	Similar to TS-70, but borax stable.
"Gelva" D-874	4	55	1000–1500	1–4	Similar to TS-70, but more flexible and tackier films.
"Gelva" D-875	4	55	1000–1500	0.25–0.75	Excellent film properties. For adhesives and coatings where excellent filming is desired.
"Flexbond" 800	3	52	550–850	0.7	High molecular weight copolymer primarily for coatings. Permanently flexible films.
"Flexbond" 811	3	52	400–600	<1	Color stable, flexible films. For industrial applications on composition board. Copolymer.
"Flexbond" 855	3	55	300–500	0.3	Terpolymer. High pigment binding. High molecular weight. Primarily for coatings.
"Polyco" 678-W	2	55	1000–1500	<1	Clear flexible films. Outstanding water resistance. Adhesion to many surfaces. Barrier and paper coatings.
"Polyco" 804	2	55	1700–2300	0.2–0.4	Non-ionic, borax and freeze-thaw stable. Excellent water resistance.
"Polyco" 804PL	2	55	600–900	0.2–0.4	
"Everflex" A	10	55	1000–1400	<2	Moderate flexibility. Heat sealable. Adhesives and paper coatings.
"Everflex" B	10	55	1000–1400	<2	Same as "Everflex" A, but more flexible. Adhesives and mastics.
"Everflex" G	10	52	300–600	<2	Outstanding film water resistance.
"Everflex" BG	10	51	200–500	<2	Same as "Everflex" G, but more flexible.
"Everflex" GT	10	55	1500–3000	1	Same as "Everflex" G, but borax stable. Mastics and spackling compounds.

Product					Description
"Everflex" MA	10	55	200–700	0.1	Borax compatible. Improved pigment binding. Heat-sealable adhesives and paper coatings.
"Everflex" MB	10	55	200–700	0.1	Same as "Everflex" MA, but more flexible.
"Everflex" MF	10	55	1300–2300	0.1	Same as "Everflex" MA, but better water resistance. Freeze-thaw stable.
"Vinrez" 3-R-58	9	55	800–1400	<1	Excellent film former. For adhesive, binder and coating uses.
CL-201	11	55	1000–1500	0.1–1.6	Adhesives, coatings and finishes.
CL-202	11	55	1900–2500	0.05–0.4	Specialty adhesives, industrial coatings, paper coatings and textile finishes.
CL-200	11	55	1400–2100	0.1–1.3	Adhesives, coatings and finishes.
"Resyn" 1255	12	55	600	0.2	For coatings. High binding power and good water resistance.
"Resyn" 1251	12	55	3700	0.5	Binder. Adhesive base. Good water resistance and adhesion to cellulose acetate.

Class VIII: Vinyl Acetate-Alkyl Acrylate Copolymer Emulsions

Product					Description
"Gelva" TS-100	4	55	1000–1500	0.05–1	Adhesive base for difficult surfaces. Good film flexibility and tack.
"Gelva" D-242	4	55	1000–1400	1–2	Adhesive base for difficult surfaces. Good film flexibility and tack.
"Flexbond" 306	3	55	200–300	0.3	Terpolymer. High pigment binding. Water-resistant films. Color coat paper adhesive. Pick resistant. Nonwoven fabrics.
"Polyco" 2170	2	55	1000–2000	0.4–0.8	Primarily for industrial coatings such as ceiling tiles. Excellent adhesion to fiber glass.
"Polyco" 806	2	55	1000–2000	0.2–0.3	Primarily for glass coatings and concrete coatings.
CL-203	11	55	1900–2500	—	Paint, textile, adhesive and paper coatings use.
CL-204	11	55	300–600	—	For coatings. Excellent pigment binding capacity.
VX-551	11	46	50–200	—	Paint, textile and specialty coatings use.
SX-3	11	46	75–1000	—	Textile and paper coatings. Non-woven fabric binder.
"Resyn" 1203	12	42	70	<0.5	For pigmented paper coatings. Glossy, water resistant films.
"Resyn" 1234	12	51	1800	0.3	Adhesion to difficult surfaces. Packaging adhesives. Good binding power. Terpolymer.
"Resyn" 2211	12	55	600	<1	High molecular weight and good water resistance for adhesives. Nonwoven binder.

Class IX: Other Polyvinyl Ester Emulsions

Product					Description
"Gelva" D-845	4	55	1000–2000	0.5–2.0	Very soft and tacky resin. Pressure sensitive adhesives.
"Gelva" RS-4066	4	55	1000–2000	1–2	Very soft film. Film properties intermediate to "Gelva" TS-63 and D-845.

TABLE 7. VINYL ACETATE HOMOPOLYMER AND COPOLYMER EMULSIONS FOR ADHESIVES. (cont'd.)

Product	Supplier	Solids (%)	Emulsion[a] Viscosity (cps)	Particle[b] Size (microns)	Remarks
					Class X: Other Types
"Resyn" 2507	12	49	2000	0.3	A non-film forming copolymer with vinyl chloride. Plasticized films have good water resistance and fire retardancy. Borax stable latex. Specific adhesion to PVC1 films.
"Gelva" D-809	4	10–30	—	0.1	Non-filming tetrapolymer latex. Plasticized or heat-formed films have excellent water resistance. High softening point.
"Gelva" D-806	4	200–500	—	<0.1	Tetrapolymer latex giving excellent film and binding properties. For surface coatings and adhesives.
"Gelva" D-805	4	200–500	—	<0.1	Same as D-806, but finer particle size.
S.C.L. Emulsion	13				
"Emultex"	14				
"Texibond"/"Texicote"	15				
"Vinamul"	16				
VR	17				All foreign manufacturers listed supply a broad range of homopolymer and copolymer dispersions for adhesives, paper, textiles and paper coatings.
"Vinavil"	18				
"Edivil"	19				
"Rhodopas"	20				
"Mowilith"	21				
"Vinnepas"	22				
MC(A)L Emulsion	23				

a Methods of measurement are not necessarily the same among different manufacturers.
b As listed in manufacturers' literature.

Class III with Class I or II emulsions are often utilized with unique results.

Class IV: Homopolymer Latices. In the last decade, several polyvinyl acetate latices have become commercially available. These products are characterized by a particle size in the range of 0.1 to 0.4 micron or less. Their clear, glossy and water-resistant films make them particularly useful as adhesive coatings. Class IV emulsions are stabilized primarily by surfactants. Batch or gradual monomer addition processes are used.

Class V: Vinyl Acetate-Acid Copolymer Emulsions. Polyvinyl acetate emulsion films or adhesives can be redispersed in alkaline media when the resin is a copolymer containing acid groups. The presence of acid groups also confers better adhesion to many surfaces. The degree of adhesion and alkali-redispersibility can be controlled by varying the number of acid groups in the polymer chain. The emulsion or adhesive viscosity can also be controlled by varying the pH of the emulsion. Aqueous solutions of polyvinyl acetate alkali-soluble resins can be prepared from some of these emulsions. In other respects, the properties and applications of emulsions in this class will depend on the similarity of the emulsion system to the other classes listed here.

Class VI. High-Colloid Content Emulsions. Under the proper conditions, vinyl acetate can be polymerized in the presence of two to five times the amount of protective colloid used in making general-purpose adhesive emulsions. In this case, the colloid functions in a primary way to impart special properties to the emulsion. Important examples are the emulsions offered as remoistenable adhesives for high-speed machine application. Class VI emulsions are extraordinarily stable to compounding with thickening agents and with water-soluble resins, gums, starches and dextrins in general. This class would include emulsions polymerized in the presence of pigments, fillers, extenders and other modifying agents, but not emulsions modified after polymerization.

Class VII: Vinyl Acetate-Alkyl Maleate Copolymer Emulsions. Copolymers of vinyl acetate and maleate or fumarate esters are available in emulsion systems that fit most of the preceding classifications. Although designed initially for emulsion paints and other surface coatings, these copolymer emulsions have rapidly become important as adhesive bases. Tack properties, compatibility with solvents and plasticizers, and film and resin properties generally are different from those of the vinyl acetate homopolymer emulsions. Consequently, better adhesion to certain surfaces is obtained with adhesives based

on Class VII emulsions—in addition, it is often unnecessary to add large amounts of plasticizer or coalescing agents.

Class VIII: Vinyl Acetate-Alkyl Acrylate Copolymer Emulsions. The comments on Class VIII are the same as those on Class VII. 2-Ethyl hexyl, ethyl and butyl acrylates are currently most often copolymerized with vinyl acetate. Class VII and VIII emulsions are maturing rapidly because of their specific adhesion to difficult-to-adhere surfaces.

Class IX: Other Polyvinyl Ester Emulsions. Polymer emulsions of vinyl propionate, vinyl butyrate, vinyl stearate and other vinyl esters are appearing as adhesive bases—either as homopolymers or copolymers with vinyl acetate. Esters such as vinyl propionate or vinyl butyrate give soft, sticky, and in some cases, permanently tacky films. Small amounts of vinyl stearate copolymerized with vinyl acetate give water-resistant nonblocking films. Class IX emulsions are limited to small volume specialty uses at present.

Class X: Other Types. A few examples of emulsions that do not fall in Classes I to IX are listed here. These products could be specifically classified by a more detailed scheme, of course. Also listed are the trade names of emulsions obtained from literature received from several major foreign manufacturers. Most of these companies also supply polyvinyl acetate resins, solutions, copolymers and polyvinyl alcohol.

The varied applications and properties of polyvinyl acetate emulsions are noted in Table 7.

Alkali-Dispersible or Soluble Resins

Resins soluble or dispersible in aqueous alkalies are obtained by copolymerizing vinyl acetate with monomers containing carboxyl groups. As little as 1 to 5 mole per cent of such monomers as acrylic, methacrylic, itaconic, crotonic and maleic acids has been used. The initial work on these as with most vinyl acetate resins was reported in Germany.[28] Patents were obtained in the United States in the early 1940's.[29]

Clear and glossy films are obtained from aqueous alkaline solutions of polyvinyl acetate-acid resins. Aqueous solutions are readily prepared by sprinkling the resin into water containing a base with constant agitation. The time, temperature and amount of base required to effect solution vary with the molecular weight and degree of carboxylation of the resin. The viscosity of the solution can be varied within certain limits by adjustment of solids content and pH. Prescribed pH should be maintained for maximum stability of the solutions. When ammonium hydroxide or other volatile alkalies are used, the films become water insoluble; they remain soluble or dispersible in aqueous alkalies. Sodium hydroxide or carbonate give salts whose films are water soluble or dispersible.

The carboxyl groups improve adhesion to a variety of materials including metals, leather and cellulosics; otherwise the properties are similar to those of polyvinyl acetate resins. Vinyl acetate-acid resins are soluble in many organic solvents; moreover they can be compounded with plasticizers, pigments, dyes, fillers and modifying resins.

Vinyl acetate-acid resins are widely used in hot-melt form as well as from aqueous alkaline or organic solvent solution. Book-binding adhesives where easy scrap recovery is desired and textile sizing of rayon, cotton and acetate warp yarns are important uses. Paper coatings for heat sealing, gloss, grease and abrasion resistance, electrostatic properties, improved ink and varnish holdout as well as improved printability are interesting uses. The sensitivity of aqueous solutions of the resin-salts to alum suggests wet-end addition to pulp. Other uses include anti-tarnish lacquers for silver, hair-set sprays, temporary protective coatings on metals, surface conditioners for chalked paint surfaces, pigment binders for economical high PVC paint dispersions, high gloss finishes, self-polishing floor waxes and thickening and stabilizing resin dispersions. Most commercial grades are supplied in bead form; some are coated with anti-caking agents.[30] However, bead grades, particularly those of low molecular weight, should be stored under cool, dry conditions to guard against caking. Table 8 lists the regularly available products.

Copolymer Resins and Solutions; Higher Vinyl Esters

Several copolymers of vinyl acetate are available commercially in solid form or dissolved in organic solvents. Numerous patents on their preparation and use exist. Most reference books on vinyl polymers list some of the original literature.[16] These same remarks are true of polymers of higher vinyl esters and copolymers of them with vinyl acetate. Table 9 illustrates the types of resins available. Other types that should be noted are: vinyl acetate-chloride resins; vinyl acetate-maleic anhydride copolymer resin used in suspension polymerization and other specialties; vinyl acetate-alcohol resins in organic solvent solutions used in bonding impervious as well as porous surfaces;

and, most recently available, copolymer resins of vinyl acetate and ethylene which seem destined for novel adhesive applications.

The resins noted in this section are used primarily in specialty or unique adhesive applications now. It is reasonable to predict that many of them will move into large volume adhesive uses as they become more well known and their potential applications are more widely investigated.

POLYVINYL ALCOHOL

Polyvinyl alcohol is one of a small group of synthetic polymers which competes in the 3-billion-pound market for water-soluble resins. Over 95 per cent of the market is served by natural products such as starch, dextrin, and casein; however sales of synthetic water-soluble polymers have grown substantially in recent years, reaching approximately 80 million pounds in 1960. The synthetics, though higher priced, compete in a variety of applications by virtue of uniform quality and unique properties.

The major markets for polyvinyl alcohol are adhesives (11 million pounds in 1960), textiles (4½ million pounds), emulsifier[62] and protective colloid in polymerization (3 million pounds), paper (2¼ million pounds) and plastic film (1 million pounds). There is an amazing number of smaller specialties, including synthetic sponges, cosmetics, pharmaceuticals, photosensitive coatings, ceramics, moldings, extrusions, release agents and many others. These miscellaneous markets account for about 3½ million pounds, bringing the total 1960 consumption of polyvinyl alcohol in the United States to approximately 25 million pounds. None of the major markets is mature. The growth potential in adhesives, paper, and particularly in film is excellent.

Preparation and Properties

Polyvinyl alcohol is produced by replacing the ester groups of polyvinyl acetate or other polyvinyl esters with hydroxyl groups. Processes[31, 32] involve alcoholysis in methanol or ethanol using an acid (e.g., sulfuric) or alkaline (e.g., sodium methoxide) catalyst. The extent of replacement of acetate groups can be controlled in both processes. The extent is described variously as degree of saponification, per cent hydrolysis and per cent residual acetate groups. Most polyvinyl alcohols contain 60 to 100 per cent replacement of acetate by hydroxyl groups. Commercial grades of polyvinyl acetate-alcohols that are water-soluble or

TABLE 8. VINYL ACETATE-ACID RESINS.

(Alkali-Soluble Beads)

Product	Supplier	Viscosity Grade (V-Number)	Softening Temperature (°C)	Remarks
"Vinac" ASB-10	3	9–11	130–140	Excellent film clarity. For adhesives, paper and textile applications.
"Lemac" 541-10	2	9–11	120–125	Paper coatings. Warp size.
"Lemac" 541-20	2	18–21	150–155	Hot-melt adhesives.
"Gelva" C-3 V-10	4	9–11	120–125	Low, medium and high molecular weight grades of the same basic resin. General adhesive use and for difficult-to-bond surfaces. Paper coatings, textile finishes. Paints.
"Gelva" C-3 V-20	4	18–22	150–155	
"Gelva" C-3 V-30	4	27–33	175–180	
"Gelva" C-5 V-10	4	9–11	120–125	Higher degree of carboxylation. Uses similar to C-3 grades. Slightly different solution and film properties.
"Gelva" C-5 V-16	4	15–17	130–135	
"Gelva" C-5 V-16R	4	15–17	130–135	Special hot-melt grade.
"Gelva" M-7 V-100R	4	90–110	175–180	Resistance to high temperature degradation. Hot melts. High molecular weight.

TABLE 9. COPOLYMER RESINS AND SOLUTIONS. HIGHER VINYL ESTERS.

Product	Supplier	Composition	Remarks
"Resyn" 26-1404	12	40% solids solution of vinyl acetate copolymer in toluene:isopropyl acetate, 7:2.	Superior adhesion to foil, cellulose acetate and other polar materials.
"Resyn" 26-2404	12	40% solids solution of vinyl acetate-acrylic copolymer in toluene:ethyl acetate, 7:3.	Tacky films.
"Resyn" 26-1244	12	40% solids solution of vinyl acetate copolymer in toluene:isopropyl acetate, 3:2.	Laminating plastic films, foils and paper. Packaging. Pressure-sensitive and specialty adhesives. Printing inks. Versatile adhesion to a wide range of packaging sheeting.
"Resyn" 26-1206	12	40% solids solution of vinyl acetate copolymer in toluene:ethyl acetate, 1:2.	Very flexible almost tacky dry films. Laminating packaging materials.
"Gelva" C-254-B	4	35% solids solution of vinyl acetate copolymer in benzene.	Release coatings. Laminating adhesives. High gloss, grease-resistant paper coatings.
"Gelva" C-254-H	4	35% solids solution of vinyl acetate copolymer in hexane:heptane.	
"Gelva" D-267	4	55% solids solution of vinyl acetate-acrylate copolymer in toluene:isopropyl acetate, 1:2.	Similar to D-266, but more tacky. Pressure-sensitive adhesives.
"Gelva" D-269	4	55% solids solution of vinyl acetate-maleate copolymer in toluene:isopropyl acetate, 1:2.	Uses similar to D-266 and D-267, but harder. Particularly effective on polyvinyl chloride film. Surface coating primer.
"Gelva" D-264	4	55% solids in anhydrous ehanol.	Similar to D-269. Ethanol solvent is more adaptable to certain surface, e.g., polystyrene. Flexographic printing inks.
"Gelva" D-256	4	Beads.	Bead-form of "Gelva" C-254-B. Allows choice of solvents. Also alkali-redispersible.

dispersible are termed polyvinyl alcohols along with the "fully hydrolyzed" grades.

Preparation of polyvinyl alcohol was disclosed in the 1920's.[33, 34, 35] Considerable study of its preparation, structure, properties and reactions has continued,[12, 16, 18, 36] although significant commercial exploitation did not occur in the United States until the 1940's.

Physical properties common to most grades of polyvinyl alcohol made by one manufacturer are given in Table 10. Particle size, bulk density, color, ease of solution, foaming tendencies, stability and similar characteristics vary among "equivalent" grades supplied by different manufacturers depending upon their processes.

The characteristics of aqueous solutions of polyvinyl alcohol vary with the per cent hydrolysis and the molecular weight of the intermediate polyvinyl acetate resin. Low molecular weight, low (ca. 70 to 80) per cent hydrolyzed grades dissolve rapidly in water at room temperature. High molecular weight, high (ca. 95 to 100) per cent hydrolyzed grades are best dissolved by dispersing in cold water and heating to 85 to 95°C with stirring. Heating may be accomplished with hot water coils, jackets or steam injection. Medium molecular weight, medium (ca. 80 to 95) per cent hydrolyzed grades are dissolved or dispersed by slow addition to cold water with stirring. The temperature can then be raised to 60 to 80°C to hasten the dissolving process. Variations in solution viscosity, pH and viscosity stability, and surfactant properties among the different grades are discussed in the manufacturers' literature. Films of different grades of the resin also differ in water, grease and solvent resistance; adhesion; flexibility;

TABLE 10. PHYSICAL PROPERTIES OF POLYVINYL ALCOHOL.[a]

Physical form	White to light straw granular powder
Specific gravity	1.19–1.27
Bulk density:	30–40 lb/ft^3
Refractive index, n_D, 25°C	1.51
Tensile strength, 50% relative humidity	to 22,000 psi
Elongation, 50% relative humidity	to 300% unplasticized; to 600% plasticized
Thermal coefficient of linear expansion	1×10^{-4}/°C, at 0–50°C plasticized
I.C.I. Sward hardness	27–57% vs glass at 50% relative humidity
Heat-sealing temperature	110–150°C
Heat stability	Darkening, slow degradation >100°C. Rapid degradation, decomposition >200°C
Effect of light	Negligible
Burning rate	Slow
Gas impermeability	High
Mold resistance	Good
Organic solvents	Generally insoluble

[a] Average values of "Gelvatols," depending on grade of polymer and ambient conditions.

elongation; and plasticizer compatibility. Some of the properties that vary with molecular weight and per cent hydrolysis are given in Table 11.

Commerical Grades

There are four manufacturers of polyvinyl alcohol in the United States, and they are listed as 2, 3, 4 and 7 in the key to product suppliers on page 381. The major commercial grades are listed in Table 12.

Reactions and Modifications

Compared to polyvinyl acetate, polyvinyl alcohol not only has unique properties but also greater chemical reactivity. The arrangement of hydroxyl groups in predominantly 1,3-glycol units, and the possibilities for hydrogen bonding in solution and film form are keys to its versatility.

One of the most useful reactions of polyvinyl alcohol is condensation with aldehydes to form acetal resins. Polyvinyl alcohol reacts with boric acid to form a readily hydrolyzable and methanol-soluble ester. Boric acid is used with aqueous solu-

tions of polyvinyl alcohol in textile sizing. Borax is added to aqueous solutions of the resin to increase viscosity or, in larger amounts, to form a heat-reversible gel. Hydrogen peroxide can be added to polyvinyl alcohol solutions to decrease viscosity upon heating. Acid esters or their sodium salts formed with polyvinyl alcohol are useful in drilling muds, cation exchange resins and other applications. Esters formed with unsaturated acids are interesting where solvent-soluble, light-sensitive films are desired. Polymeric acids such as polyacrylic acid react with polyvinyl alcohol to form an insoluble gel whose mechanical properties vary with pH and temperature. Formation of ethers with such materials as benzyl chloride gives films of low water-vapor permeability. Graft copolymers formed with acrylonitrile can be spun into fibers or molded. A host of other chemical reactions exist which are generally typical of long-chain polyhydric alcohols.

Polyvinyl alcohols are readily compounded with various materials to modify properties. Glycerin, ethylene and butylene glycols, sorbitol and other water-soluble organic compounds are effective plasticizers. Their ability to impart softness and flexibility is augmented by the presence of a small amount of water. Although many grades have water resistance, this property can be improved by heat or incorporation of insolubilizing agents. Formaldehyde, furfural, benzaldehyde, dimethylol urea, monomethylol dimethylhydantoin and water-soluble phenol-, urea-, or melamine-formaldehyde resins will insolubilize polyvinyl alcohol in the presence of acid catalysts. A number of chromium and other inorganic metal compounds insolubilize the resin. Dyes, pigments, starches, clays, dextrins, casein, urea, cement, wetting agents, antifoaming agents, flame retarders and other modifying or extending materials may be combined with polyvinyl alcohol to increase its uses.

Applications

The largest use of polyvinyl alcohol is in adhesive formulations, usually in combination with polyvinyl acetate emulsions or other resin dispersions. Polyvinyl alcohol got its start in the adhesives industry in the United States during World War II in the packaging industry. It was widely used at that time as an adhesive in waterproof V-board packing cases that could be floated ashore from cargo carriers. Since that time, polyvinyl alcohol has become firmly established in the burgeoning markets for synthetic adhesives in packaging, paper-converting, furniture, bookbinding, envelopes, etc. The polyvinyl alcohol func-

370 ADHESIVE MATERIALS—VINYL RESINS

TABLE 11. Gelvatol Characteristics.

Grade	Viscosity[a] (cps)	Hydrolysis (%)	Molecular Weight (wt. avg.)	Tensile Strength[b] (psi)	Elongation[b] (%)	Second Order Transition Temp. (°C)	Surface[d] Tension (dynes/cm)	Abrasion[c] Resistance	Concentration of 10,000 cps Solution %[e]
"Gelvatol"									
40-10	1.3-2	72.9-77	1,900	1,000	5	ca. 10	46	129	57
40-20	2-3	72.9-77	3,100	1,750	5	—	46	—	46
0-365	4-6	80-84	10,800	9,000	225	43	46	—	—
20-30	4-6	87.7-89	9,800	9,300	225	46	49	—	35
1-30	4-6	98.5-100	8,600	9,700	170	54	62	—	29
20-60	21-25	87-89	96,000	9,300	250	—	52	—	17
3-60	23-28	99.9-99	88,000	10,500	200	—	65	—	16
1-60	28-32	99-100	86,000	12,000	175	—	69	—	15
20-90	34-45	87-89	125,000	9,500	250	73	52	24	13
3-90	45-55	97.9-99	118,000	13,300	200	84	65	—	12
1-90	55-65	99-100	115,000	14,500	175	86	69	15	11
3-91	55-65	97.9-99	126,000	13,300	200	—	65	—	—

[a] 4% aqueous solution at 20°C.
[b] Films conditioned one week at 50% RH, 74°F and tested at 2″/min crosshead speed.
[c] Same test as Table 3.
[d] 4% aqueous solution at 23°C.
[e] At 20°C.

TABLE 12. COMMERCIAL POLYVINYL ALCOHOL RESINS.

Product	Supplier	Hydrolysis (%)	Viscosity[a] (cps)	Remarks
"Lemol" 5-88	2	87-89	4-6	Suspending agent, emulsifier, protective colloid.
"Lemol" 22-88	2	87-89	21-25	
"Lemol" 42-88	2	87-89	38-45	
"Lemol" 5-98	2	98.5-100	4-6	Adhesive compounding, mold release.
"Lemol" 16-98	2	99-100	15-20	
"Lemol" 24-98	2	99-100	22-28	Adhesives, mold release—cast films, tubing.
"Lemol" 30-98	2	99-100	28-34	
"Lemol" 51-98	2	99-100	47-54	
"Lemol" 51-98 GF	2	96.2-97.5	47-54	Adhesive compounding, mold release, non-gelling solutions.
"Lemol" 60-98	2	99-100	55-65	Adhesive compounding, mold release.
"Lemol" 60-98 GF	2	96.2-97.5	55-65	Adhesives, mold release, non-gelling solutions.
"Lemol" 30-77	2	76-79	—	Suspending agent—primarily in polymerization of vinyl chloride.
"Lemol" 65-98	2	98-100	62-70	Adhesive compounding, mold release.
"Vinol" PA-5	3	86-89	4-6	Emulsifiers in emulsion polymerization, remoistenable adhesives, textile warp size, thickeners and modifiers of adhesive formulations.
"Vinol" PA-20	3	86-89	19-25	
"Vinol" PA-40	3	86-89	35-45	
"Vinol" PA-100	3	86-89	90-100	Remoistenable adhesives; adhesion to smooth surfaces.
"Vinol" FH-100	3	98.5-100	4-6	Laminating and water-resistant adhesives; modifier and thickener in liquid and dry-mix adhesives; greaseproofing and promoting ink holdout on paper; textile warp size; ceramic binder; release coating; precast film used in vacuum bag molding.
"Vinol" FH-400	3	98.5-100	22-32	
"Vinol" FH-500	3	98.5-100	35-45	
"Vinol" FH-600	3	98.5-100	50-70	
"Vinol" FH-1500	3	99.5	155	
"Vinol" CWS	3	92-95	4-6	Cold water-soluble films for unit packaging; dry-mix products (joint cements, spackling compounds.
"Vinol" 125	3	—	—	Clear, color-free solutions. Superhydrolyzed grade.
"Elvanol" 51-05	7	87.7-89	4-6	Remoistenable adhesives; adhesion to smooth surfaces; ceramic and fabric binders; filament and spun yarn sizing; cold-water soluble film; emulsifying agent; temporary protective coatings; cosmetics.
"Elvanol" 70-05	7	98.5-100	4-6	Ceramic binders; low foaming; mold release.

TABLE 12. COMMERCIAL POLYVINYL ALCOHOL RESINS.

Product	Supplier	Hydrolysis (%)	Viscosity[a] (cps)	Remarks
"Elvanol" 52-22	7	87–89	19–25	Remoistenable adhesives; adhesion to smooth surfaces, ceramic and fabric binders; filament yarn sizing; extrusion molding; cold-water soluble film; emulsifying agent; cosmetics.
"Elvanol" 71-24	7	97.9–98.7	23–28	Similar to 71-30, but gel-free and slightly less water resistant.
"Elvanol" 71-30	7	99–100	28–32	Glassine paper; paper coatings; extrusion molding; solvent-resistant film; mold release; temporary protective coatings.
"Elvanol" 50-42	7	87–89	34–45	Compression molding; emulsifying agent; cosmetics.
"Elvanol" 72-51	7	97.9–98.7	45–55	Similar to 72-60, but gel-free and slightly less water resistant.
"Elvanol" 72-60	7	99–100	55–65	Water-resistant paper adhesives; textile thermosetting finishes; grease-resistant coatings; compression molding; solvent resistant film; emulsifying agent.
"Gelvatol" 0-383	4	37–45	5–8*	Water-dispersible, detergent-soluble, solvent-soluble binding systems.
"Gelvatol" 40-10	4	77–72.9	1.3–2	Remoistenable adhesives; emulsification; binders; rapid water solubility at room temperature.
"Gelvatol" 40-20	4	77–72.9	2–3	
"Gelvatol" 0-365	4	80–84	4–6	Emulsifier and protective colloid.
"Gelvatol" 20-30	4	87.7–89	4–6	Adhesion to a variety of surfaces; formulation with resin emulsions to improve adhesion or increase viscosity; emulsification and protective colloid properties; 20–30 for water-soluble packaging and remoistenable adhesives.
"Gelvatol" 20-60	4	87–89	21–25	
"Gelvatol" 20-90	4	87–89	35–45	
"Gelvatol" 3-60	4	97.9–99	23–28	Similar to 3-90, but lower viscosity. Gel-free grade.
"Gelvatol" 3-90	4	97.9–99	45–55	Paper coating and sizing; textile sizing and finishing; grease-resistance; gel-free grade.
"Gelvatol" 3-91	4	97.9–99	55–65	Similar to 3-90, but higher viscosity; gel-free grade.
"Gelvatol" 1-30	4	98.5–100	4–6	High wet strength paper adhesives; formulation with resin emulsions for water resistant adhesives; paper laminating; 1-90 for textile sizing and finishing and for paper coating; sizing and grease-resistance; molded articles.
"Gelvatol" 1-60	4	99–100	28–32	
"Gelvatol" 1-90	4	99–100	55–65	
"Gelvatol" 2/75	4	99	35 minimum	Acid-hydrolyzed grades for film and other specialties.
"Gelvatol" 2/55	4	98.5	23–29	

[a] 4 per cent aqueous solution.

* 4 per cent solution in 1:1 water:isopropanol.

tions as a protective colloid, emulsifier and thickener as well as a resin in adhesive formulations. It promotes incorporation of water-immiscible solvents, plasticizers, waxes, and oils. It contributes improved adhesion and tensile strength. Fully-hydrolyzed grades are particularly important in promoting increased water resistance. High molecular weight grades facilitate lower adhesive solids by maintaining high solution viscosity; they also impart excellent machining properties. Medium hydrolyzed grades give the best combination of adhesion, viscosity control, and emulsifier-protective colloid action. Polyvinyl alcohols are used universally in the polymerization of polyvinyl acetate emulsions. Low hydrolyzed grades have excellent cold-water solubility, and their films exhibit remoistenability, gloss and non-curling properties on paper. Such grades are widely used as binders and additives. Low-cost paper laminating adhesives are obtained by combining polyvinyl alcohol with starches, dextrins, and clays. Polyvinyl alcohol is generally considered safe for food packaging adhesives. It has specific FDA approval for use on fatty food packages.

Among the many paper applications should be mentioned the use of dilute solutions of fully hydrolyzed grades applied by conventional equipment to impart improved wet strength, flexibility, grease-resistance, better appearance and printing qualities. Plasticizer is usually incorporated in these paper coatings formulations.

In textile warp sizing and finishing applications, excellent adhesion to natural and synthetic fibers, high tensile strength and abrasion resistance, good filming, ease of preparation and uniformity of solutions, ease of removal of size and low BOD requirements make polyvinyl alcohol desirable.

Polyvinyl alcohol, an effective binder, is used in the preparation of ceramics, sand molds, and metal slip castings. It is also used as a binder for nonwoven fabrics and is gaining importance as a concrete additive in the building products industry.

Polyvinyl alcohol film is tough, resistant to organic solvents, and impermeable to most gases. It has been used for vacuum molding of reinforced plastics, as a polarizer in optical instruments and in protective packaging. More recently, it is being utilized in water-soluble packaging for detergents, dyes, bleaches, etc.

Mention of fibers and photosensitive coatings completes the list of current major or interesting applications. Numerous new applications are being explored, which combined with the many miscellaneous applications mentioned, will contribute to the continued rapid growth of this truly versatile resin.

ADHESIVE FORMULATIONS

One way of classifying polyvinyl acetate adhesives is by the type of the formulation: emulsion and aqueous solution, dry-mix, hot-melt and solution in organic solvent. The tables in this section present "starting" formulations that illustrate a few of the many adhesive uses of polyvinyl acetate. Thousands of actual "working" formulations exist in the laboratories of adhesives manufacturers. Formulating principles are thoroughly reviewed in the literature of the resin manufacturers.[37]

Adhesives for paper or paper-composition substances is one of the largest uses for polyvinyl acetate emulsions. Often the emulsions can be used with little, if any, modification. Usually, however, it is necessary to alter physical properties such as viscosity, solids and water resistance; to vary application characteristics such as tack and machinability; and to reduce cost.

Starches, polyvinyl alcohol solutions and clays are examples of cost-reducing agents. Starches provide high viscosity and "body." Polyvinyl alcohol builds viscosity, improves machinability and water resistance. Clays improve setting properties by controlling penetration into porous substrates.

Improved fast-setting and tack characteristics are achieved by addition of plasticizers, solvents, and film-coalescing agents. Thin boiling starches and clays also facilitate the speed of set by raising the solids content. Examples of formulations of several paper adhesives are in Table 13.

Fast-setting packaging or case sealing is a particular class of paper adhesives. High wet tack, machinability, low cost and, often, water resistance are required in addition to fast set. The fast set generally inherent in Classes I and II emulsions noted previously is improved by addition of solvents (aromatic and chlorinated types) and plasticizers and by maintaining a high non-aqueous content in the adhesive. Addition of rosin derivatives in the solvent or plasticizer improves wet tack. Machinability can often be improved by addition of polyvinyl alcohol solutions. Most emulsions in Classes I and II (and selected products in the other classes) have sufficient machinability to prevent "cottoning" and "throwing" at high speed operation and coagulation under shear. They also have good "clean-up" properties. Fast-setting packaging and case sealing adhesives are illustrated in Table 14.

Polyvinyl acetate emulsions, polyvinyl alcohol and combinations of the two are well suited for remoistenable adhesives on envelopes, stamps, sealing tapes, and ribbons. Major requirements of remoistenable adhesives on paper are rapid reac-

TABLE 13. GENERAL ADHESIVES FOR PAPER SURFACES.

Material	Supplier	1 Bag Bottom Paste	2 Bag Bottom Paste	3 Kraft Surfaces	4 Seam Adhesive	5 Tube Winding	6 "Quilon" Paper
"Gelva" S-55	4	20–30[a]	10–20	X	39–41	X	
"Gelva" S-51	4	X	X	10–20	X	X	
"Gelva" TS-23	4	X	X			38–40	
Dibutyl phthalate	24					2	
"Santicizer" 160	24					X	
"Benzoflex" 9-88	25					X	
"Hercoflex" 900	26				7–9		
Pearl Starch	27	10–20	10–15	1–2			8–10
"Globe" 341 Starch	28	X	X				X
"Gelvatol" 1-90	4		2–5	2–5	2–4	2	5–7
"Gelvatol" 1-90G	4		X	X	X		X
"Gelvatol" 3-90	4		X	X	X		X
"Gelvatol" 1-60	4		X	X	X		X
ASP-400	29			10–20	5	24–26	3–4
ASP-602	29			X		X	X
CWF Clay	30			X		X	X
"Hercolyn"	26				7–9		
"Abalyn"	26				X		
Trichloroethylene	7				2–4	1–2	
Benzene	31				X		
Ethanol	32						4–6
Preservative		0–2	0–2	0–2			0–2
Water		70–50	78–60	77–53	38–28	33–28	80–73
Remarks		Low cost, high viscosity.	Low cost, water resistant.	Low cost, fast setting, water resistant.	Medium cost, rapid setting.	Low cost, water resistant.	High viscosity, water resistant.

[a] Parts by weight in all cases.

X—Other suitable components.

tivation with water (after aging), glossy film with low coefficient of friction (slip), and resistance to blocking (temperature and humidity) and to curling. "All-synthetic" remoistenable adhesives can be obtained by adding polyvinyl alcohol (20 to 40 percent acetate content) to Class I, III A and some VI emulsions. The polyvinyl alcohol improves remoistenability, gloss, and block resistance. Addition of humectant-type plasticizers controls undesirable curling and improves remoistenability. An optimum balance of these properties and non-blocking and gloss is achieved by specific formulating techniques of the envelope and stamp adhesive companies. Classes III A and VI emulsions furnish good gloss. Addition of special plasticizers such as butyl ricinoleate improves blocking resistance. "Resin-dextrin" remoistenable adhesives have such advantages as lower cost and gloss when a large proportion of dextrin is used with the emulsion. However, they present problems such as curling and possible loss of remoistenability with age. Most of the Class VI emulsions are specially designed to be compatible with large amounts of dextrin. Usually ingredients that promote post-addition of dextrin are incorporated during polymerization. Even "all-dextrin" systems can be improved by the addition of polyvinyl acetate emulsions. In tape, ribbon and paper applications, high-quality remoistenable adhesives can be obtained with polyvinyl alcohol systems. Table 15 contains several remoistenable adhesive formulations.

Polyvinyl acetate and polyvinyl alcohol are important raw materials for wood adhesive applications. High bond strength, fast set, controllable open and closed assembly times, colorless glue lines and ease of application at room temperature are some of the many advantages of polyvinyl acetate emulsion adhesives over natural and thermosetting resin adhesives. Classes I, II and V emulsions require only a little compounding with plasticizers, solvents and fillers to perform well as general wood or household adhesives. Water and heat resistance are improved by special compounding by adhesive manufacturers.

TABLE 14. FAST TACK AND PACKAGING ADHESIVES—PAPER.

Material	Supplier[b]	1 General Packaging	2 General Packaging	3 Carton Sealing	4 Cup Adhesive	5 Box-Board	6 Glassine to Paper	7 General Packaging	8 Difficult Surfaces
"Gelva" S-55	4	X		95			30	X	
"Gelva" S-51	4	90[a]			75		X	25	65
"Gelva" TS-63	4		65	X		90			
"Gelva" TS-71	24			1.5		5		5	2
Dibutyl phthalate	24	10	5						
"Santicizer" 160	25	X							
"Benzoflex" 9-88	33	X							
"Pycal" 94	34						10		
Hexylene glycol	7					3			
Trichloroethylene	31			3.5	6		10		
Benzene	26							25	
"Vinsol" Resin	24							25	5
"Santolite" MS-80	24					1			
Phosphoric acid	4		30		19		40	10	28
"Gelvatol" 1-90 (10% solution)							10	10	
Water						1	10	10	
Remarks		Fast tack.	Water resistant, medium cost.	Fast set, high wet tack.	Water and heat resistant.	Very fast tack.	Low cost, colorless.	High wet tack, dark color.	Fast set, water resistant.

a Parts by weight.
b See supplier p. 381.
X—Other suitable components.

TABLE 15. REMOISTENABLE ADHESIVES.

Material	Supplier	1 All Synthetic	2 All Synthetic Lay-Flat	3 Anti-Block	4 Resin Dextrin Combination	5 Lay-flat Resin Dextrin	6 High Dextrin
"Gelva" S-55	4	50[a]		50			
"Gelva" TS-63	4	X	50	X			
"Gelva" S-98	4				35	35	10
"Gelvatol" 20-30	4	15	10	10			
"Gelvatol" 40-10	4					3	
"Gelvatol" 40-20	4					X	
Dibutyl phthalate	24		3		3		1
Butyl ricinoleate	36			3			
Polypropylene glycol	35			3	3	3	8
"Arlex"	33					3	X
70% Sorbitol	33					X	X
Dextrin	9				35	30	40
Water		35	37	34	24	26	41
Remarks		Colorless film, good aging, fair gloss	High gloss, non-curling.	Fair gloss, good aging.	Good gloss, tan color.	Non-curling, good gloss, tan color.	Low cost, improved aging.

[a] Parts by weight.   X—Other suitable components.

Polyvinyl acetate emulsions, specifically plasticized or copolymer emulsions, are bases for successful adhesives for difficult-to-adhere surfaces to a variety of porous substrates. Heat-sealing or wet-bond methods are applicable. Homopolymer emulsions of Classes I–V are suitable with appropriate plasticizer and solvent depending on the surfaces involved. Class VII and VIII copolymer emulsions and certain Class VIII higher vinyl ester emulsions frequently possess specific adhesion not obtainable with the others. Some of the formulations in Table 16 are capable of bonding such difficult surfaces as polyvinyl chloride, pyroxylin, aluminum foil, polystyrene film and cellulose acetate to paper, chipboard, wood and cloth.

Where extreme water, heat and abrasion resistance are required, polyvinyl acetate emulsions can be compounded with water-soluble thermosetting resins. Plywood lamination, metal-to-wood, metal-to-metal, plastic-to-metal and particle board are possible applications. General limitations are those of thermosetting systems: reduced storage stability, short pot life, colored glue lines and use of heat or catalyst for curing.

Dry-mix adhesive formulations containing redispersible polyvinyl acetate powder, polyvinyl alcohol, starches, clays and thermosetting resins are in Table 17. Particular advantages of dry-mix adhesives not mentioned previously are found in "on-the-job" preparation of adhesives and in the stability of components mixed dry which would interact or gel in paste or liquid form. Wallboard joint adhesive and concrete additives are special applications of dry-mix adhesives in the building products industry (not mentioned in Table 17).

The technology of hot-melt adhesives based on polyvinyl acetate resins has been described.[38] Polyvinyl acetate resin is considered as the basic film-forming and adhesive component. "Fluxing" resins are added to lower viscosity, melt temperature and cost; plasticizers improve film flexibility and adhesion and affect flow and tack; waxes improve flow, spreading, slip and non-blocking. Fillers, pigments, dyes and antioxidants are also added depending on the end use. Several hot-melt starting formulations are reviewed in Table 18.

Adhesives are formulated with polyvinyl acetate in organic solvent using plasticizers and other materials similar to those mentioned with emulsions and hot-melts—with the limitation of solubility or dispersibility in the solvent system. Such solvent system adhesives are specifically tailored to particular uses.

The final Table contains a few miscellaneous "starting" formulations to illustrate further uses for polyvinyl acetate/alcohol adhesives.

Several articles[38-45] appearing in recent issues of *Adhesives Age* relate to the formulation and use of polyvinyl acetate products in adhesives. Such papers exemplify the growing importance of polyvinyl acetate and its derivatives to the adhesive industry.

TABLE 16. ADHESIVES FOR DIFFICULT-TO-BOND SURFACES.

Material	Supplier	1 General. Porous to Nonporous Surfaces	2 Porous Surfaces to PVC1 and Aluminum Foil	3 Cloth Backed PVC1 to Porous Surfaces	4 Porous Surfaces to Polyethylene and "Mylar"	5 Porous Surfaces to Polyester Films	6 PVC1 Film to Wallboard	7 Aluminum Foil to Paper and Chipboard	8 Bookbinding Cover Stock	9 General Pressure-Sensitive Adhesives	10 Aluminum Foil to Chipboard	11 Polyethylene to Porous Surfaces
"Gelva" S-55	4	X										
"Gelva" TS-30	4			60								
"Gelva" TS-70	4	73[a]							90			
"Gelva" TS-71	4								X		85	
"Gelva" TS-100	4	X	85		76	90	90	65		65		65
"Gelva" D-845	4	7	10									
"Santicizer" 160	24			5			5				10	10
Dibutyl phthalate	24								6			
"Hercoflex" 900	26				19							
"Santicizer" 8	24							10			5	
Ethyl acetate	32	8										
Butyl acetate	32	12										
Methyl isobutyl ketone	34		5									
Toluene	31			10		10						
Butyl lactate	32											
Cyclohexanone	31						5					
Xylene	31									15		
"Santolite" MS-80	24								4			
"Hercolyn"	26									20		
"Staybelite Ester" No. 10[b]	26			25								
"Gelvatol" 1-90 (10% sol'n.)	4											25
NH4OH (3% aqueous)	—							5				
FF-30 casein (15% aqueous)	2							20				
"Santomerse" SX	24									0.1		0.1
Water	24				6							
Remarks		High tack, high viscosity.	Low viscosity.	Low cost, water resistant.	Tacky film.	Clear film, low viscosity.	Low viscosity, fast setting.	Heat setting, water resistant.	Fast setting, clear film.	High viscosity.	Fast setting, water resistant.	High viscosity, tacky film.

[a] Parts by weight.   X—Other suitable components.   [b] 60 per cent in butyl acetate.

Table 17. Dry Mix Adhesives.

Material	Supplier	1 Bag Bottom Paste	2 Wood Adhesive	3 Wood Adhesive	4 Wood Adhesive	5 Remoistenable	6 Wood Laminating	7 Kraft, Bag Seams Paperboard	8 Bag Side Seams
"Gelva" Powder 700	4		20	20	39	49	15	2	
"Gelva" Powder 702	4								4.4
"Gelvatol" 1-90	4	6[a]		3.3				2	
"Gelvatol" 3-90	4								
"Gelvatol" 40-10	4					7			
"Lauxein" 888P	24		40						
"Urac" 110	37				13		100		11
"Amrez" 1400	38							12	
ASP-100 clay	29								
ASP-400 clay	29						10		
Walnut shell flour	—								
Pearl starch	27	9						5	8.6
Amioca starch	9				1.5				
"Cato" 8	12			7	1.5				
Ammonium sulfate	—								
Ammonium chloride	—								
"Dowicide" A	35	1						1	
Reconstitute to		16% solids	60% solids	30% solids	55% solids	56% solids	desired viscosity	22% solids	24% solids
Remarks		High viscosity, water resistant.	High bond strength, short pot life, water resistant.	High viscosity, low cost	Thermo-setting.	Add 3 parts DBP.	Heat curable 300° F.	Water resistant.	Low viscosity, water resistant.

[a] Parts by weight in all cases.

X—Other suitable components.

TABLE 18. HOT MELT ADHESIVES.

Material	Supplier	1 Basic Hot-Melt General Use	2 Alkali-dispersible Pick-up Labeling	3 Alkali-dispersible Bookbinding	4 PVC1 Coated Paper Adhesive	5 Particle-board	6 Paper-board Con-tainers	7 Heat-Sealing	8 Hot Pick-up Label-ing
"Gelva" V-1½	4					33			25
"Gelva" V-2½	4						50		
"Gelva" V-7	4	46ª				33	50		9
"Gelva" V-15	4				60			80	
"Gelva" C-3 V-10	4		50	40	X				
"Gelva" C-5 V-16R	4								
Dibutyl phthalate	24	28	13	8	20		20		
"Aroclor" 1254	24		12	26					
"Santicizer" 8	24					33			
"Santicizer" B-16	24							20	12
"Santicizer" 160	24								
Rosin WW	26		25				50		45
"Nevillac" soft	39								
"Nevillac" hard	39	24		24					
Ethyl cellulose N-4	26				10				
Hoechst wax W	40							20	
"Acrawax" C	41	2		1					
Sodium benzoate				0.75					
Remarks		3000 cps at 170°C.	Low melt temp. 2000 cps at 120°C.	Non-blocking 3500 cps at 175°C.	Water-resistant 2500 cps at 170°C.	Permanent-tacky 1000 cps at 150°C.	Non-blocking 6000 cps at 170°C.	Flexible films 1000 cps at 150°C.	Low melt temp. 1500 cps at 130°C.

ª Parts by weight in all cases.
X—Other suitable components.

TABLE 19. MISCELLANEOUS POLYVINYL ACETATE ADHESIVES.

Adhesive Formula	Supplier	1	2	3	4	5	6	7	8
Product									
TS-70	4	41ᵃ							
S-55 VH	4		90						
C-3 Emulsion	4			40	80				
S-55	4						24	51	60
TS-100	4			55ᵇ		9			
"Gelvatol" 20-30	4							11.5ᶜ	
"Gelvatol" 20-90	4								
Ethylene glycol	31								
Dibutyl phthalate	24		10	5	1				
"Resoflex" R-296	42	3				10		3.5	3
Toluene	31				6				7
Glycerin	31						4		
GMC-LV-70	26						4		
80 TBA Amioca starch	9						8		
ASP-400 clay	29	29.4						34	30
ASP-100 clay	29						16		
Titanium dioxide	43	5							
Antimony oxide	44	5							
TKPP	24	0.1							
Epoxy resin ERL-2795	1				13				
Water		16.5				81	44		
Comments		Fire retardant lagging compound.	Pad-ding.	Concrete bond coat.	Cure 320°F, 20 ft. Exc. water resistance PVAc/Epoxy.	Solvent and oil resistance-paper and paperboard.	For PVC1 backed wall-paper.	Parquet wood flooring.	Mastic composition.

ᵃ Parts by weight in all cases.
ᵇ 25% solution.
ᶜ 10% solution.

Acknowledgments

We wish to acknowledge the contribution of Mr. D. H. Fraser in supplying marketing information, Mr. L. J. Monaghan in supplying data on polyvinyl alcohol, Dr. R. N. Crozier and Dr. A. F. Price in reviewing, and Mrs. B. Uihlein in typing the manuscript.

Key to Product Suppliers

1. Union Carbide Plastics Co. Div., Union Carbide Corp.
2. Borden Chemical Co., Div. The Borden Co.
3. Colton Chemical Co., Div. Air Reduction Co., Inc.
4. Shawinigan Resins Corp.
5. Reichhold Chemicals, Inc.
6. Polyvinyl Chemicals, Inc., Affiliate of Stahl Finish Co.
7. Electrochemicals Dept., E. I. du Pont de Nemours & Co., Inc.
8. B. F. Goodrich Chemical Co. Div., The B. F. Goodrich Co.
9. Stein Hall and Co., Inc.
10. Dewey and Almy Chemical Div., W. R. Grace and Co.
11. Celanese Chemical Company Division, Celanese Corporation of America
12. National Starch and Chemical Corp.
13. Shawinigan Chemicals, Ltd., Canada
14. Revertex, Ltd., England
15. Scott Bader and Company, Ltd., England
16. Vinyl Products, Ltd. England
17. Societa Edison, Italy
18. Societa Rhodiatoce, Italy
19. Compagnie Rousselot
20. Societe Rhone-Poulenc
21. Farbewerke Hoechst, AG
22. Wacker-Chemie, GMBH
23. Monsanto Chemicals (Australia) Ltd.
24. Monsanto Chemical Company
25. Tennesee Products and Chemicals Corp.
26. Hercules Powder Co., Inc.
27. A. E. Staley Manufacturing Co.
28. Corn Products Refining Co.
29. Minerals and Chemicals Corporation of America
30. J. M. Huber Corp.
31. Allied Chemical Corp.
32. Commercial Solvents Corp.
33. Atlas Powder Co.
34. Shell Chemical Corp.
35. Dow Chemical Co.
36. Baker Castor Oil Co.
37. American Cyanamid Co.
38. American-Marietta Co.
39. Neville Chemicals Co.
40. Hostawax Co.
41. Glyco Products, Inc.
42. Cambridge Industries
43. Titanium Pigments Corp.
44. Metal and Thermit Corp.

Key to Monomer Suppliers

1. Union Carbide Chemicals Co. Div., Union Carbide Corp.
2. Air Reduction Chemical Co. Div., Air Reduction Co., Inc.
3. Electrochemicals Dept., E. I. du Pont de Nemours & Co., Inc.
4. Celanese Chemical Co. Div., Celanese Corporation of America
5. Shawinigan Resins Corp.
6. Pacific Carbide Chemicals Co.

References

1. Zahrndt, H. J., *Am. Paint J.,* **43,** (7-A), 30–32 (Oct. 28, 1958).
2. German Patent 271,381 (1912).
3. German Patents 582,544 (1930); 604,640 (1933); 636,212 (1934); 637,257 (1935); 638,003 (1953).
4. Morrison, G. O., and Shaw, T. P. G., *Trans. Electrochem. Soc., 63,* 425 (1933).
5. German Patents 403,784 (1921); 485,271 (1927).
6. Ushakov, S. N., and Feinstein, J. M., *Ind Eng. Chem.,* **26,** 561 (1934).
7. U. S. Patent 2,425,389 (1947).
8. *Vinyl Acetate Monomer,* Air Reduction Chemical Co., New York, N. Y.
9. *Vinyl Acetate Monomer,* Celanese Corporation of America, New York, N. Y.
10. *"Niacet" Vinyl Acetate Monomer,* Union Carbide Chemicals Co., New York, N. Y.
11. *Vinyl Acetate,* Shawinigan Chemicals Limited.
12. Kirk-Othmer, "Encyclopedia of Chemical Technology," Vol. 14, pp. 686–722, New York, Interscience Encyclopedia, Inc., 1955.
13. Horn, O., *Chemistry and Industry (British),* 1748–1755, (Dec. 1955).
14. DeBell, J. M., Goggin, W. C., and Gloor, W. E., "German Plastics Practice," Hazardville, Conn., DeBell & Richardson, 1948.
15. Dunlop, R. D., and Reese, F. E., *Ind. Eng. Chem.,* **40,** 654–60 (1948).
16. Schildknecht, C. E., "Vinyl and Related Polymers," New York John Wiley & Sons, Inc., 1952.
17. Staudinger, Frey and Starck, *Berichte,* **60B,** 1782–92 (1927).
18. Blaikie and Crozier, *Ind. Eng. Chem.,* **28,** 1155 (1936).
19. German Patent 281,687 (1913).
20. U. S. Patent 1,241,738 (1918).
21. U. S. Patent 1,872,834 (1932).
22. Canadian Patents 288,639–44 and 313,027.
23. U. S. Patents 1,725,362 (1929); 1,746,615 (1930); 1,746,665 (1930); 2,007,557 (1935).
24. Schildknecht, C. E., "Polymer Processes," New York, Interscience Publishers, Inc., 1956.
25. FIAT Final Report 1108 (1947).
26. U. S. Patent 2,800,463 (1957).
27. U. S. Patent 2,733,995 (1956).
28. German Patents 727,955 (1934) and 746,788 (1937).

29. U. S. Patents 2,228,270 (1941); 2,263,598 (1941); 2,317,725 (1943) and 2,047,398 (1936).
30. U. S. Patent 2,816,877 (1957).
31. U. S. Patent 2,424,110 (1947).
32. U. S. Patent 2,478,431 (1949).
33. Canadian Patent 265,172 (1926).
34. German Patent 450,286 (1924).
35. U. S. Patent 1,672,157 (1928).
36. Wheeler, O. L., and Crozier, R. N., *J. Polymer Sci.,* **8,** 409 and **9,** 157 (1952).
37. "Elvacet" Polyvinyl Acetate Emulsions, Electrochemicals Department, E. I. du Pont de Nemours & Co., Inc.
38. Kopyscinski, W., Herman, S. C., and Norris, F. H., *Adhesives Age,* **3,** (1), 31–36 (May 1960).
39. Nichipor, A. E., *Adhesives Age,* **1,** (3), 16–20 (Dec. 1958).
40. Miller, H., *Adhesives Age,* **2,** (3), 37–39 (Mar. 1959).
41. Butts, G. T., *Adhesives Age,* **2,** (10), 20–24 (Oct. 1959).
42. Larsen, P. H., *Adhesives Age,* **3,** (10), 34–36 (Oct. 1960).
43. Bird, V., *Adhesives Age,* **3,** (11), 27, (Nov. 1960).
44. *Adhesives Age,* **4,** (2), 38–39 (Feb. 1961).
45. Reed, H. B., *Adhesives Age,* **4,** (3), 41 (Mar. 1961).
46. Whitney, W., and Herman, S. C., *Adhesives Age,* **3,** (1), (Jan. 1960).
47. Dupre, A., *Brit. Plastics,* 89–98 (Feb. 1950).
48. FIAT Final Report 1102 (1947).
49. French, D. M., *J. Polymer Sci.,* **32,** 395–411 (1958).
50. O'Donnell, J. T., and Mesrobian, R. B., *J. Polymer Sci.,* **28,** 171–177 (1958).
51. Priest, W. J., *J. Phys. Chem.,* **56,** 1077–1082 (1952).
52. Warson, H., *Paint Technol. (British),* **24,** 19–27 (1960).
53. Mills, J. A., *Brit. Plastics* (Dec. 1955).
54. Olson, W. Z., and Blomquist, R. F., *Forest Products J.,* **5,** 219–226, (Aug. 1955).
55. Blomquist, R. F., *Forest Products J.,* **9,** 59–67 (Feb. 1959).
56. Grouse, D., *Forest Products J.,* **7,** 163–167 (May 1957).
57. *Modern Plastics* (Sept. 1953).
58. Weitz. P., *Paper, Film and Foil Converter,* 25–29 (Jan. 1960).
59. Shapiro, L., *TAPPI,* **40,** 387–396 (1957).
60. Andrews, W. J., *et. al., TAPPI,* **40,** 744–749 (1957).
61. *Paper Ind.,* 545–546 (Nov. 1959).
62. Coker, J. N., *Ind. Eng. Chem.,* **49,** 382–385 (1957).

Polyvinyl Acetal Adhesives

Edward Lavin and James A. Snelgrove

Shawinigan Resins Corporation
Springfield, Massachusetts

Polyvinyl acetal resins depend for most applications on their excellent adhesive characteristics to a variety of surfaces. They are used in many structural adhesive applications involving metal, glass and paper as well as in hot-melt adhesives for paper, metal foil and plastic films. Excellent adhesion to glass makes polyvinyl butyral the almost universal interlayer for safety glass. As coatings, they serve admirably in wire enamels, wash primers, metal coatings, textile coatings, etc. In each use, their excellent adhesive characteristics are a prime consideration.

In the following pages, the chemistry of their preparation, their reactions, physical properties and compatibilities, the commercial types available, etc., are summarized prior to the discussions of their use in adhesives and coatings.

CHEMISTRY

Acetals are formed by the well-known reaction of one molecule of aldehyde and two molecules of alcohol:

$$R—CHO + 2R'OH \longrightarrow$$
Aldehyde   Alcohol
$$R—CH—(OR')_2 + H_2O$$
Acetal

Polyvinyl acetals are prepared from aldehydes and polyvinyl alcohol. The polyvinyl alcohol is in turn prepared from polyvinyl acetate by hydrolysis. Since polyvinyl acetate is made by the polymerization of vinyl acetate monomer, the precursor of the polyvinyl acetals is vinyl acetate monomer. It would be easier to start with vinyl

alcohol monomer and polymerize to polyvinyl alcohol to avoid the hydrolysis step. Unfortunately, this is not possible because vinyl alcohol monomer does not exist as such. It is a tautomer of acetaldehyde with the equilibrium in favor of the acetaldehyde. The polyvinyl alcohols which are prepared from polyvinyl acetate are high molecular weight resins containing varying percentages of hydroxyl and acetate groups, i.e.,

$$-CH_2—CH—CH_2—CH—CH_2—CH—$$
$$\quad\quad\ \ OH \quad\quad\quad OH \quad\quad\quad OAc$$

The conditions of the acetal reaction and the concentration of the particular aldehyde and polyvinyl alcohol used are closely controlled to form polymers containing predetermined proportions of acetal groups, hydroxyl groups and acetate groups. The final products may be represented by the following stylized structure:

PV Acetal (A)   *PV Alcohol* (B)   *PV Acetate* (C)

The A, B, and C moieties are randomly distributed along the molecule. The polyvinyl acetal is a cyclic acetal because the hydroxyl groups are attached to the same chain; moreover the polyvinyl acetals may also be crosslinked by heating or with a trace of mineral acid. Crosslinking in this case is thought to be caused by transacetalization but it may also involve more complex mechanisms such as a reaction between acetate or hydroxyl groups on adjacent chains.[1]

Polyvinyl acetal films are characterized by high resistance to aliphatic hydrocarbons, mineral, animal and vegetable oils with the exception of castor and blown oils. They withstand strong alkalies but are subject to some attack by acids; however when employed as components of cured adhesives or coatings, their stability to acids as well as solvents and other chemicals is improved greatly. The polyvinyl acetals will withstand heating up to 100°C for prolonged periods without discoloration.

Many applications for the polyvinyl acetal resins involve curing with a thermosetting resin in order to obtain the balance of properties desired. In general, any chemical reagent or resinous material which reacts with secondary hydroxyl groups will react with the acetals. The following reactions illustrate the probable mechanism of crosslinking polyvinyl acetals with various materials. Of course, the properties vary greatly with the type and amount of crosslinking agent used.

The reaction of an aldehyde with polyvinyl alcohol to form acetal rings involves two vinyl alcohol units per aldehyde molecule. Since information in terms of molar quantities is often desired for systems where crosslinking reactions are involved, the necessary calculations are given below.

If A and B = weight per cents of polyvinyl acetate and polyvinyl alcohol, respectively, then the number of acetal units per hundred vinyl units in the chain backbone is given by

$$\frac{189\,(100-A-B)}{0.044A\,(x-86) + 0.086B\,(x-44) + 378}$$

where x is half the gram molecular weight of the repeating acetal unit, i.e., one half of

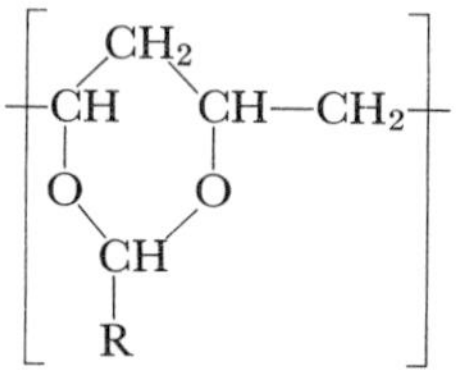

The number of grams of resin containing 1 g mole of this unit is given by

$$\frac{2x}{1 - .01\,(A + B)}$$

(1) *Reaction with Isocyanates*

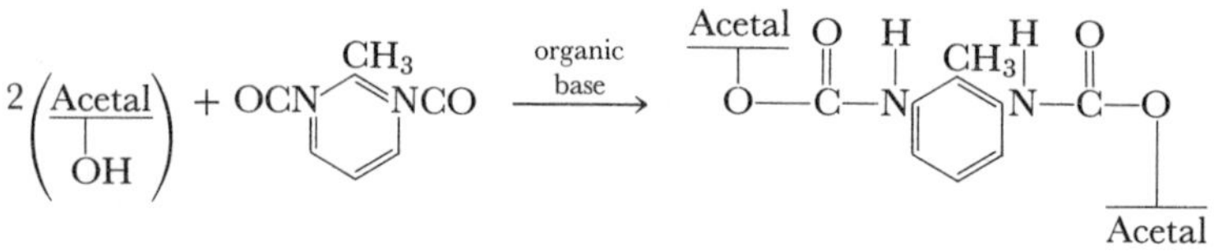

(2) *Reaction with Phenolics*

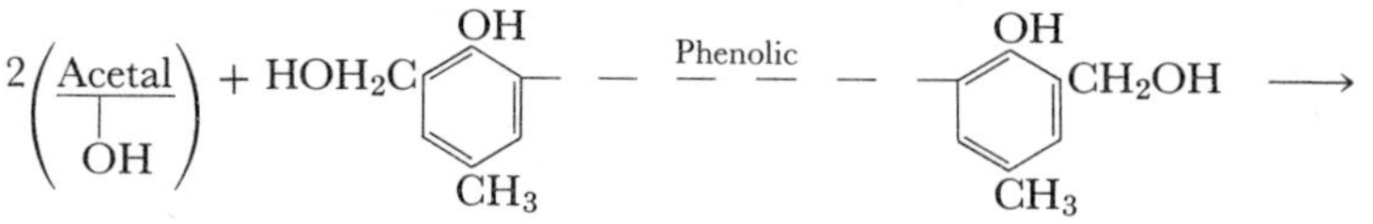

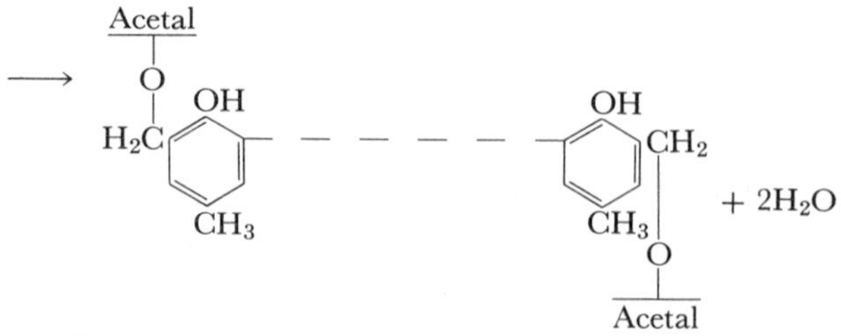

(3) *Reaction with Dialdehydes*

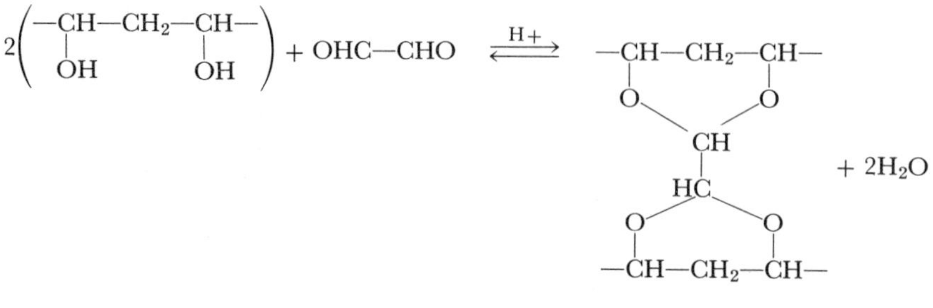

(4) *Reaction with Melamines*

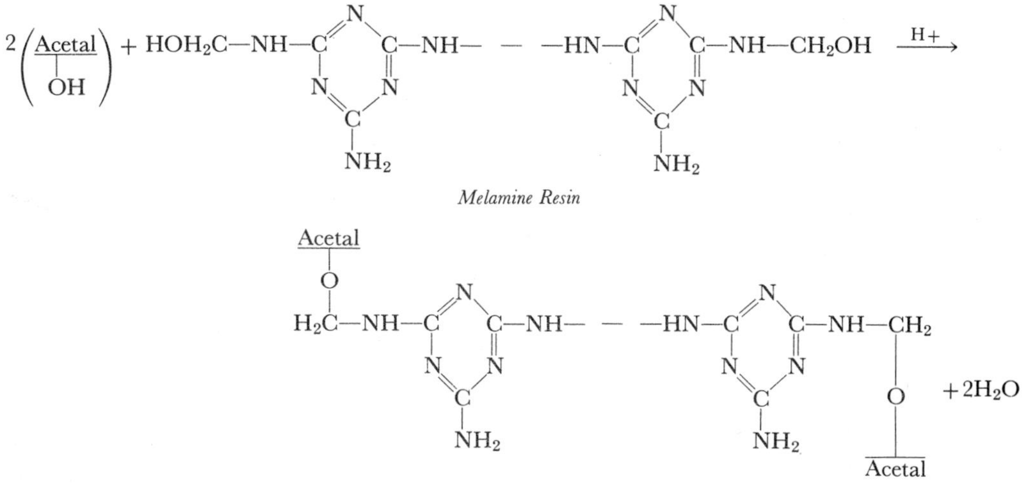

$$2\left(\overset{\text{Acetal}}{\underset{\text{OH}}{|}}\right) + \text{HOH}_2\text{C—NH—C} \cdots \text{C—NH— — —HN—C} \cdots \text{C—NH—CH}_2\text{OH} \xrightarrow{\ H+\ }$$

Melamine Resin

$$+ 2\text{H}_2\text{O}$$

(5) *Reaction with Epoxies (Anhydride Cure)*

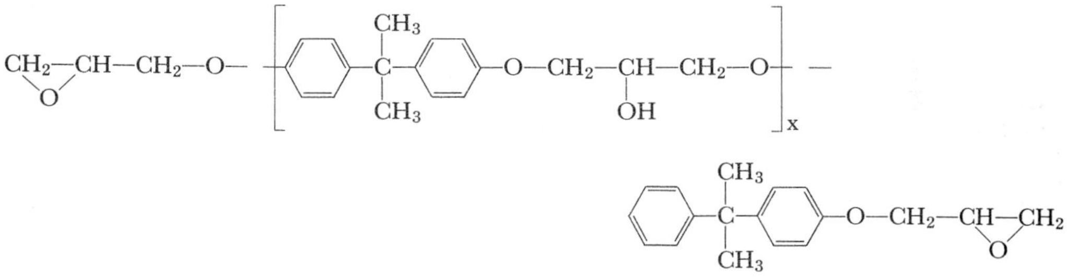

Typical Epoxy Resin

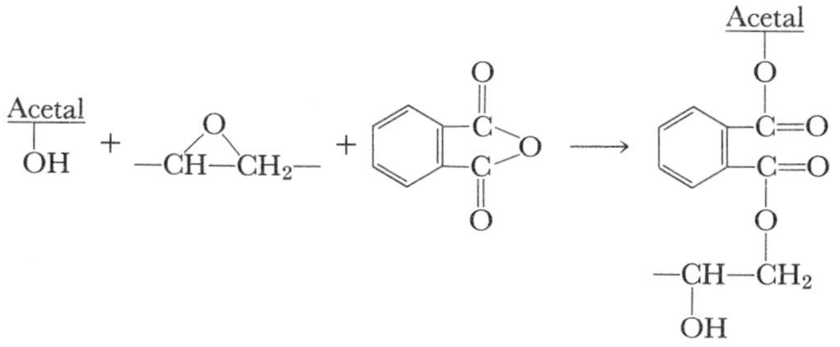

Similarly the numbers of vinyl alcohol and vinyl acetate units per hundred chain vinyl units are, respectively

$$\frac{8.6Bx}{0.044A\,(x-86)+0.086B\,(x-44)+378},\ \text{and}$$

$$\frac{4.4Ax}{0.044A\,(x-86)+0.086B\,(x-44)+378}$$

while the numbers of grams of resin containing respectively 1 g mole of hydroxyl and acetate groups are given by

$$\frac{44}{0.01B}\quad\text{and}\quad\frac{86}{0.01A}$$

As an illustration of this type of calculation, consider the reaction of polyvinyl formal "Formvar" 15/95E and tolylene diisocyanate. The reaction, illustrated schematically on page 384, involves the formation of urethane links between the isocyanate groups and the hydroxyls of the polyvinyl formal. Suppose we wish to find that weight of the polyvinyl formal which is equivalent to 1 g mole of the diisocyanate (174 g). Since "Formvar" 15/95E contains 6 per cent by weight of polyvinyl alcohol, 1 g mole of hydroxyl groups is contained in 44/.06 = 733 g. Since tolylene diisocyanate is difunctional, 2 × 733 or 1466 g of "Formvar" 15/95E is equivalent to 174 g of the diisocyanate.

If we wish to react only a specified number of hydroxyls per resin chain, e.g., 2 we proceed as follows. The number of hydroxyl groups per hundred vinyl units is given for "Formvar" 15/95E by

$$\frac{8.6 \times 6 \times 50}{0.044 \times 12(50-86) + .086 \times 6\,(50-44) + 378}$$

or 7.1. The weight average degree of polymerization from Table 1 is 650; thus there are, on the average, 46 hydroxyl groups per chain. We therefore require only $2/46 \times 174$ or 7.6 g of tolylene diisocyanate per 1466 g of "Formvar" 15/95E to react 2 hydroxyls per chain.

TYPES

Since the condensation of polyvinyl alcohol with aldehydes is a general reaction, the chemical and patent literature contains many examples.[2-17] Aliphatic and aromatic compounds as well as mixtures have been used. Commercial development, however, has been limited to the reaction products of formaldehyde, acetaldehyde and *n*-butyraldehyde with polyvinyl alcohol. Production of one or more of these products has been undertaken in Europe, Japan and Russia, but the bulk of the production is in North America.

Examples of some of the commercial resins

TABLE 1. PARTIAL LIST OF COMMERCIAL POLYVINYL ACETAL RESINS.

Trade-mark	Type	Manu-facturer	Vinyl Alcohol (Weight %)	Vinyl Acetate (Weight %)	Vinyl Acetal (Weight %)	Weight Av. Degree of Polymerization (approx.)*
Alvar 5/80	A	SC	5	28	67	300
Alvar 7/70	A	SC	5	40	55	350
Alvar 13/80	A	SC	5	28	67	600
Alvar 15/70	A	SC	5	40	55	650
Vinylite XYHL	B	UC	19	0.5	80.5	650
Vinylite XYSG	B	UC	19	0.5	80.5	2000
Butvar B-98	B	SR	19	1.5	79.5	500
Butvar B-90	B	SR	19	0.5	80.5	650
Butvar D510	B	SR	11	1.5	87.5	500
Butvar B-76	B	SR	11	1.5	87.5	750
Butvar D511	B	SR	11	1.5	87.5	3500
Butvar B-73	B	SR	19	1.5	79.5	1000
Butvar D509	B	SR	19	1.0	80.0	2000
Butvar B-72A	B	SR	19	1.5	79.5	3500
Mowital B-30H	B	H	18	2.5	79.5	500
Mowital B-30T	B	H	24	2.5	73.5	500
Mowital B-60H	B	H	18	1.5	80.5	1000
Mowital B-60T	B	H	24	1.5	74.5	1000
Pioloform BL-18	B	W	19	3	78	200
Pioloform BL-24	B	W	25	5	70	200
Pioloform BW	B	W	23	3	74	1000
Pioloform BS	B	W	23	3	74	2000
Formvar 7/70	F	SR	6	45	49	350
Formvar 7/95S	F	SR	8	12	80	350
Formvar 12/85	F	SR	6	26	68	550
Formvar 15/95S	F	SR	8	12	80	650
Formvar 15/95E	F	SR	6	12	82	650
Mowital F-40	F	H	6	13	81	650
Rhovinal FM	F	AI	11	8	81	350
Rhovinal FH	F	AI	6	12	82	650

Legend:

A = polyvinyl acetal.   SC = Shawinigan Chemicals Ltd. (Canada).
B = polyvinyl butyral.   SR = Shawinigan Resins Corp.
F = polyvinyl formal.   UC = Union Carbide Corp.
AI = Alsthom-Isolants.   W = Wacker-Chemie.
H = Fabwerke Hoechst A. G.

* = Shawinigan Resins Corporation unpublished data.

appear in Table 1; however the list is not intended to be complete. Wide variations in degree of polymerization, residual hydroxyl and ester content, as well as the nature of the substituent are available. The similarity between these resins and vinyl terpolymers can be discerned. By analogy with the work of Flory[18] on the removal of chlorine from polyvinyl chloride, it can be predicted that the residual hydroxyl content of polyvinyl acetal resins can never be reduced to zero in the acetalization reaction. Studies carried out in the authors' laboratories have confirmed this prediction.

PHYSICAL PROPERTIES OF POLYVINYL ACETAL RESINS

The properties of polyvinyl acetal resins depend chiefly on the types and amounts of functional groups present, and on the resin molecular weight.[19,20]

Tensile strengths vary from 6000 to 11,000 psi, increasing with molecular weight and as we go from butyral to acetal to formal. Elastic modulus values also increase in the same order, ranging from 3 to 7×10^5 psi. Elongation at yield is about 3 per cent for formals, 6 per cent for acetals and 9 per cent for butyrals. Specific gravity is between 1.1 and 1.2 for all the commercial polyvinyl acetals. Heat distortion temperatures range from 50°C for some of the polyvinyl butyrals of low molecular weight to approximately 90°C for the high molecular weight polyvinyl formals.

Solubility. In general the polyvinyl butyrals are soluble in alcohols, glycol ethers and certain mixtures of polar and nonpolar solvents. Polyvinyl formals are soluble in chlorinated hydrocarbons, dioxane, and mixtures of polar and nonpolar solvents; furthermore those types having the higher acetate contents are also soluble in glycol ethers, esters and ketones. Polyvinyl acetals have a wider range of solubility than either polyvinyl formals or butyrals. A representative list of solvents is shown in Table 2.

Viscosity. For a given type of polyvinyl acetal, the solution viscosity increases sharply with molecular weight. For a given molecular weight the viscosity of a polyvinyl formal is greater than that of a polyvinyl butyral in the usual alcohol-aromatic solvent blends. The viscosities in ethanol-toluene of several commercial resins are shown in Fig. 1.

Viscosities of polyvinyl butyral resin solutions in alcohol-aromatic solvent mixtures depend on the ratio of alcohol to aromatic. Viscosity curves for some commercial polyvinyl butyrals (see Fig. 2) show minima in the vicinity of 60 per cent alcohol to 40 per cent aromatic. Within the range of 40 to 60 per cent alcohol, the ratio of alcohol to aromatic solvent has no appreciable effect on polyvinyl formal or polyvinyl acetal solution viscosities.

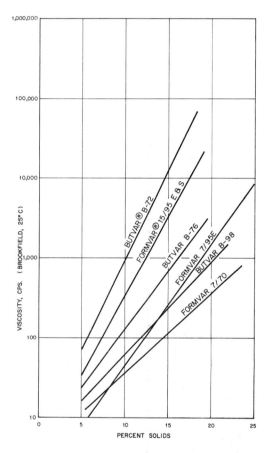

Fig. 1. Solution viscosities of some polyvinyl acetal resins in 40/60 ethyl alcohol (95%)/toluene (by weight).

For polyvinyl butyral formulations, methyl alcohol will tend to give lower viscosities than ethyl alcohol and therefore will permit the use of higher solids when used as a component of a solvent blend. However, when much more than 10 to 15 per cent methyl alcohol is used in a formulation for spray application, blushing probably will result.

Selection of a suitable solvent system involves a

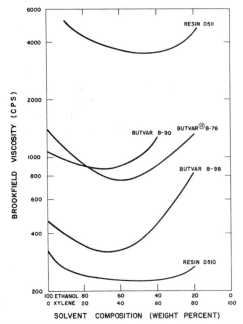

Fig. 2. Polyvinyl butyral solution viscosities in ethyl alcohol (95%)/xylene mixtures at 15% solids and 25°C.

number of factors. The end-use and the application technique used will necessitate consideration of solution viscosity, cobweb formation, blushing, evaporation rate and solvent release. In most cases, the choice of components of the solvent blend will involve compromises in at least some of these factors so that a desired combination of properties may be obtained.

The solvent blends in Table 3 are suggested for use with all grades of polyvinyl butyral and high acetate polyvinyl formal. They are useful as starting points in the development of solvent blends for the other types.

Plasticizers. Low temperature flexibility of adhesives, coatings, films, etc., of polyvinyl acetal resins may be improved and brittleness reduced by the incorporation of plasticizers, which may also be employed to reduce the viscosity of hot-melt formulations.

Many of the common phthalate, phosphate, glycolate and other ester types may be used. An excellent plasticizer for producing a flexible or elastomeric polyvinyl formal composition is "Santicizer" E-15. A representative list of plasticizers is shown in Table 4.

AQUEOUS POLYVINYL BUTYRAL DISPERSIONS

Although methods of producing dispersions of other polyvinyl acetal resins have been described

in the patent literature, only those containing polyvinyl butyral have been developed commercially.

These dispersions are usually produced by a mixer process somewhat similar to that used for making rubber latex from reclaimed stock.[29, 30] They are generally about 50 per cent solids and have a particle size below 1 micron. Plasticizer contents vary upward from zero, the usual maximum being 40 to 50 parts per hundred resin. Commercial types are anionic and have a pH range of about 8.5 to 10.5.

Films of polyvinyl butyral dispersions exhibit the toughness and transparency for which the resin is noted. Physical properties vary with plasticizer content. Unplasticized dispersions show tensile strengths of the order of 6000 to 7000 psi, while those containing 40 to 50 parts of plasticizer break at about 2000 psi. Elongations at break show a similar variation. If the plasticizer content is of the order of 20 parts per hundred and above, the films develop full strength properties when cast and dried at room temperature. If the plasticizer content is lower, it is necessary to dry the film above room temperature (preferably 40 to 50°C) to achieve continuity and non-redispersibility.

The plasticizer content of polyvinyl butyral dispersions can be increased by emulsifying the required amount of plasticizer in water and adding it to the dispersion with gentle agitation. An emulsifying agent which is anionic or nonionic must be used with the commercial dispersions now available to avoid coagulation of the dispersion. The mixed emulsion should be allowed to stand overnight to achieve uniform plasticization.

The following types of polyvinyl butyral dispersions are available commercially from Shawinigan Resins Coporation.

Name	Resin M. W.	Plasticizer Content (parts per hundred resin)	Total Solids (%)
"Butvar" dispersion Br	High	40	50
Resin D-564	High	5	50
Resin D-565	Low	0	40
Resin D-566	High	20	50

The low adhesion of films cast from most polyvinyl butyral dispersions on impervious surfaces such as glass, metal, etc., together with their toughness and abrasion resistance, have led to their use as temporary, strippable protective coatings.[31] Formulated strip coatings are available from several manufacturers.

TABLE 2. SOLVENTS FOR POLYVINYL ACETAL RESINS.

	Polyvinyl Formal			Polyvinyl Butyral		Polyvinyl Acetal
	Low Acetate	Medium Acetate	High Acetate	Low Hydroxyl	High Hydroxyl	
Acetic acid (glacial)	S	S	S	S	S	S
Acetone	I	I	S	S	I	S
n-Butanol	I	I	I	S	S	S
Butyl acetate	I	I	I	S	I	S
Carbon tetrachloride	I	I	I	I	I	I
Cresylic acid	S	S	S	S	S	S
Cyclohexanone	I	S	S	S	S	S
Diacetone alcohol	I	S	S	S	S	S
Diisobutyl ketone	I	I	I	S	I	I
Dioxane	S	S	S	S	S	S
Ethanol, 95%	I	I	I	S	S	S
Ethyl acetate, 99%	I	I	S	S	I	S
Ethyl acetate, 85%	I	I	S	S	S	S
Ethyl "Cellosolve"	I	I	S	S	S	S
Ethylene chloride	S	S	S	S	S	S
Hexane	I	I	I	I	I	I
Isopropanol, 95%	I	I	I	S	S	S
Methyl acetate	I	I	S	S	S	S
Methanol	I	I	I	I	S	S
Methyl "Cellosolve"	I	S	S	S	S	S
Methyl "Cellosolve" acetate	I	S	S	S	I	S
Methylbutynol	S	S	S	S	S	S
Methylpentynol	S	S	S	S	S	S
Methylethyl ketone	I	I	S	S	I	S
Methylisobutyl ketone	I	I	I	S	I	S
Nitropropane	I	S	S	I	I	
Toluene	I	I	I	S	I	I
Toluene-ethyl alcohol (60:40 by weight)	S	S	S	S	S	S
Xylene	I	I	I	I	I	I
Xylene-n-butanol (60:40 by weight)	I	I	S	S	S	S

Key: S = Completely soluble.
      I = Insoluble or not completely soluble.

TABLE 3. SUGGESTED SOLVENT BLENDS.

	A %	B %	C %	D %
Diacetone alcohol*	22.5	20.0	15.0	—
n-Butanol	22.5	20.0	15.0	—
Ethanol, 95%	10.0	20.0	20.0	55.0
Xylene	45.0	40.0	30.0	—
Toluene	—	—	20.0	45.0
	100.0	100.0	100.0	100.0
Relative viscosity	High	Medium	Low	Low
Relative evaporation rate	Slow	Medium	Medium	Very fast
Application technique	Spray	Dip, roll	Dip, roll	Brush
Drying technique	Bake	Bake	Bake	Air-dry

* "Cellosolve" may be partially substituted here to give lower viscosity.

TABLE 4. PLASTICIZERS FOR POLYVINYL ACETAL RESINS.

Type	Name or Trade-mark	Type	Name or Trade-mark
(A) Polyvinyl Formal Resins			
Phthalate	Diphenyl phthalate	Pelargonate	"Plastolein" 9055
	Diethyl phthalate	Furfuryloleate	"Plastolein" 9250
	"Methox"	Glycolate	"Santicizer" B-16
	"Santicizer" 160		"Santicizer" E-15
	Dicyclohexyl phthalate		"Santicizer" M-17
Phosphate	"Santicizer" 141	Epoxidized	
	Triphenyl phosphate	soybean oil	"Admex" 710
	Tricresyl phosphate	Polyester	"Resoflex" R-296
	Tributyl phosphate	Adipate	"Adipol" BCA 4720
Polyester	"Paraplex" G-20		"Plastolein" 9720
Dibenzoate	"Flexol" 2GB		"Pycal" 29
Chlorinated			"Pycal" 40
naphthalene	"Halowax" 1014		"Pycal" 94
(B) Polyvinyl Butyral Resins			
Glycol	"Pycal" 94	Glycol	
Glyceryl monooleate		derivatives	"Flexol" 3GH
Petroleum	"Conoco" H-300	Dibutyl sebacate	
Phosphate	"Santicizer" 141	Raw castor oil	
	"Flexol" TOF	Process caster	
	Tricresyl phosphate	oil	K Castor
Dibutyl phthalate			No. 15 Castor
Polyester	"Paraplex" RG-8		No. 30 Castor
	"Resoflex" R-296		No. 40 Castor
Ricinoleate	"Flexricin" P-3		No. 300 Castor
Rosin derivatives	"Hercolyn"	Blown linseed oil	Diamond K linseed
(C) Polyvinyl Acetal Resins			
Phosphate	Triphenyl phosphate		
	Tricresyl phosphate		
	Tributyl phosphate		
	"Santicizer" 141		
Phthalate	Diphenyl phthalate		
	Diethyl phthalate	(Note: The criterion used to determine plasticizer	
	Dibutyl phthalate	compatibility was 50 parts plasticizer to 100 parts	
	Dicyclohexyl phthalate	resin. In many cases the plasticizer will be found	
Dibutyl sebacate		compatible in higher concentrations.)	
Butyl ricinoleate			
Triacetin			

Although most polyvinyl butyral dispersions illustrate low adhesion to impervious surfaces such as glass and metal, Resin D-566 adheres strongly when the film is cured at elevated temperatures. This enables impervious surfaces to be given permanent, tough, abrasion-resistant coatings from a aqueous system. Reactive thermosetting resins such as water-soluble or dispersible phenolics can be incorporated.

Polyvinyl butyral dispersions are widely utilized in the textile industry to impart increased abrasion resistance, durability, strength and slippage control, and reduced color crocking. Nylon webbing for parachute harnesses and seat belts is thus given improved abrasion resistance.

STRUCTURAL ADHESIVES

An adhesive system based on a polyvinyl formal-phenolic combination was the first synthetic resin adhesive used in the structural bonding of metals.[21] Since that time numerous commercial adhesives combining a polyvinyl acetal resin with a phenolic in a thermosetting system have appeared.[22] In addition, combinations of

TABLE 5. COMPATIBILITY* OF POLYVINYL ACETALS WITH VARIOUS RESINS.

Name or Trade-mark	Polyvinyl Butyral		Polyvinyl Formal			Polyvinyl Acetal
	Low OH	High OH	High Acetate	Medium Acetate	Low Acetate	
Acrylate	I	I	I	I	I	I
Alkyd						
"Rezyl" 807-1	P	P	P	P	P	—
"Duraplex" C-49	P	P	P	P	P	—
"Beckosol" 1334-50EL	P	P	P	P	P	—
Alpha-pinene						
Newport V-40	C	C	C	C	C	C
Cellulose						
Cellulose acetate	I	I	I	I	I	I
Cellulose acetate butyrate	P	P	P	P	P	—
Cellulose, ethyl	P	P	I	I	I	I
Cellulose, nitro	P	P	I	I	C	C
Chlorinated rubber	I	I	I	I	I	—
Coumarone-Indene	I	I	P	P	P	—
Epoxy						
"Epi Rez" 540	C	C	C	C	C	C
"Epon" 1001, 1007	C	C	C	C	C	C
"Araldite"	P	P	P	P	P	—
Fossil						
Dammar	C	C	I	I	I	C
Isocyanate						
"Mondur" S	C	C	C	C	C	C
Ketone formaldehyde						
"Advaresin" KF	P	P	P	P	P	—
Melamine formaldehyde						
"Resimene" 881	P	P	I	P	P	—
Phenolic, unmodified						
"Amberol" ST-137	C	C	I	—	—	—
BKR-2620	C	C	P	P	P	—
BV-1600	C	C	I	—	—	—
BV-2710	P	P	C	C	C	C
GE-75-108	C	C	C	C	C	C
"Resinox" P-97	C	C	C	C	C	C
Rosin derivatives						
"Pentalyn" H	P	P	I	—	—	—
"Staybelite" ester 10	P	P	I	—	—	—
"Vinsol"	C	C	C	C	C	C
Shellac	C	C	I	I	I	P
Silicone						
Resin 840	P	P	I	I	I	—
Sulfonamide						
"Santolite" MHP	P	P	P	—	—	C
Urea formaldehyde						
"Uformite" F-240	P	P	I	P	P	—
Vinyl chloride copolymer						
VAGH	P	I	P	I	I	—

Key: C–Compatible in all proportions; P–Partially compatible; I–Incompatible.
  * Refers to film compatibility providing mutual solvents are used.

these resins with other reactive thermosetting resins such as epoxies yield adhesives with unique properties.[23-25] Although the early development of structural adhesives based on polyvinyl acetals was in the aircraft industry, similar formulations satisfy many other needs today. Examples are honeycomb construction, brake linings, printed circuits, and curtain walls. Proper balancing of the formulation with respect to both amount and type of polyvinyl acetal resin can produce adhesives which are admirably suited to any of the above applications.

Structural adhesives based on polyvinyl acetal resins can be applied as a solution, an unsupported film, a supported film on paper or cloth, or as a mixture of liquid and solid.

Formulations

Many commercial structural adhesives are based on combinations of polyvinyl acetals and thermosetting resins, usually phenolics. A list of some manufacturers of adhesives of this type is given in Table 6.

TABLE 6. SOME MANUFACTURERS OF STRUCTURAL ADHESIVES CONTAINING POLYVINYL ACETAL RESINS.

Adhesives Engineering Co.
Bloomingdale Rubber Co.
Ciba, Inc.
Cycleweld Cement Products Div.
General Veneer Mfg. Co.
Lebec Chemical Corp.
Minnesota Mining & Mfg.
Narmco Adhesives & Plastics Co., Inc.
Palmer Products, Inc.
Permafuse Corp.
Permalastic Products
Reichhold Chemicals, Inc.
Rubber & Asbestos Corp.
Swedlow Plastics Co.

Wide variations in performance are possible by varying the formulations of polyvinyl acetal-phenolic adhesives.[26] Acetal-phenolic ratios of from 10:1 to 10:20 have been used. In Fig. 3 the

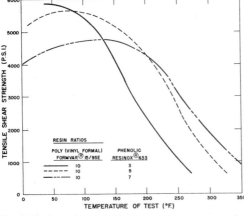

Fig. 3. Variation in tensile shear—temperature properties of aluminum lap shear samples bonded with polyvinyl formal—phenolic adhesives, as a function of resin ratio. (Cured 1 hour at 350°F.)

effect of this ratio on the variation in tensile shear strength of aluminum samples bonded with a polyvinyl formal phenolic adhesive is shown. The room temperature tensile strength of the cured adhesive is. at a maximum at about 10 polyvinyl acetal to 4 phenolic. If the phenolic content is higher, the adhesive crosslinks more completely, and the resultant shrinkage during cure induces strains which lower the tensile strength. This same increase in crosslinking does, however, increase the shear strength at elevated temperature. The increased flexibility imparted by the polyvinyl acetal tends to increase the peel strength of the bond at high polyvinyl acetal-phenolic ratios.

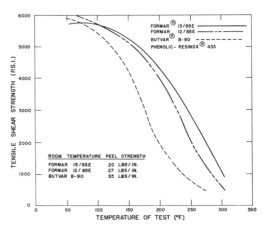

Fig. 4. Shear and peel strength of aluminum bonded with polyvinyl acetal—phenolic adhesives, showing the effect of type of polyvinyl acetal resin. (Polyvinyl acetal/phenolic ratio 2/1; cure at 1 hr at 330°F.)

Another way to affect the performance of a polyvinyl acetal-phenolic adhesive is to vary the type of acetal resin. In general, polyvinyl formal-phenolic adhesives have better high temperature shear properties but lower peel strength than do polyvinyl butyral-phenolic types. However, as shown in Fig. 4, the use of a polyvinyl formal with about 25 weight per cent residual polyvinyl acetate groups allows retention of most of the high temperature properties of an adhesive based on a polyvinyl formal with about 10 weight per cent residual polyvinyl acetate groups, while giving a peel strength approaching that of a polyvinyl butyral-phenolic adhesive. Higher molecular weight polyvinyl acetal resins generally produce adhesives with higher shear strengths but lower peel strengths.

Polyvinyl butyral and polyvinyl formal resins are compatible with many epoxy resins and can confer such improvements on epoxy-based systems as increased impact resistance, peel strength, and room temperature shear strength. Properly formulated, only slight high-temperature strength losses are incurred.[23] In epoxy systems, as in phenolic systems, a polyvinyl acetal resin can serve as coreactant, flexibilizer, and flow control agent.

Examples of adhesive formulations combining polyvinyl acetal resins with epoxy-phenolic blends have been given.[25] A one-package solution system is:

	parts
Polyvinyl butyral	100
Phenolic resin	150
Epoxy resin	100
Aluminum powder	200
Isopropyl acetate	200
95% isopropyl alcohol	100

The polyvinyl butyral type used in this formulation contains 18 to 20 per cent vinyl alcohol groups. The phenolic and epoxy resins used in this and the following examples are described in detail in reference 25.

A two-package polyvinyl acetal-epoxy-phenolic system[25] involves coating the substrate with an epoxy-phenolic solution, sprinkling polyvinyl formal powder onto the wet surface, and shaking off the excess powder. The solution used is:

	parts
Epoxy resin	100
Phenolic resin	100
Methylethyl ketone	200

The addition of small amounts of a compatible plasticizer to an adhesive system combining a polyvinyl acetal resin with a thermosetting resin increases the flexibility and impact resistance of the bond with only slight sacrifice in high temperature shear. This increased flexibility is most evident when peeling thick adherends and at high peeling speeds. The tack or heat seal temperature of the uncured adhesive is also appreciably lowered by the addition of plasticizer. When necessary the heat-seal temperature of the uncured formulation may be lowered to room temperature while maintaining a cured room-temperature shear bond strength of more than 1000 psi. Fillers and extenders, of course, can also be used.

The solubility characteristics of the various polyvinyl acetal resins have been given in Table 2. Typical solvent systems for polyvinyl acetal-phenolic structural adhesives are shown below. In general, for brushing, polyvinyl acetal solids contents of 10 to 15 per cent are used, while spray formulations are 5 to 10 per cent polyvinyl acetal solids. Most applications require a dry adhesive film of 3 to 10 mils.

SOLVENTS FOR POLYVINYL
ACETAL-PHENOLIC ADHESIVES

(1) Polyvinyl Butyral	% wt.
(for brushing)	
95% ethyl alcohol	60
Toluene	40
(2) Polyvinyl Formal	% wt.
(for brushing)	
Ethylene chloride	50
Methylethyl ketone	25
95% ethyl alcohol	25
(3) Polyvinyl Formal	% wt.
(for spraying)	
Diacetone alcohol	40
Ethylene chloride	35
"Cellosolve" acetate	25

The choice of solvents is important also for proper drying and filming characteristics in solution adhesives. A small amount of residual solvent can greatly affect the final bond strengths; however the solvent should not be so volatile that blushing occurs.

Bonding

For high strength bonds, substrate cleaning is important. Usually the removal of surface contamination such as oil, film, dust, etc. is sufficient. Such cleaning normally is achieved by solvent or detergent wash; however for highest strength bonds, chemical surface preparation is employed. The following metals require the preparation noted: aluminum alloys—acid oxidation; copper—alkaline oxidation; and steel—a pickling bath to remove oxide scale.[27, 28]

Care should be taken to avoid touching the cleaned panels with the hands or exposing them to any contaminated atmosphere. The adhesive should be applied to the cleaned surface as soon as possible.

A dry glue line of from 3 to 10 mils has been found quite satisfactory. With solvent systems, this thickness usually can be achieved with two to four brushed coats of adhesive on each adherend. With very thin glue lines, it is imperative that even pressure be applied to the laminate during cure in order that consistent bonds be obtained. Thicker glue lines are able to flow more and absorb unequal curing pressures.

The curing schedule of a polyvinyl acetal-phenolic adhesive is determined both by the curing rate of the phenolic used and by the bond qualities desired. For most purposes, a cure temperature of about 325°F for 15 to 30 min is suitable. Certain high strength aircraft uses require 1 or 2 hr at 350°F. The minimum temperature for most polyvinyl acetal-phenolic adhesives is about 280°F. Lowering the time and/or temperature of cure usually increases the room-temperature peel strength of a bond but decreases its high temperature shear strength. Within the limits of resin degradation, the high temperature strength of a polyvinyl acetal-phenolic adhesive increases as the bond is held at an elevated temperature. This effect is shown in Fig. 5. In combinations with epoxies, the cure schedule is determined by the epoxy formulation.

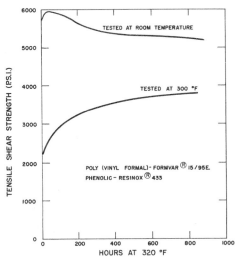

Fig. 5. Variation in tensile shear strength of aluminum lap shear specimens as a function of aging at 320°F. for a polyvinyl formal—phenolic (2/1) adhesive.

General

The quality of a structural bond for a particular application is usually described in terms of its shear strength, peel strength, creep properties, fatigue and environmental resistance. In aircraft applications, high temperature shear strength, fatigue resistance, creep, oil and gasoline resistance are most important. The applicable tests and specifications are given in MIL-A-5090B, MIL-A-8431 and MIL-A-25463. Polyvinyl acetal-phenolic adhesives are now qualified under MIL-A-5090B and pass many of the tests of MIL-A-8431 Type I and MIL-A-25463 Type II (300°F).

For printed circuits, the most important qualifications are dielectric properties, peel strength and blister resistance. The cure conditions are generally determined by the cure cycle of the board which is used as substrate, but 1000 psi pressure and 300 to 350°F for 20 min. to 1 hr are common conditions. Peel strengths of the order of

10 lb per in. width are required, and the bond must not blister when immersed in molden solder at about 500°F for 5 to 15 sec. Polyvinyl acetal adhesives of the type shown on p. 264 (the one-package system) perform well under these conditions. Test methods have been standardized by the National Electrical Manufacturers' Association and the American Society for Testing Materials.

For architectural use, high peel strength and long time resistance to dead load and extremes of atmospheric environment are paramount requirements. Little standardization of tests or specifications has occurred in this new field to date, but adhesives based on polyvinyl acetals are performing well.

HOT-MELT ADHESIVES

This type of formulation is characterized by a solid form at room temperature and the ability to become fluid and tacky on heating. Polyvinyl butyral resins, when properly compounded, form excellent hot-melt adhesives providing a tough, clear film with good adhesive strength.

A recent surge of interest has been evident in the hot-melt field. For many adhesive applications, hot-melt formulations are more advantageous than solution or emulsion types. For example, no solvent release problems are present, they are easy to handle below their melt temperature, they give quick initial tack yet little shrinkage on hardening and are often more economical. These properties adapt them particularly to those applications where mass-production techniques are used. A good example is packaging, where the coating or adhesive must set quickly enough to permit economic rates. Other areas of use are coatings for paper, metal foil, plastic film, fresh meat and adhesives for labels, bookbinding, wax paper bags, metal foil, etc.

Most hot-melt formulations employing polyvinyl butyral have a working range of about 125 to 150°C. The necessary additives to the base resin are plasticizers, waxes, fluxing-extending resins, and stabilizers. Pigments, dyes and fillers may also, of course, be added. Suitable plasticizers for polyvinyl butyral resins are listed in Table 4. The choice of wax is dictated by the requirements of the particular application. Fluxing-extending resins, which lower the melt temperature and often reduce the raw material cost, include "Santolite" MHP (Monsanto Chemical Co.), Resin 861, Rosin WW, or "Pentalyn" A or G (Hercules Powder Co., Inc.). If the ingredients are not completely compatible, a blending agent such as "Armid" HT (Armour Chemical Division) may be used. To improve the thermal stability of the melt and to prevent oxidative degradation, antioxidants such as para-substituted phenols, phenothiazine, substituted thioureas, "Sopanox" (Monsanto Chemical Co.), etc. may be added in small amounts.

The preparation of hot melts is simple. The ingredients other than the polyvinyl butyral are added and melted to a homogeneous state. The resin is then gradually added and the temperature raised until the melt is uniform. Extruders, mixers, and kettles are used.

Application of the hot melt may be carried out immediately, or the material may be cooled, chopped, or extruded into rope. Hot melts are usually applied by roller coating, spraying, dipping, or doctoring.

As stated earlier, polyvinyl butyral forms an excellent base for hot-melt formulation, particularly where difficult-to-bond surfaces are involved. The wide range of polyvinyl butyral types makes possible the selection of a resin with characteristics best suited to the individual application. For example, hot melts with high or low viscosity characteristics but with similar chemical properties can be made by merely choosing the appropriate type of resin. Similarly, the range of available chemical compositions in commercial polyvinyl butyral resins makes it possible to vary such properties as oil and water resistance, compatibilities, etc., while maintaining a desired viscosity.

A typical starting formulation for a polyvinyl butyral hot melt is shown herein:

	parts
Low hydroxyl polyvinyl butyral	60–100
"Santicizer" 141	10–20
Resin 861	100–200
"Armid" HT	2–4
"Castorwax"	100–200

By varying the preceding proportions, this formulation can be used for adhering or coating numerous surfaces. Such properties as specific adhesion, flow, melt temperature, film hardness, setting time, etc., can be varied at will. More specific supplementary formulations are shown in Table 7, and parts are by weight.

APPLICATIONS

Safety Glass

The original and largest use of polyvinyl butyral, containing 18 to 20 per cent vinyl alcohol groups, is as the interlayer in laminated automotive safety glass. The laminate consists of two pieces of glass permanently bonded together under heat and pressure with a plasticized polyvinyl butyral interlayer. In this application the excellent

TABLE 7. POLYVINYL BUTYRAL HOT-MELT ADHESIVE FORMULATIONS.

Formulation No.	1	2	3	4	5	6	7	8
Low hydroxyl polyvinyl butyral	—	—	—	10	15	18	—	20
High hydroxyl polyvinyl butyral	40	10	15	—	—	—	10	—
"Santicizer" 141	—	6	—	—	—	—	—	2.5
"Santicizer" B-16	—	—	3	10	0–9	—	—	—
"Santicizer" 8	30	—	—	—	—	—	—	—
Dibutyl sebacate	—	2	—	—	—	—	—	—
Resin 861	—	24	43	90	43	25	45	—
Rosin WW	—	—	—	—	—	—	—	60
"Castorwax"	—	24	36	10	36	44	35	25
"Acrawax" C	—	—	—	—	2	—	—	—
"Armid" HT	—	2.4	3.6	1	3.6	4.4	3.5	2.5
Titanium dioxide	—	—	—	—	—	1.9	—	—
Aluminum silicate	—	—	—	—	—	10.4	—	—
"Ethocel" N-10	—	—	—	—	—	—	3	—
Polyvinyl methyl ether	5	—	—	—	—	—	—	—

The above formulations can be used as follows:

Formulation
1 Aluminum-to-steel adhesive
2 Label adhesive
3 Low melting coating
4 Label adhesive for tin cans
5 Wax paper adhesive
6 and 7 Frozen food container adhesive
8 Leather-to-wood adhesive

adhesive properties of the plasticized film prevent fragments of glass from flying off from a suddenly cracked or broken pane of safety glass. The particles adhere so tightly to the interlayer that a shattered laminate can literally be rolled on itself without particles of glass falling off. In addition, the elastic properties of the plasticized film allow the dissipation of momentum to occur over a longer time period, reducing the force of impact. The impact area also becomes larger as the laminate gives way, reducing the stress concentration. The excellent optical, chemical, adhesive and tensile properties of the interlayer are retained after long-term exposure to the elements, although the edges of the laminate are exposed.

Laminated architectural glass is currently being manufactured to meet specific structural requirements by permanently bonding two or more pieces of glass with polyvinyl butyral interlayers. Variations in structure and design can be accomplished by varying the glass or the polyvinyl butyral interlayer, pigmentation, printing, screening or painting with dyes or pigments on the glass or plastic interlayer, and by the inclusion of paper, botanicals, fibers and a wide variety of colorful objects. Laminated architectural glass offers a broad range of light control from transparent to opaque. It is manufactured to reduce glare, exclude ultraviolet, and diminish solar energy or heat. The colors and designs are permanently bonded between the layers of glass. Again the adhesive polyvinyl butyral interlayer reduces the hazard from shattering glass, an important safety factor in heavy traffic areas such as school corridors.

Wire Enamels

The first and most extensive application of polyvinyl formal resins is in the manufacture of a tough, adhesive, heat-resistant wire enamel. In this application a standard enamel based on "Formvar" 15/95E polyvinyl formal and phenolic would consist of 100 parts of polyvinyl formal and 50 parts of an alkyl phenolic resin dissolved in a solvent mixture composed of naphtha solvent and cresylic acid. After application to the wire, this coating is dried and cured at high temperatures to a crosslinked film which is extremely tough, heat resistant, and adherent with excellent dielectric properties.[32]

Many enamel formulations based on polyvinyl formal resins have been developed which have desirable properties for specific applications. Among these are solderable enamels, bonding enamels,

and most recently, an enamel with excellent resistance to common refrigerants.

The high degree of adhesion, toughness, and abrasion resistance of wire enamel containing polyvinyl formal resins enables the magnet wire to maintain its coating integrity during high-speed motor winding and service. Today approximately 75 per cent of magnet wire made in this country has the polyvinyl formal type coating, superseding oleoresinous enamel. Polyvinyl formal and polyvinyl butyral resins may also be used to overcoat magnet wire so that coils made therefrom can be adhered with heat or by solvent action.

Surface Coatings

The acetal resins, polyvinyl formal and polyvinyl butyral, may be used alone or in combination with various resins to give functional surface coating compositions. Films which may be air-dried, baked or cured at room temperature are obtained by proper compounding. The presence of hydroxyl groups in the polymer molecule not only enables good wetting of most substrates but also furnishes a reactive site for chemical combination with thermosetting resins.

Wash Primers. In protective coatings for metal, the best known polyvinyl acetal application is in "wash primers," also referred to as "metal conditioners." Wash primers are more effective than other corrosion-inhibiting materials, because they offer, in a single treatment, several means of preventing corrosion. These anticorrosive primers apply easier, adhere better, and dry faster than the more conventional materials.

The action of wash primers over steel, for example, is threefold. First, an iron oxide and zinc phosphate film, similar to that formed in the common phosphating processes, is deposited on the metal. Second, unlike other methods, wash primers provide a continuous supply of chromate ions for the repair of any pinholes present in the phosphate film, eliminating the need for a special chromate rinse. And third, the polyvinyl butyral or formal film is chemically bound in the inorganic layers through a chromium complex, providing additional mechanical protection to the metal surface. Thus the primer phosphatizes the metal at the surface, supplies a corrosion-inhibiting pigment in a tenaciously adhering binder, and dries to take any kind of top coat.

In finishing house trailers fabricated of phosphated or galvanized steel, or aluminum, wash primers provide corrosion resistance and adhesion under single-coat styrenated alkyd and other modified alkyd enamels. On metal subject to immersion and corrosion conditions, wash primers are specified under urethane and vinyl top coats.

A typical wash primer formulation is shown below:

WP-1 MIL C-15328A (BUREAU OF SHIPS)

GSSO Exception No. 8030—302   10 Mar. 1958

Base Grind Material	% by wt.
Polyvinyl butyral (18 to 20 per cent vinyl alcohol groups)	9.15
n-Butanol	20.44
Isopropanol, 99%	57.72
Water	2.45
Basic zinc chromate	8.83
Talc (WCD 399SF)	1.31
Lamp black	0.10
	100.00

Grind to Hegman 6

Reducer	% by wt.
85% Phosphoric acid (U.S.P.)	18.42
Water	16.45
Isopropanol, 99%	65.13
	100.00

Application: Dilute 4 parts base grind with 1 part reducer by volume. For spray, add sufficient isopropanol or ethanol, 95 per cent, to equal volume of reducer. To reduce blushing under humid conditions, the preferred alcohol is n- butanol. 0.3 to 0.8 mil dry film thickness is specified over a clean surface. Pot life is 8 to 12 hr.

Metal Coatings. Polyvinyl formal and polyvinyl butyral are used in phenolic and epoxy can linings. In this application, the polyvinyl acetal resin increases toughness, adhesion, and flexibility of the film. The incorporation of a polyvinyl acetal resin improves application properties by promoting leveling of the coating. By suitable compounding, it is possible to obtain baked coatings that will withstand postforming. Curable coatings containing either polyvinyl formal or polyvinyl butyral may be formulated to meet the extractability requirements of the Food and Drug Administration.

Clear, baked coatings based on a polyvinyl acetal-thermosetting resin combination may be formulated to resist strong acids such as aqua regia and boiling concentrated caustic soda. These coatings are particularly recommended for chemical milling resists. In this application the coating functions as an adhesive for subsequent top coats.

A typical formulation for a can coating is given below:

POLYVINYL BUTYRAL-PHENOLIC CAN COATING

Material	% by wt.
Low hydroxyl polyvinyl butyral solution (20% in n-butanol)	13.5
Phenolic	51.0
Methyl isobutyl ketone	35.5
	100.0

NVM: 28.2%
Application: Roller or knife
Baking schedule: 15 min at 400°F
                                 or 60 min at 300°F

Wood Finishes. In coatings for wood, polyvinyl acetal resin not only furnishes good adhesion but also increases intercoat adhesion, cold check resistance, and toughness. In furniture finishing, polyvinyl acetals usually are combined with nitrocellulose to give outstanding wood sealers.

Combined with phenolic, polyvinyl butyral has enjoyed widespread use as a knot sealer. The polyvinyl acetal resins as a class are excellent barriers to bleeding of terpinaceous matter from knots, heartwood, and resin ducts.

WESTERN PINE ASSOCIATION KNOT SEALER, WP578

Material	% by wt.
Polyvinyl butyral	3.3
Phenolic	33.3
Ethanol, 95% (proprietary)	63.4
	100.00

NVM: 23%
Application: Brush

Textile Coatings. In textile coatings, polyvinyl butyral can be compounded to make fabrics waterproof and stain resistant without conspicuously affecting the appearance, feel, drape, and color of the fabric. Cotton, wool, silk, nylon, viscose rayon and other synthetics can be successfully coated. Almost any fairly tightly woven fabric with a flat surface can be made waterproof and stain resistant. Polyvinyl butyral textile coatings have good adhesion, transparency, hand and appearance, and functional properties. During the drying and curing operations, it is transformed to an elastomer which becomes a permanent part of the fabric.

Polyvinyl butyral is almost unique among vinyl resins in its ability to be cured in a manner somewhat analogous to rubber, with improved heat resistance, solvent resistance and adhesion to the

TRADE-NAME PRODUCTS

	Type	Source
Acrawax C	Octadeceneamide	Glyco Products Co., Inc.
Adipol BCA, 4720	Adipate plasticizer	Ohio Apex Div., Food Machinery & Chemical
Admex 710	Epoxidized soybean oil	Archer-Daniels-Midland Co.
Advaresin KF	Ketone-formaldehyde resin	Advance Solvents & Chem. Corp.
Amberol ST-137	Phenolic resin	Rohm & Haas Co.
Araldite	Epoxy resin	Ciba Co., Inc.
Armid HT	Fatty acid amide	Armour Chemical Div.
Beckosol 1334-50EL	Alkyd resin	Reichhold Chem., Inc.
BKR-2620	Phenolic resin	Union Carbide Plastics Co.
BV-1600, -2710	Phenolic resin	Union Carbide Plastics Co.
Castorwax	Hydrogenated castor oil	Baker Castor Oil Co.
Catalyst AC	Urea and melamine resin catalyst	Monsanto Chem. Co.
Cellosolve	Ethylene glycol monoethyl ether	Union Carbide Chemical Co.
Cellosolve Acetate	Acetic ester of "Cellosolve"	Union Carbide Chemical Co.
Conoco H-300	Hydrocarbon plasticizer	Continental Oil Co.
Diamond K. Linseed Oil	Linseed oil	Spencer Kellogg & Sons, Inc.
Duraplex C-49	Alkyd resin	Rohm & Haas Co.
Epi Rez 540	Epoxy resin	Jones Dabney Co.
Epon 1001, 1007	Epoxy resins	Shell Chemical Corp.
Ethocel N-10	Ethyl cellulose	Dow Chemical Co.
Flexol 2GB	Dibenzoate plasticizer	Union Carbide Chemical Co.
Flexol 3GH	Glycollate plasticizer	Union Carbide Chemical Co.
Flexol TOF	Phosphate plasticizer	Union Carbide Chemical Co.
Flexricin P-3	Butyl ricinoleate	Baker Castor Oil Co.
GE 75-108	Phenolic resin	General Electric Co.
Gum Dammar	Natural resin	Wm. H. Scheel, Inc.
Halowax 1014	Chlorinated naphthalene plasticizer	Koppers Co., Inc.
Hercolyn	Rosin derivative plasticizer	Hercules Powder Co., Inc.
Methox	Phthalate plasticizer	Ohio Apex Division
Mondur S	Isocyanate	Mobay Chemical Co.
Newport V-40	Alpha-pinene resin	Heyden-Newport Chem. Corp.
Paraplex G-20, RG-8	Polyester plasticizers	Rohm & Haas Co.
Pentalyn A, H, G	Pentaerythritol esters of rosin	Hercules Powder Co., Inc.
Plastolein 9055	Pelargonate plasticizer	Emery Industries, Inc.
Plastolein 9250	Furfuryloleate plasticizer	Emery Industries, Inc.
Plastolein 9720	Adipate plasticizer	Emery Industries, Inc.
Pycal 29, 40, 94	Adipate plasticizers	Atlas Powder Co.
Resimene 881	Melamine formaldehyde resin	Monsanto Chemical Co.
Resin 840	Silicone resin	Dow Corning Corp.
Resin 861	Thermoplastic resin	Hercules Powder Co., Inc.
Resinox P-97	Phenolic resin	Monsanto Chemical Co.
Resloom M-75	Liquid melamine	Monsanto Chemical Co.
Resoflex R-296	Polyester plasticizer	Cambridge Industries Co.
Rezyl 807-1	Alkyd resin	American Cyanamid Co.
Rosin WW	Wood rosin	Hercules Powder Co.
Santicizer 8	Sulfonamide plasticizer	Monsanto Chemical Co.
Santicizer 141	Phosphate plasticizer	Monsanto Chemical Co.
Santicizer 160	Phthalate plasticizer	Monsanto Chemical Co.
Santicizer B-16, E-15, M-17	Glycollate plasticizers	Monsanto Chemical Co.
Santolite MHP	Sulfonamide-formaldehyde resin	Monsanto Chemical Co.
Sopanox	Ortho-tolyl biguanide	Monsanto Chemical Co.
Staybelite Ester 10	Rosin derivative	Hercules Powder Co., Inc.
Uformite F-240	Urea-formaldehyde resin	Rohm & Haas Co.
Vinsol	Rosin derivative	Hercules Powder Co., Inc.
Vinylite VAGH	Vinyl chloride copolymer	Union Carbide Plastics Co.

fabric. Curing is accomplished by incorporating crosslinking resins such as urea, phenolics, melamines and isocyanates. Since the reaction involves the hydroxyl groups on the polyvinyl butyral chain, only a small amount of a modifying resin is needed to increase the heat and solvent resistance substantially. A formulation incorporating such a crosslinking resin would be:

Material	parts by wt.
Polyvinyl butyral	48.0
Tricresyl phosphate	48.0
Ethanol (2B) 95%	84.2
Toluene	64.8
Water	8.0
"Resloom" M-75	3.5
Catalyst AC	.7
p-Nonyl phenol	.2

Acknowledgments

The authors wish to acknowledge the contributions of many members of the staff of Shawinigan Resins Corp., who over the years obtained much of the information presented in this chapter.

References

1. Cohen, S. M., Kass, R. E., and Lavin, E., *Ind. and Eng. Chem.,* **50,** 229 (1958).
2. Morrison, G. O., Skirrow, F. W., and Blaikie, K. G. (to Canadian Electro Products Co., Ltd.), U. S. Patent 2,036,092.
3. Matheson, H. W., and Morrison, G. O. (to Shawinigan Chemicals, Ltd.), U. S. Patent 2,116,635.
4. Robertson, H. F. (to Carbide and Carbon Chemicals Corp.), U. S. Patent 2,162,678, 9 and 80.
5. Morrison, G. O. and Price, A. F. (to Shawinigan Chemicals, Ltd.), U. S. Patent 2,168,827.
6. McNally, J. G., Fordyce, C. R., and Talbot, R. H. (to Eastman Kodak Co.), U. S. Patent 2,326,048.
7. Lavin, E., Marinaro, A. T., and Richard W. R. (to Shawinigan Resins Corp.), U. S. Patent 2,496,480.
8. Wilson, C. L., U. S. Patent 2,609,347.
9. Lavin, E., Fitzhugh, A. F., and Crozier, R. N. (to Shawinigan Resins Corp.), U. S. Patent 2,917,482.
10. Farbwerke Hoechst (W. Starck and W. Langbein, inventors), German Patent 947,114.
11. Kurashiki Rayon Dabushiki Kaisha. British Patent 745,219.
12. Société Nobel francaise French Patent 895,992–4 and 900,341.
13. PB 32,997.
14. PB 40,822.
15. Schildknecht, C. E. "Vinyl and Related Polymers," pp. 358–365, New York, 1952, John Wiley & Sons, Inc.
16. Motoyana, T., and Okamura, S., *Chem. High Polymers,* (Japan) **8,** 321 (1951).
17. Blaikie, K. G., and Small, M. W. S., "Encyclopedia of Chemical Technology," Vol. 14, pp. 716–723, New York, Interscience Publishers, Inc.,
18. Flory, P. J., *J. Am. Chem. Soc.,* **61,** 1518 (1939).
19. Fitzhugh, A. F., Lavin, E., and Morrison, G. O., *J. Electrochem. Soc.,* **100,** 351 (1953).
20. Fitzhugh, A. F., and Crozier, R. N., *J. Polymer Sci.,* **8,** (2), 225 (1952).
21. de Bruyne, N. A. (to Rohm & Haas Co.), U. S. Patent 2,499,134.
22. Merriman, H. R., W. A. D. C. Tech. Rept 56–320.
23. Naps, M., and Hopper, F. C., W. A. D. C. Tech. Rept 53–126.
24. Martin, T. J., W. A. D. C. Tech. Rept 57–513.
25. Been, J. L., and Grover, M. M. (to Rubber and Asbestos Corp.), U. S. Patent 2,920,990.
26. Whitney, W., and Herman, S. C., *Adhesives Age,* 22, (Jan. 1960).
27. Shane, R. S., Eriksson, T. L., Korczak, A., Conklin, D. B., W. A. D. C. Tech. Rept 53–477.
28. Miller, M. A., *Adhesives Age,* p. 28 (Mar. 1960).
29. Pratt, W. B. British Patent 233,370.
30. Bromley, W. H., Jr. (to Shawinigan Resins Corp.), U. S. Patent 2,455,402; 2,532,223; 2,611,755.
31. Mahoney, P. L. (to U. S. Rubber Co.), U. S. Patent 2,487,254 and 5.
32. Kass, R. E., and Lavin, E., *Wire and Wire Products,* p. 1207 (Oct. 1956).
33. Kopyscinski, W., Norris, F. H., and Herman, S. C., *Adhesives Age,* p. 31 (May 1960).

Polyvinyl Ether Adhesives

Julian L. Azorlosa

General Aniline and Film Corporation
Easton, Pennsylvania

During the decade preceding World War II a technological breakthrough was achieved by the I. G. Farben in the handling of high-pressure acetylene. Under the direction of Dr. J. W. Reppe this work led to the development and commercialization of many new vinyl polymers. Of particular interest to the adhesives industry were the polyvinyl ethers. In 1948 vinyl ether monomers and polymers were made commercially available in the United States.

For a more complete treatment of the vinyl ethers, the reader is referred to other sources.[1,2] In this chapter, emphasis will be given to those polymers which have achieved development or commercial interest within the United States (see Table 1).

SYNTHESIS OF POLYVINYL ETHERS

Preparation of Vinyl Ethers

Two methods have been used for the commercial synthesis of vinyl ethers:

(1) The pyrolysis of the corresponding acetal:

$$CH_3-CH(OR)_2 \xrightarrow{\Delta} CH_2=CHOR + ROH$$

(2) Direct vinylation of the alcohol with acetylene:

$$HC{\equiv}CH + ROH \xrightarrow{KOH} CH{=}CHOR$$

Method (2), the "vinylation process" of Reppe, offers the easiest and most economic approach. The following reaction conditions are representative:[2]

Temperature: 130 to 170°C
Catalyst: 1 to 3% KOH (K alcoholate formed
  in situ)

Acetylene pressure: 100 to 150 psi (diluted
  with nitrogen)
Yield: 90 to 95 per cent

The physical properties of various vinyl ethers are described in detail elsewhere.[1,2,3]

Polymerization of Vinyl Ethers

Vinyl ethers may be polymerized by free radical catalysts, e.g., peroxides; however only very low molecular weight products are thus obtained. Acid-type catalysts result in low to high molecular weight polymers, lower temperatures favoring higher molecular weights. Among the catalysts which have been cited are BF_3 (hydrate or etherate), $SnCl_4$, $FeCl_3$, $AlCl_3$, SO_2, and iodine.[1,2]

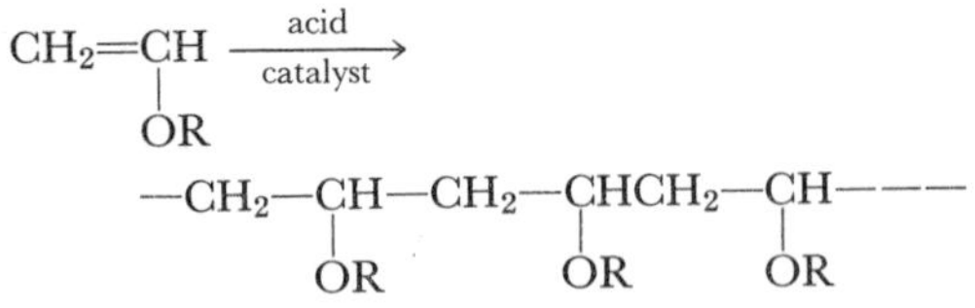

$$CH_2{=}CH \xrightarrow[\text{catalyst}]{\text{acid}}$$
$$\underset{OR}{|}$$

$$-CH_2-\underset{OR}{\underset{|}{CH}}-CH_2-\underset{OR}{\underset{|}{CH}}CH_2-\underset{OR}{\underset{|}{CH}}-{-}{-}{-}$$

To obtain low and medium viscosity polyvinyl ethers, the polymerization may be conducted in bulk at 0 to 10°C by portion-wise addition of the monomer and catalyst to a brine-cooled, stirred reactor. The reaction is rapid and exothermic and the rate of monomer addition must be closely regulated.

The high viscosity grades of polyvinyl isobutyl ether, for example require a much lower temperature, e.g., −50°C. A low boiling solvent such as propane may be used to control the exotherm. A continuous flash polymerization process using an endless revolving belt has been patented abroad.[4] Recently the Union Carbide Plastics Corpora-

TABLE 1. PRODUCT DESIGNATION—POLYVINYL ETHERS.

	U.S. Product Designation	Corresponding German Trade Names[c]
Polyvinyl methyl ether[a]	PVM, 100%	"Lutonal" (Igevin) M-40
	PVM, 50% in water	
(medium viscosity)	PVM, 50% in isopropanol	
	PVM, 50% in toluene	
Polyvinyl ethyl ether[b]		
(low viscosity)	EHBC[b], 80% in heptane	
	EDBC[b], dry form	"Lutonal" (Igevin) A-50
(high viscosity)	EHBM[b], 25% in heptane	
	EDBM[b], dry form	
Polyvinyl isobutyl ether[a]		
(low viscosity)	PVI-L	
(med. viscosity)	PVI-M	"Lutonal" (Igevin) J-60
(high viscosity)	PVI-C	"Oppanol" C

[a] These products have been offered on a development basis by the General Aniline and Film Corp.

[b] These resins are sold by the Union Carbide Plastics Corp.

[c] Badische Anilin and Soda Fabrik.

tion has patented a process for obtaining high molecular weight polyvinyl ether by polymerization at temperatures above 10°C using an aluminum hexahydrosulfate catalyst.[5]

Copolymerization of Vinyl Ethers

Vinyl ether monomers may copolymerize with such monomers as acrylonitrile, acrylates, chloroprene, vinyl chloride, vinyl esters, maleic anhydride, maleates, methacrylates, and vinyl chloride using free radical catalysts. Since the tendency for homopolymerization is practically nil under these conditions, a theoretical maximum of only 50 mole per cent vinyl ether can be introduced.

Copolymers and terpolymers of the vinyl ether with acrylates and vinyl chloride are produced commercially in Germany. Those of interest in the surface coating fields are listed in Table 2.

PROPERTIES OF POLYVINYL ETHERS

Three vinyl ether homopolymers have been offered commercially within the United States:

polyvinyl methyl ether (PVM), polyvinyl ethyl ether (PVE), and polyvinyl isobutyl ether (PVI). All are essentially of the atactic, noncrystalline type. The low or medium viscosity grades are sticky, viscous gums; whereas the high molecular weight grades are tough, rubbery solids. A high molecular weight PVM has not been made commercially available to date. Some of the physical properties are listed in Table 3.

Solubility

PVM, PVE, and PVI are soluble in a wide variety of industrial solvents. A partial listing appears in Table 4.

PVM is unique among the polyvinyl alkyl ethers in being both water-soluble and organic solvent-soluble; moreover its aqueous solubility is thermally reversible. PVM is soluble in dilute aqueous solution at temperatures below 32.5°C; whereas at higher temperatures it will precipitate from water but redissolve on cooling. The effect of concentration on the cloud point is shown in Fig. 1. Aqueous solutions of PVM can tolerate

TABLE 2. COMMERCIAL VINYL ETHER COPOLYMERS (GERMANY).

Trade Name	Form (% solids)	Vinyl Isobutyl Ether (%)	Methyl Acrylate (%)	Ethyl Acrylate (%)	Styrene (%)	Acrylic Acid (%)	Vinyl Chloride (%)
"Acronal"* 400D	Emulsion, 40	22	66	—	12	—	—
"Acronal"* 450D	Emulsion, 40	20	—	66	12	2	—
"Acronal"* 550D	Emulsion, 50	50	50	—	—	—	—
"Acronal"* 600D	Emulsion, 40	20	—	80	—	—	—
"Vinoflex"* MP 400	Powder	25	—	—	—	—	75

* Badische Anilin and Soda Fabrik.

TABLE 3. PHYSICAL PROPERTIES OF POLYVINYL ETHERS.

	PVM	PVE-Low	PVE-High	PVI-Low	PVI-Med.	PVI-High
Reduced viscosity at 20°C	0.50	0.2–0.4	3.5–4.5	0.07	0.6	3–4
Specific gravity at 20°C	1.05	0.97	0.97	0.91	0.91	0.93
Refractive Index n_D 25°C	1.47	1.45	1.45	1.45	1.46	1.46
Plasticity (Williams)			1.6–2.0			1.5–1.9
Dielectric constant (50 cycles/sec)	3.5	3.0			2.2	
Brittle point (90-mil. specimens)	−27 to −30°C			−29 to −27°C	−19 to −17°C	−19 to −17°C
Softening point (ASTM Ball and Ring Method)	62°C			10 to 16°C	44 to 46°C	

small amounts of inorganic salts without precipitation. The concentration-viscosity relationship for PVM, PVE, and PVI solutions are shown in Fig. 2, 3, and 4.

Compatibility

PVE and PVI are compatible with a limited number of commercial resins. Of particular interest in adhesive formulations are their compatibilities with rosin derivatives and some phenolics. Conversely, PVM exhibits a wider range of compatibilities as shown in Table 5. In borderline cases, compatibility data should be treated with some skepticism, since observations will vary among several investigators. There are a number of materials which may be termed "practical modifiers," since they do not form true polymeric alloys but may be useful in formulating quasi-compatible

TABLE 4. SOLUBILITIES OF POLYVINYL ETHERS.

	PVM	PVE	PVI
Water	S (below 32°C)	I	I
Ethanol	S	S	I
n-Butanol	S	S	S
Acetone	S	S	I
Cyclohexanone	S	S	S
Ethyl acetate	S	S	S
Butyl acetate	S	S	S
Ethyl ether	S	S	S
Benzene	S	S	S
Toluene	S	S	S
Turpentine	PS	S	S
Heptane	I	S	S

S = soluble
PS = partly soluble
I = insoluble

systems. Often the macroscopic compatibility may be improved by hot milling or by the addition of a compatible third component, e.g., polyisobutylene or natural rubber. PVM exhibits a limited compatibility in film form with several of the commercial water-soluble resins, e.g., methyl cellulose, tragacanth gum, sodium alginate, and some dextrins.

Stability

The stability of the polyvinyl ethers is reduced by the presence of residual acidic polymerization catalysts. Stabilizers such as beta-naphthyl phenyl-

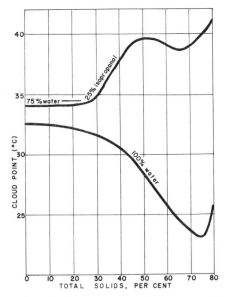

Fig. 1. Cloud point vs. concentration-aqueous polyvinyl methyl ether solutions.

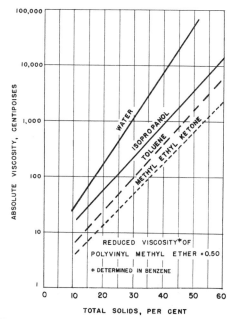

Fig. 2. Viscosity of polyvinyl methyl ether solutions at 25°C.

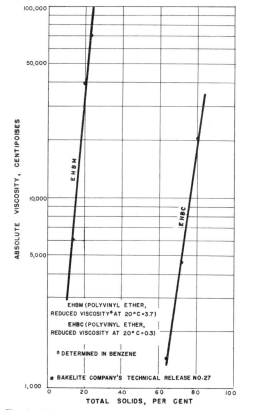

Fig. 3. Viscosity of Bakelite polyvinyl ethyl ether solutions in heptane (20°C).*

* Bakelite Company's technical release no. 27.

TABLE 5. COMPATIBILITY OF AMORPHOUS POLYVINYL ETHERS (CAST FILMS).

	PVM	PVE	PVI
Wood rosin	C	C	C
Methyl abietate	C	C	C
Ester gum	C	C	C
Phenolics (oil soluble)	C	C	C
Phenol-modified coumarone-indene resin "Nevillac Hard"[a]	C	C	C
Nitrocellulose	C	PC	I
Ethyl cellulose	C	I	I
Cellulose acetate	PC	I	I
Polystyrene	C	I	I
Polyvinyl acetate	PC	I	I
Polyvinyl butyral	C	I	I
Vinyl chloride-vinyl acetate copolymers	I	I	I
Neoprene[b] CG Soft	PC	I	I
Chlorinated rubber "Parlon"[c]	C	I	I
Paraffin wax	I	I	C
Polyethylene	I	I	I

C = Compatible.
PC = Partially compatible.
I = Incompatible.

[a] Neville Co.   [c] Hercules Powder Co.
[b] E. I. du Pont Co.

amine have been used to prevent degradation (depolymerization) during storage. Where exceptional heat and oxidative stability are required, addition of 0.25 to 0.5 per cent of an antioxidant is recommended. Some effective types are:

> 2,6-ditertiary butyl *p*-cresol
> 2,5-ditertiary butyl hydroquinone
> Butyl-*p*-aminophenol
> "Santowhite"* (dialkylphenol sulfide)
> Hydroquinone monobenzyl ether

Degradation by ultraviolet light may be controlled by incorporation of 0.1 per cent of an ultraviolet absorber such as "Uvinul"** 400 (2,4-dihydroxybenzophenone). PVE and PVI are stable toward dilute and concentrated alkalies and dilute acids, but concentrated mineral acids will degrade or crosslink PVM eventually.

Color

The polyvinyl ethers are intrinsically colorless. The yellow-to-orange color of some commercial samples can be attributed to impurities introduced in the manufacturing process, e.g., residual vinyl

* Monsanto Chemical Co.
** General Aniline and Film Corp.

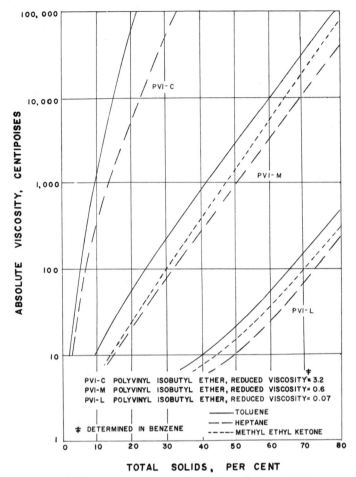

Fig. 4. Viscosity of polyvinyl isobutyl ether solutions at 25°C.

ether monomer may hydrolyze under acidic conditions to give acetaldehyde and colored condensation products thereof. Alcoholic solutions of PVM, for example, may be quite color stable since the alcohol converts any residual vinyl ether to the corresponding acetal in the presence of trace acids. The presence of antioxidants will stabilize against discoloration by heat at 135°C. [6]

Toxicity

The literature indicates that these polyvinyl ethers have a low order of toxicity.[6,7] Skin irritation studies indicate that they are non-allergenic.

Adhesive Characteristics

Properly compounded adhesives based on PVE and PVI show excellent adhesion to porous surfaces such as cloth, paper, and wood as well as to smooth substrates such as cellophane, "Mylar,"* and

TABLE 6. HYGROSCOPICITY OF PVM.

Relative Humidity (%)	H₂O Pick-up (%)
50	1.0
70	1.2
93	6.0

cellulose acetate, and vinyl sheet. Adhesion of PVE and PVI to polyethylene and silicone-treated surfaces is questionable; however PVM does adhere to polyethylene. Although it is water-soluble, PVM's tackiness is substantially constant over a wide range of humidity, which may be attributed to its low degree of hygroscopicity (Table 6).

The tackiness of a PVM-containing formulation is dependent on its compatibility with the cohesive component. With a resin of borderline compatibil-

* E. I. du Pont Co.

ity such as polyvinyl acetate, 10 per cent PVM will impart tack. Where true polymeric alloys are possible with high softening point resins, e.g., polystyrene, 50 to 60 per cent PVM is necessary to impart tack at room temperature.

Handling

Solutions of polyvinyl ethers may be prepared with a Werner-Pfleiderer, Baker-Perkins, or a similar type masticator and are also available from suppliers. Specific recommendations for milling and extrusion lamination of polyvinyl ethyl ethers are available.[6]

ADHESIVE APPLICATIONS

The polyvinyl ethers are advantageous in most types of adhesives. In the following section their applications are classified primarily by the mode of application.

Remoistenable Adhesives

PVM is the only polyvinyl ether discussed here which is water-soluble, hence remoistenable. This polymer is unique in being a permanently tacky and flexible water-soluble polymer. The incorporation of PVM into dextrin and animal glue-based adhesives imparts improved adhesion toward many surfaces including polyethylene, metals, and coated papers; in addition the tendency toward adhesive failure in a dry atmosphere is corrected. The following formulation has been suggested for remoistenable label stock.[8] The function of the isopropanol is to raise the cloud point above that of aqueous PVM. The PVM/MA ("Gantrez"* AN-119) reduces the blocking tendency.

Dextrin	100
PVM	35
"Gantrez" AN-119 (methyl vinyl ether-maleic anhydride copolymer, reduced visc. = 0.5)	7
Isopropanol	35
Water	200

The relative insensitivity of PVM to changes in relative humidity permits the formulation of non-curling gummed paper. A. E. Davis has patented an ingenious solution to the curling problem of re-moistenable gummed paper,[9] which consists essentially of coating the following formulation onto paper stock.

Dextrin	80
PVM	20
Toluene	45

The 80 parts of dextrin, previously ground to a fine mesh size, is uniformly dispersed in the PVM-toluene solution. Macroscopically the dry, gummed surface appears homogeneous although microscopically it consists of minute, discrete particles of dextrin in a continuous matrix of PVM. The gummed paper exhibits no tendency to curl with radical changes in humidity. In lieu of dextrin, finely divided animal glue or CMC (carboxymethylcellulose) may be used.

An adhesive composition that is particularly effective for adhering paper labels to printed surfaces such as magazines has been disclosed.[10]

Bentonite (less than 200 mesh)	2
Polyvinyl methyl ether	22
Water	72

The PVM gives excellent adhesion to the hard, glossy printed magazine surface and because of its water solubility presents no problem in reworking the magazine scrap.

Laminating Adhesives

The polyvinyl ethers have been suggested as an adhesive component of interlayers for safety glass. An interesting study by F. T. Buckley illustrates the effect of PVM in decreasing the water sensitivity of polyvinyl butyral/glass bonds, as shown in the following table.[11]

Examples

Polyvinyl butyral resin (parts)	100	100	100	100	100	100
Dibutyl cellosolve adipate (parts)	40	40	40	40	40	40
PVM (parts)	5	5	10	10	—	—
Water, % of total composition	0.2	1.0	0.2	1.0	0.2	1.0
Adhesion**	7	5	8	6	6	2

A curable laminating adhesive has been patented which employs PVM to obtain improved adhesion to copper and zinc.[12] The following composition is typical.

* General Aniline and Film Corp.

** Adhesion is graded on an arbitrary scale after hammering a safety glass laminate at 0°F and determining the amount of unexposed interlayer. A value of "8" corresponds to 95 per cent unexposed interlayer (an excellent value), while "2" corresponds to 10 per cent unexposed interlayer (a poor value).

PVM	33.1
Propylene glycol-maleate-phthalate resin	40
Methyl methacrylate monomer	26.6
Dimethyl p-toluidine	0.3
Hydroquinone	0.05

When admixed with 1.5 per cent benzoyl peroxide and cured at room temperature between copper sheets, a shear strength of 3100 psi results.

For laminating paper wadding to polyethylene, PVM may be used by itself. A 20 per cent PVM solution in water is coated onto polyethylene film; then the paper wadding may be adhered with slight pressure.

In the preparation of cellulose acetate laminates, the following solution can be coated onto the acetate film by conventional methods, dried, and calendered onto paper or aluminum foil.[8]

"Vinylite" AYAT[a]	100
"Vinylite" VAGH[b]	100
PVM	100
Methylethyl ketone	500
Toluene	500

[a] Polyvinyl acetate, Union Carbide Plastics Co.

[b] A modified vinyl chloride-vinyl acetate copolymer, Union Carbide Plastics Co.

Pressure-Sensitive Adhesives

In this type of adhesive the polyvinyl ethers have attracted the most interest to date. Their outstanding adhesiveness and stability coupled with a low order of toxicity or dermatological effect make them particularly suitable.

A properly formulated pressure-sensitive adhesive must have the correct balance of adhesion, cohesion, plasticity, and tack. It should include at least one elastomeric compound plus one or more compounds which have a tackifying and plasticizing function. Where age resistance is necessary, antioxidants and sometimes UV absorbers are included. Fillers are optional, and the most practical arrangement in a finished adhesive tape is:

> Adhesion to Backing > Cohesive Strength
> (or primer coat)
>
> > Adhesive Strength > Tack
> > (adhesion to adherend)

The specific end use must be considered in adjusting the ratio of the components, e.g., in a formulation for a freezer tape a larger proportion of plasticizer would be necessary than in a formulation where the product is used at room temperature. The polyvinyl ethers provide adhesives usable over a temperature range of -20 to $160°$ F. The acrylonitrile-butadiene copolymers, e.g., "Hycar"[*]

Latex 1516 have been found to be effective primers for tape backings of paper, cellophane, and vinyl.[6]

Starting formulas for transparent cellophane-backed adhesives, which are given below, may be coated onto primed cellophane from a 20 per cent heptane solution by conventional means.

Formulation 1

PVI-C (high viscosity, polyvinyl isobutyl ether)	80
PVI-M (medium viscosity, polyvinyl isobutyl ether)	20
Ester gum	5

Formulation 2[6]

"Bakelite" resin EHBM (PVE, high viscosity)	90
"Bakelite" resin EHBC (PVE, low viscosity)	10
"Lucite"[a] 42 (polyethyl methacrylate)	5
"Staybelite"[b] Ester No. 10	2.5

[a] E. I. du Pont Co.

[b] Hercules Powder Co.

A composition for surgical adhesive tape non-irritating to human skin has been described.[13]

Polyvinyl isobutyl ether (medium viscosity)	44
Polyvinyl isobutyl ether (high viscosity)	28
TiO_2	15

By coating the above composition at 100°C onto a cloth backing, the use of solvents is eliminated. The opposite side of the backing is maintained at a substantially lower temperature to effect a quick set of the coating paste as a porous mass. This technique produces an air-permeable, hence less skin-irritating, adhesive tape.

Hot-melt Adhesives

The adhesive nature of the polyvinyl ethers as well as their compatibility with the cheaper resins make them suitable for hot-melt adhesive formulations. The following compositions are effective for adhering labels to metal surfaces.[8]

FORMULATION	1	2
Polyvinyl methyl ether	15 parts	100
Wood rosin	85 parts	—
"Vinsol"[*]	—	100

[*] Hercules Powder Co.

The following composition for "glueing off" books has been suggested.[8]

N-Wood rosin	100
"Belro"[a] rosin	100

[a] Hercules Powder Co.

[*] B. F. Goodrich Chemical Co.

"Vinylite"[b] AYAT	50
Polyvinyl methyl ether	40
Butyl benzyl phthalate	12
Paraffin wax	4
"Santovar"A[c]	0.3

[b] Polyvinyl acetate (Bakelite Co.)

[c] Monsanto Chemical Co.

Emulsion-Type Adhesives

Stable oil-in-water emulsions of the polyvinyl ethers can be prepared. The following formulation has been recommended for use as plywood, leather, and fabric adhesives.[8]

	parts (dry basis)
PVI-M	100
Casein	18
Stearic acid	6
Boric acid	1.8
Salicylic acid	1.8
Ammonia (25%)	6.9
Water	130.5
2,6-ditertiarybutyl-p-cresol	0.3
n-Heptane	27

A hot solution of casein (18 parts), water (48 parts) and ammonia (1.8 parts), is mixed with stearic acid (6 parts), water (15 parts), and ammonia (3 parts), An 80 per cent PVI-M in heptane solution is warmed to 50°C; then it is added, with agitation, to the above mixture. A solution of boric acid (1.8 parts), salicylic acid (1.8 parts), water (18 parts), 2,6-ditertiary-butyl-p-cresol (0.3 part) and ammonia (2.1 parts) is finally added.

The *hot* water insolubility of PVM has been utilized in formulating heat-sensitive rubber latices: natural, GR-S, neoprene, and acrylonitrile-butadiene copolymers.[8] While the prime function of PVM in such applications is as a heat sensitizer, the coagulated rubber film exhibits improved adhesion to fabric and paper. A typical heat-sensitized latex formulation follows:

	parts (dry basis)
Centrifuged natural rubber latex (60% solids)	100
"Emulphor" ON-870[a] (10% aqueous)	1.5
H$_2$SO$_4$ (5%)	Adjust pH to 7.5
Vulcanizer dispersion (40%)[b]	20
PVM (20% aqueous solution)	4

"Emulphor" ON-870 is thoroughly mixed with the latex before adding H$_2$SO$_4$

[a] A nonionic surfactant produced by General Aniline and Film Corp.

[b] These ingredients are ball-milled together with water to prepare a 40 per cent dispersion, and they are added in the order given above.

Vulcanizer Dispersion[b]	parts by wt. (dry basis)
Kaolin	10
Zinc oxide	5
Sulfur	3
"Captax"[c]	1
"Blancol" N[d]	1

[c] A mercaptobenzothiazole accelerator, R. T. Vanderbilt Co.

[d] A sodium salt of a sulfonated naphthalene condensate, General Aniline and Film Corp.

Stable emulsion systems containing PVM have been prepared. The following formulation has been recommended as a cellophane bag adhesive.[8]

	parts (dry basis)
"Vinylite" WC 130[a]	100
Dibutyl phthalate	30
PVM (as 50% aqueous)	20
"Santolite" MHP[b]	45

[a] Polyvinyl acetate emulsion, Union Carbide Plastics Co.

[b] An aryl sulfonamide-formaldehyde condensate, used as 60 per cent perchloroethylene solution. (Monsanto Chemical Co.)

Surface Coatings

Polyvinyl ethers improve the adhesion of surface coatings, e.g., by adding 2 to 4 per cent PVI-L (based on solids content) to a PVC organosol used as a prime coating for metal, good adhesion and resistance to salt-spray corrosion are obtained.

German literature cites the use of PVM or PVE in nitrocellulose lacquers to improve adhesion without undue increase in water sensitivity or tendency to blush. The use of up to 20 per cent PVM based on lacquer solids is recommended; furthermore PVM has been found effective as an additive to chlorinated rubber-based swimming pool paints for improved adhesion to cement surfaces. A starting formula follows:[8]

Chlorinated rubber[a]	100
"Aroclor" 1254[b]	40
PVM	20
Methylethyl ketone	100
Toluene	60

[a] "Parlon" (20 cps), Hercules Powder Co.

[b] A polychlorinated biphenyl, Monsanto Chemical Co.

PROSPECTS

At the present, the polyvinyl ethers represent only a fraction of the polymeric adhesives produced in the United States; however in recent years the polyvinyl ethyl ether resins have made rapid strides in the adhesives field. With sufficient volume, the low viscosity (tackifying) polyvinyl ethers derived from C_1 to C_4 alcohols could sell in the 35 to 45¢/lb range; whereas projected large volume prices for the high viscosity (elastomeric) polyvinyl ethers might be 50 to 60¢/lb.

Considering the multitude of hydroxyl-containing chemicals (alcohols, phenols, etc.) which are commercially available and readily vinylated, the vinyl ethers are a versatile family. As a means of introducing new functions into adhesives, the vinyl ether presents some interesting opportunities, e.g., the vinyl ethers of amino alcohols are capable of imparting a cationic character to copolymers.[14] The vinyl ethers of the fluorinated alcohols can contribute flame and solvent resistance;[15] moreover the vinyl ethers of the fatty alcohols may be incorporated into copolymers designed as release coatings for adhesive systems.

Although too premature to assess their commercial significance, mention should be made of the isotactic polyvinyl ethers. By slow heterogeneous, cationic polymerization, a crystalline polyvinyl isobutyl ether was obtained with properties distinctly different from the elastomeric PVI discussed herein.[16] The use of a Ziegler-Natta type catalyst for producing isotactic PVM has also been described.[17] All these factors indicate that a real potential exists for the vinyl ether-based polymers.

Acknowledgment

The author wishes to acknowledge the invaluable cooperation of General Aniline and Film's Research and Commercial Development Departments; especially, Dr. Margaret Flannery and Mr. Frank Prescott.

References

1. Schildknecht, C. E., "Vinyl and Related Polymers," New York, John Wiley & Sons, Inc., 1952.
2. Copenhaver, J. W., and Bigelow, M. H., "Acetylene and Carbon Monoxide Chemistry," Ch. 2, New York, Reinhold Publishing Corp., 1949.
3. "Monomers" (Ch. "Vinyl Ethers," by C. A. Schildknecht), New York, Interscience Publishers, 1951.
4. Otto, M., *et al.* (to Jasco), U. S. Patent 2,311,567 (Feb. 16, 1943).
5. Mosley, S. A. (to Union Carbide and Carbon Corp.), U. S. Patent 2,549,921 (Apr. 24, 1951).
6. Bakelite Company (now Union Carbide Plastics Co.), Technical Release No. 27.
7. General Aniline and Film Corp., New Product Bull. No. P-104.
8. General Aniline and Film Corp., Bull. No. P-123.
9. Davis, A. E. (to Nashua Corp.), U. S. Patent 2,793,966 (May 28, 1957).
10. Allegretti, A. J. (to R. R. Donnelley & Sons), U. S. Patent 2,884,396 (Apr. 28, 1959).
11. Buckley, F. T. (to Monsanto Chemical Co.), U. S. Patent 2,628,950 (Feb. 17, 1953).
12. Bader, E., and Koert, H. (to Deutsche Gold-und Silber-Scheideanstalt Vormals Roessler), U. S. Patent 2,894,932 (July 14, 1959).
13. Salditt, F. (to Scholl Mfg. Co.), U. S. Patent 2,647,100 (July 28, 1953).
14. Cupery, M. E., and Sauer, J. C. (to E. I du Pont), U. S. Patent 2,720,511 (Oct. 11, 1955).
15. Codding, D. W. (to Minnesota Mining and Mfg. Co.), U. S. Patent 2,732,370 (Jan. 24, 1956).
16. Schildknecht, C. E., *et. al., Ind. Eng. Chem.,* **39**, 180 (1947); **40**, 2104 (1948).
17. British Patent 820,469 (to Hercules Powder Co).

—31—

Cyanoacrylate Adhesives

H. W. Coover, Jr.

Research Laboratories
Tennessee Eastman Company
Division of Eastman Kodak Company
Kingsport, Tennessee

Alkyl 2-cyanoacrylates exhibit properties which make them the basis of a new type of adhesive. These properties are manifested in (1) their ability to polymerize, or harden, at room temperature without the addition of a catalyst when they are pressed into a thin film between two adherends, (2) the rapidity with which the bonding occurs, and (3) the strength of the bonds produced with a wide variety of adherend combinations. Conventional adhesives, on the other hand, function by application of heat and pressure, addition of catalyst, or evaporation of a solvent.[1] Adhesives composed of vinyl monomers in partially polymerized form or in a mixture with a powdered polymer are well known; for example, vinyl acetate and methyl methacrylate are often employed as adhesives in this manner, but these, as in the case of some conventional adhesives, require the addition of a catalyst.

The alkyl 2-cyanoacrylates are prepared by pyrolyzing the poly (alkyl 2-cyanoacrylates) which are produced when formaldehyde is condensed with the corresponding alkyl cyanoacetates.[2,3]

mers also undergo polymerization induced by free radicals. Successful inhibition of premature polymerization of the alkyl 2-cyanoacrylates depends on the ability of an inhibitor or inhibitor system to prevent or retard both types of polymerization. Among the effective liquid-phase-polymerization inhibitors are poly(phosphoric acid), phosphorus pentoxide, and o-sulfobenzoic acid anhydride.[4] Vapor-phase-polymerization inhibitors are nitric oxide and sulfur dioxide.[5]

Although the monomeric alkyl 2-cyanoacrylates are excellent adhesives, their fluidity makes them undesirable for many applications. The monomer can be formulated with properly purified thickening agents, however, to produce materials ranging from thin sirups to thick gels. Also, the addition of plasticizers to the adhesive formulation prevents embrittlement of the bond during aging. This improvement is accomplished without materially reducing the tensile strength of the bond.

The physical properties of the adhesive formulation based on methyl 2-cyanoacrylate are given in Table 2.

$$nCH_2O + nCH_2(CN)COOR \xrightarrow{\text{Base}} \left[-CH_2-\overset{\overset{\textstyle CN}{|}}{\underset{|}{C}}-COOR \right]_n + nH_2O$$

$$nCH_2 = C(CN)COOR \xleftarrow{\quad \Delta \quad}$$

Redistillation of the crude monomers resulting from the pyrolysis is necessary to provide materials suitable for use as adhesives. The physical properties of the methyl ester are given in Table 1.

The pure monomers undergo autopolymerization in both liquid and vapor states. The mono-

The only commercial cyanoacrylate adhesive on the market at present is "Eastman 910 Adhesive,"* which is based on methyl 2-cyanoacrylate. Several patents assigned to Eastman Kodak Company de-

* Trade-mark, Eastman Kodak Co.

TABLE 1. PHYSICAL PROPERTIES OF METHYL 2-CYANO-ACRYLATE.[16]

Appearance	Clear, colorless liquid
B.p. (°C)	48–49 at 2.5–2.7 mm
Viscosity at 25°C (Brookfield), cp	2.2
Heat of polymerization in water	10.15 ± 0.2 kcal/mole
n_D^{20}	1.4406
Specific gravity, 27°/4°C	1.1044

TABLE 2. PHYSICAL PROPERTIES OF METHYL 2-CYANO-ACRYLATE ADHESIVE.[16]

Appearance	Cloudy, colorless liquid
n_D^{20}	1.4517
Viscosity at 25°C (Brookfield), cp	~100
Specific gravity, 27°/4°C	1.0959
Weight/gal., lb	9.15
Flash point and fire point (Cleveland Open Cup), °F	180
Solvents	Nitromethane, toluene, methylethyl ketone, and acetone

scribe this and related adhesive systems.[2-13] The chemistry and performance of cyanoacrylate adhesives were described in 1959 by Coover and co-workers.[14] In most respects, the methyl 2-cyanoacrylate adhesive compared favorably with a representative epoxy adhesive with regard to bond strength and the effects of moisture and temperature on the bond strength.[15]

Since the cyanoacrylates represent a new type of adhesive, this chapter is primarily concerned with the application of the adhesives and the properties of the bonds thus formed. The mechanism of the adhesive action and the uses of these adhesives are also discussed. A number of 2-cyanoacrylic esters have been prepared, but only the data obtained using the adhesive formulation based on methyl 2-cyanoacrylate are presented to illustrate the adhesive properties exhibited by this class of compounds.

THEORY OF ADHESIVE ACTION

Negatively disubstituted ethylenes of the type represented by (I) polymerize by a base-catalyzed

$$(I) \quad CH_2 = C \underset{Y}{\overset{X}{<}}$$

ionic mechanism; for example, the alkyl 2-cyanoacrylates readily undergo a highly exothermic polymerization which may be initiated at low temperatures by even very weak bases such as water and alcohols. This reaction is represented by the equation on page 411.

All such negatively disubstituted ethylenes do not possess the phenomenal activity associated with the alkyl 2-cyanoacrylates, however. Monomers possessing electronegative groups which function primarily through a strong inductive ($-I$) effect do not possess the sensitivity of the 2-cyanoacrylates toward weak bases; for example, 2-(trifluoromethyl)acrylonitrile and methyl 2-(trifluoro-

methyl)acrylate are not polymerized by weak bases such as water or alcohols, although the trifluoromethyl group is strongly electronegative.

The sensitivity of the alkyl 2-cyanoacrylates to weak bases is probably due to the strong electromeric ($-E$) effects of both the nitrile group and alkoxycarbonyl group. Under the influence of the catalyst, the strong $-E$ effects which are brought into play render these groups strongly electronegative. When the $-E$ effects of groups of this type are strong and are operating, the electronegativity generally overshadows that of any group operating only through a strong $-I$ effect. Thus, the combined $-E$ effects of the nitrile group and the alkoxycarbonyl group, stimulated by even very weak bases, are apparently sufficient to result in an unusually strong polarization of the double bond in the alkyl 2-cyanoacrylates:

$$CH_2=C-\overset{\overset{O}{\parallel}}{C}-OR \underset{}{\overset{Base}{\rightleftharpoons}}$$
$$\underset{C\equiv N}{\overset{|}{}}$$

$$\overset{\oplus}{CH_2}-\overset{\ominus}{C}-\overset{\overset{O}{\parallel}}{C}-OR$$
$$\underset{C\equiv N}{\overset{|}{}}$$

It may be concluded that for monomers of the type shown (I) to be useful in the new type of adhesives represented by the alkyl 2-cyanoacrylates, strong $-E$ effects must be capable of operating in both X and Y.

The bonding action observed when a 2-cyanoacrylate adhesive is placed between two adherends is the result of the anionic polymerization described

$$
\underset{\substack{\delta+ \qquad \delta-}}{\overset{\displaystyle CN}{CH_2=\overset{|}{C}-COOR}} \;\; \underset{}{\overset{A^-}{\rightleftharpoons}} \;\; \overset{\displaystyle CN}{CH_2-\overset{|}{C}-COOR} \;\; \overset{A^-}{\rightarrow} \;\; A-CH_2-\overset{\overset{\displaystyle CN}{|}}{\underset{\ominus}{C}}-COOR
$$

$$
\overset{\displaystyle CN}{CH_2=\overset{|}{C}-COOR}
$$

$$
Polymer \; \xleftarrow[\text{reaction}]{\text{Further}} \; A-CH_2-\overset{\overset{\displaystyle CN}{|}}{\underset{\underset{\ominus}{COOR}}{C}}-CH_2-\overset{\overset{\displaystyle CN}{|}}{C}-COOR
$$

above. The effect of minute amounts of water vapor or other weak bases on the bonding action is maximized by spreading the adhesive into a very thin film.

APPLICATION OF THE ADHESIVE

The cyanoacrylate adhesives are applied in a different manner than that used for conventional adhesives. Consequently, general precautions and directions concerning the use of this adhesive are presented in this section rather than in the general chapter on adhesive use.

General Precautions

The extreme reactivity associated with cyanoacrylate adhesives has already been indicated. Water or water vapor is sufficiently basic to cause deterioration of the adhesive. Acidic substances do not cause rapid solidification of the adhesive, but contamination with such substances renders the adhesive inactive.

Since the cyanoacrylate adhesives polymerize rapidly on contact with skin or clothing, spillage should be prevented. The cyanoacrylates are also mild lachrymators.

Preparation of Adherend Surfaces

To obtain the best bonding action, the surfaces should be thoroughly cleaned and dried before the adhesive is applied. In most cases, no extensive pretreatment is necessary other than removal of loose dirt, acidic deposits, grease, and other foreign matter.

When bonding metals, cleaning the surfaces with a toluene-acetone mixture is usually sufficient to ensure good bond formation. Cleaning with chlorinated hydrocarbons such as trichloroethylene or

carbon tetrachloride is also satisfactory. Vapor degreasing methods may be used successfully. It has been shown that strong bonds result when the bonding surfaces make smooth, close contact.

Formation of the Bond

Cyanoacrylate adhesives can be applied directly from polyethylene containers equipped with dispensing spouts or by means of medicine droppers. Only one of the surfaces to be bonded should be coated with the adhesive. The adhesive is spread as thinly as possible by means of a wooden or metal spatula or a putty knife, without exerting undue pressure on the adhesive film. The bond is then prepared by placing the properly aligned, uncoated surface in contact with the coated surface. For the bonding of areas of 1 sq in. or less, the adhesive can be spread uniformly over the contact area by rubbing the two surfaces together very quickly once or twice before the final adjustment is made. Since the set time[a] of the adhesive is short, the final adjustment should be made within a few seconds after the bonding surfaces are placed together. A good bond is assured if sufficient manual pressure is applied to the bonded surfaces to provide close contact until the bond is set.

The amount of adhesive required to form a satisfactory bond depends on the type of material to be bonded and on the condition of the surface. Smooth, nonporous materials such as glass, or closely fitting pieces of metal, require less than one drop of adhesive per square inch. Porous materials such as pottery, cork, leather, or wood require a larger amount. Trial bonds should be prepared, when possible, to determine the amount of adhesive required for a given application. The use of excess adhesive produces bonds which generally

[a] Elapsed time after which two surfaces that have been pressed together can no longer be moved.

set more slowly and are weaker than those prepared using only the required amount.

The open time[(b)] of the adhesive depends on the type of surface and on the atmospheric temperature and humidity. Under the ideal conditions of low humidity and temperature and a clean surface, this time could be as long as several hours. Under practical conditions, the open time should be restricted to several minutes. Once the adhesive has been spread or pressed into a very thin film, the surfaces should be placed together within a few seconds.

The adhesive should not be brushed or rolled onto a surface prior to bonding. Application of the adhesive by these methods might cause polymerization of the adhesive on the surface as well as on the brush or roller.

Setting and Curing of the Adhesive

The most important factors affecting set time are the types of material being bonded and the condition of the bonding surfaces. Factors of minor importance are viscosity of the adhesive, temperature, and humidity. Bonds involving smooth, hard surfaces set more rapidly, in general, than those between porous or rough surfaces. The presence of a slight amount of alkalinity, as with glass, causes formation of unbreakable bonds within 10 to 30 sec, while the presence of a slight amount of acidity, as with wood, produces bonds which required three or more minutes to set.

In Table 3, rapidity of bonding action and bond strengths are qualitatively described for a wide variety of adherend combinations. Some bonded thin plastic films showed good tensile properties, but exhibited poor strength under a stripping action. Bonded acetate film had good resistance to both peeling and stripping action; on the other hand, bonded pieces of poly(ethylene terephthalate) film had good tensile properties but could be peeled apart with relative ease. Apparently, there are few materials which do not bond to some extent with alkyl 2-cyanoacrylate adhesives.

PROPERTIES OF THE BOND

The general physical properties of the methyl 2-cyanoacrylate bonds are listed in Table 4.

Unless otherwise indicated, all the values in the following discussion are for metal-metal bonds.

Bond Strength

Bonds formed with methyl 2-cyanoacrylate adhesive have high initial tensile strength, and bonded

TABLE 3. EFFECT OF ADHEREND COMBINATIONS ON BONDING ACTION AND STRENGTH.[16]

Type of Bond	Bonding Action[a]	Bond Strength[b]
Glass-glass	Rapid	Strong
Aluminum-aluminum	Intermediate	Intermediate
Steel-steel	Intermediate	Strong
Glass-rubber	Rapid	Strong
Porcelain-porcelain	Rapid	Strong
Polyethylene-polyethylene	Intermediate	Intermediate
Polyester-polyester[c]	Rapid	Intermediate
"Tenite" Acetate-"Tenite" Acetate	Intermediate	Strong
"Tenite" Butyrate-"Tenite" Butyrate	Intermediate	Strong
Metal-cork	Rapid	Strong
Metal-felt	Rapid	Strong
Glass-cork	Rapid	Strong
Glass-felt	Rapid	Strong
Wood-wood (maple)	Slow	Strong
Metal-leather	Intermediate	Strong
Metal-rubber	Rapid	Strong
Rubber-rubber	Rapid	Strong
Rubber-cardboard	Rapid	Strong
Glass-steel	Intermediate	Strong
Nylon-nylon	Rapid	Intermediate
Glass-"Tenite" Butyrate	Intermediate	Intermediate
Steel-neoprene	Rapid	Strong

[a] Rapid denotes bond-setting within <1 min; intermediate, within 1 to 3 min; slow, after 3 min.

[b] Bonds of intermediate strength could be peeled apart without breaking the adherends. Strong bonds could not be broken manually; in many cases, the weaker of the adherends was broken. Data in this table are qualitative.

[c] Poly(ethylene terephthalate).

articles can be handled within minutes after the bond is formed. However, as shown by Table 5, with steel specimens maximum strength of bonds cured at room temperature was attained after about

TABLE 4. PROPERTIES OF THE CURED BOND.[16]

Softening point (°C)	165
n_D^{20}	Approx. that of glass
Dielectric constant at 1 mc[a]	3.34
Dissipation factor at 1 mc, %[a]	2.02
Solvents	Nitromethane, N, N-dimethylformamide
Nonsolvents	Hydrocarbons, alcohols

[a] ASTM D150–54T.

[(b)] Length of time the adhesive can be exposed to air without autopolymerization.

TABLE 5. EFFECTS OF CURING TIME AT ROOM TEMPERATURE ON BOND STRENGTH.[16]

Curing Time	Tensile Strength of Steel-Steel Bond (psi)	Shear Strength (psi)	
		Steel-Steel[a]	Aluminum-Aluminum[b]
2 hr	2000		
4 hr	2600		
24 hr	3800	1700	2400
40 hr		1775	
48 hr	5000		2600
72 hr			2700
1 wk	4900		
2 wk			2700
4 mo	3950		

[a] Modification of ASTM D1002–49T.
[b] Modification of MIL-A-S090B.

48 hr. Only slight reduction in bond strength occurred in specimens aged for 4 months.

Data from shear strength tests on steel-steel and aluminum-aluminum bonds are presented in Table 5. Bodnar and Schrader[15] reported shear strengths in the range of 3800 psi for steel-steel bonds that had been cured for 24 hr at room temperature. Similar bonds aged for 1 wk had shear strengths of about 4100 psi. These tests were run according to Federal Specification MMM-A-175.

Bonds formed with materials such as glass, wood, and rubber are generally stronger at the glue line than the material bonded.

Resistance to Heat

Data in Table 6 indicate that steel-steel bonds exposed to temperatures up to 80°C show a marked increase in tensile strength. The ultimate temperature tolerance is governed by the softening point of the bond, which is approximately 165°C. The bond strength was somewhat reduced by exposure to 120°C for 24 hr. Higher temperatures or longer exposure times had a more drastic effect on bond strength. Bonds stored at −17°C for 24 hr retained their high initial tensile strengths.

TABLE 6. EFFECT OF HEAT ON BOND STRENGTH OF STEEL-STEEL BONDS.[a 16]

Temp. (°C)	Time	Tensile Strength (psi)
70	1 wk	8900
70	10 days	8500
80	24 hr	8400
120	24 hr	3400
−17	24 hr	4600

[a] Cured 24 hr at room temperature.

TABLE 7. RESISTANCE OF STEEL-STEEL BONDS TO CHEMICALS AND INDUSTRIAL FLUIDS.[16]

Testing Conditions[a]	Fluid	Tensile Strength After Test (psi)
I	Ethyl alcohol	3400
I	Acetone	4450
I	Benzene	4350
I	10% sodium hydroxide solution	1700
I	10% hydrochloric acid solution	3100
II	Gasoline	5300
II	SAE 30 engine oil	4300
II	Synthetic lube—7808	3600
II	Dioctyl phthalate	4200
II	Hydraulic brake fluid	3600

[a] Conditions: I, bonds were cured for 1 day at room temperature and then immersed in test solvent for 1 day at room temperature; II, bonds were cured for 48 hr at room temperature and then immersed in test solvent for 2 wk at room temperature.

Qualitative examination of bonded specimens cooled in dry ice for several hours revealed no observable deterioration in the quality of aluminum-aluminum and glass-glass bonds.

Resistance to Chemicals and Solvents

The effects of common solvents, chemicals, and industrial fluids on steel-steel bonds are shown in Table 7. In general, bonded steel specimens had excellent resistance to common organic solvents and industrial fluids. Bonds immersed in dilute alkali solution were weakened noticeably, but dilute acid solution had less effect. Bonded areas were gradually dissolved by N,N-dimethylformamide.

Resistance to Weathering

Weathering properties of properly cured steel-steel bonds are good. The data in Table 8 indicate that bonds having excellent resistance to high humidity at 100°F were produced by curing for 24 hr at room temperature and then for 24 hr at 70°C.

The qualitative effect of weathering was examined for various bond combinations. Simple lap joints were prepared with the following combinations and the specimens were then exposed on a test rack to normal weather conditions:

1. Wood (maple)-"Tenite" Butyrate
2. Wood (maple)-aluminum
3. Wood-wood (maple)
4. Steel-steel
5. Aluminum-rubber

6. Aluminum-"Tenite" Butyrate
7. "Tenite" Butyrate-"Tenite" Butyrate
8. Glass-glass

These bonds, with the exception of those involving aluminum and glass, withstood the effects of weathering for 8 months or longer.

TABLE 8. EFFECT OF WEATHERING ON STEEL-STEEL BONDS.[16]

Curing Time Prior to Tests (hr.)[a]	Weathering Time (days)	Temp., (°F)[b]	Tensile Strength After Test (psi)
24	8	77	2700
0	2	100	3100
24	4	100	2700
24	7	100	2400
24	19	100	1800
24	28	100	1150
48	13	100[c]	4400
48	14	100[d]	6300
48	15	100	3800
24[e]	5	100	4400

[a] Cured at room temperature.
[b] Humidity was 93 ±2%.
[c] Weathering test followed by aging for 2 days at room temperature.
[d] Weathering test followed by aging for 24 hr at 70°C (dry heat).
[e] Curing time followed by heating at 70°C for 24 hr.

USES OF THE ADHESIVE

The properties which make methyl 2-cyanoacrylate adhesive unique have been used to solve numerous assembly problems in industries making a wide variety of products. The rapid set time of the adhesive is used to speed the assembly of trophies, fountain pens, rubber imprinting plates, optical lenses, tools, and high-fidelity phonograph cartridges. The ability of the adhesive to bond dissimilar materials is also used advantageously, particularly in the assembly of rubber swimming masks and in radiation-measuring instruments. In some of the applications noted above, the design of the product itself was dependent on the use of methyl 2-cyanoacrylate adhesive. The combination of rapid setting action and high bond strength (without heat cure) differentiate this adhesive from other industrial bonding materials.

References

1. De Bruyne, N. A., and Houwink, R., "Adhesion and Adhesives," New York, Elsevier Publishing Co., 1951.
2. Joyner, F. B., and Shearer, N. H., Jr. (to Eastman Kodak Co.), U. S. Patent 2,756,251 (July 24, 1956).
3. Joyner, F. B., and Hawkins, G. F. (to Eastman Kodak Co.), U. S. Patent 2,721,858 (Oct. 25, 1955).
4. Joyner, F. B. (to Eastman Kodak Co.), U. S. Patent 2,784,215 (Mar. 5, 1957).
5. Coover, H. W., Jr., and Shearer, N. H., Jr. (to Eastman Kodak Co.), U. S. Patent 2,794,788 (June 4, 1957).
6. Coover, H. W., Jr. (to Eastman Kodak Co.), U. S. Patent 2,816,093 (Dec. 10, 1957).
7. Shearer, N. H., Jr., and Coover, H. W., Jr. (to Eastman Kodak Co.), U. S. Patent 2,748,050 (May 29, 1956).
8. Coover, H. W., Jr., and Shearer, N. H., Jr. (to Eastman Kodak Co.), U. S. Patent 2,763,585 (Sept. 18, 1956).
9. Coover, H. W., Jr. (to Eastman Kodak Co.), U. S. Patent 2,768,109 (Oct. 23, 1956).
10. Joyner, F. B., and Coover, H. W., Jr. (to Eastman Kodak Co.), U. S. Patent 2,784,127 (Mar. 5, 1957).
11. Coover, H. W., Jr., and Dickey, J. B. (to Eastman Kodak Co.), U. S. Patent 2,765,332 (Oct. 2, 1956).
12. Shearer, N. H., Jr., and Coover, H. W., Jr. (to Eastman Kodak Co.), U. S. Patent 2,776,232 (Jan. 1, 1957).
13. Jeremias, C. G. (to Eastman Kodak Co.), U. S. Patent 2,763,677 (Sept. 18, 1956).
14. Coover, H. W., Jr., Joyner, F. B., Shearer, N. H., Jr., and Wicker, T. H., Jr., *SPE Journal,* **15,** (5), 413–417 (1959).
15. Bodnar, M. J., and Schrader, W. H., *Modern Plastics,* **36,** (1), 142–148 (1958).
16. Tennessee Eastman Co., unpublished data.

— 32 —

Unsaturated Polyester Resins

William J. Eakins
De Bell & Richardson, Inc.
Hazardville, Connecticut

Unsaturated polyester resins are one of many matrices for laminates of glass fibers. At 25 to 35 per cent glass content, the bulk of the commercial use, laminates of polyester resin reinforced with cut glass strands are made as corrugated sheets, boats, bodies for trucks, truck trailers and sports cars. For this use, the adhesive bond between the glass and the resin must be sufficient to allow the glass fiber to stiffen the resin; stress transfer capability is relatively low.

When polyester resin is laminated with glass fabric (60 to 65 per cent glass content), e.g., to make electrically transparent components for aircraft, the strength and modulus values are considerably higher. Although the glass fabric carries the bulk of the applied stress, the resin elongates to transfer about 50 per cent of this stress between the fabric and yarn elements, allowing more of the glass to load simultaneously. For high glass loadings, as in continuous filament wound rocket motor cases (78 to 83 per cent glass content), piping, etc., the glass carries over 90 per cent of the load and the resin acts as an adhesive. To date, the bulk of the high glass content applications have been in epoxy resin because this resin apparently forms a superior bond to the coupling agent on the surface of the glass and thus transfers the high stresses between glass fibers required to obtain simultaneous loading. In all cases, the environmental resistance of the adhesive layer is critical in a successful application. At these low resin contents the bond between the resin and the glass is the most critical area. At high glass contents, when the resin is a true adhesive, the resin as well as the resin-glass bond should resist moisture attack to minimize strength loss.

REINFORCED PLASTICS TECHNOLOGY

During World War II, a new technology was born—laminating at low glass densities by hand-layup contact molding. Previously, materials were fabricated into parts either by forming into sheets, rods, bars or beams, and piecing together or by putting the material into a press and molding under temperature and pressure. The first technique uses thermoplastic materials, that is, the metals and the plastics that soften on heating. Tooling is generally inexpensive. On the other hand, molding under high temperature and pressure utilizes costly molds, hence it requires a large volume run on a single item. Its advantage is that complex shapes, difficult to fabricate from sheet, cylinders or bars can be made in one operation. Since thermosetting materials that polymerize in a three-dimensional structure have a memory, they cannot be thermoformed from sheet. Molding under heat and pressure was the only method possible until the advent of the polyester fiber-glass structure through the hand-layup molding technique.

Polyester resins became practical when the low temperature catalyst promoter system, methylethyl ketone (MEK) peroxide-cobalt naphthenate (CN), was discovered. The polyester resin could be mixed with large additions of styrene and approximately 25 per cent by weight glass strand and gelled through the addition of small amounts of MEK peroxide and cobalt naphthenate. Final hardening or curing was accomplished by heating the gelled object, removed from its mold, to temperatures in the order of 200°F. Thus, large objects such as boat hulls could be formed on waxed wooden molds by impregnating cut strand fiberglass mat with a paint brush or a spray gun having two heads, one for catalyst and the other for resin and promoter. The mold is first sprayed with catalyzed resin, the mat applied, sprayed and rolled. For each pair of subsequent mats applied and sprayed with resin, a lamb's wool roller is used to remove the air and push the mats sufficiently close together to form a layup of 25 to 30 per cent glass content. As the resin begins to polymerize, heat is given off. The thicker the section or the lower the glass content, the more heat is evolved per unit of exposed area. The heat that cannot be conducted away increases the temperature of the gelling mixture. When the temperature of any part of the gelling mass exceeds about 425°F, the resulting laminate becomes excessively brittle and is filled with small voids caused by vaporized styrene.

Three-component Spray

Recently, a new variation has gained acceptance by hand-layup fabricators, the three-headed spray gun.[1] Besides resin and catalyst heads, this gun has a roving cutter that is continuously fed an end or more of 60 end roving. As the cut glass strand is thrown toward the mold surface, it is blended with the resin and catalyst. It is claimed that since the glass and resin go down simultaneously, there is less occluded air to roll out, and that as consistent high quality a part can be made as is made using cut strand mat. There is a considerable material price saving involved in using roving in place of cut strand mat.

Preform Technique

The preform technique is a method for preparing the glass strand for press-molded parts. In a sense, a cut strand mat is formed in the shape of the part to be molded. Roving fed through a cutter is chopped into cut strand and directed toward a rotating screen mold of the desired shape. From inside this mold down through the bottom of the table, a fan is exhausting air; thus the strand as it contacts the screen is held on the screen by air pressure. As the cake builds on the screen mold, it is sprayed with a binder emulsion. The screen molds with their cakes are then removed from the spraying and dried in a circulating air oven. The dried preforms are placed in heated matched metal die molds, a measured quantity of resin added, and the part made within a few minutes after the mold is closed if a high temperature activation catalyst such as di-t-butyl peroxide is used

with a polyester resin. The object made from a preform may be a washing machine tub or a lamp shade.

CHEMISTRY

Unsaturated polyester resins are generally the reaction product of a dibasic unsaturated acid and a glycol. The most reactive types have the vinyl group in the α,β position relative to the acid. The reaction is as follows for maleic anhydride plus 1,2-propylene glycol to make a high reactivity unsaturated alkyd:

$$H_2C-C \begin{matrix} O \\ \\ \\ O \end{matrix} \qquad CH_3 \\ \\ H_2C-C \diagdown_O + HOCH_2-CH-OH \longrightarrow$$

(10% excess)

$$HOCH_2-\overset{CH_3}{\underset{|}{CH}}-O-\overset{O}{\underset{\|}{C}}-CH_2=CH_2-\overset{O}{\underset{\|}{C}}-$$

$$O[CH_2-\overset{CH_3}{\underset{|}{CH}}-O-\overset{O}{\underset{\|}{C}}-CH_2=CH_2-\overset{O}{\underset{\|}{C}}-O-]_x$$

$$\overset{CH_3}{\underset{|}{CH_2}}-CH-OH + (x+1)H_2O$$

Molecular weights for these resins are approximately 4000. Ten per cent excess of propylene glycol is added to drive the reaction to completion. Water is removed as the solution is heated by passing carbon dioxide under the surface of the reaction mixture. The carbon dioxide also seals the surface from air and protects the mixture from discoloration. The degree of completion of the reaction can be measured at first by the quantity of water removed and later by the number of acid groups still available for reaction, determined by titration with alcoholic potash (KOH).

The substitution of phthalic anhydride for maleic anhydride is the classic method of reducing unsaturation and increasing aromatic or, generally, styrene compatibility. For example, 1 mole maleic anhydride, 1 mole phthalic anhydride, and 2.2 moles propylene glycol give a polyester of medium reactivity, while 1 mole maleic anhydride, 2 moles phthalic anhydride, and 3.3 moles propylene glycol yield a polyester of low reactivity. Even in the high reactivity polyester, a ratio of 2 maleic to 1 phthalic is used.

Either styrene, vinyl toluene or α-methyl styrene are used with general-purpose polyesters as crosslinking agents. At least 16 per cent of styrene is necessary to furnish sufficient crosslinks, and usually 28 per cent or more is added by the resin manufacturer as a part of his formulation.

Inhibitors

Were inhibitors not added by the resin manufacturers prior to the unsaturated monomer addition, the resins would crosslink in lumps as the monomer is added, setting to a hard, useless mass. The inhibitor in most common use is hydroquinone, added at approximately 0.015 per cent by weight of alkyd. This inhibitor retards the formation of free radicals. When a catalyst is added, it must first use up a portion of the hydroquinone. Unfortunately, a retardant-type inhibitor is consumed during storage; therefore it gives limited protection. Also, it protects to almost the same degree at an elevated temperature as at room temperature. Consequently, the retardant-type inhibitor gives either long gel-cure times at an elevated temperature with a long pot life at a lower temperature or a short gel time at the elevated temperature with a short pot life at the lower temperature.

Some other inhibitors are classed as stabilizers. They stabilize the resin for long pot life at room temperature; yet they allow a complete cure at molding temperatures in a short cycle. They are used in making resins for corrugated fiber-glass sheeting manufacture, for example. Salts of substituted hydrazines,[2] quaternary ammonium salts,[3] substituted benzoquinones[4] and triphenyl phosphite are among the stabilizers.

RECENT ADVANCES

Combinations of glass fabric and polyester resins have found considerable use in the aircraft industry for nonsupporting structures, e.g., in radar equipment for weather protection and as a lense for the scanning devices. They use glass fabric to make a uniform high quality piece containing 60 to 70 per cent glass, and many new techniques have been developed.

Vacuum Bag Molding

To handle small numbers of parts, generally 500 or less, the "vacuum bag" technique of low-pressure molding is suitable. Resin-wetted layers of fabric are stacked one on another on a nonporous mold surface and covered with a polyvinyl alcohol (PVA) film. Gutters are formed by a coiled spring and a roll of clay just outside the periphery of the resin-soaked fabric area. A vacuum pump is connected to this gutter area, and the pressure inside the sealed off area is reduced to a few inches of mercury. A hard rubber roller is applied from the center of the laminate to the periphery, removing a small quantity of resin and a large quantity of air. As much as 30 to 50 per cent of the resin is removed by this rolling until all visible voids are removed to the gutter area. This method can result in uniform parts, but as with all wet layup, the skill of the operator is critical.

Catalysts Activated by UV Light

Another advance was the development of UV light-sensitive catalysts such as benzoin and various homologues. In this manner, the pot life problem was circumvented and gel-cure times decreased substantially by using a combination of a UV light catalyst to gel and a free radical temperature-activated type (benzoyl peroxide) to cure. Generally, this catalyst system allowed the operator to produce a larger percentage of high quality parts.

Allyl Resins

Greater uniformity in layup was also obtained by the mechanical impregnation of rolls of fabric with a hot polyester resin using diallyl phthalate as the crosslinking agent in place of styrene. Diallyl phthalate has a much lower reactivity as well as a higher viscosity; consequently it must be heated for flow and cure. The storage life of the diallyl phthalate-modified formulations is superior to that of styrene, and there is less squeeze-out of resin during layup. A high-temperature activation catalyst is employed with diallyl phthalate polyesters. Diallyl phthalate and diallyl isophthalate are also used alone as casting resins and are co-polymerized with other monomers such as diallyl diglycol carbonate for electrical potting.

Prepregs

Since 1956, the use of preimpregnated fabrics has swept through the aircraft industries. Once it became apparent that the number of reject parts could be reduced 80 per cent or more by the use of "prepregs," economics catalyzed the change. Preimpregnated fabrics are prepared by dip coating fabric in an organic solvent solution of a mixture of polyester resin and diallyl phthalate monomer. The resin is modified to give flow on molding and tack to handling. In a typical prepreg polyester, an amorphous and a crystalline resin are mixed to give the desired tack and flow characteristics. The crystalline formulation might be ethylene adipate fumarate and the amorphous formulation 1,2-propylene maleate isophthalate. About 13 per cent diallyl phthalate is added to a mixture of 1 part crystalline to 2 parts amorphous resin. One part acetone to 5 parts toluene are used as mixed solvent to make an application mixture.

Another interesting and growing use for cut strand mat laminates is in tanks, duct work and drainage piping for acidic and salt solutions, both hot and cold, particularly those used in plating. For trouble-free use, the polyester fiber-glass laminates are best suited for duct work. Except for strong, hot phenolic or acid fumes these ducts will resist almost any vapor. If condensate damages a duct, the part can be repaired in place with a patch kit and the duct drained at the points of condensation to prevent further damage. Polyester resin plus 20 per cent silica powder will make a satisfactory coating for a gutter inside the duct.

In the beginning, a polyester resin was available that gave excellent hot water resistance when laminated in tank forms. These vessels were in demand for hot water rinse tanks. This resin was a high reactivity type (a large number of crosslinks were formed during the gelling and hardening process). It had a large percentage of fumaric acid that improved the high temperature stiffness and gave excellent resistance to embrittlement. Fumaric acid-based tanks lasted over 3 yr. When this and other formulations changed to a maleic base, the newer plating tanks for hot water rinses fell apart as a result of embrittlement in as short a time as 4 months. To overcome this problem, a special formulation was developed using a polyester resin based on the reaction product of an alkylene glycol of bisphenol-A and fumaric acid. This solid resin is mixed with equal parts by weight styrene and for this use may be catalyzed by a complicated system consisting of Amine No. 220,* high temperature catalyst, cobalt naphthenate promoter, N,N-dimethylaniline and a low temperature catalyst. The high temperature catalyst, two amines and promoter are mixed with the alkyd and the styrene. The low temperature catalyst, methylethyl ketone peroxide, is diluted with diallyl phthalate as a carrier and sprayed as a mist through a separate auxiliary head of a spray gun while the resin mixture is sprayed through an enclosed type main head in a continuous stream. The low vapor pressure of the diallyl phthalate aids the catalyst to reach its target.

Flexible Polyesters

Brittleness is a characteristic difficulty in the polyester resins of medium and high reactivity. Resilience can be introduced by adding 15 to 30 per cent of a flexible polyester resin of the formula: 3.0 moles fumaric acid, 3.0 moles adipic acid, 3.3 moles ethylene glycol, and 3.3 moles diethylene glycol with 30 per cent styrene. However, the shrinkage increases appreciably, from about 7 to 14 per cent, and water resistance decreases markedly because of the saturated aliphatic chains in the flexible resin.

Isophthalic Acid Polyesters

Isophthalic acid has been used in increasing quantities in the manufacture of polyester resins. It does not depress the impact strength as does a phthalic addition and, aromatic in nature, it tends to reduce water adsorption in the resin. Also, the thickening property of the isophthalic acid tends to allow larger styrene additions, thus further reducing water adsorption. It has been claimed that in laminate structures, as the isophthalic acid proportion increases in the resin at the expense of maleic anhydride, there is increased adhesion to the glass fibers. It is likely that, rather than increasing the adhesion, the isophthalic acid lowers the solubility of water in the resin and therefore decreases the rate of attack of water on the glass-resin bond. The use of isophthalic acid in a resilient polyester formulation will improve the modulus and heat distortion point if it can be substituted for aliphatic dibasic acids. Information on the formulation of polyester[5] and isopolyester[6] resins versus the physical properties of the casting is available.

Although polyester resins do not appear to bond well to uncoated E glass fiber, they have a comparatively high shrinkage,[7] and it appears that it is this shrinkage that maintains high dry strength in a laminate. However, when this laminate is subjected to moist conditions, the water penetrates through the resin to the glass-resin interface. The adsorption of water in the resin changes the distribution of stress at the resin-glass joints.[7] With glass fabric laminates the stress pattern is entirely different from that obtained with continuous strand unidirectional mat.[8]

"Buton" Resins

In 1959, a new radically different type of unsaturated thermosetting resin[9] entered the commercial field. A liquid copolymer of butadiene and styrene, it was known as "C-oil" and now "Buton" resin. In the copolymerization the butadiene reacts for the most part as a mono-olefin, re-

* Union Carbide Chemical Co., New York, N. Y.

sulting in vinyl groups attached to a polymer chain. Thus, when a hydrocarbon crosslinking monomer is used, it is possible to have a hydrocarbon end product with extremely low water adsorption. Because it has a high boiling point, vinyl toluene is used instead of styrene in a 60:40 or 50:50 ratio with the resin as a crosslinking agent. Since these resins have relatively inactive vinyl groups near room temperature, it is necessary to use high temperature activation catalysts such as mixtures of dicumene peroxide and di-*t*-butyl peroxide at temperatures above 260°F, usually 290 to 300°F, to gel and cure. Fabric laminates finished with vinyl alkoxy silane type finishes will have flexural strength and modulus values equivalent to values obtained with unsaturated polyester resins. Because of the absence of polar compounds in the cured resin, this type of cured thermoset has negligible water adsorption and should be a candidate in those mechanized operations that can use a high temperature catalyst system, e.g., the manufacture of glass-reinforced pipe.

Other Resins

Finally, the triallyl cyanurate and maleimide modified unsaturated polyester resins merit a short discussion. Since the early fifties, the armed forces have been requiring high temperature properties in laminating resins for many aircraft applications. To meet this need, a number of suppliers developed a triallyl cyanurate-modified polyester. Although these commercial resins represented the highest realizable heat resistance for the cyanurate type of resin, they had deficiences: high shrinkage of the triallyl cyanurate monomer, oxidation of the alkyd portion, and craze-cracking of the co-polymers due to further curing of the partially hardened resin. A good, reasonably craze-free,

heat-resistant formulation can be made from 2.0 moles propylene glycol, 1.5 moles maleic anhydride, 0.5 mole cinnamic acid, and 0.25 mole chlorophthalic anhydride, with 1.8 moles acrylonitrile and 1.1 moles triallyl cyanurate as monomers. These resins require very careful curing techniques. If the temperature rises too rapidly within the thicker areas, crosslinks will be formed when the resin is below the strength required to resist the shrinkage that results from polymerization. The use of maleimide as a monomer has been found to reduce crazing at elevated temperatures substantially.

Regardless of the improvement in the heat resistant properties of the polyesters, they cannot be compared to the acid-based phenolics such as CTL-91-LD (Cincinnati Testing Laboratories) and its competitive equivalents.

References

1. Anderson, D. F. (to Canadian-Ingersoll-Rand Co. Ltd.), U. S. Patents 2,787,314 (Apr. 2, 1957) and 2,933,125 (Apr. 19, 1960).
2. Parker, E. E. (to Pittsburgh Plate Glass Co.), U.S. Patent 2,570,269 (Oct. 9, 1951).
3. Parker, E. E. (to Pittsburgh Plate Glass Co.), U.S. Patent 2,593,787 (Apr. 22, 1952).
4. Anderson, T. F. (to Libbey-Owens-Ford Glass Co.), U. S. Patent 2,610,168 (Sept. 9, 1952).
5. Parker, E. E., and Moffett, E. W., *Ind. Eng. Chem.*, **48**, 1615 (1954).
6. Parker, E. E., *Modern Plastics*, **36**, 135 (June 1958).
7. Outwater, J., Section 10-F, 15th Annual Conference, Reinforced Plastics Division, S.P.I. (1960).
8. Desai, M. B., and McGarry, F. J., Section 16-E, 14th Annual Conference, Reinforced Plastics Division, S.P.I. (1959).
9. Clark, H., and Vanderbilt, B. M., Section 17-C, 14th Annual Conference, Reinforced Plastics Division, S.P.I. (1959).

─ 33 ─

The Resin to Glass Bond

William J. Eakins
De Bell & Richardson, Inc.
Hazardville, Connecticut

Reinforced plastic parts are made of two widely dissimilar materials: a high modulus, high strength, low elongation material—the glass—and a low modulus, low strength, relatively higher elongation material—the resin. These materials are mated together across a region called an interface. This interface region has been broadened by definition to include that portion of the glass and the resin that is affected by the presence of the other, as well as the coupling agent or finish that may form a chemical link between phases. Inorganic or organic contaminants also are frequently present on the surface of the glass.

COUPLING AGENTS

The coupling agents are chemically designed to react with both glass and laminating resin (see Fig. 1). Two classes of coupling agents have extensive commercial use: the alkyl alkoxy silanes and the chromic chloride complexes. The chemical structures indicate the most efficient method of application to be a monolayer, the glass-reactive side, combining with the silanols of the glass and the resin-reactive side at the surface ready to co-polymerize with the laminating resin during the gelling and curing period. Data published to date[1] have indicated that considerably more than a monolayer is necessary to obtain maximum strength in the laminate and retain that strength in a moist atmosphere.

It has been shown that under certain conditions the coupling agent does react with the glass surface. When a chlorosilane is applied in the vapor phase to dehydrated E glass, hydrochloric acid is removed as a reaction product after the choloro-silane has been cured on the glass.[2] *P*-nitrobenzyl bromide[3] and epichlorohydrin,[1] applied similarly, provide evidence that an ionic reaction occurs between the halogen and the silanol group on the glass surface. β-chloroallyl trichlorosilane has been applied in the vapor phase to heat-cleaned glass fabric with indications, by the superior results obtained, of a strong bond to the glass and to the resin.

The alkyl alkoxysilanes, however, are applied commercially from water solution rather than vapor. It has been shown that the alkoxy groups react with the water to form silanol groups, which react in turn, to form siloxane ($-Si-O-Si$) bonds with water as the by-product. It has been suggested[1] that these siloxanes remain soluble in the water.

These alkyl alkoxy siloxanes can be removed partially from the surface of hydrated E glass by solvent extraction. In every case, an unextracted layer is left on the surface of the glass. This indicates that the surface layer or layers of siloxane were probably oriented toward the glass and thus formed a siloxane structure that was uniform and complete, which therefore dissolved with difficulty. This also indicates the probability of a reaction with the glass surface silanols.

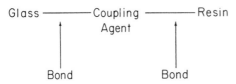

Fig. 1. Idealized reactions of the coupling agent.

THE GLASS FILAMENT

It may be inferred from the work of a number of investigators that the surface of a glass tends to adsorb both oxygen and water. One investigator[4] carefully measured the adsorption of oxygen by lead glass and other glasses and indicated that oxygen can be adsorbed as a surface layer of semi-chemical bond strength, when there are vacant oxygen sites in the surface octahedra. In E glass with 15 per cent alumina and 5 per cent magnesia, such vacancies are possible. In another study,[5] working with single filaments of E glass, it is demonstrated that maintaining the glass in a vacuum results in retention of original tensile strength of 525,000 psi over the 28-day test period. In dry air, however, the glass steadily loses strength at a diminishing rate, 0.5 per cent the first day, 0.1 per cent the 28th day, 0.05 per cent on the 128th day, etc. In humid air (100 per cent relative humidity) the initial loss was 8 per cent the first day, 0.3 per cent the 28th day, 0.02 per cent on the 128th day, etc., as shown in Fig. 2. Handling also reduces the tensile strength, especially of the larger diameter filaments.[5, 6]

a spray to apply a size or binder solution. This coating is necessary to handle the strand for subsequent operations. This solution may be starch-oil, a loom size to improve weaving, consisting of hydrogenated cottonseed oil, partially dextrinized starch, fatty acid esters, polyvinyl alcohol, and emulsifiers.[7]

For use with polyester resins, the size applied at the bushing may be a "Volan"* size consisting of methacrylato chromic chloride ("Volan"), polyvinyl acetate lubricant, and emulsifiers. It may be a "Garan"** size having as its coupling agent the sodium salt of vinyl triethoxysilane, or it may be an epoxy-resin-compatible formulation[8] useful in continuous filament winding at high glass content. The base formula disclosed is: saturated polyester resin, lubricant, polyvinyl alcohol, and polyvinyl pyrrolidone. This patent is a variation of another one[9] that shows the advantages of using saturated polyester resins in glass size formulations.

Note that the above formulations are all emulsions. The fiber glass producers prefer water systems, since organic solvents are combustible and the bushing operates at over 2000°F. The materials generally found best for giving the glass

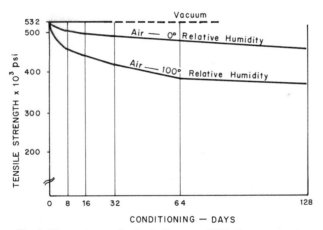

Fig. 2. The exposure of a single filament of "E" glass vs. retention of tensile strength.[5]

SIZES

Glass filaments for reinforced plastics are 0.0002 to 0.0005 in. in diameter. They are formed from a 204-hole bushing operating at a temperature of 2300°F and at a rate exceeding 10,000 ft/min. The glass flows through the holes in the bottom of a platinum alloy pot by gravity and is drawn or formed at an "onion" or lump just under each tip. After forming, the glass strand is immediately and continuously drawn over a pad or passed through

strand good lubricity and satisfactory resistance to self-abrasion are organic polymers, for the most part water insoluble.

The glass strand as it is drawn in air has a tremendous tensile strength of 525,000 psi. Air and moisture weaken the filament at or near its surface, but the sizes that are applied give considerable protection against further damage. The

* E. I. du Pont de Nemours & Co., Inc., Wilmington, Delaware.

** Johns-Manville Corp., Toledo, Ohio.

water and chemicals present promote further surface degradation of the glass to >90,000 and <300,000 psi in accordance with the degree of handling to which the glass filament has been subjected.

Cured resin-glass composites lose considerably less strength in moist air or water when sized with a binder containing a coupling agent. This effect may be specific for certain coupling agent/resin combinations. For example, a "Volan" size at 85 per cent glass in continuous filament winding does fairly well with a general-purpose polyester resin, but poorly with an anhydride-hardened epoxy. The strand treated with "Volan" alone, without the other ingredients of the size, is much more difficult to handle; nevertheless it will show comparatively excellent strength retention with both the polyester and the anhydride-hardened epoxy. The epoxy-compatible-sized rovings are supplied for use with epoxy resins in continuous filament winding.

CUT STRAND MAT

Rovings sized with "Volan" binder or "Garan" binder are used to make cut strand mat or preforms. The cut strand mat is an interesting product. Sixty end roving is chopped continuously into strands 1 to 1½ in. long, shot out a chute upon a moving screen bed. The air is moving through this bed to a low pressure area underneath the screen, and the glass is placed on the screen by this moving air. Into the moving stream of cut glass strand is discharged either powdered solid resin or a spray of liquid resin. The prepared, supported mat enters a tunnel oven to set the binder and thus hold the cut strands together so that they may be rolled as a flat, porous mat. Some of the latest improvements in cut strand mat manufacture may be seen in reference.[10]

The binders for cut strand mat fall into the following classifications:

(1) Soluble—a powdered form of the reaction product of the diglycol of bisphenol-A and fumaric acid.
(2) Partially soluble—a water-emulsified reaction product of phthalic anhydride, maleic anhydride and propylene glycol.
(3) Insoluble—a water-emulsified melamine phenolic combination.

Cut strand mats are also available mechanically tied on a modification of an Axminister loom. Rovings in counts up to 60 ends are woven in a basket weave on a similar loom to obtain a material having high glass density at low cost. Neither of these modifications requires additional binder.

PREPARING GLASS FABRIC

To withstand the abrasion of intensive handling operations, glass fabrics are woven of twisted and plied yarns coated at the bushing with starch-oil (No. 630) size. When the fabrics are used in reinforced plastics, they require a batch heat-cleaning step to remove the starch-oil size and a dip-drying or "finishing" step to coat with a coupling agent.

Fabrics for reinforced plastics are mainly of two kinds: the open plain weave, highly plied fabrics for the outer surfaces of boat hulls, to spread the load on impact, and the seven harness satin weaves that provide high glass density and maximum draping properties. The satin weave is used for high quality aircraft and missile laminates providing 60 to 70 per cent glass content.

Each of the fabric preparing operations—weaving, heat-cleaning and finishing—has been studied.[11, 12, 13] It was found[12] that the binder can change from tacky to dry as a function of humidity and temperature during the weave processing. This affects the thickness and tightness of the fabric. In an unpublished continuation of this work, the author has shown that variable thicknesses of fabric in weaving is due to variations in the quantity and composition of the solids deposited from an aqueous starch-oil emulsion. The weaving characteristics of the yarn change to provide a loose weave when more oil is present, or a tight weave of powdery yarn with an excess of starch in the size.

Batch heat cleaning at 650 to 800°F shrinks or densifies the glass to "set" the weaving pattern in the yarn.[13, 14, 15] Densifying glass filament by heating, called compaction, increases both the strength and modulus.[13] Highest dry flexural strength and modulus, but poorest strength retention on boiling, were found in polyester laminates made with the finished fabric heated to the highest temperature. Most recent studies[15] have shown that the chemical activity of the glass surface is affected by heating. The improvement in the strength and modulus of the glass made possible by heating is not severely influenced by the degrading effect of surface deterioration up to 775°F. Removal of size is sufficient to permit a finish such as "Volan" to bond securely and give excellent retention of strength properties in boiling water with room-temperature-cured polyesters.

The maximum temperature and time at that temperature during heat-cleaning also affect the drape of the fabric after it is finished with "Garan" or "A-172."* This drape can be made to vary over 50 per cent by changing the degree of compaction obtained in the heat-cleaning operation.[15] The finishing line is composed of fabric unwinding and tensioning apparatus, finish dipping tank and padder rolls to squeeze finish liquid from fabric, drying tower or cans, water-dipping tank, padder rolls and drying tower or cans. The heat-cleaned fabric containing residual organic matter of less than 0.10 per cent is dipped in a large reservoir of aqueous finish solution. Occasionally the residual solids are reduced by a weak acid wash, but generally the heel of the finish solution accumulates some of the organic residual. After padding of the pick up, the finish application solution is reduced to 30 to 50 per cent for most fabrics. The cloth is then dried, either on steam-heated cans or in a vertical tower containing a series of slots through which the air passes at high velocity (2500 + ft/min) and a temperature of 300 to 400°F.[1] In the second bath, the chloride salts formed by neutralization of the "Volan" with 1 per cent ammonia are dissolved. The cans, either of stainless steel or "Teflon" coated, are steam heated to a surface temperature of 300 to 350°F.

In the application of a finish, a sufficient concentration must be used to not only cover the filament area with a monolayer but also to fill a considerable portion of the spaces between the fila-ments of a twisted strand. Optimum laminate physical properties are obtained with approximately 0.16 per cent "Volan" solids (0.05 per cent chromium) or about 0.25 per cent or more of the vinyl siloxane coating-type finishes such as "Garan" and "A-172" each based on dry weight of glass.

It is important to note that the proper functional group must be on the finish to obtain a bond to a particular class of resin.

Note: All laminates with 12 plies, except where noted, Style 181 fabric.

(1) Polyester: "Paraplex" P-43 catalyzed with 1 per cent benzoyl peroxide heated slowly through activation temperature, i.e., about 160 to 250°F to cure.

(2) Epoxy: 100 parts "Epon" 828, 14 to 15 parts meta-phenylenediamine. Cured in press at 235 to 250°F for at least 1 hr.

(3) Melamine: "Cymel" 405 applied from water and B-staged for 2½ min at 275°F. The 12 plies were pressed at 300°F for 15 min at 1000 psi.

(4) Phenolic: "Plaskon" V-204 coated and B-staged for 2 to 3 min at 275°F. Thirteen plies of the preimpregnated material were molded at 290°F., first at contact pressure for 6 to 8 min, then at 200 psi. A post-cure of 24 hr each at 250, 300, and 400°F followed.

TABLE 1. DRY AND WET FLEXURAL STRENGTH PROPERTIES OF FABRIC LAMINATES WITH FABRIC SURFACE FINISHED WITH VARIOUS COUPLING AGENTS.

Finishing Agent			Flexural Strength (psi)		
Class	Functional or Modifying Group	Resin	Dry	Wet	Hr Boil
Chrome complex	Methacrylate	Polyester	70,000	58,000	2
Chrome complex	Isobutyric	Polyester	60,000	30,000	2
Alkoxy silane	Vinyl	Polyester	72,000	68,000	2
Alkoxy silane	Ethyl	Polyester	43,500	30,000	2
Alkoxy silane	Aminopropyl	Polyester	37,500	18,000	2
None	None	Polyester	60,000	35,000	2
Chrome complex	Methacrylate	Epoxy	80,000	72,000	2
Chrome complex	Methacrylate	Epoxy	80,000	35,000	72
Alkoxy silane	Vinyl	Epoxy	80,600	84,400	2
Alkoxy silane	Vinyl	Epoxy	80,600	38,000	72
Alkoxy silane	Aminopropyl	Epoxy	81,000	75,000	2
Alkoxy silane	Aminopropyl	Epoxy	81,000	55,000	72
None	None	Epoxy	73,600	53,500	2
Alkoxy silane	Vinyl	Melamine	31,500	28,000	2
Alkoxy silane	Aminopropyl	Melamine	90,000	85,000	2
None	None	Melamine	38,000	27,000	2
Alkoxy silane	Vinyl	Phenolic	60,000	18,000	2
Alkoxy silane	Aminopropyl	Phenolic	80,000	55,000	2
None	None	Phenolic	69,000	14,000	2

For polyester resins, Table 1 shows that glass fabrics heat-cleaned and finished with either the methacrylic chrome complex or a vinyl alkoxy silane are markedly superior to those treated with the saturated counterparts, isobutyric[16] chrome complex and ethyl alkoxy silane.[1] The dry flexural strength values for laminates with ethyl and aminopropyl alkoxy silanes are so low because these groups do not form a chemical bond with the polyester resin as does the vinyl group. The wet strength retention with "A-1100,"* aminopropyl silane, is very poor because, unlike the ethyl counterpart, it is water soluble even as a polymer when it is not reacted to the resin as well as to the glass. Both the ethyl and the aminopropyl alkoxy silanes act as plasticizers next to the glass surface. The high shrinkage of the polyester is responsible for the high dry strength indicated for heat-cleaned fabric laminate.

In the epoxy resin series, a resin-reactive group in the coupling agent is seen to provide better resistance to boiling. The aminopropyl group of the finish ("A-1100") reacts with the epoxy groups of the resin gives water resistance. A new chrome complex with a similar epoxy-reactive group[15] gives similar strength retention in boiling water.

In laminates of melamine and phenolic, the aminopropyl alkoxy silane again ranks high, indicating reaction of the finish with the laminating resin as well as with the surface of the glass.

References

1. Sterman, S., and Bradley, H. B., Section 8D, 16th Annual Conference, Reinforced Plastics Division, S.P.I., Feb. 1961.

2. Gutfreund, K., and Weber, H. S., Section 8D, 16th Annual Conference, Reinforced Plastics Division, S.P.I., Feb. 1961.

3. Haller, W., and Duecker, H. C., *Nature,* **178,** 376–7 (1956).

4. Anderson, S., and Kimpton, D. D., *J. Am. Ceramic Soc.,* **43,** 484–488 (1960).

5. Thomas, W. F., *Physics and Chemistry of Glasses,* **1,** 1–18 (1960).

6. Kies, J. A., and McVicker, R. E., 13th Annual Conference, Reinforced Plastics Division, S.P.I., Feb. 1958.

7. Horton, R. C., and Falls, H. S., 13th Annual Conference, Reinforced Plastics Division, S.P.I., Feb. 1958.

8. Marzocchi, A. (to Owens Corning Fiberglass), U. S. Patent 2,931,739 (Apr. 5, 1960).

9. Collier, T. J. (to Owens Corning Fiberglass), U. S. Patent 2,801,189 (July 30, 1957).

10. Moore, L. D., and Cole, W. G. (to Ferro Corp.), U. S. Patent 2,925,117 (Feb. 16, 1960).

11. Eakins, W. J., Section 3A, 13th Annual Conference, Reinforced Plastics Division, S.P.I., Feb. 1958.

12. Eakins, W. J., Section 13A, 14th Annual Conference, Reinforced Plastics Division, S.P.I., Feb. 1959.

13. Eakins, W. J., Section 39–1, Volume V, Technical Papers, Society of Plastics Engineers, Jan. 1959.

14. Otto, W. H., presentation of paper, Glass Division, American Ceramic Society, Bedford Springs, Pa., Oct. 1956.

15. Eakins, W. J., unpublished work.

16. Yates, P. C., and Trebilcock, J. W., Section 8B, 16th Annual Technical Conference, Reinforced Plastics Division, S.P.I., Feb. 1961.

* Silicones Division Union Carbide Corp., Tonawanda, N. Y.

Polyamide Adhesives

Don E. Floyd

Research Laboratories
General Mills, Inc.
Minneapolis, Minnesota

Polyamide resins are used in two main classes of adhesives. These are (1) the thermoplastic heat-seal or heat-activated adhesives and (2) the thermoset, structural adhesives. The polyamide resins used in heat-seal adhesives are generally linear and neutral or non-reactive. Polyamides used in thermoset and structural adhesives are highly branched and are very reactive with epoxy resins because they contain unreacted amino groups. Consequently, the thermoset, structural polyamide-containing adhesives are really reacted or cured blends of reactive polyamides and epoxy resins. The following equation will serve to differentiate and identify the two classes of "Versamid"* polyamide resins to be covered in this chapter for the above uses. It will be noted that both such classes of polyamide resins are made from the polymerized fatty acids, commonly referred to as "dimer" acid.

When they are condensed with diamines, such as ethylene diamine, polyamide resins of a generally linear nature and a relatively neutral character are produced. Here, neutral means there are very few remaining unreacted amino and carboxyl groups in the molecules and the quantities of those present are nearly equal.

Resin Grades

Several grades of polyamide resins are produced by General Mills, Inc., and of these, the ones most frequently used for thermoplastic adhesives are "Versamids" 900, 930, 940, 950 and 100. What has been said heretofore about the composition and general properties applies to all of these, with the exception of "Versamid" 100. "Versamid" 100 is a branched amino-containing resin made from a

$$C_{34}H_{62}\diagup\!\!\!\!\!\diagdown \begin{array}{l} COOH \xrightarrow{\text{diamines}} \\ \\ COOH \xrightarrow[\text{polyamines}]{\text{higher}} \end{array}$$

Linear "Versamid"
Resins 930, 940, 950, 900

Branched chain, reactive
"Versamid" Resins 100, 115, 125, 140

HEAT-SEAL ADHESIVES

"Versamid" polyamides for heat-seal adhesives are the reaction products of dibasic acids with di-amines. All of these polyamides are based on polymerized fatty acids or dimer acids, made by polymerizing unsaturated fatty acids. Dimer acids consist of a mixture of 36 carbon atom dibasic acids probably containing several isomers and also a small amount of trimer and higher polymers.

polyamine rather than a diamine. Also, it is a semi-solid or balsam-like material, whereas "Versamids" 900, 930, 940 and 950 are all solids at room temperature. Typical data on these products are given in Table 1 for perspective.

These polyamides have certain characteristics in common. Because of the long chain structure of the dimer acids, they have a fatty character and

* Registered trademark of General Mills, Inc., Chemical Div.

TABLE 1. DATA ON "VERSAMID" POLYAMIDE RESINS.

| | "Versamid" | | | | |
| | Solid Series | | | | Semi-Solid |
	900	930	940	950	Series 100
Amine value	3	3	3	3	83–93
Color-Gardner (solid resin)	NDT 12	NDT 12	NDT 12	NDT 12	NDT 12
Melting point (ASTM 1240)	180–190	105–115	105–115	90–100	43–53
Viscosity (poises) 40°C*	—	—	—	—	—
Viscosity (poises) 150°C*	—	35–45	20–30	7–15	10–15
Viscosity (poises) 200°C*	3–4	—	—	—	—
% Ash (by weight)	0.05	0.05	0.05	0.05	0.05
Specific gravity	0.98	0.98	0.98	0.98	0.98
Pounds per gallon	8.2	8.2	8.2	8.2	8.2
Penetration—25°C—ASTM D5–52	2	3	4	15	100

* Brookfield Viscometer

show a high degree of flexibility. Because of this composition, they have considerable resistance to water, but are more soluble than the more familiar nylon polyamides. Except for "Versamid" 900, which is a high-melting product, all of the resins named so far have fairly low melting points, around 100°C or slightly lower, and have relatively high solubility in alcoholic solvents. Some solubility data are given in Table 2. Solubility is improved somewhat by addition of other substances to the alcohol, including water, aromatic hydrocarbons, and aliphatic hydrocarbons. The choice of the particular solvent or solvent combination will depend upon the equipment to be used in applying the solution of the material and the needs or requirements for evaporation of the solvent. Like other polyamides, these "Versamids" have sharp melting points and low-melt viscosities.

The characteristics which make the polyamides especially useful for thermoplastic adhesives are: (1) low and sharp melting points, which give quick grab when the adhesive is activated with heat or solvent, (2) low viscosities in the molten state, which makes for ease of application, (3) strong adhesion to a variety of surfaces and substrates including various grades of paper, cellophane, cellulose ace-

TABLE 2. SOLUBILITY OF "VERSAMIDS" 930 AND 940.

Solvent	% N.V.	24 Hr at 25°C	Reflux Hot	After Cooling
n-Butanol	10	S	S	S
n-Butanol	35	S	S	S
Ethanol	10	I	S	Sep
Ethanol	35	I	S	Sep
Isopropanol	10	S	S	S
Isopropanol	35	PS	S	Gel
Isopropanol 91, water 9	10	S	S	S
Isopropanol 91, water 9	35	PS	S	S
Isopropanol 90, methyl butynol 10	10	S	S	S
Isopropanol 90, methyl butynol 10	35	PS	S	S
Isopropanol 30, toluene 70	10	S	S	S
Isopropanol 30, toluene 70	35	S	S	S
Isopropanol 30, hexane 70	10	S	S	S
Isopropanol 30, hexane 70	35	SlS	S	Gel
Methyl butynol	10	S	S	S
Methyl butynol	35	S	S	S
n-propanol	10	S	S	S
n-propanol	35	PS	S	S
n-propanol 95, water 5	10	S	S	S
n-Propanol 95, water 5	35	S	S	S

I—Insoluble	PS—Partly soluble	Sep—Separates
SLS—Slightly soluble	S—Soluble	N.V.—Non-volatile

tate, polyethylene, other plastic films, metal foils, paper board, etc., and (4) resistance to moisture and grease.

Hot Melts

"Versamids" 930 and 940 are the polyamides most widely used in hot melt cements. "Versamid" 950 is a modified product for special needs in having a low melting point and low viscosity, and good blocking resistance (in spite of lowered melting point). "Versamids" 900 and 100 are most often used as modifiers in hot-melt formulas, where they may be added to "Versamids" 930 and 940 to raise or lower the melting point, improve resistance to solvents, or to contribute some other characteristic.

Polyamide-based adhesives are employed for a number of different kinds of service. They are most widely used as heat-activated or heat-seal adhesives for flexible packaging materials such as paper, cellophane, aluminum foil, and cellulose acetate. They are used for packages of all sizes, shapes, and kinds and for the fastening of labels on containers. In some instances, heat-activated adhesion makes possible the design of a package which would not be possible with other adhesive forms. It is readily adapted to the assembly line packaging of numerous articles which requires rapid activation, nearly instantaneous adhesion, and high strength.

The polyamide-based adhesives are used for paper board boxes, for shoe, leather and metal cements. They are used also in adhesive formulas for plastic films such as "Mylar" and polyethylene.

Polyamide resins and the adhesives made from them are noted for strong adhesion, toughness, high cohesive strength and quick-set.

Application Techniques

The polyamides may be applied by various kinds of equipment. The paper converter often melts them in a resin pot connected with hot melt coating equipment and applies them by roller or knife coating equipment to a continuous web of paper. Occasionally, they are applied as melts to individual sheets or individual board pieces by similar techniques. Similar methods are also used in applying melts to plastic film and metal foil. However, for application to sheet metal as a sealing adhesive, as in a fabricated can, the adhesive composition is generally squirted in place as narrow beads along the area or seam to be adhered. Occasionally, the adhesives are spot printed or spot applied, as on paper and foil heat seal packages.

They may also be applied by spraying or even manually by brush or spatula from a melt pot, but these methods are used less frequently.

The liquid resin in the melt state must be relatively stable. Otherwise the pot would have to be cleaned out frequently or the material discarded. Frequently, new resin is added to the melt pot, rather than clean it out during an operation or as each new operation is started. The "Versamids" have been stabilized during manufacture to prevent air oxidation, and to prevent discoloration and skinning or gelling by the combination of heat and exposure to air. In spite of these precautions, as is the case with most organic substances, prolonged exposure to high temperature and oxygen, will cause some darkening, some skinning, and some gelation effect. These can be minimized by certain careful techniques. One is to avoid exposure to oxygen wherever possible. This may be done by operating under reduced pressure, or in an atmosphere of carbon dioxide or nitrogen, or simply by enclosing the resin mixture so that air has difficulty in reaching its surface. Other precautions include keeping the material at the minimum temperature needed for application, and heating only the minimum amount of material needed to keep the equipment operating properly. It is often helpful to stir the material gently to reduce the tendency of the surface to skin and dissolve any broken skins. It should not be stirred so rapidly that an air vortex develops in the hot resin. Additional antioxidants and stabilizers can be added to the resin mixtures if desired, but generally these are not necessary if proper mechanical techniques are followed.

Formulation

The polyamide resins may be used in a variety of ways as hot melt adhesives or in hot melt adhesive formulas. Frequently, additives are included in a formula to get special benefits, i.e., lowering of the melting point, increasing mar resistance, increasing peel strength, or increasing low temperature flexibility. Polyamides are compatible with a wide range of substances, including phenolic resins, rosin and its derivatives, maleic resins, waxes (except for paraffin), most plasticizers, shellac, nitrocellulose, and some cumarone-indene resins, which may be used for these purposes. Most of these resins tend to harden the composition and give added block resistance, although rosin and resins based on rosin generally increase tack or quick grab and may reduce blocking resistance. Waxes serve to lower viscosity and give smear and blocking resist-

TABLE 3. HEAT-SEAL CHARACTERISTICS OF "VERSAMID" POLYAMIDES.

| | "Versamid" | | | | |
	900	930	940	950	100
Sealing range (°C)	100–150	80–110	80–110	70–100	25
Blocking at 50°C, 1 psi, 50% relative humidity, 24 hr					
Face-to-face	None	None	Very slight	None	100%
Face-to-back	None	None	None	None	100%

ance, while plasticizers generally lower the viscosity and the melting point to give greater flexibility and less blocking resistance.

Hot melt cements based on straight polyamides generally have fairly narrow sealing ranges. Some of these are apparent from the data summarized in Table 3 on sealing range and blocking resistance. The sealing range is the temperature at which the material will form a fiber tearing bond on label paper on submission to very slight pressure for five seconds. The adhesive bond must be strong within less than one second after removal of heat. The sealing range can be broadened to some extent by addition of other substances, especially materials which do not have sharp melting points. It is also possible to incorporate substances which have only limited compatibility by use of a fluxing agent having high compatibility with both ingredients. Rosin and its derivatives are excellent fluxing agents.

Polyamides can also be used in solvent-based adhesive formulas. These solvents are usually alcohols or blends of alcohols with hydrocarbons. Application techniques are similar to those for hot-melts except that the solutions are applied at room temperature, and facility must be provided for removal of solvent from the coated material by evaporation or drying with heat.

Formulas have been developed for a wide variety of purposes. Representative examples of starting formulas given here include a general purpose adhesive for use in packaging, an adhesive of good low temperature flexibility, an adhesive for label paper and glassine, a wax-extended formula, an adhesive for polyethylene, and a hot-melt adhesive with delayed-tack effect.

GENERAL-PURPOSE PACKAGING ADHESIVE

	parts by wt.
"Versamid" 940	100
"Staybelite" Ester No. 10*	10
130°F Paraffin	4
"Santicizer" 8**	10

* Hercules Powder Co.
** Monsanto Chemical Co.

The "Staybelite" Ester No. 10 serves as a tackifier, while the paraffin improves blocking resistance and offsets the effect of the plasticizer in this respect.

ADHESIVE FOR LOW-TEMPERATURE PERFORMANCE

	parts by wt.
"Versamid" 940	85
"Versamid" 900	4
Paraffin	2
Dibutyl phthalate	9

Again, the paraffin is included to improve blocking resistance. The dibutyl phthalate is added to improve low temperature flexibility. Because of the presence of "Versamid" 900, which reduces the solubility of this formula, the hot-melt application technique is preferred.

ADHESIVE FOR LABEL PAPER AND GLASSINE

	parts by wt.
"Versamid" 940	50
"Versamid" 950	50

This simple composition has excellent quality and is useful as a general-purpose heat-seal adhesive.

FLEXIBLE ADHESIVE

	parts by wt.
"Versamid" 940	80
"Versamid" 100	20

"Versamid" 100 serves to soften and flexibilize the formula. This adhesive should not be used where blocking resistance is considered important. Hot-melt or solution may be used for its application.

POLYETHYLENE ADHESIVE

	parts by wt.
"Versamid" 940	40
"Versamid" 100	60

The tacky nature of "Versamid" 100 gives this formula good adhesion to polyethylene.

WAX-EXTENDED FORMULA

	parts by wt.
"Versamid" 940	85
"Zeco Wax" 6660	
(G. S. Ziegler Co.)	15

The wax serves as an extender which does not harm adhesive strength and it also improves blocking resistance. Such combinations may be prepared in solution or hot-melt for application.

DELAYED-TACK ADHESIVE

	parts by wt.
"Versamid" 940	70–80
"Santicizer" 9	20–30
Candelilla wax	2–4

This blend, applied as a hot-melt, goes through a stage of super-cooling after heat activation and remains tacky for a period of time below the actual melting point. The wax helps control the length of time the adhesive remains tacky.

All "Versamids" are compatible with each other and all may be used to modify the properties of the others. "Versamid" 900 is frequently added to "Versamid" 940 to raise the melting point and increase blocking resistance. It also greatly increases the solvent resistance of the blended adhesive. In contrast, "Versamid" 100 is often added to "Versamid" 940 to lower the melting point, to increase tackiness, and to give greater flexibility. Typical

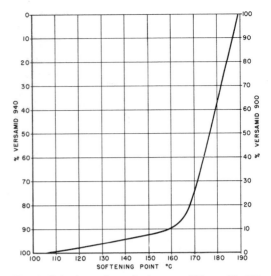

Fig. 2. Softening points of mixtures of Versamids 900 and 940.

melting point curves for these compositions are given in Figs. 1 and 2. They show that when two polyamides are blended, the higher melting one generally exerts a very profound effect on the melting point of the blend. In other words, a small amount of the higher melting resin markedly raises the melting point of the mixture.

A particularly interesting adhesive formula is made from a blend of "Versamids" 900 and 100, which represent extremes in melting point in this group of resins, "Versamid" 900 melting near 180°C and "Versamid" 100 being balsam-like and semi-solid at room temperature.

Blends of two "Versamids" will also interact with each other, going through a phase of block copolymerization followed by random copolymerization on prolonged heating at elevated temperatures. Normally, these interaction effects require high temperatures and prolonged heating times to bring about noticeable change. Interaction may be accompanied by change in viscosity and in melting point.

While this discussion has been aimed primarily towards adhesives and adhesion, there are other effects obtained which are frequently used to advantage. For example, a heat seal adhesive on paper may also be used as a barrier against moisture, moisture vapor, and grease to protect the contents of a heat sealed package. In addition, it may give a glossy effect. It is frequently applied over printing, usually from solvent. Typically, these are called over-print finishes.

In summary, the polyamide resins based on polymerized fatty acids have melting characteristics, viscosity, adhesion, and resistance properties

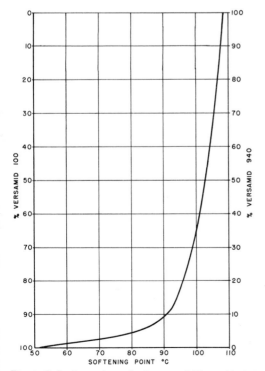

Fig. 1. Softening points of mixtures of Versamids 940 and 100.

which make them useful as heat seal adhesives for application to paper, foil, plastic film, metal sheeting, and other surfaces and substrates. Their performance is fine for quick grab, high speed application, strong bonds, and flexible character. They are most often compounded with other ingredients in heat-seal adhesive formulas, particularly for specialized uses.

THERMOSET STRUCTURAL ADHESIVES

Reaction of the amino-containing or branched-chain polyamide resins with epoxy resins produces thermoset reaction products possessing structural strength. These reaction products show strong adhesion to steel, aluminum, magnesium and other metals, wood, glass, masonry, and many plastics. Notable exceptions are fluorocarbon polymers. The adhesive blends may be cured at room temperature (60 to 80°F) or at elevated temperature, although cohesive strength is usually a little higher after cure at elevated temperature. Because they "set" or cure at room temperature, the adhesive blends have limited pot life and consequently are considered to be two-package adhesive systems. Only contact pressure is needed to form adhesive bonds.

Fields of Application

The polyamid-epoxy adhesive compositions are especially useful in several fields, including:

(1) metal to metal bonding
(2) wood bonding
(3) bonding of dissimilar metals
(4) metal to plastic bonding
(5) bonding or repair of masonry structures
(6) metal seam filling and metal weld sealing

These adhesives are used for aircraft and automotive applications as well as general industrial uses. Their principal limitation is loss of strength above 250°F; consequently they cannot be recommended for general service on prolonged exposures above this temperature.

Resin Grades

Four different grades of "Versamid" polyamide resins, capable of reacting or curing with epoxy resins, are available. Their properties are given in Table 4.

Characteristics of Polyamide-Epoxy Systems

The reaction between a polyamide and an epoxy resin is essentially the reaction of aliphatic amino groups with epoxy groups, and, therefore, parallels the amine-cured epoxy resins. However, there are several important differences. The polyamides are resins and polymers, and can serve as film formers and adhesives in their own right. Therefore, they play a strong role in modifying the properties of the cured adhesive. Not only do they contribute strong specific adhesion to metals, wood, glass and many other materials, but they also confer a "built-in" resilience and toughness not found in the epoxy resin alone. This shows up in bend tests and impact tests. Polyamides offer an interesting balance of peel strength and tensile strength.

Furthermore, these polyamides, since they are polymers, are relatively nonvolatile. They are not skin sensitizers and do not present the toxic hazard associated with ordinary amine curing agents. Therefore, less caution is needed in handling and application.

The polyamide-epoxy adhesives have much longer pot lives than most amine-cured epoxy adhesives and also have much lower exotherms. This permits mixing of several gallon quantities from the two components at one time. Handling and application are thus facilitated and control simplified.

Formulation

In blending polyamide resins with liquid epoxy resins, there is an optimum ratio for maximum

TABLE 4. "VERSAMID" POLYAMIDE RESINS FOR THERMOSET ADHESIVE COMBINATIONS.

	"Versamid"			
	100	115	125	140
Physical state	Semi-solid	Liquid	Liquid	Liquid
Viscosity (poises)				
40°C	—	500–750	80–120	—
25°C	—	—	500–750	125–175
Amine value	83–93	210–220	290–320	350–400
Relative cure rate	Slow	Moderate	Rapid	Moderate

TABLE 5. HARDNESS OF "VERSAMID"-EPOXY FORMU-
LATIONS.

Ratio	Hardness	
	Barcol*	Shore Durometer A
"Versamid" 125 : Bakelite ERL 2795		
40:60	60–65	—
50:50	20–25	—
60:40	—	90
65:35	—	85
70:30	—	50
75:25	—	30
80:20	—	5

* Barcol Impressor Model GYZJ-935

structural strength. Increasing the polyamide content serves to make the composition more flexible,
with greater elongation, higher peel strength at the
expense of lower structural strength and reduced
creep resistance. Adjusting the ratios of the two
reactants thus gives differences in structural
strength and peel strength or, in other terms, different degrees of flexibility (Table 5).

Before bonding metals, accepted practice in
metal cleaning and pretreatment should be followed. This may be done by sanding, sandblasting, and chemical treatments. It is best to clean
aluminum with solvent first and then apply an acid
chromate chemical pretreatment.

Table 6 gives typical starting formulas for "Versamid" 115 and various epoxy resins (without necessary fillers) for high strength structural adhesive
formulas.

"Versamids" 125 and 140 may be used in place
of the "Versamid" 115 in these formulas, if the
epoxy resin content is increased by 10 to 20 per
cent in each case (Table 7).

Adhesive Properties

Tables 9 and 10 show the impact resistance
values and bend strength test results, respectively,
for representative structural adhesive formulas.
Both reflect the effect of the polyamide resin portion on resilience and "built-in" flexibility.

Numerous environmental test studies on several
of these adhesive formulas have been made to test
resistance to chemicals, solvents, and various storage conditions. The effects are shown for some
formulas in Tables 11 and 12.

Plastic solders and sealants for seam filling and

TABLE 6. "VERSAMID" 115-EPOXY* ADHESIVE FORMULATIONS.

Parts by Weight		Epoxy Resin*	Company
"Versamid" 115	Epoxy		
40	60	"Araldite" 502	Ciba Co.
45	55	"Araldite" 6010	Ciba Co.
50	50	"Araldite" 504	Ciba Co.
50	50	ERL 2795	Bakelite Co.
40	60	ERL 2774	Bakelite Co.
40	60	ERL 3794	Bakelite Co.
40	60	"Epon" 828	Shell Chemical Co.
50	50	"Epon" 815	Shell Chemical Co.
45	55	"Epon" 834	Shell Chemical Co.
35	65	"Hysol" 6020	Houghton Laboratories
45	55	"Epi-Rez" 510	Jones-Dabney

* Equivalent epoxy resins also available from other suppliers.

TABLE 7. "VERSAMID" 125-EPOXY* ADHESIVE FORMULATIONS.

Parts by Weight		Epoxy Resin*	Company
"Versamid" 125	Epoxy		
40	60	ERL-2795	Bakelite Co.
30	70	"Araldite" 502	Ciba Co.
40	60	"Epon" 815	Shell Chemical Co.
30	70	ERL-2774	Bakelite Co.
30	70	"Araldite" 6010	Ciba Co.
35	65	"Epi-Rez" 510	Jones-Dabney

* Equivalent epoxy resins also available from other supplies.

TABLE 8. RECOMMENDED CURE CONDITIONS FOR FULL STRENGTH FOR SELECTED VERSAMID-EPOXY ADHESIVES.

Temp. (°F)	"Versamid" 115	"Versamid" 125	"Versamid" 140
300°F	20 min	10 min	20 min
250°F	45 min	30 min	45 min
200°F	60 min	45 min	60 min
150°F	3 hr	2 hr	3 hr
75°F	36–48 hr	24–36 hr	36–48 hr

Typical pot lives are:

Composition	Ratio	Size of Batch (Gal)	Usable Pot Life (Min)	Temp. at Gel Time (°F)	Max. Temp. Reached (°F)
"Versamid" 125: "Bakelite" ERL 2795	40:60	½	60	185	355
"Versamid" 115: "Bakelite" ERL 2795	50:50	½	110	140	140
"Versamid" 140: "Bakelite" ERL 2795	30:70	½	90	180	430

TABLE 9. IMPACT TESTS ON "VERSAMID"-EPOXY ADHESIVES.

(ASTM D1002–49T) (MIL A–5090–B) (USAF)

Composition	Tensile Shear Before Impact	Tensile Shear After Specified Impacts*		
		40 in. lb (psi)	60 in. lb (psi)	80 in. lb. (psi)
"Versamid" 115:ERL 2795: Surfex MM (50:50:20)	2,730	2,180	2,260	2,240
"Versamid" 115:ERL 2795: AFD filler (50:50:20)	3,420	2,870	2,460	2,260
"Versamid" 115:ERL 2795: Tabular alumina (50:50:20)	3,200	3,220	3,350	2,940
"Versamid" 115:ERL 2795: Nylon powder (50:50:20)	2,940	3,530	2,680	2,250
"Versamid" 115:ERL 2795: Atomized aluminum powder #101 (50:50:50)	3,025	2,780	2,930	2,840

* Impacts were applied by placing the adhesive specimens with the center of the glue line on the anvil of a Gardner Impact Tester, and striking the joint with a ½-in. diameter spherical impresser at the specified force.

TABLE 10. BEND STRENGTH.

(MIL-A-5090-B, 4.3.2.9)

Composition	Average Load at Failure (lb)
"Versamid" 115: ERL 2795: AFD filler (50:50:20)	201
"Versamid" 115:ERL 2795: Tabular alumina (50:50:20)	194
"Versamid" 115:ERL 2795: Atomized aluminum (50:50:20)	182

for repair of damaged sheet steel (as in automobile bodies) have been studied.[8]

Continuous metering and mixing devices for two-component adhesives of this nature are under evaluation. Among the manufacturers of such equipment are Pyles Industries, Detroit, Michigan; H. V. Hardman Company, Bellevue, New Jersey; Kish Resin Co., Lansing, Michigan; Bell and Gossett, Morton Grove, Illinois; Meter-Mix Corporation, Boston, Massachusetts; and others. Ideally, the use of such equipment can eliminate pot life problems and facilitate blending of components.

TABLE 11. THE EFFECT OF SOLVENTS AND CHEMICALS ON ADHESIVE FORMULATIONS.
(ASTM D1002-49-T) and (MIL A-5090-B)

	Tensile Shear Before Immersion	Hydraulic Fluid (psi)	Motor Oil (SAE #10) (psi)	Aviation Gasoline (psi)	Tap Water (psi)
"Versamid" 115: "Araldite" 502: "Metronite" (40:60:20)	3,060	3,080	3,130	2,890	2,790
"Versamid" 115:ERL 2795: AFD filler (50:50:20)	3,420	2,870	2,730	2,730	2,710
"Versamid" 115:ERL 2795: Nylon powder (50:50:20)	2,940	2,760	2,760	3,060	2,880
"Versamid" 115:ERL 2795: Tabular alumina (50:50:20)	3,200	3,170	3,250	3,270	3,170

TABLE 12. RESISTANCE TO ENVIRONMENTAL CONDITIONS.

Composition Tested: "Versamid" 115: "Araldite" 502: Tabular Alumina (40:60:20)

Exposed to:	Ultimate Tensile Shear Before Exposure (psi) (Ave. of 5)	Ultimate Tensile Shear After Exposure (psi) (Ave. of 5)
250 hrs salt spray (MIL-A-5090-B, 4.2.4)	3,130	2,050
7 days in isopropanol (MIL-A-5090-B, 4.3.1.4.3)	3,200	3,000
7 days in hydrocarbon (MIL-A-5090-B, 4.3.1.4.3)	3,270	3,300
7 days in hydraulic oil (MIL-A-5090-B, 4.3.1.4.3)	3,160	2,770
60 hr in Weatherometer (MIL-A-8623, 4.5.10)	2,440	2,680
7 days in JP4 fuel (MIL-A-5090-B, 4.3.1.4.3)	2,440	2,680
30 days in tap water (MIL-A-5090-B, 4.3.1.4.3)	3,130	2,600

References

1. Del Monte, John, "Technology of Adhesives," New York, Reinhold Publishing Corp., 1947.
2. Elam, D. W., *Product Eng.,* **25,** 167 (1955).
3. Epstein, George, *Adhesives & Resins,* **3** (3), 66 (1955).
4. Epstein, George, "Adhesive Bonding of Metals," New York, Reinhold Publishing Corp., 1954.
5. Floyd, D. E., "Polyamide Resins," New York, Reinhold Publishing Corp., 1958.
6. General Mills Tech. Bull. 11-B, "Heat-Seal Coatings and Adhesives."
7. *Progress Thru Research,* General Mills Quarterly Publication, **9** (3), 1 (1955).
8. Peerman, D. E., and Floyd, D. E., SPE, Upper Midwest Section, Epoxy Resin Symposium, Minneapolis, Minn., 1958.
9. Peerman, D. E., Floyd, D. E., and Mitchell, W. S., *Plastics Technol.,* **2** (1), 25 (1956).
10. Peerman, D. E., Tolberg, W., and Floyd, D. E., *Ind. Eng. Chem.,* **49,** 1091 (1957).
11. Wittcoff, H., and Dyck, A. W. J., "Technology of Paper Coatings," Chicago, Ill., Fritz Publications, 1957.
12. Wittcoff, H., and Peerman, D. E., *Modern Packaging,* **26** (3), 135 (1952).

Water-Based and
Solvent-Based Adhesives

Jacob Lichman

Key Polymer Corporation
Lawrence, Massachusetts

All adhesives must be fluid for application and bonding. Solid adhesive film-forming materials may be made fluid by dissolving or dispersing them into organic solvents or water. Thermoplastic materials may be made fluid by heat alone or with heat and pressure. Some materials that are liquid at room temperatures can convert into solid materials by chemical reactions such as polymerization or condensation. While this chapter is concerned with water and organic-solvent based adhesives, a discussion and review of other forms will be useful to point out the features and advantages of each type. In addition to adhesives that are made from materials that are capable of being dispersed in water or solvent, there are 100 per cent solids types such as hot melt, mastic, tape, film, plastisol, monomer, epoxy, polyester, polyurethane, polysulfide and polychloroprene (neoprene) rubber as well as calendered rubber and plastic compounds.

WATER-BASED ADHESIVES

Water-based adhesives are made from materials that can be dispersed or dissolved in water alone. Animal glue, starch, dextrin, blood albumin, egg albumin, methylcellulose and polyvinyl alcohol would fall into this class. Other adhesive materials can be dissolved or dispersed in water by means of alkali. Casein, rosin, shellac, copolymers of vinyl acetate or acrylates made to contain carboxyl groups by using crotonic acid, methacrylic acid or maleic anhydride, and carboxymethylcellulose are examples of this class.

Many adhesives today are made from water-based dispersions or emulsions frequently referred to as latex. Historically, latex meant the natural rubber dispersion as it came from the tree. In recent years, however, water dispersions of synthetic resins and rubbers made by emulsion polymerization are also called latex. In addition to natural rubber, the latices include styrene-butadiene, nitrile, and chloroprene emulsion polymer synthetic rubbers and vinyl acetate, acrylic, methacrylic, vinyl chloride, vinylidene chloride and styrene emulsion polymer synthetic resins. Water dispersions are also made by emulsifying or dispersing solid rubbers or resins. Dispersions of reclaim rubber, butyl rubber, rosin, rosin derivatives, asphalt and coal tar as well as synthetic resins derived from coal tar and petroleum are made by this procedure. Urea formaldehyde and phenol formaldehyde resins are also made and sold as water dispersions.

Water-based adhesives, unless applied as thermoplastic heat seal or contact adhesive coatings, are used for applications where at least one surface is permeable to water and water vapor. If two water-impermeable surfaces were used, the adhesive would never dry or develop useful bond strength. An exception would be a class of internal setting water-based adhesives that are made from Portland cements and natural or synthetic rubber latices. These are two-part adhesives that

TABLE 1.[1] RANGES OF SOLIDS, VISCOSITIES AND pH OF LATICES USED FOR ADHESIVES.

Polymer	% Solids	Viscosity (cps)	pH
Natural rubber			
Normal	38–41	<25	10.5
Centrifuged	>61.5	50	10.2
Creamed	>64	50	10.5
Heat concentrated	72–74	(pasty)	11–11.5
Neoprene	50–58	8–35	12.2–12.5
Butyl rubber	55	900	5–6
SBR rubber			
High solids	>55	200–2500	10–11.5
Medium solids	39–55	15–300	10–11.5
Low solids	24–27	8–20	9–11
Nitrile	40–55	12–200	8.5–11
Styrene-butadiene resin	45–50	10–80	9.0–11.5
Polyvinyl chloride	50–55	20–100	8.0
Vinylidene chloride copolymers	50–52	20–50	6–8
Polyacrylic	47–55	25–47	7.0–9.5
Polyvinyl acetate	55	800–1500	4–5

are blended just prior to use. The water present is absorbed by the cement for cure.

Properties of Resin or Rubber Latices

The more important properties of resin or rubber latices or dispersions for adhesives are:

Per cent solids or nonvolatiles.
Viscosity.
Emulsifiers used.
Surface tension.
pH.
Particle size and particle size distribution.
Film-forming temperature.
Mechanical stability.

In a latex or dispersion, the polymer is suspended in water. Each particle is separated or protected from adjacent particles by a layer of emulsifier or protective colloid.

Solids contents of 40 per cent or more at less than 1000 cps are achieved easily, regardless of the molecular weight of the dispersed phase. Table 1 lists typical polymer dispersions used for adhesives together with solids, viscosity and pH ranges.

The type and amount of emulsifier and protective colloid have a great effect on the properties of the latex. A greater amount will decrease water resistance. Lesser quantities may result in poor stability. The emulsion may then break or start to coagulate during pumping or application or perhaps separate during storage in the package.

Poorer stability may sometimes be an advantage when fast-breaking or fast-setting adhesives are needed.

Surfactants are commonly used during manufacture to lower the surface tension so that water can wet the dispersed phase during processing. Three types are available; anionic, non-ionic and cationic. Most latices are made with anionic emulsifiers, and these together with a few made with non-ionic types are used for adhesives. Cationic emulsions have not found general application as adhesives; but cationic asphalt emulsions have interesting wetting and adhesive properties. Nonionic polyvinyl acetate emulsions are widely used for adhesives. Natural and synthetic rubbers, as well as other types of resins, are anionic.

Some surfactants can cause foaming, which presents application problems. Compounds which will prevent foaming or which will break troublesome foam once formed—antifoams or defoamers—are frequently employed with water-based adhesives.

Emulsion and other water-based adhesives can be frozen when left exposed for long enough times at cold temperatures. Compounds which lower the freezing point of water are sometimes used to lower the freezing point of the adhesives. Some water-soluble adhesives are not harmed by freezing. When thawed back to the liquid state, they are still satisfactory and useful. Emulsions or dispersions, however, may be damaged irreversibly by freezing. Some surfactants are recommended to improve freeze-thaw stability. Although marketers and consumers of adhesives frequently request freeze-thaw stability, there are still no adequate test procedures or meaningful correlation with actual or possible conditions. Freezing rates, minimum temperature reached, and the length of time in the freezing cycle all have a bearing on the number of freeze-thaw cycles an emulsion-based adhesive will pass. An adhesive that would resist five cycles of 16 hr in the freezer and 8 hr at room temperature might not stand up to one cycle of 5 days in the freezer and one thaw.

Surfactants added to improve freeze-thaw lower water resistance. The expansion that occurs during freezing can damage containers. A frozen adhesive must be kept in a warm area for many hours depending on the size of the package before it will be warm enough for use. Conservative practice, even with so-called freeze-thaw stable adhesives, is to protect them from freezing during shipment and storage.

The pH of the emulsion as well as emulsifier type is also important to the adhesive formulator in order to know what types of additives or modifying ingredients can be used. The pH and emulsifier type may also affect application and bond strength when adhesives are applied to some reactive types of adherends.

Everything else being equal, a finer particle sized emulsion will have a higher viscosity and will generally be more stable both in the package and during application. When compounding resin or rubber latices into adhesives, it is frequently necessary or desirable to increase the viscosity. For example, where only a small amount of solids is needed, thickeners may be added for economic reasons to a diluted polymer emulsion. High viscosities may be desirable for adhesives used on porous and absorptive surfaces. Viscosity also affects the pick up or coating weight of adhesives when applied by mechanically driven rolls.

Widely used thickeners for anionic emulsions are casein, bentonite, methyl cellulose and sodium polyacrylates. Polyvinyl alcohol is used to thicken non-ionic polyvinyl acetate emulsions. Most latex thickeners increase viscosity by coalescing the individual dispersed particles, at least to some degree. When the compound is thickened to a few hundred centipoises or less, there is danger of destabilization. At higher viscosities, thickeners frequently improve stability.

The temperature of the adhesive and adherends is important for some type emulsion adhesives. Some resin emulsions, when used without plasticizers, do not deposit continuous films at ordinary room temperatures or may form discontinuous films at somewhat lower temperatures. One type of a polyvinyl acetate adhesive, when used at 40 to 50°F to bond wood, gave only a fraction of the bond strength obtained when adhesive and wood were at 70°F or higher.

Emulsions and adhesives made from emulsions vary widely in their ability to resist coagulation when subjected to mechanical shear. Mechanical stability can be evaluated by subjecting a quantity of the emulsion under standard conditions to high speed shear in a malted mixer or similar equipment. Surfactants and protective colloids are used to improve mechanical stability.

SOLVENT-BASED ADHESIVES

The natural and synthetic rubber and synthetic resins previously referred to are also capable of being dissolved in organic solvents; then they are referred to as cements, resin solutions, or lacquers. In addition to these, there are many cellulose derivatives such as nitrocellulose, ethyl cellulose, and cellulose acetate butyrate used in preparing solvent-based adhesives. Solvent-based adhesives are also made from cyclized rubber, chlorinated rubber, polyvinyl ethers, butyl rubber, polyamide and polyisobutylene. Low molecular weight polyurethane and epoxy compounds can be used with or without solvent; but high molecular weight types or prepolymers require solvent to make application possible.

Solvents or solvents containing small amounts of resin are used for bonding some types of thermoplastic resins and films. For example, toluol can be used to soften and dissolve polystyrene molded articles so that two softened pieces can be joined. Vinyl chloride films can be similarly bonded by using ketone solvents that will dissolve the film. A small amount of resin can be used to thicken the solvent so that a sufficient amount will stay in place to dissolve the substrate; however solvent welding of molded plastics can cause stress cracking and weakening of the structure as the parts age. If the use is critical, this contingency should be carefully checked.

Another class of solvent-based dispersions is the organosols. Here, vinyl chloride copolymer resins are dispersed in suitable nonvolatile plasticizers and solvent. For use, the solvent is evaporated and the remaining film heated to approximately 350°F. The heat causes the resin to dissolve in the plasticizer, resulting in a tough and flexible film when cooled to room temperature.

The major polymers for water- and solvent-based adhesives are listed in Table 2.

TABLE 2. PRINCIPAL POLYMERS FOR WATER AND
SOLVENT-BASED ADHESIVES.

Water base
  Starch and dextrin
  Gums
  Glue
  Albumin
  Sodium silicate
  Casein
  Sodium carboxymethylcellulose
  Lignin
  Polyvinyl alcohol

Water or solvent base
  Natural rubber
  SBR rubbers
  Butyl rubbers
  Neoprene rubbers
  Nitrile rubbers
  Reclaim rubbers
  Polyvinyl acetate and copolymer
  Polyvinyl chloride and copolymer
  Polyvinyl ether
  Polyvinylidene chloride and copolymers
  Polyacrylate and polymethacrylate
  Polyamide
  Asphalt
  Urea formaldehyde
  Phenol formaldehyde
  Rescorcinol formaldehyde
  Rosin esters

Solvent base
  Nitrocellulose
  Cellulose acetate butyrate
  Cyclized rubber
  Polyisobutylene

Comparison and Properties

Now that adhesive forms have been introduced, the characteristics of each together with the advantages and disadvantages of the various types will be presented.

Water-based adhesives are lower in cost than the equivalent solvent-based compound. Even inexpensive organic solvents are costly when compared to water. When water is used as the vehicle for adhesives, the problems of flammability and toxicity associated with organic solvents are eliminated. However, in most instances water-based adhesives must be protected from freezing during shipment and storage because of possible permanent damage to both container and contents.

It is relatively easy to compound water-based adhesives to give extreme ranges of viscosity and solids content. High solids at low viscosity or low solids at high viscosity can be more readably obtained with water-based than solvent-based adhesives. The usable concentration of polymer or resin can be considerably higher as a water dispersion than a solvent dispersion or hot melt. Penetration and wetting of water-based adhesives can be controlled by the use of surfactants or the particle size of the dispersion. The formulator can use thickeners so that viscosity can be increased to prevent penetration into porous surfaces. A disadvantage is that the water present shrinks fabrics and curls and wrinkles paper. It also presents corrosion and rusting problems to iron and steel application equipment and storage facilities.

Solvent-based adhesives do not have these drawbacks; moreover they usually make more water-resistant bonds than the water-based product. They are generally more tacky and can be used to provide high early strength.

Solvent-based adhesives also wet oily surfaces and some plastics considerably better than water. The formulator has at his disposal a wide variety of organic solvents which vary in evaporation or drying rate; thus the drying or setting rate of films from organic solvent-based adhesives can be more readily varied than from water-based.

With organic solvents, however, explosion-proof equipment must be used and other precautions taken for handling and application. In addition, ventilation to eliminate toxic hazards must be provided for personnel exposed to the solvent vapors when the adhesive is used.

One hundred per cent solids adhesives have some advantages. Petroleum wax and asphalt hot-melt adhesives, for example, are not only low in initial cost but also have lower actual freight costs than solvent- or water-based adhesives because every pound of material shipped is film-forming and useful in the final bond. Packaging costs of hot melts are less than for solvent- or water-based adhesive per pound of useful product. The cost of packaging a dry material is usually less than that required for the liquid-tight containers needed for water-based and solvent-based adhesives. With hot melts and other 100 per cent solids adhesives, there is no danger of freezing and the hazards of using flammable and toxic solvents are eliminated. No drying equipment is necessary to remove water or solvent. The stability or shelf ageing is not usually a problem with hot-melt adhesives as is frequently the case with water-based or solvent-based compounds.

Asphalts and waxes, however, when used as adhesives lack cohesive strength for many applications. High molecular weight polymers such as rubber, butyl or vistanex can be added to improve bond strength.

Other types of hot melts are based on high molecular weight polymers such as ethyl cellulose, cellulose acetate butyrate, and polyvinyl acetate. With these materials, waxes or resins or plasticizers that would give low viscosity solutions of the polymer when heated are needed to prepare useful compounds. The principle here is comparable to solvent-based adhesives where the solvents are capable of dissolving the film-forming polymer and keeping it fluid at room temperature. With the hot melts, however, the waxes, resins or plasticizers used are capable of making the polymer liquid only at elevated temperatures.

Hot melts must be heated until fluid for application. When polymers are present, heating times and temperatures are critical since the polymers used can decompose on continued heating. Polymers also increase the viscosity of hot melts in direct proportion to the molecular weight and the amount present. Since higher molecular weight and higher percentages are usually needed to give high bond strengths and toughness, application problems occur. A compromise is usually required between molecular weight, concentration and temperature to obtain workable stability, application and bond strength. Accurate control of coating, particularly in the low ranges, is also difficult. Unlike hot melts, high molecular weight materials can be used for solvent-based adhesives

without too much difficulty. With emulsion polymers, extremely high molecular weights are available at high solids and low viscosity. The fact that solutions and dispersions are considerably less than 100 per cent solids gives more accurate control of coating weight since the final variation is only a fraction of the original variation.

Hot melts usually do not wrinkle paper, nor do they disturb the dimensions of fabrics. They can be used with one or more impermeable surfaces since there is no volatile solvent or water to be removed. In many instances, the surfaces or parts need preheating to get proper wetting and adhesion.

The use of hot-melt adhesives will probably increase when equipment is available for handling high viscosities at temperatures and times which will not interfere with stability. Perhaps by adapting equipment now used for injection molding, the adhesives industry could overcome the problems inherent with hot melts. Equipment is available to handle extremely high viscosity materials and to avoid stability problems by heating only small quantities of materials for short times.

Many of the advantages that apply to hot melts also apply to other 100 per cent solids types of adhesives. Polymerizable monomers, epoxy polyester polyurethane, "Thiokol," and liquid neoprene adhesive usually require either a two-component system or elevated temperatures for

TABLE 3. ADHESIVE FORMS.

	Advantages	Disadvantages
Water base	Lower cost	Poorer water resistance
	Nonflammable	Subject to freezing
	Nontoxic solvent	Shrinks fabrics
	Wide range of solids content	Wrinkles or curls paper
	Wide range of viscosity	Can be contaminated by some metals used
	High concentration of high molecular	for storage and application
	weight material can be used	Corrosive to some metals
	Penetration and wetting can be varied	Slow drying
		Poorer electrical properties
Solvent base	Water resistant	Fire and explosive hazard
	Wide range of drying rates and open times	Health hazard
	Develop high early bond strength or tack	Special explosion proof and ventilating
	Easily wets some difficult surfaces	equipment needed
Hot melt	Lower package and shipping cost per	Special applicating equipment needed
	pound of solid material	Limited strength because of viscosity and
	Will not freeze	temperature limitations
	Drying and equipment for drying are	Degrades on continuous heating
	unnecessary	Poorer coating weight control
	Impervious surfaces easily bonded	Preheating of adherends may be necessary
	Fast bond strength development	
	Good storage stability	
	Provides continuous water vapor impermeable and water resistant adhesive film	

cure. Tapes and films while considered as 100 per cent solids adhesives are frequently made by coating from solvent-based dispersions. Calendering may also be used, but this is a relatively expensive method and requires a substantial capital investment for equipment.

Methods of Use

There are many methods of using adhesives to obtain bond. Where one or more of the surfaces to be bonded is permeable, the simplest method would be one of "wet stick." Here, the fluid adhesive, as would be the case with solvent- or water-based adhesives, is applied to one of the surfaces and the surfaces are immediately joined. The solvent or the water in the adhesive is absorbed into one or both of the substrates. A hot melt could also be used by the wet-stick method. In this case, before application the adhesive is made fluid by heating, and bonding occurs when the adhesive has solidified. With a hot melt, both surfaces can be impermeable since there are no solvents or water to be dissipated.

A wet-stick adhesive, if not capable of initially holding together the surfaces being joined, must be kept under pressure until enough strength has developed for subsequent handling. Adhesive compositions vary widely in tack or strength development. A higher rate of strength development makes higher production rates possible. On the other hand, if one of the assembly parts has to be placed and then positioned, a slow rate is indicated.

Another method of bonding would be to coat one surface, completely or partially dry and then bond the two surfaces desired with heat or pressure or both. When the adhesives are capable of being completely dried and then used with heat or pressure or both, the adhesives can be factory-applied at high production rates with consequent low cost, together with good quality control.

Pressure-sensitive tape would be an example of an adhesive requiring subsequent pressure only. The "iron-on" patches and tapes used for fabric mending at home would be an example of an adhesive that required both heat and pressure for subsequent use. Delayed tack paper coatings are used that become pressure-sensitive on heating.

Another class of adhesive is similar to the pressure-sensitive or heat-seal types; but in this instance the adhesive film or layer is reactivated with a small amount of organic solvent. Considerably less solvent is needed to reactivate an adhesive film than is used for the original coating. Occasionally, diluted adhesive rather than solvent alone is used to get a better working viscosity and drying rate.

Another interesting class of adhesives is the contact or dry stick type. With this class, both surfaces are coated and dried. Bonding occurs immediately with pressure only. An example of this type would be the dry-seal adhesive used on mailing envelopes.

Adhesive Requirements

Adhesive selection therefore is based on a combination of adhesive type and engineering or methods. To meet the ever-present economic requirements of lowest possible cost, the cost of the adhesive itself is important; however it is only part of the cost of bonding. What is desired is the lowest cost per bonded unit taking into consideration labor, equipment, depreciation and maintenance, rejects and quality. An adhesive or procedure that would eliminate or diminish a high percentage of rework, seconds or rejects, even if it appears expensive on first examination, may actually increase profits by reducing cost per finished unit.

A discussion of adhesive requirements will serve to illustrate the reasons for commercial use for either water-based or solvent-based adhesives as well as other types. Of course, the adhesive selected must be capable of bonding the two surfaces required. Unless one or both of the materials are a recent commercial development, however, there generally is no problem in getting an adhesive to make a good initial bond. Where adhesives have been used previously and a change is desired, there are usually equipment and space limitations at least until it is definite that no satisfactory adhesive can be found to be used with existing equipment procedures. If adhesives have not been used previously, still more decisions must be made prior to starting a large-scale commercial use. After determining production rate and schedules desired, space requirements, and capital available for equipment, one can give consideration to other factors.

Adhesives can be applied by simple hand tools such as brushes, paint rollers, or squeeze bottles. The rheology or flow properties of the adhesive must fit the method of application desired. An adhesive that could be applied easily and satisfactorily to a floor might not be satisfactory for application to a ceiling if it dripped or fell off from the tool used to apply it. If production requirements are large, the adhesive could be applied by spray, paint roller, motorized roller or gravure cylinders as well as many other types of machinery. Drying could be at room conditions or with ovens heated by various methods such as hot air or infrared or with heated calenders.

Some adhesives are not utilized in the factory but in the field. Here adhesives may be applied by brushes, trowels, or caulking guns. All these methods of application require somewhat different viscosity characteristics. An adhesive that would be suitable for one method of application and drying would not necessarily be satisfactory for all other methods.

The adhesive viscosity, therefore, must be suitable for use with the equipment selected. It must have the proper flow for easy application, particularly by hand tools; nevertheless it must not run, drip or otherwise present excessive cleaning problems.

The adhesive selected must also wet the surface to which it is to be applied. The adhesive should remain uniform where applied and not penetrate excessively into the substrate. To save adhesive costs, it is usually applied to the smoothest and densest of the two surfaces. In rare instances, except for contact types, it may be necessary to coat both surfaces in order to obtain satisfactory quality under conditions that are available.

The adhesive must be capable of being applied within specified coating weight limits. Insufficient as well as excessive adhesive can be a cause for bond failure. Insufficient adhesive may not allow enough contact for required bond strength; whereas too much adhesive may retard the drying rate and also give low bond strength.

During application, the adhesive should not foam, skin, dry, coagulate, string or web. For critical machine applications, pans containing adhesive can be enclosed or covered and the adhesive continuously filtered. The adhesive should be stable for use with the equipment required or conventionally used.

Ease of cleanup both for equipment and surfaces is also a factor; furthermore pot life preferably should be unlimited.

The adhesive selected must have sufficient bond strength to work with the normal variables in stock and the temperatures and humidity range that will be encountered in production. The rate of strength development should be sufficient for the next handling step whatever and whenever that may be; moreover it must meet the drying requirements. These can vary from simple ambient room temperature drying to large and highly engineered oven installations. The rate of strength development for the drying conditions used must be sufficient for the next handling step to meet production rates.

The final bond strength of course must be sufficient and suitable for end-use requirements. The bond must be sufficiently durable to withstand any and all exposures to which it may possibly be subjected. On ageing, the adhesive film must not be harmed by migration or chemical change from the materials being bonded. It must be capable of maintaining useful bond strengths at temperature extremes to which the bonded article may be exposed. Other requirements may be various degrees of water resistance or water proofness and resistance to solvents, detergents, acids, alkalies and other chemicals.

The bond strength and end-use requirements will probably limit the type of adhesives that can be used, thus limiting the methods of possible use. The adhesive will then be selected from a class of compounds that would meet all the requirements at the lowest possible finished cost per unit. Finally, the adhesive itself must be capable of accomplishing all this with no harmful change as the packaged adhesive itself ages.

Other Names for Adhesives

Adhesive forces and properties occur in many products and uses not ordinarily associated with the term "adhesive"; for example, a coating could be considered to be a one-sided non-blocking adhesive. A binder size or saturant has to adhere materials composed of small particles. Problems of adhesion and wetting are present. Final bond strength and durability, as with adhesives, are also factors. Caulking compounds and sealants can also be called adhesives in that they must adhere strongly to the substrates being used. Even release coats for tapes are adhesives, but here a lack of adhesion rather than high bond strength is the requirement.

WATER-BASED ADHESIVES FROM STARCH AND DEXTRINS

Some typical formulations of starch and dextrin adhesives have been compiled for this chapter as examples of widely used water-based adhesives. The properties of various types of starch and dextrin that make them useful for adhesive manufacture will be outlined and discussed. Manufacturing procedures and compounding practices will be correlated with properties. Commonly used modifiers will be mentioned and their need or effect on the adhesives described. Typical adhesive applications will be tabulated together with formulations.

It should be understood that the formulations are by necessity only typical and would require changes to meet all possible conditions and requirements for use. By providing data on important types of starch-based adhesives, chemists and engineers, engaged in developing or applying adhesives, as well as adhesive buyers and users, may learn how the properties of an unfamiliar raw material and its method of use may solve an existing problem. Adhesive development and manufacture is carried on by companies or departments that specialize only in certain raw materials. It is hoped that the data presented here will provide useful background to those unfamiliar with starch so that they may understand all the possible varieties.

Frequently commercial adhesives contain more than one principal raw material. In a brief summary of this type, it is not possible to describe all useful combinations. An attempt has been made to limit the formulations to those commercially important at the present time, are the most simple and which will still provide good background on properties and end uses.

To provide formulations as close as possible to those used commercially, trade names are used. Enough details and properties are given so that other sources of supply can be easily used.

Starches and modified or converted starches are used in great quantities for adhesives. Starch is abundant and available at low cost; it can be dissolved by heating with water. Chemically, it is very similar to cellulose; thus it has good adhesion to paper, wood and cotton. It is insoluble in organic solvents, fats, and oils and adhesive bonds made with starch or converted starches would be resistant to these materials.

Commercial starches are made from a wide variety of plants; seeds, piths and roots are raw material sources. There is some variation in properties from one type starch to another.

Starch granules when heated in water suddenly begin to swell, and this swelling is referred to as *gelatinization*. Gelatinization for any particular starch occurs over a range in temperature, and the range is different for various starches. The clarity and viscosity or rheology of the water solutions of different starches also varies.[2, 3, 4]

Corn, tapioca, sago, wheat and potato starches are available commercially; however about ten times as much corn starch is used in the United States as all the other varieties together. The data that follows are confined to corn starch and its conversion products.

Starch and its common modifications, being soluble in water, are unsuitable for applications where waterproofness or a great amount of water resistance is needed. Converted starches, i.e., dextrins, are commonly used to make water-remoistenable adhesives.

Starch solutions are extremely viscous even at low solids content. To provide lower viscosities and higher solids solutions, starch is modified or converted by breaking up the molecule. Thin boiling starches are made by heating a suspension of starch in water with a small amount of acid to a temperature below its gelatinization point. Oxidized starches are made the same way except that sodium hypochlorite is used instead of acid. The use of oxidized starches in adhesives generally is confined to being a thickening agent for dextrins.

These treatments still do not convert starch sufficiently so that the solution will be low enough in viscosity and sufficiently fluid for many adhesive applications.

Dextrins, made by roasting starch, are most commonly used for adhesive manufacture. Three types of dextrins are produced. British gums are made by roasting starch at high temperature. Sometimes a small amount of acid is used to accelerate the process, and the resultant product has been referred to as semi-British gum. White dextrins are made with acid, but at a lower temperature; whereas yellow or canary dextrins are made with less acid, but at a higher temperature than white dextrins.

Thin boiling starches and dextrins dissolve in water with heat more readily than unmodified starch because the starch cell has been ruptured in processing. Important properties are pH, viscosity, rheology, cold water solubility, color, moisture, and cost. The pH of dextrins is acidic; thin boiling starches are neutralized or partially neutralized, and the pH varies from acidic to neutral or slightly alkaline according to the grade.

Starch, thin boiling starch, and oxidized starch contain about 12 per cent moisture when packed. British gum contains approximately 1 per cent moisture, white dextrins contain about 5 per cent, and yellow or canary dextrins from 1 to 2 per cent.

Converted starches and dextrins are sold at a fixed premium over the price of raw, or as it is termed, pearl starch. The premiums per hundred pounds in 1959 for the wet corn-milling industry were as follows: thin boiling starch $0.60; white dextrin $1.59; oxidized starch and yellow dextrin $1.75; and British gum $2.00.

Cold-water solubles are determined by mixing 5-g samples of powder with 200 ml of water at 77°F. The mixture is kept at 77°F and filtered after 2 hr. A portion of the filtrate is evaporated to dryness, and the per cent cold-water solubles are calculated. Per cent cold-water solubles usually correlates with viscosity or rheology as well as the maximum solids content that is practical for solutions. Low cold-water solubles give higher viscosity, pasty solutions at relatively low solids. High cold-water solubles allow for higher solids content with good flow properties.

Thin boiling starches generally vary from 2 to 20 per cent cold-water solubles although some grades are available up to 40 per cent. Solutions are light colored and have a high viscosity; they are generally made at 5 to 35 per cent solids content. Solutions usually have a tendency to gel on standing. Thin boiling starches are used in preparing low cost adhesives where a narrow specification range and stability are not required.

In some cases the differences between white and yellow dextrins is arbitrary. Generally, white dextrins have lower cold-water solubles and are white in color. Cold-water solubles range from 2 to 90 per cent. Solutions can range from very thick and starchy to water thin at solids content varying from 25 to 55 per cent. Cooks of white dextrins which are low in cold-water solubles have a tendency to gel on storage. White dextrins with 80 to 90 per cent cold water solubles enter the range of yellow or canary dextrins.

Yellow dextrins vary in cold-water solubles from 80 to 100 per cent. The color ranges from light cream to dark tan. Solutions with 40 to 65 per cent solids can be made that are low in viscosity and stable. High solids solutions provide fast drying and tacky adhesives useful for high-speed operations.

British gums encompass many of the properties of both white and yellow dextrins and in addition have some unusual properties of their own. Cold-water solubles range from 10 to 100 per cent and vary in color from light tan to dark tan. Their viscosity is always higher than a comparable white or yellow dextrin of the same solubility. The high soluble British gums are usually somewhat cold-water swelling and can sometimes be used without cooking.

Some cold water-soluble powdered adhesives are made by converting a starch slurry with acid under heat and pressure and then spray or drum drying. The adhesive can be prepared for use with or without cooking. Small consumers without cooking facilities use this type of adhesive to save freight and packaging costs that are necessary for liquid adhesives.

Another type of cold water-soluble adhesive is made from borated dextrin, which is made by cooking dextrin, borax, and water and then adding a small amount of caustic soda after cooking. The mixture is then spray dried and packed into bags.

Equipment for dissolving starch or dextrin can vary from a simple vessel heated with live steam to special kettles equipped with both slow- and high-speed agitators and a jacket so that the kettle and contents can be heated with steam or cooled by circulating cold water.

The corrugated box industry consumes large tonnages of starch adhesives for bonding corrugated paper to smooth kraft paper using a process patented over 20 years ago by Jordan V. Bauer of Stein Hall and Company.[5] By a process of gelatinization *in situ,* he overcame the drawbacks of low solids and high viscosity associated with completely cooked starches. Starch, and not the more costly dextrins, is used to secure high solids; in addition, bond strength develops extremely fast. All this is accomplished by suspending a large amount of dry starch in a solution of almost completely gelatinized starch. During the heating of the starch after the adhesive has been applied, the suspended starch suddenly gels. This provides the immediate tack and bond strength required, much faster in fact than can be obtained with dextrins.

Caustic soda is used to hasten gelatinization and to lower the gelatinization temperature of starch cooks. Borax increases the viscosity of starch and dextrin solutions and also makes the solutions more cohesive, thus giving greater initial tack. Caustic when used with borax increases this effect.

Aqueous solutions of starch and its modification are readily attacked by bacteria and mold. Formaldehyde and water-soluble phenol derivatives are used as preservatives to prevent putrefaction and mildew.

CORRUGATED PAPER-BOX ADHESIVE[6]

Primary Mixer:

(1) Add 50 gal of water; heat to 100°F.
(2) Add 80 lb pearl corn starch; agitate until dispersed.
(3) Add 15 lb caustic soda which has been dissolved in 3 gal of water.
(4) Heat to 160°F; hold 15 min under agitation.
(5) Add 60 gal cold water. This is the completed carrier and is ready for use in Step (9) below.

Secondary Mixer:

(6) Add 185 gal water.
(7) Add 15 lb 10 mole borax.
(8) Add 520 lb pearl corn starch.
(9) Slowly drop carrier portion prepared in Step (5).

(10) Add 1 qt formaldehyde.

(11) Agitate approximately 15 min before checking viscosity.

Water dispersions of urea formaldehyde resins are used to increase the water resistance of starch and converted starch-based adhesives. Acid catalysts such as alum, ammonium chloride and ammonium sulfate are used to help cure the resin. A reduction in machine speed is usually required in order to allow the starch to gelatinize *in situ* on the acid side. Recently introduced urea formaldehyde resins are available which can cure on the alkaline side and permit full production speeds.

CORRUGATED PAPER-BOX ADHESIVE—WATER-RESISTANT[7]

Primary Mixer:

(1) Fill with 56 gal of water.

(2) Heat to 120°F.

(3) Add 80 lb pearl corn starch.

(4) Agitate 5 min.

(5) Add 15 lb caustic soda dissolved in water.

(6) Agitate 15 min.

(7) Add cold water to a total volume of 125 gal.

Secondary Mixer:

(1) Add 182 gal water.

(2) Heat to 90–100°F.

(3) Add 500 lb pearl corn starch.

(4) Add 45 lb "Casco" Resin PR-195 (urea formaldehyde resin 65 per cent solids).[12]

Final Mix:

(1) Drop contents of primary mixer into secondary tank using 20 to 30 min to transfer.

(2) Agitate at least 15 min.

(3) Check viscosity. If heavy, continue mixing for an additional 10 min and recheck. If still heavy, add water to adjust. On subsequent batches vary starch in primary mixer so that adjustments will not be required.

Note: Borax can be used as part of the suspension prepared in the secondary mixer, but better water resistance can be obtained if none is used. Where borax is included, it is suggested that not more than 9 lb of 10 mole borax be used and that 1 extra lb of caustic be added to the primary for each 3 lb of 10 mole borax. Add borax before addition of "Casco" Resin PR-195.

Grocery bags must use the lowest possible priced adhesives because of the very low price of the paper bags. For this reason, pearl corn starch or thin boiling starch at fairly low concentrations is used for the bottom flap and borated starch or dextrin for the seam adhesive.

Adhesive films from starch and converted starches are brittle when dry. To render the film flexible, hygroscopic or water-holding compounds or some fatty compounds may be added. Corn syrup, glycerin, urea, sorbitol, and invert sugars are some of the materials used as humectants. Soaps, sulfonated oils and sulfated alcohols are examples of the fatty type. Plasticizers are used in remoistenable and lay-flat adhesives to prevent curl and cracking. Fatty plasticizers in remoistenable adhesives help prevent blocking or adhering of the coated sheets. Soaps also help pumpability by eliminating or minimizing tendency of solution to gel.

BAG PASTING GROCERY TYPE, FLATS, SQUARES AND NOTION—NON-WATERPROOF.[8]

Seam paste

Staley's 83SU adhesive*[17]

Cook 30–33 per cent solids

Bottom paste	parts
Pearl corn starch	98
Soap (sodium stearate type)	2

Cook 12 to 14 per cent solids

Add 0.1 per cent on total weight of formaldehyde

* Borated starch, 25 per cent cold-water solubles, pH 8.8–9.0.

Multiwall bags are made with two or more plies of paper. Generally, a "tuber" machine combines the separate plies of paper, pastes the seams, and then cuts the tubes to length. The cut tubes are then placed on the bottomer to form and paste the bottoms or both ends of the bag. Seam adhesives are made from dextrin and thin boiling starch; and bottom adhesives from thin boiling starch alone, or from borated white dextrins of low conversion and low borax content.

Soda ash, rather than caustic soda, is frequently used to adjust pH since it is a milder alkali, thus giving better control.

BAG PASTING, SEAM, MULTIWALL—WATER RESISTANT.[8]

	parts
"Stadex" Dextrin No. 5*[17]	300
"Staclipse" KST starch**[17]	100
"Casco" Resin PR-205 (urea formaldehyde resin 65 per cent solids)	52
Ammonium chloride	11
Soap flakes (sodium stearate type)	2.5

Cook at 25 per cent solids

Heat to 190°F and hold for 15 min

Cool

Add soda ash to adjust pH to 5.0 to 5.5

* White dextrin, 5 per cent cold-water solubles, pH 4 to 5.

** Thin boiling starch, 7 per cent cold-water solubles, pH 7 to 8.

Bag Pasting, Bottom, Multiwall—Water Resistant.[8]

	parts
"Staclipse" KST starch[17]	500
"Eclipse" "F" starch*[17]	100
"Casco" Resin PR-205 (urea formaldehyde resin 65 per cent solids	72
Ammonium chloride	16
Soap flakes (sodium stearate type)	3
Cook at 28 per cent total solids	
Heat to 190°F and hold for 15 min	
Cool	
Add soda ash to adjust pH to 5.0 to 5.5	

* Thin boiling starch, 1 per cent cold-water solubles, pH 4.4 to 5.5.

Completely hydrolysed high viscosity grades of polyvinyl alcohol form extremely strong, cold water resistant films. Water resistant adhesives complying with government specification for laminating solid fiber for boxes and bonding multiwall bags are made from this type polyvinyl alcohol clay, and starch. Adhesives of this type are covered by U. S. Patent 2,487,448 and are generally marketed as dry powder blends to be cooked in the user's plant at solids ranging from 15 to 30 per cent.

Bag Pasting, Seam, Multiwall—Water Resistant.[9]

	parts
Low micron clay	45.5
Pearl corn starch	26.0
"Lemol" 60-98[12] (polyvinyl alcohol)	28.0
"Myrj" 45[11] (polyoxyethylene stearate)	0.2
"Dowicide" A[13]	0.3

Dextrins and thin boiling starches are used for paper laminating, a process of combining two or more plies of material together to form a useful combination. In some cases the adhesive is applied at a temperature of 135 to 165°F to increase the bonding rate. When two or more dissimilar sheets are being combined, care must be taken to prevent excessive warp.

High solids adhesives contain less water and are thus preferred for laminating where curl is a problem.

Asphalt emulsions are used to raise solids, improve water resistance, and lower cost of laminating adhesives.

Box—Weatherproof Solid-Fiber Laminating.[8]

(1) Fill secondary mixer with 383 gal of water.
(2) Add 2 lb soda ash; start agitator.
(3) Add 1500 lb "Stadex" Dextrin No. 5[17]
(4) Add 800 lb "Stadex" Dextrin No. 135*[17]

(5) Mix to smooth slurry.
(6) Heat to 195°F; hold at least 15 min.
(7) Cool to 170°F and pump to storage tank.
(8) Add 110 gal "Bitusize" A[10] asphalt emulsion.
(9) Add 378 lb "Casco" Resin PR-205[12] (urea formaldehyde resin 65 per cent solids).
(10) Add 33 lb ammonium sulfate**

The ingredients should be mixed well before pumping to machine. Adjust pH to be 5.5.

* Canary dextrin, 95 per cent cold-water solubles, pH 3 to 4.
** Solution should be no hotter than 130°F when adding ammonium sulfate.

Defoamers and anti-foams such as sulfonated castor oil, tributyl phosphate and non-ionic surfactants are useful to eliminate the air that gets occluded during the preparation of solutions. They are also used to prevent foaming during adhesive application.

In some adhesives, the compounder can further convert a modified starch by using hydrochloric acid in the cook.

Sodium nitrate and calcium chloride are used as humectants; they have less effect on tack than corn syrup.

Layflat Laminating.[8]

	parts
Water	130
"Staclipse" JUB*[17]	100
Sulfonated castor oil, 75 per cent	0.5
Hydrochloric acid ⎫ Mix	0.3
Water ⎭	1
Heat to 140°F	
Sodium nitrate	40
Calcium chloride	40
Formaldehyde	0.5
Viscosity—5,000 cps	

* Thin boiling starch, 20 per cent cold-water solubles, pH 7 to 8.

Borated dextrins are used for carton and casesealing adhesives. Very fast tack with good final bond strength is required for these uses.

Carton Sealer—Top and Bottom.[8]

	parts
Water	400
"Stadex" Dextrin No. 121*[17]	100
"Stadex" Dextrin No. 79**[17]	75
Sulfonated castor oil 75%	1
Heat to 140°F	
Borax, 5 mole	18
Heat to 190°F for 30 min	
Cool to 140°F	
Caustic soda flake	4

Water to dissolve caustic soda	8
Formaldehyde	1

Add water to adjust viscosity which can vary between 1000 and 4000 cps depending on operating conditions.

* Canary dextrin, 95 per cent cold water solubles, pH 3 to 4

** White dextrin, 80 per cent cold water solubles, pH 3.5 to 5.5

CASE SEALING.[8]

	parts
Water	300
Tributyl phosphate	1
"Stadex" Dextrin No. 50*[17]	200
Borax, 10 mole	30
Heat to 185°F using jacketed steam only	
Hold at 185°F for 20 min	
Cool to 140° and add:	
Caustic soda (40 per cent solution)	10
Formaldehyde	1

Allow to mix for 10 min then check pH. If pH is not between 9.2 and 9.4, add sufficient caustic soda solution to reach the desired range. Then adjust to final viscosity by the addition of water.

Solids	38–40%
pH	9.2–9.4
Viscosity	3000–4000 cps

If this viscosity is too heavy, the adhesive may be thinned with water to the proper operating viscosity.

* White dextrin, 45 per cent cold water solubles, pH 3.5 to 4.5.

Envelopes require both a seam and a flap or front-seal adhesive. Corn dextrin is usually used for the seam adhesive; moreover a special waxy corn dextrin because of its better gloss and remoistening properties is used for the flap adhesive.

Corn dextrins are used for gummed papers such as labels, trading stamps, and tapes. The better grades of gummed tape are made with animal glue extended with about 25 per cent of yellow dextrin.

Frequently in order to reduce viscosity, starch and dextrin adhesives are used slightly warm. To prevent degradation, precautions should be taken to maintain heating times and temperatures to a minimum. Urea, dicyandiamide and similar chemicals can be added during compounding to lower the viscosity of the final cook and to keep the viscosity from rising as the solution ages. The use of such chemicals also allows for higher solids content adhesives.

Monosodium phosphate is as a buffer to adjust pH.

ENVELOPE GUM, BACK SEAM.[8]

	parts
Water	250
"Stadex" Dextrin No. 79[17]	500
Urea	250
Monosodium phosphate	10
Tributyl phosphate	2
Heat to 160°F for 20 min	
Cool to 120°F	
Formaldehyde	2

Adjust viscosity for application equipment as follows:

	cps
Plunger	15,000
Wide range	10,000
Rotary	2,500

ENVELOPE GUM, REMOISTENABLE, FRONT SEAL.[8]

	parts
Water	150
"Stadex" Dextrin No. 106*[17]	300
Tributyl phosphate	1
Heat to 190°F for 30 min	
Cool to 140°F	
Corn syrup, regular 43° Baume	5

Adjust viscosity for application equipment as follows:

Plunger	10,000 cps
Wide range	7,000 cps
Rotary	5,000 cps

* Canary dextrin, 95 per cent cold-water solubles, pH 3 to 4.

Polyvinyl acetate resin emulsions are also used for remoistenable adhesives. They are less affected by humidity and are thus characterized by non-curl and non-block. Canary dextrins are added to provide a more glossy coating.

ENVELOPE ADHESIVE—REMOISTENABLE.[8]

	parts
"Polyco" 694 dextrin compatible polyvinyl acetate emulsion[12]	60
"Stadex" Dextrin No. 120[17]	25
Glycerin	5
"Santicizer" M-17[16] plasticizer	5
Water	5

Materials are added in order given with agitation in a steam-jacketed kettle. Heating is started at the same time the dextrin is added. After all materials are in, heat and stir until dextrin has completely dissolved and cool.

Solids	68 per cent
Viscosity	12,000 cps

A wide variety of library pastes are on the market all having different solids and consistency. The usual type is made at approximately 40 per cent solids and sets up to a stiff paste after being cooked. During application when pressure is applied with a finger or a brush, the paste will soften sufficiently so that it will apply smoothly.

LIBRARY PASTE.[8]

	parts
"Staclipse" JUB[17]	100
Corn syrup regular, 43° Baume	15
Preservative	0.3
Water	200

Heat to 190°F for 20 min and package hot. It takes from 2 to 7 days for the paste to set up, depending on the rate of cooling. Oil of wintergreen is sometimes added to provide a characteristic odor.

Canary dextrins highly plasticized with corn syrups are used for adhering paper labels to glass. Phosphoric acid is used to improve wetting and adhesion to paper.

PAPER TO GLASS—NON-WATERPROOF.[8]

	parts
Water	40
"Stadex" Dextrin No. 1170X*[17]	60
Heat to 190°F and hold until the dextrin is dispersed; add	
Corn syrup regular, 43° Baume	300
Phosphoric acid	0.5
Adjust viscosity from 10,000 to 20,000 cps	

* Canary dextrin, 95 per cent cold-water solubles, pH 3 to 4.

Thin boiling starch is used as an adhesive to bond cartons or bags together so that a number of them can be handled on a pallet without danger of the loading slipping and sliding off. "Vinsol" emulsion is included in the formula to provide good shear strength, but give a brittle bond in tension. Thus bags and boxes can be separated from each other without tearing paper, when the bags or boxes are lifted upwards with a jerking motion.

PALLETIZING.[8]

	parts
Water	135
"Staclipse" J*[17]	100
Corn syrup regular conversion, 43° Baume	25
"Pluronic" L-61 non-ionic surfactant[18]	0.25
"Dowicide" A[13]	0.25
Cook to 190°F; hold for 20 min	
Cool to 130°F; add	
"Vinsol" emulsion[14]	100

	Viscosity	1000–2000 cps
	Solids	40 per cent
	pH	8.2

* Thin boiling starch, 20 per cent cold-water solubles, pH 7 to 8.

Borated dextrins at 30 to 50 per cent solids are used to bond paper and board into spiral wound tubes. The adhesive is used hot to provide the very fast tack required.

Clays and other inert fillers can be used to reduce cost, to prevent excessive penetration, and in some instances improve adhesion to various surfaces.

TUBE WINDING.[8]

	parts
Water	400
"Stadex" Dextrin No. 120*[17]	200
"Stadex Dextrin No. 78**[17]	100
ASP 400 clay[15]	15
Sulfonated castor oil 75 per cent	1
Heat to 140°F; add	
Borax, 5 mole	20
Heat to 190°F for 30 min.	
Cool to 140°F; add	
Caustic soda flake	4
Water to dissolve caustic	8
Formaldehyde	1
Viscosity 100 to 4000 cps	

* Canary dextrin, 98 per cent cold water-solubles, pH 3 to 4.

** White dextrin, 75 per cent cold water-solubles, pH 3.5 to 5.5.

References

1. *The Vanderbilt News,* p. 22–27, New York, R. T. Vanderbilt Co., Inc., Oct. 1959. Also supplier's literature.

2. Brautlecht, C. A., "Starch—Its Sources, Production and Uses," New York Reinhold Publishing Corp. 1953.

3. *"Corn Starch,"* Corn Industries Research Foundation, Inc., Washington 6, D. C., 1955.

4. Kerr, Ralph W., "Chemistry and Industry of Starch," New York, Academic Press, Inc., 1944.

5. U. S. Patents 2,051,025 and 2,102,937.

6. Brekke, M. G., and Lipman, L. H., "Economics of Corrugating Adhesives," *Adhesives Age,* p. 26, May 1959.

7. Private communication—Sept. 7, 1959, Britton, R. K., The Borden Chemical Co., Resins and Chemicals Dept., Bainbridge, N. Y.

8. Private communication, Sept. 15, 1959, Wrightsman, John H., A. E. Staley Manufacturing Co., Dextrin and Adhesives Laboratory, Decatur, Ill.

9. Private communication, Nov. 23, 1959, Breslauf, M., The Borden Chemical Co., Polyco-Monomer Department, Leominster, Mass.

SOURCES OF SUPPLY

10. American Bitumuls Co., San Francisco, Calif.

11. Atlas Powder Co., Wilmington, Del.

12. The Borden Chemical Co., New York, N. Y.

13. The Dow Chemical Co., Midland, Mich.

14. Hercules Powder Co., Wilmington, Del.

15. Minerals and Chemicals Corp. of America, Menlo Park, N. J.

16. Monsanto Chemical Co., St. Louis, Mo.

17. A. E. Staley Manufacturing Co., Decatur, Ill.

18. Wyandotte Chemicals Corp. Wyandotte, Mich.

— 36 —

Hot-Melt Adhesives

E. M. Crowell
Research Division
United Shoe Machinery Corporation
Beverly, Mass.

and

J. C. Eldridge
B. B. Chemical Company, Subsidiary
United Shoe Machinery Corporation
Cambridge, Mass.

Hot-melt adhesives are bonding agents which achieve a solid state and resultant strength by cooling, as contrasted with other adhesives which achieve the solid state through evaporation or removal of solvents. Prior to heating, a hot-melt adhesive is a thermoplastic, 100 per cent solid material, all adhesive. Application of heat brings the material to the liquid state, and after removal of the heat, it sets by simple cooling. Hot melts offer the possibility of nearly instantaneous bonding, especially when joining previously uncemented or smooth impermeable surfaces.

When a hot-melt adhesive comes in close contact with the surface to be bonded, a molecular layer of film at the surface of this substrate immediately attains a temperature approaching that of the hot melt; furthermore a high degree of wetting, almost coalescence, of the hot melt and the surface material occurs. Directly afterward, the melt loses heat to the film over the whole area and temperature equilibrium is attained. Since the adhesive is in contact with a mass much larger than itself, the temperature of the entire system drops to where the melt sets to a solid with adequate cohesive strength to hold the films together.

Why Hot-Melt Adhesives Are Used

Ordinarily, a hot-melt adhesive is sought for the economic reasons associated with process speed, simplicity, or mechanization. Where these factors are unimportant, a solvent cement or a thermosetting-type adhesive is usually available to provide a bond with greater strength and durability.

Hot-melt adhesives are unique primarily because of the speed with which they produce a bond. Although their use eliminates the cost of solvents used with cements, the main cost reduction results from the time saved in their application. Usually a lesser quantity of the hot melt can be utilized to produce an equivalent bond, resulting in a further saving in cost.

The sequence of operations involving hot-melt adhesives is necessarily rapid; consequently they are rarely considered for hand application. They are sought for processes using maximum mechanization, and their ultimate economic advantage is reached only through full automation and where high production speeds are required.

Prices of polymers and plastics usually increase with strength. The strength of an adhesive need not exceed the strength of the materials being joined. Materials of low laminar strength such as some papers, normally need adhesives of relatively low strength and cost. Here, one of several alternate adhesives may frequently be used. The selection is based therefore primarily on costs rather than technical qualities.

When to Specify A Hot-Melt Adhesive

However, if the process becomes critical due to a desire for automation with a demand for high speeds of work travel through the joining process, the limiting factor may not be the bond quality but the melting and "freezing" characteristics of the adhesive. This situation conceivably might demand a special, and therefore high-cost adhesive for its solution and yet be economically attractive because of the magnitude of savings realized in automation and speed-up.

The development of a successful hot-melt adhesive process is almost always a twofold operation: the evolution of a machine for controllably melting, feeding, and positioning the adhesive in the joint between the work surfaces, followed by immobilization of the joint while the adhesive cools and develops mechanical strength; and the creation of an adhesive to meet the engineering requirements imposed by the machine-and-product specifications.

Hot-melt technology is in a stage of rapid evolution. Early examples gave fastenings of relative rigidity, low mechanical strength, and slow adhesive setting time. With the introduction of newer polymers and modern techniques of adhesive handling, these limitations are being overcome to make available highly shock-resistant, flexible joints of greatly increased ultimate strength, having in some instances a unique resistance to solvents.

Composition of Hot-Melt Adhesives

In the past, there has been a wide selection of low-molecular-weight, natural and synthetic waxes and resins that served as hot melts when formulated. Among these are:[1, 2]

> Coumarone-indene resins
> Rosin and its derivatives
> Mineral, vegetable, and petroleum waxes
> Alkyds
> Terpene resins
> Heat-stable phenol-formaldehyde resins

All of these have typically low strength and melt easily to low viscosity fluids. To be converted into useful adhesives, they are reinforced or toughened by blending with limited proportions of higher molecular weight polymers selected from the following:

> Ethyl cellulose
> Polyvinyl acetate and its derivatives
> Butyl methacrylates

> Polyethylene
> Polystyrene and styrene copolymers
> Polyisobutylene

The finished adhesives usually contain, additionally, some proportion of a liquid plasticizer, resinous or monomeric. The natural asphalts and the vegetable and coal-tar pitches also represent base materials useful as hot-melt adhesives, alone or in compounds. Generally considered, these formulations have only moderate shock resistance, tensile strength, and freedom from creep when compared with solution-grade or structural plastics.

Some of the most outstanding modern hot-melt adhesives are compounded from polyethylene, polyvinyl acetate and its derivatives, and a polyamide derived from dimerized fatty acids and diamines. These have had gratifying success in bonding papers, metal foils, plastic films, fabrics, and light leathers.

All these raw materials, whether natural products or synthetic materials, were manufactured for use in the plastics, coating, or rubber industries. Very few, if any, synthetic polymers have been developed to suit the particular needs of hot-melt technology since it is a highly specialized and limited market. The adhesive technologist's contribution has been to modify pre-existing materials by blending them to suit adhesive requirements.

Knowledge has been accumulating over the past two decades relating the mechanical properties of polymers to their chemistry and structure. When this information is exploited in the synthesis of new polymers for adhesive use, many vexatious limitations in the available general-purpose resin materials will be overcome. In a number of instances involving highly mechanized processes, new synthetic polymers have been successful after conventional formulating efforts with stock commercial polymers had failed.

Recent Formulations[3,4, 5]

Considerable success has been reported in the formulating of hot-melt adhesives in rapid melting cordlike form containing resins such as polyethylene, polyamides or polyvinyl acetate. These can be compounded to give superior bonding action with less concern for the heat stability of the ingredients. A rod or cordlike adhesive melts rapidly, and only a small amount of adhesive is retained in hot and melted condition before use; consequently, there is less thermal degradation than with pot-type hot melts. Control of temperature and quality is facilitated.

The bonding of polyethylene surfaces, a task formerly requiring fusion, has been accomplished with an adhesive composition. The adhesive is applied in hot molten condition at a temperature well above the melting point of polyethylene, in a quantity carrying sufficient heat to melt the surface of the polyethylene and cause mutual solution of adhesive and polyethylene surface. One formulation useful in this method comprises polyethylene, isobutylene polymeric material, and a hydrocarbon resin having at elevated temperatures at least limited solvent power toward the polyethylene. The most effective proportions are:

Polyethylene, from 15 to 60 per cent, preferably 40 to 55 per cent

Isobutylene polymeric material, from 10 to 35 per cent, preferably 20 to 30 per cent

Hydrocarbon resin, 20 to 60 per cent

It is possible to use mixtures of more than one hydrocarbon resin and more than one molecular weight of the isobutylene polymeric material. However, it is important to select components of sufficiently high molecular weight and melting point. Other materials may be added including antioxidants, very fine mineral fillers, etc.

Polyamide resinous materials are useful in various hot-melt adhesive problems because of their high strength and ability to hold strongly to a wide variety of materials, including paper, rubber, leather and metal.

The bonding of leather, with almost instantaneous setting, has been accomplished by the reaction product of a polyamide resin with another resin. Although the reaction product has higher molecular weight, it still melts readily. It is capable of bonding a wider range of materials than the polyamide itself.

Many combinations of resins are known in which the resins are miscible in molten condition to form a homogeneous liquid but are incompatible and would tend to separate when the molten material is cooled to solidify it. One such mixture comprises polyethylene, polyvinyl acetate, and a hydrocarbon resin having at elevated temperatures at least limited solvent power toward the polyethylene. Another combination which has been found useful as an adhesive is a mixture of from 2 to 10 parts of polyethylene and 10 to 15 parts of polymerized resin with from 60 to 75 parts of polyamide resin which has been reacted with epoxide resin insufficient to cure it.

A cordlike body of one of these mixtures, when melted quickly, forms a uniform, clear adhesive liquid. After application of the molten material, relatively long open-time is attained if the various components are in the right proportions. Polyvinyl acetate-polyethylene compositions have the milky look of incompatibility when solid. Apparently this incompatibility in solid form introduces a delay of the setting up without lessening the bonding ability. Notwithstanding the relatively long open-time, the adhesive has high resistance to "cold flow."

Bonding Technology

The ideal hot-melt adhesive would be solid at room temperature and capable of being stored and handled easily without blocking. Color would be light. Upon heating, it would melt sharply and flow freely. It would be stable to prolonged heating and able to withstand local overheating.

In liquid-melt form, it could be applied to the work by nozzle, wheel, or spray. Its point of solidification would be such that ample time would be available to close the bond with only minimum pressure. Of course, bonds accomplished with this ideal hot melt would be strong and the range of materials which it could bond would be wide.

Finally, the composition of the hot melt would be such that paper products bonded with the adhesive could be reclaimed by some simple process. These are general requirements. A quality that might be particularly desirable for one application could be unimportant for another.

In any case, a polymer must be a fluid liquid at some elevated temperature in order to meet requirements as a hot melt; yet it must set to a strong solid.

Physical Forms of Hot Melts

Hot melts are available in many different forms. Some of these are (1) tapes or ribbons, (2) films or thin sheets, (3) granules, (4) pellets in various shapes such as cylinders and cubes, (5) block, (6) others such as cordlike. Heat reactive adhesives may come as liquids, pastes or foams, which are not identified as hot melts. Many materials are applied as solvent or aqueous solutions or emulsions to be dried and later heat-activated.

Methods of Applying Hot Melts

One of the limitations of hot melts is the special equipment required. This has led to the development of many different systems for applying them.

Doctored rolls and intaglio techniques are common. Individual pieces are often dipped.

A recent system uses an extruder as a melting and feeding device or heat pump. The latest system, widely used, embodies a new concept: a hot-melt adhesive in cordlike form and an applicator to melt, meter and apply it.*

Types of Equipment

Equipment for applying hot melts is of two principal types: melt reservoir and "progressive feed." In the former, a quantity of the adhesive is melted in a pot and delivered by a metering pump from the pot to a heated nozzle. The adhesive is in the form of blocks, chips, or granules. A charge is put in the melting pot, heated to a predetermined temperature under thermostatic control, and the melt is fed to a nozzle or cementing wheel by a pump. The components are bonded together immediately with pressure.

Wherever a melting pot must be used, there are some inherent drawbacks. A considerable quantity of adhesive needs to be kept above the fusion temperature for considerably long periods. There is difficulty in controlling the temperature throughout this mass accurately, especially when fresh solid must be added periodically. With many compositions, there is only a narrow range between the fusion and decomposition temperatures, which often leads to thickening and gelling by oxidation; moreover carbonized deposits may form in the melting pots. Few compositions will remain stable under these conditions.

With "progressive feed" applicators, only a minimum quantity of hot melts must be molten at any one time because the adhesive is fed continuously in the form of an elongated cord. The adhesive is supplied as a flexible, grooved cylindrical cord coiled on reels. The rate of feed of the cord is synchronized with the rate of delivery of the melt through the nozzle. In between the feed and delivery point, the adhesive passes around a heated melt wheel running in an eccentric groove. The melt chamber is formed, in fact, by the small tubular space between the wheel and the casing. The internal capacity of the unit is so small that only a few grams of material are held above the melt temperature within the applicator. The use of thermostatically controlled heating elements located at carefully selected points enables the adhesive to be maintained at its maximum application temperature without overheating. The first-in,

first-out principle of adhesive application is a further safeguard. The width of bonds may be controlled by the design of the nozzle or applying wheel and by the relationship between the rate of adhesive output and the speed of the moving web. Many variations are possible, including the application of several parallel beads of adhesive by using a number of nozzles from the same applicator, or a wide band from many small orifices in a single nozzle.

Uses of Hot Melts

There are many diverse applications of hot melts. As production speeds increase, economics of hot melts will become more favorable, and new uses will certainly be found.

At present, the most common uses are the following:

1. Protective coating of paper, cloth, foil and plastic film.
2. Lamination of the same materials.
3. Structural bonding of paper, wood and other materials.
4. Pick-up gums and spot labeling.
5. Bonding of ceramics, cork and metal.
6. Production of articles made from paper, foil or film webs including several forms of containers and packages.
7. Sealing of packages and spot joining of small articles.

With modern application equipment using "progressive feed," and especially with the wide range of adhesive formulations available in cordlike form, a number of varied bond properties have been made possible. Some of these are:

(1) Effective bonding of flexible package at $-40°F$.
(2) Oil-resistive bonds retaining strength on papers with 4 to 6 per cent mineral oil.
(3) Effective bonding of lightly waxed surfaces.
(4) Strong uniform bonding and sealing of polyethylene films and coatings.
(5) Strong foil bonding.
(6) Fast, effective bonding of leathers.

Expression of formulations contained in the foregoing does not constitute a license to practice of the invention of patents.

---

* "Thermogrip" adhesives and applicators, United Shoe Machinery Corp.

References

1. Seymour, R. B., "Hot Organic Coatings," New York, Reinhold Publishing Corp., 1959.

2. Kopyscinski, W., Norris, F. H., and Herman, S., *Adhesives Age,* p. 31 (May 1960).

3. Johnson, C., and Clarke, D. (to B. B. Chemical Co., subsidiary of United Shoe Machinery Corp.) U. S. Patent 2,975,150 (Mar. 14, 1961).

4. Morris, C., and Johnson, C. (to B. B. Chemical Co., subsidiary of United Shoe Machinery Corp.), U. S. Patent 2,894,925 (July 14, 1959).

5. Morris, C., and Chaplick, A. M. (to B. B. Chemical Co., subsidiary of United Shoe Machinery Corp), U. S. Patent 2,867,592 (Jan. 6, 1959).

37

Plasticizers for Adhesives

David H. Bechtold, Peter W. Spink and Walter F. Waychoff

Monsanto Chemical Company
St. Louis, Missouri

A plasticizer is a high-boiling liquid or low-melting solid organic compound which is added to a synthetic resin adhesive formulation to impart desirable end properties, improve processing, and possibly reduce cost. Plasticizers are capable of improving such important characteristics as tack and flexibility. In the processing operations the use of proper plasticizers will result in decreased drying time, better machine processing, and improved film formation.

THE MECHANISM OF PLASTICIZATION

Thermoplastic resins are normally long-chain chemically bonded polymers. There is no primary bond between chains; instead, the polymer molecules are held together with Van der Waals' secondary bonds. Since these between-chain bonds are physical rather than chemical in nature, they are susceptible to modification by external forces. Consequently, when a plasticizer is incorporated into the resin, the plasticizer is thought to enter between the chains, physically separating the polymer molecules. This separation decreases the Van der Waals' forces or secondary bonds between polymer molecules, resulting in increased flexibility.

The Van der Waals' forces or secondary bonds between the chains vary in magnitude and number with the resin. The polymer chains of some resins are strongly bonded together by many cross-tying attractive forces; whereas others are more loosely knit. The stronger the bonding forces be-tween the molecules of the polymer, the more highly polar must be the plasticizer for the resin; thus a strongly bonded resin, e.g., cellulose acetate or a polyamide resin, requires plasticizers of high polarity. Compounds that are less strongly bonded such as rubber require plasticizers that are less polar in nature.

Plasticizers, like solvents, are attracted by their polar groups to polar polymers, replacing the secondary polymer-polymer bonds with polymer-plasticizer bonds. The sheer bulk of a plasticizer molecule and the configuration of its grouping disrupts the forces between chains, thereby separating them with resulting increased flexibility and tack.

SELECTING THE RIGHT PLASTICIZER

More than 350 plasticizers are now made commercially. This multitude of products plus the synthetic resins available makes possible an almost infinite number of plasticizer and resin combinations. There are five basic evaluations to help determine the right plasticizer for a specific resin, namely: compatibility, processing, performance, permanence, and cost.

The first consideration when choosing a plasticizer is compatibility with the resin to be used. Table 1 lists some of the more common plasticizers and gives their compatibility with synthetic resins in the adhesive field. In addition, the product must process well. Reaction to machine handling, drying time, and adhesive build-up on applicators must be evaluated.

One of the most serious problems in formulation of adhesives is toxicity. Several plasticizers have had prior sanction from the Food and Drug Administration for use of synthetic resins in food packaging, an important application for adhesives. Other characteristics to be evaluated include flexibility, heat sealability, bond strength, and shock resistance.

Next to be determined is the degree of permanence. Considerations here are the material's volatility, resistance to extractions by water and solvents, migration of the plasticizer from the adhesive to the substrate and chemical stability.

Finally, cost of the plasticizer should not be excessive.

APPLICATION IN ADHESIVES

Plasticizers are used in emulsion, solution, hot-melt, delayed tack, pressure-sensitive, and miscellaneous adhesive formulations.

Emulsion Adhesives

Emulsion adhesives are based on water dispersions of plasticized or unplasticized resins. They offer the advantages of reduced fire and toxicity hazards because of the elimination of volatile, flammable and possible toxic solvents.

Polyvinyl acetate emulsion adhesives are perhaps the most widely used of this type. They offer quick tack, good adhesion to many surfaces,

grease resistance, nontoxicity (by selection of other compounding ingredients) and many other desirable features.

Dibutyl phthalate is probably the most popular plasticizer for this type of adhesive. It imparts good flexibility and softening action with relatively low volatility. Butyl benzyl phthalate and butyl cyclohexyl phthalate are also widely used, providing lower volatility, better moisture resistance and film toughness than dibutyl phthalate. Diethyl phthalate is utilized in fast tack, nontoxic applications. Dimethyl phthalate is preferred for polyvinyl acetate adhesives for cellulose acetate film, covering cutout windows in cartons, or laminating it to paper. Dipropylene glycol dibenzoate and diethylene glycol dibenzoate are used where long open tack time is desired.

Among the phosphate esters, tricresyl phosphate, cresyl diphenyl phosphate, and alkyl aryl phosphates provide flame resistance, oil resistance, and low volatility. The phthalyl glycollates are nontoxic, moreover, methyl phthalyl ethyl glycollate gives superior light stability, quick tack, and ability to dissolve cellulose acetate.

Among the sulfonamides, N-ethyl-o-p-toluene sulfonamide offers excellent grease resistance plus improved bonding of rubber to metal.

Low cost plasticizers for polyvinyl acetate emulsion adhesives, the chlorinated biphenyls and terphenyls are used principally because of their quick tack, good adhesion to many surfaces and excellent performance. The following six formulations, which represent major applications for polyvinyl acetate, are typical of many starting formulations.

	Formulation 1: Quick Tack Adhesive	Formulation 2: Quick Tack, Low Cost Adhesive	Formulation 3: Wood Adhesive	Formulation 4: Combining Adhesive	Formulation 5: Padding Adhesive	Formulation 6: Cellophane, Aluminum Foil, Paper Adhesive
Polyvinyl acetate emulsion (55% solids)	100.0	100.0	100.0	100.0	100.0	100.0
N-ethyl-o,p-toluene sulfonamide	12.0	—	—	—	—	—
Butyl benzyl phthalate	12.0	—	3.2	—	—	9.0
Chlorinated biphenyl (32% chlorine)	—	11.0	—	—	—	—
Diethylene glycol dibenzoate or dibutyl phthalate	—	—	—	40.0	—	—
Tricresyl phosphate	—	—	—	—	14.0	—
"Santolite"* MS (80%)	—	—	—	—	—	13.5
Water	9.0	—	2.2	13.0	5.5	13.5

* Monsanto Chemical Co.

TABLE 1. PLASTICIZER COMPATABILITY WITH VARIOUS RESINS.

	Polyamide	Urethane	Nitrile and Neoprene Rubber	Chlorinated Rubber	Epoxy	Asphalt	Proteins	Acrylic	Ethyl Cellulose	Cellulose Acetate Butyrate	Cellulose Acetate	Cellulose Nitrate	Polystyrene	Polyvinyl Butyral	Polyvinyl Chloride	Polyvinyl Acetate
Butyl benzyl phthalate	C	C	C	C	C	I	P	C	C	C	P	C	C	C	C	C
Butyl cyclohexyl phthalate	C	C	C	C	C	I	P	C	C	C	P	C	C	C	C	C
Butyl decyl phthalate	P	C	C	C	P	P	I	C	C	C	I	C	C	C	C	I
Butyl octyl phthalate	C	C	C	C	P	P	I	C	C	C	I	C	C	P	C	I
Dibutyl phthalate	C	C	C	C	C	I	P	C	C	C	P	C	C	C	C	C
Dicyclohexyl phthalate	P	P	C	P	P	I	I	C	C	P	I	C	P	C	C	C
Diethyl phthalate	I	P	C	C	P	I	P	C	C	C	C	C	C	C	I	C
Diisodecyl phthalate	P	C	C	C	P	P	I	C	C	C	I	C	C	P	C	I
Dimethyl phthalate	I	P	C	C	I	I	P	C	C	C	C	C	C	C	C	C
Dioctyl phthalate	C	C	C	C	I	P	I	C	C	C	I	C	C	P	I	I
Diphenyl phthalate	P	P	C	P	P	I	I	C	C	C	I	C	C	C	C	C
Cresyl diphenyl phosphate	C	C	C	C	C	I	P	C	C	C	C	C	P	C	C	C
Octyl diphenyl phosphate	C	C	C	C	C	P	C	C	C	C	P	C	C	C	C	C
Tricresyl phosphate	C	C	C	C	C	I	C	C	C	C	P	C	P	C	C	C

Plasticizer	1	2	3	4	5	6	7	8	9	10	11	12	13	14	15	16
Trioctyl phosphate	I	C	C	—	C	P	P	C	I	I	C	I	P	C	C	C
Triphenyl phosphate	C	C	C	P	C	C	C	C	I	P	C	C	C	C	C	P
Diethylene glycol dibenzoate	C	C	C	C	C	P	P	C	C	P	C	C	C	C	C	P
Dipropylene glycol dibenzoate	C	C	C	C	C	P	C	C	C	P	C	I	C	C	C	C
Butyl phthalyl butyl glycollate	C	C	C	C	C	C	C	C	C	C	C	I	C	C	C	C
Ethyl phthalyl ethyl glycollate	C	P	C	C	C	C	C	C	I	C	C	C	C	C	C	I
Methyl phthalyl ethyl glycollate	C	P	C	C	C	C	C	C	C	P	C	I	C	C	C	I
N-Cyclohexyl-p-toluenesulfonamide	C	I	C	P	C	C	C	P	C	C	C	P	P	C	P	C
N-Ethyl-o,p-toluenesulfonamide	C	I	C	P	C	C	C	C	C	C	C	C	C	C	P	C
o,p-toluenesulfonamide	C	I	C	P	C	C	C	C	C	C	C	C	C	C	P	C
Chlorinated biphenyls	C	P	C	C	C	I	I	C	C	P	C	C	C	C	C	C
Chlorinated paraffins	C	P	P	C	P	I	I	C	P	P	C	P	P	C	C	C
Didecyl adipate	I	C	C	C	C	I	I	C	I	I	C	I	C	C	C	C
Dioctyl adipate	I	C	C	C	C	C	C	C	I	I	C	C	C	P	P	C
Dioctyl azelate	I	C	P	C	C	C	P	C	I	P	C	I	C	C	P	C
Dioctyl sebacate	I	C	P	C	C	C	I	C	I	I	C	I	C	C	P	C

C = Compatible (over 25 phr)
P = Partially Compatible (5–25 phr)
I = Incompatible (less than 5 phr)

Emulsion adhesives of the heat-sealable type frequently contain a solid plasticizer, which must be ground and dispersed. Typical dispersions of solid plasticizers are:

Ingredient	Formulation:	(7)	(8)	(9)
		parts by wt.		
Diphenyl phthalate		100	—	—
N-cyclohexyl p-toluenesulfonamide		—	100	—
Triphenyl phosphate		—	—	100
Water		100	100	100
Polyvinyl pyrrolidone		4.7	4.4	4.4
Sodium carboxymethylcellulose		1.3	1.3	1.3

These formulations are prepared as follows:

(1) Grind the solid plasticizer with dry ice to the desired particle size. Dry ice prevents coagulation of the solid plasticizer as a result of softening from frictional heat.

(2) Add the thickening agents to the water, and agitate until solution is effected.

(3) Slowly add the solid plasticizer to the viscous solution with good agitation. This dispersion may be used in any desired polyvinyl acetate emulsion formulation.

Solution Adhesives

Solution synthetic resin adhesives differ from the emulsion types in that solvents instead of water carry the adhesive. The use of solvents improves the bite or adhesion. Almost any thermoplastic resin can be used in solution adhesives.

Vinyl resins are widely used in heat-sealable, grease-resistant paper coatings. Formula 10 is typical:

Formulation 10: Vinyl Solution Coating.

Ingredient	parts by wt.
"Vinylite"* VYHH	80
"Vinylite"* VMCH	10
"Vinylite"* VAGH	10
Alkyl aryl phosphate	20
Acetone	250
Methylethyl ketone	100

* Union Carbide Plastics Co.

Nitrocellulose lacquer coatings are frequently applied to make cellophane heat-sealable and moisture-resistant. Formula 11 is suitable, for this type of application. For a household adhesive, nitrocellulose cement is compounded according to Formula 12.

	Formulation 11: Nitrocellulose Heat-Sealable Cellophane Lacquer	Formulation 12: Nitrocellulose Cement
Nitrocellulose (½ sec SS)	56	—
Nitrocellulose (30–40 sec KS)	—	10
Dibutyl phthalate	13	—
Dicyclohexyl phthalate	20	—
Butyl benzyl phthalate	—	5
Dammar wax	8	—
Paraffin wax	3	—
"Santolite" MS (80%)	—	12
Ethanol	50	—
Ethyl acetate	104	34
Acetone	—	34
Toluene	50	—

	Formulation 13: Paper to Paper or Cellulose Acetate Butyrate	Formulation 14: Grease-Resistant Coating	Formulation 15: Ethyl Cellulose Cement
Cellulose acetate butyrate (½ sec)	15.0	—	—
Cellulose acetate (LL-1)	—	20.0	—
Ethyl cellulose (N-14)	—	—	10.0
"Santolite" MHP	15.0	—	—
Methyl phthalyl ethyl glycollate	—	10.2	—
N-ethyl-o,p-toluene sulfonamide	—	2.5	—
Dibutyl phthalate	—	—	1.5
"Lewisol" 28	—	—	5.0
Ethanol	15.0	—	17.0
Toluene	35.0	—	67.5
Hi-Flash naphtha	10.0	—	—
Acetone	—	16.8	—
Methylethyl ketone	—	37.0	—
Methyl cellosolve acetate	—	7.0	—
Ethyl lactate	—	7.0	—

Cellulose acetate butyrate, cellulose acetate, and ethyl cellulose are widely used in solution adhesives as shown in Formulas 13, 14, and 15.

Polyurethane. The advent of urethane foam has increased the need for adhesives to bond it to itself or to other materials. Formula 16 is a good starting formulation for this application.

Formulation 16: Polyurethane Adhesive

Ingredient	parts by wt.
"Multranil"* 176	100
"Mondur"* C	5
Ethyl acetate	50
Chlorinated biphenyl (54% Cl)	20

* Mobay Chemical Co.

Formulation 16 has a maximum work life of 48 hr; however excessive humidity or temperature will shorten the work life. It is recommended, therefore, that only enough adhesive for 1 day be mixed at a time. The formula may be diluted with acetone or ethyl acetate if desired. This adhesive may be applied cold and subsequently be allowed to stand at room temperature for 10 to 30 min until the solvent evaporates. The pieces are joined and compressed at 50 psi for a minimum of 15 sec.

Chlorinated rubber is used in heat-sealing adhesives because of its low moisture-vapor transmission, chemical resistance, and heat sealability. Formulation 17 is a suggested starting formulation for a heat-sealing chlorinated rubber adhesive. When 5 to 7 lb are applied per ream of paper, this coating allows only $\frac{1}{16}$ g of moisture vapor to pass through 100 sq in. of paper in 72 hr.

	Formulation 17: Heat-Sealing Chlorinated-Rubber Adhesive	Formulation 18: Chlorinated-Rubber Label Adhesive
Chlorinated rubber (125 centipoise type)	60	20
Chlorinated biphenyl (54% chlorine)	—	6
Chlorinated terphenyl (60% chlorine)	—	6
Dibutyl phthalate	14	—
Paraffin wax	5	—
"Pentalyn"* H	21	—
Toluene	—	68
Solvent	As needed	—

* Hercules Powder Co.

Plasticizers make possible many unique compounds. Formulation 19 illustrates their versatility in formulating coatings or adhesives.

Formulation 19: Zein Label Varnish

Zein	100
Rosin WW	100
"Santolite" MHP	20
N-ethyl-*o,p*-toluenesulfonamide	25
Isopropanol (91%)	190

Hot-Melt Adhesives

Hot-melt adhesives are utilized because they set rapidly after application. Here plasticizers play an important part. Liquid plasticizers are added to impart flexibility. Solid plasticizers are employed in many applications since they melt at the processing temperature but resolidify on cooling, thereby overcoming the problem of excessive softness frequently encountered with hot-melt adhesives.

Hot-melts are frequently used to make bookbinding adhesives. Formula 20, an alkali-dispersible nonblocking adhesive, is suggested for this application.

Formulation 20

"Gelva"* C-5 V-16	38.0
"Nevillac," soft	28.3
Butyl benzyl phthalate	7.0
Chlorinated biphenyl (54% chlorine)	27.0
"Acrawax" C	1.0
Sodium benzoate	0.76
Viscosity 3500 cps at 175°C	

* Shawinigan Resins

"Mylar" can be bonded to paper with Formulation 21:

Formulation 21

"Gelva" V-1½	50
"Gelva" V-7	50
N-ethyl-*o,p*-toluenesulfonamide	50

Polyvinyl butyral hot-melt adhesives are useful for joining cellophane, aluminum foil, glassine and wax glassine to themselves. The sealing temperature is usually 250 to 350°F, and the pressure for application usually ranges between 0.5 and 30 psi. The advantage of polyvinyl butyral hot-melts is their extremely fast rate of setting, i.e., from 0.5 to 2 sec. The molten bulk adhesive is applied to both surfaces to be bonded, allowed to cool and set; then the surfaces are joined under heat and pressure for adhesion. Formulation 22 shown below is typical of a polyvinyl butyral hot-melt adhesive.

Formulation 22: Polyvinyl Butyral Hot-Pickup Adhesives

"Butvar"* B-76	10.0
Resin 861	74.4
"Castorwax"	8.3
Butyl phthalyl butyl glycollate	10.0
"Armid" HT	0.2

* Shawinigan Resins.

To make Formula 22, the polyvinyl butyral is dissolved in ethanol; then the wax is added with agitation and slight heating until a homogenous slurry is obtained. The alcohol is then distilled from the mixture and the other ingredients are added to the molten polyvinyl butyral wax mix. To obtain a perfectly smooth formulation the

Solid plasticizers such as diphenyl phthalate, N-cyclohexyl-p-toluene sulfonamide, o-p-toluenesulfonamide, and dicyclohexyl phthalate make possible the delayed-tack properties of these unusual adhesives. The solid plasticizers are chosen for their crystallizing characteristics, their compatibility and solvating power for the base resin as well as the temperature at which the adhesive is to be activated.

Such compositions are broadly covered by patents, for example United States Patents 2,462,029, 2,408,542, 2,608,543, 2,613,156, and 2,613,191. Formulation 27 depends on the n-cyclohexyl-p-toluenesulfonamide for its delayed-tack characteristics.

	Formulation 23: Polymethyl Methacrylate Combining Hot-Melt	Formulation 24: Cellulose Acetate Hot-Melt	Formulation 25: Cellulose Acetate Butyrate Hot-Melt	Formulation 26: Ethyl Cellulose Hot-Melt
Polymethyl methacrylate	100.0	—	—	—
Chlorinated rubber	20.0	—	—	—
Cellulose acetate	—	50.0	—	—
Cellulose acetate butyrate (½ sec)	—	—	35.0	—
Ethyl cellulose (50 cps)	—	—	—	24.0
Butyl cyclohexyl phthalate or				
Butyl benzyl phthalate	10.0	—	—	—
Methyl phthalyl ethyl glycollate	—	88.0	—	—
Chlorinated terphenyl (60% chlorine)	—	—	30.0	7.0
Di 2 ethylhexyl phthalate	—	—	15.0	—
"Newport" V-40	—	—	19.9	—
"Santonox"*	—	—	0.1	1.0
Lopor No. 45 mineral oil	—	—	—	57.0
Bakers No. 15 castor oil	—	—	—	5.0
Epoxy soybean oil	—	—	—	3.0
Paraffin wax (135°F M.P.)	—	—	—	3.0

* Monsanto Chemical Co.

finished compound should be strained through cheesecloth or other suitable filter material.

Formulations 23 through 26 indicate the versatility of plasticizers in preparing hot-melts based upon other synthetic resins.

Delayed-Tack Adhesives

Delayed-tack adhesives differ from hot-melts adhesives in which tackiness terminates on cooling; moreover they are normally tack-free at ordinary temperatures after they are spread and dried on a surface. After subsequent heat activation, tackiness is maintained from several hours to several days over a fairly wide temperature range. This slow setting property permits necessary mechanical handling before the adhesive cools and sets.

Formulation 27: Delayed-Tack Adhesive
(United States Patent 2,462,029, Example 96)

Ingredient	parts by wt.
N-cyclohexyl-p-toluenesulfonamide	50
"Vinsol" resin	50
Thinned amine dispersant[a]	250
"Acrysol" M. R.	10

[a] "The thinned amine dispersant is a mixture composed of 1 part stearic acid, 1 part poly-pale resin, a polymerized rosin containing approximately 40 per cent dipolymers of abietic acid (Hercules Powder Co.), 1 part 2 amino-2-methyl-1-propanol (Commercial Solvents Corp.), and 3 parts water. This composition is designed solely as a dispersion assistant . . ." (from Column 10 of this patent).

Formulation 28 illustrates the use of diphenyl phthalate as a plasticizer in delayed-tack adhesives.

Formulation 28: (United States Patent 2,462,029)

Ingredient	parts by wt.
Diphenyl phthalate	52.5
"Nevindene" R-3	30.0
Thinned amine dispersant (see Formula 25)	198.0
"Hycar" OR-25	43.5

Formulation 29

Ingredient	parts by wt.
"Versamid" 940	100.0
o,p-toluenesulfonamide	31.6
Candelilla wax	5.9
Isopropyl alcohol	29.5
Toluene	29.5

This formulation is nontacky at ordinary temperatures and is heat-activated at about 150°F; then the compound remains adhesive through temperatures as low as 50°F. Once set, the adhesive continues to hold at ordinary temperatures.

Formulation 29 is based on polyamide resins and gets its delayed tack characteristics from o-p-toluenesulfonamide.

Pressure-Sensitive Adhesives

Pressure-sensitive adhesives are those materials which require little or no pressure to develop their adhesive characteristics; they can be made from emulsions, hot-melts, solution, or by straight mixing of the adhesive. Formulations 30 through 32 illustrate three typical pressure-sensitive adhesives.

	Formulation 30: Pressure-Sensitive Cellulose Acetate Adhesive (calender on fabric)	Formulation 31: Pressure-Sensitive Polyvinyl Acetate Adhesive (calender on fabric)	Formulation 32: Pressure-Sensitive Chlorinated- Rubber Adhesive (solution type)
Cellulose acetate (type A, 40 mesh)	1.0	—	—
"Vinylite" AYAF	—	5.0	—
"Arofene" 700 (100% phenolic resin)	—	36.0	—
"Parlon"* (1259 type)	—	—	5
"Staybelite"* Ester No. 10	—	—	10
Dibutyl phthalate	—	—	10
Acetone	—	—	52.5
Hexane	—	—	22.5
N-cyclohexyl-p-toluenesulfonamide	3.5	—	—
"Santolite" MHP	1.5	—	—
Butyl phthalyl butyl glycollate	—	18.0	—

* Hercules Powder Co.

— 38 —

Ceramic and Other High-Temperature Adhesives

D. V. Rosato

Telecomputing Corp.
Waltham, Massachusetts

Outstanding developments in the fields of missiles, jet aircraft, and atomic-powered heat engines have created the need for structural adhesives resistant to temperatures. Ceramics and inorganic materials are playing an important role in these developments. Some ceramic mixtures give satisfactory adhesives after maturing at temperatures ranging from 1000 to 2000°F. Adhesive tensile lap-bond strengths have been developed ranging from 2000 to 5000 psi at room temperature, retaining 1000 to 3000 psi at 1000°F.

In the past two decades, new organic base adhesives have provided reliable adhesive joints with higher strengths, simplicity in quality control, and/or low cost processing. Typical applications are truck bodies, table tops, automotive brake bands, automotive bodies, building partitions, ceramic tool bits, oil well tubes, aircraft structures, jet engine shrouds and missile motor bodies. These structural adhesives are combinations of epoxy-phenolic, vinyl-phenolic, nitrile-rubber-phenolic, nylon-phenolic, etc.

Modern aerospace vehicles and ordnance equipment also rely on the use of these structural type organic adhesives. Typical examples include missiles (Atlas, Terrier, Titan, Honest John, etc.), aircraft (B-36, B-52, B-58, etc.), ground and water vehicles, etc. The B-58 Hustler high-speed aircraft uses over 1000 lb of adhesives; however as aerospace temperature requirements increased, the available adhesives became limited in new applications. Military research and development efforts in improving the heat resistance and thermal stability of adhesives are primarily in (1) inorganic or metallic fillers providing for non-oxidation reactions with organic binders, (2) inorganics, and (3) ceramics.

ORGANICS

The organic programs have developed adhesives operating up to 500°F for relatively long-time service. Organic adhesive polymers are being developed to withstand short-time exposures at temperatures above 500°F. As an example, tensile shear strengths of 2000 to 3000 psi have been developed at room temperature. Retention of approximately 50 per cent strength exists after 10 min at 700°F, and retention of approximately 20 per cent exists after 10 min at 1000°F. Major development programs to date regarding organic adhesives involve the preparation of special fillers (metallic oxides, etc.) and additives to provide closer molecular bond (arsenic pentoxide, etc.).

SEMIORGANICS AND INORGANICS

Semiorganic polymer adhesives have recently been developed which provide structural strength up to 1000°F for short periods of time. The most promising systems are modified phenolics, e.g., inorganic filled epoxy-phenolics and silicone-phenolics. Narmco Industries developments with arsenic pentoxide are discussed in Chapter 39. Unmodified, the tightly crosslinked phenolics are extremely susceptible to oxidation degradation; whereas the weaker crosslinked epoxy alone becomes thermoplastic at the higher temperatures.

The epoxy-novolacs are converted to tightly crosslinked polymers with curing agents such as melamine (semiinorganic compound) and arsenic pentoxide (inorganic compound).

Compounds showing improved high temperature properties are prepared by the interaction of a phenolic compound with siloxane. Siloxane-phenolic resin adhesive compound systems prepared with an equal weight of aluminum powder have good strength retention at 500°F or above.

Other inorganic adhesives include sodium silicate, Portland cement, magnesium oxychloride, magnesium oxysulfide, plaster of Paris and ceramics. All except the last are discussed in Chapter 6.

CERAMICS

One of the spectacular technical developments of recent years has been in the field of ceramic adhesives. Supersonic aerospace vehicles require high-temperature-resistant bonded structures. Wright Air Development Division, Bureau of Naval Weapons, Army Ordnance, and industrial subcontractors have successfully developed ceramic adhesives for bonding steels and other alloys with operational conditions ranging from 700°F up. These new materials are being evaluated in sample end items.

Work of the mid-'50's resulted in providing high strength bonds using ceramic-oxide glassy bonded adhesives. However, these possessed poor moisture resistance and consequently had limited application alone. Recently, this and other problems are being overcome, and a new materials industry is emerging.

When cermets (ceramic/metallics) are used directly as adhesives, they are too refractory; however, if the component materials are finely ground and incorporated in a glassy matrix, they become suitable as structural adhesives. The original work in this area involved equal weights of lead borosilicate glass and metallic cobalt.

The general procedure for preparing ceramic adhesives is not complex but requires detailed controls. A typical formulation contains 25 per cent by weight of silica, 9 per cent sodium nitrate, 65 per cent boric acid, and 1 per cent ferric oxide. Laboratory batches, from 1000 to 2000 g, are made by heating the smelting crucible to approximately 2400°F and adding approximately ½ of the mixed raw materials. Heating the mix for approximately 20 min will stop the frothing action prior to adding the remaining mix. After adding the remaining mixed batch, the procedure is to continue heating for 60 to 90 min until all frothing has ceased. The temperature of the smelting crucible varies, depending on formulation, from 1000° to at least 4500°F.

The molten glass is then quenched in a bucket of cold water. After the hard frit is formed, it is dried and milled in a ball mill until it is of uniform size. Control is established by passing it through a screen (e.g., 48 mesh). After adding oxides (or other fillers) and approximately an equal weight of water in the ball mill, a slip is formed, which can be made into bisque, prepared for dip operations, or sprayed on the metal sheets to be bonded. All metal sheets are properly cleaned (degreased, chemically etched, etc.). The influence of surface conditions of the base metal on shear strength of ceramic adhesive has been quite evident. Tests have indicated that pre-oxidation of the substrate greatly increases strength. Preheating the metal in the temperature range of 350°F results in a more tenacious bisque.

When the bonding of metal-to-metal is occurring, pressures ranging from 2 to 15 psi are developed with maturing temperatures ranging from 1000 to 2000°F. The pressure and temperature depend on the composition of the adhesive properties to be obtained, type of metal, type of structure, and desired bond line thickness of adhesive. The maturing temperature time can range from a few minutes up to 1 hr. The final operation is cooling of the unit at controlled rates to eliminate internal stresses, etc.

An important development has been the reduction of maturing temperature of glassy system adhesives from 2000 to 1000°F. Various techniques have been used, e.g., low melting flux additives (lead oxide and barium oxide) and low melting porcelain enamel frits. Other compositions are based on lead silicate glasses with varying amounts of sodium oxide and titanium oxide. The target is a maturing temperature even below 1000°F.

On the other hand to produce bonds having high strength above 2000°F, the ceramic compositions apparently require maturing temperatures of at least 3200°F. Also, more stable and higher temperature-resistant crucibles are necessary to prepare the adhesive frits.

Air setting and low heat cured systems are now available. The aluminum phosphate type ceramic adhesives can provide some strength maturing at room temperature or temperatures up to 600°F. Other promising air-setting adhesive systems contain approximately 30 per cent by weight iron oxide.

Oxidizing atmospheres are usually present during the maturing phase. If uncoated graphite pressure plates are used, the ceramic adhesive may discolor and becomes granular in consistency. Apparently the graphite reacts with the oxygen, producing a carbon monoxide reducing atmosphere.

Indications are that metal additives in ceramic compositions promote excessive oxidation during setting when fired unprotected in air atmospheres. Cracking or spalling may result on cooling, yielding irregular surfaces. On the other hand, oxides such as ferric oxide, aluminum oxide, barium oxide, and copper oxide in ceramic adhesives generally result in increased physical properties. Aluminum oxide also introduces more porosity. A relatively new additive system, which shows some degree of increase in strength of adhesives as well as preparation advantages, is phosphatized carbonyl iron.

Strength changes from small amounts of additives generally do not become evident until tests are conducted at elevated temperatures.* The addition of approximately 5 per cent metal powder of aluminum, copper, silicon, carbonyl iron, or carbonyl nickel to ceramic adhesive slip does not change room temperature shear strength appreciably; however significant change occurred with carbonyl iron when tests were conducted at 800°F.

In the *metal-glass-forming system,* the metal phase is deposited on the steel and the glassy carrier phase is ejected by pressure. The resultant joint has a continuous metal bond. The fluid glass phase (flux) is extruded out of the bond line. In the *oxide-metal system,* a homogeneous mixture of oxides and metals remains in the bond line. All exothermic products are retained within the bond lines. Isopropyl alcohol is incorporated into these two systems during the ball milling operation.** The alcohol suspensions are partially dried on a hot plate to produce a thick paste. This slurry is used for wet applications. When dry applications are to be used, the alcohol is evaporated completely to form dry powders.

These exothermic reactive systems provide a glass-metal phase separation, the glass phase being extruded from the bond line, leaving behind a continuous metal bond. Phase separation and extrusion are further developed by the addition of small amounts of alumina and/or fine copper powder. Preliminary work in this system was with borax, barium, silicone dioxide and copper oxide.

Adhesive systems consisting of combinations of metals and oxides can react exothermically when fired. The resultant product produces stable oxides and less reactive metals. A typical example con-

sists of 45 per cent glass and 55 per cent copper. Basic glass composition is 17.7 per cent $Na_2O \cdot 2B_2O_3$ (borax), 16.4 per cent SiO_2, 6.4 per cent Ba, 59.5 per cent CuO. Other metal-glassy systems have basic formulations of 5.3 per cent Mg + 79.8 per cent Cu_2O + 9.9 per cent SnO_2 + 5.0 per cent Ti.

A major new development is the low-cost bonding of temperature-resistant structures by ceramic-braze adhesives.† The structural bonds are reported to be superior to present ceramic adhesives and may surpass currently available brazed bonds. The resultant ceramic-braze bond is primarily metallic in composition after firing. This process simplifies the manufacture of large and reliable heat-resistant structures.

Stresses due to uneven thermal contraction are minimized through the use of adhesives with thermal expansion similar to type 17-7 pH stainless steel. Adhesive formulations based on titania-sodium-borosilicate-glasses are applicable. The frits are smelted at a temperature of 2300°F. The maturing cycle is 1750°F for 20 min with a 15 mil thick adhesive bond line.

Ceramic adhesives should be resistant to moisture, which can cause failure due to corrosion of metal-bonded surface or metallic additives in the ceramic compositions. Additions of approximately 30 per cent iron oxide, after preliminary heat treatment of 1 hr at 1000°F, have provided some success. However, lower shear strengths occur. Compositions such as SiO_2 (38 parts), Na_2O (5 parts), and B_2O_3 (57 parts) can be made insoluble or less soluble in water by the addition of approximately 5 per cent by weight of calcium oxide. Other additives that show similar gains are aluminum oxide, zinc oxide, and barium oxide.

Tensile shear strength increases as the bond line thickness decreases; however too low a thin bond line, i.e., below 12 mils, produces adhesvie starved joints of low strength. The tensile shear strength is dependent on the bond line pressure only to the extend that bond pressure affects the resultant bond line thickness.

Developments in the field of ceramic adhesives are continuing; adhesives are sought with the best combination of chemical compatibility, thermal expansion, low maturing or firing temperature, strength, and cost. A composition for high strength includes 70.4 parts by weight of a frit, 1.4 parts of

---

* The usual metal for preparing structural test specimens is 17-7 PH stainless steel. Elevated test temperature exposure period is generally 10 min followed immediately by testing at the same elevated temperature.

** Narmco Industries, Inc.

† Boeing Airplane Co.

colloidal silica, 28.2 parts of water, and 10 parts of metal powder (carbonyl iron). The frit may contain 38 parts of SiO_2, 5 parts of Na_2O, and 57 parts of B_2O_3.

Ceramic adhesives are already used in some missile component parts, heavy-duty truck and aircraft brakes, electronic units, and bearing blocks. It is expected that within the next several years, the ceramic adhesive industry will be of substantial size.

References

"Adhesive Bonding," Merriam, J. C., *Materials in Design Engineering.* (Sept. 1959).

Kelly, K. K., Contributions to the Data on Theoretical Metallurgy—High Temperature Heat Content, Heat Capacity, and Entropy Data for the Elements and Inorganic Compounds Bull. 584, Bureau of Mines, 1960.

"Densification of AlO_2 During Studies of Hot Pressing," *ACS J.* (Feb. 1960).

"Design Manual on Adhesives," *Machine Design* (Apr. 1954).

"Nature of Ceramic-Metal Bonds Investigation," *Elec. Mfg.* (June 1959).

Lang, S. M., "Properties of High-Temperature Ceramics and Cermets," National Bureau of Standards, Monograph 6, Mar. 1, 1960.

"Water in Glass," *Refractory J.* **35**, (5), 178 (1959).

"Plastic Deformation of Ceramic-Oxide Single Crystals," National Bureau of Standards, Wachtman & Maxwell PB139626, 1954.

Navy Bureau of Aeronautics, Quarterly Report No. 5, "Development of Exo-reactant Inorganic Adhesive System," W. Bassett, W. Boram and R. A. Long, Oct. 1, 1959.

Navy Bureau of Aeronautics, Quarterly Progress Report No. 2, "Development and Test of Ceramic Bonded Stainless Steel Structural Components," Dec. 31, 1959.

Navy Bureau of Naval Weapons, Quarterly Report No. 1, "Development of Exo-reactant Inorganic Adhesive System," W. Bassett and R. A. Long, Jan. 1, 1960.

Navy Bureau of Naval Weapons, Quarterly Report No. 2, "Development of Exo-reactant Inorganic Adhesive System," W. Bassett and R. A. Long, Apr. 1, 1960.

Navy Bureau of Naval Weapons, Quarterly Progress Report No. 3, "Development and Test of Ceramic Bonded Stainless Steel Structural Components," Mar. 31, 1960.

Navy Bureau of Weapons, Quarterly Progress Report No. 4, "Development and Test of Ceramic Bonded Stainless Steel Structural Components," June 30, 1960.

WADC Technical Report 53–126 (Part IV), "Elevated Temperature Resistant Modified Epoxy Resin Additives for Metals" (1956).

WADC Technical Report 53–353, "Survey of the Literature on Antioxidants and Anti-corrosion Additives for Lubricants at Elevated Temperatures" (1954).

WADC Technical Report 55–491, "Research on Elevated Temperature Resistant Ceramic Structural Adhesives," R. M. Spriggs, H. G. Lefort and D. G. Bennett (Sept. 1956).

WADC Technical Report 55–491, Part III—"Research on Elevated Temperature Resistant Ceramic Structural Adhesives," R. M. Spriggs, C. N. Williams, H. G. Lefort, and D. G. Bennett (Dec. 1957).

WADC Technical Report 55–491, Part IV—"Research on Elevated Temperature Resistant Ceramic Structural Adhesives," G. H. Haertling, K. N. Parik, H. G. Lefort and D. G. Bennett (June 1959).

WADC Technical Report 55–491, Part V—"Research on Elevated Temperature Resistant Ceramic Structural Adhesives," G. H. Haertling, K. N. Parik, H. R. Thornton, H. G. Lefort, J. H. Lauchner and D. G. Bennett (Feb. 1960).

WADC Technical Report 58–450—"Survey of Adhesion and Adhesives," F. W. Reinhart and I. G. Callomon (July 1959).

WADC Tech. Rept 59–82, "Inorganic High Temperature Adhesives for Metals and Sandwich Constructions," R. A. Long and W. Bassett (June 1959).

WADC Tech. Rept 59–113 (Part I), "Research and Development in Inorganic High Temperature Adhesives for Metals and Composite Constructions," J. Bayer and W. A. Patterson (July 1959).

WADC Tech. Rept 59–113 (Part II), "Research and Development on Inorganic High Temperature Adhesives for Metals and Composite Constructions," J. Bayer, O. E. Johnston and W. A. Patterson (May 1960).

— 39 —

New Developments in Adhesives

A. Silicones and Miscellaneous Adhesives

Don Kingsley

Permacel

New Brunswick, New Jersey

Progress in adhesives has closely paralleled advances in high polymers. Almost daily, new polymers become available which can serve as adhesive materials, and plastic materials are developed which present new bonding problems in their varied applications.

Although synthetic polymers are not the only driving force in the adhesives industry today, they have certainly been one of the most important. This chapter reviews some of the recent developments in adhesives polymers, concentrating on materials not treated extensively in other chapters.

SILICONES

Silicone-Based Adhesives

Dimethyl-silicone elastomers are useful because they remain rubberlike over a wide temperature range; however, they are attacked by solvents and consequently are ruled out for many applications. A new class of silicone elastomers, the cyanoalkyl-silicones has been prepared that shows excellent resistance to many solvents.[1] The cyanoalkylsilicones also have improved low temperature flexibility and are stable up to 250°C.

The methods used to prepare these new polymers are similar to those for the preparation of dimethyl-silicone elastomers. The cyanoalkyl function can be attached to silicone by adding silanic hydrogen to olefinic nitriles, which is similar to the addition of trichlorosilane to acrylonitrile.

The cyanoalkychlorosilanes are hydrolyzed, alone or with other organochlorosilanes, to form partially condensed siloxane polymers, which are converted into gums by further condensation. Cyanoalkylsilicone copolymers varying from free-flowing liquids to viscous gums are made by adjusting molecular weight, structure of the cyanoalkyl group and concentration of the cyanoalkylsilicone component in the copolymer. Totally condensed cyanoalkylsilicone gums are clear, viscous polymers similar in appearance to dimethyl-silicone gums.

Cyanoalkylsilicone can be prepared in a variety of forms: fluids, pastes, solvent solutions, and solid stocks suitable for solution coating, molding, calendering, and extrusion. Cyanoalkylsilicone elastomers show promise as adhesives, solvent barriers, encapsulating compositions, electric cable components, sealing compounds, and automotive and aircraft components.

A product having high heat resistance is obtained by allowing α-hydroxy carboxylic acids or their esters to react with silica tetrahalides at 60°C and polycondensing the reaction product.[1] The reaction product of methyl salicylate and silica tetrachloride is an amberlike material, which is soluble in boiling chloroalkanes and suitable as an adhesive.

For some time "bouncing putty" or "silly putty" has been an interesting but commercially unimportant silicone polymer. The material has the unusual combination of properties of very high cold flow under slow stressing and very high elastic rebound under rapid stressing. It is made by heating dimethyl silicone with about 5 per cent boric oxide for a few hours at 150 to 250°C.[2]

Relatively recently however two adhesive uses have been reported for this silicone. If it is mixed with an epoxy resin (powder) in the ratio of 1:3, a heat-curable adhesive results that is particularly suitable for bonding metals.[3] Kneaded intimately with 44 to 48 per cent polyvinyl chloride powder, it gives a multipurpose adhesive which displays less cold flow than "bouncing putty" itself. The material resembles glazier's putty, but does not stick to the hands. A firm bond is obtained when this adhesive is pressed between metals, glass or plastic parts; moreover the parts can be separated and reassembled.[4]

Organopolysiloxane elastomers can be applied and cured in thin films on metal surfaces with a small amount of organic polybasic acid or anhydride, e.g., maleic anhydride, as a crosslinking agent.[5] The polysiloxane must be heat convertible and should contain alkyl radicals. Fillers can be compounded with the material.

To form friction elements such as brake linings, a finely divided heat-flowable thermosetting resin is superimposed on a layer of finely divided uncured siloxane resin containing a cohydrolyzate of a mixture of 70 to 90 mole per cent phenylsilicon trihalide and 10 to 30 mole per cent ethyl silicon trihalide. Heat and pressure are then applied for a sufficient time to ensure flow of both layers.[6]

Polyphenylethoxysiloxanes can be combined with alkyd resins to produce heat-resistant polymers having adhesive properties.[7]

Vinylalkoxysilanes can be polymerized with dibutyl peroxide as a catalyst to form polymers ranging from liquid to solid.[8] The action of the catalyst is quite specific as other peroxides give poor results. The reaction is quite sensitive and care must be taken to exclude air, water, and oxygen since they inhibit polymerization.

The vinylalkoxysilane homopolymers can be used as plasticizers and modifiers for synthetic resins, as insolubilizing and toughening agents for polyvinyl alcohol, or as adhesives and sizing agents.

A viscous amber liquid suitable for casting, impregnating, and as a laminating resin is reported.[9] This epoxy-substituted organosilicon compound has been identified as 1,4-bis-2,3,-epoxypropoxy-dimethylsilyl benzene.

Peroxide vulcanized silicone elastomers or adhesives are bonded better to solid surfaces when the surface is first coated with an air-dried film of an amine-containing organosilicon compound. The general formula given for the organosilicon primer coat is

$$R_n R'_m Si (ORCHR'''CH_2NR''_2HY)4—M—N$$

The elastomer or adhesive containing an organic peroxide curing agent is applied to the treated surface and cured. It can be bonded to flexible or nonflexible solid material such as metal, glass, ceramics, asbestos, glass cloth, wood polymers, elastomers and textiles.[10]

Silicone Pressure-Sensitive Tape

A siloxane resin suitable for pressure-sensitive adhesive tape was prepared in the following manner. Hydrochloric acid and sodium silicate are mixed. Isopropyl alcohol, trimethylchlorosilane and hexamethyldisiloxane are added. The mixture is then refluxed. After cooling, xylene is added and the resin layer is separated from the acid layer.[11]

A silicone pressure-sensitive adhesive containing 1.5 per cent benzoyl peroxide, on a glass tape, is cured at 150°C. The initial adhesion of this tape to steel is 20 oz/in.[12]

A method is described for preparing pressure-sensitive unsupported silicone rubber tape.[13] A thin section (10 to 50 mil) of raw unvulcanized silicone rubber containing a peroxide vulcanizing agent is heated on one side at 160 to 222°C for 5 to 30 sec. Simultaneously, the opposite side of the web is maintained below 40°C.

A siloxane adhesive compound suitable for tape can be cured at room temperature.[14] It contains diphenylsiloxane 10, dimethylsiloxane 30, and monomethylsiloxane 60 mole per cent. The copolymer is dissolved in toluene and .2 per cent by weight benzyl trimethyl ammonium hydroxide is added. The solution is then applied to silicone resin impregnated glass tape and dried for 4 hr at room temperature to give a bond strength of 600 g.

A heat-resistant tape with good insulating qualities consists of an organosilicone pressure-sensitive adhesive anchored to a polyethylene, polyethylene terephthalate or polytetrafluoroethylene tape. The tape is first primed with a primer coat of organosilicone resin, a butadiene-acrylonitrile copolymer and a coal tar and polyterpene resin. A typical receipt for the primer coat is as follows:

	parts by wt.
"Hycar" 1042	10
Butadiene-styrene copolymer	2
Mill together and dissolve in nitropropane and toluene then add	
"Piccolyte" S-85	3

	parts by wt.
Coumarone indene resin	5
Dow SC-269	15
Hydrated alumina	.75
Benzoyl peroxide	small amount

The primer is coated at a weight of 12 lb per ream and dried at 140 to 180°F for 1 to 5 min. Dow SC-269 blended with 50 per cent of a filler such as titanium dioxide and 0.1 to 2.0 per cent benzoyl peroxide is then coated at 30 lb per ream over the primer coat and dried at 140 to 200°F. The tape is cured at 300°F for 5 min.[15]

MISCELLANEOUS ADHESIVES

Compounds containing at least one oxacyclobutane ring per mole condense on heating in the presence of ether-splitting catalysts to form resins. Typical ether-splitting catalysts employed are zinc chloride, aluminum chloride, and tin chloride. Compounds with only one such ring (trimethylene oxide) give noncurable resins. Compounds with several such rings (dioxaspiro-heptane) give either curable or crosslinked products. Mixtures of the two types of monomer give various plastics with a wide range of properties. Liquid or even solid partially polymerized materials can be used as stabilizers for polyvinyl halides or as cements or adhesives. The polymers adhere firmly to all types of surfaces, including ceramics, glass, and metal.[16]

Rubber and plastics can be joined to each other or to metals, paper or fabrics by using diazo compounds. The contact surfaces are coated with solutions of aliphatic mono- or polydiazo compounds. These compounds react with the carbon hydrogen bonds in the rubber or plastic. The groups thus formed can react with each other or with isocyanates. Isocyanate treatment alone does not cement certain plastics and rubbers, particularly vulcanized rubber. If polyazo compounds are used with rubber, no isocyanate treatment is necessary.

Vulcanized rubber can be bonded to itself using a 10 per cent solution of bisazodicarboxylic acid ester in benzene. The surfaces are pressed gently together for 2 min at 120°C.

Vulcanized rubber covered with a solution of bisazodicarboxylic acid ester and a polyisocyanate in benzene can be bonded to a metal plate covered with diiscyanate. The joint is kept under compression for 10 min at 140°C, and the bond formed is stronger than that obtained using dissocyanate alone.[17]

Coatings of polyisocyanate adhesives on metal can be stabilized to atmospheric moisture by addition of chloroparaffins. Fillers can also be added, which improve the tack of the coating as well as the solution stability.[18]

A mixture of isobutylene (100), isoprene (20) and butadiene (150) is copolymerized in a chlorinated solvent at 100° with aluminum chloride as catalyst. The resulting polymer is hot-milled and dissolved in hexane. This cement is especially useful for bonding dissimilar rubbery materials.[19]

If an alkylenimine such as ethyleneimine is allowed to react with an organic cyclic carbonate such as ethylene carbonate, an intermediate hydroxyimine is formed which can then be polymerized to a linear polymer. This type of polymer is useful as an adhesive, a paper additive, and for the treatment of textiles.[20]

A vinyl-to-metal adhesive that obviates expensive metal pretreatment is given by the following formula.

"Hycar"-10723	3.81
"Durez"-12687	.954
"Vinylite" VMCH	14.3
Methylethyl ketone	37.61
Isobutyl ether	18.51
Toluene	20.00
Mercaptobenzothiazole	.066
Carbon disulfide	4.75

The material can be roller coated or sprayed on film or metal; then the two materials are laminated at speeds up to 200 ft/min at 40 to 80 psi and 400°F. The resulting lamination can be formed, bent, deep drawn, stamped, or crimped without failure of the bond, even after aging.[21]

A new "delayed tack" adhesive suitable for heat-seal applications is based on 1,2-bis-2-phenylyloxyethane as the dispersed solid plasticizer.[22] The adhesive is tack-free and nonblocking when dried; however when it is exposed to heat, the solid plasticizer melts, giving a pressure-sensitive adhesive that has a tack life of 15 min. A typical formulation is:

60/40 Styrene-butadiene	40
1,2-bis-2-phenylyloxyethane	100
Water	363
Casein	8

Rubberlike copolymers containing multivalent phenols and lower aliphatic ketones condense in the presense of an acid catalyst, giving resinous products suitable for adhesives. A copolymer prepared from butadiene and methyl isopropenyl ketone is dissolved in a nonaqueous solvent, and a ketone and resorcinol are added. The reaction is catalyzed by hydrogen chloride. Alternatively, a phenol ketone resin obtained by acid condensation is linked with the polymer while heating on a roll mixer. These adhesives have good bond strength for styrene-butadiene resins and rubber-polyvinyl chloride mixtures. They are soluble in ethyl acetate, benzene, and methyl isobutyl ketone but insoluble in acetone.[23]

GRS and neoprene form the basis of adhesives with excellent heat fatigue resistance and a good tack range. By the changing of ratios of polychloroprene and butadiene-styrene polymer and the kinds of resins to be blended with the rubbery constituents, adhesives of different physical properties can be prepared. They can be made to vary from products that are permanently tacky to those with high heat resistance and substantially shorter tack range. One formulation is as follows:[24]

GRS 1013	35.0
Neoprene W	65.0
Zinc oxide	37.0
"Accelerator" 833	0.5
"Poly-pale" resin	62.0

The above materials were placed in a Banbury mixer and blended for 30 min at 300°F; then the material was cooled and dissolved in naphtha. This produced an adhesive having extraordinary heat fatigue resistance and a tack range of 2 hr.

Rubber can be bonded to metal effectively in the following manner. A phenol aldehyde resin containing free polyphenol is applied to the metal. A layer of a vulcanizable rubber is then applied which contains an aldehyde or aldehyde generator capable of reacting with the polyphenol in the first layer. Thus a 12 per cent solution of phenol formaldehyde resin in methylethyl ketone, containing 200 per cent resorcinol based on resin solids, is coated on metal. To this first layer is applied the following formulation in a 10 per cent solids solution in ethylene dichloride:

Rubber	100
Carbon black	50
Zinc oxide	5
Stearic acid	2
Sulfur	2.5
Mercaptobenzothiazole	.8
Hexamethylenetetramine	40.0

When vulcanized, the adhesion of the rubber layer to the metal is 59 kg/sq cm.[25]

A good bond between an organic glass (made from polyacrylate derivatives) and synthetic rubber is obtained by impregnating the rubber surface before vulcanization, first with an adhesive solution such as a solution of chlorinated rubber and then with a solution of a polyacrylate. After vulcanization of the rubber, the organic glass is held tightly in contact until the bond hardens.[26]

Adhesives or lacquers of polymerizable compounds which adhere well to copper or zinc are obtained by adding small amounts of acetylacetone, benzoylacetone or oxyquinolines to the poly-

meric mixtures. For example solution A was prepared by dissolving 84 parts of polystyrene in 100 parts of a mixture of 77 per cent styrene, 9 per cent maleic acid glycol polyester, 8 per cent acrylic acid, 4 per cent diethanol-*p*-toluidine, and 2 per cent acetylacetone. The mixture was stabilized with .01 per cent hydroquinone. For solution B, 84 parts of polystyrene and 5 parts of benzoyl peroxide were dissolved in 100 parts of a mixture of 89 per cent styrene, 9 per cent maleic acid glycol polyester and 2 per cent acetylacetone. For stabilization .2 per cent hydroquinone was added. One surface was coated with solution A and another with solution B. The two surfaces were pressed together forming a good bond.[27]

A homogeneous mixture of a thermosetting phenol formaldehyde resin and a butadiene-acrylonitrile polymer is suitable as a liquid cement for metals. The polymer mixture is applied from a solution of a volatile ketone solvent. The liquid cement forms ductile, stable, heat-resistant connections on smooth metal surfaces.[28]

References

1. Williams, T. C., Pike, R. A., and Fekete, F., "Cyanosilicone Elastomers," *Ind. Eng. Chem.,* **51,** (8) (Aug. 1959).

2. Billmeyer, F. W., "Textbook of Polymer Chemistry," p. 367, New York, Interscience Publishers, Inc.

3. Jedlicka, Helmut, German Patent 956,711 (Jan. 24, 1957).

4. Jedlicka, Helmut, German Patent 957,156 (Jan. 31, 1957).

5. Seidel, M. P., and Murrin, T. J. (to Westinghouse Electric Corp.), U. S. Patent 2,858,241 (Oct. 28, 1958).

6. Dereich, John E. (to Diamond Alkali Co.), U.S. Patent 2,845,378 (July 29, 1958).

7. Zhinkin, D. Y., and Losev, V. B., U. S. S. R. Patent 118,351 (Mar. 5, 1959).

8. Bailey, Donald L., and Mixer, Robert Y. (to Union Carbide Corp.), U. S. Patent 2,777,869.

9. Rogers, Dow A., Jr., and Lewis, Daniel W. (to Westinghouse Electric Corp.), U. S. Patent 2,883,-395 (Apr. 21, 1959).

10. Ken, Joseph W. (to Dow Corning Corp.), U. S. Patent 2,902,389 (Sept. 1, 1959).

11. Currie, Chester C., and Keil, Joseph W. (to Dow Corning Corp.), U. S. Patent 2,814,601 (Nov. 26, 1957).

12. Bond, Herbert M., and Groff, Gaylord L. (to Minnesota Mining and Manufacturing Co.), U. S. Patent 2,882,183 (Apr. 14, 1959).

13. Midland Silicones Ltd., British Patent 792,041 (Mar. 19, 1958).

14. Midland Silicones Ltd., British Patent 813,889 (May 27, 1959).

15. Bolraty, Gene (to Mystik Adhesive Products Inc.), U. S. Patent 2,878,142 (Mar. 17, 1959).

16. Henkel & Cie G. M. B. H. (to Rudolf Kohler and Helmut Pietsch, inventors) German Patent 931,-130 (Aug. 1, 1955).

17. Phoenix Gummiwerke Akt-Ges (to Walter Stegemann and Gottfried Reuter), German Patent 930,655 (July 21, 1955).

18. Continental Gummiwerke Akt-Ges, Erich Christopher and Richard Behrens, inventors), German Patent 944,327 (June 14, 1956).

19. Wilson, Howard L., Robinson, Samuel B., and Smith, Winthrope C. (to Esso Research and Engineering Co.), U. S. Patent 2,825,675 (Mar. 4, 1958).

20. Drechsel, Ernest K. (to American Cyanamid Co.), U. S. Patent 2,824,857 (Feb. 25, 1958).

21. Kiernan, C. E., Clark, W. K. (to United States Rubber Co.), U. S. Patent 2,872,366 (Feb. 3, 1959).

22. Rigterink, R. H., Miller, R. L., Silvernail, L. H. (to Dow Chemical Co.), U. S. Patent 2,885,306 (May 5, 1959).

23. Dunlop Rubber Co. Ltd.—Derek W. Searl, inventor, German Patent 953,918 (Dec. 6, 1956).

24. Moore, C. D. (to Armstrong Cork Co.), U. S. Patent 2,884,400 (Apr. 28, 1959).

25. Societe Anou des Pneumatiques Dunlop, French Patent 1,127,785.

26. Wetzell Gummiwerke Akt-Ges (to Ernest Mattaei, inventor), German Patent 1,004,369 (Mar. 14, 1957).

27. Deutsche Gold und Silber—Scheideanstalt Vorm. Roessler (to Erich Bader and Otto Schweitzer, inventors), German Patent 953,454 (Nov. 29, 1956).

28. Minnesota Mining and Manufacturing Co. (Gordon F. Lindner, James M. McClellan and Alfred L. Finn, inventors), German Patent 956,617 (Jan. 24, 1957).

B. s-Triazine Polymers

Harold H. Levine

Narmco Research and Development Division
Telecomputing Corp.
San Diego, California

Among the many approaches to inorganic and semi-inorganic polymers, the s-triazine compounds deserve more attention. One compound, melamine, is used in considerable quantities to prepare commercially important polymers; however these are not stable at or near 1000°F.

By arbitrary definition, an inorganic polymer is a macromolecule which is devoid of carbon-to-carbon bonds. For high temperature environments, a semi-inorganic polymer should be a macromolecule that contains some carbon-to-carbon bonds which are known to be heat stable, such as the phenyl or methyl groups or a "blocked" group such

as $R - \underset{\underset{CH_3}{|}}{\overset{\overset{CH_3}{|}}{C}} - CH_2 -$ which prevents β-elimina-

tion reactions at high temperatures.

The s-triazine nucleus has the following structure:

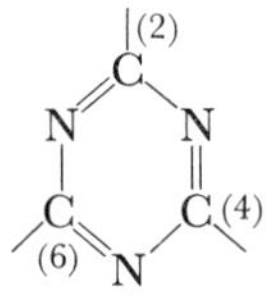

melamine is the 2,4,6-triamino derivative, ammeline is the 2-hydroxy-4,6-diamino derivative and triallyl cyanurate (TAC) is the 2,4,6-tris(allyloxy) derivative.

Although s-triazines have been described in organic texts, the ring itself can be considered inorganic according to the above definition.

The s-triazine compounds react via the functional groups attached to the three carbon atoms of the ring rather than via the ring itself. However, the ring does affect the behavior of the functional groups; for example, the amino group cannot be diazotized as its aromatic counterpart, and the hydroxy group is difficult to acylate and is non-phenolic in character. These effects are ascribed to the six extra electrons in the ring which come from the three nitrogen atoms. The high heat stability of the s-triazine ring is at least partially due to a high resonance stabilization energy, 82 kcal/mole, compared to that of benzene, 39 kcal/mole.

To use such thermal stability to its fullest advantage, it is necessary to link the s-triazine rings together with groups which are as heat stable as the ring itself, since the polymer degrades at its weakest point. Thus melamine-formaldehyde polymer fails at the methylene linkages. Heat stability is improved when inorganic linkages are used to connect the rings. Various inorganic halides and oxides appear promising for reaction with amino groups in melamine and/or ammeline.

Interaction of melamine with phosphorus pentoxide gave rise to a heat-stable material which did not blacken when heated in a Meeker burner flame. At 800°F, the solid rapidly lost weight during the first 15 to 30 min, but the glassy residue maintained almost constant weight for the next 3½ hr. However, the solid lacked adhesive properties. Ammeline, which has a hydroxyl group that is absent in melamine, was next reacted with phosphorus pentoxide. The solid product displayed weak adhesion, 65 psi, on No. 302 stainless steel. The tensile shear strength was increased to 285 psi by extraction of the solid with dimethylformamide and the use of tetraisopropylorthotitanate to deposit a polymeric titanium dioxide prime-coating on the steel.

Many difficulties must be faced in s-triazine research. There is a lack of suitable solvents for either melamine, ammeline or the oxides; consequently the reactions are heterogeneous and probably lead to complex mixtures. Further, all the products to date have been solids with high melting or decomposition points. As a result, proper bond fabrication is extremely difficult, requiring high temperatures and pressures to permit the solid adhesive to wet the surface; moreover the adhesive must be finely powdered and spread on the bond area and carefully assembled to prevent spillage. A glass fabric carrier proved useless because the material attacked the glass, resulting in an extremely brittle, weak supporting medium.

As work on inorganic polymers continues, new knowledge and techniques may permit a more sophisticated approach. In addition to being a source of high thermal stability, the s-triazine nucleus is admirably adapted to polymer formation because of its trifunctionality. Future research on s-triazine polymer adhesives is recommended.

C. Structural Adhesives For Use Above 700°F

Frank J. Riel and Harold H. Levine

Narmco Research and Development Division
Telecomputing Corp.
San Diego, California

When organic adhesives are used at elevated temperatures, the temperature of exposure is not the only important variable. Other factors, especially time of exposure and the composition of the atmosphere in contact with the test specimen, must also be considered. Loss of strength, when the temperature is raised to 500°F and higher, is the result of two factors:

(1) Simple thermal effects.

(2) Secondary effects caused by chemical reactions between the polymer and other materials, such as the adherend surface, the atmosphere, or some component within the adhesive, e.g., a filler or carrier.

The second factor is relatively unimportant if the time is relatively short (several hours) and the temperature is moderate (500 to 600°F). As the time increases, at a moderate temperature, or the temperature increases for a fixed exposure time, the second factor becomes increasingly dominant and may result in 100 per cent strength losses. The major cause of these rapid strength losses under the more adverse conditions is the air oxidation of the organic material within the polymer. This fact is illustrated by the following data (Fig. 1), which compare the performance of a representative high temperature adhesive aged at 600°F in air and in nitrogen atmospheres.

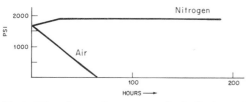

Fig. 1. Effect of atmosphere on strength of adhesive aged at 600°F.

Air oxidation apparently occurs at temperatures considerably lower than 500°F. Recent data on very long time exposures at temperatures as low as 250°F reveal substantial degradation. For example, a representative high temperature adhesive lost 50 per cent of its strength at 250°F after a 6-months exposure in a circulating air oven. These observations indicate that those adhesives which can operate in the 500°F and higher region probably do so mainly because they do not reach chemical equilibrium with their environment. Therefore, other factors such as bond line porosity, surface condition of the metal (which, in some cases, can catalyze the oxidation reaction), chemical and physical nature of any carrier or filler, and geometry of the test specimen influence the strength retention of the adhesive. In fact, one or more of these factors may overshadow the more basic considerations of chemical stability. A test specimen which contains less bond line porosity has less surface area exposed to the air atmosphere; consequently the rate of reaction is slower.

Retention of bond strength at elevated temperatures after short-time exposures (only thermal equilibrium) is less complex. The ability of the resin to retain high strength is a function of the degree of crosslinking, and only the more tightly, highly crosslinked structures retain strength at temperatures above 500°F. Even the best structures available—phenolic resins—may have only marginal strength at temperatures of 700 to 1000°F. These materials are extremely rigid at conventional temperatures and have very low peel strength.

Polymers which revert at temperatures below 500°F, e.g., the isocyanates, which depolymerizes

rapidly at 400°F, are obviously unsuitable as high-temperature adhesives.

Two general approaches have been followed in the development of new and improved structural adhesives suited to operation at 500 to 1000°F.

(1) Improvement of conventional organic polymers.
(2) Development of new polymers, based on organic, semi-organic, or inorganic linkages.

The relative emphasis appropriate to these two approaches is a function of the exposure condition under consideration.

Recent work has indicated that certain organic polymers are capable of surprisingly good performance at 700 to 1000°F for periods up to 1 hr. For some new devices such as missiles, outer space vehicles and high-speed aircraft, the time requirements at temperature have been reduced; 200-hr tests at temperature are usually not needed. This change in requirements has brought the organic materials back into consideration.

A series of tests was carried out on the best commercially available organic adhesives. Tensile shear strength was determined at 700 to 1000°F for periods up to 1 hr. Bonds were prepared with annealed 17-7 stainless steel that was degreased and etched with a mixture of phosphoric, hydrochloric and hydrofluoric acids. The adhesives included:

(1) Phenolic adhesives—Monsanto's SC-1008 and Narmco's "Metlbond" 309.
(2) An epoxy phenolic of the Shell "Epon" 422 type—"Metlbond" 302.
(3) A silicone modified phenolic—Monsanto's SC-1013.
(4) A newly developed semi-inorganic type adhesive containing a silicone-phenolic condensation product and an epoxy novolac —"Metlbond" 311.

The SC-1008 and SC-1013 resins were filled with 100 parts of aluminum, based on solids content, and put on 112 to 112 glass cloth; the other adhesives were used as received, and all were cured and post-cured at 25 psi according to the manufacturer's recommendations. It can be seen that the epoxies and epoxy-based adhesives have poorer performance than phenolics, although the former are more oxidation resistant. The crosslinking density in epoxies is too low to prevent thermoplasticity, even though the epoxies suffer oxidative attack at a slower rate than phenolics. Thermoplasticity is virtually nil in a phenolic; the greater number of crosslinks per unit volume also indicates that oxidation has to break a much larger number

TABLE 1. SUMMARY OF TEST DATA.

Cure Temperature (°F)	Test Temperature	Soak Time (min)	SC-1008	"Metlbond" 302	"Metlbond" 309	SC-1013	"Metlbond" 311
				Tensile Shear Strength, psi			
250	Room temp.	—	2737	3000	2373	2360	1520[a]
	700°F	10	1453	1145	1162	528	1050[a]
	900°F	10	1003	531	951	910	995[a]
	1000°F	10	959	663	756	1000	NT
	700°F	30	1273	970	1343	781	960[a]
	900°F	30	1001	578	580	997	1015[a]
	1000°F	30	645	533	843	589	NT
	700°F	60	1412	816	1413	810	1235[a]
	900°F	60	936	392	724	784	605[a]
	1000°F	60	490	98	231	0	NT
300	Room temp.	—	3070	3273	2963	2727	NT
	700°F	10	1465	1128	1360	978	NT
	900°F	10	1071	848	945	1010	NT
	1000°F	10	1069	625	1007	847	NT
	700°F	30	1490	994	1597	1298	NT
	900°F	30	1070	658	918	1103	NT
	1000°F	30	867	352	835	652	NT
	700°F	60	1509	808	1448	1402	NT
	900°F	60	900	517	657	803	NT
	1000°F	60	417	102	650	470	NT
350	Room temp.	—	2927	3252	3017	2563	2820
	700°F	10	1523	981	1291	824	306
	900°F	10	999	853	1183	997	409
	1000°F	10	917	752	893	1054	255
	700°F	30	1198	771	1425	1087	472
	900°F	30	907	805	930	890	325
	1000°F	30	560	468	701	579	152
	700°F	60	1467	855	1475	1147	463
	900°F	60	884	233	360	947	241
	1000°F	60	425	80	565	390	—

[a] Recommended cure for "Metlbond" 311.

NT = No Test. "Metlbond" 311 ignites after 3 min at 1000°F resulting from a thermite-type reaction between aluminum and arsenic pentoxide present in the adhesive.

of these linkages to produce the same degree of degradation and that this tighter, more cross-linked system retards the entry of oxygen, provided a nonporous structure is obtained during the processing.

There is, however, still a need for long time aging adhesives. Research into this area has resulted in "Metlbond" 311, a semi-inorganic. This adhesive contains an epoxy novolac, the reaction product of a poly(ethoxy phenyl siloxane) and "Bis Phenol-A," aluminum powder and arsenic pentoxide. In this system, the oxide and aluminum are not merely fillers. Reaction mechanism studies have shown that the pentoxide acts as a true catalyst in promoting polyether formation from the epoxy novolac and reacts with the ethoxy siloxane linkages to produce a $Si-O-As^{+5}$ bonding. It is also believed that the arsenic compound reacts with

the iron in the steel to form a thin coating of iron arsenate and prevents the oxidative attack of iron and oxygen upon the adhesive at the interface. Table 2 illustrates the data of "Metlbond" 311 when tested in accordance with MIL-A-8431,

TABLE 2.

Test Temperature	Time	Tensile Shear (psi)	MIL-A-8431 Requirements (psi)
Room temp.	—	1590	2250
300°F	10 min	1430	2000
300°F	192 hr	1061	2000
500°F	10 min	1344	1850
500°F	192 hr	716	1000
−67°F	10 min	2420	2250
600°F	10 min	1216	—
600°F	192 hr	753	—

Type III Adhesives. Bonds were made with 17-7 PH stainless steel using the phosphoric, hydrochloric, hydrofluoric acids etch solution.

This adhesive system had a zero deformation in room temperature creep rupture tests (0.015 in. specified) and 0.007 in. at 300°F after 192 hr (0.015 in. specified). Bend strength was 98 lb compared to the 130 lb required; however for many applications such a system could be of use. Of even greater importance is that this type of adhesive is an important forerunner and guide into areas of semi-inorganic polymer research.

Section C

ADHERENDS

— 40 —

Bonding Paper

Arthur Hirsch

Skeist Laboratories, Inc.
Newark, New Jersey

The combination of paper and adhesives has gained a place of importance in modern technology. Without paper and adhesives life would be quite different—no milk cartons, paper bags, and paperboard boxes for food; no paper cups, envelopes, stamps; not even books as we know them.

Per capita consumption of paper in the United States is placed at 430 lb per year. It is estimated that this figure may rise to 1000 to 1500 lb by the year 2000. In contrast, the rest of the world has a per capita paper consumption of only 42 lb.

After a brief review of paper making and paper testing, we shall study the role of paper as an adherend in the manufacture of numerous products. Finally, the types of adhesives most commonly employed will be critically assayed.

PAPER MAKING

Paper making, an ancient art, is becoming a science in more than 800 mills throughout the United States. Paper making consists of eight basic operations:[7]

(1) Fiber pretreatment.
(2) Fiber blending.
(3) Furnish cleaning and screening.
(4) Slurry distribution and metering, and fiber dispersion.
(5) Web formation, with water removal by filtration.
(6) Web compaction, with water removal by mechanical means.
(7) Web drying, with water removal by heat.
(8) Sheet finishing, by one or more of the following:

(a) Calendering
(b) Sizing
(c) Coating
(d) Glazing

The Raw Material

The most important source of raw material remains the forest. Seventy per cent of all paper is derived directly from new wood pulp. The remaining 30 per cent is supplied by waste paper and other natural and synthetic fibers. Wood is 50 per cent cellulose fibers, 30 per cent lignin, and the remaining 20 per cent hemicellulose, sugar, etc.

Pulping

The first step then in paper making is *pulping*—the separation of fibers. There are five major processes presently in use. Each attempts to either pull the fibers apart mechanically, or remove the lignin binder by chemical means.

(1) *Mechanical Pulp.* Wood is simply ground up. This is a very cheap process. It requires neither expensive equipment nor chemicals. The yields are very good. Only about 7 per cent of raw materials are lost, as compared with 50 per cent in the chemical pulping processes. However, this method yields only short fibers of inferior strength, for tissues, towels, and similar weak products.

(2) *Soda Pulp.* Wood chips are cooked in caustic under pressure. The product formed is pure cellulose. However, once more the fibers are rather short.

(3) *Sulfite Pulp.* Here again wood chips—soft-

wood or hardwood—are cooked under pressure, with either calcium, magnesium, or ammonium bisulfite and sulfur dioxide. The fiber yield is only 45 per cent of the original wood. This process consumes large quantities of chemicals, and fuel, and corrodes equipment rapidly. Sulfite pulp forms paper with high bursting but low tearing strength.

(4) *Sulfate Pulp* (Kraft). Chips of hard- and sometimes softwood are cooked in a "liquor" consisting of caustic soda and sodium sulfide. The sulfate process is the largest and fastest growing pulping process. It produces very strong paper.

(5) *Semichemical Pulp.* Woodchips are treated in a buffered alkaline solution with sulfur dioxide. This process, developed by the U. S. Forest Products Laboratory in 1926, is an economical pulping method because of high yield and low chemical consumption.

Paper Machine

After bleaching, fiber preparation, and the addition of binders, there are two basic processes available to convert the cellulosic fibers into a paper sheet.

The *Fourdrinier* machine, invented by Louis Robert in France in 1799, has evolved into machines of great capacity. Widths of in excess of 300 in. and machine speeds of up to 3000 ft/min have been reported.

Sheet formation is accomplished by depositing prescreened fibers from a headbox onto a moving wire belt. The excess water drains through the wire. Suction accelerates this dewatering stage. At the far end of the wire, the matted sheet of fibers passes on to a suction couch roll and is carried from there, supported by felts, through pressure rolls and finally heated dryers, in order to drive off the remaining water.

The *cylinder paper machine,* less common, is similar to the Fourdrinier except for the wire section. Instead of the continuous flat wire screen belt, it employs a cylinder covered with fine wire screen. This cylinder revolves in a vat containing an aqueous fiber suspension. The fibers thus picked up are transferred to a felt at the apex of the cylinder. There are usually several such devices in series, forming a multilayer sheet. It is thus possible to combine several grades of fiber to good advantage.

Fillers

Powders such as clay, calcium carbonate, talc, calcium sulfate, silica, titanium dioxide, etc., are added to paper stock prior to sheet formation.

Fillers should have a high degree of whiteness, high refractive index, small particle size, low water solubility, low specific gravity, low cost, and inertness. The quantity of filler may vary from 2 to 40 per cent based on the weight of the fiber. The addition of 10 per cent of clay may reduce the burst strength of paper by 20 per cent.

Sizing

Sizes are used to impart resistance to liquid penetration and a better surface for writing or printing. Depending on the degree of sizing, paper is referred to as:

(*a*) hard sizing—strongly sized.
(*b*) slack sizing—weakly sized.
(*c*) water leaf—unsized.

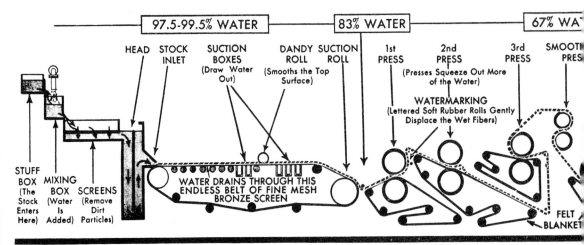

Fig. 1. Fourdrinier machine. (Courtesy Hammermill Paper Co.)

Internal sizing may be accomplished by adding rosin soap or an aqueous dispersion of rosin to the pulp slurry and setting it with alum.

Beater sizing may involve the addition of from 1 to 3 per cent of starch to the pulp in the beater. It increases the tear, fold, and wet strength by bonding individual fibers.

Calendar sizing is added after web formation, to improve surface characteristics.

Tub sizing is accomplished by immersing the preformed sheet in dilute size solution.

Surface sizing—most important in this category is clay coating. Clay in combination with titanium dioxide may be coated on the paper either on or off the machine. Prior to 1930 only casein and animal glue were employed as binders. Starch is today the major bonding agent; but styrenebutadiene resins and acrylics are gaining in importance.

PAPER TESTING

The properties of paper depend on many factors such as the choice of pulp, the type of bleaching, thickness, degree of pressing in water removal, degree of pressing in finishing, chemical additives, and others. The adhesives technologist is concerned with some of the physical as well as chemical properties of paper as an adherend.*

Physical Test Methods and Definitions

Conditioning. Since paper is highly susceptible to changing atmospheric conditions, it is conditioned at $73 \pm 3°F$ and 50 ± 2 per cent relative humidity for 24 hr before testing.

Basis Weight. This is the weight in pounds of one ream of paper. There are many definitions of the term "ream." It means to most people a number of sheets (480 or 500) of a certain size (anywhere from 17 x 22 in. to 25 x 38 in.). One common "ream" in the paper mill is 500 sheets of 24 x 36 in., i.e., 3000 sq ft. Attempts have been made to standardize the ream. Some day it may come to mean one million square inches, i.e., 1000 sheets each 1000 sq in. in size. *Thickness,* measured with a micrometer, is expressed in thousandths of an inch. *Bulk* or *apparent density* is the ratio of basis weight to thickness.

Tensile strength measures the rupture point under unidirectional loading. *Bursting strength,* using the "Mullen" tester, involves the application of air or hydraulic pressure (via a rubber diaphragm) to one side of a paper until it bursts. *Tear strength,* by the Elmendorf Tear Tester, measures the force required to tear a piece of paper after a cut has been started.

Chemical Test Methods

Tappi standard test methods are available for moisture (T-412m-53) and (T-484m-58), ash (T-413m-58), pH (T-435m-52), as well as for sulfate, chloride, nitrogen, copper, zinc, iron, and many others.

PAPER PRODUCTS

Adhesives make it possible to convert the raw paper into a host of useful products. The major outlet for this three and one half billion dollar converting industry is packaging.

* Test methods have been prepared by and are available from the Technical Association of the Pulp and Paper Industry, 360 Lexington Avenue, New York City.

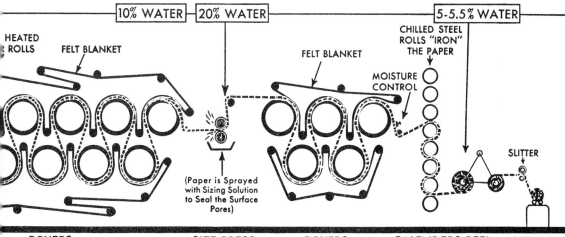

10% WATER — 20% WATER — 5-5.5% WATER

HEATED ROLLS — FELT BLANKET — FELT BLANKET — CHILLED STEEL ROLLS "IRON" THE PAPER — MOISTURE CONTROL — SLITTER

(Paper is Sprayed with Sizing Solution to Seal the Surface Pores)

DRYERS — SIZE PRESS — DRYERS — CALENDERS REEL — WINDER

Corrugated and Solid Fiber Containers

This industry now consists of 400 companies operating 800 plants in the United States. It is an important segment of the U. S. economy, having an annual output of 1,750 million dollars.

Corrugated board is produced by laminating several plies of paper. The adhesive employed is usually starch, although some silicate is still used for this purpose. The Stein-Hall process has contributed greatly to the acceptance of starch in the corrugated industry. In this method, ungelatinized starch is suspended in a starch solution in order to obtain a slurry of maximum solids and minimum viscosity. (For details see Chapters 12 and 48.)

Folding Cartons

These are produced at the rate of approximately three million short tons per year and are valued at 950 million dollars. These containers can be produced rapidly, filled automatically, and used for display.

Set-Up Boxes

These are made on machinery that glues the corners together with gummed or heat seal tape. The shell is then covered with a finish paper. The adhesive employed in this operation is commonly a low-grade animal glue, plasticized with sugar and dextrin. Production is estimated at more than 15 billion boxes annually.

Paperboard Milk Containers

Here is a good example of how adhesives can aid in capturing new markets. The milk container has in a few short years displaced the traditional glass bottle from the supermarket. This feat was made possible by high-speed gluing operations which permit low-cost production of milk containers. It is estimated that more than 12 billion of these are produced annually.

Paper Bags

These are finding increasing use both in the retail business and as shipping containers for industrial products. Considerable quantities of adhesives are consumed annually in the manufacture of an estimated one hundred billion paper bags.

Stamps

Stamps account for the consumption of a considerable quantity of low-grade starch and dextrin adhesives. In the last few years this figure has risen sharply due to the introduction of premium stamps into retail commerce.

Labels

Labels are placed on most bottles, cans, cartons, or packages in order to identify content, brand name, manufacturer or sales agent, and/or the addressee. Most labels are attached to the container with an adhesive, usually precoated so that it may be activated by solvent, water, pressure, or heat.

Adhesive Tapes

These account for a considerable quantity of paper and adhesives consumption. The market in regular gummed sealing tape may be declining. However, reinforced sealing tapes, consisting of two plies of paper reinforced with glass or some other fiber, are gaining in popularity.

ADHESIVES

A large variety of adhesives are employed in the paper converting industry. Because of differences in machinery and paper stock, it is almost impossible to standardize adhesive production. Thus, in a bag plant, two production lines running side by side may require different adhesives. This divergence of equipment and raw materials make the task of the adhesive technologist a difficult one.

The physical and chemical properties expected of the adhesive for paper products are usually not too severe. Since paper has relatively poor tear strength, a strength of 100 psi may be adequate for the adhesive bond. Even at this low value, the paper will tear prior to the rupture of the adhesive bond. Moisture resistance is in many instances unimportant, since most papers will disintegrate upon exposure to water. High heat resistance, too, is of minor importance because of paper's tendency to char or burn at elevated temperature. This lack of stringent requirements has made it possible to utilize inexpensive adhesives and thus produce an array of low cost products.

In the last few years, however, increasing labor costs have brought about production changes which have affected adhesive requirements. Many manual and semi-automatic operations have been replaced by fully automatic high-speed machines. The adhesives that worked under the old conditions no longer perform at today's tempo. Newer, more costly adhesives must take the place of the old standbys such as animal glue and starch.

Adhesives for the paper converting industry may be classified according to their origin.

(A) *Protein Adhesives*

(1) *Animal glue* (Chapter 7) is prepared from bone, hides, and connective tissues of animals. It is estimated that more than 60 million pounds of animal glue are used annually by the paper industry; but the market is shrinking. Major causes for the decline are poor odor, poor water resistance, poor flexibility, and relatively high price.

(2) *Fish glue* (Chapter 8) is extracted from the bones and skins of fish. It is similar to animal glue but remains liquid at room temperature even without liquefiers.

(3) *Casein* (Chapter 9) is derived from skim milk. Casein glues are used for labeling of bottles, cans, and case sealing. They are usually formulated with alkalies, mold inhibitors and bactericides. They have good cold water resistance, but are easily dissolved in caustic soda solution. This combination of properties is taken advantage of in adhering labels to beer and soft-drink cans and bottles.

Large tonnages of casein are used in the clay coating of paper.

(4) *Vegetable Proteins.* Soya protein (Chapter 10) is an ingredient of compositions used to bind clay coatings to paper.

(B) *Vegetable Adhesives*

(1) *Gums* are materials of plant origin which dissolve or swell in water. Gum arabic extracted from acacia trees is the best known vegetable gum adhesive and has been used in postage stamps. Vegetable gums do not give as strong adhesives as animal glues, but do have quick tack. Gum tragacanth is a water-dispersible gum used as a thickening agent for starch and protein adhesives.

(2) *Starch and dextrin* (Chapter 12) may be dissolved or dispersed in water to yield a large array of adhesive products. Degradation of starch by either heat, acids, or enzymes results in the formation of dextrins. These are used in envelope or stamp adhesives. Starch is the adhesive employed in the manufacture of corrugated board. The Stein-Hall, Hot-Drop, and other processes which permit a high solids, low viscosity slurry, are discussed elsewhere.

Newer starch derivatives such as ethers and esters, are offering improved properties at slightly higher cost.

Starch is also playing an important role in the clay coating of paper.

(3) *Natural and Reclaimed Rubber* (Chapter 15) are the basis for most pressure-sensitive adhesives and contact cements. In the last few years, however, competition from vinyl ethers, butyl and other synthetics has been felt.

(4) *Natural Resins.* A number of naturally occurring resinous substances from the basis for adhesive products. Rosin, its esters and derivatives, has occupied an important position among these. Recently, however, rosin has been in short supply and synthetics have taken over many of its traditional applications.

Asphalt, perhaps the cheapest adhesive, is utilized in paper lamination, where color is of minor importance. It offers the added advantage of forming a moisture barrier.

Shellac is not, strictly speaking, a vegetable product; it is a conglomeration of ester-alcohol-acid polymers deposited on trees by lac insects. Formerly popular for such favorites as de Khotinsky cement, it has declined in use because of high cost and lack of flexibility.

(C) *Inorganic Adhesives*

(1) *Sodium Silicate* (Chapter 6). This inorganic salt has been widely used to laminate paper-to-paper in the manufacture of corrugated board, and in the sealing of shipping containers. However, it is losing ground to both starches and synthetics.

(D) *Synthetic Resin Adhesives*

(1) *Formaldehyde-based condensates* with phenol, resorcinol, urea, and melamine. These are of greatest importance in the wood industries; but urea-formaldehyde resins are utilized in conjunction with starch to provide improved water resistance (Chapter 24).

(2) *Vinyls.* The most important "vinyl" for paper adhesion is polyvinyl acetate. It offers many advantageous properties: high solids at low viscosity, emulsion form which is nonflammable and eliminates cost of solvent, good compatibility with many natural and synthetic resins, good initial tack, rapid "set." The thermoplastic nature of polyvinyl acetate makes it suitable for hot-melt adhesives as well. Bookbinding, bag sealing, lamination, folding and set up boxes are just a few of the industries consuming large quantities of vinyl acetate polymer. Both homopolymer, which re-

quires addition of plasticizer and compounding prior to use, and copolymer, which may have the plasticizer built into the molecule, are employed by the paper converting industry. Polyvinyl alcohol, which is produced by the partial or complete hydrolysis of the acetate, is an excellent adhesive as well. It is a water-soluble powder and may be extended with starch, dextrins, and other products. Solubility and water resistance depend on chemical composition (Chapter 28). The polyvinylethers have been mentioned above as newer raw materials of interest especially in pressure-sensitive formulations. Acrylics seem even better suited for this purpose and are finding application in clay coating of paper as well.

(3) *Synthetic Rubber.* These materials are employed to adhere paper to more difficultly bonded surfaces such as metal (foil), rubber, leather, glass, etc. The synthetic rubbers include butyl, polyisobutylene, neoprene, butadiene-acrylonitrile, butadiene-styrene, chlorinated rubber, etc. Some of them find application in pressure-sensitive adhesives and in the coating of paper.

(4) *Miscellaneous Synthetics.* The polyamides are of special interest as hot-melt adhesives for bread wraps and similar applications. The silicones offer unique adhesive as well as *ab*hesive properties. Silicones are often employed as release coatings on paper, to prevent adhesion thereto.

Paper because of its high porosity and weak structure makes an excellent adherend. Almost any adhesive will perform well with paper either by specific or mechanical adhesion. It is thus not important to select adhesives specifically for this adherend. Rather, they should be chosen according to the conditions of application and use.

References

1. Ainsworth, I. H., "Paper the Fifth Wonder," Thomas Publishing Co., Kankauna, Wisc., 1959.
2. Brecht, W., "Conditioning of Paper Testing Rooms in European Countries," *TAPPI,* **44,** (6), 153A–154A (1961).
3. Calkin, J. B., "Modern Pulp and Paper Making," New York, Reinhold Publishing Corp., 1957.
4. Casey, J. P., "Pulp and Paper, Chemistry and Chemical Technology," New York, Interscience Publishers Inc., 1952.
5. Clark, J. d'A., "Conditioning for Paper Testing," *TAPPI,* **44,** (6), 154A–157A (1961).
6. Meredith, R., "Mechanical Properties of Wood and Paper," New York, Interscience Publishers Inc., 1953.
7. Wrist, P. E., The Science of Paper Manufacture, *TAPPI,* **44,** (1), 181A–199A (1961).
8. U. S. Industrial Outlook for 1961.

— 41 —

Bonding Plastics

M. J. Bodnar

Picatinny Arsenal
Dover, New Jersey

Plastics can be bonded to themselves, other plastics, or other type adherends. The bonding method chosen and the techniques used will depend on the adherends being bonded, facilities available, and the end item application.

Bonding of plastics offers several advantages over mechanical methods of attachment. These include (1) a more uniform distribution of stresses over the fastened area; (2) high strength-to-weight ratio; (3) smooth contour; (4) ability to join components having complex geometrical configurations; (5) ability to join thin sheets, rigid or flexible; (6) effective sealing against moisture, chemicals, fuels, and gases; (7) dampening of vibration; (8) increase in electrical resistivity or providing of electrical conductivity if specially compounded; (9) often simpler and more economical operation.

Plastics are generally classified as thermoplastic or thermosetting. The thermoplastics are characterized by their ability to exhibit plastic flow when subjected to heat or to prolonged stress. The amorphous thermoplastics are soluble in selected solvents. Crystalline thermoplastics are insoluble except at elevated temperatures. Thermosetting plastics are crosslinked polymers which are characterized by infusibility and insolubility. These do not demonstrate appreciable plastic flow when subjected to heat. Although they may swell when immersed in solvent, they will not go into solution. It becomes readily apparent that the thermosetting plastics cannot be bonded by either heat welding or solvent cementing techniques. Only adhesives will bond these thermosetting materials effectively. The thermoplastics on the other hand can in many cases be bonded to themselves or to other thermo-plastics by heat welding or solvent cementing. These techniques will be described shortly.

In order to understand better the principles of adhesion, it should be mentioned briefly that adhesion is a surface phenomenon, independent of the subsurface layers in the adherends. There are two types of adhesion, mechanical and chemical. Mechanical adhesion consists solely of mechanical interlocking of the adhesive with a porous adherend. The adhesive flows into the pores or through the interstices of an adherend, and upon cure, effects mechanical interlocking as of plastic threads sewn through the mesh of a fabric. Chemical or specific adhesion usually results from residual valence forces of the same type that cause cohesion. Generally the selection of an adhesive will depend, among other factors, on the polarity or polarizability of the adherends.

Regardless of the bonding method used, it should be emphasized that the bonding surfaces must always be very clean just before the bonding operation. The cleaning may be accomplished by a suitable solvent, mechanical abrasion, or chemical treatment.

Heat Welding

Most thermoplastics can be joined by welding, by heating the plastic to be joined sufficiently to permit fusion under slight pressure. Cellulose nitrate is not heat welded because of the fire hazard. Most other thermoplastics can be heat sealed or welded by heating the plastic surfaces to be joined to temperatures of 325 to 400°F depending on the plastic. The surfaces should be brought into contact immediately (preferably within less than a second) and sufficient pressure applied to allow intimate contact and uniform fusion without excessive squeeze-out. Overheating is undesirable since either bubbling may occur is to depolymerization, or charring may take place due to decomposition. The exact temperature of the welding tool, time of contact with the plastic surfaces, and pressure applied will depend on the specific type of plastic and upon the thickness of the plastic components. Figure 1 shows flexible thermoplastic film being heat sealed with a hand sealer.

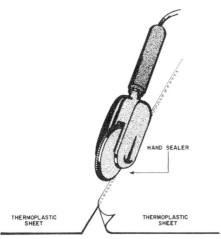

Fig. 1. Heat sealing.

Since heat welding and solvent cementing are very much a matter of utilizing proper techniques and developing skills for specific end item applications, it is recommended that, when possible, the user conduct a simple test on small pieces of the plastics to be joined prior to joining either two large pieces or a number of pieces. Testing this sample to destruction upon completion of the bond will give the user an indication of the strength of the bond he may expect.

Hot gas welding is a technique often used to join thermoplastics to themselves. As with other heat welding methods, polyvinyl chloride and the olefin polymers—low- and high-density polyethylene as well as polypropylene—are especially suitable for hot gas welding. A heat gun which utilizes either electrical or gas heat sources is used, with an orifice temperature of 425 to 700°F. For olefin polymers, the gas must be inert since oxygen in the air will oxidize the surfaces of the plastics and decrease their welding properties. The surfaces, as always, must be thoroughly cleaned before the welding operation. A welding rod of the same plastic material as the parts being joined is usually employed

to butt-join two pieces of the plastics. The ends to be joined are aligned to allow a 30 to 60 mil gap between them. The heat is directed at the tip of the welding rod which is held in close proximity to the gap to be filled. Figure 2 shows two rigid thermoplastic sheets being joined by hot gas welding. To obtain maximum strength it is preferable to allow all heat-welded joints to cool for several hours before stressing them severely. This is particularly true for the highly crystalline polymers, e.g. the polyolefins, nylon, and polyformaldehyde or polyoxymethylene ("Delrin").

Heat sealing is commonly used to join plastic films. The heat may be applied from both sides of the joint to be bonded or from only one side. The former method is generally easier to master since both pieces of plastic are heated more uniformly than when the heat penetrates from one side only. Either heated jaws or heated rollers are employed. A "Teflon" coating is often used on the heater jaws to prevent the plastic being heat sealed from sticking to them. Other heated tools also used include hot irons, welding irons, strip heaters, and hot plates. Care must be taken with heated-tool welding to supply a sufficient heat-time-pressure cycle to attain uniform and complete fusion but to refrain from melting through the plastics being joined. This is especially important if heat is applied from one side only to accomplish a weld when either one or both of the films to be joined are very thin. Uncoated cellophane and uncoated polyethylene terephthalate ("Mylar") cannot be heat sealed.

Spin welding is a technique which utilizes the heat of friction created by a spinning rod of the plastic when in contact with another piece of the plastic. Cylinders, rods, and discs are often joined by spin welding. A high degree of polymerization in the plastic is a desirable characteristic since

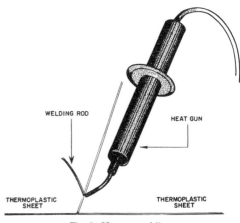

Fig. 2. Hot gas welding.

residual monomer in the plastic evaporates at the high temperatures created by friction and tends to leave a somewhat bubbly, weaker joint. Sufficient pressure should be applied during the spin welding process to force out excess bubbles. This pressure should be maintained until the weld has set. Large-diameter cylinders are often crowned or machined to cone-shaped contact areas in order to equalize the temperatures of friction between the centers and peripheries of the two rods. Since the centers travel at much lower velocities than the outer peripheries of the rods, the pressure is concentrated on the centers during the spinning to initiate the welding process.

Heat welding in general should give bonds approaching or equal to the strength of the parent plastic.

SOLVENT CEMENTING

Noncrystalline, amorphous-type thermoplastics can be joined to themselves by utilizing suitable solvents, solvent-polymer solutions, or monomer compositions. When two dissimilar plastics of this type are to be bonded, polymeric adhesives are generally desirable. Solvents and polymers should be chosen which match closely the solubility parameters of the plastics to be bonded.[23] By using the solubility parameters, it is easier to find an appropriate solvent for each plastic.

Solvents should be chosen which evaporate neither too rapidly nor too slowly. Fast-evaporating solvent tends to give unbonded areas, stressed joints, crazing, and blushing. Slow-evaporating solvents are more suitable from this point of view but require a much longer time to produce a satisfactory bond. Mixtures of slow and fast solvents are usually preferred. Crazing or the appearance of fine striations occurs most often in the hard brittle plastics. It is most common in polymethyl methacrylate and unmodified polystyrene. Fast-evaporating solvents are, therefore, not recommended when bonding these plastics. Apparently, highly stressed joints are much more subject to crazing than are lightly stressed joints. Special consideration should be given in selecting solvents for bonded joints which will remain under a continuous static load.

Solvents are often bodied with the polymer resin or chips of the polymer to provide gap-filling properties for the cement, to decrease its rate of set so that the solvents can better penetrate the mating surface of each adherend, and to decrease shrinkage at the joint which would increase internal stresses.

Methods of Application Commonly Used for Solvent Cementing of Similar Plastics

Brush Application. Cement is brushed onto both adherends, and the parts are joined while wet. As in all solvent cementing, it is usually preferable to jig the parts in place so that they are in intimate contact until the bond is firmly set. Last traces of high-boiling solvents will often take several days or more to completely evaporate. Therefore, the joint should not be subjected to very high stresses before the setting is completed. It is sometimes desirable to mask the areas immediately adjacent to the joint to be made, since running cement will ruin the appearance of the plastic.

Spraying. This method is often used when either large or numerous pieces are to be cemented. Uniform application of cement is a prime advantage of this method but masking of the plastic is usually required. Adequate ventilation is necessary for protection of personnel. Although spraying provides a rapid means of application, more cement is often used than when brush coating.

Dipping. Surfaces to be bonded are often dipped into the cement for periods ranging from one second to more than 30 min, depending on the plastic and cement used. The surfaces to be butt joined are immersed in the cement until softened, then removed and brought into contact.

Felt Pad. This method involves the use of a thick felt pad partially immersed in a pan of solvent. The solvent "wicks" through the felt fibers by capillary action so that the surface of the pad is constantly wet. Plastic surfaces to be joined are brought into contact with the pad until properly softened. This method is especially suitable for quick assembly where extremely strong bonds are not a prime criterion and masking is undesirable.

Hypodermic Syringes. These are sometimes used to introduce cement into small, otherwise inaccessible areas where a bonded joint is desirable.

Typical Solvent Cements for Major Plastics

Since discussion of the innumerable solvent cement mixtures available for the various plastics would take us beyond the intended scope of this chapter, what follows will be limited primarily to one or two working methods for each type of plastic that can be cemented to itself.

Acrylics. Acrylics can usually be bonded by utilizing a mixture of 60 parts methylene chloride, 40 parts methyl methacrylate monomer, and 0.2 part benzoyl peroxide. Polymer chips can be dissolved in this adhesive to obtain the desired consistency. Due to their relative softness, molded or extruded acrylic parts are wet with the cement by brush or spray application and joined immediately. Strain must be avoided since these acrylics are highly susceptible to stress-crazing. Cast sheets usually require soaking in adhesive to allow thorough softening before joining. A 15 to 30 min soak in ethylene dichloride is satisfactory. Glacial acetic acid will also soften the acrylics but may need as long as 60 min to work effectively. As with most cemented plastics, the cemented joints can be handled after several hours at room temperature and machined after a 24-hr cure.

Cellulose Polymers. Cellulose acetates are very easy to cement. Acetone can be used for very quick bonds. A highly satisfactory cement consists of 60 parts acetone, 30 parts methyl "Cellosolve," and 10 parts dissolved cellulose acetate. It is applied to the mating surfaces and the surfaces are joined immediately. Light pressure should be applied for the first 5 to 15 min to ensure intimate contact as the setting takes place.

Cellulose acetate butyrate has been cemented to provide excellent bonded joints by using the following mixture: 40 parts acetone, 40 parts ethyl acetate, and 20 parts cellulose acetate butyrate. Mating parts, as always, should be kept in contact until the joint has had time to become rigid.

Cellulose nitrate, acetate and acetate butyrate may be bonded with numerous solvents. Commonly used are acetone, methyl or ethyl acetates, and Cellosolve. Dope lacquer consisting of cellulose nitrate, ethyl acetate, and acetone provides a very effective and strong cement for all three of these cellulose polymers.

Ethyl cellulose can be bonded to itself readily with solvent solutions of the polymer dissolved in a mixture of 80 parts ethyl acetate with 20 parts alcohol.

Polycarbonate ("Lexan"). Polycarbonate can be effectively cemented to itself by utilizing the following solution: 40 parts polymer, 147 parts methylene chloride, and 80 parts ethylene dichloride. This plastic can also be heat welded with hot nitrogen or hot air at a jet temperature of 600 to 650°C. It can also be joined by liquefying the surfaces with a hot metal bar, about 350°C, for 2 to 5 sec.

Polyvinyl Alcohol. Water with 10 or 20 per cent glycerine can be used to cement polyvinyl alcohol (PVA) although heat is desirable. Heat sealing of PVA requires the use of water.

Polystyrene. Many large-scale production items such as housewares and children's toys are cemented quickly by wetting the surfaces of the polystyrene with a suitable solvent, such as toluene or xylene, holding the surfaces in contact for 30 sec to 1 min while allowing to set. In many cases it is preferable to body the adhesive by dissolving some polymer into it. Quick-drying solvents should be avoided because of their tendency to craze the plastic. Very slow drying solvents like ethyl naphthalene will give craze-free joints with good optical clarity for several years, but long times are needed to effect a bond. Mixtures of slow- and fast-drying solvents can be used. Fast-drying solvents include ethyl acetate, methylethyl ketone, and methylene chloride. Other medium drying solvents are perchloroethylene and trichloroethylene.

Polymethylstyrene can be bonded effectively with a bodied solvent solution of trichloroethylene.

Polyvinyl Chloride. Polyvinyl chloride (PVC) and its acetate copolymers can be cemented by using solvent solutions containing ketones. In the vinyl chloride-acetate copolymers, solubility is increased as the acetate fraction is increased. Chlorinated hydrocarbons are good solvents for these copolymers. Methylethyl ketone (MEK) and methyl isobutyl ketone (MIBK) are commonly used as solvents or components of solvent solutions for cementing low- and medium-molecular-weight polyvinyl chloride-acetate copolymers. High-molecular-weight PVC-acetate copolymers and vinyl chloride homopolymers usually require the more powerful cyclohexanone or even tetrahydrofuran. A trace of plasticizer, such as 2 to 5 per cent of dioctylphthalate (DOP), may be added to improve the flexibility at the joint and to reduce stresses. Acetic acid is added sometimes to solvent solutions to increase the "bite" of the cement. A mixture utilizing solvents and nonsolvents is commonly employed. One such mixture consists of the following: 20 parts dioxane, 12 parts methanol, 60 parts MEK, 3 parts DOP, 2 parts glacial acetic acid, and 3 parts isophorone. Dissolved chips or shavings of the resin will increase the viscosity of the solution and make the cement more effective in joining mating surfaces that are not perfectly smooth, thereby producing uniform contact throughout the bonding area. In bonding unsupported flexible polyvinyl chloride film or sheet to itself, the following formulation has worked very satisfactorily:

Parts by Weight	Material
100	polyvinyl chloride resin, medium molecular weight
100	tetrahydrofuran
200	methylethyl ketone
1.5	tin organic stabilizer
20	dioctylphthalate
25	methyl isobutyl ketone

This cement can also be used in bonding rigid PVC to itself. Care must be used in handling this adhesive due to the slightly toxic nature of the tetrahydrofuran. Good ventilation is recommended.

ADHESIVES BONDING*

Adhesive bonding of plastics is the most versatile method of joining one type of plastic to another type, or a plastic to a nonplastic adherend. Unlike heat welding, which involves mechanical fusion at the softening temperature of the plastic, or solvent cementing, which utilizes physical solution of the plastic adherend and subsequent volatilization of the residual solvent, adhesive bonding depends primarily upon specific or chemical adhesion. Unlike components are held together by a common material, usually foreign to both adherends.

The selection of the proper adhesive depends upon many variables. Proper design of adhesive joints and the choice of an adhesive best qualified for specific applications should be considered carefully. The adhesive joint should be designed primarily to withstand the most severe type of stress to which it will be subjected. Selection of the adhesive will depend upon the following factors:

1. Type, magnitude, and duration of the stresses to which the joint will be subjected.
2. Environmental conditions the bonded joint may encounter.
3. Types of adherends.
4. Geometry of the bonded area.
5. Maximum allowable time, temperature, and pressure for cure.
6. Available facilities (presses, sources of heat, methods of chemical treatment, jig fixtures, etc.).
7. Economy.
8. Method of application desirable (brush, dip, spray, trowel, etc.).

In many cases the tendency is to over-engineer, that is, to select the strongest adhesive available. For reasons of economy it is sufficient to select an adhesive that will meet the strength requirements for the end item under all the conditions that it must encounter in service. If only low stresses are to be encountered, a cheap adhesive can be used. Maximum strength of the joint is often limited by the mechanical strength of one of the adherends. The adhesive selected need not provide higher strength adhesive bonds than the strength of the weaker adherend.

Thermoplastic adhesives are often satisfactory for bonding plastics when the bonds will not be subjected to high temperatures or to continuous loads. These adhesives are generally less expensive. However, they are, as a rule, less resistant to solvents and have poor creep characteristics. Effects of solvents in the adhesives on vulnerable (noncrystalline, amorphous type) thermoplastics should be considered. The curing temperature of the adhesive should always be below the softening point of the plastic. The amount of pressure that can be effectively applied will be governed by the geometrical configurations of the adherends as well as by the jigging and pressure facilities available. For these reasons contact-pressure, room-temperature-curing adhesives are popular for many applications.

Generally speaking, epoxies or modified epoxies provide good adhesion to thermosetting plastics.

Surfaces of the thermosets can be wiped with a clean cloth dampened with an effective degreasing solvent such as acetone, MEK, toluene, low-boiling petroleum naphtha, or trichloroethylene to remove excess grease, grit, dust, and other foreign matter. It is usually advisable to sand the bonding surfaces of the plastics to remove traces of mold-release agents such as silicone grease, which are often very difficult to completely remove otherwise. Traces of grease or other impurities may drastically reduce the strength of the bonded joint. Crystalline thermoplastics may be acetone wiped. Some require chemical treatment to obtain good surface adhesion characteristics. Amorphous, noncrystalline plastics should be cleaned with solvents that do not affect the plastics. Sanding may be advisable in some instances.

When bonding plastics to metals, ceramics, glass, etc., the selection of the adhesive should be governed in part by the differences in the thermal coefficients of expansion of the adherends if the bonded joints are to be subjected to either high or very low temperatures. Since the thermal coefficients of plastics are considerably higher than those for the other adherends mentioned, the adhesive should be of such a nature as to allow distribution of stresses at the temperature extremes by virtue of its elastic nature. On the other hand the polymeric adhesive may be filled with inorganic fillers which will tend to lessen the gap between the thermal coefficients of the adherends.

An example of the stresses that may be encountered due to different thermal coefficients is given here. A polysulfide-modified epoxy used to bond cellulose acetate butyrate to magnesium gave good bond strengths at room temperature. When the specimens were subjected to $-65\,°F$, they fell apart at the adhesive joints because of the difference in thermal coefficients. The problem of the thermal coefficient of the adherends did not exist with cellulose acetate butyrate bonded to itself, or magne-

* Since solvent cements were discussed earlier, they will not be discussed again under Adhesives Bonding although they are types of adhesives.

sium bonded to itself with the same adhesive, and these specimens retained good bond strength at $-65°F$. Thicker layers, or a two-coat system of adhesive, is found to be highly desirable where the thermal coefficient problem is encountered.

In some instances an adhesive that will bond well to one adherend will bond poorly to the other. In this case a suitable primer, which will adhere to both the adhesive and to the adherend which bonds poorly, should be used. For example, in bonding nylon to steel a resorcinol-formaldehyde adhesive will provide excellent bonds to the nylon but poor bonds to steel. By priming the steel with either a nitrile-phenolic or an epoxy, and curing this primer, resorcinol-formaldehyde can then be used to provide excellent bonds between the nylon and the primed steel. If the bonded joint is to be subjected only to shear or tensile stresses, the epoxy primer may be preferable. On the other hand, if high peel stresses or impact loads are to be encountered, a rubbery primer is required. A fairly thick coat (up to several mils dry film thickness) is recommended.

As mentioned earlier, choice of the adhesive depends on many factors. In general, brittle-type adhesives should not be used where high peel, cleavage, or impact strengths are required. They can, however, be used in many instances if a heavy layer of a suitable elastomeric adhesive is first applied as a primer.

The types of adhesives which can be used when bonding various plastics, and the bonding techniques required to obtain effective bonds will be described shortly. For a quick general idea which will tell the reader what type of adhesive to select to obtain a bond to a specific type plastic a limited reference chart is presented in Table 1.

Unlike the usual type adhesives reference chart, this table shows the adhesion obtainable to any one plastic by code numbers for the different types of adhesives. For bonding one type of plastic to another, the reader should select where possible an adhesives code number common to both plastics. This is the type adhesive that will bond both plastics. In some instances, especially for some of the crystalline thermoplastics, a chemical pretreatment

TABLE 1. ADHESIVE SELECTOR FOR SPECIFIC PLASTICS.

Plastics	Adhesives*	Plastics	Adhesives*
I. Thermoplastics		Flexible polyvinyl chloride,	
Polymethyl methacrylate	15, 14, 17	fabrics	10, 11, 7, 9
Cellulose acetate	1, 14, 2	Vinylidene chloride	10
Cellulose acetate butyrate	1, 14, 2	Polystyrene	17, 2, 14, 3, 5
Cellulose nitrate	1, 14, 2	Polyurethane	14, 15, 5
Ethyl cellulose	3, 10, 8, 1	Polyformaldehyde	8, 14, 17, 5
Polyethylene	16, 13	Polyformaldehyde (treated)	5, 3, 14, 17
Polyethylene (treated)	3, 5, 10	"Penton"	14, 17, 5
Polypropylene	16	"Penton" (treated)	14, 17, 5
Polypropylene (treated)	3, 5, 10	Nylon	15, 3, 10, 8
Polymonochlorotrifluoroethylene	16		
Polymonochlorotrifluoroethylene		*II. Thermosets*	
(treated)	3, 5, 12	Diallylphthalate	3, 5, 6, 17
Polytetrafluoroethylene	16	Polyethylene terephthalate	10, 8, 16, 17
Polytetrafluoroethylene		Epoxy	3, 17, 15, 6, 12
(treated)	3, 5, 12	Polyester	10, 19, 4, 3, 17, 14
Polycarbonate	17, 14, 5, 2	Furane	6, 3, 4, 14
Rigid polyvinyl chloride	14, 17, 3, 5	Melamine	3, 4, 14
		Phenolic	3, 4, 10, 15, 17, 18, 14

Adhesive Reference Numbers

1. Cellulose nitrate
2. Cyanoacrylate
3. Epoxy
4. Phenolic epoxy
5. Polysulfide epoxy or polyamide epoxy
6. Furane
7. GRS-rubber-based, solvent type
8. Neoprene-based, solvent type
9. Neoprene-based, water emulsion
10. Nitrile phenolic

11. Nitrile-rubber-based, water emulsion
12. Phenol formaldehyde
13. Polybutadiene
14. Polyurethane
15. Resorcinol formaldehyde
16. Silicone resin in xylene solvent
17. Unsaturated polyester-styrene
18. Urea formaldehyde
19. Vinyl phenolic

is required to obtain high bond strength to that plastic. The treatment changes the surface properties of the plastic and makes it more adhesionable. Except where specifically stated otherwise, the reference chart lists untreated plastic surfaces. "Untreated" surface is meant to imply only solvent wiping and/or sanding. Treating the surfaces, as discussed here, refers to chemical pretreatment of the bonding surfaces of the plastic, such as acid etching. Adhesives that bond poorly to untreated plastic may provide bonds stronger than the plastic itself if the plastic is chemically pretreated.

Adhesives for bonding to various plastics and methods utilized in the various processes are described in this section. In many instances the bond strengths described were obtained in controlled laboratory tests. Information on adhesives for specific end item applications can usually be obtained in more detail from the manufacturers of the adhesives. The bond strengths reported were usually obtained as follows: shear strengths, based on ½ sq in. single-lap tensile shear specimens, ASTM type D1002-53T; tensile strengths, based upon 1 sq in. bonding surface, button-type specimens, ASTM type D897-49. Higher relative bond strengths are usually reported in shear tests where the bonded area is less than ½ sq in. or where compressive shear tests are conducted. Higher relative tensile bond strengths are usually reported when tensile specimens have a relatively small bonding area. The reported tensile strength of the bond is then a calculated value. Therefore, the bond strengths reported here should be considered as relative.

Thermoplastics

Acrylics. Excellent adhesion can be obtained to polymethyl methacrylate with resorcinol-formaldehyde adhesives. Before the adhesive is applied, the plastic should be wiped clean of all traces of grease, dust, and other foreign matter with a clean cloth dampened with methanol. Bond strength at room temperature will exceed the strength of the plastic.

Polymethyl methacrylate (PMMA) can be bonded effectively with polyurethane adhesives but bond strength may decline as the environmental temperature approaches 160°F. By priming an aluminum surface with a polysulfide epoxy and bonding PMMA to it with a polyurethane adhesive, strong bonds were obtained at temperatures ranging from −65 to 160°F. On testing, failure occurred in the PMMA in all cases, in spite of the differences in the thermal coefficients of expansion of the aluminum and the plastic, largely due to the elastomeric nature of the polyurethane adhesive. Except where relatively low bond strengths are

satisfactory, epoxy adhesives should not be used for bonding PMMA.

Unsaturated polyester-styrene adhesives can be used for bonding PMMA. Shear-strength bonds are relatively poor at −65°F, however, due to the brittle nature of this adhesive at low temperatures.

Acrylic resin solvent cements are available that will bond PMMA to vinyl, cellulosics, and rubber. Cementing of PMMA to other plastics should be considered carefully since plasticizers in the other plastics may migrate into the PMMA, with subsequent harmful effects on the plastic, such as crazing.

Cellulose Polymers. Methanol is recommended for cleaning the surfaces of these polymers.

Cellulose nitrate can be bonded to a wide variety of substrates with a solvent solution of the polymer. The adhesive known commonly as "Duco" cement will provide bond strengths equivalent to the strength of the plastic. The solvent in this cement will soften the surface of the cellulose nitrate. As in other cases where solvent softens the plastic, care must be taken not to apply so much pressure that the plastic at the joint interface is deformed. This adhesive also bonds well to cellulose acetate (CA) and to cellulose acetate butyrate (CAB). The cellulose nitrate adhesive can be used for bonding to ethyl cellulose but not as effectively.

Polyurethane adhesives provide good to excellent bonds to cellulose nitrate, CA, and CAB at temperatures from −65 to 160°F, but the strength of the bond diminishes somewhat at the upper temperature limit.

Cyanoacrylate adhesives bond well to cellulose nitrate. They can also be used to bond effectively to CA and CAB.

By utilizing epoxy adhesives, ethyl cellulose can be bonded with fairly good bond strengths. Relatively low bond strengths can be obtained with nitrile-phenolic and neoprene solvent-type adhesives.

Nylon. An acetone wipe can be used to clean the nylon surface. 6,6-nylon can be bonded very effectively with resorcinol-formaldehyde adhesives. The strength of the bond may exceed the strength of the plastic. As mentioned earlier, high-strength bonds to metals such as steel, aluminum, and titanium can be obtained by priming the metal surface with an epoxy adhesive, curing the adhesive, then bonding the nylon to the primed surface with the resorcinol-formaldehyde.

Epoxies give only fair bonds to nylon, with shear strengths reaching only about 450 psi. Low-strength bonds to nylon are obtainable with nitrile-phenolic and neoprene solvent-type adhesives.

Adhesion between nylon or rayon and rubber is

obtainable by using a mixture of butadiene-styrene-vinylpyridine latex and resorcinol-formaldehyde.[20] The proportion of resin to rubber is 10–20/90–80 for the treatment of tire cord and 50–95/50–5 for the lamination of wood or metal.

"Penton." The surface should be cleaned with acetone. Polyurethane adhesives can be used to give tensile strength bonds in excess of 800 psi. Unsaturated polyester-styrene adhesive gives tensile strength bonds exceeding 600 psi while polysulfide-modified epoxy gives only 500 psi. By pretreating the "Penton" with a concentrated sulfuric acid-dichromate solution for 5 min at 160°F, washing thoroughly with clean tap water to remove all acid, then drying, the adhesion characteristics of the "Penton" are somewhat improved. Tensile strength of the bonded pretreated plastic exceeds 1200 psi when bonded with polysulfide epoxy adhesive. The acid solution used for this and other sulfuric-chromate treatments discussed in this chapter consists of the following:

	parts by wt.
sulfuric acid, concentrated (sp. gr. = 1.84)	150
distilled water	12
potassium dichromate	7.5

Polycarbonate. The surfaces of this plastic can be cleaned satisfactorily with methanol prior to adhesive application. Very high bond strengths are obtainable to this plastic with several types of adhesives. Shear strengths in excess of 1800 psi have been obtained when bonding this plastic to steel with a rigid-flexible type resin mixture of an unsaturated polyester-styrene adhesive. A urethane prepolymer adhesive gave 1500 psi shear strength when bonding this plastic to steel, while a polysulfide epoxide gave 1200 psi. A cyanoacrylate adhesive gave 1100 psi.

Olefin Polymers. Untreated olefin polymers cannot be bonded to give high bond strengths for most applications. For bonding thin films (1 to 2 mils thick) or for laminating, however, adhesives are available that will give satisfactory adhesion. These are tacky type solvent adhesives that never harden completely.[24] Their peel strength is invariably very poor at 160°F. One such adhesive is a silicone resin adhesive with xylene solvent. This adhesive remains slightly tacky for a long time. A coating of talc may be dusted onto the edges of the bonded joint to keep it from adhering to other surfaces with which it may come in contact. This adhesive will also give slight adhesive bonds to untreated "Teflon" and "Kel-F."

In order to obtain strong and reliable adhesion to any surface, it is important that the adhesive wet that surface. Adhesionability to low-density polyethylene, high-density polyethylene, and polypropylene can be increased greatly by pretreating the bonding surfaces to make the nonwettable plastic wettable.[25] A highly satisfactory method[1] for obtaining a good bonding surface utilizes treatment of the polyethylene with the sulfuric-dichromate solution used on "Penton." This treatment changes the normally nonpolar surface to a polar surface by oxidizing surface units of the molecular structure. This oxidation process does not depend on the degree of branching since the acid treatment greatly improves specific adhesion to the surface of both the highly branched low-density polyethylenes and the essentially nonbranched high-density polyethylenes. The shear-strength bonds obtainable to typical low-density and high-density polyethylenes when the bonding surface of the plastic is pretreated with concentrated acid solution are shown in Table 2. Results obtained for both types of polyethylene after treatment at 73°F are compared with results obtained after treatment at 160°F.[24] A polysulfide-epoxy adhesive was used as the bonding agent in this evaluation.

TABLE 2. EFFECT OF STRONG ACID PRETREATMENT TIME ON SHEAR STRENGTH ADHESION OF POLYETHYLENE BONDED WITH A POLYSULFIDE EPOXY ADHESIVE.

Time of Treatment	Low-Density Polyethylene		High-Density Polyethylene	
	Shear Strengths (psi) Obtained When Treated at		Shear Strengths (psi) Obtained When Treated at	
	73°F	160°F	73°F	160°F
2 sec	294	303	220	279
5 sec	294	330	228	298
1 min	327	404	283	608
5 min	331	422	289	747
15 min	336	440	347	753
1 hr	354		521	
4 hr	370		674	
24 hr	383		756	

As the upper bond strength limits were reached in the above test series, the ⅛ in. thick polyethylene adherend usually broke. Table 3 shows the peel strength obtainable to low-density polyethylene. It will be noticed that while relatively good shear-strength adhesion properties are obtained when the polyethylene is immersed in the acid solution only momentarily, longer treatment is required to improve peel-strength adhesion. This is in accordance with numerous other data obtained which indicate that peel stresses are much more sensitive to surface pretreatment than are shear stresses.

TABLE 3. EFFECT OF STRONG ACID PRETREATMENT TIME ON PEEL STRENGTH ADHESION OF LOW-DENSITY POLYETHYLENE

Time of Treatment	Peel Strength, lb/in. When Treated at 73°F
5 sec	8.1
1 min	8.5
5 min	13.5
15 min	21.0
1 hr	27.6
4 hr	30.3
24 hr	44.0

At the higher stress levels failure always occurred in the polyethylene during application of load.

The sulfuric acid-dichromate pretreatment can also be used to provide high bond strengths to polypropylene. Pretreatment of the polypropylene in the acid solution for one minute at 160°F provides a bonding surface which will give tensile adhesion values of 1400 psi with a modified epoxy. Safety precautions, including the use of protective clothing and glasses, must be taken when using this strong acid solution. The acid pretreatment method is usually undesirable for large-scale operations. It is recommended mainly where a limited number of polyolefin pieces of unusual bonding surface contour are to be bonded.

Several other processes can be used to improve the adhesion characteristics of polyethylene surfaces. One such method involves subjecting the surface of the polyethylene to a hot flame for a very short time.[2] The surface is then oxidized but the heat source must be removed before the subsurface polyethylene softens sufficiently to deform. Another method which utilizes heat involves subjecting the polyethylene surface momentarily to a blast of hot air.[3] Both of these heat treatment methods are used in production to make polyethylene sheet bondable. Intense electron bombardment of the polyethylene surface has also been used to make polyethylene more adhesionable.[4] Another

electrical method involves passing a brush discharge from the high voltage side of a Tesla spark coil over the polyethylene.[5]

All of the methods mentioned above could probably be used to improve the surface bonding characteristics of any of the olefin polymers. Little design data has appeared in the open literature on the actual bond strengths available to the different treated plastics. Treated polyethylene surfaces cannot be heat sealed effectively. Where heat sealing is required, chemical or electrical treatments should be avoided.

Excellent bonds have been reported between polyethylene and brass as well as between polyethylene and rubbers including GR-S, natural, and neoprene types.[6] The process utilizes as the adhesive a specially compounded, partly hydrogenated polybutadiene with 3 to 30 per cent unsaturation. An adhesive layer 2 to 3 mils thick is used between the adherends. Cure is normally effected at 250 to 350°F at pressures up to 100 psi. Bond strengths obtainable upon vulcanization are reported to include peel strengths up to 100 lb/in. and tensile strengths of 1000 psi. This bonding method is probably suitable for the other olefin polymers. Good bonds are reported between polyethylene and metals at a cure temperature as low as 85°C.[13]

Treating polyethylene with ozone and ultraviolet light at 300°F or above and quenching in an aqueous solution of inorganic compounds produces an adhesionable surface.[15]

High-strength bonds of polyethylene to steel and aluminum are obtained by preheating the metal surfaces to 450 to 500°F, and then applying the plastic. Adhesion occurs as the surface of the polyethylene is oxidized at this high temperature. This process is undoubtedly satisfactory for other olefin polymers. Where dimensions are critical, this process is usually undesirable since some deformation of the plastic occurs near the interface.

Polyethylene and other polymers can be made to adhere more readily to surfaces by adding as a modifier 0.02 to 20 per cent α,β-unsaturated acids, their salts, esters or their precursors such as acrylic, malonic, fumaric, or itaconic acids, diallyl fumarate, and antioxidants to the molten surface of the polyethylene.[16]

Polyethylene film can be heat-sealed to numerous other types of polymer film and sheets including vinylidene-chloride, vinyl chloride polymers and copolymers, polyamides, and polyesters. The mating surfaces are treated with a polyalkylenimine, then the sheets are pressed together at a temperature close to the softening point of one of the resins.[17]

Fluorinated Polymers. Polymonochlorotrifluoro-ethylene ("Kel-F") and polytetrafluoroethylene ("Teflon") can be bonded with the tacky-type adhesives described for the olefin polymers to give very low bond strength. For reliable, high-strength bonds the surfaces must be pretreated.[24, 25]

The DuPont bonderizing process for making "Teflon" adhesionable treats the surface with a sodium-ammonia complex.[14] Tensile values of 1400 psi have been obtained to this treated "Teflon." Epoxies and phenol-formaldehyde adhesives bond well to this surface.

A sodium-naphthalene treatment of "Kel-F" and "Teflon" produces surfaces which can be effectively bonded with epoxies to give high-strength bonds.[7] Tensile values of 1800 psi have been obtained with bonded "Teflon" which had been pretreated with the sodium naphthalene solution for 15 min. Shear strengths of 530 and 1360 psi have been obtained for "Teflon" and "Kel-F," respectively, when the plastics were pretreated for 15 min. Tensile strengths in excess of 2500 psi have been obtained for treated "Teflon" bonded to brass with an epoxy adhesive. Failure occurred in the plastics.

To prepare the treating solution, 128 g of naphthalene and 1 liter of tetrahydrofuran are placed in a 2-liter flask containing a drying tube outlet and a stirrer with a mercury seal. Then, 23 g of sodium metal, in small cube form, are dissolved in this solution, one cube at a time. The mixture is allowed to stand for 16 hr and is then stirred for 2 hr at room temperature. Specimens are treated by immersion for the desired period of time, removed, acetone rinsed, then water washed and allowed to dry. It was found that "Teflon" which was treated in this manner, then bonded to steel with an epoxy adhesive, was deleteriously affected when exposed to ultraviolet light for a prolonged period of time. Since ultraviolet light will penetrate the fluoropolymers, plastic treated in this manner should not be used if it is to be subjected to long periods of sunlight.

Treatment time of "Teflon" with the sodium naphthalene solution is reported to be satisfactory from as little as 3 sec up to 24 hr. The bath itself is said to be satisfactory for as long as 2 months and does not need refrigeration. It can be used in intermittent small-scale laboratory operations with ease, but an exhaust system for ventilation is desirable.

A 1957 patent describes a method of treating synthetic resins of high fluorine content with a solution of alkali metal in a polycyclic carbon.[12] A substantial part of the treatment described above is discussed. In this case, however, sodium is added to a solution of naphthalene in dimethyl glycol ether, under nitrogen. After the solution turns green, a strip of fluorinated polymer is immersed in it for 5 min. Other effective treating solutions consist of either sodium biphenyl or sodium anthracene in dimethyl glycol ether.

Untreated "Teflon" can be bonded to itself or to other materials by using a copolymer of 5 to 50 per cent hexafluoropropylene and 50 to 95 per cent tetrafluoroethylene and bonding at 330 to 390°C.[18]

Vinyl Chloride Polymers and Copolymers. Rigid polyvinyl chloride should be cleaned with an inert solvent such as low-boiling petroleum naphtha prior to adhesive bonding. It can be bonded effectively with a variety of adhesives. Shear-strength bonds in excess of 1500 psi have been obtained with polyurethane adhesives when bonding filled polyvinyl chloride. Shear strengths of over 1300 psi were obtained with an unsaturated polyester-styrene adhesive. Epoxies have provided shear-strength bonds in excess of 650 psi.

An adhesive consisting of vinyl resin, methyl-ethyl ketone, dioctyl phthalate plasticizer, and methylene bis(4-phenyl isocyanate) has been reported to give good bonds between vinyl films and nylon or polyester ("Dacron") fabrics.[8] Peel-strength bonds of 20 lb/in. of width are claimed.

High-strength bonds to vinylidene chloride are not readily attainable. Fair bonds can be obtained by using nitrile rubber-phenolic resin solvent adhesives or specially compounded vinyl chloride-acetate resin solvent adhesives.

Supported polyvinyl chloride fabrics can be bonded effectively to themselves or to other materials such as wood, most metals, fiberboard, and phenolics with nitrile-phenolic adhesives. Trouble can be encountered because the plasticizers from the vinyl fabrics migrate into the adhesives. For this reason the nitrile-phenolics are ideal for the bonding applications from an adhesion point of view since they resist plasticizers, and therefore, are not usually softened by them. The degree to which an adhesive may be softened by the migrating plasticizers will vary with the composition of the adhesive and with the thickness of the adhesive film, as well as with the quantities and types of plasticizers in the vinyl fabric.

In the aircraft and furniture industries, special care has been exercised in bonding vinyl-coated fabrics since many adhesives will "bleed through" or stain the plastic. This may occur even though the adhesive itself is colorless.

Plasticizer that migrates into the adhesive also migrates back into the vinyl again. The tendency is toward an equilibrium. Plasticizer returning into the vinyl from the adhesive can carry traces of contaminants which, if not staining by themselves, will often cause staining when subjected to heat or light. Ultraviolet light has been found to produce staining in a few hours, while exposure of similar type specimens to incandescent light for a month produced no discoloration in the vinyl. When contemplating using adhesive to bond vinyl-coated fabrics where discoloration is undesirable, it is suggested that a small sample of the fabric be bonded and then subjected to either ultraviolet, Fade-Ometer, heat, or Weather-Ometer test, whichever best suits the individual application, to determine staining characteristics.

A specially formulated GR-S rubber adhesive that permits long open times and provides a very high degree of tack, is used to bond many vinyl-coated fabrics if the plasticizer content is low. Vinyls backed with uncoated fabrics have been bonded satisfactorily with water emulsion adhesives of both nitrile rubber and neoprene rubber bases. The adhesives are either sprayed or brushed onto the bonding surfaces, allowed to dry until clear, then bonded within several hours by applying firm hand and/or roller pressure. Care is taken to eliminate air bubbles in laying down the fabric. This is done by positioning the fabric, bringing it into contact with the other mating surface on one end, then smoothing out the fabric gradually while laying the fabric down slowly. Trapped air may be removed by making small pin holes and working the air out manually. Excess adhesive should be removed from the surface area of vinyls while the adhesive is still fresh. If it cannot be rolled off by finger, then a cloth dampened in either kerosene or petroleum naphtha can be used to clean the vinyl.

When vinyl-coated fabric must be stretched to fit around a curved surface, a high-tack adhesive is preferred. Coating the mating surfaces with a coat or two of nitrile phenolic adhesive, allowing it to dry thoroughly, then lightly dampening the adhesive surfaces with either methylethyl ketone or methyl isobutyl ketone will usually provide enough tack to effect a bond. The fabric can in many cases be stretched if it is carefully preheated with either infrared heat lamps or with a heat gun prior to the actual bonding. Care must be taken, however, not to stretch the surface grain out of the vinyl.

Vinyl films are reported to bond well to rubber by utilizing the following process.[19] A solution which consists of 5 g synthetic rubber and 2 g sulfur in 100 ml ethyl acetate, 100 ml butyl acetate, and 50 ml ethyl acetoacetate is coated over the surfaces to be bonded. Upon assembly the adhesive joint is heated at 120°C while subjected to a pressure of 70 psi.

Polyformaldehyde. When polyformaldehyde is sanded and solvent wiped prior to bonding with a

neoprene rubber solvent type adhesive, shear-strength bonds of 500 psi have been claimed. Tensile-strength bonds obtained to a surface prepared in this manner were 800, 600, and 650 psi when using polyurethane, unsaturated polyester-styrene, and polysulfide-modified epoxy adhesives, respectively. When the polyformaldehyde was treated for 10 sec with a concentrated sulfuric acid-dichromate solution at room temperature, the surface adhesion characteristics were improved. Tensile adhesion values up to 2260 psi were obtained by bonding with the polysulfide-modified epoxy. Since the surface of the plastic is decomposed to liberate formaldehyde, precautions should be taken during the treatment. The concentration of the acid and time of treatment might be varied to obtain a more desirable treating process.

Polystyrene. For light bond strength applications where porous adherend surfaces are available, a solution of polystyrene resin in toluene with 2 to 3 per cent dioctylphthalate plasticizer will provide satisfactory bonds. Paper or wood can be attached to polystyrene effectively with this adhesive. Rubber-solvent adhesives are sometimes used to bond rubber to polystyrene. To prevent crazing, fast-drying adhesives should be avoided.

High-strength bonds to polystyrene are obtained with a variety of adhesives. When bonding to glass-filled polystyrene with either polyurethane or cyanoacrylate adhesives, bonds obtained are sufficiently strong to insure failure in the plastic at room temperature. Bond strength of the polyurethane-bonded plastic decreases considerably at 160°F.

High-strength bonds to polystyrene and poly-methylstyrene are obtainable with unsaturated polyester-styrene adhesives. A mixture of 3 parts rigid to 1 part flexible resin is satisfactory. This adhesive is excellent for bonding polystyrene to itself as well as to phenolic, melamine, epoxy, or polyester laminates. Slightly lower bond strengths are obtained with epoxy adhesives. These two types of adhesive can also be used to bond the high-impact, rubber-modified polystyrenes as well as the acrylonitrile-styrene copolymers.

Polyurethane. Acetone can be used to clean the polyurethane surface. Urethane prepolymer adhesives provide excellent adhesion to polyurethane. Elastomeric polyurethane adhesives provide a bond which resists not only shear and tensile stresses satisfactorily but have high impact resistance and perform well even at cryogenic test temperatures. A high degree of adhesion is also exhibited by resorcinol-formaldehyde adhesives. However, due to the brittleness and higher rigidity of these adhesives, failure occurs in the polyurethane adherend at considerably lower loads than when the more flexible urethane prepolymer adhesive is used. Unsaturated polyester-styrene and epoxies give the relatively low shear-strength bonds of only 180 to 260 psi, respectively.

Thermosets

Diallyl Phthalate. Considerable difficulty is experienced in bonding to orlon-filled diallyl phthalate if the faying (or bonding) surface has been solvent wiped only. Sanding is a prerequisite to obtaining high-strength adhesive bonds. Excellent bonds can be obtained by sanding the plastic with medium-grit sandpaper to remove all surface gloss, wiping clean with acetone, then bonding with an epoxy adhesive. Bonds obtained with a polysulfide-modified epoxy are sufficiently strong at temperatures of −65 to 160°F to withstand applied loads until the orlon-filled diallyl phthalate fails. Equally good bonds are obtainable with a diallyl phthalate modified polyester resin, but a glue line temperature of 220°F for 30 min is required to cure the adhesive. Furanes and unsaturated polyester-styrene adhesives also provide relatively good bonds to the presanded, solvent-wiped plastic.

Polyethylene Terephthalate. Polyethylene terephthalate film ("Mylar") is difficult to bond. Adhesion of a relatively low order can be obtained with a variety of adhesives including some nitrile rubber-phenolic solvent adhesives, thermoplastic resin solvent adhesives, lacquers, and emulsion adhesives. Specific commercially available adhesives for bonding the "Mylar" to numerous other plastic and nonplastic adherends are given in the manufacturer's literature. A process which involves the immersion of "Mylar" in vinyl halosilane is reported to improve the adhesion properties of the plastic surface considerably.[9] The manufacturer reports a number of modified synthetic rubber and polyester type adhesives which give fair-to-good adhesion to "Mylar."

"Dacron" polyester fiber is reported to bond well to SBR (styrene-butadiene rubber) and neoprene by utilizing phenol-blocked diphenylmethane diisocyanate dispersed in butadiene-vinylpyridine-styrene latex as an adhesive.[11] The "Dacron" cord is dip-coated with the water-based latex adhesive. It is cured at 420 to 435°F for 1 to 2 min to give a relatively high peel-strength bond between the polyester cord and the rubber.

The surface adhesion properties of polyethylene terephthalate film, which has been molecularly oriented by drawing, improve when it is subjected to high-voltage electrical stress accompanied by corona discharge.[21] "Mylar" film can be satisfactorily heat sealed if the surfaces to be joined are lightly coated with benzyl alcohol or anisole, pressed together firmly, then heated to 250 to 280°F.[22]

Reinforced Plastics. This section will be devoted primarily to the bonding of reinforced plastics. It should be apparent that a type of adhesive that bonds well to a reinforced plastic will also bond well to the parent plastic. The reinforcing material may be cloth, mat, wound fiber, or paper form. These materials are usually glass, asbestos, cotton, nylon, or rayon, although other type fibers may be used. Discussion here will include bonding to epoxy, polyester, furane, melamine, phenolic, and silicone laminates. Emphasis will be on the epoxy and polyester.

Numerous factors should be considered before bonding reinforced plastics for structural applications. In addition to the factors mentioned earlier in this chapter, plasticity, inelasticity, and differential elasticity of adhesive and adherends are also important. They may significantly affect the degree or magnitude of stress concentrations created in a bonded joint when subjected to load.[10] In reinforced plastics, e.g., where glass-cloth laminates are to be bonded, the anisotropic properties of the laminates should be taken into account, since the strain will vary with the direction of the load.

As with other plastics, the bonding surfaces of reinforced plastics must be clean. Wiping with acetone or a similar type cleaning solvent is recommended. Sanding with a light- to medium-grit sandpaper sufficiently to remove the surface gloss is usually desirable. This treatment will remove traces of difficult-to-dissolve contaminants such as silicone mold-release agents. Care should be taken not to rupture the surfaces of the laminating fibers during the sanding process, especially if the laminates are to be used for high-strength structures, or for structures that will be subjected to prolonged loads.

In bonding sheets of plastic laminate the usual precautions which pertain to bonding materials should be taken. Application of excessive pressure to bring the bonding surfaces of poorly mated joints into intimate contact may result in joints with starved areas. Properly mated joints require less pressure and make possible the formation of a uniformly thin continuous bond line which provides optimum adhesion characteristics. When the joint is heat cured, uniform mating is highly desirable since uneven heating will produce uneven expansion. This will stress the adhesive bond and possibly warp the laminate structure. When bonding parts with different thermal coefficients of expansion, it is desirable to refrain from exerting high pressure on the adherends until they have been heated to approximately the curing temperature of the adhesive. The use of elastomeric type adhesives, or the incorporation of inert fillers into rigid type adhesives, is usually desirable when bonding adherends with different thermal coefficients of expansion. Longer cure at elevated temperatures usually provides a more heat resistant bond due to additional crosslinking, but the adhesive often suffers a loss in strength properties at room temperature due to increased brittleness.

Epoxy laminates are often bonded with epoxy adhesives. The adhesives may be either of the room-temperature-curing type or heat-curing type, depending on the heat resistance and strength requirements of the bonded assembly. Normally, failure should occur in the adherend. An adhesive composition that has been used very effectively for elevated temperature applications in the bonding of epoxy-glass laminates consists of the following (parts by weight):

> 100 epoxy resin
> 20 aromatic diamine
> 100 aluminum silicate filler

Cure is effected by contact pressure and heating the adhesive for 1½ hr at 85°C to B stage it, then for 2 hr at 150°C for the post cure. The B staging is required to allow the adhesive to partially polymerize so that excessive adhesive flow and subsequent starved joints are not encountered when completing polymerization at 150°C. Relatively good adhesion can be obtained to epoxy laminates with unsaturated polyester-styrene adhesives, resorcinol-formaldehyde, phenolics, and furanes. For lower strength bonds numerous types of adhesives can be used including polyurethanes, nitrile rubber-phenolic and neoprene solvent adhesives, and various thermoplastic resin solutions.

Polyester laminates can be bonded with either unsaturated polyester-styrene adhesives, preferably one having a composition similar to the laminate plastic, or with epoxies. For patching polyester laminate automobile chassis, boat hulls, or household furnishings and fixtures, the polyester resin adhesive is often preferable because it is cheaper and easy to handle. For high-strength bonding of polyester laminate to other types of adherends, an epoxy adhesive may in many instances be preferable because it shrinks less during the curing process. The adhesives described for the epoxy laminates will provide bonds to polyester laminates in the same general range of mechanical strength. Good bonds have been obtained to both type laminates when adhered to aluminum with nitrile rubber-phenolic, vinyl phenolic, and phenolic-epoxy adhesives as well as with various epoxy

resins. Most of these adhesives require high temperatures and application of pressure to form effective bonds.

Phenolic laminates are likely to have traces of mold-release agent on their surfaces since they are compression molded. A light sanding of the surface is advisable. Resorcinol-formaldehyde and urea-formaldehydes provide excellent bonds to the phenolics, but the former adhesive is more water resistant. Epoxy adhesives provide excellent bonds to phenolics as well as to furanes and melamines. High-temperature-curing phenolic-epoxy and nitrile rubber-phenolic adhesives give excellent bonds to these plastics. General-purpose nitrile rubber-phenolic solvent adhesives can be used to obtain bonds of a lower degree of strength to all three of these plastics. Polyurethane adhesives can be used to obtain fair to good bond strengths.

Silicone laminates are often bonded with silicone resins. Specific adhesive formulations and bonding techniques should be obtained from the manufacturer.

Plastic Foams. High-strength adhesives are not usually required for bonding plastic foams since the mechanical strengths of the foams are relatively low. Mastic- or rubber-based adhesives may be used to bond elastomeric or flexible foams to themselves or other flexible materials. They may also be used to bond rigid foams when high bond strengths are not required. Solvent-type adhesives such as the rubber- and mastic-based adhesives should not be used to bond two nonporous surfaces, e.g., closed-cell foam to metal. However, these adhesives may be used where at least one of the surfaces is porous and will therefore allow solvent evaporation, e.g., open-cell foam to metal or to itself. When using adhesives containing solvent, care should be exercised to avoid solvents that will attack the plastic since these solvents may cause the cellular structure to deform or collapse at the bond interface.

Some expanded plastics are available that can be foamed in place, with fair adhesion to a large variety of adherends. Polyurethane and styrene-epoxy are examples of foams which adhere chemically. However, primers are often used on adherends to increase adhesion properties of other types of foams.

When bonding rigid foams to themselves or other rigid materials or to flexible materials, room-temperature-curing thermosetting adhesives are normally recommended for maximum adhesive properties. When bonding to rigid-type foams which have a skin, sanding of the mating surface is sometimes desirable to remove traces of mold-release agents.

In conclusion it might be well to emphasize that in order to be assured of a good bond, selection of the right adhesive for the application, proper design of the joint to be bonded, clean (in some cases chemically treated) surfaces, and good techniques or process control are required.

References

1. Horton, P. V. (to Plax Corp.), U. S. Patent 2,668,134 (Feb. 2, 1954).
2. Kritchever, M. F. (to Traver Corp.), U. S. Patent 2,648,097 (Aug. 11, 1953) and 2,683,894 (July 20, 1954).
3. Kriedl, W. H., U. S. Patent 2,632,921 (Mar. 31, 1953).
4. Traver, U. S. Patent pending.
5. Rossman, K., *J. Polymer. Sci.,* **19,** 141 (Jan. 1956).
6. *Mech. Eng.,* **79,** 11, 1050 (Nov. 1957).
7. Benderly, A. A., Kilduff, T. J., and Nelson, E. R., *Ind. Eng. Chem.,* **50,** 3, 329–30 (1958).
8. *Plastics Technol.,* **4,** p. 948 (Oct. 1958).
9. Sayre, K. L. (to Bjorksten Research Laboratories), U. S. Patent 2,785,085 (Mar. 12, 1957).
10. Perry, H. A., "Adhesive Bonding of Reinforced Plastics," New York, McGraw-Hill Book Co., Inc., 1959.
11. Thompson, W. L., *et al., Adhesives Age,* **2,** 30 (Feb. 1959).
12. Rappaport, G. (to General Motors Corp.), U. S. Patent 2,809,130 (Oct. 8, 1957).
13. Wright, D., and Parkman, N., *Brit. Plastics,* **31,** 255, (June 1958).
14. E. I. du Pont de Nemours & Co., British Patent 793,731 (Apr. 23, 1958).
15. Wolinski, L. E. (to du Pont), U. S. Patent 2,801,446 (Aug. 6, 1957).
16. Busse, W. F., and Boxler, J. A. (to du Pont), U. S. Patent 2,838,437 (June 10, 1958).
17. Rosser, C. M. (to American Viscose Corp.), U. S. Patent 2,828,237 (Mar. 25, 1958).
18. Sandt, B. W. (to du Pont), U. S. Patent 2,833,686 (May 6, 1958).
19. Nakamura, G., Sugimoto, K., and Tansho, I., Japan Patent 4137 (1957).
20. Wolfe, W. D. (to Goodyear Tire & Rubber Co.), U. S. Patent 2,817,616 (Dem. 24, 1957).
21. Gates, E. F. (to I.C.I., Ltd.), British Patent 796,341 (June 11, 1958).
22. Smith, W. M., Jr. (to Firestone Tire & Rubber Co.), U. S. Patent 2,849,359 (Aug. 26, 1958).
23. Skeist, I., *Modern Plastics,* **35,** 1A (Encyclopedia Issue), 818 (1957).
24. Bodnar, M. J., and Powers, W. J., *Plastics Technol.,* **4,** 721 (1958).
25. Schrader, W. H., and Bodnar, M. J., *Plastics Technol.,* **3,** 988 (1957).

— 42 —

Bonding Textiles to Rubber

Roy H. Moult

Koppers Company, Inc.
Verona, Pennsylvania

The problem of bonding textile fibers to rubber involves the great difference between two types of surface; the necessity for a bond which exceeds the strength of both substrates, and the ability of the bond to be able to resist extremes of temperature, cyclic tension and compression loads, shock, creep, and distortion. Thus a large responsibility is placed on the adhesive component. It must have optimum adherence to both rubber and fiber without tendering or stiffening the latter in any way, without affecting the curing properties of the former, and it must be at least equal in physical properties to both components.

Textile-to-rubber adhesives are used most extensively in the manufacture of automobile tires for bonding tire cords and other textile components to the rubber carcass. Other important uses are in rubber belts, hose, rubberized fabrics and rugs.

Until World War II, cotton was the principal textile cord used in automobile tires. However, with the advent of synthetic rubber, stronger cords were needed for tire building. The new synthetic rubbers did not lose heat as well as natural rubber; consequently it was necessary to reduce the size of the tire carcass. To achieve this, higher strength fibers became necessary, and both rayon and nylon were considered.

At this stage it was found that the adhesion of the textile to the rubber was an important consideration. Cotton, a staple fiber, adhered well to rubber because of the numerous fiber ends which protruded from the surface of the cord, giving a good mechanical bond.[1, 2] The synthetic fibers were continuous filament cords with smooth, wax-like surfaces and would not adhere satisfactorily to the rubber stock. The cords are laid up in plies which cross each other diagonally and are continually subjected to rolling, compression, and tension forces during service; consequently they tend to separate from the rubber and abrade, thus weakening the carcass unless adequately bonded.

The development of suitable adhesives for rayon soon led to the supremacy of this material in tires during the postwar period.[3] In 1946, 40 per cent of the entire 500-million pound tire cord market had been captured by rayon. In 1950, the proportion had risen to about 90 per cent. Attempts to substitute the higher strength nylon, which could result in further reduction of the size of the tire carcass, were not very successful because of the problems of adequate bonding, cold stretching, and higher cost. During the past 10 yr these difficulties have been gradually reduced and the bonding problem for nylon has been solved; consequently it commands about one-third of the tire market.

A third potential competitor, "Dacron"* polyester, has always suffered a great disadvantage due to the lack of an adequate bonding system for it. The discovery of a good adhesive, which could be applied economically and safely, could immediately promote this type of cord to the status of a serious candidate. At present its use is limited to belt manufacture, where solvent-type adhesives are acceptable.

TIRE CORD ADHESIVES

The adhesive predominantly in use at the present time for the bonding of rayon and nylon tire cords is the resorcinol-formaldehyde latex type.

* E. I. du Pont de Nemours & Co.

495

RFL adhesives, as they are popularly known, are generally prepared by the condensation of resorcinol or resorcinol resins with formaldehyde in the presence of a rubber latex. Many variations are in use in secret formulations of the individual tire and rubber companies. They vary with respect to the following factors:

(1) Type of latex
    (a) Natural
    (b) Hot styrene-butadiene
    (c) Cold styrene-butadiene
    (d) Vinylpyridine terpolymer
(2) Resorcinol resin
    (A) Method of preparation of resin
        (a) Prepared *in situ* from resorcinol and formaldehyde
        (b) Prepared in the kettle beforehand
    (B) Component ratios
        (a) Resorcinol-formaldehyde ratio
        (b) Resorcinol resin to latex ratio
(3) Catalyst
    (a) Sodium hydroxide—"fixed alkali"
    (b) Ammonium hydroxide—"volatile alkali"
    (c) Mixtures of (a) and (b)
    (d) Amines

The usual practice in compounding this type of adhesive is to prepare an aqueous resin solution of about 5 to 15 per cent solids, either by direct reaction of resorcinol with formaldehyde or by reaction of a preformed, partially condensed resorcinol resin with additional formaldehyde. In both cases an alkaline catalyst is used at this stage. The solution is "ripened" for 2 to 4 hr, carefully maintaining it at room temperature or below. It is then added to the blended and diluted latices and aged for at least 1 day before use. In this form

the adhesive is generally referred to as a "dip" since it is applied by passing the cord or fabric through a bath of the adhesive, the operation of "dipping."

EFFECTS OF DIP FORMULA VARIATIONS

A study of the various factors involved in the compounding of dip formulations shows that optimum adhesion is secured only by careful control of the resorcinol-formaldehyde ratio, the resin-formation conditions, the pH of the resin solution, the selection of latex used, the relative amounts of resin and rubber solids, the catalyst composition, and the final total solids content of the dip. Some of these factors have been described by Dietrick.[4]

Using the base formulas shown in Table 1, effects of variation of the above factors have been studied.

The nature of the resin solution is controlled by the formaldehyde ratio. Figure 1 shows that optimum adhesion to rayon is attained when 1.5 to 2 moles of formaldehyde are present for each mole of resorcinol. Similarly, nylon has maximum adhesion at a ratio of 2.0 to 3.0 moles formaldehyde per mole of resorcinol. The higher formaldehyde requirement is ascribed to the nonparticipating amide groups present inside of the nylon cord, which nevertheless use up additional formaldehyde to form methylol groups. Such ratios of formaldehyde to resorcinol are possible only as long as the solution is dilute and kept cool. At higher concentrations, higher temperature, or long times, these resin solutions gelatinize and are thereafter useless.

The resin solutions show differences due to conditions under which they are aged.[6] In Fig. 2 the adhesive strengths obtained from dips ripened at

TABLE 1. TYPICAL FORMULATIONS OF RFL TYPE ADHESIVES.

	Ingredients in Parts per 1000					
	A	B	C	D	E	F
Resorcinol-technical grade	18.5	—	21.5	—	—	18.5
Preformed resorcinol-formaldehyde resin (75% total solids)	—	31.5	—	37.5	34.5	—
Aqueous sodium hydroxide solution (10%)	11.0	9.5	13.0	11.0	10.5	11.0
Ammonium hydroxide (28%)	—	—	—	—	84.0	80.0
Water	645.0	644.0	568.0	572.0	525.0	569.0
Formaldehyde (37%)	21.5	16.0	39.5	28.5	26.0	21.5
Synthetic rubber latex (styrene-butadiene type), 40%	243.0	239.0	—	—	—	240.0
Vinylpyridine-styrene-butadiene terpolymer (40%)	61.0	60.0	358.0	351.0	322.0	60.0
Type cord used in evaluation	Rayon	Rayon	Nylon	Nylon	Nylon	Rayon

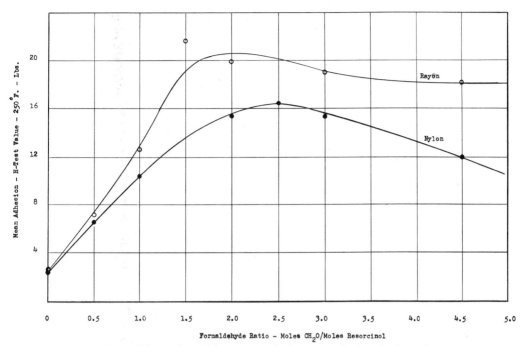

Fig. 1. Effect of formaldehyde to resorcinol ratio on adhesion of nylon and rayon cords to rubber.

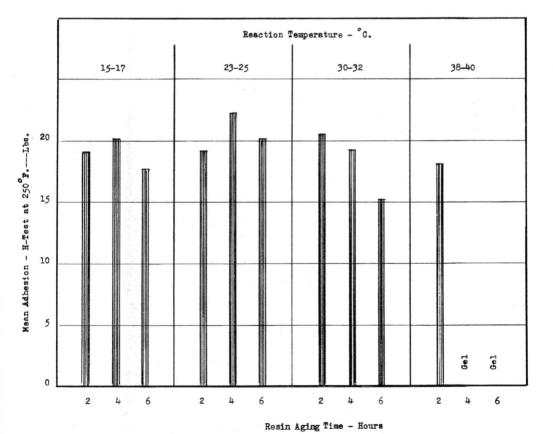

Fig. 2. Effects of resin aging time and temperature on adhesion.

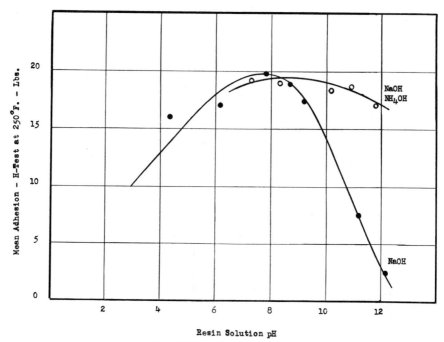

Fig. 3. Effect of catalyst and pH.

various temperatures and times are compared. The evidence indicates that best adhesion is obtained when the resin solution is aged 4 hr at room temperature. Similar results are also found when a preformed resorcinol-formaldehyde resin solution, which is infinitely stable at less than 1 mole of formaldehyde per mole of resorcinol, is ripened in dilute solution in the presence of an alkaline catalyst with the required amount of formaldehyde to give the desired formaldehyde ratio.

A third major factor in the control of the resin solution is the nature and amount of catalyst. Both sodium hydroxide and ammonium hydroxide are currently in use. Adhesion values obtained with sodium hydroxide are at the optimum value in the pH range of 7 to 9, as shown by Fig. 3. When ammonium hydroxide is employed as the only catalyst, adhesion values obtained throughout the same range are lower. However, when the pH of the system is adjusted to 8 with sodium hydroxide and additional ammonium hydroxide is supplied to raise the pH above 10, the adhesion is considerably greater than with sodium hydroxide alone. In additional, the stability of the adhesive dip prepared in this way may be lengthened to several weeks.

The selection of latex composition also has a pronounced effect on the adhesion value. A comparison of several types of latices and latex combinations is shown in Table 2. It is noted that a considerable increase in adhesion results with the use of vinylpyridine-containing latices and that this advantage is retained even when 80 per cent of the vinylpyridine latex is replaced with a cold rubber latex. Other influences on adhesion are the temperature of polymerization of the latex, the styrene-to-butadiene ratio, and the similarity of the latex composition to the carcass rubber.[4]

The advantage of the use of vinylpyridine-modified latices is generally thought to be related to the exceptionally high strength of the vinylpyridine terpolymer itself. The higher tensile strength of the vulcanized cold rubbers probably explains the higher adhesion strength of the cold-rubber latices.

The bonding strength of the adhesive latex is also affected by the resin-to-rubber ratio. Adhesion increases abruptly as the amount of resin is raised

TABLE 2. COMPARISON OF VARIOUS LATICES USED IN THE BASIC FORMULA IN BONDING TO NATURAL RUBBER.

Latex		Mean Adhesion H-Test (¼ in.)-Lb. (250°F)
Styrene-butadiene-heat polymerized		12.3
Natural rubber		11.1
Styrene-butadiene—(cold rubber)		13.8
Vinylpyridine terpolymer		19.4
Cold rubber	80%	18.5
Vinylpyridine terpolymer	20%	

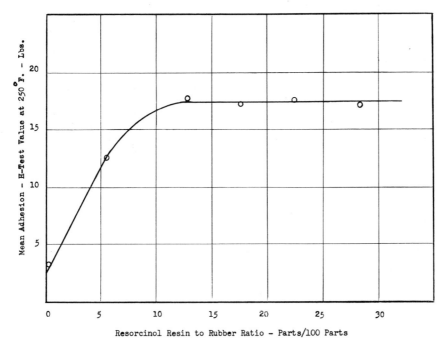

Fig. 4. Effect of resorcinol resin content in dip.

from 0 to 15 parts per hundred of rubber solids; thereafter, further resin addition does not affect the static adhesion value (Fig. 4). It is generally recognized, however, that excessive resin results in poor tire performance, which is due to the stiffening of the tire cord resulting from the high modulus of the cured adhesive film. If the bonded cord-to-rubber system is insufficiently flexible to withstand the dynamic forces imposed upon it, it rapidly fails.

A significant factor in the attainment of good fiber-to-rubber adhesion is the precondensation of the resorcinol-formaldehyde resin in the kettle before preparation of the tire cord dip. The advantage of this procedure is that the resin is further advanced and has a greater uniformity of composition when produced at higher reaction velocity than when the resin is slowly formed in the dip in dilute solution at room temperature by direct reaction of resorcinol and formaldehyde.

The precondensed resorcinol resin solutions are produced in the presence of either strong acids or strong bases as catalysts. Since proportion or formaldehyde to resorcinol of 1 mole per mole or greater will result in the formation of a gel at high temperature and concentration, these resins are usually prepared with a minor amount of formaldehyde, generally in the range of 0.6 to 0.9 mole of formaldehyde per mole of resorcinol. Under reflux conditions and under the influence of strong catalysts, the resin can be formed so that

it consists exclusively of long-chain, methylene-linked resorcinol units, with no resitol or resite particles. Reactions under less vigorous conditions give rise to local crosslinking, resulting in the formation of particles having low reactivity or low solubility. These reduce the reactivity of the RFL dip which is made from them, and ultimately impairs the strength of the fiber-to-rubber bond.

Precondensed resins of the above type are available from several companies either in the form of brittle, solid resins which may be dissolved in water or as stable, concentrated solutions which may be diluted with water to be used directly in RFL dips. They are activated by addition of formaldehyde as shown in Table 1. In addition to their superior adhesion properties, these resins minimize compounding variations, reduce aging time, and yield dip compositions with better storage stability.

ADHESION OF RUBBER-TO-FIBER— THEORETICAL CONSIDERATIONS

Although there have been numerous opinions concerning the nature of the fiber-to-rubber bond, there has been no published attempt to integrate these views. It is generally recognized, however, that there are two primary considerations: the nature of the resin-to-rubber bond and the nature of the resin-to-fiber bond.

The bond between the resorcinol resin and rubber has generally been deemed to be the same as other phenolic resin-rubber linkages; the precise nature of this linkage however has been disputed for many years. Hultzch[7] proposed that resoles react with the unsaturated carbon-to-carbon bonds of various substances to form chromanes.

In later work this was explained as taking place through the intermediate formation of o-methylene quinone intermediates, and that the latter combined with an unsaturated carbon-carbon bond by a form of Diels-Alder reaction.[8]

This mechanism has been used by Hultzch and others[9, 10, 11] to explain the chemical linkage of phenolic substances to rubber.

Another viewpoint was that of Van der Meer[12] who maintained that the vulcanization of rubber by means of dimethylol phenols is explained by the conversion of the latter to intermediate o-methylene quinone compounds which then react at the methylene group adjacent to the unsaturated carbon in the rubber molecules.

A third proposal is that advocated by Piccini[13] who concluded that resorcinol resins afford a strong contribution toward vulcanization of rubber when added during the latex stage, but that no direct chemical linkage is involved. He explained the action as an entanglement of the resin in the rubber matrix and termed it "reinforcement." The Hultzch and Van der Meer theories were rejected on the basis that methylol groups are unavailable in the resorcinol resin.

It should be argued in rebuttal, however, that under the conditions cited in the Piccini experiments, as well as those obtaining in RFL dips, methylol groups must be present if only momentarily; otherwise resin formation would not occur. It is therefore quite probable that methylene quinone compounds are formed which react with the unsaturated carbons in the rubber latex to form structures of the following chromane type:

Portion of Rubber Molecule	Portion of Resorcinol Resin Molecule

ADHESION OF RESORCINOL RESINS TO FIBER SURFACES

The nature of the fiber plays a most important role in the bonding of tire cords to rubber. In practice it has been found that rayon cords are relatively easy to bond; nylon cords more troublesome; and "Dacron" cords extremely difficult. As stated previously, this has been a prominent factor in deciding which type of cord will capture the large textile market in automobile tires.

Viscose rayon is regenerated cellulose. In its natural state, a cellulose molecule has an average of 500 cellobiose units; however during its processing to form rayon fibers, it suffers some degradation to form molecular chains containing 150 to 200 of these units. X-ray studies have shown the units to be about 10.28Å in length.[21]

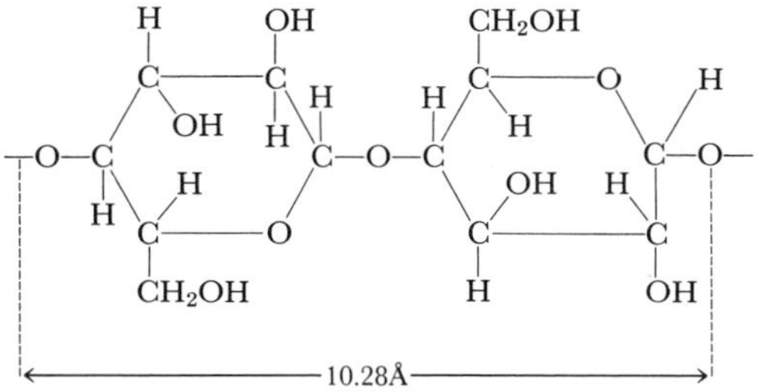

It is noted that the cellulose molecules are characterized by a high proportion of —OH groups which are conducive to good adhesion. The mechanism of this bonding action has not been established unequivocally. Various authors have alluded to direct reaction between the phenolic resin and the cellulose fiber,[14,15] hydrogen bonding,[16] dipole-dipole bonding,[17] and molecular entanglement.[18] None of these have shown sufficient evidence to gain wide acceptance; therefore it must be left to future research to decide the question.

If a direct covalent linkage between the resorcinol resin and the cellulose fiber were assumed to be the mechanism for bonding, it could possibly be due to direct reaction of transient methylol groups in the resin with —OH groups of the cellulose, as shown below.

The reaction of methylol groups on phenolic resins with various alcohols and polyols was reported by Greth[19] and Krumbhaar.[20]

The bonding of nylon cords to rubber was initially a more difficult problem than the bonding of rayon due to the scarcity of polar groups on the nylon surface. The relative proportion of amide groups on nylon to —OH groups on cellulose can

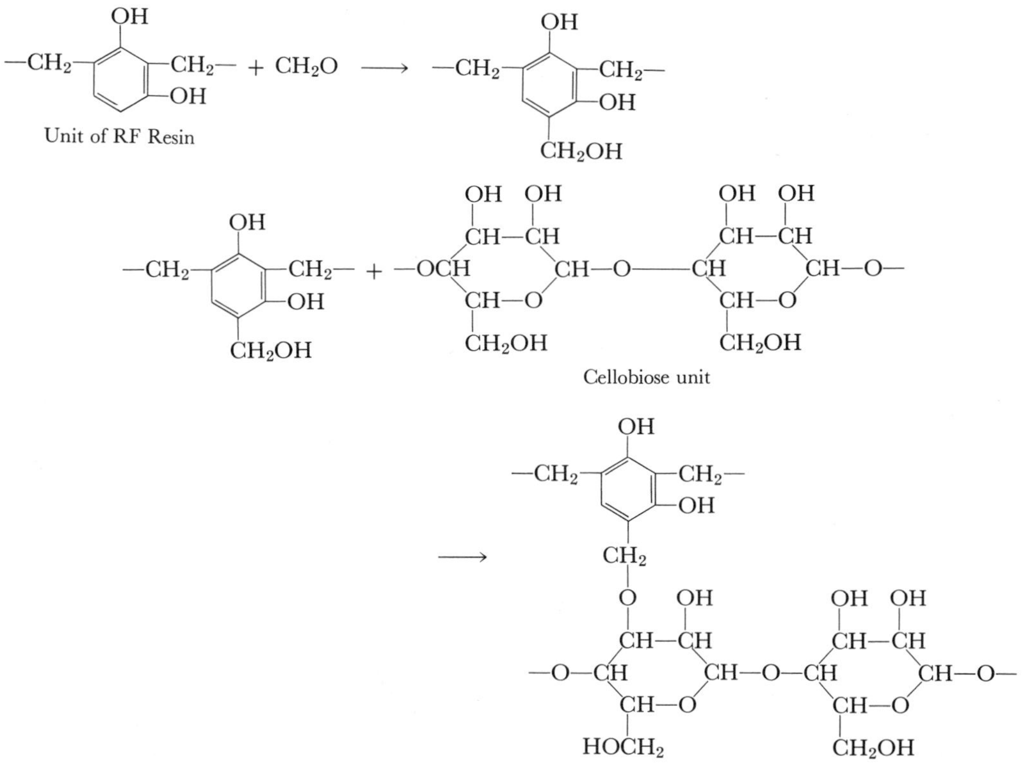

Unit of RF Resin

Cellobiose unit

be seen by comparing their structures. A unit of a nylon 66 molecule is:[21]

←——————————————— 17.2Å ———————————————→

It is notable that there are six —OH groups per unit of cellulose, which is 10.28Å long, hence an average distance of 1.7Å along the chain between —OH groups; whereas on the polyamide chain, there are two —NH groups on a unit 17.2Å long, or an average distance of 8.6Å between —NH groups. The advantage of using resorcinol resins with nylon may again be due to direct chemical linkage of the resorcinol resin with the nylon surface. Methylols may be formed by reaction of formaldehyde with —NH groups,[21] which in turn react with resorcinol resins through methylene bridges.

A typical adhesive contains a styrene-butadiene-vinylpyridine terpolymer latex into which is dispersed the phenol-blocked diisocyanate and sodium alginate in the presence of a wetting agent. The diisocyanate is reportedly regenerated during the hot-stretching of the tire cord at 220°C and interacts with both rubber and fiber to form a substantial bond. The reaction of blocking and unblocking is depicted as shown on page 503.

MEASUREMENT OF ADHESION

A number of methods have been proposed for estimating the adhesion of tire cord to rubber,[23, 24, 25] but the one in most general use is

The bonding of "Dacron" directly with resorcinol resins is inadequate because of the lack of suitable polar groups on the fiber surface. "Dacron" is made by the condensation of ethylene glycol and dimethyl terephthalate by ester interchange to form a polymer which may be represented as shown at top of page 503.[21]

Successful results on the bonding of "Dacron" to rubber have been reported by Thomson, et al,[27] and Blackley,[26] using phenol-blocked isocyanates.

known as the H-test so named because the test piece resembles an H. The two vertical members of the H are 2-ply strips of reinforced rubber, joined together by a single segment of tire cord which is embedded in each rubber block. These blocks are generally 1 × ¼ × ⅛ in.; however they may alternatively be ⅜ in. wide to allow for deeper embedment of the cord. The test is not standard at present, and there are many variations in current use; nevertheless recent study by

$$O-\overset{\overset{\displaystyle O}{\parallel}}{C}-\langle\text{benzene}\rangle-\overset{\overset{\displaystyle O}{\parallel}}{C}-\left[OCH_2CH_2O\overset{\overset{\displaystyle O}{\parallel}}{C}-\langle\text{benzene}\rangle-\overset{\overset{\displaystyle O}{\parallel}}{C}-\right]_n OCH_2CH_2O-$$

ASTM Committee D-11 may soon result in a standard method. A study of the variables in this test is described in Ref. 23.

To determine the "pull-out" force, the specimen, previously heated to some predetermined temperature, is pulled apart by two hook-like

tire cord as received from the suppliers is continuously fed from cones, passed through a bath of RFL adhesive under low tension, squeezed, shaken, or blown to remove excess latex and then passed through a hot-air dryer. During the drying stage the cord is subjected to sufficient tensile pull to

$$OCN-\langle\text{benzene}\rangle-CH_2-\langle\text{benzene}\rangle-NCO + 2\;\langle\text{phenol, OH}\rangle$$

$$\downarrow 220°C$$

$$\langle\text{OH}\rangle-O\overset{\overset{\displaystyle O}{\parallel}}{C}NH-\langle\text{benzene}\rangle-CH_2-\langle\text{benzene}\rangle-NH\overset{\overset{\displaystyle O}{\parallel}}{C}-O\langle\text{OH}\rangle$$

clamps in a tensile testing machine such as the Scott X-3 or Instron. The force required to rupture the specimen is designated "static adhesion." A number of specimens are tested, and a mean value is used for comparison.

Although satisfactory static adhesion values are required in order to produce good, long-wearing, safe tires, it is not sufficient to determine the value of the cord-to-rubber bond in this way. Correlation of this test with the performance of tires on automobiles has often been shown to be erroneous. Tire cords in service are subjected to continual changes in extension, compression, temperature, cold-stretch, and high-speed loading forces. Although none of these may exert sufficient force to equal that given in a static test, the repeated application of such forces over millions of cycles gradually weakens the cord-rubber bonded system until failure occurs.

Many methods of testing the so-called "dynamic adhesion" have been suggested,[17, 27, 28] but none has been generally accepted. The only reliable method presently known is the "fleet-test" where a given system of cord, adhesive, and rubber stock combination is tested by making a number of tires and testing them in fleets of cars under observable conditions.

APPLICATION OF ADHESIVES

The application of latex adhesives to tire cords is done by "dipping," stretching, and drying. The

stretch the cord several per cent, thus removing part of the tendency for tire cord to cold-stretch in use. In commercial practice many cords are treated simultaneously and conducted through the treating machine in parallel with the cords close together so that they appear to form a single fabric. Frequently this is referred to as "weftless fabric," and in the building of tires, it is generally applied directly to the freshly calendared carcass stock, and subsequently into the built tire.

References

1. Borroff, E. M., and Wake, W. C., *Trans. Inst. Rubber Ind.,* **25,** 190 (1949).
2. Lyons, W. J., *Textile Research J.,* **20,** (9), 654 (1950).
3. Gillman, H. H., and Thoman, R., *Ind. Eng. Chem.,* **40,** 1237 (1948).
4. Dietrick, M. I., *Rubber World,* **136,** 847 (1957).
5. Whitby, G. S., "Synthetic Rubber," p. 698, New York, John Wiley & Sons, Inc., 1954.
6. Doyle, G. M., *Trans. Inst. Rubber Ind.,* **36,** 177 (1960).
7. Hultzch, K., *J. prakt. Chem., N. F. Band,* **158,** 275–294 (1941).
8. Hultzch, K., *Ber.,* **74B,** 898–904 (1941).
9. Hultzch, K., *Kunststoffe,* **37,** 43 (1947).
10. Cunneen, Farmer, and Koch, *Rubber Chem. and Technol.,* **17,** 277–284 (1944).
11. Towney, Little and Viohl, *Rubber Chem. and Technol.,* **33,** (1959).
12. Van der Meer, S., *Rubber Chem. and Technol.,* **18,** 853–873 (1945).
13. Piccini, I., *Rubber Chem. and Technol.,* **26,** 207–219 (1953).

14. Schmidt, A. X., and Marlies, C. A., "Principles of High-Polymer Theory and Practice," pp. 405, 651, New York, McGraw-Hill Book Co., 1948.

15. Wake, W. C., "Adhesion of Rubber and Textiles" in "Adhesion and Adhesives Fundamentals and Practice," Edited by Clark, Rutzler, and Savage, New York, John Wiley & Sons, Inc., 1954.

16. McLaren, A. D., "The Adhesion of High Polymers to Cellulose," p. 57, in "Adhesion and Adhesives Fundamentals and Practice," Edited by Clark, Rutzler, and Savage, New York, John Wiley & Sons, Inc., 1954.

17. Wilson, M. W., "Characteristics and Performance of Rayon Tire Cords," *Tappi*, **43**, (2), 129 (1960).

18. Marsh, J. T., "An Introduction to Textile Finishing," p. 431, New York, John Wiley & Sons, Inc., 1949.

19. Greth, *Angew. Chem.* **51**, 719 (1958).

20. Krumbhaar, U. S. Patent 2,268,946 (1942).

21. Moncrieff, R. W., "Artificial Fibres," New York, John Wiley & Sons, Inc., 1957.

22. Thomson, *et al., Adhesives Age,* (Feb. 1959).

23. Lyons, Nelson, and Conrad, *India Rubber World,* **114,** 213 (1946).

24. Lessig, E. T., and Compton, J., *Rubber Chem. and Technol.,* **19,** 223 (1946).

25. Wood, J. O., *Trans. Inst. Rubber Ind.,* **32,** (1), 1 (1956).

26. Blackley, D. C., *Adhesives and Resins,* **8,** 1–2 (1960).

27. Lyons, W. J., *Anal. Chem.,* **23,** (9), 1255 (1951).

28. Williams, K. R., *et al., Ind. Eng. Chem.,* **45,** (4), 796 (1953).

— 43 —

Wood Gluing

Charles B. Hemming
United States Plywood Corp.
Brewster, New York

In the formation of adhesive bonds in which wood is one or both of the faying surfaces, the nature of wood controls the choice of material used as adhesive as well as the manner of bonding. All too often the technician fails to realize this, probably because wood has been adhered by means of adhesives for so many centuries. Wood was probably the first material to be joined for structural purposes, beginning in the distant past; whereas other structural bonding had to wait for the so-called age of adhesives commencing approximately in the middle of World War II.

In the early 1940's the common concept was mechanical adhesion; indeed only a few advanced workers realized that mechanical adhesion played a minute role. Mechanical adhesion presupposed adequate porosity in the surface of the wood to permit the adhesive to sink into the upper layers while in the liquid stage. This formed stalactites which hardened in the pores. It was thought that if the cohesive strength of the adhesive film was adequate, the stalactites did the rest. We now know that any penetration due to porosity will increase the strength of the bond but only because greater areas are thus made available for wetting and specific adhesion. There may be reinforcing action as a result of the penetration; however this is a secondary effect.

Specific adhesion is a term generally used to contrast with mechanical adhesion just described. In some cases, particularly with phenol-formaldehyde resin adhesives, there is evidence of an actual reaction between the cellulose and the phenol-formaldehyde compound when in its reactive stage. The bonding mechanism may be hydrogen bonding, valence forces and/or van der Waals forces, depending on the adhesive. Normal wood is hydrophilic in nature and highly porous. Since it is a basic tenet that you cannot adhere something if you do not first wet the surface involved, it becomes obvious that an adhesive must be used that is hydrophilic in the uncured stage and that it would be wise to use a pore-filling compound.

Based on these considerations it would seem that very high orders of bonding efficiency should almost always be reached; unfortunately this is not the case. From the purely theoretical standpoint we have loss of efficiency due to steric hindrance. We also have losses in efficiency due to failure to understand the true nature of the material being bonded as well as certain facts of surface chemistry which will be discussed later.

Wood can be said to be a "living" material. This is not true in the organic sense; however it is true in the mechanical sense. Wood is normally hygroscopic regardless of age or how well seasoned if it has not been altered chemically. Because of this it changes its moisture content with changes in relative humidity; these changes are sufficiently reliable to be predicted with surprising accuracy. In fact wood can be used as an element of a hydrostat or hygrometer.

As wood takes on moisture during a rise in relative humidity to which it may be exposed, it swells; conversely after a fall in relative humidity it shrinks. These dimensional changes are three: radial, tangential and longitudinal. The radial change which is across the ring structure is the greatest. The tangential is second, and the longitudinal changes, i.e., those occurring along the fiber are very small and generally can be neglected. The radial and tangential changes cannot be neglected for two reasons. These dimensional changes must be dealt with in any bonding operation. The distortion forces so induced can be very high; furthermore if they occur during the period when the thermosetting adhesive is in the soft gel stage, the gel will be permanently cracked with a weak final bond resulting. Warp will often occur unless high bonding pressures are used, and any movement may cause a fit change with a resultant weak bond. High bonding pressures are not always the remedy. If the structure is unsound resulting in warp forces, the bond may be put in tension during service; consequently it will support a far lower load than if there is no built-in stress or all stresses are kept in as nearly pure shear as possible.

Hygroscopicity shows its effect in other ways. Wood containing too much moisture at the time of bonding may cause excessive absorption of the adhesive during application or over-penetration during bonding conditions. Conversely, excessively dry wood may cause poor wetting of the surface, and under-penetration results in a joint with superficial strength. Finally, hygroscopicity will control the amount of volatile material capable of building up pressures in the case of hot-press bonding. If the sum total of all the volatiles is excessive, a steam explosion is the inevitable result and the bond is again worthless.

Grain direction must also be considered by the designer who would use wood as an adherend in a bonding operation. Wood is anisotropic, and the strength along the grain is many times that across the grain. In plywood this effect is used to make wood split-resistant by aligning the grain directions in alternate plies as nearly 90 degrees to each other as possible. This produces what is called balance or restraint of grain movement by orientation. Normal wood is thus converted from an anisotropic material to one that is isotropic, or at least biaxial. Plywood thus tends to balance out expansion and contraction effects due to moisture content changes resulting in a plywood construction which is more stable than lumber of the same species. Plywood constructions do not completely avoid what may be called a hygroscopic couple, and if one face receives more moisture than the other in a change of ambient conditions, the plywood will tend to warp; however it will recover its flatness at the new level after the retarded face has a chance to reach the same moisture content as the first.

Wood, as we normally use it, is actually a complex chemical mixture which is by no means all cellulose. Often subsidiary constituents have profound effects on bonding efficiency. Lignin, the second major constituent of wood, can generally be neglected as not interfering with the bonding operation; but resin content, wax content, and oxidation products on the surface have significant actions. Manuals on adhesive bonding of wood stress the importance of clean, freshly machined surfaces. This is especially true of the softwoods because of their high resin content and because as the resin tends to oxidize on the surface with time, it becomes increasingly difficult to wet properly with the adhesives normally used in wood bonding. Wax and oil content are special problems in such woods as gum, teak, and Brazilian rosewood.

Finally, wood can be caused to become hydrophobic on the surface. When this occurs, the effect is not easily recognized but the result with normal adhesives is invariably a poor bond. The commonest cause of the hydrophobic surface on wood is overheating. Plywood bonded over 300°F is likely to have a hydrophobic surface, and waterborne adhesives will not wet properly. While the effects are not generally macroscopic, cold, clean water spilled on such a surface will not wet it. The surface will react as though it were oily or greasy. These materials can be ruled out by means of ultraviolet light since most waxes or greases likely to contaminate the wood surface will fluoresce; whereas the hydrophobic condition does not fluoresce. Strips of wood immersed in xylene or some other nonpolar solvent will be wetted, and the meniscus at the point of contact between the hydrophic wood and the liquid will rise. Similar strips immersed in water will not be wetted, and the meniscus will be depressed. The preventive is obviously not to overheat the wood. The remedy is to sand the surface in the hope that the damage may not go deeply into the wood.

SPECIES SENSITIVITY

Generally, hardwoods and softwoods do not require different adhesives or different bonding techniques. There is more likelihood that variations among hardwoods and among softwoods would be greater than the variations between hardwoods and softwoods. The major differences are that softwoods generally have a little lower compressive strength so that pressures are lighter. They have a high resin content which adds to the volatile materials which encourage blows. Therefore they should be somewhat drier, particularly when hot bonded, and the importance of a freshly cut surface at the time of bonding is greater.

Open-grain woods may cause difficulty because of excessive penetration resulting in starved glue lines. Adhesives are generally formulated to prevent this; conversely close-grain woods must be given a lighter spread to avoid excessively thick glue lines. Ring-porous woods present a compromise problem; but they are generally very strong in compression, thereby permitting the use of higher bonding pressures.

There are some special problems. The Philippines, constituting up to twelve different species, all with different bonding characteristics, will not necessarily give uniform results with the same adhesive. Most of the species tend to be ropy or stringy in nature, and some reinforcement of surface by means of slight but controlled penetration is desirable. Maple is so powerful—particularly in dimension stock form—that if the grain orientation of the machined parts is not wisely chosen, the section may warp and rupture the best adhesive line. Gum contains a wax which appears to concentrate between the spring and summer wood and makes bonding with phenolic resins difficult, resulting in the general use of aminoplasts. Oak with high tannic acid content can interfere with the durability of the bond, particularly under severe exposure such as in the planking and beams or hulls of boats; for utmost durability, special resorcinol adhesives resistant to tannic acid are required. Larch contains galactans, and these gummy substances may also interfere with the proper wetting of the wood by the adhesive or even contaminate the adhesive, impairing its cohesive strength. Birch is subject to case hardening and burnishing. These defects may be hydrophobic in nature but in any event interfere with good wetting and good strength development. Dense ring growth and dwarfed, old-growth woods also present bonding problems because the surface is difficult to wet.

PHYSICAL CONDITION

Heartwood and sapwood do not bond similarly. Sapwood tends to be absorptive, encouraging starved glue lines. If heartwood and sapwood cannot economically be separated, a compromise adhesive must be effected so that adequate wetting of heartwood is obtained.

Springwood and summerwood represent minor problems although if the adhesive is chosen which will wet the summerwood properly and if the spread is adequate to take care of the springwood, a good over-all bond will result.

In wood that is cut in a rotary lathe, i.e., peeled for use in plywood manufacture, there is a tight and loose side. It will be recognized that if a log is peeled, the veneer which in effect was wrapped around the trunk of the tree is now laid out flat, which tends to compress the outside and stretch the inside. The compressed side is no problem, but the inside may be torn and be full of tiny checks or cracks. In plywood manufacture it is preferred that the loose side, particularly of the face and back, be toward the center of the panel in order to reduce finishing problems and checking in service, and to give better balance. On the other hand, loose sides require a bit more adhesive because of the increased porosity. Proper operation of the lathe can reduce the severity of the checks on the loose side, and this must be done; otherwise the adhesive will bleed through excessively.

The machining process may introduce contaminants. Oil or oil vapors from machinery or dirty tools will interfere with the wetting of the adhesives. Waxes used as caul or platen lubricants may be transferred to the surfaces of laminated timbers or plywood. When secondary bonding is attempted, the adhesive will fail to function properly. Any water repellency in a clear water test should be regarded with suspicion and the contaminant removed before bonding is attempted.

Machining is important. Adhesive materials by their nature develop their best strengths in extremely thin films, which means that the glue line should be as nearly nonexistent as possible and certainly not over 0.005 in. thick. Machining which is proper ensures a good fit of the faying surfaces without excessive pressures.

Compression wood, incipient rot, and similar factors which reduce the fiber strength may prevent wetting of the adhesive; however even if they do not, they will give a bond of low structural strength because the adherend itself has been weakened.

Over-drying causes difficulties which have been described above. Solvent seasoning can be troublesome. If residual solvent is not removed or if the solvent used contains a nonvolatile tailing, the wood will behave as though it were waxy; thus wetting by the adhesive will be prevented. While adhesives vary in their sensitivity to this effect, the proper remedy is to dispose of the solvent rather than pick a tolerant adhesive.

CHEMICAL MODIFICATION

The virtues of wood are well known, but recent competition from aluminum and plastics has brought to sharp focus some of the disadvantages.

This in turn has brought about renewed efforts to modify or eliminate these defects.

From the structural standpoint, improved dimensional stability would accomplish more than any other change. It would prevent shifting or movement within structures, stop warping, twisting, sticking of moving parts, enhance the durability of applied finishes, and make glued assemblies more reliable and stronger. Since wood has a very low thermal coefficient of expansion, it would be a more stable material than either metal or plastics if it could be rendered incapable of swelling and shrinking with changes in moisture content.

Some of the better known attempts at stabilization have been at least partially successful commercially. One such is "Impreg," the process for which is patented and belongs to the citizens of the United States. It involves treatment of wood by soaking in a low molecular weight water solution of phenol-formaldehyde resin. Drying and curing of the absorbed resin results in a remarkably stable material. Unfortunately it is still too expensive for most purposes, and it has very low impact resistance. It is outstanding in patternmaking where it enjoys a large commercial use.

Attempts to substitute the phenol-formaldehyde by lower cost materials have only been of limited technical success and little commercial use to date. Alternate impregnants include water-soluble salts and polyethylene glycols. These agents, which are inert or unreacted, are known as "cell stuffers" because they fill the wood cells in the expanded or green conditions and prevent normal shrinkage.

"Compreg" is a modification of "Impreg" in which very high pressure is applied to the phenol-formaldehyde treated wood at the onset of the curing step. The resulting densified material is extremely strong, but the high cost of the process has restricted its commercial use to specialties such as knife handles, nonmetallic gears and certain military items.

A somewhat different approach is acetylation. If the terminal hydroxyl groups of the cellulose molecule could be eliminated, the normal hygroscopicity of wood would be greatly reduced and the stabilization proportionately increased. Obviously, a chemical reaction is called for, and one is the reaction between aliphatic acids such as acetic and the cellulose of the wood. Acetyl groups replace hydroxyl groups, and the desired result is partially achieved. Cost, incompleteness of reaction, loss of impact resistance, and introduction of other undesirable physical properties have reduced its usefulness.

There are many other reactions involving removal of hydroxyl groups, but none so far as is presently known has reached a practical degree of success without severe lowering of some important physical property.

Another weakness of wood is its susceptibility to decay, which leads to different approaches in attempts at modification. If wood could be kept dry, its decay resistance would be greatly enhanced. "Impreg" and "Compreg" will not mold or decay. However, the popular approaches have involved almost exclusively impregnation of the wood with toxic substances such as pentachlorophenol, sodium pentachlorophenate, "Wolman" salts, creosote oil, metallo-organic compounds based on copper or zinc and others too numerous to mention.

Some of these are very effective and long-lasting even under conditions of severe exposure; nevertheless they add appreciably to the cost and do little for the stability problem. Some interfere with subsequent painting or gluing; whereas others discolor the wood. Even so, the results are very valuable commercially, and the use of wood treated against decay is rapidly increasing.

The last major weakness of wood is combustibility. Treatments involve impregnation with inorganic salts, all of which are incombustible and some of which are particularly effective in protecting the wood. Of course no treatment can prevent fire penetration indefinitely since wood, being organic, will distill out of the mixture eventually, leaving some charcoal and a salt residue without strength; but flame is not propagated, and fire penetration is greatly delayed.

ADHESIVES FOR WOOD

Many plastics and most film-forming substances can act as adhesives for wood. Since the durability of the assembly is dependent on the durability of the adhesive used, the service requirement of the bonded structure most often dictates the choice, which is balanced against cost. Secondary requirements also enter such as heat resistance or necessary setting or curing conditions.

Phenolic-resin adhesives and their room-temperature-setting relatives, the resorcinol and phenol-resorcinol adhesives, are the most durable of all and more indestructible than the wood itself. They are generally dark in color; in places where this is an objection, melamine resin adhesives—a close second in extreme durability—are used. Less durable are urea resin adhesives, which are amply adequate for indoor services where elevated temperatures or prolonged exposure to moist conditions are not involved.

These adhesives are known as thermosetting types even when they cure at room temperatures since they cannot be "remelted" or heat softened, once cured. Some hybrid types for special purposes, also in this class, are melamine-ureas, phenol-resorcinols mentioned above, thiourea resin adhesives, furfurylated ureas, and protein phenolic adhesives.

Some new and old miscellaneous types having commercial value for certain classes of work include polyvinyl-acetate emulsion adhesives known as white glues; casein glues; vegetable glues based on processed starch; blood protein glues, soya protein glues; nitrocellulose solutions similar to lacquers but designed for adhesive purposes; epoxy resin adhesives which are new and versatile but expensive; polysulfide adhesives where elasticity is required, and naturally, the ancient and well-known animal glues. Table 1 included herein is a brief summary for convenient reference. For further information, please see the chapters on the respective adhesives.

ADHESIVE MODIFIERS

The basic film forming substance or resin is rarely used without modification. One or more of the following are likely to be necessary:

(1) Extenders have inherent adhesive action and are used to lower cost. Wheat flour in ureas is an example.
(2) Diluents have no adhesive action and are used to lower cost or control flow and penetration. Walnut shell flour in phenolics is an example.
(3) Reinforcing agents strengthen the glue line. Wood flour in ureas is a very desirable component illustrating this action.
(4) Fortifiers are full adhesives in their own right and contribute to increased durability or some other useful property.
(5) Catalysts are often necessary to ensure cure or set in a reasonable time.
(6) Tougheners may or may not be adhesives in their own right but serve to make glue lines more shock or peel-resistant.
(7) Consistency modifiers are special diluents, often with some adhesive action, and are used to control consistency for correct application action.

BOND STRENGTHS

Traditionally the criterion of a successful wood bond has been that the strength of the bond ex-ceed the strength of the wood itself. This does not tell much about the strength of the adhesive, and the American Society for Testing Materials has done a great deal in its Committee D-14 on Adhesives to develop a better criterion. However, the wood failure approach is practical if understood.

The troubles with this approach stem from weak species, poor grain orientation, presence of decay and other defects, and degradation as from exposure, acids or alkalies. One should not assume that all is well because destruction of the bond results in wood failure. It is important to see that the bonded structure as a whole is adequately strong. If this is done and the durability is adequate, there should be no trouble provided that an adhesive of known quality is chosen initially. Of course, if research is being done on a new adhesive, this concept must be abandoned in favor of determining the inherent strength of the adhesive.

In weak or porous woods it is often important to reinforce the upper layers so that gluing occurs in depth; thus stresses are beneficially transferred deep into the wood. This is best done by using some of the same adhesive without extenders or fillers and perhaps thinned below normal as a priming coat. When this coat is dried but not fully cured, bonding proceeds in a manner normal for the chosen adhesive.

Balsa wood is an extreme example in which even the priming coat may have to contain a little filler to prevent excessive penetration. In any event, starvation of the glue line due to excessive penetration and strengthening of the upper layers often concur.

End grain joints are always a problem and are best solved by scarfing, fingerjointing or similar devices. However butt joints can occasionally be made adequate with good machining, proper regard for ring oriented and unoriented grain structure, adequate priming and an adhesive carefully chosen for toughness, high cohesive strength, freedom from excessive rigidity and freedom from self-crazing. Certain modified phenolics fulfill these requirements.

It is fundamental to good structures that bonds be so contrived as to be properly oriented concerning the forces they must resist. The best performance can be expected from a bond used in compression. Normally the great majority of joints are chosen to be stressed in shear—the purer the better. Tension loads a glue line severely; hence tension forces must be minimized. Peel and cleavage forces should be kept at an extremely low level since it is against these forces that bonds are most vulnerable.

TABLE 1. APPROXIMATE COSTS AND PRINCIPAL PROPERTIES OF WOOD ADHESIVES.

Type Resin Used	Cost/ Neat Pound[a] (¢)	Cost/Pound of Adhesive (¢)	Resin Solids in Glue Mix (%)	Cost/ sq ft Glue Line (¢)	Principal Use	Method of Application	Principal Property	Principal Limitation
Urea formaldehyde, primary bonding	Hot press—12.5–19.5 Cold press—12.5–19.5	3.0–5.0 5.2–7.8	23–30 40–45	0.19–0.26 0.30–.48	Wood to wood interior	Spreader rolls	Bleed-through free; good adhesion	Poor durability
Furfurylated urea formaldehyde	25–30	23–28	50–53	1.17–1.75	Wood to plastic interior	Spreader rolls	Non-crazing; good adhesion to plastic	Long cure time
Phenol formaldehyde	24.5–27.5	6.50–8.50	23–27	0.3–0.4	Plywood exterior	Spreader rolls	Durability	Comparatively long cure times
Melamine formaldehyde	45–50	31.5–34.7	68–72	1.5–2.7	Wood to wood Splicing Patching Scarfing	Sprayed Sprayed Combed	Adhesion Color Durability	Relative cost; poor washability; needs heat to cure
Melamine-urea 2/1	25–30	20–22	55–60	.97–1.11	End and edge gluing exterior	Applicator	Colorless Durability and speed	Cost
Resorcinol formaldehyde	62–65[b]	62–65	50–56	2.5–3.5	Exterior wood to wood (laminating)	Spreader rolls	Cold sets durability	Cost, odor
Phenol-resorcinol 10/90	37.5–46.5[b]	36–43.6	50–56	2.0–2.5	Wood to wood exterior (laminating)	Spreader rolls	Warm-set durability	Cost, odor
Polyvinyl-acetate Emulsion	45–55	25–30	45–55	2.5–3.0	Wood to wood interior	Brushed, Sprayed Spread. rolls	Handy	Lack of H_2O and heat resistance
Cresol formaldehyde	25–30	—	—	—	Wood to wood exterior			
Nitrocellulose	40	35	—	—	Wood to wood interior			
Urea forml., sec. bonding	19.5	12.5	60–65	1.0–1.5	Wood to wood interior	Spray, Brush, Spread. rolls	Speed, adhesion	Poor durability

a Resin solids.   b Liquid.

Impact resistance will depend on the nature of the impact force, i.e., whether it is a shear, tension or other force and whether the glue line is tough or brittle. This is best ascertained by actual measurement. Wood itself has very high impact strength; whereas some adhesives used for wood binding do not.

Fatigue and hysteresis effects seldom enter the picture for well-made bonds made with phenolic, resorcinol, melamine or urea adhesives. However, such effects may be appreciable for some of the other adhesives.

Plastic effects can be expected in thermoplastic or water-sensitive adhesives, and consideration to these limitations must be given if adhesives of these types are used. Highly stressed parts or parts subjected to high temperatures or high relative humidities long sustained must be bonded only with thermosetting adhesives.

DURABILITY

The purchaser of a glued assembly actually buys a glue line. He expects that it will never fail before the wood itself and will last for the life of the wood under the service conditions normally anticipated in the use of the assembly. For example, the requirements of exterior plywood are quite different from those of interior plywood. Similarly, laminated boat beams have a far different durability requirement from those of furniture for use indoors. It would be foolhardy to use a furniture assembly adhesive for boat work and uneconomic to use a boat adhesive in the manufacture of household interior furniture.

Regardless of type of exposure, there are some basic requirements of durability not discussed above which must also be met. As we have learned, wood expands and contracts with changes in moisture content which are in turn induced by changes in relative humidity. These cyclic conditions are severe in some areas of our country and exist to some extent in all areas. Cyclic stresses thus induced can load a bond severely, and the adhesive must be capable of withstanding these stresses as well as the normal expected loads.

A final factor is resistance to biological agents and particularly molds and bacteria. Adhesive bonds may have to be chosen for resistance to these agents, either for interior or exterior service. A common approach is to "poison" the glue line with a suitable toxic agent; needless to say this may be undesirable in some cases for health and safety reasons. If such is the case, the best answer is to choose an adhesive immune to such attack.

Testing for resistance to these destructive effects must of necessity be most often on an accelerated basis. The reader is referred to Chapter 5 of this volume, the Standards of the American Society for Testing Materials and the publications of the Forest Products Laboratory, United States Department of Agriculture for further information.

Acknowledgments

The author wishes to acknowledge with appreciation the assistance and critical comment of Mr. J. R. Ash and his staff at Monsanto Chemical Company, Seattle, Washington, in the preparation of this chapter.

References

Wise, Louis E., "Wood Chemistry," New York, Reinhold Publishing Corp. 1946.

"Wood Handbook," Forest Products Laboratory, U. S. Department of Agriculture.

Meyer, Louis H., "Plywood What It Is—What It Does," New York, McGraw-Hill Book Co., 1947.

Dietz, Albert G. H., "Engineering Laminates," New York, John Wiley & Sons, Inc., 1949.

"ASTM Standards 1958," Part 6, American Society for Testing Materials, Philadelphia.

DeBruyne, N. A., and Houwink, R., "Adhesion and Adhesives," New York, Elsevier Publishing Co., 1951.

"Plastics Engineering Handbook," Society of the Plastics Industry, Ch. 23, New York, Reinhold Publishing Corp. 1960.

— 44 —

Structural Metal Bonding

Nicholas J. DeLollis
Sandia Corp.
Albuquerque, New Mexico

Adhesives have been known for a long time, but throughout most of their history they have been used principally for the bonding of wood and paper products. Now, however, adhesives are available for almost every material.

One of the relatively recent developments for adhesives has been in the structural bonding of metal-to-metal. Today there are adhesives which bond many metal assemblies more effectively than do conventional fastening methods. Unlike many older adhesives which are restricted to non-critical assemblies, these new materials add to the composite strength.

Adhesives are as numerous as adherends, and there are adhesives to bind virtually any two materials provided the requirements of the bonded system are not severe. However, the universal adhesive is usually not the most satisfactory in a specific application, and a thorough evaluation of all possible adhesives is necessary to determine the best one for any particular situation. To be acceptable, an adhesive must perform as well as or better than conventional fastening methods, and/or it must be economically competitive with the conventional methods.

ADVANTAGES OF ADHESIVE BONDING OF METALS

The advantages of an adhesive bonded joint over a mechanically fastened joint are as follows:

(1) An adhesive distributes stresses uniformly throughout the bonded area, and thereby avoids the localized stresses to which a riveted joint is subject.

(2) A bonded joint in an airplane or missile presents a smooth aerodynamic surface to the elements, thus eliminating the drag caused by a surface dotted with rivet heads.

(3) The use of an adhesive usually reduces the weight of the system.

(4) An adhesive is generally a good dielectric and thus can bond and insulate simultaneously.

(5) When an adhesive is used with dissimilar metals, it isolates the metals and thus minimizes the possibility of electrolytic corrosion.

(6) Adhesives seal a joint completely and allow only minimal escape or entrance of moisture and gas. Because of this property and because of the inertness of certain adhesives to general environment, to reaction with organic solvents, and to thermal cycling, adhesives are especially suitable for the incorporation of fuel tanks into structures.

(7) The use of elastomeric adhesives permits the bonding of dissimilar materials with widely differing coefficients of expansion.

As one striking example of the improved performance of a structure as a result of several of the above factors, the operational life of a helicopter rotor blade was increased from approximately 200 to more than 2000 hr.[1]

SOME THEORETICAL CONSIDERATIONS

Adhesives are improved by allowing the forces of attraction to operate between materials and by minimizing the forces which work against adhesion. The forces working against adhesion are measurable, and methods have been developed to reduce their effect in individual situations. At present, however, what actually constitutes the force of attraction in adhesives is still a matter of theoretical speculation.

Forces of Attraction

At some stage in its application, an adhesive becomes fluid. It can be a solid dissolved in a liquid, a chemically reactive liquid, or a solid made liquid, either by melting or by the application of both heat and pressure. As a fluid which actually saturates the surface of the adherend, the adhesive achieves the proximity to the surface necessary for the forces of attraction to operate. Then, through solidification by drying, by polymerization, or by cooling, the adhesive gains strength.

Bikerman maintains that the comparative roughness of solid surfaces is a major factor in adhesion.[2] When considered on a molecular scale, even a polished surface is very rough and has an actual surface area considerably greater than the simple planar area apparent to conventional measurement. Once the wet adhesive has spread itself into the crevices of a surface by capillary and/or wetting action and has hardened in place, its adhesive force must be measured according to the actual surface; whereas any force applied to the adhesive interface tending to break the bond must be measured according to the conventional unit area of the adhesive surface. If the adherend is stronger than the adhesive, the physical strength of the adhesive determines the breaking point of the bonded system, and, if the adhesive is stronger, the strength of the adherend is the limiting factor.

Houwink[3] analyzes three types of cohesive forces between molecules: (1) London, or dispersion forces, which are similar to Van der Waals forces; (2) Debye, or inductive forces; and (3) Keesom, or electrostatic forces. He finds the London forces, the nonpolar forces which act between all atoms, to be the most significant, accounting for 80 to 100 per cent of the total forces between molecules.

Primary valence bonds may also be important in adhesion.[4, 5]

These primary bonds holding molecules together are of essentially two types: (1) valence bonds, in which electrons are transferred between atoms, and (2) covalent bonds, in which electrons are shared.

The relative importance of surface area, intermolecular forces, and primary valence forces varies with each adhesive problem.

While polar adhesives are preferred for metals, bond strengths up to 4000 psi were obtained by fusing polyethylene to aluminum surfaces at 200 to 210°C. The aluminum undoubtedly had a layer of aluminum oxide on the surface, and it is possible that the polyethylene surface became oxidized when it came in contact with the hot aluminum surface. Table 1 shows that the tensile adhesion values increase with the molecular weight of the polyethylene.

Forces Working Against Adhesion

In developing a satisfactory adhesive, the forces working against adhesion must be considered as important as the forces which work for attraction.

TABLE 1. TENSILE ADHESION STRENGTH OF POLYETHYLENE TO ALUMINUM BOND.

	Polyethylene Designation	Form	Probable Molecular Wt.	Tensile Adhesion Value (psi)	No. of Spec.	Range (psi)
A	"Agilene" No. 1	Fine powder	20,000	2075	6	1890–2380
B	"Marlex" 50	Pellets	50,000	3740	6	2860–4280
C	208176-2	Fluffy powder	20,000	1390	6	1020–1800
D	208176-1	Fluffy powder	30,000	3010	9	2530–3690
E	208176-4	Fluffy powder	50,000	3490	6	3030–3760
F	208176-3	Fluffy powder	100,000	4130	6	3380–4670

A = Supplied by American Agile Co.
B = Supplied by Phillips Petroleum Co.
C, D, E, F = Experimental polyethylene resins supplied by Monsanto Chemical Co.

The contact areas on the aluminum tensile plugs were abraded with medium emery paper, wiped with acetone and heated to 200° to 210°C. The polyethylene was fused onto the hot surfaces. The plugs were assembled into the jig while hot. Plugs were kept hot under slight spring pressure until squeeze-out indicated complete contact, then cooled under slight pressure.

When an adhesive in contact with an adherend solidifies through drying, cooling or chemical reaction such as polymerization, it shrinks, and stresses develop in the bonding system. There may be a tendency for liquids and vapors, both organic and inorganic, to be attracted to the adhesive and ultimately adsorbed on the surface of the adherend in preference to the adhesive itself. To the extent that the adhesive is displaced by these compounds, there is a loss of joint strength. Some adhesives, especially when they have absorbed moisture, tend to corrode the surface of the adherend, thus lessening the adhesion, presumably by forming a weaker interfacial layer. Inadequate cleaning of the surface of the adherend frequently leaves an adsorbed layer of some substance which is incompatible with the adhesive.

Any difference between the coefficients of expansion in the adhesive and adherend can also cause stresses in the system. The intensity of the stress depends on the relationship between the moduli of the adhesive and adherend.[6] When both the adhesive and the adherend have low modulus, as when paper is bonded with a rubber substance, the stresses which develop are generally negligible. When a low-modulus adhesive is bonded to a high-modulus adherend, or vice versa, the tendency of the flexible substance to deform under the stress partially relieves the tension. For example, high-modulus phenolic adhesives can bond to wood, and low-modulus rubber can bond to metals. The strength of the bonding ultimately depends on the strength of the adhesion itself and the strength of the weaker material in this bonded joint. But serious problems arise when adhesives are used to bond two high modulus materials such as metals. To get high bond strength with metals, it is necessary to create a high-modulus glue line. At the same time, however, the bonding agent must have sufficient adhesive power and toughness to resist stresses resulting from solvent evaporation, polymerization, or differing coefficients of expansion.

Counter-adhesive forces can often be minimized through compromise, e.g., phenolic elastomer adhesives for metals combine two materials, each with strong adhesion characteristics, to give a mixture of medium modulus. The high-modulus phenolic gives strength; the low-modulus elastomer provides toughness. Metal-to-metal bonds with this type of adhesive have developed strengths of 3000 psi, accompanied by good impact, peel, and fatigue properties.

The epoxy resins, latest development in high-strength adhesives for metals, combine fairly high modulus with relatively low shrinkage. They have very strong adhesive qualities, great enough to overcome the stresses created by any shrinkage in the adhesive-adherend interface. The addition of an inert inorganic filler to an epoxy resin can decrease its coefficient of expansion, bringing it closer to that of the metal, thus reducing the interfacial stresses between adherend and adhesive. Interfacial stress in epoxy-bonded assemblies can also be lowered by the addition of various flexibilizers such as polysulfide liquid polymers and polyamide curing agents; these facilitate the movement of the glue line to relieve stresses.

THE STRUCTURAL ADHESIVES

Practically all structural adhesives for metals are phenolic resins modified by addition of rubber, vinyl, or epoxy resins. Metallic and inorganic fillers are important additives for these adhesives.

Phenolics, nitrile rubbers, neoprenes, polyvinyl butyrals, and epoxies have been discussed in detail in earlier chapters. They will now be reassessed as metal-bonding adhesives.

Phenolic Resins

The first adhesives of this type for metal bonding were rubber-phenolic combinations. Chemically, rubber consists of a basic four-carbon molecule which builds up to a linear polymer.[7a] In natural rubber the building block is isoprene, C_5H_8.

Synthetic rubbers used with phenolic resins are based chiefly on (1) chloroprene to give neoprene rubber, and (2) butadiene plus acrylonitrile to give nitrile rubber (buna-N).

While it may be that rubber-phenolic resins are simply physical mixtures, there is some evidence that the polymers are united chemically. Martin describes one possible reaction of phenol dialcohols with rubber.[7]

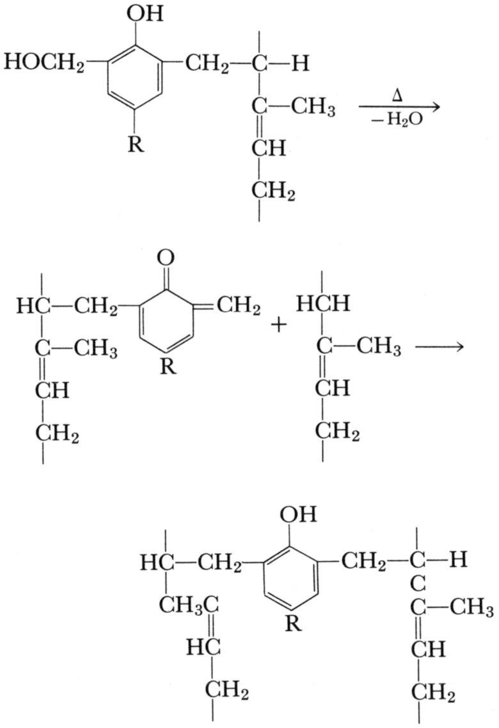

The dialcohol results from the following phenol-formaldehyde reaction:

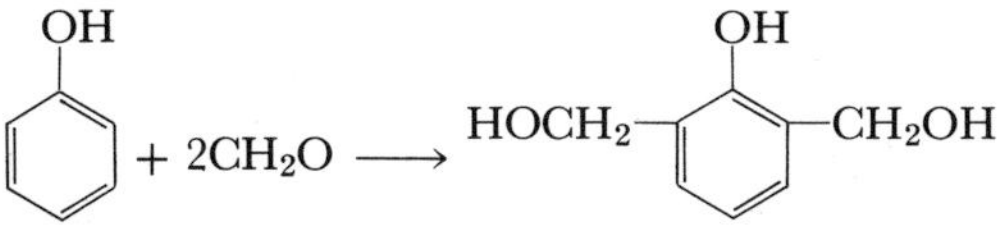

The proportion of phenolic resin to rubber in these mixtures determines the physical properties of the cured resin.[10] An increase in the phenolic content of the mixture increases the modulus and tensile strength and decreases the elongation. Table 2, taken from Reference 8, illustrates the change in physical properties of the mixture concomitant with changes in the rubber-phenolic ratio.

A typical two-part, phenolic buna-N adhesive formulation, designated PA 101 by the Bloomingdale Rubber Company,[9] is prepared according to the following formulation:

Part I

Constituents	parts by wt	
(1) "Hycar" OR-25ST	100	Band on cold rolls
(2) "Pilletex" carbon black SRF	50	Add to rubber and mill 16 min
(3) Stearic acid	1	Add items 3, 4, and 5 and mill for 5 min
(4) Zinc oxide	5	
(5) "Agerite Resin" D	1	Dissolve in methyethyl ketone at 20 per cent solids
(6) "Butyl 8"	7	Add to above solution

Part II

Constituents	parts by wt	
(1) "Bakelite" 18773	50	Grind item 3 and thoroughly disperse with Items 1 and 2 to form homogeneous dry powder. Sift.
(2) "Durez" 7031A	50	
(3) "Captax"	2	
(4) Sulfur	3	

When the adhesive is to be used, 12.5 parts of Part II powder are added to 100 parts of Part I solution and stirred thoroughly for 3 to ·5 min. The two parts must be kept separate before actual use because the combined mixture has a limited shelf life.

Generally, however, the rubber-phenolic type of adhesive is prepared as a one-component solution. It is also prepared as a film. The advantage of using an adhesive in film form is that it can be applied much more conveniently and results in a more easily controlled bond thickness. The data in Table 3, summarized from the Engel article,[9] give a good idea of what to expect from this type of adhesive in resistance to various temperatures and environments. At 180°F the adhesive has 50 per cent of its strength at room temperature. The adhesive is remarkably inert to the effect of various liquids used as immersants.

Another variation of the phenolic-elastomer adhesive is the phenolic-polyvinyl butyral type. The synthesis of polyvinyl butyral starts with the polymerization of vinyl acetate monomer, ·which is hydrolyzed to the polyvinyl alcohol. Reaction with butyraldehyde yields polyvinyl butyral. The conversion to the butyral is not complete, however, and commercially available polyvinyl butyral usually contains up to 20 per cent of unreacted hydroxyl groups.

Polyvinyl butyral is too soluble to be useful in a structural adhesive, but a cured vinyl phenolic adhesive is relatively insoluble (see Table 4B). This suggests that the principal components of a phenolic-vinyl adhesive are probably linked chemi-

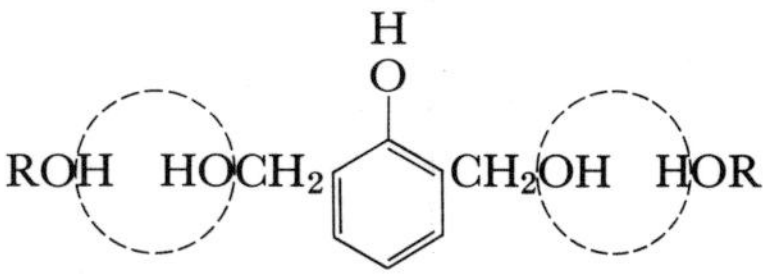

TABLE 2. EFFECT OF VARYING HYCAR-PHENOLIC RATIO.

1002-D17-HCR	234			235			236			237			238			239		
"Hycar" OR-25 EP[a]	100			100			100			100			100			100		
Phenolic resin[b]	50			60			70			80			90			100		
Zinc oxide	5.0			5.0			5.0			5.0			5.0			5.0		
Sulfur	1.5			1.5			1.5			1.5			1.5			1.5		
Benzothiazyl disulfide	1.5			1.5			1.5			1.5			1.5			1.5		
Stearic acid	1.5			1.5			1.5			1.5			1.5			1.5		
	159.5			169.5			179.5			189.5			199.5			209.5		
Minutes Cure at 310°F	15	30	45	15	30	45	15	30	45	15	30	45	15	30	45	15	30	45
Ultimate tensile strength (psi)	2700	2750	2900	3000	3100	3200	3300	3300	3600	3350	3500	3800	4250	4700	4800	4400	4150	4250
Ultimate elongation (%)	250	200	200	250	250	200	200	200	200	150	150	150	100	100	50	100	100	50
Specific gravity	1.08			1.08			1.09			1.10			1.10			1.10		
ASTM freeze test																		
1 hr at −10°F	Pass			Pass														
1 hr at −20°F	Fail			Fail			Pass			Pass			Pass			Pass		
1 hr at −30°F							Fail			Fail			Fail			Fail		
Hardness (Duro D)	43			48			54			60			68			73		
Crescent tear-die B																		
with grain (lb/in.)	420			460			460			470			500			540		
across grain (lb/in.)	330			420			390			400			550			590		
Abrasion resistance "B" stds. (%)	320			325			320			360			220			225		

a B. F. Goodrich Chemical Co.
b "Durex" 12687, Hooker Chemical Co.

TABLE 3. SINGLE-LAP TENSILE SHEAR STRENGTH OF
PA-101 FORMULATION.

Cure Temp. (°F)	Post-Cure Conditioning	Test Temp. (°F)	Av. Shear Strength (psi)
300	None	76	4325
300	None	180	2500
300	None	−70	5250
300	7 days isopropanol	76	4114
300	7 days ethylene glycol	76	4151
300	7 days hydraulic oil	76	4185
300	7 days hydraulic fluid	76	4265
300	30 days in water	76	3970
250	None	76	4300
250	None	180	1952
250	None	−70	4975
250	7 days isopropanol	76	4130
250	7 days ethylene glycol	76	4282
250	7 days hydraulic oil	76	4501
250	7 days hydrocarbon fluid	76	3885
250	30 days in water	76	4535

TABLE 4B. CHARACTERISTICS OF FM-47 PER AIR FORCE
SPEC. 14164.

Property	Average Value
(A) Standard temperature shear strength (psi)	4200
(B) Elevated temperature shear strength (psi)	3300
(C) Low temperature shear strength (psi)	2700
(D) Standard temperature fatigue strength (psi)	over 650
(E) Standard temperature long time shear strength (psi)	3500
(F) Elevated temperature long time shear strength (psi)	over 2000
(G) Standard temperature impact strength (ft lbs)	over 20
(H) Standard temperature bend test (lb)	210
(I) Shear strength after 30 days immersion in water (psi)	5000
(J) Shear strength after 7 days immersion in either ethylene glycol, anti-icing fluid, hydraulic fluid or hydrocarbon fluid (psi)	over 3600

Cure cycle:
Dried 1 hr at 150°F.
Preheated 5 min at 335°F without pressure.
Cured 25 min at 335°F, 200 psi.

cally in the cured state via hydroxyls of the polyvinyl butyral and phenol alcohols. A similar process is described by Martin.[10] Tables 4A and 4B give the characteristics of FM 47, a phenolic-vinyl adhesive.

The "Redux" type of phenolic-vinyl adhesive, consisting of a liquid phenolic primer and a polyvinyl formal powder, is widely used in Europe. Usually the surfaces to be bonded are coated with

TABLE 4A. CHARACTERISTICS OF FM-47* A PHENOLIC
VINYL ADHESIVE.

A. Single Lap Shear Strength

Metal Thickness	Cure Temp. (°F)	Pressure (psi)	Depth of Lap (in.)	Failing Strength (psi)
0.064	300	200	0.3	7200
0.064	300	200	0.5	5400
0.064	300	200	1.0	3200
0.064	300	200	2.0	1750
0.064	300	200	3.0	1100
0.064	300	200	4.0	845

Metal Thickness	Cure Temp. (°F)	Pressure (psi)	Depth of Lap (in.)	Temp. of Test (°F)	Failing Strength (psi)
0.064	300	200	0.5	−70	2600
0.064	300	200	0.5	+76	4200
0.064	300	200	0.5	+160	4000
0.064	300	200	0.5	+200	3000
0.064	300	200	0.5	+250	1700
				+300	700

* Made by Bloomingdale Rubber Co.
Data from company literature, Jan., 1954.

the liquid, and the powder is then added. The surfaces are assembled with heat and pressure. More recent versions of this adhesive combine the powder and liquid in both a supported and unsupported film. A comprehensive investigation of the "Redux" adhesive and FM 47 was made in Sweden and described in a report by Bryan R. Noton.[11]

Epoxy Resins

The epoxies were the first metal-bonding adhesives which could be applied and cured as solvent-free, fully reactive resins. The transition from the liquid to the solid state in epoxy resins occurs with no water or other volatile by-products and with a minimum of strain, as there is very little shrinkage, perhaps less than 2 per cent after gelation.

The epoxies are endowed with good wetting action in the liquid state. They have highly active groups which are probably helpful in allowing them to become preferentially adsorbed on the adherends to which they are applied. When the epoxies solidify, they become hard, inert, and impermeable. All these properties and characteristics combine to make the epoxies the favorite adhesives wherever low peel strength and lack of flexibility are not crucial factors. Other disadvantages in their use may eventually be eliminated such as their high cost and the fact that some are two-component systems.

One of the important advantages of using epoxy resins is that very little pressure is needed ordinarily to achieve the complete contact which ensures a good bond. Where rough or warped surfaces are to be bonded, filled thixotropic epoxy adhesives are available which create solid, void-free bonds, without the use of excessive pressures which tend to introduce strains in the bonded assembly.

The great variety of organic acids and amines which are available as curing agents[12] make possible systems which perform well at a wide range of temperatures. The more durable epoxy adhesive resins require cures at 200 to 350°F, especially if resistance to high temperature (up to 500°F) is desired. These high temperature-resistant formulations have the advantage of being one-component systems.

Epoxy resins may be cured with primary, secondary, or tertiary amines or with organic acid anhydrides. The primary and secondary amines react with epoxide to form secondary and tertiary amines, respectively, and secondary hydroxyl resultant.

$$R-NH_2 + CH_2 \overset{O}{-\!\!\!\triangle\!\!\!-} CH \longrightarrow$$

$$R-NH-CH_2-\underset{\underset{OH}{|}}{C}H-$$

The secondary amines continue the reaction.

$$R-NH-CH_2-\underset{\underset{OH}{|}}{C}H- + CH_2 \overset{O}{-\!\!\!\triangle\!\!\!-} CH- \longrightarrow$$

$$-\underset{\underset{OH}{|}}{C}H-CH_2-\underset{\underset{R}{|}}{N}-CH_2-\underset{\underset{OH}{|}}{C}H-$$

The hydroxyl groups cannot compete with the amines for reaction with epoxide.[13]

Diethylenetriamine and triethylenetetramine are primary amines in common use for adhesives cured at room temperature. The five and six active amine hydrogens respectively in these compounds available for chemical action are a good indication of their comparative reactivity.

Tertiary amines cure by catalytic action, causing the epoxy groups to react with each other, forming ether linkages.

Diethylaminopropylamine (DEAPA) is a curing agent frequently used with adhesives which cure at intermediate temperatures. Since it contains both a tertiary and a primary nitrogen, it is both a catalytic and a reactive hardener. If it were used as a reactive hydrogen-type curing agent, its concentrations would have to be 34 parts per hundred parts of the commoner liquid epoxy resins. However, it is almost always used in a concentration of approximately 6 per cent, giving good adhesive cures at intermediate temperatures.[14] Table 5 lists a group of epoxy adhesives cured with DEAPA. The tensile strength values both before and after environmental conditioning emphasize the usefulness of these adhesives in structural applications.

Epoxies are not always the best choice, however. If the joints are subjected to peel forces, for example, epoxies are inferior to phenolic-elastomers. Peel strengths for epoxies vary from 2 to 15 lb/in., depending on modifiers; whereas for rubber-phenolics they can be as high as 80 lb/in.[15]

Epoxy adhesives can be formulated as one-component systems with a shelf life greater than 1 yr. These adhesives require cures of 1 or 2 hr at temperatures of 300 to 350°F.

One hardener used in these systems is dicyandiamide, a solid at room temperature, which is incorporated into the adhesive by milling into a thick paste or a solid epoxy system. As seen in Table 6, this type of adhesive has good properties over a wide range of temperatures up to 300°F and is not noticeably affected by environmental exposure.

The continuing effort to develop adhesives for use at temperatures in excess of 500°F has met with the greatest success to date with epoxy-phenolic combinations using amine curing agents.[16] This type was first developed by the Shell Chemical Company as "Epon" 422J. A typical formulation is:

	parts
"Epon" 1001	49
Phenolic resin	100
Aluminum dust	149
Dicyandiamide	9
Copper-8-quinolinolate	1.5

The data in Table 7 and Figs. 1 and 2, taken from Shell Technical Bulletin SC-52-45R show that "Epon" 422 and other similar phenolic-epoxy formulations (HP 422, Fig. 1, and "Metlbond" 302, Fig. 2) still retain more than 50 per cent of their original strength at temperatures up to 500°F. Table 8 identifies the adhesives in Figs. 1 and 2.

The epoxy-phenolics are noted primarily for their low creep properties at high temperatures. As a result, they find their principal use in the aluminum skin panels of supersonic aircraft such as Convair's B-58.[17]

Table 5. Tensile Adhesion Strength of Epoxy Adhesives Cured with Diethylaminopropylamine (6 phr) 2 hr at 165°F.

Conditioning	Spec. No.	"Epon" VI	Armstrong A-2	R&A M-606	"Epibond" 123
Controls[g]	1	5400	6200	7500	5540
	2	6600	7500	7520	6000
	3	7380	6560	7400	7100
	4	7020	5380[a]	6720	7080
	5	7820	4620[b]	7220	6720
Specimens given four 24 hr cycles, −65°F 8 hr; 165°F 16 hr	1	7470	8340	8020	5660
	2	8340	6040	8550	7310
	3	7520	7010	9100	7190
	4	8530	6620	8790	7330
	5	7410	8600	9310	7330
SCEL[h] humidity cycle 20 days	1	6360	6180	6780	6360[f]
	2	5100	5940	7200	6900
	3	6220[c]	5000[c]	7640[f]	6400
	4	6460	6880	7820[f]	6620[f]
	5	6200[c]	6160	7460	6760

[a] Specimen did not break; threads stripped out at load of 5380 lb.
[b] 75% adhesion failure.
[c] 10% adhesion failure.
[d] 15% adhesion failure.
[e] 20% adhesion failure.
[f] SCEL—Signal Corps Electronics Lab.
[g] All specimens cured 2½ to 4 hr at 165°F.
[h] SCEL—Signal Corps Electronics Lab.

Specimens consisted of aluminum (6061-T6) tensile plugs 1½ in. long, 1.129 in. in diameter. They were abraded and wiped with clean acetone before being coated with the adhesive and assembled in a jig under sufficient spring pressure to maintain contact during cure.

Table 6. Characteristics of a Dicyandiamide-Cured Epoxy Resin.[a]

	Test Temp. (°F)	Mil-A-8331 Minimum Requirements (psi)[b]	"Epon" Adhesive IX
Tensile shear	77	2500	2810–3320
Tensile shear	180	1250	3200–4170
Tensile shear	250	—	2200
Tensile shear	300	—	1000–1300
Tensile shear	−70	2500	2900–3200
Impact strength	77	—	21 ft lb
Bend test	77	150 lb	175 lb
Long time test—200 hr	77	1600	3000
Long time test—200 hr	180	800	2700
Tensile shear after:			
30 days—tap water	77	2000	3390
7 days—ethylene glycol	77	2000	3500
7 days—anti-icing fluid	77	2000	3225
7 days—hydraulic oil	77	2000	3500
7 days—hydrocarbon	77	2000	3735
30 days—salt-spray exposure	77	2000	3590

[a] Data taken from Shell Chemical Corporation Technical Bulletin SC: 54-57.
* Unless otherwise noted.

TABLE 7. STRENGTH CHARACTERISTICS OF AN EPOXY-PHENOLIC.[a]

	Test Temp. (°F)	Mil-A-8331 (USAF) Specification (psi)	"Epon" Adhesive 422
Tensile shear	77	2500	2200–2500
Tensile shear	−70	2500	2200–2500
Tensile shear	300	—	1800–2000
Tensile shear	400	—	1800–2000
Tensile shear	500	—	1400–1800
Tensile shear after 200 hr at 500°F	500	—	600–800
Tensile shear after 100 cycles 77 to 500°F	500	—	1000
Tensile shear after:			
30 days—tap water	77	2000	2000–2500
7 days—ethylene glycol	77	2000	2000–2500
7 days—anti-icing fluid (MIL-F-5566)	77	2000	2000–2500
7 days—hydraulic oil (MIL-0-5606)	77	2000	2000–2500
7 days—hydrocarbon (MIL-H-3136, III)	77	2000	2000–2500
30 days—salt spray exposure (QQ-M-151)	77	2000	2000–2500

[a] Data taken from Shell Chemical Corporation Technical Bulletin SC: 54-34.

[b] Unless otherwise indicated, samples were held ½ hr at temperature before testing.

In spite of its resistance to high-temperature deterioration, the components of this adhesive tend to react at room temperatures so that the adhesive has a shelf life of only a few months under ambient conditions; however the shelf life may be extended by keeping the adhesive in refrigerated storage.

The chemistry of this reaction is rather complex. Apparently the epoxy group can react with both the phenolic hydroxyl group and with the methylol

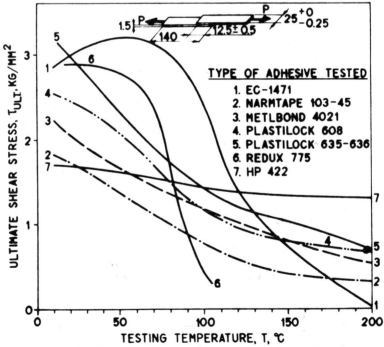

Fig. 1. Variation of ultimate shear stress with testing temperature for a tensile-shear lap joint bonded with different types of metal adhesives.

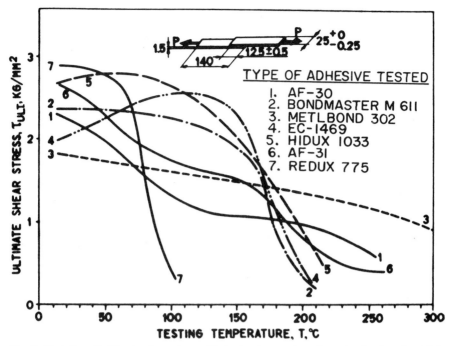

Fig. 2. Variation of ultimate shear stress with testing temperature for a tensile-shear lap joint bonded with different types of metal adhesives.

groups.[18] The dicyandiamide probably acts as both a reactive and a catayltic curing agent.

Since temperature requirements for aircraft and missile adhesive applications have passed the 500°F mark and are approaching the 1000°F mark and higher, there is a need for new adhesive materials which will meet these demands. Both organic and inorganic structures are being investigated:

(1) It is hoped that a combination of phenol group and epoxy resins with silicones may retain the good features of both. Silicone polymers are structurally weak but chemically inert at high temperatures.

(2) Since the phenol group is inherently heat-stable, and polyphenyls are already finding considerable use as high-temperature oils, there is a possibility that they can be used in adhesives, provided they can be prepared as workable polymers.[19]

TABLE 8. IDENTIFICATION OF ADHESIVES IN FIGS. 1 AND 2.

Adhesive	Type	Source
EC 1471	Epoxy	Minnesota Mining & Manufacturing Co.
"Narmtape" 103–45	Nitrile rubber-phenolic	Narmco Resins and Coatings Co.
"Metlbond" 4021	Nitrile rubber-phenolic	Narmco Resins and Coatings Co.
"Plastilock" 608	Nitrile rubber-phenolic	B. F. Goodrich Co.
"Plastilock" 635–636	Nitrile rubber-phenolic	B. F. Goodrich Co.
"Redux" 775	Polyvinyl formal-phenolic (two-phase, liquid and powder)	Aero Research, Ltd. (England)
HP 422	(Probably an epoxy phenolic)	
AF-30	Nitrile rubber-phenolic	Minnesota Mining & Manufacturing Co.
"Bondmaster" M611	Epoxy	Rubber and Asbestos Corp.
"Metlbond" 302	Epoxy phenolic	Narmco Resins and Coatings Co.
EC 1469	Epoxy	Minnesota Mining & Manufacturing Co.
"Hidux" 1033	(A heat-resistant version of "Redux" 775)	
AF-31	Nitrile rubber-phenolic film	Minnesota Mining & Manufacturing Co.

(3) Shell Chemical has tried to build heat resistance into the epoxy molecules with their resin "Epon" 1310.[20] The idealized structure is given as:

(4) Another approach is to build polymers based on the chemistry of such elements as nitrogen, boron, and phosphorus.[21]

(5) Perhaps the greatest possibility for the future lies in the development of ceramic adhesives.[22] These are inherently heat stable at temperatures in excess of 2000°F, and are used extensively where their brittleness and low coefficient of expansion are not limiting factors. Proper compounding minimizes the stresses due to differences in coefficients of expansion. As of now, however, ceramics are still too brittle for use in structural adhesive systems.

References

1. Bair, F. H., "Space Age Adhesives," *Adhesives Age,* **2,** 20 (Feb. 1959).
2. Bikerman, J. J., "The Fundamentals of Tackiness and Adhesion," *J. Colloid Sci.,* **2,** 174 (Feb. 1947).
3. DeBruyne, N. A., and Houwink, R., "Adhesion and Adhesives," p. 19, New York, Elsevier Publishing Co., 1951.
4. Kline, G. M., and Reinhart, F. W., "Fundamentals of Adhesion," *Mech. Eng.,* **72,** 717 (Sept. 1950).
5. DeBruyne, N. A., "Structural Adhesives," pp. 1–6, London, Lange, Maxwell, Springer, 1952.
6. DeLollis, N. J., Rucker, Nancy, and Wier, J. E., "Comparative Strengths of Some Adhesive Adherend Systems," *Trans. ASME,* **73,** 183 (Feb. 1951.
7. Martin, R. W., "The Chemistry of Phenolic Resins," p. 206, New York, John Wiley & Sons Inc., 1956.
7a. Fieser, L., and Fieser, M., "Organic Chemistry," p. 325 Boston, D.C. Heath & Co., 1944.
8. B. F. Goodrich Chemical Company, Service Bull. H-4 "Hycar Phenolic Blends," (Sept. 1950).
   Bascom, R. C., *et al.* "Rubber Resin Blends," *Rubber Age,* **74,** 547 (1954).
9. Engel, H. C., "Improved Structural Adhesives for Bonding Metals," *WADC Tech. Rept 52–156* (June 1952).
10. Martin, R. W., *loc. cit.,* p. 233.
11. Noton, B. R., "Swedish Aeronautical Research on Metallic Honeycomb Sandwich Construction," A Lecture Presented at the Conference on Adhesive Bonded Structures for Aircraft, Los Angeles, Calif., Jan. 31–Feb. 2, 1957.
12. Lee, Henry, and Neville, Kris, "Epoxy Resins," pp. 63–140, New York, McGraw-Hill Book Co., Inc., 1957.
13. *Ibid.,* p. 42.
14. Shell Chemical Corporation *Tech. Bull.* SC-52-45R.
15. Humke, R. K., "Sandwich Panel Materials," *Product Eng.,* **29,** 56 (May 26, 1958).
16. Black, John M., and Blomquist, R. F., "Metal-Bonding Adhesives for High Temperature Service," *Modern Plastics,* **33,** (10), 225 (June 1956).
17. Bundaruk, William, "B-58 Uses Bonded Honeycomb in Primary Structures," *Aviation Age,* **28,** (3), 72 (Sept. 1957).
18. Martin, R. W., *loc. cit.,* p. 40.
19. Trilling, C. A., *et al.,* "A Study of Polyphenyls for Use as Moderators and Coolants in Nuclear Power Reactors," Geneva Conference AEC Papers No. 733 and No. 738.
20. Shell Chemical Corporation Tech. Bull. SC-58-68.
21. Postelnek, W., "Search for High Temperature Elastomer," *Ind. Eng. Chem.,* **50,** 1602 (Nov. 1958).
22. Spriggs, R. M., *et al.,* "Research on Elevated Temperature Resistant Ceramic Structural Adhesives," WADC Tech. Report 55–491, Contract No. AF 33(616)-2556, (Sept. 1956).

— 45 —

Bonding Glass

Frank Moser

Glass Research Center
Pittsburgh Plate Glass Company
Harmar Township, Pennsylvania

The commercial availability of transparent polymers and elastomers has encouraged the use of adhesives for bonding glass either to itself or to other materials. The glass industry utilizes polymers for laminating glass and for numerous other fabrications where glass is one of the structural members. In the manufacture of safety glass and bullet-resistant glass, polyvinyl butyral supplies the interlayer and has excellent specific adhesion to glass. Other adhesive applications are for the installation of glass store fronts; adherence of glass letters to the structural glass; sealers in the construction of double-glazed windows and building panels; rubber-glass assemblies; glass-metal attachment; installing foam glass; and for bonding numerous miscellaneous items to glass.

Adhesive development for glass products has always been a tedious procedure. Physical and optical properties such as clarity, flexibility, and moisture resistance are important in the selection of a glass adhesive for the particular end use, for example, an application of adhesion in the glass industry was in the production of frosted and chipped glass. Animal glues are spread on the surface of the glass, and during the setting the glue shrinks pulling portions of the glass out of the surface giving a decorative effect.

In the development of a suitable interlayer for laminated glass, cellulose nitrate, modified cellulose acetate, polyacrylate and polyester-maleic anhydride resin were investigated. However, polyvinyl butyral resulted in a superior interlayer for glass lamination as well as a glass adhesive material. The other resinous materials continue to serve as adhesives in a minor capacity. Increased emphasis on adhesion as a means for fastening materials resulted in the formulation of structural adhesives for glass using polyvinyl resins as the base resin. Polyvinyl acetate and polyvinyl butyral were used in combination with phenolic, cellulose nitrate, buna-N, and neoprene rubbers to develop formulations for bonding glass to a wide variety of materials.

Numerous applications for bonding glass require special formulations to match adhesive composition with the polarity of the bonding surface and to meet the service conditions to which the adhesive assembly is subjected. For instance, neoprene and buna-N rubber bumper strips are bonded to the edges of tempered glass plates for use as backstops in indoor hockey arenas; whereas in industry the bumper strip is attached to the edges of plate-glass shields used in textile plants. The requirements under the two service conditions are vastly different. In the case of glass plates for hockey arenas the bond is subjected only to interior exposure, while in textile plants the adhesive bond must have moisture, heat, and acid resistance.

For interior use modified cellulose acetate, vinyl acetate, polyacrylates and amine-catalyzed epoxies are satisfactory adhesives for bonding glass in the construction of glass showcases, and for attaching glass finger pulls to sliding glass doors. In installation of decorative glass walls and structural glass panels, elastomeric and rubber-based materials are more suitable for bonding the basic structure in place. The attachment of foam glass requires instantaneous tacky adhesives for holding the insulation in place. This and many other applications emphasize the importance of adhesives for glass fabrication.

GLASS AS A BONDING SURFACE

Physical and chemical properties of glass influence the selection of an adhesive for joining glass. Glass composition varies; essentially it is a silicon-oxygen network containing network modifiers as sodium, calcium, potassium, magnesium, iron and aluminum. Other compositions may substitute either lead dioxide or phosphorus pentoxide for a major portion of the silicon and, in addition, may contain various percentages of arsenic, barium, boron, iron, strontium, and antimony. However, the soda-lime glass is the most commonly used composition for industrial application.

The chemical composition of a freshly prepared glass surface has Si-O and Si-O-Na groups extending into space. However, glass is very absorptive and hydration occurs immediately to form Si-OH groups on its surface. Thus, polar adhesives are suitable for glass bonding, joining to the glass either by hydrogen bonding or primary valence.

Flexibility, expansion and contraction coefficients of the polymeric materials are important for obtaining maximum strength and durability of glass-glass bonds. For example, certain structural adhesives require heat and pressure for setting, and often these curing requirements may induce stress concentrations at the glass surface causing premature glass failures. Therefore, certain precautions are necessary when curing glass-adhesive-glass assemblies at elevated temperatures. If bonding temperatures are 150° C or above, the assembly should be cooled rather slowly from the curing temperature down to room temperature. Often flexible polymers, plasticizers and fillers are added to offset brittleness and differential stresses of adhesive assemblies.

Normally, annealed glass is under compression with approximately 500 psi (for the ½ in. thickness) compression stress at the surface; whereas 250 psi is the tension stress at its center. Thus, unequal stress concentration caused by high shrinkage of adhesives on setting may produce glass failure well below the normal tensile strength of the assembly. Polyvinyl acetate forms good bonds between glass, but excessive stress concentration (750 to 1100 psi) develops at the glass-adhesive interface, and when tested to destruction, glass chipping failure occurs. However, the addition of 20 per cent dibutyl phthalate or any other appropriate plasticizer to the polyvinyl acetate formulation gives normal stress concentrations in the glass and at the glass adhesive interface, while strength of the assembly is materially increased.

Generally, glass is considered as a smooth transparent surface; however, microscopically the glass surface consists of peaks and valleys due to numerous small irregular sized pits which were not entirely removed by the finishing operations. Wetting of the glass and penetration of adhesive into pits depend on the size of the long-chain molecules, their orientation, and entrapped air in the pit. Only in the very flat pits is intimate contact possible. The irregularities of the glass surface provide sufficient variation in surface area which again may influence the ultimate bond strength of glass assemblies.

TESTING BOND STRENGTH

Test Specimens

Evaluation of glass adhesion requires a convenient design for a test specimen. Three designs were considered for tensile test specimens (Fig. 1): the round-center, the square-center and the simplified cross-lap. The round-center and square-center are made using two 1½ x 1½ x ½-in. pieces of glass, which are adhered to both surfaces of either a 1-in. square or a 1 in. in diameter cylinder of glass; whereas the cross-lap is bonded by crossing at a right angle two 1 x 1½ x ½-in. pieces of glass so as to have 1 sq in. of bonded area with a ¼-in. overlap on all four sides.

A statistical evaluation of these designs was made,[1] and the analysis of variance shows that no significant difference in strength was found between the three designs; therefore; the cross-lap specimen was adopted as the standard tensile test,[2] (ASTM D-1344-54T).

For tensile shear testing, either block shear or cross-lap specimens may be used. Figure 2 shows the construction. The block-shear test specimen is made by using 1½ x 1½ x ½-in. pieces of tempered glass with a ½-in. overlap. The cross-lap specimen is constructed in the same manner as for the tensile test, but it is placed in the testing machine jig so that the line of pull is parallel to the bonded area.

Standard testing machines may be used for bond evaluation; moreover either hydraulic loading or cross-head separation types are suitable. Glass is difficult to grip with serrated type grips; therefore special jigs were designed. Figures 3 and 4 show the cross-lap fixture and the tensile shear grips for glass; these jigs may be adapted to any standard testing machine.

Fig. 1. Design for tensile specimens, cross-lap, square-center and round-center types.

Cure

The curing cycle is extremely important in the bonding of transparent materials, since a good bond includes an adhesive film free from voids and other imperfections, as well as sufficient strength to support the fabrication. The studies on the curing of thermoplastic and phenolic adhesives were undertaken because the suitability of commercial adhesives for glass had not been established. Previously these were designed either for metals or other varied materials. For metal-to-metal bonds, strength and elasticity of the adhesive film are perhaps the more important

requisites; whereas a glass-glass bond must possess the same requisites, furthermore a transparent film, free from voids and cracks upon aging, is desirable.

Solvents and monomeric liquids are utilized in the formulation of solution adhesives and are essential to enable the polymeric material to wet the surface of the adherend. Since manufacturers' recommendations vary widely for the same based adhesive material, the adhesive types should be compared by identical curing cycles. Imperfect bonds may be attributed to either entrapped air or an incomplete volatilization of solvent, which may cause the adhesive film to bubble on the

Fig. 2. Shear specimens for testing glass adhesives.

application of heat and pressure. If solvent is still present, voids may form when pressure is removed after the completion of the cure. Curing cycles may be further complicated if the adhesives are copolymerizing mixtures. The open portion of the curing cycle should be long enough to remove the last traces of solvent, but not of such length as to induce set. The film must be capable of plastic flow when composited, to provide intimate contact of the adhesive to the solid surfaces being joined.

For many systems, the following procedure for heat-curing adhesives was successful: After coating the glass, a 1 hr air-drying period was allowed, which was followed by a 10-min open heat activation at 250°F and assembly under 200 lb pressure for curing at 275°F for 45 min. For room-temperature epoxies, the glass was coated with the catalyzed adhesive, assembled under contact pressure, and allowed to age for 7 days at room temperature before testing. Heat-cure epoxies (100 per cent solids) were bonded according to the recommendation of the manufacturer.

FORMULATION OF GLASS ADHESIVES

Polymeric materials are the main constituents for glass adhesives. The more promising materials

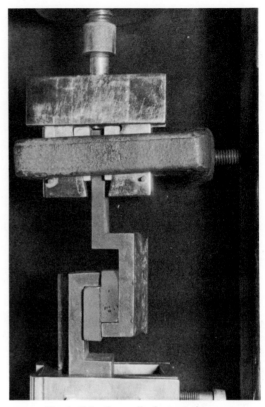

Fig. 4. Grips for tensile shear specimens.

are selected on the basis of polarity, available functional groups, and compatibility. Polar polymeric substances containing functional groups, such as —OH, —COOH, —C=O, and —COOCH$_3$, are suitable for bonding glass. Chemical structures containing the above molecular end groups are the epoxies, butyrals, polyvinyl acetate, copolymer vinyl-chloride-acetate alcohols, and polyacrylates. Various combinations of these resins with either phenolic or butadiene-acrylonitrile polymers are used for formulating glass adhesives.

Polarity of the material is a very convenient guide for selecting the polymer combination for a specific adhesive application. N. deBruyne[3] claims that similar polarities are desirable for compatibility and adhesion. The adhesion of dissimilar material is more difficult, and other writers[4, 5] have reported that an adjustment in polarity is accomplished by the application of a primer coating on the solid before applying the adhesive for bonding. In other cases, the difference in polarity between two structural members is compensated by formulation of a bifunctional adhesive molecule which by orientation of the end groups will align the respective polar groups of the adhesive molecule toward the respective polarities of the adherends.

Fig. 3. Grips for cross-lap specimens.

Fig. 5. Contact angle indicator.

Polarities of polymers and solid adherends are determined on a comparable basis using contact angle measurements in air-water systems. A modified captive-bubble apparatus[6] was used as shown in Fig. 5. The solid is placed in the glass cell containing distilled water; subsequently, an air bubble is placed on the holder which is lowered until the bubble makes contact with the solid surface. After the bubble and solid are in equilibrium, the contact angle is read by positioning the cross-hairs in the telescope on line with the tangent to the curvature that the bubble makes with the solid.

For classifying material by this method, contact angles 0 to 20° are polar; 21 to 44° are slightly polar materials; 45 to 70° are moderately nonpolar; and 71 to 100° are nonpolar.

Figures 6 to 9 illustrate the contact of the air bubble with various solids. Contact angles are as follows: glass 0°, a butadiene-acrylonitrile film 18 to 20°, and "Durez" phenolic 12687 film 48 to 50°. These contact angles indicate possible compounding combinations and group compatibility of materials for adhesive formulation. Table 1 may serve as a guide in adhesive formulations for glass, of which the lowest contact angles are preferred.

Fig. 6. Contact angle photograph of a glass surface.

Fig. 7. Contact angle photograph of butadiene acrylo-nitrile.

Fig. 8. Contact angle photograph for "Durez" 12697.

Compatibility of materials and adhesion are most likely to result if the adhesive materials have the same range of contact angles. For example, resins such as polyvinyl butyral, polyvinyl acetate, "Vinylite" 28-18, "Durez" 12987 and "Hycar"

TABLE 1. CONTACT ANGLES OF POLYMER FILM IN AIR-WATER-SYSTEM.

Film	Degrees
Polymethyl methacrylate	63–64
N-propyl methacrylate	63–65
Polyvinyl butyral (XYHL)	30–32
Polyvinyl acetate (AYAF)	25–28
Copolymer "Vinylite" (VMCH)	65–67
Copolymer "Vinylite" (VYHH)	60–62
"Vinylite" 28–18	15–18
"Durez" 12987	22–23
"Durez" 12687	48–50
"Bakelite" (BR 2432)	35–38
"Bakelite" (BV 1112)	43–44
Cellulose nitrate	36–37
Cellulose acetate	38–40
Ethyl cellulose	60–61
"Pliolite" S-50	33–35
"Pliolite" S-5	70–72
"Parlon" 125	69–71
"Hycar" OR-15	35–36
"Polyblend"	55–57
Polystyrene	80–82
Neoprene GNA	32–34
Aryl sulfonamide formaldehyde	33–35
Amine catalyzed epoxy	18–21
"Hycar" OR-15-"Vinylite" VMCH	60–62
Oil-modified phenol butyral	43–45
Silicate-vinyl-phenolic	40–42

OR-15 have contact angles in the polar range and are used for glass adhesives. If polyvinyl butyral (XYHL) is plasticized with dibutyl phthalate, the contact angle is changed from 30 to 20°, resulting in increased adhesion. When two similar contact angle materials as "Durez" 12987 and "Vinylite" XYHL are mixed in a ketone solvent, a homogeneous composition forms; however, if the "Durez" 12687 phenolic, a more nonpolar material (50°

Fig. 9. Contact angle photograph of "Durez" 12897.

contact angle) is used, it is inadequately compatible with "Vinylite" XYHL, resulting in no appreciable adhesion.

Compounding of adhesives for glass to nonpolar solids is accomplished by formulating bifunctional resinous molecules which are obtained by mixing the different polarity resins in a mutual solvent. "Vinylite" VMCH (65° contact angle) can be mixed with a cyclized rubber (35° contact angle); in order to avoid a gel, however, the solution of the higher contact angle material must be combined gradually with the lower contact angle material.

An example of adhesives for bonding glass to dissimilar material is the adhesion of a clear cast phenolic sheet plastic to glass. Formulation requires a polyfunctional adhesive having polar and nonpolar groups in the same adhesive molecule. During the preparation and bonding of the adhesive, an intermolecular arrangement occurs which allows for the polar groups to be aligned to the glass, while nonpolar groups align toward the phenol aldehyde. The 50 to 52° contact angle cast phenolic surface is bonded to a 0° glass surface by copolymerizing resins which are miscible in a common solvent. Table 1 shows that "Bakelite" BV 1112, a substituted phenolic resin, has a contact angle from 44 to 45°; whereas "Vinylite" resin has a contact angle from 15 to 30°. These are miscible in a ketone solvent and the "Vinylite" XYHL-BV 1112 formulation shows excellent adhesion for bonding the glass to the cast phenolic.

Dissimilar materials may also be bonded with the aid of a polyfunctional-type primer. For example, glass may be treated with a silicate-vinyl-phenolic primer. A thin multimolecular film changes the glass surface to a nonpolar one. Here again, the theory of molecular rearrangement of the complex primer molecule is that the silicate portion attaches to the glass and leaves a phenolic radical to give a nonpolar surface. Another example of bifunctionality is the treatment of glass with a vinyl-chloro-silane. Here the silicone portion links with the glass surface by a hydration mechanism,[7] leaving the nonpolar CH_2 groups exposed.

Table 2 shows adhesion secured with various resins and resinous combinations on glass treated with the silicate-vinyl-phenolic primer before bonding with the adhesives.

The data in Table 2 show the effects of surface polarity on bonding with various adhesives. Phenolics are only moderately polar and have little or no adhesion to glass; however an increase in adhesion results if the glass is first primed. The contact angle of the glass surface is changed from 0 to 50°. Bond strength of the modified phenolic adhesives

TABLE 2. COMPARISON OF ADHESION SECURED ON GLASS WITH AND WITHOUT A PRIMER SURFACE.

Type of Adhesives	Bonding Strength Under Tensile Loading	
	Glass Surface (psi)	Glass-Treated Silicate-Vinyl-Phenolic (psi)
Modified phenolic	1600	3200
Phenol butyral	1650	2250
Phenol aldehyde	0	700
Resorcinol	0	400
Alkyd styrene	200	700
Modified buna-N	1200	1200

is increased from 1600 to 3200 psi. Resorcinol and phenoladehyde adhesives increased from 0 to 700 psi, while the slightly nonpolar adhesive (modified VMCH buna-N type) showed no appreciable effect. These results confirm that adhesion is improved where the adherends and the adhesives are in the same polarity range.

The combining of two or more polymers is often desirable. Indication of the type of bond failure and bond strength of polymers together with the polarity classification, which are given in Table 3, are useful in selecting polymers and polymer mixture for formulating adhesives for glass. Often an improvement in strength or in physical properties is obtained either by combining resins or adding a plasticizer. A further examination of the polymers listed in Table 3 shows that each of the materials used individually gives relatively low bond strength between glass surfaces and fails adhesively. The ones giving appreciable adhesion are the vinyl-chloride-acetate-alcohol copolymer, plasticized polyvinyl acetate, and plasticized polyvinyl butyral. The phenolic resins and slightly nonpolar substances produce contact failures. Some of the epoxies show fair strength, but these also can be improved by addition of a flexible polyamide resin or plasticizer. The amount of adhesion is influenced by the physical properties of the polymer. In case of the pure polymers, assembly strength is impaired by brittleness, while in others the lack of wetting of the nonpolar polymer causes the resinous material to squeeze out at the edges of the bonded adherends leaving an insufficient adhesive film and little, if any, adhesion.

Combinations which increase flexibility and wetting properties determine the selection of the polymers for formulating glass adhesives. Polymeric substances that were compatible were tested as adhesive formulations for glass. Polyvinyl butyral is an excellent base material for a glass adhesive,

TABLE 3. POLYMERIC SUBSTANCES AS GLASS ADHESIVES.

Polymers	Bond Strength under Tensile Load (psi)	Type of Bond Failure	Polarity (Contact Angle) Degree
Polyvinyl acetate ("Bakelite" AYAF)	550	Adhesion	25–28
Polyvinyl acetate-dibutyl phthalate	1200	Adhesion	18–20
Polyvinyl chloride-acetate ("Bakelite" VMCH)	400	Adhesion	65–67
Polyvinyl chloride-acetate ("Bakelite" VYHH)	100	Contact and adhesion	60–62
Polyvinyl butyral	600	Adhesion	30–32
Polyvinyl chloride-acetate alcohol	1200	Largely glass	24–26
Polyvinyl butyral-dibutyl phthalate ("Bakelite" XYHL)	1200	Adhesion	18–20
Methyl methacrylate	0–100	Very little if any adhesion	62–64
N-propyl methacrylate	200	Adhesion	63–65
Polyvinyl alcohol	400	Adhesion	14–15
Polyvinyl chloride	0–100	No adhesion	66–68
Cellulose nitrate	200	Adhesion and contact	36–37
Ethyl cellulose	0–50	No appreciable adhesion	60–61
Phenolic ("Durez" 12987)	500	Adhesion	22–24
Phenolic ("Bakelite" BR 17620)	300	Adhesion	38–40
Substituted phenol aldehyde ("Bakelite" BV-1112)	100	Adhesive too brittle	43–44
Aryl sulfonamide formaldehyde ("Bakelite" MS-80)	100	Cohesive	33–35
Styrene butadiene ("Pliolite" S-5)	0–100	No appreciable adhesion	70–72
Cyclized rubber ("Pliolite" S-50)	100	Little adhesion	37–40
Neoprene Type GN-A	0–100	Adhesive	35–38
Butadiene acrylonitrile ("Hycar" OR-15)	200	Cohesive	35–36
Epoxy: "Epon" 1062	500	Adhesion	20–23
"Epon" 824	200	Adhesion	50–52
"Epon" 1001	400	Adhesive	60–62

but it is somewhat lacking in moisture resistance and in low temperature flexibility. Consequently, the formulations of glass adhesives are centered around modifications of this polymer. Additions of compatible material to polyvinyl butyral included phenolics, substituted phenol aldehydes, cyclized rubber and butadiene-acrylonitrile polymers. Combinations of the above polymers were tested, and the results are given in Table 4.

A substituted phenolic resin ("Bakelite" BV 1112), which was used for modifying the butyral,

is moderately nonpolar but is soluble with the butyral in mutual solvents. When mixed in equal portions on a solid basis, the cured bond gives 2800 psi under tensile loading with improved weathering qualities.

A combination of a terpene-phenolic resin with polyvinyl butyral did not increase strength considerably (1100 psi), but this mixture gave a glass surface bond failure which indicated stress concentrations at the glass-adhesive interface. More desirable adhesives with respect to normal stress

TABLE 4. COMBINATIONS OF POLYMERIC SUBSTANCES AS GLASS ADHESIVES.

Polymer Combination	Bond Strength (psi)	Type of Bond Failure
Polyvinyl butyral-cresylic phenol	2800	Adhesive
Polyvinyl butyral-oil and ester gum-modified phenolic	1900	Cohesive
Polyvinyl butyral-terpene phenolic	1100	Glass surface
Vinyl copolymer(chloride-acetate-alcohol)vinyl butyral-phenolic	1700	Cohesive
Polyvinyl chloride-acetate-alcohol with phenolic	1800	Cohesive
Polyvinyl chloride-acetate with a phenolic	800	Cohesive
Phenolic-buna-N ("Durez" 12987-"Hycar" 1032)	1400	Glass
Phenolic-butadiene-acrylonitrile ("Durez" 12687-"Hycar" 1032)	1000	Adhesive and some cohesive
Cyclized rubber-polyvinyl chloride acetate	500	Adhesive
Polyacrylate buna-N ("Hycar" 1032)	400	Adhesive
Polyamide-epoxy	1200	Adhesion

concentrations at the interface are obtained with cohesive-type failures; therefore, additional combinations were tested. One of the better formulations was obtained by combining a tung oil ester gum-modified phenolic resin with a polyvinyl butyral. Such modified phenol-butyral adhesives give excellent adhesion to glass, with good clarity and moisture resistance. Assembly strengths up to 2000 psi may be obtained.

Other polymer mixtures producing a cohesive-type failure were obtained by combining a copolymer vinyl chloride-acetate-alcohol, a polyvinyl butyral, and a substituted phenolic. A bond strength of 1700 psi was obtained; however 1800 psi was the strength when the copolymer was mixed only with a phenolic resin. In both cases cohesive failure was prevalent.

Butadiene-acrylonitrile-phenolic and the vinyl-butadiene-acrylonitrile combinations are desirable where more flexible bonds are needed. These combinations are used in quite a number of available commercial adhesives which are suitable for glass as well as for glass-metal bonding. A "Durez" phenolic resin 12987-"Hycar" 1032X1 formulation gave 1400 psi under tensile loading with glass failure; whereas the "Durez" 12687-"Hycar" 1032 resins gave only 1000 psi with adhesive failure from the glass.

This type of adhesive failure can be attributed to the phenol portion of these combinations. The "Durez" 12687 resin is decidedly more nonpolar than the 12987 resin; therefore it is less noncompatible with the glass surface, resulting in adhesive failure. The acrylate buna-N resinous mixtures are not suitable for glass, giving only 400 psi, with adhesion failure. This mixture contains a polymethyl methacrylate and undoubtedly was somewhat too nonpolar for the glass surface. More adhesion occurs if a polyethyl acrylate is used with the "Hycar" 1032X1 resin for bonding glass.

Heat-curing epoxies are ideally suited for glass surfaces. A mixture of "Epon" 1001 with polyamide "Versamid" 100 makes a very desirable adhesive, and this combination is further improved by the addition of tricresyl phosphate plasticizer.

COMMERCIAL ADHESIVES

Polymers and polymer combinations constitute the bulk of the adhesives offered for glass adhesion; moreover the ones on the market are either viscous polymers or prepolymers which set by further heating and/or the adding of hardeners. The solution-type is another form in which the polymeric materials are dissolved in suitable solvents. Both types are satisfactory for glass provided that in case of the solvent-type, the volatiles are allowed to completely evaporate before assemblying the adhesive coated surfaces.

Glass adhesives can be classified according to the basic polymeric ingredients. Usually, for bonding glass, transparent materials are desired to meet specifications, but occasionally dark-colored bonds are acceptable depending on the end use. The bulk of structural adhesives are heat-setting, as curing at elevated temperatures produces the durable weather-resistant bonds. Phenolic-polyvinyl butyral and the modified phenolics are in this category, having transparency, high bond strength, and moisture resistance. Commercially available adhesives of this type include "Bostik" 7026 by the B and B Chemical Company, BJ-16320 by Bakelite Corporation, Cycleweld 55-105 by Chrysler Cycleweld Division, FM 45 and FM 46 by Bloomingdale Rubber Company. There are other manufacturers and suppliers of modified phenolics adhesives, but only the above were tested.

Commercial adhesives for each representative type are listed in Table 5. All these adhesives were tested for adhesion and are classified according to the tensile strength, the type of assembly failure, and durability. These adhesives are most satisfactory for strength and durability provided heat and pressure are applied during curing according to the recommended procedure presented earlier (pages 525–526). Strengths as high as 5500 psi were obtained. These bonds have excellent weathering qualities, and glass failure results when these assemblies are tested to destruction.

Polyvinyl butyral is the adhesive for laminated glass and bullet-resistant glass. du Pont's "Butacite" and Monsanto's "Butvar" are supplied in sheet form for this fabrication; also, butyrals, which are available in granular form, may be dissolved in an appropriate solvent to give a solution adhesive for bonding glass-to-glass. Excellent adhesion results provided the solvent is completely volatilized before assembly of the glass. The bond strength of the butyral adhesives range from 2000 to 2500 psi. Plasticized polyvinyl butyrals (20 to 45 parts of triethylene glycol di-2-ethyl butyrate to 100 parts of resin) give good glass adhesion ranging from 2000 to 4000 psi.

Phenolic-nitrile rubber formulations are compounded by numerous manufacturers. Generally, this type of adhesive varies in color from light amber to black; also, adherends other than glass may be bonded with the phenolic nitrile. Some of the representative adhesives for this class are designated in Table 5 as EC826, EC776 by the Minne-

TABLE 5. COMMERCIAL ADHESIVES MOST DESIRABLE FOR GLASS.

| Trade Name | Chemical Type | Bond Characteristics | | |
		Strength (psi)	Type of Failure	Weathering Quality
"Butacite," "Butvar"	Polyvinyl butyral	2000–4000	Adhesive	Fair
"Bostik" 7026, FM-45, FM-46	Phenolic butyral	2000–5500	Glass	Excellent
EC826, EC776			Adhesion and glass	
N-199, "Scotchweld"	Phenolic nitrile	1000–1200		Excellent
"Pliobond" M-20, EC847	Vinyl nitrile	1200–3000	Adhesion and glass	Fair to good
EC711, EC882				
EC870	Neoprene	800–1200	Adhesion and cohesive	Fair
EC801, EC612	Polysulfide	200– 400	Cohesive	Excellent
EC526, R660T, EC669	Rubber base	200– 800	Adhesive	Fair to poor
"Silastic"	Silicone	200– 300	Cohesive	Excellent
"Rez-N-Glue," du Pont 5459	Cellulose vinyl	1000–1200	Adhesive	Fair
"Vinylite" AYAF, 28-18	Vinyl acetate	1500–2000	Adhesive	Poor
"Araldite," "Epon" L-1372,				
ERL-2774, R-313, C-14,				
SH-1, J-1152	Epoxy	600–2000	Adhesive	Fair to good

sota Mining and Manufacturing Company. Unsupported tapes such as "Scotch-Weld" and N-199 were designed more for metal bonding but they are also suitable for glass bonding. Tensile strength evaluation shows that 1000 to 1200 psi are obtained with excellent moisture resistance; however, the adhesive film is brittle when cured at high temperatures which may result in a chipping of the glass surface upon failure.

"Pliobond" M-20 and EC847 are representative of the vinyl-nitrile-type adhesives which were tested for glass. Strength will vary from 1000 to 3000 psi depending on the type of curing. For example, if room-setting cure is attempted the strength is relatively low, i.e., below 1000 psi because solvent remains entrapped between the glass surfaces. If the glass-coated adhesive film is heat activated before assembly under pressure, strength increases to approximately 1200 psi, while 3000 psi is obtained by a post cure of 30 min. at 150°C.

Neoprene-based adhesives will bond glass-to-glass, but give opaque and dark-colored bonds. These are largely solvent-type adhesives for bonding glass to other materials. They cure slowly at room temperature, but heat activation improves bond strength. Applications for such adhesives include bonding felts to glass, rubber to glass, and foam glass to basic structures. Manufacturers of this type of adhesive are too numerous to list.

The rubber-based group takes in a wide variety of materials and may be compounded from natural, buna-N (nitrile), buna-S (butadiene-styrene) and reclaimed rubbers. Numerous adhesive applications can utilize this type and are suggested for interior use to adhere glass to innumerable surfaces. Bond

strengths are sufficient for this end use although tensile strengths vary from 200 to 800 psi. Most suppliers have such adhesives for sale. The adhesives tested (Table 5) were obtained from the Minnesota Mining and Manufacturing Company and from the B. F. Goodrich Company.

Polysulfide and silicone types are primarily for special requirements giving low bond strength, but good durability. The use is usually limited to sealers. Manufacturers of these types are General Electric, Lord Manufacturing Company, Minnesota Mining and Manufacturing Company, Thiokol Corporation, and Dow Chemical Company.

The vinyl acetate and cellulose-vinyl acetate adhesives are transparent and give fair bond strength for interior use, e.g., joining glass to itself, to wood, and to other materials. They are room-setting provided adequate time is allowed for solvent evaporation and that they are assembled while the adhesive film still has some tackiness. Heat activation and heat cures, which are permissible, will depend on the fabrication. This type of cure gives bond strengths ranging from 1500 to 2000 psi. "Rez-N-Glue" by Schwartz Chemical, du Pont 5459, and "Vinylseal" 28-18 by Bakelite are representative of the above adhesives.

The epoxy adhesives are especially desirable for glass because of their setting properties and the need for only contact pressure during the cure. Both room-setting and heat-setting-types are available. These resins are well adapted for glass surfaces due to low shrinkage, clarity and high bond strength; however, some are lacking in moisture resistance especially under high humidity. Manufacturers of epoxy adhesives are numerous, and new formulators are constantly beginning production. Recently, epoxidized polyolefins have been introduced into the field to improve high temperature stability. Epoxy adhesives were supplied for testing by Ciba Corporation, Bakelite Corporation, Chrysler Cycleweld Division, Armstrong Cork, Borden Company, Carl H. Biggs Company, Shell Corporation, and other formulators. "Araldite" I, L-1372, "R"-313, C-14, ERL-2774, "Epon" 828, SH-1 and J1152 are epoxies which give desirable glass adhesion. "Araldite" I, a high temperature curing epoxy, has good adhesion giving over 2000 psi with a good moisture-resistant bond; hence it will withstand temperature to 250°F without degradation. The majority of the above epoxy adhesives are room-temperature setting with addition of the appropriate hardener. All give satisfactory bonds with glass. Some variation in strength and color was obtained, but all of them are suitable for glass bonding.

References

1. Rutzler, J. E., and Savage, R. L., "Adhesion and Adhesives," pp. 84–90, New York, John Wiley & Sons, Inc., 1954.
2. ASTM Standards 1954, pp. 160–163.
3. de Bruyne, N. A., "The Nature of Adhesion," *Aircraft Engineer,* **167,** 51 (1939).
4. Thinius, Kurt von, "Zur Kenntnis der Haftfestegkert Zwichen Schifschten Aus Verschiedenen Polymerem," *Kunstoffe,* **37,** 36 (1947).
5. Moser, F., "Approximating the Attractive Forces of Adhesion for Glass and Other Surfaces," *ASTM Bull.,* **169,** 169–249 (1950).
6. Moser, F., "Polymeric Adhesives for Glass," *Plastic Technol.,* **2,** 799–805 (1956).
7. Weyl, W. A., "The Theoretical Basis of Adhesion," *Proc. Amer. Soc. Testing Materials,* **46,** 1506–1516 (1946).

Section D

BONDING TECHNOLOGY

Applying the One-Part Adhesive

Arthur Hirsch

Skeist Laboratories, Inc.
Newark, New Jersey

The selection of the correct method of application of an adhesive may be as important to the success of the bond as the choice of an adhesive itself. Previous chapters have established that the adhesive layer should be applied: (a) as a fluid, (b) uniformly, (c) thinly, and (d) leaving no voids.

These requirements seem simple enough, but it has taken great effort to even approach these ideal conditions.

The application of adhesives may be performed on a piece by piece, or on a continuous mass production basis. Most of this chapter has been devoted to discussion of these latter methods. However, not all operations can be converted to a continuous application process. The gluing of furniture, for instance, requires that each *piece* be handled separately. In such instances, the adhesive may be applied with a: (a) brush, (b) spray gun, (c) dip, (d) trowel, (e) knife, (f) roller, (g) special applicator.

In all these instances, it is most difficult to apply a reproducibly uniform quantity. It is quite possible, however, that these "custom assemblies" are not sufficiently alike to require identical quantities of adhesive. It is therefore common practice to furnish the joint with an excess of adhesive and eliminate the unnecessary portion by pressure, wiping, or some other means.

CONTINUOUS APPLICATION

In some instances, it becomes possible to convert from manual to the automated, continuous application of the adhesive. This offers not only increased speed of operation but highly improved quality as well. This mechanical process consists of several interdependent operations, a brief discussion of which will serve as an introduction to the problem of the applicator.

Feed

The material (substrate) to be coated with an adhesive must be fed to the applicator. A good feed mechanism must fulfill the following requirements:

(1) *Speed.* It must keep up with the applicator, delivering as much as 2000 fpm of material.
(2) *Continuity.* It must deliver substrate continuously. Stoppages for reloading are intolerable. Each interruption in production is costly, necessitating wasteful clean-up and start-up operations.
(3) *Positioning.* It must deliver the substrate in proper position to the coater. Mechanical, pneumatic, or electronic devices are generally employed to maintain the substrate in proper position.
(4) *Tensioning.* It must maintain uniform tension on the substrate. This is especially important for flexible webs. Any change in tension may cause shifting of position, uneven application, wrinkles, or breaks.

Applicator

This part of the mechanized adhesives application will be discussed in detail on pages 538–542.

Dryer

In most instances, the adhesive is applied from a solution. It is necessary to evaporate all or most of the solvent before assembling adhesively joined parts. The dryer fulfills this function.

The design of the dryer will vary depending on the substrate, the desired drying speed, the type of solvent to be eliminated, and a host of other factors. Basically, however, dryers are essentially nothing more than ovens for the purpose of evaporating solvents.

For hot-melt adhesives, the conventional dryer may be replaced by a cooling compartment.

Assembly

Adhesively coated materials may be joined immediately on leaving the drying chamber. At times, however, it may prove more convenient or desirable to postpone this operation for some time, in which case the dried material will be stacked for storage or shipment.

In the case of porous substances, such as paper, some films, or wood, for instance, assembly may actually precede the drying operation. This, however, requires that the assembled parts be held in proper juxtaposition throughout the drying period. Such alignment may be achieved with the aid of pressure rollers, clamps, or any one of many similar devices.

EXCESS APPLICATORS
(Post-Metering Applicators)

One of the methods of applying adhesives in a continuous process involves deposition of an excess of adhesive on the substrate, followed by removal of all but the required amount. This may be accomplished in a number of ways, but only a few basic examples will be cited here. Many combinations of these basic processes are of course possible.

The Knife Applicator

This is probably the simplest type of adhesive applicator. In most instances, the adhesive is deposited on the web in large excess. One might actually consider the moving substrate as the adhesive reservoir. The knife (or doctor blade) both spreads and meters the adhesive.

This method has many advantages. Initial installation as well as operation and maintenance cost are relatively low. Clean-up time is held to a minimum. The system can accommodate almost any type of adhesive from a watery liquid consistency to a heavy paste. It can operate at fairly high speeds.

Some, however, oppose this as a crude method of application, emphasizing that it is difficult to avoid streaking and uneven adhesive distribution.

A few of the more important variations of the knife coater will be discussed in the following paragraphs.

The Supported Knife. This nomenclature might possibly be misleading. The support does not apply to the knife—it is meant for the substrate. The material to be coated passes over a support such as a roller, belt, or blanket at the instance it passes under the knife.

Figures 1 and 2 show the knife-over-roller and the knife-over-blanket applicators, respectively. These are especially suitable for thin, fragile substrates. Coating weight is controlled by tension as well as angle and contour of the knife.

The Unsupported Knife. Here, too, it is the substrate, not the knife, that is unsupported. There are several such arrangements in use.

In the "floating knife" coater (Fig. 3), the web has no support when it passes under the knife. This is probably the simplest type of arrangement. The substrate, however, must have a high tensile strength and low degree of elongation. The quantity of adhesive applied is a function of the tension and the characteristics of the knife.

The "inverted knife" arrangement (Fig. 4) is often employed with adhesives of lower viscosity.

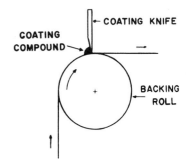

Fig. 1. Knife-over-roller applicator. (*Courtesy John Waldron Corp.*)

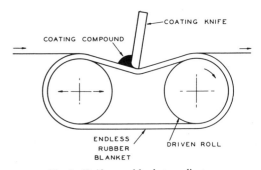

Fig. 2. Knife-over-blanket applicator. (*Courtesy John Waldron Corp.*)

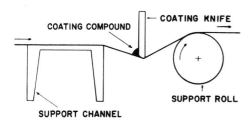

Fig. 3. Floating knife applicator. (*Courtesy John Waldron Corp.*)

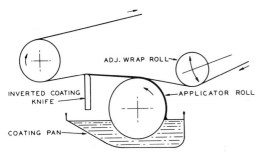

Fig. 4. Inverted knife applicator. (*Courtesy John Waldron Corp.*)

This method departs from one of the fundamentals of knife coating—the adhesives reservoir on the web. The adhesive is no longer "stored" on the moving substrate. Examination of Fig. 4 will reveal the introduction of a trough designed to hold the adhesive. A roller transfers adhesive in excessive amounts from the trough to the substrate. The knife is placed in such a position as to remove all but the required quantity of adhesive from the web and return it to the trough.

The Air Knife. Compressed air may be employed in place of the steel blade to remove excess adhesive. Numerous variations in the arrangement of components are possible. One such applicator is shown in Fig. 5.

Air-knife coaters do have certain limitations:[3]

(a) They are unable to handle high viscosity, high solids adhesives.

(b) They do not operate satisfactorily at speeds in excess of 1200 rpm.

(c) They do not perform well with organic solvents of high volatility.

(d) They cannot produce a uniform glue line on an irregular surface.

Nevertheless, the air knife does offer many advantages over other adhesive applicators, and it is highly recommended[3, 4] for the following reasons:

(1) Simple to operate.
(2) Inexpensive to install and maintain.
(3) Uniform results.
(4) Very good at low weight applications (range between 0.01 and 5 lb per 1000 sq ft).
(5) Relatively high speed.

The Trailing Blade. Several U. S. Patents[8, 9, 10, 11] disclosed a somewhat unique method which combines some of the features of the previously discussed applicators. Figure 6 shows a trailing blade coater. The adhesive is applied to the web by rollers prior to reaching the blade. The flexible blade is pressed against (or supported by) a rubber-coated roll and thus meters the adhesive, any excess being returned to the trough. Various modifications of this method are possible.

Spray Applicator

The spraying of adhesives has many limitations. Some of the difficulties encountered are due to:

(1) Shutdowns due to clogged nozzles.
(2) Waste—inability to confine spray to designated area.
(3) Variations in coating weight.
(4) Slow speeds.
(5) High solvent content—increased fire and health hazards.

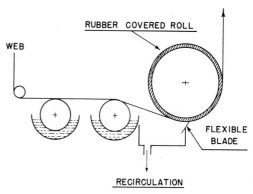

Fig. 6. Trailing blade applicator. (With permission of G. L. Booth and N. H. Laughraty *Tapp,* **43,** No. 5, p. 200A–203A.)

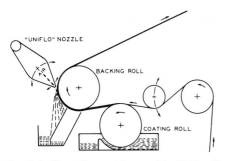

Fig. 5. Air knife applicator. (*Courtesy John Waldron Corp.*)

The spray applicator however may find increased use with two-component adhesive systems.

Various modifications of the basic spray system have been designed to overcome some of its shortcomings. One such innovation introduced a transfer roll and the adhesive is sprayed onto the roll rather than the substrate. This method is claimed to yield a more uniform coating.

PREMETERED APPLICATORS

The favored, more sophisticated method of applying adhesives employs an apparatus which measures the desired quantity prior to dispensing it, thus depositing the exact amount on the substrate.

Roll Applicator

The roll rotating in an adhesive reservoir acts like an endless brush. It dips into the adhesive, carries it out of the trough, and wipes it onto the substrate or some intermediary which, in turn, deposits it on the web. The clean roll (or, rather, its clean portion) returns to the reservoir to start the transfer cycle once more. Roll coaters vary somewhat in the method of metering and transferring the adhesive onto the substrate.

Dip Coating. This is a simple but not too satisfactory type of applicator. The substrate travels around a roll that is partially or fully immersed in the adhesive bath. One or both faces of the web could thus be coated in one pass. This is not a premetered application.

Speed of operation is very slow and metering of adhesive applied is nearly impossible.

Kiss Roll Applicator. This may consist of an arrangement of one or more rolls, the lowermost partially immersed in adhesive. The substrate passes under tension over the top roll. Both web and kiss roll are traveling in the same direction. The adhesive film carried by the roll transfers only partially onto the web. There is no wiping action which would remove all the adhesive from the roll. Instead, there is a "kiss"—a contact between web and roll which causes the adhesive film to "split," transferring only partially onto the substrate.

The "split" is often responsible for "kiss marks" (a rippled pattern in the coated application). If the adhesive has sufficient flow, these "marks" will eliminate themselves. Otherwise, it may be necessary to install smoothing bars.

Metering may be accomplished by adjusting the clearance between the two rolls in Fig. 8, or by employing a doctor roll or blade to remove excess not from the web, but from the roll before application to the web.

There is a tendency for the web to lash at high speeds or at lowering of tension. This may be overcome by installation of a rubber backup roll as shown in Fig. 9.

Reverse-Roll Applicator. As its name implies, the reverse-roll applicator consists of one or more rolls in which the applicator roll travels in a direction opposite to that of the web, thus creating a wiping effect which transfers all the adhesive from the roll to the substrate.

A large number of modifications and variations of the basic reverse-roll applicator are in actual use. The simplest type, consisting of a single roll, has

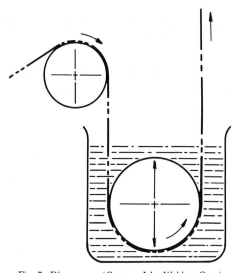

Fig. 7. Dip coater. (*Courtesy John Waldron Corp.*)

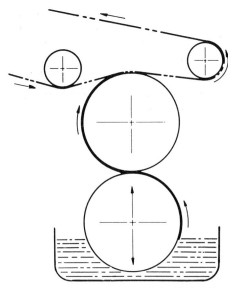

Fig. 8. Kiss applicator. (*Courtesy John Waldron Corp.*)

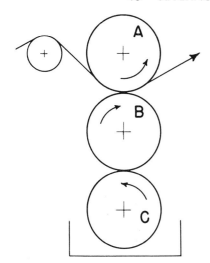

Fig. 9. Kiss applicator. (*Courtesy Dilts Div., The Black-Clawson Co., Inc.*)

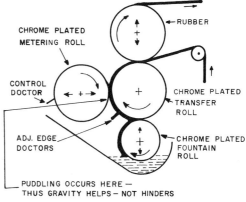

Fig. 11. Reverse roll applicator.

limited value since it cannot apply a measured amount of adhesive.

A vertical two-roll arrangement in which the web passes between the rolls is often referred to as "nip roll applicator." Thickness of the coating is controlled by the distance between the rolls. To compensate for variations in web thickness, it is customary to employ at least one rubber roll.

Metering can be achieved by using two rolls and a doctor blade as shown in Fig. 10. The two horizontally positioned rolls travel in the same direction, opposite to that of the web. The thickness of adhesive applied will be determined not only by the gap between the two reverse rolls, but also by the relative speeds of the web and rolls, and the viscosity of the coating material.

The applicator can be improved greatly by adding two more rolls to the above unit. This device, depicted in Fig. 11, has the following features:

(*a*) The fountain roll is smaller than in the two or three roll applicator. This eliminates splashing and reduces foaming.

(*b*) The metering roll is not in the fountain, thus

curtailing splashing. Closer metering is possible.

(*c*) The rubber backup roll assures complete transfer, eliminates "kiss" marks, and reduces high tension requirements.

The reverse-roll applicator can deposit adhesives coatings from less than 1 mil to approximately 20 mils in one pass.

Engraved-Roll Applicator. This method, employed where very accurate control of coating uniformity is desired, is often referred to as rotogravure coating.

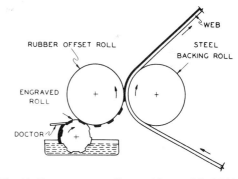

Fig. 12. Rotogravure applicator. (*Courtesy John Waldron Corp.*)

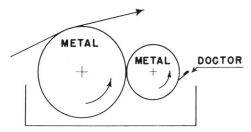

Fig. 10. Reverse roll applicator. (*Courtesy Dilts Div., The Black-Clawson Co., Inc.*)

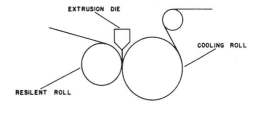

Fig. 13. Extrusion applicator. (*Courtesy F. W. Egan Co.*)

The essential parts are an engraved roll and a doctor blade. The depth and pattern of engravings will determine the adhesive capacity. The doctor blade removes excess adhesive from only the top of the engravings.

Transfer of adhesive may be achieved by "direct" contact with the web or by an intermediary "offset" rubber roll. The latter contributes substantially to a smoother application.

Extrusion Applicator

This type of mechanism offers many advantages where applicable. It applies adhesives from an extrusion head directly onto the substrate. This is accomplished by heat and pressure. The thermoplastic composition is melted and forced out through a slot onto the moving web. Neither solvents nor drying are required. This lowers the cost and reduces the hazards associated with the application operation. It also permits increased coating speeds.

It is a simple device and easy to operate, provided both adhesive and substrate can tolerate the high temperatures involved.

CONCLUSION

A few of the more important methods of applying adhesives on a continuous basis have been presented. In selecting an applicator, one should attempt to obtain the best for the job at hand. Automatic equipment should be installed wherever possible. Manually operated devices do not lend themselves to accurate, uniform metering.

Some companies have improved their products and saved money by using Beta gauges, which employ radioactive materials to measure the thickness of an applied coating. They are absolutely safe to operate.

References

1. Egan, F. W., "Coating Machines," *Paper, Film and Foil Converter* (Dec. 1955, Jan. and Feb. 1956).
2. Holt, F. W., Lorenz, C. H., and Reif, R. B., "Electrostatic Coating Process for Making Flat Gummed Paper." *Tappi,* **44,** 54–57 (1961).
3. Booth, G. L., and Laughrey, N. H., "Comparison of the Air Doctor and Blade Coating Methods," *Tappi,* **43,** (5), 200A–203A (1960).
4. Frost, F. H., "Air Knife Coater," *Tappi,* **40,** (8), 152A–153A (1957).
5. Richardson, Charles A., "Trailing Blade Coater," *Tappi,* **40,** (8), 155A–156A (1957).
6. Booth, G. L., "Take Your Choice of Coating Methods," *Modern Plastics,* **36,** (1), 91–95 (Sept. 1958).
7. Booth, G. L., *Modern Plastics,* **36,** (2), 90–99 (Oct. 1958).
8. Trist, A. R., U. S. Patent 2,368,176 (Jan. 30, 1945).
9. Trist, A. R., U. S. Patent 2,593,074 (Apr. 15, 1952).
10. Trist, A. R., U. S. Patent 2,796,846 (June 25, 1957).
11. Rush, J. A. (to Consolidated Water & Paper Co.), U. S. Patent 2,746,877 (May 22, 1956).
12. Gunning, J. R., and Kohler, J. B., "The Kohler Method of Coating," *Tappi,* **43,** 183–187 (1960).
13. Smith, B. W., "Scanning Basis Weight and Moisture Gage Systems on Paper Machines," *Tappi,* **43,** (3), 226–234 (1960).

— 47 —

Proportioning Multiphase Adhesives

Walter A. Gammel, Sr.
Modular Electronics, Inc.
Ossea, Minnesota

The desirability of many two-component adhesives—epoxies, polyurethanes, polyesters—is forcing advances in many manufacturing techniques as well as equipment. The handling of multicomponent adhesives creates problems, and there are some costs involved. Control of these costs and improved manufacturing efficiency require selection of proper processing equipment.

Truly efficient operations are quite different from standard operations of only several years ago. Although there are few completely automated installations, there are many semiautomated. Improvements are being made daily.

ADHESIVE PREPARATION

Mixing

Preparation of a multicomponent adhesive begins and ends with adequate mixing. If a commercially filled resin is used, it will be advantageous to place the unopened can upon a paint shaker and vibrate the contents for a period of time.[4] For base resin-filler or hardener-filler combinations blended by the user, test data rather than theory should be used to determine equipment required. If simple mixing is entirely adequate, use it. Where mechanical mixing is not satisfactory, as when a filler such as chopped glass fibers is extremely hard to wet, a mill may be required. A study of mechanically mixed versus milled adhesives indicates that mechanical mixing is generally satisfactory for most compounding operations. Since mechanical mixing is usually more controllable, less costly, and more versatile, it should be employed if possible.

For mechanical mixing a variable speed mixer, preferably air-driven, and a container are often all that are required. Perhaps a vacuum attachment for evacuation of air from the mixed compound may be added later. An air-driven mixer is safer, less costly, and more easily regulated than an electrically driven mixer. A typical installation is shown in Fig. 1.

For the most reliable mixing operation, the temperature of the compound in the mixing vessel should be uniform. This may be accomplished by use of a hot liquid jacket around the vessel. An air-driven motor to power the mixer will allow high speeds when stirring fillers into the resin and, later, low speeds to prevent settling out of the filler. Should the viscosity of the mix increase because of premature gelling, failure of the heater with a consequent rise in viscosity of the mix, or some other unforseen reason, the air motor will simply stall out, whereas an electric motor may burn out.

Where the mixing container is to be reused, there are several choices of materials. Since the inside surface should be noncorrosive and smooth, stainless steel or polyethylene is suggested.

Design of Mixing Apparatus

The most efficient use of a mixer is obtained when the initial interfacial surface is optimally oriented with respect to the flow streamlines in the system—usually parallel, so that $\cos \alpha_x = 1$. The designer of mixing apparatus generally does not know, however, how the user is going to orient the components in the mixer at the start of the process; therefore he must design the equipment

Fig. 1. Well vented hood with negative air slots at bench, eye, and top levels. Equipped with airmotor mixer and quick balancing scales. Vacuum chamber is in right foreground. (*Courtesy Western Electric Co.*)

to give flow patterns which achieve the same time of mixing when the minor component is a very small fraction of the batch, regardless of where that minor fraction is placed in the equipment. This result is not necessarily the most efficient use of the mixing power for the orientation used in practice, and it should be appreciated that efficiencies can be improved when the initial orien-

tation of components can be specified before the mixing equipment is designed.[1]

Provide Adequate Ventilation

Displaced-air ventilation should be provided, and when resin mixes are worked hot, it should be considered indispensable. Hoods should be used to cover the working benches and the fumes exhausted to the atmosphere through air ducts.[8]

Pot-Life

One of the most frequently asked questions about epoxy adhesives is how to extend the pot-life without appreciably increasing the time to cure. There are, of course, several answers, of which the most obvious is to use a less reactive hardener. Unfortunately, unless the curing temperature may be increased, a longer processing time which in turn means added costs will result. The problem can be solved, however, in both batch and machine-controlled operations as shown in Fig. 2. In this example, if 16 per cent of the catalyzed adhesive is drawn off every 15 min and replaced with freshly mixed material, the pot-life may be extended almost indefinitely. The amount that must be replaced per unit of time is dependent on the reactivity of the constituent and on the total mass involved.

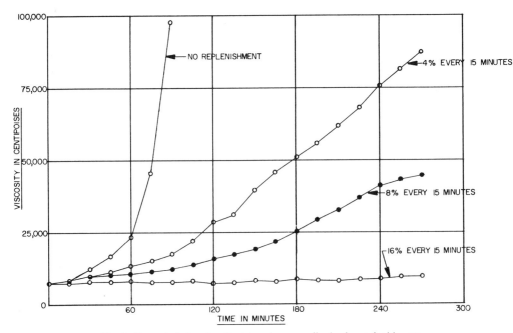

Fig. 2. Control of viscosity of catalyzed epoxy adhesive by replenishment.

Degassing

For maximum strength glue lines it is necessary to remove all air from the adhesive before using it for the actual bonding operation. Entrapped air represents a source of voids in the cured line and hence the possibility of failure.

Two methods are commonly employed to degas the adhesive, namely, (1) centrifuging and (2) subjecting to a "high" negative pressure.

For batch-type operations the centrifuge is convenient and effective. Beaver and Hamilton have designed such a centrifuge for the elimination of encapsulated and entrapped air in sealants. The unit, shown in Fig. 3, has a series of holes bored at a 45 degree angle. This inclination was chosen because it eliminates high stress components in the yoke. The value of centrifuging is vividly portrayed in Fig. 4.[6]

If the adhesive is degassed in the vessel in which it is mixed, the level of the compound should be low enough to allow for a foam head to rise and break during the operation. If the compound level is too high, the foam head will not break. Since it is desirable to know when the foam head has broken, the vacuum tank should be provided with two sight windows, one for the tank illumination light, and the other for observation of the foam head. If the mixing vessel and the storage vessel are one

and the same, equipment costs and space requirements will be reduced.

Transfer of Adhesives

The use of pumps for transferring multicomponent adhesives often has drawbacks. Filled compounds have an abrasive action on the moving parts. This is particularly true with fillers like silica. Compounds that polymerize without added catalyst or heat will tend to gum the pumps and make them inoperable.

Transfer is best done under some type of pressure. Although it may require special designs, pressure transfer does eliminate the problems which occur with gear pumping methods.

Epoxy adhesives may be moved from the original drums by air pumps. Transfer distances should be as short as possible. The transfer lines should be smooth and resistant to corrosion. In some instances barrel warmers and heated lines will be required to reduce the viscosity and hence the pressure required to transport the materials.

METERING, MIXING, AND DISPENSING EQUIPMENT

Use of epoxy adhesives has generated great interest in the development of equipment to handle these adhesives on a continuous basis. There are a number of reasons for this development. A large-scale operation using hand-mixing operations is costly, messy, and slow. Potential health hazards become a major consideration, and operator errors may occur. Manual mixing also allows considerable variation from operator to operator, and even periodically with the same operator.

In addition to the above reasons for switching to automatic equipment, there is the need for short curing cycles to ensure manufacturing efficiency. Short curing cycles typically mean short pot-life adhesive compounds. To avoid premature gelling, an epoxy is mixed with its hardener in the smallest practical quantities. It is possible to meet all of these problems, overcome the objections, and more readily assure a quality product with automatic metering, mixing, and dispensing equipment or specially designed spray gear. Both classes are discussed in later paragraphs.

It must be remembered, however, that probably no one piece of equipment can be ideal for all adhesives. There are too many variables such as (1) catalyst-to-compound ratio, (2) filler concentration, (3) pot-life, (4) temperature requirements, and (5) viscosity—not to mention speed of operations required.

Fig. 3. Centrifuge for de-aerating mixed adhesives for critical applications. (*Courtesy Douglas Aircraft Corp.*)

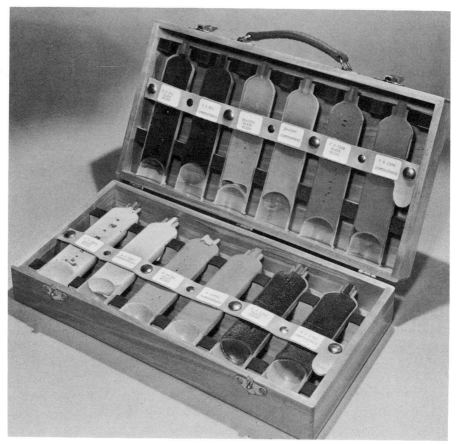

Fig. 4. Six different types of resin adhesives showing effect of centrifuging. Note the uniform absence of air on each second sample, the result of centrifuging. (*Courtesy Douglas Aircraft Corp.*)

In earlier reports[2, 3, 5] the author described many systems and listed suppliers of metering, mixing, and dispensing equipment. These studies and lists have been updated. Equipment available from the several suppliers has a wide range of sophistication, varying from simple weighing controls to nearly automatic degassing mixing and dispensing with shot size and frequency control. Costs range from a few hundred to over ten thousand dollars.

Methods of operation vary considerably. Some machines use pumping arrangements for material proportioning and transfer, others have pressurized feed with proportioning cylinders, whereas still others use pressurized feed through a preset orifice. For each case, a study of the equipment operation should be made since inherent limitations and advantages exist for any material-equipment combination.[7]

The usefulness of any of the features of any particular piece of equipment depends on individual desires, constituents of the adhesive and other speci-

fics. Equipment listed in the Appendix at the end of this chapter as well as that described in detail should be considered.

The bonding of parts may be accomplished by (a) bringing them to the equipment that will dispense the adhesive or (b) bringing the equipment to the part. Procedure (a) will be discussed first.

Automatic Batch Weighing

A first step away from a strict manual operation is the use of automatic component weighing.

Figure 5 depicts a balance instrumented for controlled weighing and dispensing of liquid components on a batch scale. In use, it is only necessary to set the scale for the required weight of liquid and to press a control switch, which actuates an electrically controlled valve to dispense the liquid and terminate the flow when the proper amount has been dispensed. This arrangement also allows the use of multiple valves for controlling batch weighing of several components.[7]

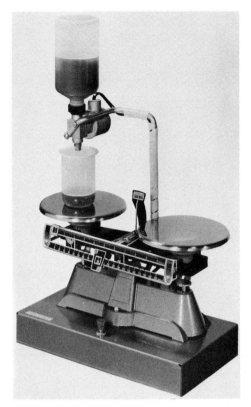

Fig. 5. Automatic weighing scales. To operate, set scale for required weight and press control. (*Courtesy Delsen Corp.*)

The Hull-Standard System

This machine employs a combination of gravity and low pressure to drive material from stainless steel storage tanks through micrometer flow control valves. The catalyzed resin stream may be continuous rather than delivered in a definite preset time. The shot size therefore can be varied as required for each shot. The amount of adhesive dispensed is determined by actuation of a foot control pedal. There is no recharge time as required with the positive-displacement principle. The ratio of epoxy to hardener or curing agent is preset by a combination adjustment of both the micrometer flow control valves and the pressure, which is outlined schematically in Fig. 6.

The Hardman Positive-Displacement System

In the Type III, Series 600 Hardman machine an electromechanical drive operates the positive-displacement metering pumps, which force the adhesive resin, modifier, and activator by the high shear agitator in the mixing chamber. The volume of material entering the chamber displaces an equal quantity of previously mixed material which is dispensed from the nozzle. Because all metering components are mounted in an insulated cabinet, even hot-melt systems requiring temperatures to 450°F may be processed effectively.

Abrasive materials may also be successfully handled in this series of machines because of the unique design of the pump valve which is a rotating disk type. The disk itself seats on a spring loaded composition base. Abrasive materials do wear the disk, but the wear is uniform. The composition base is unaffected.

A range of standard mixing chamber sizes allows the selection of the smallest one consistent with job requirement. The chambers have an activator by-pass valve. When in by-pass position the chamber may be purged with resin. A positive cutoff mechanism is provided.

Dispensers Using Gear Pumps

The first meter, mixing, and dispensing unit reported employed gear pumps to deliver fixed proportions of resin and activator to a mixer. Gear pumps are still used in most of the dispensers available today. There are many reasons for this, e.g., cost is relatively low and reliability is good. There are some design limitations; however these can be overcome. When no fillers are used in the adhesive formulation, there is little to wear. If abrasive fillers are used, carefully kept records indicate that it is quite simple to predict how long a gear pump will last, how the mixing ratios will change (and so when to compensate), and finally, when the pump should be replaced.

For those seeking a low cost, virtually foolproof simple dispenser, the "PAR" LV unit shown in Fig. 7 is recommended. The ratio of resin-to-activator may be varied from 1:1 to 1:2 or more by turning the knob which regulates the variable speed transmission between the two pumps. Mixing is performed elsewhere.

A unit such as this is ideal for metering many flexible adhesive formulations where the degree of hardness is varied by changing the ratio of resin to activator. Epoxy-polyamide blends are typical of such adhesives.

The "Twin-Blend Dispenser" for Body Solders

The use of epoxy- based two-part body solders has been limited by lack of equipment and convenient packaging of the solders. Baker-Perkins and The Kenilworth Manufacturing Co., Ltd. have jointly

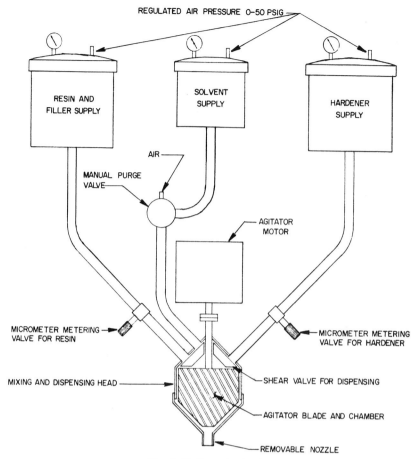

Fig. 6. Hull-standard unit.

developed the "Twin-Blend Dispenser" and "Double-Bond Autofil," respectively, to fill these needs. "Double-Bond Autofil" is an epoxy-based adhesive filling compound and body solder. It is highly thixotropic when uncured, making possible easy application and completely eliminating "slump"

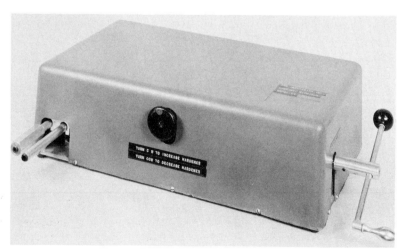

Fig. 7. Simple but effective crank operated dispenser. Proper ratio of resin to activator is discharged at the two nozzles in left foreground. (*Courtesy PARR Industries, Inc.*)

even at elevated temperatures. Unless equipment is especially designed, smooth, homogenous mixing of such compounds is unusually difficult.

Tin cans filled with the formulated epoxy base and activator are placed upside down over mushroom-shaped pistons. Hydraulic rams press each can down over its close fitting piston to drive the material through a hole in the center of the piston along a duct to one of the inlet ports of the mixing head. The epoxy and activator are intimately mixed as they pass through out to the discharge nozzle. Included air is separated and discharged elsewhere.

The dispenser-mixer-deaerator may be adjusted to handle resin-activator ratios from 3:1 to 1:3. At the 1:1 ratio, maximum shot is 15 oz, and minimum is 5 oz. The predetermined shot size is dispensed each time the operating lever is depressed. Automatic shutoff occurs when either piston reaches the end of its stroke and the can is empty, or when the safety high-pressure oil circuit is tripped. Interlocks are provided so operation is impossible unless electric and compressed air supplies are on. If the front guard doors are opened, the machine similarly becomes inoperable. The unit is shown in Fig. 8.

Fig. 8. Dispenser-mixer-deaerator for dispensing automotive body solders. (*Courtesy The Kenilworth Co., Ltd.*)

Adjustments to the dispenser are all accessible from the rear, but only by opening a pair of lockable doors. Temperature control is provided, and 80°F is optimum.

Vacuum Bonding

One representative piece of commercial equipment for performing vacuum bonding operations is available from the Red Point Corporation. In operation the resin is placed in the top container, and the parts are placed in the bottom chamber. After the lids are closed, vacuum is introduced to the system. Care, of course, must be taken in regulating the vacuum so that the reduced pressure does not fall below the vapor pressure of the constituents.

During this degassing period, the lower chamber is also evacuated. The units to be bonded are usually heated to a predetermined temperature in the range of 150 to 200°F. This drives off moisture and volatiles. Degassing and drying time typically run less than 30 min. When the components are up to temperature and the adhesive mixture has stopped bubbling, the operator opens a port in the top container to allow the adhesive to flow down into the sealing chamber. The operator observes the operation through the sight glass. The flow of resin can be stopped at the proper time. The bonded parts remain in the chamber under heat for the required period or are transfered to an oven if further care of the adhesive is required.

Spray Equipment

To cover large areas or irregular surfaces with epoxy adhesives, it is necessary to use spray equipment, which consists of the spray gun itself plus a proportioning and pumping unit to supply the resin and activator to the gun. In operation, the resultant spray is due to air or hydraulic pressure against the issuing stream which has been driven through the gun by gear pumps or positive-displacement cylinders. Mixing the resin and activator streams prior to deposition is done mechanically or hydraulically.

Air Atomization. Originally spray guns would handle only low viscosity adhesives. The spray patterns of these guns were developed by air atomization. As Perry[10] has reported, low viscosity resins were required several years ago in order to prevent the air carrier from forming bubbles likely to appear in high viscosity materials. Even today when low viscosity adhesives are applied by spray, air atomization is still most commonly used.

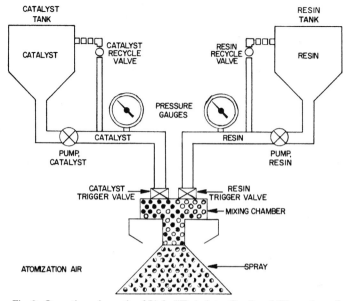

Fig. 9. Operation schematic of Binks "Turbulator Gun" and "Formulator."

Spray guns suitable for air atomization of adhesives may be obtained from Binks, Pyles, and Stuart. In each case the mixing is mechanical. Materials are fed to the Binks and Pyles guns by positive-displacement pumps, whereas a gear pump is used in the Stuart unit. (See Fig. 9.)

Hydraulic Atomization. The most common example of hydraulic atomization is the spray of water from a common garden hose equipped with a nozzle. If a liquid stream is propelled through a supply line of a given diameter at a given velocity, an increase in the velocity of the stream will occur when the stream passes through a diameter smaller than the supply line. If the stream passes through a correctly designed nozzle, the velocity of the stream will be increased to the point where atomization occurs and the proper spray pattern is developed.

Both Graco and Gusmer use hydraulic atomization in the design of the spray guns. The Gusmer gun is shown schematically in Fig. 10. The mixing, of course, is also hydraulic for both guns. Materials are fed to the Graco gun by positive-displacement piston pumps. Pressures in the order of 2500 psi are reported. The Gusmer gun is fed by four gear pumps, the arrangement of which deserves further comment.

Zero Differential Principle. When gear pumps are used to pump liquids against high spray pressures, they "slip," throwing proportions off. Certain techniques such as the zero differential principle can be applied to meet the problem, report Loesser and Pitt.[9]

In the Gusmer unit, two pumps are arranged in series to pump the resin, and two in series to pump the activator. The pressure of the material flowing to the metering pump is maintained equal to the pressure of the material flowing from the metering pumps. The pressure pumps feed the metering pump at the same pressure as the metering pump feeds the spray gun, thereby creating a zero pressure differential which eliminates pump slippage or loss of nearly perfect volumetric efficiency.[9]

The zero differential principle was developed at the Bound Brook Laboratories of Union Carbide Chemicals Company.

Curing

After the adhesive formulation has been dispensed, cure must occur before a finished unit may be delivered. Epoxy adhesives depend on optimum cure for their superior properties. An initial moderate cure of epoxy laminates yields structurally sound parts with adequate properties at moderate service conditions. At elevated temperatures, however, the chemical resistance and electrical and mechanical properties are retained only by "full" cure.

"Full" cure with its attendant bonus properties is approached by postcuring at elevated temperatures. Proper curing cycles must be determined with care and then carefully followed. To date, most parts and assemblies requiring heat-curing have been processed in batch-type gas-fired or electric ovens. The recent tendency toward in-line handling of thermoset adhesives has increased the

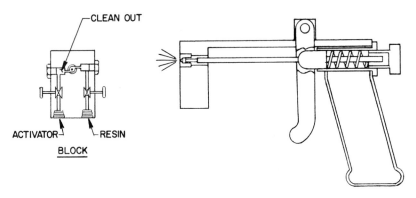

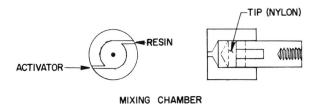

MIXING CHAMBER

Fig. 10. Gusmer spray gun.

use of curing tunnels heated by infrared lamps, fuzed quartz tubes, or conventional strip heaters.[3]

Health and Hazard Considerations

The material handling and processing of multiphase adhesive systems can be carried out successfully if precautions such as these are taken to prevent employee exposure to substances or situations that are potentially harmful:

(1) Screen out individuals with "allergic" histories.
(2) Instruct operators and their supervisors in the importance of scrupulous cleanliness.
(3) Provide work area or room that will allow good hygienic practices to be followed.
(4) Have washing facilities, including mild soaps, a good skin cream, and clean towels available at all times.
(5) Set up a systematic plan to inspect work

area and operating procedures, and follow through.

The necessity for proper facilities and clean working habits cannot be overemphasized.[5]

Skeist has reviewed the literature on exzema or dermatitis caused by epoxies and their activators. It was found that the activators, principally the amines, are mostly responsible for ailments that occasionally afflict those who work with epoxies. The best preventive, he concludes, is good housekeeping.[12]

Maintenance and Trouble Shooting

There are several cardinal points to remember:

(1) Before calling a serviceman, make sure the problem is not a burned out fuse or power failure.
(2) Keep equipment clean; provide adequate maintenance.

TABLE 1. SUMMARY TABLE OF SPRAY EQUIPMENT.

Supplier	Type of Atomization		Type of Mixing		Pumping Unit	
	Air	Hydraulic	Mechanical	Hydraulic	Positive	Gear
Binks	x		x		x	
Graco		x		x	x	
Gusmer		x		x		x
Pyles	x		x		x	
Stuart	x		x			x

(3) Servicing should be done by intelligent personnel on a regularly scheduled basis.

(4) In original order, specify the limits of service you expect as well as the length of service.

RECOMMENDATIONS ON BUYING EQUIPMENT

If the reader is considering the use of any electrically, hydraulically, mechanically, or pneumatically driven equipment, he should secure answers to the following questions before buying:

(a) Questions relating to the adhesive.

(1) *The Adhesive.* Are the parts of the equipment which come in contact with either the adhesive components or the mixed adhesive compatible?

(2) *Foreign Matter.* How is dirt kept out of the system? If there are foreign particles in the components of the adhesive, what harm is most likely to occur?

(3) *Viscosity.* Will there be variations in the viscosity of the components of the adhesive? Is it necessary to compensate for these? If so, how is this done?

(b) Questions relating to the equipment.

(4) *Purging.* In the event of trouble, how rapidly can purge be initiated? How is trouble detected?

(5) *Freeze-up.* From experience, we can almost predict this will occur at least once. When it does, what is involved? Can repetition be prevented? What means are provided to prevent it from occurring? Consider the effect of power failure.

(6) *Withdrawal.* Can components of the adhesive be conveniently drawn off, if need be, without being mixed?

(7) *Output.* Does the equipment dispense continuously or intermittently? If intermittent, is the charge-up time viscosity-dependent, so that it may lower expected output?

(8) *Quality Control.* Can the proportioning vary? For quality control purposes, is there a convenient way to check the material proportions?

(9) *Leakage.* If air or hydraulic pressure is used, what is the effect of leakage? If close regulation of pressure is required, how is it accomplished?

(10) *Temperature.* Are there temperature controls and indicators? Are they required?

(11) *Life Expectancy.* What parts of the equipment have the shortest life expectancy? How difficult is it to install a replacement part? What are the direct and indirect costs? How is wear or failure detected?

(c) Questions relating to the operation.

(12) *Operator.* Can the equipment be handled by a shop operator or does it require an engineer, a set-up man, and a maintenance man?

(d) Questions relating to the manufacturer.

(13) *Breakdown.* If breakdown should happen, are schematics, detail drawings, and parts lists provided? As new components are introduced by the equipment manufacturer, what are the problems of interchangeability?

(14) *Spare Parts.* Does manufacturer stock spare parts including purchased items?

(15) *Field Service.* What is the field service policy of the equipment supplier?

(16) *Warranty.* What is included in the warranty? Who are the individuals behind it?

(e) Questions relating to the user.

(17) *Savings.* Do I need the equipment? How will it save me money or increase my output?

(18) *Cooperation.* Will the equipment supplier work with me? Why?

Spare Parts and Operation Manual

If a decision is made to purchase a machine, an important factor to consider is a spare parts kit. Included in it should be all short-life parts, plus those which will be changed in the first major overhaul. If the equipment is located close to its manufacturer, inventory may be minimal, but in an out-of-the-way place, additional parts will be required.

The installation and operation manual should include: (1) an index, (2) a brief description of the purpose of the machine and a statement of how it is accomplished, (3) installation instructions, (4) set-up procedure, (5) operation sequence and instruction, (6) variations, (7) shutdown, (8) cleaning, lubrication, and other maintenance, (9) wiring diagrams, (10) timing charts and information, (11) recommended spare parts list, (12) drawings with complete parts lists. If the normal plane view drawings are complicated, isometrics and exploded views, with photographs, should be furnished.

A Final Word

Most progressive companies hire special mechanically inclined individuals, and they become responsible for the proper operation of all adhesives dispensing equipment. This is an age of distinct and unique adhesives. The individual close to the equipment—the man who gets his hands sticky—must not be overlooked. He may hold the key to a successful and profitable adhesive bonding production line.

References

1. Bernhardt, E. C., "Processing of Thermoplastic Materials," New York, Reinhold Publishing Corp., 1959.
2. Gammel, W. A., Sr., "Material Handling of Epoxy and Polyester Resins," *S. P. E. Technical Papers,* **4,** 108–119, (1958).
3. Gammel, W. A., Sr., "Processing System for Optimum Design Use of Casting Resins," *Elec. Mfg.,* **62,** (3), 80–85, 300, 302 (1958).
4. Gammel, W. A., Sr., "Techniques With Resins," Paper presented at First National Conference on the Application of Electrical Insulation, Cleveland, Sept. 1958.
5. Gammel, W. A., Sr., "Methods of Handling Epoxy and Polyester Resins in the U. S. A.," *Rubber and Plastics Age,* **40,** (No. 1), 55–60 (1959).
6. Gammel, W. A., Sr., "Multi-Component Resins and Machinery," *Insulation,* **5,** (12), 93–96 (1959).
7. Harper, C. A., "Electronic Packaging with Resins," New York, McGraw-Hill Book Co., Inc., 1961.
8. Lee, H., and Neville, K., "Epoxy Resins," New York, McGraw-Hill Book Co., Inc., 1957.
9. Loesser, T. S., and Plitt, C. F., "Recent Advances in Epoxy Handling Equipment," Paper presented at the University of Wisconsin Seminar on Epoxy Resins in Madison, Wisconsin, May 29, 1960.
10. Perry, H. A., "Adhesive Bonding of Reinforced Plastics," New York, McGraw-Hill Book Co., Inc, 1959.
11. Simonds, H. R., "A Concise Giude to Plastics," New York, Reinhold Publishing Corp., 1957.
12. Skeist, I., "Epoxy Resins," New York, Reinhold Publishing Corp., 1958.

APPENDIX

EQUIPMENT MANUFACTURERS AND EQUIPMENT

Admiral Equipment Corporation
661 West Market Street
Akron 3, Ohio

Admiral equipment designed initially for handling polyurethane elastomers with minimum output of 30 g.

Allied Stroud Corporation
5101 North Pennsylvania
Oklahoma City 12, Oklahoma

Moyno positive-displacement pumps driven by 1¾ H-P air-cooled gasoline motor with built-in gear reduction unit. Completely mobile and self-contained.

American Latex Products Corporation
3341 West El Segunda Boulevard
Hawthorne, California

Materials fed from pressurized pots that deliver materials through polyethylene hose to pumping unit and portable mixing head. Units known as C-10 Stafoamer.

Automatic Process Control
1001 Morris Avenue
Union, New Jersey

Positive piston-metering cylinders, mixer, and charge and recharge controls pneumatically operated. Electrical power required for sensing and temperature control.

Baker Perkins Incorporated
Chemical Machinery Division
Saginaw, Michigan

"Flowmaster Reactor" designed for 200 to 750 gal per hour thruput. Excellent heat transfer for viscosity reduction and thorough mixing.

Baker-Perkins Limited
Peterborough
England
        with
The Kenilworth Mfg. Co. Ltd.
West Drayton, Middlesex
England

"Twin Blend Dispenser" sold by Kenilworth is designed specifically to proportion, mix, deaerate, and dispense high-viscosity two-component adhesives, even those used as body solders. Is two-stage and hydropneumatic.

Bell and Gossett Company
Morton Grove
Illinois

Self-contained unit on wheels. Deaeration, positive-displacement synchronized and adjustable piston pumps, and blending head driven by electric motor(s). Temperature controlled. May be used on intermittent or continuous basis.

Binks Manufacturing Company
3114 Carroll Avenue
Chicago 12, Illinois

Air-operated portable unit. High energy internal mixer that may be used for manual or automatic dispensing by spray or pour.

Chrom-O-Lite Company, Incorporated
2701 East 78th Street
Minneapolis 23, Minnesota

Handles ratios of 1:1 to 1:4½. Air-operated mixing and dispensing. Viscosity reduction by electrical heating of components.

Conforming Matrix Corporation
Toledo Factories Building
Toledo 2, Ohio

Specialized equipment as for applying materials such as epoxies on silicone diodes to form a light-tight seal.

Delsen Corporation
719 West Broadway
Glendale 4, California

"Autogram" will dispense one component. "Variable Ratio Dispenser" will dispense metered amounts of resin and hardener through gear pumps.

The DeVilbiss Company
296 Phillips Avenue
Toledo 1, Ohio

Guns, flow meters, supply tanks, pressure equipment to handle viscosities to 5000 cps and ratios of catalyst-to-resins of 2 to 100 per cent.

Graco Products
Gray Company, Incorporated
1046 Sibley Street Northeast
Minneapolis 13, Minnesota

"Hydra-Cat" uses power unit to pump, proportion, filter, and transfer through flexible hoses to gun. Gun blends and mixes materials before applying by airless spray.

A. Gusmer, Incorporated
Barron Avenue
Woodbridge, New Jersey

"Gusco C-1" 22 oz. self-cleaning airless gun fed by compact hydraulic pumping and metering system (18½ × 18 × 22 in.) which operates from 115 V.A.C. line.

H. V. Hardman Company, Incorporated
Triplematic Pump Division
571 Cortlandt Street
Belleville 9, New Jersey

"Triplematic" series of meter, mixing, and dispensing equipment. Measured shots or continuous flow, heat, gear or positive displacement pistons, and other variables available as standard equipment.

Hull Corporation
Davisville Road
Hatboro, Pennsylvania

"Blendmaster" mixing head driven by ⅓ HP motor. Resin and hardener fed to it through stainless steel micrometer valve and Jamesbury type shutoff valve.

Hupp Engineering Associates
P. O. Box 3290
Sarasota, Florida

"Resin Depositor" allows alternate layers of reactive resin and chopped fibers to be laid.

Jennings Machine Corporation
3452 Ludlow Street
Philadelphia 4, Pennsylvania

Metering Unit Model FR50-5P with Mixing Head Model MH-8 designed for 3 to 30 lb output per minute. Recirculating.

Kenics Corporation
P.O. Box 27
Greenwood Station
Wakefield, Massachusetts

Dot, drop, bead, or strip hand dispensing. May be modified for production. Utilizes cartridges. Requires air or pressure line. Adaptable for microminiature patching. Low cost.

Kish Industries Incorporated
1301 North Turner Street
Lansing, Michigan

"Kish Ki-Pla-Blender" obtainable in low-cost hand crank or motor-operated models for simultaneous dispensing of resin and hardener. Metering achieved by nonslip gears which activate positive-displacement pumps. Portable. May be connected to material storage containers.

Marco Development Company, Inc.
4027 New Castle Avenue
Wilmington 99, Delaware

"Flow-Master" units may be assembled to meet particular requirements and is combination reactor and continuous mixer. Liquid or solid components may be added in proper proportions at correct stage of operation and at predetermined temperatures.

G. Diehl Mateer Company
776 West Lincoln Highway
Wayne, Pennsylvania

"Proportioner" units will proportion, mix, and dispense two or more component systems with or without fillers at ambient or elevated temperatures. Dispensing may be continuous or intermittent. May be operated manually but placed later into automatic conveyorized system.

Meter Mix Corporation
626 Dorchester Avenue
South Boston 27, Massachusetts

Model MM-2 has two metering pumps activated by reciprocating air cylinder. Pumps are positive displacement and will handle as little as 0.3 c.c. Purge pump is conveniently hand operated. Designed for bench use. Air operated.

Minnesota Mining & Manufacturing Co.
Adhesives, Coatings, & Sealers Div.
417 Piquette Avenue
Detroit 2, Michigan

"Formulator" with "Turbulator" gun continuously converts fluid components into mixed system at point of application. Gun mixes proportioned streams and dispenses them as a reacting fluid in either poured or sprayed form.

Mitchell Specialty Division
Novo Industrial Corporation
Edmund and Shelmire Streets
Philadelphia 36, Pennsylvania

"Novo" metering and mixing unit designed for intermittent or continuous flow. Deaerator optional. Proportioning by positive piston-type metering elements. Mixer has interchangeable heads. Many standard combinations.

Newton Tool & Manufacturing Co., Inc.
Linden Avenue at Glassboro Road
Wenonah, New Jersey

"Flowrater" metering units mounted in four-wheeled cabinet. Positive-displacement pumps meter both resin and catalyst. Resin side has heat exchanger. Recirculating. Unique mixing head offers possibility of little or no cleanup.

The E. T. Oakes Corporation
26 Commack Road
Islip, Long Island, New York

"Continuous Automatic Mixer," Model 8M is rated at approximately 100 lb per hour throughout. System is closed. One moving part in mixing head. Mixing head and product pump independent of one another. Jacketed, when required, for heating or cooling.

Par Industries, Incorporated
1800 Glenrose Avenue
P. O. Box 893
Lansing 4, Michigan

"AUTO AIR" models run from hand crank, one or more component fixed volume dispensed per revolution, to custom built meter, mixing, and dispensing units complete with vacuum. Control panel of latter permits automatic or hand actuation.

Pyles Industries, Incorporated
20855 Telegraph Road
Detroit 41, Michigan

"DUO-MIX" spray or flow guns and "DUO-FLO" metering pumps feature portability and versatility. Automatic "Shot Meter" meter, mixes, and dispenses as little as 1 g of two-part compounds. Roving chopper available for DUO-MIX spray gun.

Rand Development Corporation
13600 Deise Avenue
Cleveland 10, Ohio

Rand Fiber-Resin Depositor available for spraying gel coats (Model P22) and for spraying up laminates (Models P-24 and P-21). Latter are licensed for use.

Red Point Corporation
105 West Spazier Avenue
Burbank, California

"The Diplid" used primarily in application of highly viscous materials. "The Agitator Lid" used for mixing under controlled vacuum. Equipment is ASME coded.

Rogers Associates, Incorporated
Box 752
West Caldwell, New Jersey

Rogers equipment, although designed primarily for epoxy and urethane foams, can be adapted to handle adhesives. Present capacity of 3 lb/min.

SealZit Company of America
The Flintkote Company, Inc.
3640 Chicago Avenue
Riverside, California

SealZit spray gun, SealZit-Grover pumping system and SealZit Rock Hopper provide means for laying up to ¼ in. aggregate with plastic. Up to about 25 lb of plastic per minute can be dispensed under pressure.

Semco Sales & Service, Inc.
1313 West Florence Avenue
Inglewood 1, California

Continuous and batch mixers; guns; polyethylene liners.

Spray-Bilt
3605 East Tenth Court
Hialeah, Florida

"Fiberglaspray Gun" delivers resin, catalyst and chopped glass fiber under pressure. Materials used to date are primarily polyesters and polyurethanes.

Stuart Marine Service
P. O. Box 1318
Stuart, Florida

Spray guns, mixing heads and metering equipment. Designed primarily for polyurethane foam but may, in some cases, be used for epoxies.

The Martin Sweets Company
114 South First Street
Louisville 2, Kentucky

Pumping, metering, and mixing of multicomponent reactive resins.

Union Carbide Plastics Company
270 Park Avenue
New York 17, New York

Troweling compound mixer to demonstrate use of vibratory feeder for metering dry fillers, positive-displacement pumps, and mixing with a screw.

Gabriel Williams Company, Inc.
77 Mill Road
Freeport, L. I., New York

Automatic metering, proportioning, and mixing equipment for 2, 3, or 4 components at 150 to 450 g/min. Units designed for intermittent or continuous operation.

48

Lamination

Arthur Hirsch

Skeist Laboratories, Inc.
Newark, New Jersey

Lamination is the process of combining two or more plies of material into a new composite. The plies may be alike or different. The new product may thus be designed to possess unique properties not inherent in any of the constituents. The ever increasing demand for novel products with unusual properties results in an ever growing array of new laminates.

There are two basic types of laminated products. One consists of a combination of all flexible materials, while the other utilizes at least one rigid material. The difference is manifest not only in the final product, but in the method of manufacture as well.

FLEXIBLE WEB LAMINATION

Paper, plastic films, cloth, and metal foils are examples of flexible webs which are combined to produce laminates. These web materials can be converted by continuous manufacturing processes, with machine speeds reaching 1000 fpm.

Several methods of lamination are in common practice today.

Wet Lamination. An adhesive solution is applied to one or both surfaces to be joined. If neither surface is porous, the solvent must be evaporated prior to bond formation.

Reactivatable Adhesive Coatings. Pre-gummed webs and decalcomanias are examples of this category. Decalcomanias are printed papers coated with starch and gum arabic or with collodion. One of their many applications is the transfer of designs to pottery before firing.

Hot Melts. The adhesive is applied as a 100 per cent solids composition. Heat rather than water or organic solvent is employed to impart fluidity to this type of adhesive. Waxes, asphalt, polyethylene, polyvinyl acetate, and polyamides can be utilized as hot melts.

Thermoplastic Coatings. A thin adhesive coating on one of the webs is reactivated by heat just prior to or at the time of joining. Polyethylene and wax are typical examples.

Thermoplastic Film or Sheet. One of the base materials is softened with the aid of heat and/or pressure and thus acts as its own bonding substance. Thus a plasticized polyvinyl butyral sheet is sandwiched between glass sheets to make safety glass.

Some of these categories will be discussed in detail.

Wet Lamination

This is probably the most popular method of lamination, especially with porous substrates such as paper. Typical laminating equipment is shown in Fig. 1. It consists essentially of two or more unwind stands, one or more adhesive applicators, a combining station where webs may be brought into contact with one another under pressure, a drying station, and a rewind. Many variations of this basic arrangement are in use. For example, the drying equipment may precede the combining operation. Special machinery such as embossers or printers may be inserted.

The unwind equipment must be able to deliver a continuous web under controlled tension. Edge guides and adjustments are required to maintain proper alignment. A simple reloading system and means for splicing (on the run) are invaluable adducts to a good unwind.

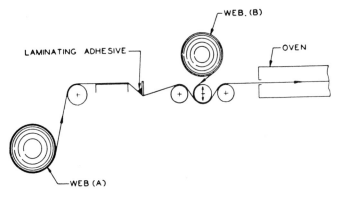

Wet laminating machine

(a)

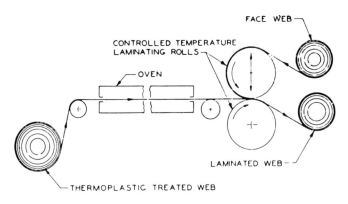

Thermoplastic laminating machine

(b)

Fig. 1. Laminating machine. (a) Wet laminating. (b) Thermoplastic laminating machine. (*Courtesy John Waldron Corp.*)

Coating equipment is discussed at length in Chapter 46. It often does not matter which web is coated with the adhesive. In some instances, however, permeability, solvent or heat susceptibility, or other properties of one of the materials may govern the choice.

Dryer type and size depends on the kind of adhesive, the solvent, the speed of operation, the web, and other factors. Explosion-proof ovens are needed to handle organic solvents safely. The heat source may be gas, steam, oil, or electricity. Evaporation of volatile solvent is hastened by the passage of hot air at high velocity countercurrent to the motion of the web. The solvent-saturated air is in most cases expelled through the chimney. In larger systems, it may be economical to recover the solvent from the vapor phase. Another system, designed to reduce fuel bills and utilize the "lost" solvent, recirculates the saturated vapors through the open flame heaters. The air is thus stripped of

solvent which burns, providing additional heat. Solvent operations are potentially hazardous; many a mishap has occurred despite the use of safety devices.

Aqueous systems are safer, but require more heat and longer periods for drying. Thus drying equipment must be either considerably longer or run at lower speeds. A closed oven or tunnel is not necessary, since water vapor is neither a fire nor a health hazard. In working with paper or other porous webs, the drying equipment is often placed after the combiner. The laminated material is then passed over drying cans (drums), and the solvent evaporated through the pores of the web.

Sometimes the drying equipment must not only eliminate solvents, but also cure a thermosetting adhesive. The temperature for cure may be higher than that sufficient for solvent removal, and extra time may be required.

No drying equipment is necessary for hot-melt

lamination. After passing through pressure rolls, the laminated material is chilled in order to "set" the hot adhesive.

The combiner joins the flexible webs into a single new material. The adhesive must be in a tacky form, although most of the solvent should have been evaporated prior to joining. Alternatively a heat reactivatable adhesive may be laminated with heated pressure rolls. Considerable quantities of solvent, especially water, can be tolerated at the combining, if at least one of the webs is porous.

The combining station consists essentially of two or more rolls arranged in such a fashion as to permit the application of pressure upon the webs to be joined. It is common practice to pair off steel with rubber rolls.

The rewind may be of the center shaft or the surface type. In the center shaft rewind, the tube on which the web is wound is driven. Multiple stations make continuous operation possible. In the surface rewind, one or two driven drums rotate the bundle. With proper control of pressure of the rewound bundle against the driven drum(s), one avoids telescoping or too hard or tight bundles.

The advantages of wet lamination are listed in Table 1,[7] which compares wet lamination, thermoplastic lamination, and calendering for the combining of vinyl film with cloth. In the last method the adhesive is on the cloth and a bond is effected as the vinyl comes off the calender. The

disadvantage of the wet process is low speed. It does, however, offer excellent adhesive economy, a good product, and low capital investment.

The importance of proper selection of adhesive is shown in Table 2.

Hot Melt Lamination

This method has been practiced for many years with waxes and resins of low adhesive strength. The introduction of thermoplastic resins of superior adhesive quality has furthered the growth of this method considerably. Hot-melt lamination offers many desirable features. Because there is no need to evaporate solvents, it can boast of: ultra-high speed, no fire hazards, no health hazards, lower cost of adhesive, lower operating cost (no need for ovens).

Foil lamination is on the increase. Sandwich structures of foil and paper are finding ever wider applications in packaging, because of:[1]

(1) Low moisture and vapor permeability.
(2) Greaseproofness.
(3) Freedom from odor, taste, and toxicity.
(4) Nonflammability.
(5) High tensile strength.
(6) Light weight.
(7) Non-rusting.
(8) Low cost.
(9) Dimensional stability.
(10) The esthetic appeal of metallic foil.

Plastic film lamination produces a composite product which may incorporate some of the most desirable properties of each of the constituents. Thus one may laminate polyethylene to a polyester film in order to obtain heat sealability from the first and dimensional stability from the second.

Most of the red cellophane tear tape used to open cigarette and other packages is a laminated material. Two thin sheets of colorless cellophane are laminated with the aid of a colored adhesive to produce a product which is stronger than a

TABLE 1. BONDING METHODS FOR VINYL AND CLOTH.

	Calender	Thermoplastic	Wet
Production speed	High	High	Low
Bond	High	Medium	High
Hand	Firm	Firm	Soft
Adhesive economy	Good	Poor	Excellent
Versatility	2 ply only	Unlimited	Unlimited
Capital investment	Very high	Varies	Low

TABLE 2. ADHESIVES FOR LAMINATION OF VINYL AND CLOTH.

	Vinyl Chloride Copolymer Emulsion	Polyvinyl Chloride Plastisol	Polyvinyl Chloride Solution	Synthetic Rubber Latex
Bond	Highest	Low	High	Fair
Hand	Fair	Very flexible	Varies	Varies
Coverage	Excellent	Poor	Good	Good
Water resistance	Fair	Excellent	Excellent	Fair
Machining	Excellent	Excellent	Poor	Poor

comparable single sheet. This method permits fabrication of smaller lots as well as a variety of colors.

RIGID LAMINATES

Wood, metal, plastic and other rigid materials are combined to form laminates for structural and decorative purposes. Among the advantages offered by rigid laminates are:

(1) Increased strength-to-weight ratio.
(2) Improved weather resistance.
(3) Economy through utilization of low-grade materials for unexposed core.
(4) Unusual architectural effects.

Wood Lamination

Wood lamination has been practiced for millenia and produces the greatest volume of rigid laminates. The raw materials as well as the method of production will vary with end use; but gluing operations are discontinuous.

The Adhesive. A great variety of adhesive materials are in current use in this industry. The selection depends on many factors, such as tradition, cost, production limitations, performance requirements. A few of the more important adhesives employed in the lamination of wood are given in Table 3. The enormous dimensions of the wood

TABLE 4. U. S. PRODUCTION OF LAMINATED WOODS—1959.

(In million square feet)

Plywood, total	8,713
Plywood, hardwood	961
Plywood, softwood	7,752
Timber	150*
Lumber	37,000*

* Million board feet.

laminating industry are indicated by the production figures for the year 1959 in Table 4.

Ideally an adhesive for wood should have the following properties:

(1) Low cost.
(2) Indefinite pot-life.
(3) Quick tack.
(4) Rapid cure at relatively low temperature.
(5) Resistance of cured bond to:
   (*a*) Moisture.
   (*b*) Solvents.
   (*c*) Heat.
   (*d*) Microorganisms.
(6) Good adhesion to a variety of materials.

The trend is away from the cheaper, but less durable products based on natural adhesives, to the synthetics.

Method of Application. The more primitive brushing, troweling, and dipping are giving way to the

TABLE 3. ADHESIVES FOR WOOD LAMINATION.

Type of Adhesive	Products	Disadvantages
Animal	Lumber	Low moisture resistance
Starch	Veneer	Low moisture resistance
Casein	Timber (interior)	Low moisture resistance
Soya	Softwood plywood	Low moisture resistance
Urea	Hardwood plywood particle board	Low moisture and heat resistance
Urea/melamine	Hardwood plywood edge gluing	Expensive
Phenol	Softwood plywood particle board	Dark color, hot press
Phenol/resorc.	Timber (exterior)	Dark color, expensive
PVAc	Doors	Low moisture and heat resistance, creep.

more sophisticated roll application. An example of such a glue spreader is shown in Fig. 2. Spraying equipment is gaining as well, especially in multicomponent or the newer foamed adhesive systems.

These methods of application require liquid adhesives. Although the concentration and kind of solvent may differ, the problem of elimination of fluid remains. Evaporation necessitates heat and time.

In a different approach, the adhesive is dispensed as a thin dry film. The finished assembly is subjected to heat and pressure which activates the adhesive and creates a permanent bond. This method permits faster spreading of a more uniform adhesive layer, and eliminates drying and the associated prolonged heating and clamping.

Products made by lamination of wood include:

Plywood. This is made from several layers of veneer, sometimes in combination with a lumber core. Generally the grain of one ply is at right angle to that of the next, thus increasing the dimensional stability of the product. Almost always an odd number of plies are used. The types of plywood produced and the corresponding adhesives are shown in Table 5. The trend in the industry is toward improved quality which will eventually eliminate the interior grade in favor of the more durable exterior plywood.

Waterproof or permanent adhesives are those

TABLE 5. TYPES OF PLYWOOD PRODUCED IN THE U. S.

Type	Glue Line Quality	Typical Glue Used
Douglas Fir:		
Exterior	Permanent	Phenolic resin
Interior	Water resistant	Soy or extended phenolic
Hardwood:		
Type I	Fully water proof	Phenolic or melamine-urea
Type II	Water resistant	Urea
Type III	Moisture resistant	Casein, extended urea

which by systematic tests and performance, have proved to be durable on exposure to weather, microorganisms, hot and cold water, and dry heat. These adhesives are normally more durable than the wood itself.

Moisture-resistant adhesives offer considerable resistance to severe conditions for a limited time, but deteriorate slowly and fail ultimately. Interior adhesives fail completely under the action of water or dampness.

Lumber and Timber. Lumber lamination involves edge or end gluing in order to produce longer or wider pieces from smaller ones. Timber on the other hand involves the lamination of several pieces of lumber into unusual structures. Some of the steps in the manufacture of such struc-

Fig. 2. Glue spreader. (*Courtesy The Black Brothers Co., Inc.*)

Fig. 3. Fabrication of laminated arches. (*Courtesy American Institute of Timber Construction*)

tures are shown in Fig. 3. These products are as yet not well suited for continuous operations. Adhesives are applied by any of the aforementioned manual or semiautomatic devices. Pieces are joined and held in contact under pressure for some time. Clamping is the usual means by which such prolonged contact is achieved. The process is often accelerated with heat.

Metal Lamination

Metal may be laminated either to itself, to to wood, plastics, or other materials. The purpose of such lamination may be either decorative or functional. Since metals are nonporous, adhesives and methods of lamination must differ from those used with the porous wood. Adhesives may be nitrile phenolic, rubber cement, or epoxy. The latter is gaining in popularity because of its 100 per cent active nature. Cements containing volatile solvents create delays in assembly. After application of adhesive, surfaces cannot be mated until solvent has evaporated, since the nonporous metal would otherwise entrap solvents. In the 100 per cent active system, however, there is no need for such delay.

References

1. Brandt, Y. M., Aluminum Foil Lamination, *TAPPI*, **44**, (1), 122A–125A (Jan. 1961).
2. Conture, J. W., High Speed Foil Laminating, *Paper Film and Foil Converter*, **32**, 28–32 (Dec. 1958).
3. Sederlund, W., "Adhesives for Lamination," *Modern Packaging*, **24**, 149–151 (Oct. 1950).
4. Blomquist, R. F., "Adhesives for the Future of the Wood Industry," *Adhesives Age*, **4**, 20–27 (June 1961).
5. *Anon.*, "How to End Creasing and Wrinkling in Laminating Foil," *Paper Film and Foil Converter*, **34**, 35–37 (Feb. 1959).
6. Haven, R. S., "Latest Developments in Board Laminating Machines," *Paper Trade Journal*, **139**, (43), 26–33, (Oct. 24, 1955).
7. Brookman, R. S., "Combining Vinyl and Cloth," *Adhesive Age*, **2**, (11), 30–33 (Nov. 1959).
8. Brown, N. C., and Bethel, J. S., "Lumber," New York, John Wiley & Sons, Inc., 1958.
9. Dietz, A. G. H., "Engineering Laminates," New York, John Wiley & Sons, Inc., 1949.
10. Perry, T. D., "Modern Plywood," New York, Pitman Publishing Co., 1942.
11. Freas, A. D., and Selbo, M. L., "Fabrication and Design of Glued Laminated Wood Structural Members," Forest Product Laboratories, U. S. Department of Agriculture, 1954.

— 49 —

Caulking and Sealing Compounds

Gordon E. Hann

The Tremco Manufacturing Co.
Cleveland, Ohio

Originally the word caulk (calk) referred to the action of driving tarred oakum, cotton twist or wicking into the seams between the planks of a ship or boat. This method of sealing openings was subsequently improved through the development of asphaltic compounds made from residual asphalt mixed with asbestos fiber and other pigments. However in the past quarter of a century, caulking compounds were developed from oil or oleoresinous vehicles, primarily bodied oils of the drying type. Tremendous volumes of caulking compound of this type have been used to seal openings around the windows in homes and for similar openings in other types of building construction. This type of caulking took place after the building was erected, and was actually a remedial action taken to reduce or eliminate the infiltration of air or moisture through openings left inadvertently, usually around windows.

Recently, with the advent of curtain-wall construction, materials were required to seal the joints between metal-to-metal sections, metal-to-glass assemblies, etc. In this modular, unit type of construction, panels and sections of uniform size fit together to form the skin of the building. The older style caulking compounds are not completely satisfactory in some of these applications, and new types of materials have been developed.

In the past few years the word "sealant" has been used to differentiate between the older types of general caulking compounds and the newer specialized materials. Often the older style caulking compounds serve excellently as sealants, but not in all cases. The word "sealant," therefore, is simply a more modern term that covers a large variety of sealing compounds, including what is frequently referred to as "the old-fashioned oil-base caulking compound."

TYPES OF CAULKING COMPOUNDS AND SEALANTS

A good caulking compound or sealant should have the following characteristics:

It should not crack cohesively.
It should not lose adhesion.
It should be easy to apply.
It should last 25 to 50 yr.

Unfortunately, there are no concise definitions as to what constitutes cracking, loss of adhesion, easy application, and life.

A sealant may not crack in some cavities because the sides of the cavity do not move. For example, ordinary mortar is a perfect sealant for some joints; however if the sides moved even slightly, the sealant might crack considerably. Consequently we must define the amount of movement that will be experienced in a joint as well as the amount of movement that the sealant can withstand without cracking.

With this approach, let us consider the various types of sealants that have been developed to solve specific problems.

Sealants are made from either pure elastomer, an elastomer plus pigment, or an elastomer plus pigment plus solvent.

An elastomer is any elastic material, for example, a rubber or even a very heavy-bodied linseed oil. If pigment is added to the elastomer, it becomes heavier in body, and usually has less flow; it has been extended and given opacity and body. If solvent is then added to the combination of the elastomer and the pigment, it may be thinned to even a pourable consistency.

Sources of the basic elastomer include raw drying oils, synthetic high molecular weight polymers and pre-polymers brought to an even higher molecular weight on the job by the addition of catalysts, as well as natural materials.

Raw drying oils, such as linseed oil, may be heated to a polymerizing temperature, at which they become as heavy in body as desired by simply controlling the length of time they are held at that temperature. The temperatures are usually in the range of 500 to 600°F.

Certain liquid organic monomers are polymerized with catalysts into elastomeric materials. Acrylics, polybutenes and butyl rubber are made in this way. Some polymers such as the currently popular polysulfides, can be brought into an elastomeric state by a curing agent and/or catalyst. Or, the elastomer may even be a natural asphalt or tree resin that the ancients used. French divers off Marseilles recently found a jug of wine in a Grecian merchant vessel sunk over 2000 years ago. The jug was sealed with tar, and the wine still was not contaminated with seawater. Records indicate the transportation of asphalt from one point to another, for sealing purposes, as early as 2700 B.C.

Although it is not common to find sealants made from pure elastomer, the basic sealing is accomplished by the elastomer. The other components—pigment and sometimes solvent—do not contribute materially to the sealing action.

Figure 1 depicts the main types of pigment that are employed with the elastomer to form the sealant. Practically all sealants have a certain amount of pigment mixed with the elastomer to provide the desired physical characteristics. Pigments are basically either crushed stone, precipitated materials such as colors, or pulverized metallic pigments, such as aluminum powder.

Pigments may be crystalline, acicular, or plate-like in form. Most common are the crystalline pigments such as ground calcium carbonate, which give body to the mass. The colors are usually crystalline also.

The acicular pigments, such as asbestos fiber, give a jackstraw or reinforcing effect; also they restrict flow. The platelike particles promote adhesion because the wet, flat plates adhere to flat surfaces better than either the acicular or crystalline shapes. However, these particles also promote flow as the plates slide over each other, and tend to cause sagging or running of a compound, which may or may not be desirable.

The third basic component of some sealants is the solvent. Some sealants have no solvents and are composed of only elastomer plus pigment. These are referred to as having 100 per cent solids. Others require solvent in order to obtain a consistency thin enough for proper handling and may

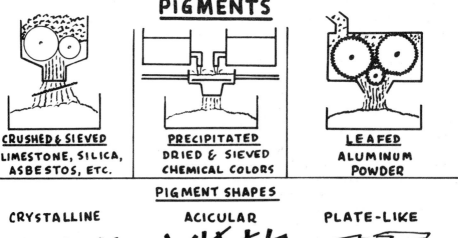

PIGMENTS

| CRUSHED & SIEVED | PRECIPITATED | LEAFED |
| LIMESTONE, SILICA, ASBESTOS, ETC. | DRIED & SIEVED CHEMICAL COLORS | ALUMINUM POWDER |

PIGMENT SHAPES

| CRYSTALLINE | ACICULAR | PLATE-LIKE |
| GIVE BODY, PROVIDE COLOR | REINFORCE, RESTRICT FLOW | PROMOTE ADHESION & FLOW |

Fig. 1

have 1 to 50 per cent solvent by volume, usually 15 to 20 per cent.

Solvents are of three general types. The petroleum solvents such as mineral spirits, gasoline, or kerosene are comparatively weak solvents, whereas the coal tar solvents such as benzene, xylene and toluene are stronger. Polar solvents such as amyl acetate, amyl alcohol, ethyl alcohol, methylethylketone, and acetone are very powerful solvents. Some elastomers are soluble only in strong solvents; some in weak solvents.

Solvents are usually added to the mixture of the elastomer and the pigment in minimum quantities to adjust the consistency downward to a point where the sealant is applicable by gun, brush, or spray. After application, the solvents usually evaporate.

Elastomers are of two basic groups: low molecular weight and high molecular weight. The low molecular weight elastomers are characterized by consistencies ranging from a thin to a very heavy syrup. These are generally used in one-part gun consistency sealers, or knife consistency sealers, employing a minimum amount of solvents. Among the low molecular weight elastomers used today are: raw drying oils, (linseed, soya, castor, fish), oxidized (blown) drying oils, polymerized drying oils, copolymer drying oils, chemically modified drying oils (dehydrated castor), fractionated drying oils, alkyd resins, polybutenes (low mol. wt.).

The high molecular weight elastomers range in consistencies from a very heavy syrup to a rubberlike solid. Some of these elastomers are used in the familiar two-part gun consistency sealers, wherein the elastomer changes after mixing with the curing agent from a heavy syrup consistency to a very heavy, rubberlike solid. Some of these elastomers are also used in one-part gun consistency sealants, along with solvent in order to bring the consistency down to the usable range. Many of these elastomers are also used to compound the extruded ribbon sealers or tapes. Among the high molecular weight elastomers currently used are: polysulfides, acrylic copolymers, butyl rubber, polyisobutene, polybutene (high mol. wt.), neoprene, polyurethanes, silicones and asphalt pitch.

The most common high molecular weight elastomer in use as a two-part gun sealant is the polysulfide type manufactured by The Thiokol Corporation. Some of these polysulfide liquid polymers lend themselves quite well to sealant manufacture. Properly compounded, mixed and applied, they have good adhesion, fairly permanent elasticity, and good resistance to ultraviolet. They cure at room temperatures, i.e., they will cure in the average building joint without the application of heat.

The most common elastomers in use in one-part consistency sealants are butyl rubber, silicone and acrylic copolymers. Butyl rubber and silicone types have good resistance to ultraviolet ozone but exhibit only fair adhesion after prolonged exposure. The acrylic copolymers have excellent adhesion after prolonged exposure.

The most common polymer in use in the manufacture of ribbon tapes is the high molecular weight polybutene. This material has fairly good adhesion and is extremely stable when exposed to ultraviolet and general weather.

These three are not interchangeable, and their own peculiar characteristics dictate the specific application of each. Of course, many modifications are possible.

The sealants made from these various elastomers fall into six basic types, as indicated in Tables 1 to 6. These data show the differences among the six basic types of compounds if all are tested under identical conditions.

TABLE 1. TYPICAL STANDARD GUN-CONSISTENCY CAULKING COMPOUND.

Use—General sealant for masonry, metal, wood, etc., where skin forming compound is required
Composition—Oxidized and/or polymerized drying oils, ground fillers, asbestos, and colors; solvent for proper gun consistency
Adhesion—Good
Shrinkage—10–20%
Approximate usable % elongation—10% after weathering
Estimated hardness Shore "A" 10 yr—65±
Life—10–20 yr if properly applied

TABLE 2. TYPICAL STANDARD KNIFE CONSISTENCY GLAZING COMPOUND.

Use—General sealant for glass to metal (small to medium size lights)
Composition—Raw, polymerized, and treated drying oils; polybutenes; ground fillers; minimum solvent
Adhesion—fair
Shrinkage—0–3%
Approximate usable % elongation—5% after weathering
Estimated hardness Shore "A" 10 yr—80
Life—10–20 yr if properly applied

TABLE 3. INTEGRAL SETTING, GUN-CONSISTENCY, SPECIAL-PURPOSE BUILDING SEALANTS (TWO-PART).

Use—Exposed, small, critical joints in building construction requiring fast cure or set. (4 to 24 hr)

Composition—Certain polysulfide polymers ("Thiokol"), minimum pigment, no solvent

Adhesion—excellent while reasonably soft

Shrinkage—0% to 3%

Approximate usable % elongation—50 to 100% after weathering

Estimated hardness Shore "A" after 10 yr—40–65

Life—20–35 yr if properly applied

TABLE 4. SKIN-FORMING, GUN-CONSISTENCY,
SPECIAL-PURPOSE SEALANT (ONE-PART).

Use—Exposed, small, critical joints in building construction where "set" in 10 to 30 days satisfactory

Composition—Butyl rubber, polyurethanes, silicone, acrylic copolymers, etc.; asbestos fiber, ground pigments, with solvent to produce gunnable consistency

Adhesion—good to excellent

Shrinkage—10–50%

Approximate usable % elongation—25% to 100% after weathering

Estimated hardness Shore "A" after 10 yr—40–70

Life—10–35 yr if properly applied

TABLE 5. NON-DRYING, GUN-CONSISTENCY, AND TOOL
CONSISTENCY, SPECIAL-PURPOSE SEALANTS.

Use—For maximum permanent elasticity—for use on nonporous surfaces, (exposed applications will hold dirt pickup because they are non-drying)

Composition—Medium molecular weight polybutenes, asbestos fiber, ground fillers

Adhesion—Excellent

Shrinkage—0–10%

Usable % elongation—50% after weathering

Estimated hardness Shore "A" after 10 yr—10–20 gun consistency, 20–30 tool consistency

Life—20–30 yr if properly applied

TABLE 6. EXTRUDED COMPRESSIBLE TAPES.

Use—Uniform joints in building construction

Composition—High molecular weight polybutene (mainly). Also—butyl rubber, buna, polyisobutene. Pigment, asbestos, ground filler, minimum solvent.

Adhesion—Fair to good

Shrinkage—0–3%*

Approximate usable % elongation—10% after weathering*

Estimated hardness Shore "A" after 10 yr—20–40

Life—20–35 yr

* Polybutene tapes.

DESIGN OF JOINT CAVITIES

Shown in Fig. 2 are typical caulking bead locations, about ½ in. wide at the base, with a maximum movement in the joint of ¹⁄₁₆ in. and a maxi-

Fig. 2

mum elongation of sealant of 10 per cent. A good caulking compound properly applied seals such joints for 15 to 20 years without any difficulty.

Figure 3 illustrates typical metal-to-glass and metal-to-metal joints, which vary from ³⁄₃₂ to ⅛ in. Movement in the joint may be ¹⁄₁₆ in. A properly formulated seal that has 50 to 100 per cent usable

Metal to
Metal

Metal to
Glass

Fig. 3

elongation should effectively seal these joints. It is easy to realize the need for types of sealants different from standard caulking compound when we visualize the actual movement within the modern joint cavity itself. Consider the joint between two sections of an aluminum cap. At 70°F the joint is approximately 0.3 in wide. If the span between fastenings is 28 ft, it is easily calculated that at 0°F, the joint opens to 0.6 in., whereas at 130°F, the joint closes to 0 in., requiring a sealant of infinite elongation. Mathematicians but not chemists can solve this problem.

Since both temperature extremes are possible, there is no sealant which will work in this joint.

The first rule to follow in selecting a specific joint sealant is to determine what movement will occur in the joint when used.

The second rule follows closely—determine what elongation the various sealants will permit.

Then make your choice of sealant.

WORKMANSHIP IN APPLYING SEALANTS

Just as the older style types caulking compounds and sealants are not applicable to all sealing problems in modern-day construction, neither are the caulking techniques that were used 10 years ago.

Extreme precautions were not necessary with the large beads of caulking compound that were placed around a window frame to seal the joint between the frame and the brick wall, especially since the seal already was partially made by a bed of mortar at the time the wall was erected. Even if there were some points of loss of adhesion, the water that went through the unsealed joint was absorbed by the thick masonry wall and did not give trouble inside.

The joint on the older style construction, as seen in Fig. 2, did not have to be wiped perfectly dry and clean before application of the sealant, as it most certainly has to be in the joint shown in Fig. 3. A very slight amount of dampness in a brick causes no serious loss of adhesion by the caulking compound.

Droplets of water in the joints of a porcelain veneer wall however do not evaporate very rapidly and definitely do interfere with the adhesion of a sealant employed in sealing the joints in this porcelain veneer wall. Figure 4 shows droplets in a joint immediately preceding the sealing operation performed by the men. The face of the wall was wiped, but not the joint where the water had actually accumulated, and where it would prevent adhesion.

Therefore, in curtain wall construction, just as a greater demand is being made upon the sealant, a greater demand is now being made upon the applier as well.

RECOMMENDATIONS FOR CURTAIN-WALL SEALING

Information to be obtained prior to making a recommendation:

(A) The basic sash or surround.
Manufacturer.
Detail drawings of the sealant location.
Type of finish; sensitivity to solvents, etc.

(B) Movement in the joint to be sealed.
Metal used for sash.
Maximum and minimum dimensions of the opening to be sealed during temperature extremes.
Handling it will undergo after it is sealed (transportation, adjustment, opening and closing) and how this will affect the joint dimensions.
If in a multiple-story building, the height and wind pressure problems of the upper stories.

(C) The glass or panel.
Manufacturer and type. Heat-absorbing glass may pose special problems.

Fig. 4

Length, width and thickness; dimension tolerances; warpage or out-of-plane dimensions.

Finish: sensitivity to handling; directions for cleaning.

(D) Placement of sealant.

Types of stops on all four sides (snap in, screwed in, fixed, etc.).

Are the fixed stops welded or sealed in the corners, or are they open butt or miter joints which require sealing?

Dimensions and tolerances.

Is a permanent stop on inside or outside or both?

Accessibility for placing and cleaning (scaffolding, height of back up walls, reversible sash, etc.).

Will it be practical to compress tapes during assembly?

Will the glass or panel be installed from the inside or outside?

(E) Exposure and general job site location problems.

Degree of ultraviolet exposure.

Expected amount of vibration shock.

Is there any abnormal exposure to chemicals?

Normal temperature range.

Is there a possibility of strong driving rains?

Is there a possibility of water getting behind the seal through the butt or miter joints?

(F) Application skill.

Type of labor; previous experience.

Estimated working temperature.

Possibility of skilled supervision.

Who has responsibility for the tightness of the curtain wall, the glazing contractor or the curtain-wall supplier?

(G) Quality of seal required.

Degree of protection required.

Is the wall protected by a screen or projection?

Degree of dependence on weep holes.

(H) Materials.

Are there any preconceived notions as to what materials are satisfactory or unsatisfactory for this particular job?

Cost limitations.

There are many possible ways of sealing a pane of glass or a panel in the standard types of sash available today. A very simple way would be to

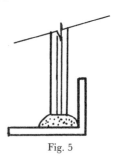

Fig. 5

put a bead of a gun-consistency sealant around the periphery of the glass after the glass is positioned and before the removable stop has been put in place, Fig. 5. This is the basic sealing procedure, that is, between the edge of the glass and the fixed portion of the sash. Any other consideration is for the purpose of compromising for cost or appearance sake.

Fundamental Considerations

Four factors are basic:

(1) The space available for the sealant.
(2) Amount of movement anticipated in the sealed joint.
(3) The real importance of the seal.
(4) Appearance requirements.

The apparent ideal recommendation based on these four factors may be impractical for other reasons. For example, it may seem advisable to use an extruded tape on both sides of the glass as the only seal, considering the four basic criteria. However, when it is discovered that outside stops are employed, this recommendation is impracticable since water could enter under the exterior stop and collect behind the sealant.

Again, polysulfide-base sealant, as the complete seal, would meet the four basic requirements in the installation of structural glass spandrels. However, the spandrels are installed in front of a concrete block back-up wall and all sealing must be done from the exterior, precluding the possibility of a gun caulking bead on the interior.

Some of the detailed requirements for the four basic factors are:

(1) Space for the sealant should be ⅛ in. min., with a "bite" (overlap of glass or panel by sash) of ⅜ in. min., Fig. 6. The glass or panel must be centered. The sealant must not be required to support mechanically the glass or panel, but properly placed shims and setting blocks must do this.

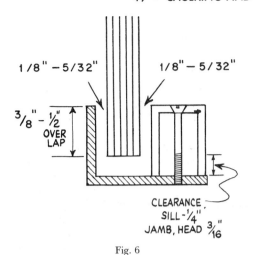

1/8" — 5/32"   1/8" — 5/32"

3/8" - 1/2" OVER LAP

CLEARANCE
SILL - 1/4"
JAMB, HEAD 3/16"

Fig. 6

(2) Movement in the sealant joint must be anticipated. Thermal movement causes strain because the expansion coefficients of glass, aluminum, steel, and masonry differ. Wind pressures cause movement in the joint, and handling of an assembled unit may cause damage to the seal. In small sizes, the movement is not critical. If the glass or panel is under 100 united inches (sum of height and width), a good quality glazing compound should provide a satisfactory, permanent seal except for excessive wracking such as in some projected sash with sliding hinges in jambs. If dimensions exceed 100 united in., the cumulative movement may be such that a more permanently elastic material, such as a polysulfide or acrylic sealant, will better serve the sealant needs. This may also be true even if the sash is under 100 united in. but is in a long continuous run which may result in accumulated movement at a few critical points.

Thermal Movement. A 10 ft aluminum extrusion, in a temperature range of 40 to 160° F will expand 2½ times more than glass, or ⅕ of an in.

Provision to Withstand Wind Pressure. The Building Research Institute Workshop Conference (Washington, D. C.) recommended that design anticipate 150 m.p.h. wind velocities. The center of a 5 ft × 10 ft light will deflect, 1¾ in., including anchorage under a 100 m.p.h. wind velocity.

(3) Seals vary in importance. The windows or panels may be protected from driving rains by large overhangs; or they may be in an isolated tall building, subject to high wind pressures and driving rains and a very small opening will permit the entrance of a large amount of water. Weep holes and baffles may be provided, especially in spandrel panels, so that even if water enters, it is led away harmlessly. The space between the glass and the sash, or at least the sill joint, (see exception below in ¶4) should be completely filled to prevent flow of water that enters at any small opening into a reservoir where it may collect and cause severe damage later by freezing or excessive vapor pressure.

(4) Appearance is excellent with polysulfide sealant. Some one-part gun consistency sealants are better than others for dirt retention. Glazing compound provides a good appearance, but will chalk, become dirty, and may even fall out if inadequate amounts were used. Extruded polybutene tape will collect dirt, but on the inside of spandrels, for example, it cannot be seen. On dark panels and sash the dirt collection may not be noticeable. If glazing compound is used to fill the joint around a ⅜ in. or thicker insulated glass or panel edge, some slight oil or compound exudation may result at the jambs and the head; consequently it will mar the appearance. Therefore, it is recommended that if a glazing compound is used on ⅜ in. or thicker glass or panel edges, a space be allowed around the periphery of the glass or panel at both jambs and the head. See Fig. 7. However, it is strongly recommended that the sill section be filled completely with the sealant.

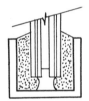

Fig. 7

Some Typical Recommendations

For a practical description of sealing procedures this text is confined to three basic materials.

(a) A gun-consistency sealant—either a two part polysulfide material or a quality one-part gun consistency sealant to fit specific job requirements.

(b) A knife-consistency glazing compound—currently a glazing compound meeting TT-G-00410—although other knife-consistency materials may fit different specific job requirements.

(c) A non-drying type of gun consistency or extruded tape.

Basic Recommendations and Examples

Aluminum Sash

(1) Lights of Glass Under 50 United Inches
    (a) Face Glazing (Inside or Out) Fig. 8.
        Bed glass in non-drying tool consistency and bedding compound.
        Set clips and face glaze with glazing compound.
    (b) Angle Glazing (Inside or Out) Fig. 9.
        Bed glass in non-drying tool consistency and bedding compound.
        Set glass. Finish with non-drying tool consistency and bedding compound and embed angle.

(2) Lights of Glass 50 to 100 United Inches
    (a) Face Glazing—Fig. 10
        Same as 1(a) above but glass must be centered in rabbet, using spacer shims in bed.
    (b) Angle Glazing—Fig. 11
        Same as 1(b) above, except that spacer must be used to ensure centering of the glass.
    (c) Channel Glazing—Fig. 12
        Same as Angle Glazing 2 (b) using spacer shims to center.

(3) Lights of Glass Greater Than 100 United Inches

Because of the much greater demands placed on the sealants through greater movement and other factors previously referred to, special precautions and the new elastomeric sealants must be used.

The following are only examples of jobs that have been completed without any leakage, and where recommendations were based on individual job situations.

Before setting any glass, all four corners where vertical members joined horizontal members must be sealed with one or two part gun consistency sealant to ensure an elastic seal (unless this had already been done in shop fabrication).

Example 1—Fig. 13
    Set glass in two-part gun consistency sealant, filling entire glazing channel to sight line.

Example 2—Fig. 14
    Bed glass in extruded tape. Apply heel bead of one or two-part gun consistency sealant, lapping on glass edge a minimum of ¼ in.

Set molding and back fill with glazing compound after overnight set of two-part gun consistency sealant.

Example 3—Fig. 15
    Bed glass in non-drying tool consistency and bedding compound.
    Set glass. All oil stains on glass or aluminum must be thoroughly removed by wiping with pure mineral spirits before application of the heel bead, to insure proper adhesion. Apply either a one- or two-part gun consistency sealant or glazing compound as in previous example. (This type of sealant placement used only where allowable variable in plane of glass prevents use of a preformed sealant, i.e., heat resisting glass).

Example 4—Fig. 16
    Bed glass in two-part gun consistency sealant to sight line. Back putty with non-drying tool consistency and bedding compound to interior sight line.

Example 5—(Screw-in molding only)—Fig. 17
    Bed glass in extruded tape with squeeze-out beyond sight line. Bed molding similarly in extruded tape. Cut off to sight line on both sides of vision glass, or on exterior only if spandrel glass is being installed. Because both tapes must be under compression to effect a seal it is important that the widths exceed designed space. Up to ¼ in. thickness the allowable tolerance of extruded tape is $\pm\frac{1}{32}$ in.

Steel Sash

(1) Lights of Glass Under 50 United Inches.
    (a) Angle Glazing—Fig. 18
        1. Apply bed of glazing compound for metal sash.
        2. Bed glass.
        3. Butter angles with glazing compound for metal sash.
        4. Install angles.
    (b) Face Glazed—Fig. 18
        1. Apply bed of glazing compound for metal sash.
        2. Bed glass and secure with clips.
        3. Face glaze with glazing compound for metal sash.

Note: When glass exceeds 50 united in., special recommendations must be obtained from the sealant manufacturer.

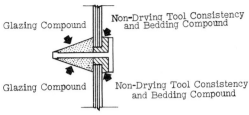

Glazing Compound

Glazing Compound

Non-Drying Tool Consistency
and Bedding Compound

Non-Drying Tool Consistency
and Bedding Compound

Fig. 8

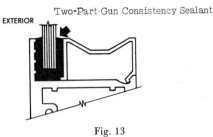

Two-Part-Gun Consistency Sealant

EXTERIOR

Fig. 13

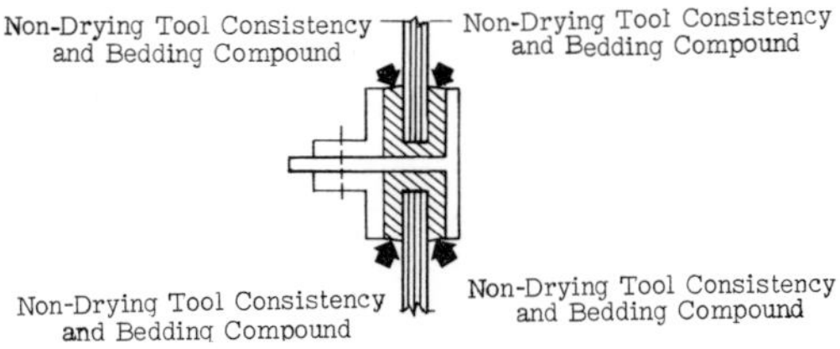

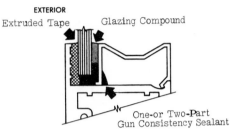

Non-Drying Tool Consistency
and Bedding Compound

Non-Drying Tool Consistency
and Bedding Compound

Non-Drying Tool Consistency
and Bedding Compound

Non-Drying Tool Consistency
and Bedding Compound

Fig. 9

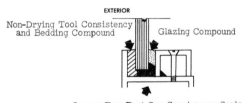

EXTERIOR

Extruded Tape   Glazing Compound

One-or Two-Part
Gun Consistency Sealant

Fig. 14

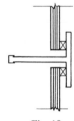

Fig. 10

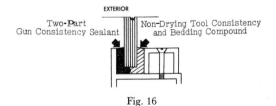

EXTERIOR

Non-Drying Tool Consistency
and Bedding Compound   Glazing Compound

One-or Two-Part Gun Consistency Sealant

Fig. 15

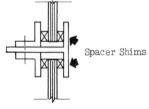

Spacer Shims

Fig. 11

EXTERIOR

Two-Part
Gun Consistency Sealant   Non-Drying Tool Consistency
and Bedding Compound

Fig. 16

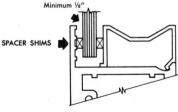

Minimum ⅛″

SPACER SHIMS

Fig. 12

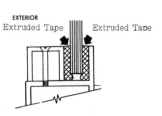

EXTERIOR

Extruded Tape   Extruded Tape

Fig. 17

Wood Sash

(a) With Molding—Fig. 19
1. Apply bed of glazing compound for wood sash to the permanent stop.
2. Bed glass and secure with glaziers points.
3. Butter moldings with glazing compound for wood sash.
4. Install moldings.

(b) Face Glazed—Fig. 20
1. Apply bed of glazing compound for wood sash to the permanent stop.
2. Bed glass and secure with glaziers points.
3. Face glaze, using glazing compound for wood sash.

Note: All wood surfaces to receive glazing compound for wood sash shall be thoroughly primed and painted.

Insulating Glass in Aluminum Sash—Fig. 21

1. Bed glass in extruded tape with squeeze-out beyond sight line.
2. Apply a heel bead of either one part or two part gun consistency sealant completely around the perimeter of the glass making a minimum ¼ in. contact on glass and metal leaving a void around the edge of glass at jambs and head.
3. At sill, fill under glass edge solidly with one or two-part gun consistency sealant.
4. Secure inside molding.
5. After sealant sets (minimum 12 hr) fill inside bed void with glazing compound or non-drying tool consistency compound.

Insulating Glass in Wood Sash—Fig. 22

(1) Shop or In-Plant Glazing
In addition to the basic considerations of adequate security of an enduring seal and economy, sound recommendations for shop glazing of heavy insulating glass units, i.e., studio windows, must include a study of:

(a) Possibility of displacement of sealants through movement or shifting of glass in handling, shipping and erection—design and extent of shimming and blocking provided by manufacturer.

(b) Type of equipment available for pneumatic, mechanical or hand applications of sealants.

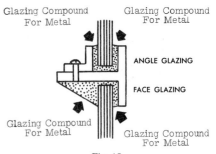

Fig. 18

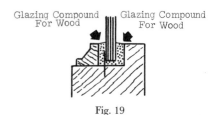

Fig. 19

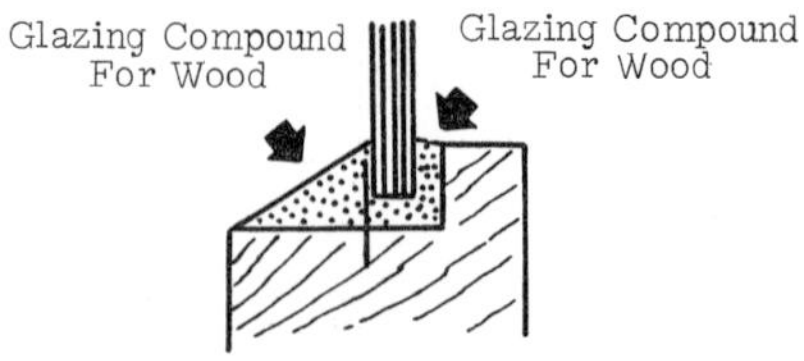

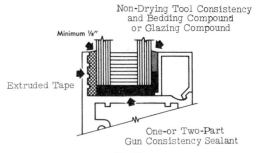

Fig. 20

Fig. 21

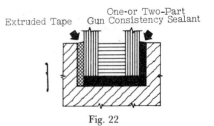

Fig. 22

(c) Speed of mass production line and time allowable for glazing operation.

Because of variables in the above, to achieve the optimum glazing procedure, special recommendations must be obtained from the sealant manufacturer.

(2) Job Site or Field Glazing

General Considerations:

Where oleoresinous glazing compound or polybutene extruded tape or non-drying tool consistency and bedding compounds are to be used, all wood rabbets should be thoroughly paint primed and sealed to prevent migration of vehicles.

Where one- or two-part gun consistency sealants are to be used contact should be made directly to virgin wood.

Considerations of size, bite, detail of rabbet will govern but in general the following might well apply:

1. Bed glass in extruded tape.
2. On jambs and head, fill rabbet to sight line with either one-part or two-part gun consistency sealant, leaving void around glass edge for expansion of compound under heat build-up.
3. At sill, repeat (2) above except pack glass edge solidly in and around and between setting blocks with one- or two-part gun consistency sealant.

Water-Remoistenable Adhesives

Armand J. Gauthier
Ludlow Papers Div.
Ludlow Corporation
Ware, Massachusetts

A water-remoistenable adhesive is a dried film of adhesive material which is capable of being activated by moistening with water. It is termed *remoistenable* because the adhesive mass was originally in water when applied to the substrate. The aqueous adhesive was spread as a film upon a backing, e.g., paper, by means of applicator rolls, and then dried by passing through a heated chamber. This dried adhesive film, on being remoistened with water, reverts almost instantly to its former gummy or tacky state, permitting the paper backing to be affixed with some degree of permanence to a variety of surfaces.

Examples of water-remoistenable adhesives are the gummings used on labels, sealing tapes, and the flaps of envelopes. The gummed labels and gummed tapes will be discussed in detail.

MATERIALS AND METHODS

Materials used to compound these adhesive films are of necessity water-soluble or water-dispersible, and include such primary components as dextrins, animal and fish glues, vegetable gums, cellulose gums, and polyvinyl alcohol. Modifying ingredients are included to impart specific properties such as flexibility, good spreading quality, ease of wetting-out, increased tackiness, and resistance to blocking. Among these modifiers are glycerin, corn syrup, sorbose derivatives, glycols, sulfonated oils, emulsified waxes and resins, salts such as sodium and calcium chlorides, sodium nitrate and acetate, urea, thiourea, dicyandiamide,

borax, soda ash, sodium silicate, and many others. Often included are preservatives such as sodium benzoate, certain quaternary ammonium salts, phenol, cresol and thymol derivatives, and occasionally mercurial and silver salts. Scenting and flavoring agents are frequently added to mask odors or unpalatable flavors of glues and resins; such agents could be synthetic oils of wintergreen, spearmint, peppermint, sassafras, lemon, clove, grape, anise, and even banana, butterscotch, maple and balsam.

The components of remoistenable-adhesive formulations are usually dispersed in sufficient water to produce a solution having a dry solids content ranging from 45 to 60 per cent, depending on the viscosity desired in the completed mix. Proper viscosity is essential for good spreading quality and for good "hold-up" on the substrate to which the liquid adhesive is being applied. An attempt is made to keep the solids content of the liquid mix as high as possible in order to speed drying and thus keep the production rate at a high level.

Depending on the size of the operation, batches of liquid adhesive are made up in quantities ranging from 50 to 250 gal. These batches are usually cooked up in steam-jacketed, stainless steel kettles at temperatures ranging from 150 to 190°F, depending on the type of adhesive being prepared. Dextrins require a cooking temperature of 190°F, whereas glues can only tolerate 150°F, for maximum adhesive quality. Moderate stirring with paddle-type or impeller-blade agitators is required to effect solution or dispersion.

The liquid adhesive is cast as a wet film onto the web of substrate, such as paper, by means of conventional kiss-feed applicator rolls, reverse-spreader rolls, and combinations of these two systems. The wet gummed paper, moving at speeds of 100 to 600 ft/min, then passes into a horizontal, usually arched, drying chamber where temperatures range from 260 to 325°F, depending on the source of heat. The dryer may be 90 to 150 ft long, with temperature controlled in two or more sections according to the substrate and the type and amount of adhesive being dried. Usually, higher temperatures are used nearest the wet end of the dryer where the bulk of the water in the gumming is driven off; the temperature near the exit end of the dryer is reduced to prevent excessive curling of the dried gummed paper. Often the gummed paper is passed over a cooling drum as it emerges from the dryer, previous to being reeled up. The cooling stabilizes the gummed paper, as nearly as possible, at its normal 5 to 6 per cent moisture content, and relieves some of the stresses set up in the product during the drying process. On a 17 × 22 in. size, 500-sheet ream basis, the dried gum film weighs 5 to 6 lb/ream, 5 lb being used on papers 17.5 to 20 lb in basis weight and 6 pounds on 23 to 28 pound papers.

Flattening

Anyone who has tried to hang wallpaper knows that paper which has been pasted and allowed to dry curls up tightly into a tube. Gummed paper destined for use as label stock will act in the same manner, unless it is processed to make it lay flat for printing. This is accomplished by drawing the gummed paper diagonally at a 45 degree angle to the grain direction over the sharp edge of a steel bar or strip, then repeating the process diagonally in the opposite direction. This action breaks the gum film into a pattern or mosaic of tiny squares, disrupting the continuity of the film and relieving the stresses set up by its contraction during drying. The processed gummed paper now lays flat, because the little squares of gum film are free to expand and contract slightly with limited changes in temperature and humidity without appreciably influencing the flatness of the paper.

The process is usually carried out under controlled conditions of temperature and humidity, ideally 70 to 75°F and 50 per cent relative humidity. Label paper flattened under these conditions will ordinarily remain flat enough to be printed even when the temperature fluctuates between 60 and 85°F and the relative humidity varies between 35 and 65 per cent.

GUMMED-LABEL STOCKS

Many types of water-remoistenable adhesives are employed in the manufacture of gummed paper designed for use as printed labels. The choice of adhesive is governed by (1) the surface to which the label is to be applied, (2) the type of paper (English finish or coated grade) to be used as the substrate or backing, (3) the basis weight or stiffness of the paper backing, and (4) whether the label stock is for domestic use, or for export to tropical and semi-tropical countries, where exposure to conditions of prolonged high humidity is frequently encountered.

Labeling of Glass

Label adhesives intended primarily for application to glass, porcelain and other vitreous surfaces contain dextrins or British gums as their major component. When coated papers or heavier weight English finish papers (23 to 28 lb on a 17 × 22 in. —500-sheet ream basis) are used as the substrate, 10 to 30 per cent of 40 to 90 g bone glue or even fish glue may be added, based on the dextrin. The glue provides added initial tack to counteract the spring-back or curl toward the backing, which often occurs when a moistened label is applied to a curved glass surface.

Stronger Labels

Labels designed for more general use are expected to adhere well to various types of paper and paper-board, corrugated cartons, wood, leather, paint finish, rubber and textiles, in addition to glass. An adhesive for these purposes might be composed of a blend of 30 to 60 per cent dextrin and 40 to 70 per cent of 40 to 90 g bone glue, with possibly some fish glue included to strengthen the final bond.

Quality Labels

Metallic-coated papers, whether casein or pyroxylin bonded, and metallic foil-to-paper laminated label stocks so popular for Christmas seals, documentary seals, anniversary seals, quality tags and labels are by nature stiffer and more expensive than run-of-the-mill labels, thereby demanding a high quality adhesive of dependable bonding strength. A gumming for seals and labels of this type might be composed mainly of animal glue, with perhaps 10 to 20 per cent dextrin added as an extender and to provide better wettability. Chances are that a scenting or flavoring agent would be included, because many of these seals would be applied by moistening with the tongue.

Stamps

Among the seals applied by tongue are the stamps, such as postage, trading, commemorative and fund-raising. Since most of these stamps are required to adhere mainly to paper stocks, the basic adhesive material need be no stronger than a dextrin of good quality. In the case of postage stamps, maximum adhesive strength is required of the dextrin; tapioca and white milo dextrin are frequently selected for this application. Corn dextrins are quite adequate for the other types of stamps.

All stamp adhesives require more antiblocking characteristics than, say, label adhesives, because most stamps suffer much more handling than labels, and are exposed to greater extremes in atmospheric conditions, such as heat and cold, excessive dryness and dampness. Antiblocking agents used in stamp adhesives include small amounts of emulsified waxes and resins, cellulose gums such as carboxymethyl and hydroxyethyl cellulose, high molecular weight polyethylene glycols, also vegetable gums such as ghatti, tragacanth or arabic, and even silica gel, diatomaceous earth and certain aluminum silicates.

Other water-remoistenable adhesives for both stamps and labels which require better than ordinary blocking resistance are formulated with polyvinyl alcohol, blends of polyvinyl alcohol and polyvinyl acetate, or blends of specially processed dextrin and polyvinyl acetate. Gummed stamp and label papers slated for export to tropical and semi-tropical countries have been known to utilize straight gum arabic adhesives.

Textile Labels

Several gummed paper manufacturers are producing a line of peelable textile labels having remoistenable adhesives designed to adhere tightly to a wide variety of textiles, but capable of being peeled away from the textile at the point of use, leaving behind no residue or stain. This enables the textile material to be utilized immediately, without the bother of soaking off the label and washing. A removable label adhesive of this type might be composed mainly of dextrin, with a small amount of low test animal glue or gelatin added, plus a considerable amount of emulsified wax or waxy material to give releasing quality on peeling away the label. Such a formulation would be adequate for cotton, cotton-rayon blends and woolen textiles; but for adhesion to the newer textiles such as nylon, "Dacron," "Orlon" and "Dynel," special additives must be added to the gumming formulation. These may be acrylic or polyvinyl acetate emulsions, polyvinyl alcohol, or cationic detergents and starches.

All-Purpose Labels

Labels designed for adhesion to more difficult surfaces such as metals, plastics, enamels, lacquers, varnishes, dried printing inks, and other water-repellent and nonporous materials require adhesives which are specially formulated. It is quite difficult to compound a single adhesive which will adhere satisfactorily to such a wide variety of surfaces, but some gummed label manufacturers have attempted it with a certain degree of success. Others formulate specifically for plastics, resinous coatings, and so forth.

Adhesives for these labels might contain animal or fish glues blended with dispersed, saponified, or emulsified resins, tackified with various oils or plasticizers, and made resistant to pressure and moisture blocking by incorporation of some inert material. Resins employed might be rosin derivatives, usually of the hydrogenated type for better stability, styrene polymers, polyisobutylenes, polyvinyl methyl ether and others. Oils and plasticizers used might be castor oil and its derivatives, sulfonated castor and tall oils, triethylene glycol, propylene glycol, hexylene glycol, hydroabietyl alcohol, to name a few. Inert materials included might be clays, bentonites and other silicaceous products, also finely ground alpha-cellulose pulp and wood flour, for example. Penetrants and wetting agents of various types could also be incorporated. Antioxidants might be added to prolong shelf-life, and scenting or flavoring agents to mask the odor and taste of the resins.

Stay-Flat Labels

A recent development in the field of water-remoistenable label adhesives is the new non-curling product now being marketed by a number of gummed paper manufacturers. This adhesive is distinctive in that it requires no mechanical "breaking" after application to the paper to make the gummed stock lay flat. The key to the success of this ingenious adhesive is the fact that it is cast on the paper backing from a nonaqueous vehicle, there being no water present to distort or swell the fibrous structure of the paper. The water-soluble portion of this adhesive is not dissolved in the vehicle, since the latter is nonaqueous, but is composed of micro-pulverized or micronized glue or dextrin. These micronized particles are merely suspended in the nonaqueous vehicle and cast as a slurry on the paper backing by means of a reverse-roll coater and then dried in the conventional manner. The adhesive film dries to a matte finish and does not contract or cause the paper to curl during drying, because it is composed of discrete tiny dextrin and/or glue particles bound to the paper by an adhesive adjunct which had been dissolved in the nonaqueous vehicle.

Preferred water-soluble components of this type of non-curling adhesive are specially prepared potato or tapioca dextrins, and bone glues of 90 to 140 g gel strength. The nonaqueous vehicle is composed of a solvent such as benzol, toluol, xylol, alcohol, naphtha, or mixtures thereof, with an adhesive adjunct such as polyvinyl methyl ether, polyvinyl acetate or other synthetic resins dissolved in the solvent. The adhesive adjunct may or may not be soluble also in water and contribute to the adhesion of the primary adhesive.

This non-curling label adhesive has an advantage over conventional mechanically flattened adhesives in that it remains flat over a wider range of relative humidity conditions, e.g., from 20 to 80 per cent relative humidity, a characteristic which pleases printers.

Decalcomanias

Decalcomanias are specialized remoistenable gummed papers which are used to transfer decorative or informative printed lacquer or ink films to a wide variety of surfaces ranging from glass and porcelain, through bananas and melons, to trucks and aircraft.

The base stock used in manufacturing the most common or "Simplex" decalcomania is a fairly heavy (80 to 100 lb on a 25 × 38 in.—500 sheet basis) unsized or absorbent waterleaf paper. It is usually coated first with a solution of either corn or wheat starch, then dried and calendered smooth. This starch coat acts as a "hold-up" medium for the second or adhesive coat, and also acts as a slip or releasing agent when the decal is wet out. The second coat, which is laid on top of the starch coat, provides the adhesion for the decal. This adhesive coat is frequently composed of a specially prepared dextrin, approximately 97 per cent cold-water soluble, supplemented by other starch derivatives, natural gums or cellulosic gums for

maximum adhesive strength. Humectant-type plasticizers may also be added to the dextrin to prevent the gum film from cracking when exposed to excessive dryness, and to help maintain flatness of the gummed sheet during the printing operation.

The manufacturer of decalcomania paper usually concerns himself primarily with production of the starched and gummed decal base stock, and may also provide it with an over-all clear, opaque white, or metallic pigmented lacquer over the gummed surface. Printing of the decal paper is accomplished by silk-screening a solid inked area directly onto the gummed surface, using special inks which dry by oxidation and/or evaporation rather than by absorption. Decorative designs or eye-appealing advertising copy are then silk-screened on top of this basic or carrier ink film. In the case of the over-all-lacquered gummed decal paper, the lacquer film acts as the carrier for the inked design.

When the completed decal design is ready to be applied to the intended surface, the decalcomania is dipped into water for approximately one-half a minute. During this immersion, the water permeates the unsized paper backing and reaches the starch coating, causing it to swell and become slippery. The water then progresses to the adhesive coat, activating it. The slippery, adhesive films beneath the surface of the silk-screened design permit it to be slid or transferred from the paper substrate directly onto the surface to be labeled.

Quite often, instead of silk-screening a solid inked area over the gummed surface of a decal paper, the printer may silk-screen a film of clear lacquer onto the adhesive coating and allow it to dry. The decorative or informative design is then silk-screened on top of this lacquer film which serves as a medium for transferring the design to the surface being labeled. It is obvious, therefore, that the decal gumming should contain neither elements which are soluble in the solvent phase of the lacquer, nor plasticizers which are compatible with the lacquer base or with silk-screen inks. In one case, release of the lacquer film might be impaired, and in either case the clear lacquer film may be clouded or etched when transferred and allowed to dry. Ingredients in the adhesive which are compatible with the ink film might soften it and prevent its release and transfer, or cause the ink film to crack or wrinkle after application to a surface and then drying.

Decals which are intended for such difficult surfaces as baked enamel, various metals and painted or varnished surfaces require a greater degree of adhesion than those which are applied mainly to glass and porcelain. To lend more versatility of adhesion, an all-purpose decal gumming might contain, in addition to the basic dextrin, a synthetic latex which is not attacked by the ketone or acetate type solvents commonly present in the clear lacquer films applied to the gumming.

GUMMED TAPES

Everyone is familiar with the gummed tapes used by shipping clerks to seal down the flaps of cartons, by grocers and butchers to seal wrapped packages of meat, and by mail order houses for sealing all shapes and sizes of shipping containers. These are but a few of the most common uses for gummed tape. There are also corrugators' box tapes, box-corner stay tapes, veneer tapes, bindery tapes and specialty gummed tapes. All are marketed in coil form, slit to any desired width, and put up in convenient yardages.

Although each of these various types of gummed tapes has a specific use, the remoistenable adhesives used on them have much in common. They are for the most part composed of animal glues, both bone and hide, with small amounts of dextrin added as extenders, also to provide quicker wetting and lasting tack. Other materials may also be included in the adhesive formulation, such as sodium chloride to provide quick penetration of the moistening water into the glue film and give it longer working life, a small amount of calcium chloride to increase the "wet tack" of the glue, and urea for rapid wetting and contribution of long thread to the glue. Sulfonated vegetable oils may be added to improve compatibility between dextrin and glues, to lend pliability to the glue film, and to add lubricity to the glue film during the slitting operation, permitting the coils of tape to be separated easily at the slitter. Scenting agents are commonly added to mask the odor of the animal glues present.

The base paper used for gummed tapes is usually a strong kraft grade, specially sized to give good hold-up of the adhesive (that is, to prevent undue penetration). Basis weights of the krafts depend on the end use of the gummed tape. Sealing tapes utilize 35, 60 and 90 lb krafts, on a 24 × 36 in.—500 sheet ream basis. Reinforced sealing tapes use two plies of kraft laminated together with asphalt or a resin-latex blend, and reinforcing yarns of glass or rayon sandwiched between the kraft plies and oriented in both machine and cross directions or diagonally for added strength. There may be two plies of 30 or 35 lb kraft, or a 60 lb kraft laminated to a 30 or 35 lb kraft.

Corrugators' box tapes, used to seal the single open corner of a knocked-down corrugated carton in its process of manufacture, are of similar reinforced laminated construction, but have their reinforcing yarns oriented mainly in the cross direction where their strength is incorporated into the box joint. Basis weight of the finished tape may run as high as 150 lb on a 24 × 36 in.—500 sheet ream basis. Box-corner stay tapes, used to stay or close the four open corners of set-up chipboard boxes such as those used to package shoes, candy, hardware and other articles, utilize a 90 or 100 lb kraft.

Veneer tapes, used to hold flitches or sections of thin wood veneer in place during the assembly of plies and panels, are made either from 35 or 50 lb kraft. Bindery tapes, used to bind the padded or stapled edge of paper tablets, pads, checkbooks or scrapbooks are usually made from "Holland" cloths or a latex-impregnated bleached sulfate paper ranging in basis weight from 45 to 90 lb on a 24 × 36 in.—500 sheet ream basis. This latex impregnated paper may or may not be embossed with a Holland, cambric, or linen-weave design to simulate these textile bases.

Sealing Tapes

Sealing tapes are applied mainly by hand to cartons, packages and shipping containers of all sizes. The size of the item to be sealed with gummed tape determines the length of strip to be moistened. The longer the strip of tape used, the longer the tape adhesive has to remain wet and tacky in order for every inch of it to bond tightly to the surface being sealed. It becomes apparent, therefore, that besides strong initial tack, one of the requisites of a good tape adhesive is an adequate amount of "working life." Without this working life, a sealing tape with a strong initial tack derived from its glue content would set-up or gel within a few seconds after wetting and provide only a superficial bond after drying in place. To lengthen working life in a sealing tape adhesive, 10 to 20 per cent of dextrin based on the total adhesive solids is added; up to 2 per cent of sodium chloride, or up to 1.5 per cent of urea will achieve this same result.

Most sealing tape manufacturers market two grades of tape, "standard" and "super-standard." The standard grade has a working life of about 30 sec, whereas that of the super-standard grade is about 20 sec. The adhesive for a standard-grade sealing tape might contain 10 to 30 parts of dextrin, 70 to 90 parts of 70 to 120 g bone glue, 0.5 to 1.5 parts of urea, 0.5 to 1.0 part of 50 per cent sulfonated castor oil, 0.5 to 1 part of sodium chloride, 0.2 to 0.5 part of calcium chloride, 0.5 to 1 part of humectant plasticizer, and 0.5 to 1 part of scenting oil. The super-standard grade tape adhesive might contain 0 to 10 parts of dextrin, 90 to 100 parts of 70 to 120 g bone glue, 0.5 to 1.5 parts of sodium chloride, 0.2 to 0.5 part of calcium chloride, 0.5 to 1 part of humectant plasticizer, 0.5 to 1 part of 50 per cent sulfonated castor oil, and 0.5 to 1 part of scenting oil. The amount of adhesive applied as a dried film to the kraft is in the order of 17 to 20 lb on a 24 × 36 in.—500 sheet ream basis, depending on the basis weight of the kraft backing. The heavier the kraft used, the more adhesive is required.

Reinforced sealing tapes, by virtue of their heavier and stiffer yarn-reinforced laminated kraft backing, and because of their somewhat higher price, demand a stronger adhesive than conventional sealing tapes. Such an adhesive formula might contain 40 to 60 parts of 70 to 120 g bone glue, 40 to 60 parts of 120 to 165 g hide glue, and possibly 10 to 20 parts of 150 to 350 g technical gelatin; also included might be 0.5 to 1 part of 50 per cent sulfonated castor oil, 1 to 2 parts of humectant plasticizer, and 0.5 to 1 part of scenting oil. Weights of glue film would vary from 20 to 28 lb on a 24 × 36 in.—500 sheet ream basis, depending on the basis weight of the backing kraft.

Corrugators' Box Tapes

There are two principal types of corrugators' box tape, one utilizing a single-ply heavy-weight kraft ranging from 120 to 140 lb on a 24 × 36 in.—500 sheet ream basis used on cartons for packaging light loads such as cereals, the other being composed of two plies of 60 lb kraft laminated with asphalt or resin-latex blend and transversely reinforced with glass or rayon yarns, or with sisal fiber, used on cartons for packaging heavy loads such as canned goods.

Adhesive formulations for both types of corrugators' box tape must adhere firmly to the carton surface to close the open joint and seal it tightly within 5 sec after application, since these tapes are applied by automatic machinery. Amount of glue film applied would range from 20 to 30 lb on a 24 × 36 in.—500 sheet ream basis, depending on the basis weight of the backing kraft.

An adhesive for the single-ply unreinforced type of closure might consist of 40 to 60 parts of 70 to 120 g bone glue, 40 to 60 parts of 120 to 165 g hide glue, 1 to 2 parts of humectant plasticizer, 0.5 to 1 part of 50 per cent sulfonated

castor oil, 0.1 to 0.3 part of phenol-derived preservative or mold-proofing agent, and 0.5 to 1 part of scenting oil.

For the two-ply reinforced tape, the adhesive might consist of 20 to 60 parts of 70 to 120 g bone glue, 40 to 80 parts of 120 to 165 g hide glue, 0.5 to 1 part of humectant plasticizer, 0.1 to 0.3 part of phenol-derived mold-proofing agent, and 0.5 to 1 part of scenting oil.

Box-Stay Tapes

The narrow strips of gummed tape used to close or "stay" the four corners of set-up chipboard boxes are known as stay tapes to the packaging trade. These are provided on a kraft backing, usually in ⅞ and 1 in. widths in coil form, either scored or creased down the center on the gummed side, or uncreased, and ranging in basis weight from 90 to 120 lb on a 24 × 36 in.—500 sheet ream basis. The 100 lb basis weight stay tape is most commonly used. Amount of glue film applied is usually 18 to 20 lb per 500 sheets 24 × 36 in.

Box stay tapes are applied by automatic machinery of two different types; the older type equipment seals one corner of the box at a time against an intermittently rotating anvil, whereas the newer machines seal all four corners of the box at the same time against a stationary anvil. The older machines are known as Single Stayers, while the newer automatics are called Quad Stayers.

The gumming formulation for stay tape to be applied by the Quad Stayers necessarily has to be much more quickly wettable and instant-grabbing than the gumming for tape to be used on the slower operating Single Stayers. Stay tape manufacturers, therefore, have a choice of producing two grades of tape, one designed specifically for the Single Stayers and one for the Quads, or else marketing only one grade with the gumming ingeniously formulated to give satisfactory performance on both types.

A tape to be used on Single Stayers should be gummed with an adhesive which has long working life or "open time," but having at the same time plenty of strong wet-tack to adhere quickly and firmly when it is formed to the box corner. Such an adhesive might be composed of 10 to 20 parts of dextrin, 60 to 80 parts of 70 to 120 g bone glue, 10 to 20 parts of 120 to 165 g hide glue, 0.5 to 1 part of 50 per cent sulfonated castor oil, 0.5 to 1 part of humectant plasticizer, and 0.5 to 1 part of scenting oil.

An adhesive formulation suitable for the quicker

grabbing tape to be used on Quad Stayers might consist of 10 to 20 parts of 40 to 70 g bone glue, 50 to 70 parts of 90 to 120 g bone glue, 10 to 20 parts of 120 to 165 g hide glue, 0.5 to 1 part of 50 per cent sulfonated castor oil, 0.5 to 1 part of humectant plasticizer, and 0.5 to 1 part of scenting oil.

Veneer Tapes

There are two grades of veneer tapes, each manufactured in both 35 lb and 50 lb weights of kraft on a 24 × 36 in.—500 sheet ream basis. One is a "standard" grade used mostly for hand-taping and other painstaking operations which demand a long open-time in the moistened tape adhesive; the other is a "high-speed" grade usually applied by automatic taping machinery.

The standard grade veneer tape adhesive might contain 10 to 25 parts of dextrin, 30 to 50 parts of 70 to 120 g bone glue, 20 to 40 parts of 120 to 165 g hide glue, and 0.5 to 1 part of humectant plasticizer.

The high-speed grade veneer tape adhesive could be composed of 40 to 60 parts of 70 to 120 g bone glue, 40 to 60 parts of 120 to 165 g hide glue, and 0.5 to 1 part of humectant plasticizer.

Ingredients used in veneer tape adhesives should be of the highest quality and purity, carefully selected so that they do not stain or otherwise mar the grain of the attractive and often expensive woods to which they are applied. Special additives such as mild alkalies and surface-active agents or penetrants may be required in small amounts, say up to 0.5 per cent, in adhesives which are to be used on oily or resinous woods such as cedar, mahogany and gum-wood, or on very dense woods such as teak and ebony.

Because of the uneven surface presented by the rough grain of some types of wood such as oak, and because of the absorbent nature of the softer woods such as pine and poplar, a heavy film of adhesive must be applied to veneer tapes to make them adhere satisfactorily. The amount of dried adhesive film used on veneer tapes is in the order of 22 to 26 lb on a 24 × 36 in.—500 sheet ream basis.

Bindery Tapes

Also called "gummed stripping tapes," bindery tapes are used to cover the binding or bound edge of checkbooks, composition books, pads or tablets of writing paper, and scrapbooks. They are also used as hinges for game-boards, gussets for file folders, and as reinforcement for the punched edge of looseleaf notebook paper.

Bindery tapes make use of a variety of backings ranging from Holland, cambric and gusset cloths, through strong latex-impregnated papers, to embossed coated krafts. These tapes are made in an attractive assortment of colors, mainly black, white, red, blue, green and brown. Most of them are applied automatically in coil form on Brackett stripping machines. The adhesive on these tapes must be of high quality and good strength, with a moderate amount of working life after wetting, and capable of bonding quickly after application.

The adhesive formulation for such tapes might consist of 60 to 90 parts of 70 to 120 g bone glue, 10 to 40 parts of 120 to 165 g hide glue, 0.5 to 1 part of humectant plasticizer, and 0.5 to 1 part of scenting oil.

Specialty Gummed Tapes

In this category would be listed dielectric and acid-free gummed tapes for use in the manufacture and protection of electrical components; water-resistant gummed tapes which meet government specifications requiring the tape to remain functional after application, even during prolonged exposure to or immersion in water; food locker tapes for sealing packages to be stored in freezers, cold-storage rooms and warehouses; mold-proof tapes with adhesives which resist the action of mold, mildew and fungus so prevalent in the tropics; and tapes with a water conditioner "built-in" or superimposed onto the surface of the adhesive to give good performance by virtue of proper wetting, even in regions where the water is extremely hard or very cold.

Dielectric glues are produced by special processing which removes acids, alkalies, electrolytic salts, metallic ions and any other conductive agents. To make a dielectric remoistenable adhesive, these non-conducting glues are simply dissolved in water to the proper concentration, then a small amount of preservative or fungicide is added, and if necessary the pH of the liquid mix is adjusted with hydrated lime to the point of neutrality. Backing papers used are usually of "vulcanized" cellulose fiber, dielectric high-density krafts, or neoprene-impregnated papers, all of neutral pH.

Adhesives for acid-free gummed papers are made from highly refined glues which have been neutralized with hydrated lime, and mold-proofed with phenolic derivatives. Substrates used are usually natural neutral krafts which are also acid-free.

Water-resistant tape adhesives are specially formulated from high-test glues which can be easily rendered insensitive to further activation by water.

This is accomplished by moistening the tape with a "tanning" solution before application to cartons. The tanning solution usually contains an aldehydic compound such as formaldehyde, glyoxal, glutaraldehyde, or combinations of these, plus a small amount of alum to implement the curing action.

Food locker tape adhesives contain additives such as sodium chloride, calcium chloride and glycerin which serve to lower the freezing point of the water used to activate them. These ingredients keep the adhesive from freeze-drying before it has a chance to bond tightly to the surface being sealed.

Mold-proof tape adhesives also have from 0.2 to 1.2 per cent of water-soluble bactericide or fungicide, based on the amount of glue present.

One gummed tape manufacturer prints onto the surface of his tape adhesive a colored identifying design, using an "ink" composed of a water-soluble surface-active agent, a sequestering compound, and a bactericide and fungicide. When the tape is drawn over the moistening brush of a tape dispenser, the "ink" on the surface of the adhesive dissolves and transfers through the brush into the water in the pan of the dispenser. The active materials in the ink reduce the surface tension of the water, tie up the metallic elements causing "hard" water and permit complete and uniform wetting of the tape even under the most adverse conditions. The fungicide and bactericide in the ink builds up to sufficient concentration in the water pan to keep the brush and pan free from mold, algae and bacterial growth which ordinarily cause odor and fouling of the equipment.

CONTROL OF QUALITY

The performance reliability of any water-remoistenable adhesive, as with any other product, depends on careful and continuous control of the quality of raw materials, in-process phases, and the finished product itself. An established quality control program, conscientiously executed by management, technical and production departments ensures that all products will consistently perform as expected and give continuing customer satisfaction.

Quality of Raw Materials

Perhaps the most important part of raw materials quality control is the physical testing of dextrins and glues, which comprise the major portion of any water-remoistenable adhesive.

Dextrins are usually tested for the following characteristics:

(1) Dextrose content, or dextrose equivalent. This is the percentage in the dextrin of invert sugar, consisting mainly of dextrose. It indicates degree of conversion of the dextrin resulting from the acid hydrolysis and torrefaction of the starch used in its manufacture. The amount of dextrose, or dextrose equivalent, commonly ranges from 3 to 7 per cent and has a direct influence on the solution viscosity, cold-water solubility and adhesive qualities of the dextrin.

(2) Viscosity, the measurement of the rheology or flow characteristics of a solution of specific concentration, determined by instruments such as the Brookfield, Stormer, MacMichael or Bloom viscosimeters and reported in centipoises.

(3) Moisture content, measured by drying out a weighed amount of dextrin to constant weight and calculating the difference in weight as moisture, reported as per cent. Moisture content may vary from 4 to 10 per cent, depending on the type of dextrin, method of manufacture, and storage conditions.

(4) Cold-water solubility, measured by suspending a weighed amount of dextrin in a fixed volume of water at room temperature for 24 hr, then determining dissolved solids in an aliquot portion of the supernatant solution by evaporating to dryness. Gumming-grade dextrins usually show 85 to 95 per cent cold-water solubility.

(5) pH, or hydrogen-ion concentration, measured with Hydrion papers, block comparators using colorimetric indicating solutions, or with glass-electrode potentiometers (pH-meters). Values range from pH of 3 to 5.5.

(6) Dirt, or insoluble material, determined by heating a specific amount of dextrin to 190°F in a measured volume of water to dissolve, and then allowing to settle. Amount of sediment reported as excessive, much, moderate, or little.

(7) Adhesiveness. A draw-down is made by dispersing an amount of the dextrin in an equal weight of water, cooking out at 190°F and then spreading the solution on a sheet of 50 lb basis weight (25 × 38 in. —500 sheets) supercalendered paper by means of a No. 24 wire-wound rod. After drying, the gummed paper is flattened and cut into 1 × 4 in. strips. These are moistened and applied to glass, to kraft paper, to 25 per cent rag-content bond paper, and to corrugated carton stock.

The strips are then allowed to dry in place for 1 hr, after which the adhesion is tested by trying to pull the strips away from the various surfaces. Satisfactory adhesion is indicated when the test strips cannot be removed without tearing apart, or when fibers are torn from the other adherend surfaces, with the exception of the glass, of course.

(8) Color, in the dry state and in solution, usually 50 per cent solids.

Animal Glues are tested for the qualities listed below:

(1) Gel strength, measured with a Bloom gelometer, which indicates the resistance in grams offered by a glue gel or jelly of fixed concentration to penetration by a plastic plunger or cylinder of specific area. The concentration of the glue gel is 15 g of glue dissolved in 105 ml of distilled water and chilled to exactly 10°C. Values range from 40 to 140 g for bone glues, 110 to 170 g for hide glues, and 100 to 400 g for technical gelatins in the grades commonly used for gumming.

(2) Viscosity, usually measured by outflow time of a 12.5 per cent solution from the Bloom viscosity pipette at 65°C. Viscosity values range from 25 to 150 millipoises, depending on the grade, gel strength and type of glue being tested. Viscosity measurements may also be taken with Brookfield or Stormer viscosimeters, but the Bloom instrument is more widely accepted among glue manufacturers and consumers.

(3) Grease, determined by extraction of a weighed sample of glue with solvent such as carbon tetrachloride, toluene, xylene or petroleum ether, or by streaking out a violet-dyed glue solution of specific concentration on a white super-calendered paper, where any grease present shows up as repel spots or "fish-eyes" against the white back-ground. Reported as per cent in the solvent-extraction method, and as excessive, much, moderate, or little in the streak-out method.

(4) Ash. A weighed amount of glue in a weighed porcelain crucible is burned in an electric muffle furnace. The weight of ash is 2.5 to 4.0 per cent, depending on the amount of treatment received by the glue during its manufacture.

(5) Foam, determined by shaking vigorously, ten times, a glue solution of concentration 15 g in 105 ml of distilled water at temperature 40°C, then noting the time required for the head of foam to break to form a clear area the size of a dime. Foam that breaks in 10 sec is recorded as "little," if up to 20 or 30 sec are required the recording is "moderate," if 40 to 60 sec are required the recording is "much," and if the foam holds for more than 1 min the recording is "persistent."

(6) Dirt, judged by allowing a 12.5 per cent glue solution to settle while holding it at temperature 40°C. Amount of sediment or dirt is reported as little, moderate, much, or excessive.

(7) Odor, evaluated by smelling of the above glue solution and recording odor reaction as normal (beefy), offensive (putrefaction) or perfumed. The presence of a perfume or deodorant in a glue may indicate that it has been added to mask some degree of spoilage, and warrants suspicion as to quality.

(8) Color, although not too important in glues utilized for sealing tape adhesives, color can be a quality factor in glues employed to compound label adhesives which are applied to white or light-colored backing papers.

(9) pH Value, usually determined on a 12.5 per cent glue solution at a temperature of 40°C. Ordinarily, glues have a pH value ranging from 5.6 to 6.0, but dielectric and acid-free glues are specially manufactured to give pH values between 6.8 and 7.2.

(10) Adhesive Strength. A specific amount of glue is dissolved in an equal weight of water by cooking out at 150°F. A drawdown of this glue solution is made with a No. 24 wire-wound rod on a sheet of 60 lb kraft and dried. After flattening, this glue-spread is cut into test strips 2 × 5½ in. and evaluated on a McLaurin adhesion tester in accordance with TAPPI Test Method T-453m-52. Tested in this manner, a 40 g bone glue has a value of about 50, 90 to 120 g bone glue about 85 or better, and bone glues of gel strength greater than 120 g have an adhesion value of 100. Hide glues and technical gelatins also have a test value of 100.

All other ingredients such as plasticizers, sulfonated oils, salts, latices, wax and resin emulsions, etc., are tested for such characteristics as moisture content, total solids, total fatty matter, pH, density, ash, and quantitatively for pertinent ions or chemical groups.

In-Process Control

Each batch of completed adhesive formulation is tested for the following characteristics before application to the paper substrate:

(1) Viscosity—by Brookfield viscosimeter or Zahn cup.
(2) Density—by hydrometer.
(3) Temperature—in degrees F by Dairy thermometer.
(4) pH Value—by Hydrion papers or pH-meter.

During production, the gummed material is tested for:

(1) Gum feed, or weight of adhesive applied.
(2) Moisture content, by drying at 110°C.
(3) Adhesion test. In the case of label stocks, strips of the gummed material are moistened and applied to glass, to 25 per cent rag-content bond paper, to 100 per cent sulfate kraft and to corrugated carton stock. Some of the strips are immediately peeled back slowly from these test surfaces to check the initial adhesion, while other strips are left on the test surfaces for several hours and then tested for final adhesion. Gummed tape stocks are tested in the foregoing manner on a corrugated carton surface, and also on the McLaurin adhesion tester for adhesion value after 5 sec.
(4) Visual examination during the gumming operation for dirt, grease, foam, blistering, penetration and streaks or misgumming in the adhesive film. During the flattening operation the gummed material is examined for flatness, width, color or shade match and uniformity of finish. Additional checks are made after subsequent operations.

THE FUTURE FOR WATER-REMOISTENABLE ADHESIVES

Perhaps the most important advantage of water-remositenable adhesives is their economy compared to pressure-sensitive adhesives. While the latter have greater versatility and ease of application, their cost is prohibitive for many labeling and sealing operations.

One of the greatest improvements in the field of water-remoistenable adhesives during the past decade has been the relatively non-curling gummed label paper. This new product, in which the adhesive film is composed of discrete water-activatable particles bonded to the substrate, has almost entirely removed the bane of distortion with change in relative humidity which has plagued printers of gummed papers for half a century.

More development work will be done on this new type of non-curling gummed paper. Further combinations of dextrins, glues, gums, resins and binders will be investigated and evaluated to produce a complete line of non-curling label grades at prices to match that of the present conventionally gummed products.

In the field of gummed sealing and specialty tapes, extensive work will be done with synthetic water-remoistenable adhesives derived from the various starches. Here, too, the goal will be greater economy.

All in all, the future for water-remoistenable adhesives remains bright.

51

Adhesive Tapes

C. W. Bemmels

Permacel

New Brunswick, New Jersey

An adhesive tape is composed of a backing element in a long strip upon which is applied an adhesive, the function of which is to attach the carrier backing to some secondary surface. The attachment is made by activating the adhesive with solvent, heat or finger pressure.

Gummed tapes, stamps, etc., are the most commonly known variety of solvent-activated tape, that is, the adhesive is activated by wetting with water. For certain industrial applications, an organic solvent-activated adhesive is used. A second type of adhesive tape is the thermoplastic or heat-activated variety. In this construction the adhesive is made sticky by the use of heat and pressure.

The most rapidly growing line of adhesive tapes is the pressure-sensitive variety. This type of tape can be applied with hand pressure in the absence of solvents or heat and sticks aggressively to most common surfaces. Because of its extreme ease of application, it has gained wide acceptance.

Rubber-based pressure-sensitive tapes were invented by Dr. Horace Day in 1845. Initially proposed for surgical use, they were used solely for that purpose for many years. With the advent of spray painting, car manufacturers began to use surgical tapes to mask the color line on the automobiles; then industrial-type pressure-sensitive tapes, more suitably designed for this application, were developed. With the advent of World War II, pressure-sensitive tapes became popular in many industries because they saved time in painting and assembly operations and speeded up production. Once their wide utility had been established, they were even more favorably received in the postwar years. Currently over 200 varieties of pressure-sensitive tapes are being manufactured.

The growth of the tape industry in 11 years is shown below:

	1947	1958
	(millions of dollars)	
Gummed tapes	65.5	65
Pressure-sensitive and heat-activated tapes (excluding surgical tapes	35.0	201

It can be seen that the use of pressure-sensitive tapes is increasing very rapidly; whereas the gummed-tape market is relatively static.

CONSTRUCTIONS

Backings

Cloth, paper, films, foils as well as many laminates have been employed as tape backings. They are always thin and flexible to conform readily to the surfaces upon which they are applied.

The most commonly used films are cellophane, polyvinyl chloride film, "Mylar,"* polyethylene and the cellulose acetate films. Aluminum and lead foils are used for specialty tapes. Films and foils are generally coated with a very thin anchor coating called a primer to improve the bonding of the adhesive to backing. Hydrophilic backings can be primed with a mixture of a water-soluble gum in water and a natural rubber or GRS latex;[1, 2] whereas hydrophobic backings may be primed with a solution of a buna-N rubber combined with GRS or a similar polymer.[3] The films are often coated on the opposite side with a release agent to reduce the adhesion of the adhesive to the back

* duPont trade name for their polyester film.

side of the next layer of tape when in roll form. Stearato chromic chloride, octadecyl acrylate-acrylic acid copolymers, vinyl stearate-maleic anhydride copolymers and similar polymers may be used.[4, 5, 6]

Cloth backings can be used without further treatment, or they may be sized with starch or other organic binders to help bind the fibers together.[8] The cloth may be coated with nitrocellulose, polyvinyl chloride, polyethylene or other film formers on the back side of the cloth to improve its appearance, unwind characteristics, and reduce its moisture vapor transmission.

Paper backings used with pressure-sensitive adhesives are almost universally impregnated with some sort of a rubbery material to improve the internal strength (ply strength or delamination resistance) of the backing. Without the necessary ply strength, the paper backings would split when unrolled from a roll, and the adhesive would be sandwiched between two layers of paper thus making the tape useless. The first paper impregnant consisted of glue plasticized with glycerin. This has been almost entirely replaced by paper saturants based on solvent-based rubber solutions and synthetic rubber latices.[9, 10, 11] The back side of the tape is coated with a film-forming polymer to improve its appearance, increase its solvent resistance and reduce the adhesion of the adhesive to the backing. In addition, a release coat may be applied with or over the back-size coat to reduce the unwind tension.[4, 5, 6, 7] As described previously, the release materials generally consist of a polymeric chain to which are attached fatty acid groups in a regular manner.

Papers used for decal tapes, as well as for heat-activated or solvent-activated tapes, do not need to be impregnated or back-sized since these tapes either are applied to release papers or develop no adhesion to backing when in roll form. Therefore such tapes are not subjected to high delaminating forces.

Laminated backings consist of a film or foil bonded to cloth or paper with a rubbery type adhesive such as a pressure-sensitive adhesive.[12] Here again the paper is impregnated in order to resist the delaminating forces when a roll of the tape is unwound. Strand reinforced backings[13] are made by bonding a plurality of strands in a lengthwise direction to a film, impregnated paper or cloth by means of a rubbery adhesive. Glass strands are used where highest tensile strength and lowest elongation are required. Rayon is used where high impact strength is needed and where the tensile strength requirement is somewhat lower. Nylon strands impart the highest impact strength.

Solvent-Activated Adhesives

Solvent-activated adhesives are made tacky by wetting the adhesive with a solvent such as water or organic solvents just before applying the tape. Upon evaporation of the solvent, a high bond is formed between the two adhering surfaces; consequently the two materials cannot usually be separated without destroying them. Water-activated adhesives are usually made from animal glue or dextrin. Hide glue is reported to give the best "quick tack" on wetting. In animal glue formulations, a small percentage of fish glue, glycerin or dextrin is often added to reduce the wet-out time and improve the tack. The amount of glycerin is adjusted for seasonal variations. Gel strength of the glue is important, and the addition of additives in large amount may adversely affect the gel strength (ability of the wet adhesive to adhere tenaciously to other surfaces).

Adhesives activated with organic solvents have not received wide acceptance because of the fire and health hazards involved and the inconvenience of activating with solvents. They are used in certain applications where a pressure-sensitive adhesive tape cannot supply the bond strength, solvent or heat resistance required.

Heat-Activated Adhesives

Heat-activated adhesives are used on tapes which can be applied with heat and pressure. They can be made from a wide variety of thermoplastic materials such as waxes, polyethylene, cellulose esters and ethers, nitrocellulose, polyvinyl acetate, polyvinyl chloride and many rubber-resin combinations. One of the widest applications of this type of adhesive tape is in garment repair. A fabric mending tape normally consists of a plasticized polyvinyl chloride adhesive applied upon a cloth backing.

A "Stay" tape used in box manufacturing consists of a kraft paper coated with a thermoplastic adhesive consisting essentially of plasticized polyvinyl acetate.

Heat-activated adhesives provide a very high, irreversible bond. No fire or health hazards are involved in their application. One disadvantage, particularly in industrial applications, is the need for special high-temperature presses to apply this type of adhesive.

The heat-seal packaging market is not considered a part of the tape market but should be mentioned in passing because of its large size. Films or paper such as waxed paper are coated with a thin layer of a heat-sealing material such as wax or resin which allows the film or paper package to be sealed by a sealing iron in automatic packaging machines.

Pressure-Sensitive Adhesives

Pressure-sensitive adhesives can be defined as those adhesives which will adhere tenaciously upon application with only light finger pressure. Tapes with these adhesives have gained wide acceptance because of their ease of application and their ability to be removed cleanly from the surfaces on which they were applied. They of necessity produce a bond of a much lower order of magnitude than the two previously mentioned adhesives.

Pressure-sensitive adhesives are composed of a rubbery type elastomer combined with a liquid or solid resin tackifier component. A mixture of resins may be used to provide a balance of properties which cannot be obtained with either resin above. Fillers are often added to change the rheological properties of the adhesive or to add color. Antioxidants are used to stabilize the adhesive against oxidation and heat and light degradation.

Adhesives for high temperature use or for electrical applications sometimes contain a minor amount of a heat-curing oil-soluble phenolic resin. An alkaline filler or zinc rezinate is added as a catalyst to promote the reaction between the phenolic resin and rubber. The adhesive is cured by the application of heat. Van der Meer[15] has postulated that crosslinking occurs through an intermediate quinone methide structure. Compatibility seems important since the higher alkyl phenolic resins are much more effective than the lower alkyl analogues. Sulfur-curing systems are not used in electrical tapes since they cause chemical corrosion of copper wires. Similarly, sulfur-curing systems are undesirable in masking tapes because sulfur and its derivatives stain light-colored painted surfaces. Light-colored resins and nonstaining antioxidants must be used for nonstaining adhesives. For masking tapes which must withstand high temperature drying and baking, adhesives containing oil-soluble heat-curing phenol formaldehyde resins as described above are used.

Typical ingredients used in pressure-sensitive adhesives are:

Elastomer	Reclaimed rubber
	SBR (styrene butadiene rubber)
	Polyisobutylene or butyl rubber
	Buna-N (butadiene acrylonitrile rubber)
	Polyvinyl ethers (ethyl or higher)
	Polyacrylate esters (ethyl or higher)
Tackifiers	Polyterpene resins
	Gum rosin
	Rosin esters and other rosin derivatives
	Oil-soluble phenolic resins
	Coumarone-indene resins
	Petroleum hydrocarbon resins
Plasticizers	Mineral oil
	Liquid polybutenes
	Liquid polyacrylates
	Lanolin
Fillers	Zinc oxide
	Titanium dioxide
	Aluminum hydrate
	Calcium carbonate
	Clay
	Pigments
Antioxidants	Rubber antioxidants (preferably nonstaining)
	Metal dithiocarbamates
	Metal chelating agents

Typical examples of pressure-sensitive adhesives are:

Adhesive A	*Parts*
Milled pale crepe	100
Poly-beta-pinene resin (m. p. 70°C)	75
Peroleum oil	5
Polymerized trimethyl dihydroquinoline	2

Adhesive B	
Milled smoke sheet rubber	100
Zinc oxide	50
Dehydrogenated rosin	75
Sym-di-beta-naphthyl-para-phenylene diamine	2
Lanolin	10

Adhesive C	
Butadiene-styrene copolymer (70:30 ratio, Mooney value 50)	50
Milled smoked sheet rubber	50
Ester of hydrogenated rosin	50
Polymerized trimethyl dihydroquinoline	2
Petroleum oil	20

Adhesive D	
Polyvinyl ethyl ether (intrinsic viscosity = 2.37)	100
Hydrogenated rosin	50
Phenyl-alpha-naphthylamine	0.35
Polyethylene glycol 400 diricinoleate	11.5

Adhesive E	
Polyisobutylene (high molecular weight polymer)	100
Polyisobutylene (viscous liquid)	70

Adhesives A, B and C are typical formulations used for most general applications; whereas adhesives D and E are employed where unusual clarity and sunlight aging are required.

The adhesive may be applied from a solvent solution or by calender coating. An appreciable weight of adhesive is needed to secure the proper wetting out or "quick stick" characteristics. A dry coating weight of 0.5 to 1.5 oz/sq yd is used on films, 1 to 3 oz on paper, and 3 to 5 oz on cloth.

THEORY

A pressure-sensitive adhesive is a high viscosity composition which may be thixotropic in nature and have some liquid characteristics. Bright[16] has characterized it as a system composed of an elastic component, a viscous component and a visco-elastic component. The adhesive must deform at a low pressure to obtain immediate wetting when a tape is applied; furthermore it must have sufficient flow so that it will retain the wet-out position after removal of pressure. Wetzel, Hock and Abbott have evidence which indicates that a pressure-sensitive adhesive is composed of an elastic member and a liquid phase.[17, 18] They have electron photomicrographs of the surface of a pressure-sensitive adhesive which suggest that there are small areas of a liquid phase in the surface of a rubber adhesive matrix. They have also shown that an appreciable quantity of a tackifying resin is necessary to build good tack in the adhesive and that the tack increases quite rapidly with the amount of resin added until it reaches a maximum. After this point the tack diminishes quite suddenly. The maximum amount of resin to be used depends on the type of resin chosen and possibly the solubility of the particular resin in the rubber phase.

The performance of a pressure-sensitive adhesive is dependent on three primary factors:

(1) The wetting ability or quick stick.
(2) The adhesion.
(3) The cohesive strength.

The proper balance of these properties is necessary in a good performing practical pressure-sensitive adhesive tape.

Wetting Ability

This property is the ability of the adhesive to immediately wet the surface to which it is applied under light finger pressure. Soft adhesives provide better wetting ability but poorer cohesive strength; however wetting ability is improved by increasing the thickness of the adhesive used. As readily seen, proper balance between wetting ability and cohe-

sion is necessary to attain good performance, for example, fly paper, which has excellent wetting ability, is not a satisfactory pressure-sensitive adhesive because of its poor cohesive strength.

With solvent- and heat-activated adhesives, wetting ability or quick tack are obtained by means of solvent or heat. Here the choice of the proper balance between "quick stick" and cohesive strength is not so critical since the cohesive strength increases rapidly on drying or cooling.

Cohesion

A highly cohesive pressure-sensitive adhesive is desirable for best performance or hold characteristics after application. The cohesiveness must be greater than the adhesiveness to prevent splitting of the adhesive on removing the tape from another object. Similarly, in all shear applications, the internal strength of the adhesive appears to be the determining factor in the performance of a tape. A partial gel structure in the adhesive appears beneficial for many uses particularly for masking applications where resistance to shear and clean removal at baking temperatures is required. To achieve good flow and wetting ability and still retain high cohesive strength, a very careful selection of components and processing conditions is necessary.

Adhesion

Adhesion is the ability of the adhesive to stick to another surface. Many methods have been designed to measure this property but the most commonly accepted test is the peel test to be described in the next section.

The work necessary to strip the tape varies, considerably with the rate at which it is stripped thereby indicating that the measured value is not the true interfacial work of adhesion, which must be independent of stripping rate, but rather a complex function of various factors. Shoberg and Hatfield,[19] through calculations involving interfacial tensions, have estimated that the work necessary to strip a pressure-sensitive adhesive tape may be as much as 10,000 times as great as the interfacial work of adhesion.

Adhesion increases with increasing weight of the adhesive. Preliminary results in this laboratory indicate that the work of stripping is much more dependent on the bulk of the adhesive than on the adhesive surface. All these factors suggest that most of the work necessary in stripping a tape is expended in deforming the adhesive and in bending the tape backing.

TEST METHODS

Pressure-sensitive tape test methods are described in ASTM-D-1000 for electrical grade tapes and in Methods published by the Pressure Sensitive Tape Council, Glenview, Illinois. The more commonly used test methods are adhesion tests, hold tests, and quick-stick tests.

Adhesion Test

180° Peel Adhesion Test. As a standard adhesion test described in ASTM-D-1000, it consists of measuring the force necessary to strip a piece of tape at a 180° angle from a stainless steel panel at a pulling rate of 12 in./min. It is a good control test to measure the uniformity of a given type tape. It does not necessarily predict the performance of a new tape since other factors play a greater role in the utility of the tape than does peel adhesion.

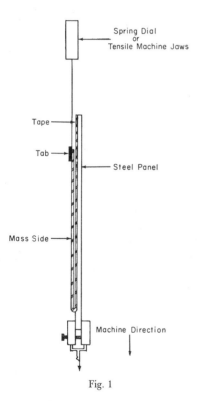

Fig. 1

Hold Tests

Hold tests are used to evaluate the performance characteristics of a tape. Many variations of the hold test have been developed depending upon the particular users application. In general, it consists of applying a weight to the end of a strip of tape attached to a given surface and measuring the time for the weight to remove the tape from the given surface. Various versions of the hold test are as follows:

0° Hold. A strip of tape 1 in. wide is attached to the clean surface of a ½ × ½ in. chrome steel bar in a direction perpendicular to the length of the bar. The tape is pressed to the surface by passing a 4½ lb rubber-covered roller slowly over the tape twice. The bar is mounted in a horizontal position and rotated to a position in which the tape makes a 0° angle with a vertical line. A weight is attached to the tape, and the time for failure is measured. A 1000-g weight is most commonly used.

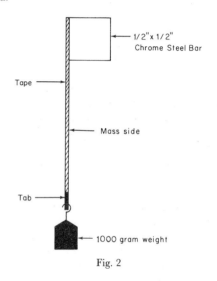

Fig. 2

A modification is the 0° hold to tape backing. In this test the test surface of the bar is covered with a strip of tape which is trimmed to the width of the bar; then the test strip of tape is applied to the back of the first strip.

A second modification is to apply a strip of container board to the test surface of the bar and trim the container board to the width of the bar before applying the test tape. The remainder of the procedure is identical to that described above.

Failure in the 0° test is almost always caused by splitting within the adhesive; hence this test measures primarily cohesive strength.

90° Hold. The test sample is attached to a chrome steel bar and mounted as described above except that the tape surface is rotated to an angle of 90° with a vertical line. A weight is attached to the free end, and the time to strip the tape is measured. In this case a 400-g weight is normally used, this test measures primarily adhesive properties of the tape.

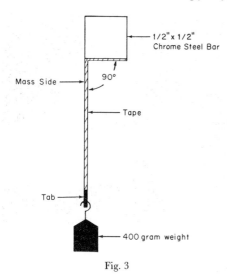

Fig. 3

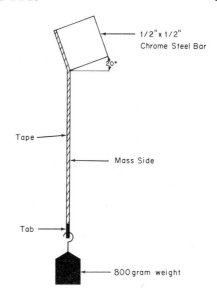

20° HOLD TEST

Fig. 4

20° Hold. The test specimen and apparatus is prepared as previously described except that the tape surface is rotated to an angle of minus 20° with a vertical line. An 800-g weight is attached, and the time for failure measured. This test measures a combination of adhesive and cohesive properties. Failure may be due to either property depending on the formulation tested.

Quick-Stick Tests

Rolling Ball Test. This test, developed by the Douglas Aircraft Company, is often called the Douglas rolling-ball quick-stick test. The apparatus consists of a steel ball and a channel iron shaped as shown in Fig. 5.

The steel ball is 1⅛ in. in diameter and weighs 111.5 g. A strip of tape is laid in the horizontal portion of the channel adhesive side up. The one end of the tape is inserted in the transverse slot and pressed against the bottom side of the channel to keep the tape from moving. The ball is cleaned with solvent and supported in the curved portion of the channel at a fixed height. The ball is released, and the distance it rolls on the tape is

an inverse measure of the quick stick. Quick stick is normally reported as the height the ball is dropped divided by the distance the ball rolls on the tape. This is a very satisfactory test for control testing but is not adequate for comparing different type tapes since the values obtained are very markedly affected by the weight of the adhesive and the compressiveness of the backing.

PSTC—11 Quick-Stick Test. A test method[20] has been developed by Chang in which the tape is applied without pressure to a stainless steel adhesion panel and immediately is peeled from the panel at 90° angle and at a speed of 12 in. per min. A special holder is required to hold the panel in the jaws of a tensile machine and to maintain an angle of 90° during stripping.

Wetzel Probe Test. A ¼-in. rod is caused to impinge on the adhesive surface of a tape and is immediately removed from the tape. The rod is attached to an Instron tensile machine so that the force of removal as well as the contact time and pressure may be controlled and measured.

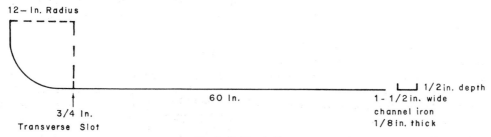

Fig. 5. Rolling ball test.

APPLICATIONS

Although the uses of surgical and cellophane pressure-sensitive tapes are widely known, the use of pressure-sensitive tapes in industry is less familiar. In this category the applications can be divided into eleven classes.

Holding or Bundling

Many objects in transit are held together with pressure-sensitive tapes; for example, doors and loose objects on appliances are taped to the frame in transit to prevent damage or scratching. Pipes, tools, lumber and numerous small objects are bundled together by means of pressure-sensitive tapes. Lead wires and start wires in transformers are held by means of pressure-sensitive electrical-grade tapes. The wire coils used in the rotor and the stator of electrical motors are bound together with electrical grade tape.

Fig. 6. Insulating.

Strand-reinforced tapes have been used quite extensively as a replacement for steel banding around cartons and palletized loads. These tapes are easier to apply, and because of their good flexibility, do not tend to crush the corners of the cartons.

Masking

Pressure-sensitive tapes are commonly used to mask surfaces which are not to be painted when spray painting is performed. For small areas the tape is used to cover the entire spot; whereas for larger areas the masking tape is utilized to make the line of demarcation between the painted and the unpainted surface and to hold up large strips

Fig. 7. Masking.

of plain paper (masking paper). Masking occurs in all types of manufacturing from small parts such as typewriters to aircraft and railway cars.

Sealing

There are thousands of packaging jobs where boxes must be sealed, tops held on tight and products protected against moisture and other elements. These sealing jobs are performed quickly and efficiently with pressure-sensitive tapes. The sealing of heating and ventilating ducts and the weather stripping of doors on trucks are additional applications where tapes are extremely practical.

Protecting

Many objects need protection from damage during fabrication or in transit. Pressure-sensitive protective papers can guard these finishes or surfaces from scratches, mars, corrosion, chipping, cracking or staining; for instance, stainless steel plate is covered with a protective paper during fabrication operations in order to retain the mirrorlike surface. "Plexiglas" windows are usually masked by a pressure-sensitive protective tape until they reach the ultimate consumer in order to avoid scratching; moreover precision gears, the cutting edges of tools, etc., are often protected by this means during storage and in transit.

Reinforcing

Pressure-sensitive tapes are used to reinforce leather, textile and paper products such as wallets, ladies handbags, linings and uppers in shoes; to reinforce edges of fiber containers, boxes and seams in fabrics; to edge and repair blueprints, maps, drawings, photographs, slides, documents as well as other valuable papers.

Splicing

Pressure-sensitive tapes are often used in industry to splice the end of a web from one roll to the beginning of the web of a second roll. Linoleum, paper and cloth manufacturers use pressure-sensitive tapes for splicing.

Stenciling

Tapes have been used often for the decorative stenciling of names and designs on metal, glass and plastic. It is ideal for this application since it can be positioned firmly in advance of the painting operation and provides clean, sharp edges to the painted designs.

Identifying

Printed and colored pressure-sensitive tapes are used frequently for identifying wires, cables, pipelines, fittings, parts, and bundles for storage and inventory. Printed tapes are used by merchants as a combination means of advertising and sealing packages.

Packaging

Many industrial manufacturers as well as retailers use pressure-sensitive tapes to seal packages and prevent pilfering or contamination. Most plastic vegetable packages are now sealed with a wrap of pressure-sensitive tape. For overseas packaging the government frequently specifies pressure-sensitive tape; moreover the use of presure-sensitive tapes for packaging provides a faster and neater job than other means.

Insulating

Electrical-grade pressure-sensitive tapes are used in the manufacture of transformers and motors for the electrical industry. Tapes are used for two purposes: (1) to hold down wires, and (2) to serve as an insulating layer between successive wires. Specially designed tapes are used as a stop-off in the electrical plating operation to prevent electroplating on the covered areas. Condensers are held together with a small strip of pressure-sensitive tape. Automotive ignition harnesses are commonly held together with tapes. Bus bars are wrapped with tapes to insulate them. Vinyl tapes

are used to insulate the splices in household and industrial wiring systems. They are commonly used to insulate the splices in underground installations. Vinyl and polyethylene backed tapes are used to wrap pipe in the installation of underground gas lines to prevent galvanic corrosion. "Teflon" tape, with a pressure-sensitive silicone adhesive and glass-cloth backings with various silicone adhesives are being used quite widely for very high-temperature (Class H) insulating applications.

Besides electrical insulation there is heat and sound insulation. In aircraft construction, for example, cloth-aluminum foil laminated tapes are applied to the inside skin of the fuselage in order to deaden the sound and reduce vibration. In the installation of air ducts, aluminum foil tape or vinyl tape is used on all the seams and joints to eliminate dissipation of heat by air leakage.

Special Applications

This category includes numerous miscellaneous uses. Tapes with conductive black adhesive or aluminized "Mylar" or metal backing are used as conductors. Tapes are used for heat and light reflection. Both antifriction and antiskid surfaces may be coated with appropriate adhesives. A transparent-colored film tape is used to mask photographic films. Narrow tapes in colors or printed designs are being sold to make graphs, layouts, signs, etc. Adhesive tapes can be applied to any surface to produce various decorative effects.

New applications are being found for pressure-sensitive tapes because of their (1) ease of application, (2) safety, and (3) labor- and time-saving features.

References

1. Drew, R. G., (to Minnesota Mining and Manufacturing Co.), U. S. Patent 2,328,066 (Aug. 31, 1943).
2. Billings, H. J., (to Johnson and Johnson), U. S. Patent 2,340,298 (Feb. 1, 1944).
3. Bemmels, C. W., (to Johnson and Johnson), U. S. Patent 2,647,843 (Aug. 4, 1943).
4. Dahlquist, C. A., (to Minnesota Mining and Manufacturing Co.), U. S. Patent 2,532,011 (Nov. 28, 1950).
5. Hendricks, J. O., (to Minnesota Mining and Manufacturing Co.), U. S. Patent 2,607,711 (Aug. 19, 1952).
6. Port, W. S. and Jordan, E. F., Jr., (to U. S. of America), U. S. Patent 2,876,895 (Mar. 10, 1959).
7. Collins, W. C., (to Johnson and Johnson), U. S. Patent 2,913,355 (Nov. 17, 1959).

8. Frantz, V. L., (to Johnson and Johnson), U.S. Patent 2,799,596 (July 16, 1957).

9. Abere, J. F., Schmelzle, A. F., and Murray, H. W., (to Minnesota Mining and Manufacturing Co)., U. S. Patent 2,725,981 (Dec. 6, 1955).

10. Eger, L. W., and Engel, E. W., (to Johnson and Johnson), U. S. Patent 2,726,967 (Dec. 13, 1955).

11. Bartell, C., (to Johnson and Johnson), U. S. Patent 2,848,355 (Aug. 19, 1958).

12. Kellgren, W., Tierney, H. J., and Drew, R. G., (to Minnesota Mining and Manufacturing Co.), U. S. Patent 2,444,830 (July 6, 1948).

13. Bemmels, C. W., (to Johnson and Johnson), U.S. Patent 2,750,314 (June 12, 1956).

14. Eger, L. W., (to Johnson and Johnson), U.S. Patent 2,697,084 (Dec. 14, 1954).

15. van der Meer, S., in Megson, N. J. L. (Editor), "Phenolic Resin Chemistry," p. 126, New York, Academic Press Inc., 1958.

16. Bright, W. M., p. 137 in Clark, J., Rutzler, J. E., Jr. and Savage, R. L., "Adhesion and Adhesives, Fundamentals and Practice," New York, John Wiley & Sons, Inc. 1954.

17. Wetzel, F. H., *Rubber Age,* **82,** 291–295 (1957).

18. Hock, C. W., and Abbott, A. N., *Rubber Age,* **82,** 471–475 (1957).

19. Scholberg, H. M., and Hatfield, M. R., in Clark, Rutzler, and Savage (Editors), "Adhesion and Adhesives Fundamentals and Practice," p. 34, New York, John Wiley & Sons, Inc., 1954.

20. Chang, F. S. C., Adhesives Age, 32–39 (Nov. 1958).

21. Wetzel, F. H., *ASTM Bull.* No. 221, p. 64 (Apr. 1957).

22. Morris, V. N., Weidner, C. L., and Landau N. St., "Adhesives," pp. 191–206, in Kirk, R. E., and Orthmer, D. F. (Editors), "Encyclopedia of Chemical Technology," Vol., 1, New York, The Interscience Encyclopedia Inc., 1947.

Coated and Bonded Abrasives

Sigmund Orchon* and Melvin L. Buike

The Carborundum Company
Niagara Falls, New York

ADHESIVES FOR COATED ABRASIVES**

The first printed information about the production of coated abrasives appeared in 1809[1] wherein a specification for so-called "Rust-Paper" was given. Pumice was first heated and subsequently quenched in water to obtain finer particles; moreover abrasive grit prepared in such a manner was dispersed to a very thin slurry and compounded with linseed oil, after which this paste was applied to paper by means of brushes and dried.

Abraded Surfaces

A description of the use of adhesives in coated abrasives must be preceded by a description of physics, chemistry and the geometry of a solid surface.

The science of abrasion is based on three basic laws of friction:

(1) Frictional resistance is independent of the area of contact.
(2) Frictional resistance is a function of load.
(3) Frictional properties of sliding material.

Preparation of microscopically perfect flat surfaces is extremely difficult, if possible. Even smooth surfaces are rough and uneven in microscopical dimensions. If a coated abrasive is placed in contact with a surface to be abraded, it will be supported in relatively few places on miniature mountains (asperities) and will contain large valleys between the points of contact.

The two basic processes, grinding and polishing, result in two different physical, chemical, and sometimes crystallographic changes of solid surfaces. In the process of grinding, comparatively large volumes of solid materials are removed along their crystallographical planes without change or with only slight change in geometry and chemistry of the ground surface.

The mechanism of the polishing process has been a controversial topic, e.g., Newton,[2] Herschel,[3] and Rayleigh,[4] claimed polishing as essentially an abrading process; whereas the tension forces theory by Bielby[5] explains the phenomenon in terms of instant mobility of surface atoms before solidification. The structure of the Bielby layer was investigated by electron diffraction, and it was established that the surface consists of either fine crystals or a completely amorphous layer with a depth of several hundreds Angstroms.

Leonardo Da Vinci[6] observed that "The very rapid friction of the two thick bodies produces fire." Heat developed on metal surfaces is visible in the form of a flame during the grinding process. Experiments provide strong evidence that high local temperatures play an extremely important role in polishing; furthermore molten solid will flow and smear into cooler areas.

Abrading action is affected by heat. The abrasive grain does not always have to be harder than the surface to which it is applied; it is possible to grind or polish a harder surface by means of softer bodies provided their melting point is higher than that of the surface. Chemical reactions at the abraded surfaces often contribute to grinding or polishing processes.

* Present address Aerojet-General Corp., Sacramento, California.

** This section by Sigmund Orchon.

Application of lubricants or coolants does not eliminate the heat of abrasion; it attracts and transfers part of the heat and localizes or confines the remainder to a limited area.

Coated-Abrasives Industry

The coated-abrasives industry was born of the necessity to have more effective tools for use in grinding and polishing metal and wood. Abrasive paper and abrasive cloth were the first coated-abrasive products on the market. With the growth of modern industry, new problems and challenges brought the coated-abrasive industry from obscurity and crude "artistry" into the light of science.

At present, products of the coated-abrasives industry are used not only in woodworking and metal trades, but also in the plastics, shoe, leather, clothing, textile, hat, and glasn industries, etc.

Backings

(1) Cloth is available as:
   (a) Drills (X) which are heavier, stronger, less stretchable; used mainly in belts and discs.
   (b) Jeans (J) which are lighter and more flexible, but less strong than drills, having more inherent stretch; used for jobs where flexibility is important.
   (c) Twills for applications which require higher tensile strength than one can obtain with drills.
   (d) Duck Cloth for applications which require maximum toughness.
   (e) Print Cloth in combination with paper to improve the physical properties of paper.

To provide a suitable coating surface and right backing, cloth must be filled prior to being put on the coating machines that manufacture coated abrasives. The greige goods are washed and dyed if desired; then to fill the cloth various modifications of glue and additives are applied, depending on the desired flexibility of the backing. Dextrins and clays provide the required flexibility, and glue mixes are applied to the cloth by coating rolls or knives on the coating machines. Filling may be applied equally to both sides of the cloth, or a "one-sided" effect may be produced by filling opposite sides with different compositions. The filled cloth is then dried by running over a series of "dry cans" prior to being wound up. The entire operation is performed under tension to eliminate as much stretch as possible from the backing.

(2) Paper backings are the most widely used for coated abrasives. To meet a wide range of requirements, they are used in four different weights:

"A"—lightest and most pliable; used in finishing operations.
"C" and "D"—used for severe hand-sanding.
"E"—used for mechanical sanding; tough and durable.

Glue is used to a small degree in the manufacture of paper backings where it is applied as a light tub sizing following the manufacture of paper.

(3) Vulcanized fiber backing is strong and durable and is used for sander disc applications.

Paper backing is preferred to cloth or fiber backing because of price differentials and similarity of physical properties; however for final choice one has to consider the strain and stress involved in the particular application.

In all cases where grinding operations require water-base coolants such as in glass polishing and in the case of varnished surfaces, waterproof-coated abrasive papers or cloth are required.

Types of Abrasives

To meet the diversified requirements of various industries, coated abrasive industry uses seven types of abrasives, five of which are natural and mined: garnet, flint, emery, crocus and tripoli.

Aluminum oxide (Al_2O_3) and silicon carbide (SiC) are produced in electric furnaces.

Many physical properties of manufactured abrasive grain are more uniform than are the corresponding natural abrasives. Hardness, one of these properties, is quite important. Other physical properties of abrasive grains are: toughness, shear and tensile strength, crystallographical planes along which grain fractures affect shape, and dimensions of grain.

The abrasive grain chosen has to be tough to resist vectorial forces of grinding and still continue to produce sharp edges by the fracture process.

Silicon Carbide. Initially made by E. G. Acheson,[7] 1891, from clay and coke; subsequently it was made of sand, coke, salt, and sawdust. It finds applications for sanding cast iron, copper, brass, aluminum beveling and polishing plastics, glass and marble.

Aluminum Oxide. Produced from bauxite, it was originally made by Charles Jacobs (1897).[8] Particularly well-adapted for grinding materials of high tensile strength such as alloy, steel, bronze, high-speed steels, stellite, high-carbon steel and malleable iron.

Flint. Relatively sharp and naturally mined abrasive which is used for hand applications, do-it-yourself projects, painting, wood finishing, leather finishing, etc.

Garnet. Tough and sharp, it is used primarily in the woodworking trade; moderate usage on leather.

Emery. Softest material used for surface finishing.

Tripoli. Natural material used for polishing.

Crocus. An iron oxide polishing powder.

All abrasive grains are crushed, milled, and screened. The quality of the grain surface is improved by chemical means, e.g., acid or caustic treatments. Preparation of abrasive raw materials into exactly defined abrasive grain is extremely complicated and requires vast experience. Current grit sizes range between very coarse grain (about 2000μ) and exceptionally fine ones (about 20μ).

Requirements of Adhesives

Requirements for adhesives in the coated-abrasives industry are extremely critical since they must produce a good bond between backings and abrasive grain, be tough and not hygroscopic. Currently employed adhesives are animal glue, resins, and varnishes.

Animal glue, having specific adhesion to abrasive grains, fast gelling properties, durability, and toughness is a most suitable and efficient adhesive for the coated-abrasives industry. The high shock absorption stability in proper storage conditions, economy, and availability are additional advantages.

Of the many types of glue available for the manufacture of coated abrasives, high-quality hide glues are used almost exclusively. Other types such as bone glue, fish glue, etc. do not have all the necessary properties requisite to the manufacture of coated abrasives, especially since the applications for coated abrasives are becoming more severe and more exacting. The grades of hide glue used range from high test (jelly value 379) to low test (135). Selection of a glue for a particular commodity or for a backing is dependent on the way the manufacturer expects the consumer to use that product. The higher grades of glue are used on products which will be employed mechanically and frequently subjected to extreme pressures during grinding; whereas the lower glues may be employed for less severe work such as hand sanding, "jitterbug" sanding or light belt work.

Frequently in the coated-abrasives industry, various additives and modifiers are utilized, of which one of the most important is ground calcium carbonate, which is mixed with coating glue to improve the resistance of the coated abrasive to both the heat of grinding and atmospheric moisture. Additives such as starches, dextrins and clays are also used in the filling of cloth backings. Starches provide stiffness and body at low cost; whereas clays and dextrins produce flexibility desired for hand sanding or contour polishing by machine.

The preparation of animal glue requires, first, dissolving of water in glue (swelling) and second, solution of glue in water. Since the first is an exothermic reaction, it is accomplished by cold soaking of ground glue for approximately ½ hr. The second, since it is an endothermic reaction, requires heating the glue mix at a temperature of 140°F for a minimum of 2 hr, after which the glue may be held at 140°F for periods up to 4 hr prior to using it in the coating or cloth filling process. Concentration of glue varies, depending on the particle size being coated. Applied glue must be free from foam.

Waterproof papers were some of the first products developed with resin binders. The early products involved the use of long-drying, long-oil-length varnishes which were used because of the flexibility and coating characteristics. More recently, varnishes with shorter oil length have been employed.

Waterproof papers of today are vastly different from those developed originally. Latex-filled paper backings have made this type of product flexible, tough, and more waterproof.

The coated abrasives industry has for years used hide glue as a principal bond. The development of mechanized operations demanded more heat-resistant binders; consequently it was necessary to develop novel materials involving resin bonds. Initially, these products were made with a hide-glue make coat[a] and a phenolic-resin size coat, possessing fast-dry and fast-cure properties. Products made in this manner show a tremendous improvement over the 100 per cent glue-bonded products due to greater heat resistance, durability, and adhesion.

A satisfactory system for making resin-bond coated abrasives has also reached commercial acceptance and is used on certain applications of moderate severity. These resins are generally ureas modified to improve flexibility on aging. Articles[b] produced with these resins are easy to process (lower cure temperatures) and are particularly adaptable to the woodworking trade.

[a] The make coat is the first coat of adhesive into which the abrasive grain is imbedded.

[b] Patent No. 2,468,056.

In cloth products of the "resin-over-resin" type, slow-curing phenolic resins are used to achieve greater bond strength and higher heat resistance. Waterproof cloth consists of cloth which is impregnated with phenolic resins modified with plasticizers and/or elastomeric materials and a phenolic make coat.

Until recently, resin cloth belts for rough snagging and grinding operations were made on conventional backings similar to those used with glue bonded belts. A new method of bonding[c] has been adopted in the manufacturing of resin bond products involving pre-sizing the backing with a thin film of phenolformaldehyde resin and drying it tack-free; the backing is then coated with abrasive grain by conventional gravity or electrostatic processes. This has given a striking improvement over materials made by techniques described previously.

With steady progress in research and development, resin bond technology is constantly changing. This change is dynamic and results in continuing advancement of techniques and products.

Production of Coated Abrasives

Paper or cloth passes, in a continuous process, through rotational printing rolls which print the trade name, quality and grit size of the abrasive on one side of the backing, with the number on the backside (print side); it then passes between two additional rolls, of which the lower one is immersed in a pan with liquid adhesive, which is transferred onto the top (coat side) of backing (make coat) and smoothed. The backing then goes around the top roll and passes under a hopper where it is sprinkled with abrasive grain, at which point adhesives must exhibit the following functions:

(1) Permit penetration of abrasive grain into the adhesive.
(2) Produce good bond qualities to grain, as well as to backings.
(3) Permit economical handling.

In the next step, the product enters a huge drying room where it is hung loosely in the form of long loops. Before completion of the drying cycle, a second coating (size coat) is applied over the abrasive grain. The size coat produces a bond with the make coat, firmly anchoring the abrasive particles. The amount of adhesive applied in either the make or size coat can be controlled by adjusting the viscosity of adhesive mix and/or by adjusting the roll pressure. Once again, the product is sent to the drying room and wound into jumbo rolls after completion of drying and/or curing cycle.

Mechanical sprinkling of abrasive grain is an every-day process in the coated-abrasives industry; however the electrostatic method of applying abrasive grain is being used more frequently, especially for fine- and medium-sized grits. The backing passes with the coat side down in this process between two electrodes. Abrasive grain is transported on a conveyor into the electrical field above the bottom electrode (cathode) possessing a varying but substantial voltage. While approaching the electrical field, abrasive grains are picked up by the anode and embedded onto the adhesive on the backing. The advantage of this method is that the grains become oriented in the direction of their longitudinal axis perpendicular to the backing, producing a superior product with regard to both sharpness and extended life. Beta-ray control gauges placed in strategic spots show the slightest variations in weight of backings, adhesives and grains without affecting speed of the manufacturing process. Other quality controls, e.g., viscosity measurements and grit-size distribution curves supplement inspection of production processes.

Two modifications of grain distributions on backings are possible with all three types of adhesives: open coat and close coat. In the case of open coat, grain is spaced in such a manner that spaces are left between adjacent particles, and depending on requirements, can be made smaller or larger. In the case of close coat, the surface is covered with grain in a continuous manner, providing an unbroken array of abrasive points over the entire surface of the backings. Such products are useful for operations where relatively large amounts of materials are ground under high pressures. Conversely, open coat is used to prevent "loading" and permit abrasives to cut freely wherever materials such as rosin, pitch, putty and other filling materials are to be abraded.

Proper removal of moisture from coated abrasives requires carefully balanced conditions of heat and humidity resulting in a comparatively slow process due to thickness of applied adhesives and presenting problems of subsequent warping in sheet, disc and belt forms. As drying progresses, the softening temperature of the adhesive increases, thereby permitting a corresponding increase in the temperature of the drying chamber. Proper humidity control prevents case hardening of adhesives.

Subsequent operations involve flexing, cutting, slitting, or dieing to the proper size and shape, inspection, and storage and/or shipment. In the case of coated-abrasive belts, the splicing process precedes storage. In the construction of abrasive belts,

[c] Patent No. 2,805,136.

the type of adhesive applied is influenced by the final use of the products. Adhesives of the highest quality are essential because many belts run under moderate tension and extreme working pressures. These adhesives are applied to spliced areas from which the grain has been removed by "skiving" from the bottom part of the lap; then the other end of the belt is put on top of this area and the splice is pressed until set. This type of splicing is employed by the coated-abrasives manufacturers as well as by many customers, especially in the woodworking trade, which produces its own belts from coated abrasives purchased in roll form. High quality animal glues and various types of resins are used for splice adhesives.

For many applications, it is necessary to increase flexibility. For this purpose coated abrasives are pulled, under tension, over a right-angle steel bar to produce "Flex-lines" at 90° or at 45° to each edge of the material. Excessive flexing can destroy the adhesion of the bond between the coating and the backing.

Most suitable for mechanical, free-hand grinding are sander discs made from cloth or preferably flexible vulcanized fiber; they are used especially in the steel industry where flat and/or contoured surfaces have to be ground to remove uneven and solder spots. These discs are quite economical. After wear at the edge, a ½ in. outside ring can be stamped off and the remaining, smaller disc reused.

A recent development of the coated-abrasives industry is "Sandscreen,"* a twenty-two square-weave filament rayon built in the form of a screen, coated on both sides with sharp abrasive grain. Due to the open mesh construction, the new product lasts longer, does not "load" so quickly, and permits easy removal of abraded particles.

Through intensive evolution, the coated-abrasives industry has come from infancy into adolescence. Its future is unpredictable, it is moving into maturity as one of the leading agents of stock removal.

References

1. Technik *Tages-Anzeiger fuer Stadt und Kanton Zuerich* Nr. 43, 20 (Feb. 1958).
2. Horsley, Samuel, "Isaaci Newtoni Opera Quae Extant Omnia," London, (1779–1785).
3. Bowden, F. P., and Tabor, D., "The Friction and Lubrication of Solids," Oxford, Claredon Press, 1950.
4. Lodge, Sir Oliver, *National Review*, (Sept. 1898).
5. Bowden, F. P., and Tabor, D., "The Friction and

Lubrication of Solids," Oxford, Claredon Press, 1950.
6. da Vinci, Leonardo, Manuscript G, Blatt 70.
7. Hofmann, K. A., "Anorganische Chemie," p. 332 Zehnte Auflage, Wien, 1943.
8. Hofmann, K. A., "Anorganische Chemie," p. 474 Zehnte Auflage, Wien, 1943; Furnas: "Roger's Industrial Chemistry," Vol. 2, New York, D. Van Nostrand Co., 1943. Holmes, J., "The Story of Aluminum," *Chemical Education,* **7**, 233 (1930).

ADHESIVES FOR BONDED ABRASIVES**

The manufacture of bonded abrasives requires the use of adhesives of many specific characteristics to perform various functions in process from the initial mixing operation to the final blottering of the finished product. The most important uses are as follows:

Temporary Binders in Ceramic-Bonded Abrasives

The two basic components of all bonded abrasive products are abrasive grains and bond. Ceramic bonds consist of glass frits, clays, or porcelain. The bond, which is in powder form and used in the initial step of processing, must be uniformly distributed as a coating on each individual grit in the mix. This is accomplished by adhesives generally called "temporary binders" in the abrasives industry.

Temporary binders most commonly used are water-base adhesives such as dextrin in water solution and wax emulsions. The adhesive is added to the dry components in the mix tub while the mixer is in motion and run until a uniform mix is achieved. The finished mix must be free flowing granules of individually coated abrasive grits to permit uniform distribution in subsequent operations.

Another important function of the temporary binder adhesive is to impart pressure sensitivity to the mix. When pressure is applied in the molding operation, the mix is compacted in the mold to a predetermined size and shape. At this stage, the molded article must have sufficient "green" strength to permit extraction from the mold cavity and subsequent handling in the green. When water soluble-type adhesives are used, the green ware may be dried at relatively low temperatures to evaporate the water thus adding to the green strength of the ware. This is particularly desirable in the case of large wheels to facilitate handling and setting on kiln cars.

* Registered trade mark, The Carborundum Co.

** This section by Melvin L. Buike.

Wax emulsion adhesives may be used in the same manner, or the mix may be predried before the molding operation.

The temporary binder adhesive has still another function to perform, i.e., to hold the molded article to size and shape in the process of firing until the vitrified bond begins to sinter and develop sufficient strength on its own. The binder, being an organic material, naturally loses its adhesive characteristics at a temperature below the build up of this initial strength in the bond; therefore it must have sufficient residual carbon in the molded article to hold the structure together in this intermediate stage in firing. The last traces of carbon must however burn out before the ware is fully matured; thus, a suitable adhesive for this purpose must possess a delicate balance in properties during its complete life span in process.

Adhesives for Organic-Bonded Abrasives

The bonds used in these products are adhesives with special properties; furthermore they must meet rigid specifications in uniformity of both physical and chemical characteristics. It is insufficient merely to hold the abrasive grains together with adequate bonding strength to withstand the centrifugal forces involved in rotating abrasive wheels at operating speed.

Bonded abrasives to be efficient must be self-sharpening, e.g., the abrasive grits in the face of a grinding wheel become dulled in use and require increased pressure to make them penetrate the work being ground. When this occurs, the bond or adhesive that holds them in place must yield to the extent that the dulled abrasive grains are released and new sharp ones exposed. Due to the wide variety of grinding operations, bonds of various controlled strengths are required.

The organic bonds or adhesives most commonly used are synthetic resins, rubber and shellac.

Resin Bonds. Synthetic resins known in the industry as "Resinoid" bonds consist of liquid one-stage phenolics, novolacs with hexamethylene tetramine catalysts, liquid and powdered alkyds. Shellac is a natural resin with some resemblance to alkyds.

The process for bonding abrasive grains with resins consists in first wetting the abrasive grains with a plasticizer or solvent in a mixer; then the powdered resin is added to the mix. If the correct amount of plasticizer or solvent has been added initially, the resultant mix will be free flowing, pressure-sensitive granules of individual grits coated with resin.

The molding of resin mixes can be either cold-pressed at room temperature or hot-pressed. The cold pressed technique is used for more porous structures; accordingly, the mix is compacted in a mold to a predetermined size and shape. It has sufficient green strength to be extracted from the mold cavity and withstand subsequent handling. The product is then oven-cured, during which the resins develop a tenacious adhesion to the abrasive and a bridge or bond post between the abrasive grains to hold them together.

The hot pressed method, which is used for very dense nonporous structures, consists of compacting the mix to a definite size, shape, and density under heat and pressure. The resin bond melts in the process and fills in the voids between the grits, thus achieving the ultimate in strength and adhesion.

Rubber Bonds. Rubber provides a very versatile bond for abrasive wheels. The rubber which may be in the form of rubber cement is mixed with abrasive grain and other compounding ingredients by a process similar to that used for resin-bonded products. It is also common practice to perform the mixing operation on rolls and calender out in sheet form from which wheels are cut and subsequently cured. The end product may be as flexible as a pencil eraser or a hard vulcanite, depending on the compounding and the use for which the product is intended.

Cementing Operations

At this stage, the use of adhesives is incomplete. To supply a bonded abrasive article of proper design and shape to a consumer, it may be necessary to perform one of the following additional cementing operations.

Cementing Wheels to Steel Plates. An adhesive to cement an abrasive wheel to a steel plate for mounting on special grinders must be of adequate strength both at room and elevated temperatures to withstand the complex forces including centrifugal, tensile and shear set up during the grinding operation. The cement must be resilient to compensate for the differential in thermal expansion between the abrasive and steel; otherwise a rigid bond may cause the abrasive to fracture. The adhesive must also have sufficient heat resistance to withstand the heat generated over prolonged periods during the dry grinding operations. There are also many wet grinding operations; hence the cement must be resistant to prolonged exposure of grinding fluids such as water, detergents, or oils.

There are several common processes for cementing abrasive wheels to steel backs.

Gammeter Process. This first successful process for cementing abrasive products to steel plates employed a laminating technique. A sheet of resilient rubber compound on the order of 1/16 in. thick was cemented between the abrasive and the plate to act as a tie bond to hold the two together. This also provided resiliency to compensate for the differential in coefficient of expansion between the two materials. Although this process is currently used to some extent, it has largely been replaced by resilient resin cements.

Resin Cements. The plasticized epoxy types, which are commonly used for this purpose, are available in a wide variety of resiliencies. With this process, it is necessary only to cement-coat the cleaned surface of the plate and bed the abrasive article on it. The assembly may be air-dried or heated for a relatively short period to cure the cement.

A layer of cement approximately 1/32 in. thick is required to absorb the stresses set up by the differential in thermal expansion between the steel plate and abrasive article; indeed this is contrary to accepted cementing practices that recommend as thin as possible a glue line.

The cementing of organic-bonded abrasive products to steel is not as critical as that of vitrified bonded abrasives. The coefficient of thermal expansion of organic-bonded abrasives is closer to that of steel, thereby allowing more rigid cements which are also more heat resistant than the flexible cements. However, the rigid cement must not shrink excessively during cure since shrinkage will set up stresses in the assembly and cause the steel plate to warp, especially in large diameters.

Epoxy Cement Hardeners. The selection of hardeners for the cement depends on the desired physical properties of the end product and the process to be used. The pot life of the cement can range from 1/2 hr using some amine hardeners, to several hours with certain organic acid anhydrides as the hardeners. Aliphatic amine hardener will usually cure at room temperature but improved strengths at elevated temperatures can be obtained by a short, low temperature oven cure. The acid anhydride hardeners give improved heat resistance over aliphatic amine hardeners but require a longer and higher temperature cure to achieve maximum strength.

The epoxy resins are comparatively new in the plastics field, i.e., new materials, processes and cures are continually being developed. If these resins are to be used, it is wise to seek the aid of a resin manufacturer or compounder in making a selection for a specific purpose.

In cases where extremely high heat is generated in grinding, present-day epoxy systems or mounting with rubber may be inadequate. Such grinding operations require the heat resistance of phenolic resin cements. Liquid, one-stage resins reinforced with fillers or powders, e.g., cryolite, flint, feldspar, magnesium oxide, etc., are suitable for this use; also powdered, two-stage resins dissolved in a reactive solvent such as furfural and filled with powders as above are used effectively.

The phenolic-type of cement should be restricted to small diameter wheels due to the shrinkage of the cement during cure. The heat resistance of this cement when properly cured is equal or superior to that of the resin used to make the bonded abrasive wheel.

Cementing Mandrels in Mounted Wheels. For this purpose, the cement must be unusually tough and hard to lock mechanically the knurled section of the mandrel in the wheel; also the cement must be heat resistant and maintain its toughness and adhesion at the high temperatures generated in dry grinding on some severe operations.

The high firing temperature in the kiln prevents the molding of metallic mandrels into vitrified bonded wheels before firing. For anchoring mandrels in these wheels after firing, various cements have been used with success.

Copper oxide-phosphoric acid cement was among the first to gain widespread acceptance; however this cement requires very exacting control of materials and processing. It also has a tendency to bleed into the wheels thus discoloring them.

Phenolic Resin Cement. Phenolic resin adhesives, which have adequate strength and function quite satisfactorily as a cement for most applications, are easily controlled, unlike copper oxide cement. For certain light applications and soft grades of wheels, epoxy resin cements have been found adequate. In many cases, they are preferred to the phenolic resin or copper oxide cement since there is less penetration and discoloration of open structure abrasives.

Organic-bonded abrasive-mounted wheels do not reach as high temperatures in the curing ovens as vitrified wheels do, and thus it is possible to mold the mandrels in the wheels as inserts. The mandrels may be primed with a phenolic resin cement before being molded into the wheel. A combination of adhesion and mechanical locking of the knurled section on the mandrel prevents it from twisting within the wheel while in use.

Threaded Metal Bushings. To fit on a threaded machine spindle, they are cemented in abrasive wheels in much the same way as mandrels for mounted wheels. For simplicity in operation, the same cements are generally used for bushings as for mandrels.

Cements Used In Pulp Wheel Assembly. Pulp wheels are very large wheels up to 6 ft in diameter used in the paper industry to grind wood to pulp; they consist of an external annular ring of abrasive anchored by bolts to a core of reinforced concrete. The abrasive ring is assembled first; then the concrete core is cast inside the ring. The abrasive ring consists of rectangular-shaped segments cemented together with a layer of resilient material between each joint. The cement used must be resistant to boiling water and provide for unequal expansion of the assembly due to heat generated in grinding. The rate of wear of the cement must match the wear of the abrasive. Too hard a cement will have raised ridges at the joints and interfere with the grinding action. A cement that is too soft will undercut between segments and not properly support the segment edges. This may cause the segments to chip or spall in use. Large flat areas are involved; therefore the cement must have a minimum of volatiles to reduce the tendency of gas pockets in the cement.

Phenolic resin cements have been used with some success. A disadvantage of this type of cement is the necessity of heat curing the wheel after assembly to achieve the desired physical properties. Also, phenolic resins cure through condensation and there is a tendency for the evolved condensation products to form gas pockets.

Epoxy resins with special amine-type hardeners will cure at room temperature. No volatiles are produced during cure; so the possibility of gas pockets is practically nil.

Finishing Operations

After the abrasive has been processed, certain components are added. Segments that are mounted in special chucks of surface-grinding machines require pads of gasket material adhered to the segment. These pads act as a cushion between the chuck and abrasive to prevent fracturing of the abrasive and to protect the face of the chuck from the abrasive.

The adhesive for this operation must have instant grip to hold the pad on the contour of segment; also it must be a coolant and water-resistant so that pads will not loosen when used wet. The rubber base-type adhesive has proved satisfactory for this purpose.

Abrasive wheels require gaskets or blotters on the sides of wheels to act as a cushion between the machine flanges and the wheel. The adhesive for this operation must have good pot life in applicators. In addition, it should be of low viscosity to prevent any unevenness in thickness of the cement film that would affect parallelism of the sides of the wheel. It must have fast grip to hold the blotters and labels in place until it dries.

A water solution of sodium silicate is frequently used as an adhesive as well as water-soluble latices.

The use of adhesives in the bonded-abrasives industry is extensive and will become ever more highly specialized.

—— 53 ——

Adhesion of Coatings

R. L. Patrick

Alpha Research and Development, Inc.
Blue Island, Illinois

and R. L. Millar

Central Research & Engineering Division
Continental Can Company, Inc.
Chicago, Illinois

Adhesion is important in many areas of our technology. Nowhere does it contribute more than in the adequate performance of coatings. Once adhesion is lost, the coating is essentially useless. It is not necessary to develop and maintain the adhesive strengths required in structural bonding; nevertheless, there are instances, such as the deep drawing of precoated metal, where strains of considerable magnitude are established between the substrate and the organic film. Other coating systems are subjected to extreme demands through such treatments as thermal cycling. Indeed, adhesion plays a most significant role in producing a satisfactory coating.

In this discussion on the adhesion of coatings, five aspects are covered: (1) a general discussion concerned with the theoretical considerations of physical and mechanical properties of films, and mechanisms of failure; (2) substrates; (3) application considerations; (4) testing and interpretation; and, (5) environmental effects.

GENERAL DISCUSSION

Theoretical Considerations of Physical and Mechanical Properties of Films

To be useful as a coating, an organic film must have a strong interaction with the substrate. The solvent or dispersant system must be compatible with (i.e., wet) the substrate surface. A zero contact angle is a prime requisite necessary to generate a system in which the dissolved polymer or prepolymer will be ideally situated to yield a continuous, tightly bound film once the volatile material is removed. There must be initial interaction with the solvent, followed by rapid adsorption of the polymer phase onto the surface. The polymer phase also causes pigment particles, when present, to be transported due to pigment-polymer interaction. Assuming that the critical pigment volume-concentration is not exceeded, the presence of pigment in the coating has no important effect on adhesion and will, therefore, not be considered.

The manner in which adsorption of the polymer phase onto the substrate occurs is of great importance. One must assume that the bonds which are formed are in most cases physical, as distinct from truly chemical bonds. The adsorption of polymer is complex, and doubtlessly involves competition between solvent and polymer molecules for active sites. Since the solvent molecules are so much smaller in magnitude, they undoubtedly attach to the surface first with subsequent displacement by the polymer molecules.

Selection of a poor solvent aids the polymer-substrate interaction by virtually pushing the polymer molecules out of solution. However, the poor solvent compacts the molecules into tighter agglomerates than a good solvent allowing less active sites per adsorbed molecule (Fig. 1A). On the other hand, the mobility of the polymer is greater in a

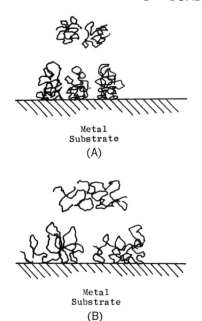

Metal
Substrate
(A)

Metal
Substrate
(B)

Fig. 1. Adsorption of polymer from a "poor" solvent, (A), and a "good" solvent, (B), onto substrate.

good solvent and thus the molecules are more able to move to the interface where adsorption occurs.

The adsorption and, hence, adhesion is affected by several factors: surface oxidation, contamination, rugosity, etc. The contribution of each of these factors to adsorption is a chapter in itself. It is sufficient here to say that in a system having an oxide-free surface, stronger adhesion occurs. Conceivably, this is due in some cases to the formation of chemical bonds. While the presence of oxide reduces the possibility of chemical bonding, the formation of physical bonds generates a sufficiently strong bond for the general mechanical stresses which a coating would be expected to withstand.

Contamination makes the formation of adhesive bonds difficult. If the contaminant is strongly adsorbed, there is a possibility that the coating cannot successfully compete for the surface sites.

Other factors which contribute to the formation of adhesive bonds are more intrinsic. For example, the molecular weight of the polymer is very significant. Coatings, as applied, usually use lower molecular weight polymers than are used for other purposes. Both low solution-viscosity and high solids are desired for ease of application in thin films. Ideally, a higher molecular weight material would yield more interfacial bonds per molecule but this effect may be offset by the lower intramolecular mobility which hinders optimum orientation at the interface. To the extent that bulk strength contributes to adhesion, the higher molecular weight coating is preferred.

An additional intrinsic factor is the release rate of the solvents. It has been demonstrated in many instances that as long as a measurable amount of liquid phase remains in the coating, adhesion is realized. As soon as the liquid phase is exhausted, the bonds fail; the liquid phase acts as a "tie-coat" between the adhesive and the substrate. In many cases primers which are softer more mobile materials are used.

In other cases, e.g., with some vinyl chloride copolymer coatings, incomplete solvent removal results in poor adhesion to metal; preferential adsorption of the more polar solvents at the interface results in a weakly bonded coating.

Polymerization, *e.g.*, of oleoresinous materials, may itself cause considerable strain to be set up in the coating. In many cases the bulk polymerization is accompanied by a diminution in volume. Even though the rate of polymerization is slow, the material frequently cannot release the strains. As the polymerization continues, the system becomes more reticulated and eventually, if not controlled, will cause shrinkage to be a major factor in film failure. Figure 2 shows, schematically, the effect of the degree of polymerization on relative adhesion in a hypothetical system.

Some of the more recently developed thermoplastic polymers may be subject to still another stress. Many of these will change from a completely amorphous condition to a state including some degree of crystallinity.[1, 2] As crystallization occurs, a corresponding decrease in polymer volume results, with high stress concentrations being generated especially in the areas approximating the interfacial zone. A graphic example is shown by 6,6-nylon. The polyamide may be coated

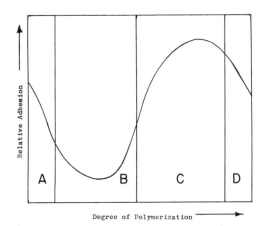

Fig. 2. A. Liquid phase present.
       B. Low MW solid phase only.
       C. Optimum high MW by polymerization.
       D. Excess polymerization, high degree of crosslinking, slight chance of stress relaxation.

onto a carefully prepared substrate from the molten state and quickly cooled to virtually a zero crystallite content. The coating has excellent adhesion initially. In time, even at relatively low temperatures, adhesion begins to degenerate as crystallites begin to form. Eventually, adhesive bonds no longer exist between the substrate and the nylon. Other materials, such as polyethylene terephthalate, are not subject to crystallization at room temperature since it occurs only when the temperature of the polymer is raised above the second order transition temperature.

Failure of adhesion is accelerated in some highly crosslinked coatings by thermal cycling. As the temperature is raised, considerable strains are generated if the coefficients of expansion of the substrate material and the organic phase are markedly different. As the cycling continues, the strain concentrations become more pronounced and eventually accumulate to the point at which film failure occurs. Ideally, coatings and their substrates should have similar coefficients of expansion and, more important, the coatings should be able to release the strains very rapidly. Unfortunately, in general, materials which release strains rapidly seldom perform as serviceable coatings.

Great strides are being made in the flexibility of coatings. The fabrication of metal coated with relatively thick films has been improved greatly over the past few years. The drawing operation causes extremely high strains to be concentrated close to the interfacial area. The coatings which are most satisfactory are able to relax and disperse the strains virtually instantaneously. In many cases, the addition of pigment to coatings aids in stress distribution, thus avoiding gross failure.

Often a material will successfully undergo the mandrel bend test without obvious failure, but if the coating of the bent sample is nicked, a crack will propagate very rapidly across the coating, and adhesive failure will occur. Obviously, coating systems which attain a high degree of hardness by extensive crosslinking will not be satisfactory in situations where flexibility is a prime requirement.

Mechanisms of Film Failure

Theoretical understanding of film failure is incomplete. Mechanically, it is virtually impossible to rupture organo-metallic interfacial bonds. It is, however, quite simple to cause interfacial bond failure by hydrolysis, solvolysis, displacement or other physical-chemical interaction. The adsorption of organic coatings on glass is quickly destroyed by water immersion, even though the sample may have only a small area of the glass ends exposed to the water. Solvents may swell the polymer or even partially dissolve the material, or solvent molecules may exchange with the adsorbed polymer.

The outward indication of impact failure is loss of adhesion; but excessive film brittleness, with a commensurate inherent strain, could be the cause of failure close to the interface. It may very well be that the materials which fail on impact are coherent coatings that have actually failed adhesively prior to the impact. Much more work must be done in these rather poorly understood areas.

SUBSTRATES

It is well known that wood and paper generate mechanical bonds with the coating. The porous substrates imbibe a certain portion of the material and a tenaciously held film results. DeBruyne[3] calculated capillary pressures of model porous systems, and found them sizeable, aiding markedly in adhesion.

Metal substrates adsorb the polymer phase, and either physi- or chemi-sorption causes very strong interfacial bonds to be formed. Even "Teflon," when rubbed on metal surfaces, is removed only with difficulty. The more coherent, nonporous coating systems are the most suitable for metals since the permeation of oxygen, moisture, etc., through the interstices of the polymer to the interface is made more difficult.

Plastic substrates generally utilize mutual solubility to obtain successful coatings. Since both materials are organic, the surface energy is low and mutual adsorptive interaction is minimal. However, mutual solution allows intertwining of chains, etc., resulting in good coatings.

APPLICATION CONSIDERATIONS

Surface Preparation

It is obvious from theoretical considerations that surface preparation is one of the most important factors affecting the adhesion of coatings. While it would be highly desirable to start with a completely uncontaminated surface, this is a practical impossibility. Adsorbed gases, water, oxide films, cleaning solvents, etc., are always present.

It is sometimes necessary, however, for economic or other reasons, to apply coatings to more or less grossly contaminated surfaces. In coating the plate from which tin cans are made, for instance, there is present a very thin film of cottonseed oil or dioctyl sebacate which has been applied as a lubricant to prevent abrasion and an excessive rate of oxidation of the tin coating on the plate. The enamels used for this type surface must be compatible with and/or have the capacity to preferentially desorb the lubricant so that good adhesion is attained.

Another type of surface contamination frequently encountered is rust on steel. Under conditions where the rust can not be removed, reasonably good adhesion may be obtained by applying a penetrating type coating such as one containing a high proportion of fish oil. In this case, the film-forming vehicle is slow-drying and penetrates to the metal surface, incorporating the rust into the film in somewhat the same fashion as a pigment.

The various methods of surface preparation may be divided into three general types: mechanical, physical, and chemical.

Mechanical Methods. Wire brushing, scraping, or sanding removes loose rust, scale or paint from a surface, but will generally not produce an entirely "virgin" surface. Shot or sand blasting of metals is much preferred, where possible, since a thoroughly fresh surface may be obtained. In addition, the resulting roughness provides an effectively (up to 20 times[4]) larger surface per unit projected area and, hence, better adhesion.

Physical Methods. The simplest form of physical cleaning is solvent washing whereby oily contaminants are dissolved. While mere dipping in solvent may be sufficient in some cases, the vapor degreasing method is preferred since condensing vapors of a liquid such as trichloroethylene present continuously fresh solvent to the surface being cleaned. Alkali washing is sometimes used alone, but more often as a prelude to phosphate treating (see Chemical Methods). It involves dipping or spraying the surface with as much turbulence as possible, using hot aqueous solutions of trisodium phosphate, sodium silicate, organic emulsifiers, wetting agents, etc., in order to displace the contaminant. This is generally followed by a hot water wash to remove the alkaline salts.

A combination of solvent cleaning and alkali washing is sometimes employed by emulsifying a solvent in an aqueous alkaline solution.

Electrolytic cleaning is classified here as a physical method in relation to the article being cleaned, although frequently some chemical reaction with the metallic surface takes place. This effective method of decontaminating many metal surfaces involves dipping the article into a hot alkaline bath and simultaneously subjecting it to a positive or negative potential. Cathodic cleaning produces a large amount of gassing, and therefore, is fast in its action. This is followed by anodic cleaning to remove bath contaminants.

Ultrasonic cleaning, although it is not of great commercial importance, is a useful tool for rapidly decontaminating a surface. Ultrasonic vibrations generated by a suitable transducer produce, in an alkaline or detergent bath, a degree of interfacial turbulence so great that surfaces can be cleaned almost instantaneously.

Chemical Methods. The simplest way of preparing hot rolled steel surfaces for coating is by weathering. The metal rusts and the scale becomes loosened so that wire brushing or sand blasting can remove it with ease. This method has been frequently used on large outdoor storage tanks. Another almost equally simple process is to burn off oily contaminants. It is obvious that subjecting steel to 500–600°F, or even to open flames, is not going to remove oxides; in fact, oxides are often formed under these conditions. On the other hand, organic matter is volatilized or decomposed and moisture thoroughly removed in this manner. This method is very adaptable for cleaning hard, relatively nonporous surfaces such as chrome, glass, etc.

The most commonly used chemical treatment for metal surfaces is phosphatizing. This general process involves immersing the metal object in solutions of phosphoric acid containing phosphates of iron, manganese and zinc. Controlled, finely crystalline, porous films of phosphate salts are deposited which are resistant to corrosion, and provide an excellent base to which a coating can adhere. From the standpoint of adhesion, however, it is possible to deposit too much zinc phosphate causing the surface to be brittle, loose, and powdery, thus forming a weak interface.

Acid pickling is often used to remove mill scale and oxide from steel surfaces before coating. This is generally carried out subsequent to some other process which has removed oily contaminants. In certain cases where the usual 2.5 per cent metal weight loss[5] is intolerable, the sodium hydride process is used. Here the steel is immersed in a bath of fused caustic containing sodium hydride which reduces surface oxides to the metallic state.

In the case of aluminum, hot solutions of soda ash or trisodium phosphate are used as a surface treatment, followed by a quick rinse in nitric acid solution.

With certain types of surfaces, such as glass, treatment with a positive adhesion promotor is desirable. Organosilanes, alkoxy titanates, and colloidal silica have been used for this purpose. These materials depend on reaction with surface moisture and/or hydroxyl groups to form a truly chemisorbed interfacial layer, thus promoting adhesion between the substrate and applied coating.

An interesting but special case involves the surface treatment of polyethylene. This polymer, to which almost nothing adheres satisfactorily, can be oxidized by flame treatment or other means to yield a surface which has excellent compatibility with many coating materials. Although the exact nature of the changes produced by this method is not known, it is apparent that surface polarity is increased to the point where other polymers can be adsorbed.

Methods of Application

Although in general the method of applying a coating to a substrate does not greatly affect adhesion, there are some important exceptions to this rule. When a coating is spread on a porous substrate, it may be necessary to employ considerable shear close to the interface in order to insure adequate contact between the coating and the surface. Brushing, reverse roll coating and knife coating are examples of this type of operation. In the process of dipping or flow coating, residual surface contaminants may be washed away or displaced, thus removing, at least in part, impediments to good adhesion.

Hot melt, fluidized bed, or other solventless coating systems may in many cases show better adhesion than the corresponding solution coatings because competition between resin and solvent for interfacial sites is avoided. The flame-spraying technique is sometimes the only practical way to gain metal adhesion with such polymers as polyethylene or polytetrafluoroethylene. By this method the powdered resin is blown through a flame which heats the polymer above its melting point but short of its decomposition temperature. In the process the surface of the resin particles is oxidized slightly to give sufficient polarity for reasonably good adhesion to clean metal.

Application methods such as spraying, printing or roller coating involve so little shear in the interfacial plane that these techniques, in themselves, should not affect adhesion.

Primers

As the name implies, a primer is a first coat; its main function is to provide adhesion to the substrate for subsequent coating of films. Depending on the industry or end use involved, a primer may be designated by any of the following terms.

Sealer	Shopcoat
Undercoater	Sizecoat
Primer-surfacer	Washcoat
Basecoat	Tiecoat

Besides promoting adhesion, the primer must perform other functions such as controlling the penetration of the topcoat into a porous substrate, preventing the corrosion of the metal, or smoothing out a rough surface. The specific character of each prime coat and the film thickness at which it is applied will obviously depend on the end use. From the standpoint of adhesion alone, it is preferable to use a thin prime coat since the main object is to create a new interface which acts as a liaison between topcoat and substrate.

For metal coatings involving the use of poorly adherent, high molecular weight materials, such as vinyl chloride copolymers, it is possible to incorporate a relatively low molecular weight component of high polarity which will migrate to the metal. Thus, by stratification, a primer and topcoat can, in effect, be laid down in a single application with resulting excellent adhesion.[6, 7]

TESTS FOR ADHESION AND INTERPRETATION OF RESULTS

Innumerable methods for evaluating the adhesion of coatings have been devised. From a scientific standpoint, most, if not all, of the test methods cannot be said to measure true interfacial adhesion. The purist cannot tolerate the knife or impact test; yet these give results which can be readily understood in the practical use of coatings. It may well be that once a theoretically sound method is found for determining the true adhesion of coatings, the resultant value will have to be modified immediately by such parameters as hardness, flexibility, film thickness, etc., for practical use. The coatings technologist continues to seek better ways to define this value.

The methods of evaluating coating adhesion can be divided into scraping, scoring, impact, bend and tensile tests (Figs. 3 and 4), or the direct fabrication of an actual shaped article from the coated substrate.

Scraping Tests

The simplest of these tests, such as the fingernail, the coin, and the knife, are entirely subjective and permit only a relative rating of one coating versus another. Attempts to make a more quantitative test have resulted in such instruments as the Interchemical Adherometer, Fig. 3A. Using an ivory cutting tool, the peeling force necessary to remove a coating from its substrate is measured. While attempts are made to correct for the various parameters other than adhesion, this instrument gives a

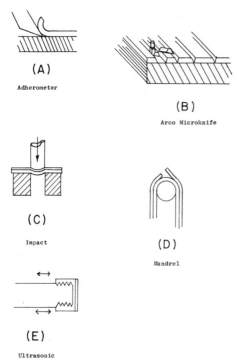

(A)

Adherometer

(B)

Arco Microknife

(C)

Impact

(D)

Mandrel

(E)

Ultrasonic

Fig. 3. Schematic diagrams of typical adhesion test methods.

value which is a direct function of film thickness. But if adhesion is defined as an interfacial phenomenon, it is obvious that film thickness cannot be involved. The Rossmann chisel adhesion test and the New York Production Club chisel test[8] have similar deficiencies. The above tests represent methods which measure the force of removal rather than adhesion since results are affected by such parameters as hardness, cohesion, flexibility, film thickness, etc. See also Asbeck et al.[16]

Scoring Tests

In its simplest form the scoring test consists of making a series of parallel cuts with a knife or razor blade at different intervals in one direction and another series perpendicular to the first. A piece of pressure sensitive tape is pressed over the crosshatched scribed area and rapidly removed by pulling one end of the tape perpendicular to the coating surface. The minimum distance between score marks is said to be inversely proportional to adhesion. A more refined version of this test is the Arco Microknife (Fig. 3B), in which a weighted diamond point is adjusted to cut through the coating just to the substrate. By a calibrated screw adjustment further parallel cuts are made successively closer until the coating is separated from

the substrate. The results obtained by this method are a function of film hardness and flexibility as well as adhesion.

Impact Tests

There are several widely used impact tests which give results relating to adhesion. The most common consists in placing the coated panel horizontally between a hemispherically tipped, ½-in. pin and a slightly larger hole in a metal block (Fig. 3C). A 2-pound weight, guided by two vertical rods, is dropped onto the pin from various heights. The force of impact, noted in inch-pounds, required to crack or peel the film, is considered to be a measure of adhesion. The Ericksen Cup test is similar except that a ball is slowly pushed into the coated metal panel over a hole in a metal block. In both tests either a concave or convex dent can be made in the panel. Impact tests are generally related to fabrication operations. In special cases, such as stamping out enamelled can ends, it is easy to evaluate a coating by the exact, rather than a simulated, production process. As an aid to observing coating failure, the specimen is subsequently immersed in a copper sulfate solution to make film breaks apparent.

It should be noted that high-speed fabrication will give a considerably different result than a relatively slow impact test. While in all cases variations in ambient test temperature can affect results, it is particularly true in a high-speed fabrication operation.

The results from an impact test are functions not only of adhesion, but also of coating flexibility (extensibility or compressability), film thickness, and the thickness and malleability of the substrate. Concave impact tests are generally more severe from an adhesion standpoint since the compressed coating film tends to be pushed away from the substrate.

Mandrel Tests

The mandrel test (Fig. 3D) is similar to an impact test except that the deformation is applied linearly and at a slower rate. The conical mandrel test provides a means of evaluating simultaneously the bends from a ⅛ in. to 1 in. radius. The radius at which the coating flakes from the panel is inversely proportional to adhesion. In measuring adhesion, this test involves the same extraneous factors as the impact tests.

Tensile Tests

From a theoretical standpoint, a tensile evaluation of adhesion would appear most satisfactory. For coatings, the difficulty arises in finding a suitable "handle" whereby the film can be pulled from the substrate. If adhesion is of a low order, pressure sensitive tape may be used, but with most desirable coating films, adhesion exceeds the tack of the tape. Numerous methods have been devised which make use of an adhesive between the coated substrate and a foil, fabric or metal block. A matter of controversy is the effect of this adhesive on the coating to be evaluated. In addition, it is necessary that the adhesive adhesion of the coating to the test fixture be greater than the adhesion of the coating to the substrate.

Several recent methods of determining the adhesion of coatings have to a large extent circumvented these objections.

The ultrasonic adhesion[9] test makes use of an electrodynamic system for producing ultrasonic vibrations in a metal cylinder (Fig. 3E). A coated metal cap is firmly attached to the free end of the longitudinally vibrating cylinder. The coating separates from the substrate as the force due to acceleration exceeds the force of adhesion. This force can be calculated from the frequency and amplitude of vibration.

The ICI adhesion gun[10] (Fig. 4A) involves applying a plug of coating to a disc-shaped "bullet" which is fired from an air gun at a hole in a metal block in such a way that the disc is stopped abruptly but the spot of coating is free to fly off. By increasing the projectile speed it is said that decelerating forces on the coating of more than $27 \times 10^6 G$ can be applied. It is most probable that some distortion of the substrate disc takes place, thus introducing other factors than true adhesion.

The ultracentrifuge[11] has been used for evaluating adhesion. A spot of coating (Fig. 4B) is applied to the periphery of the suitably balanced rotor and observed by a photocell while spinning in a vacuum. A centrifugal force of up to $50 \times 10^6 G$ can be applied, thus causing the coating to fly from the substrate. Means must be provided to cool the rotor to avoid heat effects on the coating material and adhesive interface.

From a theoretical standpoint, it appears that the most satisfactory method for determining pure adhesion is the Dannenberg[12a, 12b] Blister Method (Fig. 4C). Here a coating is applied over a masked hole in the substrate and mercury (or other suitable liquid) is pumped through the hole, thus forc-

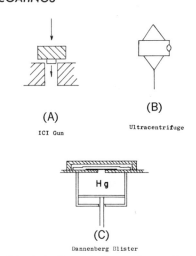

(A)
ICI Gun

(B)
Ultracentrifuge

(C)
Dannenberg Blister

Fig. 4. Schematic diagrams of more elegant adhesion test methods.

ing the coating away from the substrate and into a confining cavity which prevents film rupture. By measuring the integrated work, rather than the force of adhesion, as had been attempted previously,[13, 14] consistent values can be obtained. Film parameters other than adhesion are eliminated by subtracting the work of expansion of a free coating film measured in identical fashion.

ENVIRONMENTAL EFFECTS ON ADHESION

Once a coating has been applied so that it has good adhesion to its substrate, there are many factors which may reduce or destroy this adhesion. Besides mechanical deformation of the substrate and/or coating, various environmental conditions affect adhesion.

Contact with humidity, moisture or actual immersion in water are the most common detrimental environmental conditions. In the simplest case, moisture can permeate through a coating film and effectively, either partially or totally, desorb the coating from a metal substrate thus reducing adhesion. This is demonstrated in films such as many vinyl chloride copolymers on tinplate. Frequently the adhesion is recoverable to a large extent when the coating and substrate are dried.

In the case of a porous substrate such as wood, absorbed moisture from beneath can actually push a coating away from the substrate. This effect is enhanced by varying thermal gradients from the uncoated to the coated side of the wood. Similar effects have been noted by completely covering the outside of a polyethylene container with a relatively impermeable coating and subsequently filling the container with a volatile aliphatic hydrocarbon.

Loss of adhesion in coatings on nonporous substrates can result from relatively slight surface contamination such as fingerprints. Osmotic pressures of up to 30 atm[15] are responsible for detaching the coating from the substrate in the form of blisters. Surface contamination can in a sense be induced by corrosive mechanisms in metal surfaces. It is well established that atmospheric corrosion in metals is propagated by an electrochemical process which requires some coating discontinuity to initiate the phenomenon. The exposed metal becomes the anode at which corrosion takes place. Cathodic areas show up as blisters caused by migration of cations and moisture through the coating at these points. Electroendosmosis of water through, and hydrogen formation under, the film cause adhesion loss. The well-known Salt Spray Test accelerates this action. The bisphenol-epichlorohydrin epoxy resins, which make excellent metal adhesives, yield coatings (in combination with urea-formaldehyde or phenolic resins) with outstanding resistance to blistering in the Salt Spray Test.

Permeability to oxygen can cause adhesion failures in coatings, especially when subjected to high temperatures. Most unmodified silicone resins, having excellent thermal stability in other respects, are very permeable to oxygen. At temperatures above 500°F, oxygen reacts with the steel substrate so that on subsequent cooling, the steel-iron oxide bond fails and the silicone coating plus the oxide spalls off the substrate.

As previously discussed, an environment of changing temperature can also cause coating adhesion failures due to differences in thermal expansion.

References

1. Morgan, L. B., *J. Appl. Chem.,* **4,** 160–72 (1954).
2. Mandelkern, L., *Chem. Rev.,* **56,** 903–58 (1956).
3. DeBruyne, N. A., *Nature,* **180,** 262–6 (1957).
4. Burns, R. M., and Schuh, A. E., "Protective Coatings for Metals," pp. 313–15, New York, Reinhold Publishing Corp., 1959.
5. Kirk, R. E., and Othmer, D. F., "Encyclopedia of Chemical Technology," Vol. 9, p. 7, New York, The Interscience Encyclopedia, Inc., 1952.
6. Maier, C. E., Flugge, S. L., and Pfeffer, E. C. (to Continental Can Co., Inc.), U. S. Patent 2,380,456 (July 31, 1945).
7. Pfeffer, E. C., and DeBeers, F. W. (to Continental Can Co., Inc.), U. S. Patent 2,433,062 (Dec. 23, 1947).
8. Gardner, H. A., and Sward, G. G., "Physical and Chemical Examination of Paints, Varnishes, Lacquers and Colors," 11th Ed., Bethesda, Maryland, Henry A. Gardner Laboratories, Inc., 1950.
9. Moses, S., and Witt, R. K., *Ind. Eng. Chem.,* **41,** 2334 (1949).
10. May, W. D., Smith, N. D. P., and Snow, C. I., *Nature,* **179,** 494 (1957).
11. Beams, J. W., *Tech. Proc. Am. Electroplaters' Soc.,* **43,** 211 (1956).
12a. Dannenberg, H., *J. Polymer Sci.,* **33,** 509 (1958).
12b. Dannenberg, H., "Measurement of Adhesion by the Blister Method," Division of Paint, Plastics, and Printing Ink Chemistry, Am. Chem. Soc., Cleveland, Ohio, Apr. 1960.
13. Rossmann, E., Weise, K., and Schubbe, A., *Farben-Ztg.,* **43,** 1247 (1938).
14. Hoffmann, E., and Georgoussis, O., *J. Oil & Color Chemists' Assoc.,* **42,** 267 (1959).
15. Von Fischer, W., and Bobalek, E. G., "Organic Protective Coatings," p. 317, New York, Reinhold Publishing Corp., 1953.
16. Asbeck, W. K., Peterson, R. H., and Jenkinson, R. D., "Forces in Coatings Removal by the Cutting Mechanism," Division of Paint, Plastics, and Printing Ink Chemistry, Am. Chem. Soc., Cleveland, Ohio, Apr. 1960.

— 54 —

Adhesives in the Building Industry

George J. Schulte

Adhesives, Coatings & Sealers Div.
Minnesota Mining & Mfg. Company
St. Paul, Minnesota

This chapter covers the majority of adhesives that are used by the building trades industry. New technology is constantly taking place which will add adhesives and applications to this list. In many instances, these changes are slow; consequently most of the building adhesives mentioned will be in use for some years.

WALL COVERINGS

Ceramic Tile Adhesives

Four main types of adhesives are used for the so-called "thin-bed-setting" of ceramic tile.

(a) Rubber-base mastics with volatile solvent vehicle.
(b) Rubber-base mastics with water vehicle.
(c) Oil- and resin-base mastics.
(d) Portland cement with resin binder.

The rubber-base solvent-type mastics were the first to be used, and they have been steadily improved from the standpoint of ease of application, strength and water resistance.

The rubber-base type with water vehicle is a newer product which is also being rapidly improved. It has won some favor because of its advantages of reduced odor, simple application, and easy clean-up with water. Its principal deficiency is in reduced water resistance as compared to the solvent types. Some of the water-vehicle ceramic tile adhesives should not be used in high-moisture areas such as in shower stalls.

The oil-resin type is employed because of easy application and a long bonding time. Adhesives of this type generally have less strength than the rubber-base types; furthermore since they are relatively new, not much is known about their aging durability.

One new development is the use of a binder such as a polyvinyl acetate resin which is mixed with Portland cement and sand. This is similar to the conventional mortar method of setting tile except that this mix may be applied with a notched trowel over a variety of surfaces. The binder is mixed on the job or premixed in the cement. The applicator merely adds sufficient water to bring the mix to the proper consistency.

Application. All the above mentioned adhesives are thick or mastic in consistency, permitting two general methods of application:

(1) Floating Method. Adhesive is applied directly to wall with a notched trowel or spreader.
(2) Buttering Method. Small part of adhesive is applied to the back side of the tile.

Ceramic tile may be installed with adhesive to almost any sound, strong, dry and clean wall surface including brown coat plaster, finish coat plaster, gypsum wallboard, cement asbestos board, concrete, waterproof plywood and painted surfaces. When it is applied over a painted surface, the paint

609

Fig. 1. Applying ceramic tile adhesive to wall of bathroom by the floating method. Adhesive is applied directly to wall with notched trowel.

primer as recommended by the adhesive manufacturer. It is important to caulk or seal all open edges with the adhesive or a caulking compound. This includes all seams and corners of wallboard, plaster, plywood, etc., and is accomplished by packing the adhesive or caulking into the openings with a putty knife or caulking gun.

The adhesive is then applied either by the notched trowel or buttering method. Generally, the trowel should contain ridges about ³⁄₁₆-in. deep and about the same distance apart. This provides a sufficient volume of fresh soft mastic so that a long bonding time is attained. The wall should be completely covered with adhesive.

Tile is then set into the mastic with a slight twisting motion to break any skin coating on the adhesive. With most mastics, tile may be presoaked in water if desired. This provides moisture for proper curing of the grout cement if grouting of the joints is to be done the same day. After waiting at least 4 hr for the adhesive to dry, the tile may be sponged down to provide more moisture and grouted in the usual manner.

must be securely bonded to the sub-surface. Paint should be scraped to test for adhesion.

In moisture areas the base surface must be completely waterproofed. This is accomplished by applying a skim coat of the adhesive with the flat side of a trowel or by brushing on a waterproofing

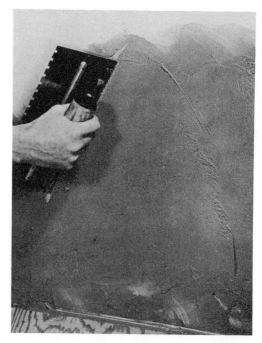

Fig. 3. When buttering method is used for installing ceramic wall tile, the wall surface is first waterproofed with a skim coat or brush coat primer.

Fig. 2. Applying ceramic tile adhesive to back side of tile. Tile is then pressed in place on wall. This is called the buttering method.

If the buttering method is preferred, the wall is skim coated or primed for waterproofing as before and a small pat of adhesive is placed on the back side of each tile. The tile is then immediately pressed into place with a twisting motion.

Specifications. The U.S. Department of Commerce has issued Commercial Standard No. 181-52 covering the performance of organic adhesives for installing ceramic tile. Products meeting this specification must provide strength of at least 40 psi under high moisture conditions.

Plastic Tile Adhesives

Since World War II, a considerable market has been developed for polystyrene plastic wall tile. Several other types of plastic tile such as melamine have been marketed but have not attained popularity. Adhesives may be:

(a) Oil- resin
(b) Resin
(c) Rubber base with water vehicle.

There have been many varieties of oil-resin type mastics used for plastic tile. Many have been satisfactory, but a few have failed to perform well. A satisfactory plastic tile adhesive must have excellent adhesion to the tile and remain permanently soft or plastic. The U.S. Department of Commerce Commercial Standard for both plastic and metal tile adhesives is No. 168-50.

Application. The application of plastic tile adhesive is similar to that of ceramic tile adhesive. Generally, the floating method is used with a notched trowel having ⅛-in. "V" notches, ⅛-in. apart. Many adhesive manufacturers recommend that the wall be primed with a special primer. The tile is left ungrouted, or it may be grouted with the tile adhesive itself. Care must be taken to avoid cleaning the adhesive from the tile with a solvent that will attack the tile. Alcohol or a special tile cleaner is usually satisfactory.

The resin-type mastics such as the vinyl acetates are applied similarly, and they may have a shorter bonding time. These types can usually be washed off with water. Some of these adhesives are unsuitable for application in moisture areas because of their water solubility. The rubber-base type mastics have similar application properties.

Metal Tile Adhesives

Metal wall tile may be enameled aluminum tile, enameled steel tile, porcelain enameled steel tile, stainless steel tile and copper tile. The same types of adhesives are utilized for installing metal tile as are used for installing plastic tile, except that not all plastic tile adhesives are recommended for metal tile. The same floating or buttering techniques of application are also used.

Hardboard Adhesives

Hardboard or resin-impregnated fiberboard is adhesive bonded to existing walls to form a decorative wall covering. This material has either a prefinished or unfinished surface, of which the former surface has an enamel coating applied to one side of the board. It is important with the prefinished hardboard to use an adhesive which will not stain through or discolor the paint. Adhesives in most common use are:

(a) Rubber-base mastics with solvent vehicle.
(b) Resin-base mastics.
(c) Oil-resin base mastics.

The rubber-base mastics with volatile solvent vehicles are the most satisfactory from the standpoint of easy application, high strength, and good water resistance.

The resin-base types are easy to apply, but have less ultimate strength and reduced water and heat resistance. Since the resin types have high initial strength, they are occasionally used where this property is desired but where final strength is not an important factor.

Oil-resin base mastics similar to the plastic tile adhesives have also been used successfully for hardboard.

Application. All of these types of adhesives may be applied by the "floating" method with a notched trowel, having notches approximately ¼-in. deep and ¼-in. apart. A primer is recommended in high moisture areas to seal the wall. The adhesive is applied to the back of the board with a notched trowel, and the hardboard is immediately pressed against the wall. The board is firmly pressed over its entire area to effect a bond. The wall surface must be clean, dry and free of contaminating material. In some instances, failure has occurred where mastics were used over old linoleum cement or bituminous adhesive which previously secured a wall covering material.

While the use of hardboard is recommended in moisture areas, it is important that all seams be carefully sealed to eliminate moisture penetration and possible swelling of the board. It is also important to fit the board loosely in mouldings so that moisture will not cause buckling of the board.

The second method of application is the buttering method. The adhesive is placed in spots (or "gobs") about 2-in. in diameter and 1-in. deep, spaced approximately 1 ft apart across the back side of the board. The board is then pressed to the wall with a sliding action to smooth the adhesive. This method is often used on an uneven wall to provide a smooth surface, but it does not provide as solid a surface as the troweling method.

Plywood or Wood Paneling Adhesives

Adhesives may be used in several ways to install plywood or wood paneling to wall surfaces. A mastic may be used in similar fashion to those used in applying hardboard. A contact bond-type adhesive may be preferred to fasten the plywood to wooden furring strips or to the wall itself. Types include:

(a) Rubber-base mastics with solvent vehicle.
(b) Synthetic rubber with solvent or water vehicle known as contact bond adhesive.

The rubber-base mastic should have high initial strength and good ultimate strength. The adhesive should dry to a flexible film to absorb any dimensional changes in the plywood. The bonding of plywood on exterior surfaces is generally not recommended because moisture can penetrate plywood to cause swelling, which may fail the adhesive bond. Adhesives may be used on the exterior if supplementary nails or screws are employed.

Contact bond adhesives should have high ultimate strength with good resistance to creep or flow.

Application. Rubber-base mastics are applied with a notched spreader of approximately the same size as that used with hardboard. The application is similar to that for hardboard except that batten strips or wood moldings may be nailed over the joints instead of metal moldings. Care must be taken not to restrict the edges of the plywood since some expansion can occur resulting from a change in moisture content.

Contact bond adhesives are used in two ways, the first of which is with furring strips. The usual precautions of having clean, dry, dust-free surfaces are important; moreover the furring strips must be plumb and in line. Any shimming must be done behind the furring strip. The contact bond adhesive is then applied by brush, spreader or roller to the surface of the furring strips and to the back side of the plywood. The adhesive should be allowed to dry for the specified time, and the board is aligned and pressed into place. A few nails are often used at the corners and at the center of the plywood. These may be finishing nails covered with wood filler or wood plugs. It is difficult to

manipulate the board once it is pressed into position using this method.

The contact bond method may also be used in installing plywood over a solid flat surface such as plaster, cement-asbestos board or gypsum wallboard. The adhesive is applied to both surfaces and allowed to dry the specified period; then the board is carefully aligned and pressed into place. Usually no nails are necessary with this method if sufficient bond contact area (at least ½ of the area) is obtained.

Gypsum Wallboard Adhesives

There are two principal applications of adhesives for gypsum wallboard (drywall) installation. One is the laminating of two layers of wallboard, which is frequently done to eliminate nail heads in the finished surface. The second use of adhesive is for bonding gypsum wallboard directly to studs or joists to reduce the number of nailing operations. This also reduces the number of nailheads to fill and finish. Some nails are used to apply pressure between the wallboard and stud so that the adhesive will spread out to give complete contact between the stud and the back of the wallboard. Because the adhesive helps hold the drywall in place, fewer nails are required in the final installation. In many instances, the use of drywall adhesive reduces the required number of nails by as much as 50 per cent. Types include:

(a) Casein or dextrin adhesives which come either in powder form or in premixed, semi-mastic form.
(b) Rubber-base mastics—solvent or water type.
(c) Contact cements.

The caseins and dextrins are primarily used for double-laminating drywall although rubber-base mastics and contact cements may be used for the same purpose. Rubber-base mastics are used for bonding wallboard (drywall) directly to studs to strengthen the wall and reduce nail usage and nail popping.

Application. The casein or dextrin adhesives of the powder type require mixing with water to form an adhesive with a paste consistency. This is applied with a fine notched trowel or by brush to the already installed drywall base surface; then the second sheet of drywall is placed on the adhesive-coated base surface. Slight sliding action provides best contact. The premixed adhesives are applied in a similar fashion, after which the joints are taped as in the usual manner. Rubber-base mastics, which are premixed, may be used in the same fashion for laminating drywall or for application directly to studs. This adhesive has high adhesion, strength and water resistance and is often utilized where moisture could occur.

Contact cement is applied by brush or roll coater to both surfaces, dried, and bonded with roller pressure.

When used on studs for minimizing nail popping, rubber-base mastics are applied with caulking guns in approximately ⅜-in. diameter continuous beads to the centers of the studs or joists. On joists where two adjacent pieces of drywall join, the bead is applied in a zigzag fashion to give best contact. Drywall is pressed into place as soon as possible after complete application of the adhesive over the area that the board is to cover. The drywall is applied with a slight sliding action to break any skin that may develop on the adhesive. Some supplementary nails are required to anchor the board to the wall until the adhesive sets. There is varying opinion as to how many nails are required; however the trend is toward the use of fewer nails, e.g., one nail in each corner and two nails in the "field." Some building codes today require a minimum of ½ the number of nails that were formerly used without adhesive. The usual methods of taping joints and finishing the board are then used.

Metal and Plastic Wall Clips and Furring Strip Adhesives

There are a variety of special metal and plastic clips for attaching such materials as furring strips, insulation or various types of wallboard including plywood. These clips are attached with mastic or heavy liquid adhesives to walls, ceilings, air-conditioning ducts, and other surfaces. They may be made of galvanized steel, aluminum, or plastic. They are used mostly where it is difficult or impractical to attach either the clip or the wall-surfacing material by mechanical means such as nailing, etc. They are especially useful on masonry and metal heating ducts. Adhesives are:

(a) Rubber-base mastics with solvent vehicle.
(b) Liquid contact cement types.

The rubber-base mastics, which are the most commonly used types, are of the very high initial strength variety. They are applied in small dabs or preferably smeared over the back side of the clip in a film ⅛-in. thick. The clip, which contains a series of perforations or holes in the bonding surface, is then pressed in place with a sliding motion

so that the mastic squeezes through the holes to provide a high strength bond. The mastic is allowed to set for 2 to 18 hr depending on the drying rate. The furring strips, which are pre-drilled, are then placed over the protruding screw or nail of the clip and fastened into position. The same general method of installation applies where insulation or other wall and ceiling surfacing material is being attached. On heating ducts an adhesive with sufficient flexibility and strength at elevated temperatures should be employed.

The contact cement types are occasionally used on very smooth surfaces such as metal or wood or where very high initial strength is desired. A coat of the adhesive is applied liberally to the back of the clip and another to the wall or ceiling surface. When the adhesive has dried as specified, the two surfaces are joined with as much hand pressure as possible.

Plastic Wall Covering Adhesives

In addition to tile, several other types of plastic wall coverings are in use today, in roll or sheet form. Flexible vinyl plastic coverings may be "supported," with a paper or fabric backing, or unsupported, in which case the vinyl itself is the bonding surface on the back side. Rigid or decorative plastic laminate is being used in tile as well as sheet form for walls. Adhesives are:

(a) Resin-base mastics.
(b) Rubber-base mastics.
(c) Linoleum pastes.
(d) Contact adhesives.

Resin-base mastics for vinyl wall coverings may be the oil-resin type similar to that used for bonding plastic tile or the polyvinyl-acetate type occasionally preferred because it may be washed off.

The rubber-base mastics are slightly more difficult to use because of their quick drying characteristics and since solvents are required to remove excess adhesive from tools and surfaces. However they have quick strength and are often preferred. The natural or synthetic rubber latex type has desirable light color. The reclaim rubber type, gray or black, is often used because of good strength and low cost. High-strength rubber-base adhesives may also be used.

For cloth or paper-backed vinyl, linoleum paste is sometimes used. This is a by-product of paper manufacturing, inexpensive and easy to clean up with water. It is satisfactory on interior wall surfaces where moisture will not be a problem, but it is not recommended on unsupported vinyl because of poor adhesion. Linoleum paste may also cause discoloration of the vinyl. There is also a possibility that the vinyl will plasticize or soften some adhesives. The synthetic-rubber types resist this action best.

Plastic laminates, either in tile or sheet form, may be bonded with a contact bond adhesive as described in previous sections.

Application. For vinyl wall coverings, the mastics are usually applied to the wall surface with a very fine notched trowel having notches approximately ⅓₂-in. deep. The sub-surfaces must be clean, dry and very smooth. The adhesive is troweled on the wall. The wall covering is usually bonded soon after application of the adhesive to prevent "ridging" or "showing through" of the mastic.

For plastic laminates, contact bond adhesives are applied by brush or roller to both surfaces. The decorative plastic laminate panel is carefully aligned and pressed into position. Rubber-base mastics are used on plastic laminates by application with a notched trowel to the back of the panel or to the wall surface. In some cases, it is necessary to shore or brace the panels until the mastic has set.

Cementitious Materials Adhesives

Adhesives have been developed for bonding cementitious materials such as concrete and plaster to themselves as well as to many sound sub-surfaces. This technique now enables the building industry to repair existing surfaces more easily and to build new buildings with greater versatility of design. Types include:

(a) Epoxy resin mastics.
(b) Synthetic rubber-water emulsions.
(c) Vinyl-water dispersions.

The epoxy resin adhesives are two-part materials requiring mixing of an amine or polyamide curing agent to cure or "set" the product. They are used primarily for applying new concrete to old concrete.

The synthetic rubber emulsions are used as admixes in cement to bond new concrete to old concrete.

The vinyl-water dispersions are employed principally for bonding new plaster to a concrete base or to other wall or ceiling surfaces.

Application:

(a) The epoxy resin mastics are mixed and applied immediately to the wall by brushing or troweling. It is important that the existing concrete be clean, dry and sound. While the epoxy is still "wet" (uncured), the new concrete is poured into place.

(b) The synthetic rubber emulsions are mixed into the concrete as recommended. A second method is to make a thin cement paste containing the rubber emulsion which is brushed or troweled on the old surface before applying the new concrete.

(c) The vinyl-water dispersions are sprayed over the new concrete. When dry, the wall is plastered.

FLOOR COVERINGS

Resilient Floor Tile Adhesives

More common resilient floor tile includes rubber tile, solid vinyl tile and cork tile. Other types are also used: cork tile with a vinyl top sheet, thin vinyl tile with an asphalt paper backing, and various kinds of linoleum tile. The same types of adhesives may usually be used with each of these tiles:

(a) Rubber-base mastics with water vehicle.
(b) Resin-base mastics with alcohol solvent.
(c) Linoleum paste.
(d) Epoxy resin mastics.

Several types of rubber-base mastics are in use, one of which is a low-cost black reclaim rubber type which has high water resistance and flexibility. A new light-colored synthetic rubber type mastic with a water vehicle has excellent water and alkali resistance and is becoming popular for on-grade and below-grade concrete applications.

The resin-alcohol mastics are popular for rubber tile and vinyl tile; moreover they may also be used for cork tile and linoleum tile. These adhesives are reasonably water resistant and usually light in color. Linoleum paste is used where water resistance is not a problem. It is not usually recommended for vinyl tile however because of poor adhesion to some vinyl products. Epoxy resin adhesives are used over on-grade concrete and below-grade concrete floors where moisture is likely to occur.

Application. Most of these various types are spread with a notched trowel having notches approximately ⅟₁₆-in. deep. Some adhesives may be brushed or rolled on the floor surface; subsequently the floor tiles are laid into the wet mastic before it becomes too dry to effect a bond. It is important, particularly with vinyl tile, to lay the tile before the ridges of adhesive have set up so that all of

Fig. 4. Applying ceramic tile adhesive to floor by the floating method. The tile is then laid in the adhesive before the adhesive dries.

the ridges will be pressed out smoothly, thus eliminating any "telegraphing" or set-up ridges showing through the tile. This is not so much of a problem with rubber, cork and linoleum tile. A floor roller, used to roll the tile securely to the floor, assists in flattening the ridges.

It is important to use only recommended adhesives over on-grade or below-grade level concrete slabs since moisture in the concrete can cause some adhesives to dissolve and/or lose strength. *Caution:* Apply these adhesives only over a *dry* concrete floor.

Linoleum and Sheet Goods Adhesives

Ordinarily the same adhesives used for resilient tile are satisfactory for linoleum and various types of vinyl sheet goods. Because sheet linoleum has so very few seams, linoleum paste is used despite its poor water resistance. In bathrooms and in other areas of extreme moisture concentrations, it is desirable to use one of the rubber-base or resin-base adhesives mentioned under the resilient floor tile section. The same methods of application apply as used for resilient floor tile.

Asphalt and Vinyl Asbestos Tile Adhesives

These two types of tile are classified together because of their semi-rigid nature. The same types of adhesives may be used for both:

(a) Asphalt emulsion.
(b) Asphalt cut back.
(c) Rubber base mastics with water vehicle.

The asphalt or bituminous emulsion is most popular because it is inexpensive and generally satisfactory. The asphalt cut-back type, which contains very slow drying solvents, is losing favor because of difficulty in application and cleanup. The reclaim and synthetic rubber-water types may be used in areas of high moisture content.

Application. The asphalt emulsion is spread with a fine notched trowel on the clean, dry and warm (room temperature, if possible) floor surface. In areas of extreme dust, a brushable primer is often used to provide better adhesion to the concrete. The adhesive is allowed to dry completely until all the moisture has escaped. This may require from 2 to 24 hr depending on the temperature and humidity; then the tile is laid without rolling. The edges may not lay flat for a few days or even weeks if the temperature is low. However, they will gradually conform to the floor. This is particularly true of asphalt tile. Asphalt cut-backs are applied in the same manner.

The rubber-water types are applied in the same manner as for resilient floor tile. It is important to lay the tile in those mastics before the adhesive is dry.

Woodblock Flooring Adhesives

There are three main types of woodblock flooring installed with adhesives. One is the block made up of strips of regular strip flooring. These are held together with a steel spline or other device usually in 9-in. by 9-in. tile form. Another very popular type is the laminated plywood tile block. Both types have tongue-and-groove edges so that they lock together. The third type, which is the single-ply or solid-sheet tile, is occasionally composed of little squares of hardwood that are glued or fastened together. In other blocks, it is a rather flexible, veneer-type tile. The adhesives used for these three types of blocks vary considerably. Types include:

(a) Rubber mastic-solvent vehicle.
(b) Rubber mastic-water dispersion.
(c) Asphalt cut-back.
(d) Asphalt emulsion.
(e) Hot asphalt or coal tar.

The rubber base-solvent type adhesive is used with plywood block and also to some extent with the solid veneer and the strip flooring type. The rubber-base water emulsion is employed with the plywood-type block. The asphalt cut-back is used primarily with the strip floor block. The asphalt emulsion is utilized with the plywood block. Where extreme moisture may occur, it is usually best to use a rubber-base product with a solvent vehicle. If there is water in a concrete floor, no adhesive should be used since expansion of wood due to moisture may break the bond.

Application. All of these adhesives may be applied with a notched trowel having notches approximately ¼-in. deep. The asphalts are frequently troweled or spread to form a flat bed of mastic. The thinner veneer tile will not require such deep notches. The rubber-base mastics require that the tile be bonded within a certain time after spreading. The asphalt cut-back and emulsion types usually require a longer waiting time with virtually no restriction upon the maximum length of time before bonding. Hot asphalt or hot coal tar is often delivered hot to the job; otherwise drum or pail heaters must be used to soften it for application.

The blocks are laid into the adhesives at the recommended time. Blocks should be rolled with at least a 100 lb roller soon after installation.

Ceramic Floor Tile Adhesives

Adhesives may be used for laying various types of ceramic floor tile, either the small unglazed or glazed ceramic mosaics or the larger quarry-type tile.

(a) Rubber-base mastics with solvent vehicle.
(b) Rubber base mastics with water vehicle.
(c) Portland cement with resin binder.

The rubber-base solvent-type mastics have gained in popularity for setting floor tile because they permit tile to be placed, in many cases, where mortar cannot be used. They are particularly good for installing floor tile over smooth concrete floors and in buildings that are being remodeled, and over plywood or underlayment board in new residential construction.

The rubber-base mastics with water vehicle generally do not have as high a water resistance; therefore they should not be used in areas of extreme moisture.

Portland cement with resin binder is a new product for installing floor tile. It has superior leveling properties and smooths out irregularities in the floor surfaces. It can be used over a number of floor surfaces such as concrete, but is not as versatile in this respect as the rubber-base mastics.

Application. The rubber-base mastics are spread with a notched trowel having notches approximately ¹⁄₁₆-in. deep over clean, dry and smooth floor surfaces. In moisture areas, a skim coat of adhesive or brush coat of sealer is recommended on plywood and other water-sensitive surfaces. After this dries, the adhesive is troweled over this primer film. The tile, whether it be ceramic mosaic or quarry tile, must be laid before the adhesive dries. Frequently the ceramic mosaics must be manipulated to straighten the small tiles; then the tile is pounded with a wooden beating block. After installation, the tile should be covered with boards to prevent the small tiles from sliding out of position. After the adhesive has set, which usually requires at least 4 hr, the tile may be grouted in the conventional method except that it should be covered with building paper or plastic film to hold the moisture and ensure a proper cure of the grout.

The Portland cement-resin binder type is sometimes troweled on using a deeper notched trowel, or it may be used in a ½ to 1 in. thick bed similar to laying tile in mortar.

Miscellaneous Floor Tile Adhesives

Cove-Base Adhesive. This is a thick mastic which is used for cementing vinyl, rubber or asphalt cove base to wall surfaces. It is usually composed of resins with a solvent vehicle. This product is applied to the back side of the cove base with a notched trowel having notches approximately ³⁄₃₂-in. deep. It can be applied over most wall surfaces with little or no preparation if they are clean and dry. Where it is applied around columns or curved surfaces, it may be necessary to brace the cove base in position until the adhesive has set.

Carpet Tack Strip Adhesive. This is a synthetic rubber thick liquid adhesive that is brushed or spread on the wooden carpet tack strip and the concrete or wood floor. When adhesive surfaces are tacky, but not completely dry, the strip is placed firmly to the floor to effect a bond. It is recommended to wait at least 1 hr before stretching the carpet over the tacks.

SINK AND COUNTER TOPS

Decorative Plastic Laminate Adhesives

There are several types of decorative plastic laminates in use. One contains a phenolic impregnated paper with a melamine plastic top sheet;

whereas another type is a solid polyester plastic. The decorative laminates are available either in sheet or tile form. The same adhesives, which are described for laminates, may be used for plastic wall coverings:

(1) Contact bond adhesives.
(2) Rubber-base mastics.

The average contact bond adhesive may be applied by spreading with a notched trowel or spreader, by rolling with a paint roller, by brushing or by spraying. The adhesive is applied to both the laminate and the other surface to be bonded in a smooth even film. Drying time of the adhesive varies with the product but is usually 15 to 30 min. Most adhesives become glossy when dry. If they do not dry glossy, more adhesive should be applied. With many of the products, the applicator has approximately 2 hr to complete the installation, during which time the adhesive on the mating surfaces will bond to itself.

Application. The plastic laminate is precut and fitted before spreading the cement. After spreading and drying, the laminate is positioned carefully and pressed into place. The paper slip sheet method, in which heavy Kraft paper is used between the plastic laminate and the base surface, makes proper alignment of the laminate easy. The paper is placed on the dry adhesive on the base surface, and the laminate is carefully positioned on top of the paper to get one corner and one side properly in place. Then the paper is pulled out and the laminate carefully pressed into position, working from one side to the other to prevent entrapment of air. The laminate is rolled firmly over the entire area with a wood or metal hand roller. A rubber mallet or a hammer and a small block of wood may be used to apply pressure if

Fig. 5. Precut plastic laminate is bonded to sink or counter top base surface. Pressure is applied with a roller.

desired. For cleanup of excess, many contact bond adhesives may be rolled off the surface by hand; others require a solvent.

When a brush is used, care must be taken not to brush over the cement after it has dried as this may cause uneveness in the film.

Some adhesives, particularly the water-vehicle types, may be sprayed. Paint spray equipment is generally satisfactory.

The rubber-base mastics are spread with a notched trowel on the base surface. After the laminate is carefully aligned, it is pressed into place with a twisting motion. With most mastics, it is possible to manipulate the panel. The laminate is then rolled with a hand roller. It may be necessary to apply additional pressure to shore or brace the panels until the mastic has set.

Resilient Covering Adhesives

Resilient coverings include vinyl, rubber, and linoleum sheet goods. It is important to use a waterproof-type adhesive on counter tops. Some of the waterproof types of adhesives that may be used are:

(a) Rubber-base mastics with water vehicle.
(b) Resin-base mastics with alcohol solvent.

These products are discussed under resilient floor tile adhesives.

Application. For counter tops, these adhesives are applied in much the same way as they are applied as resilient floor tile adhesives, but with a small hand roller. On vinyl, particularly, it is important that the adhesive be used only over a clean dry surface. When vinyl is installed over a surface that previously had a counter-top covering, all of the old adhesives must be removed by scraping and sanding to obtain satisfactory adhesion.

Ceramic Tile Adhesives

Ceramic tile may be laid on counter tops with adhesive providing that the base surface is suitably waterproof and that a waterproof adhesive is used. Because of the many joints, it is most important to have the tile joint cement, i.e., grout tight and free of cracks or openings. The rubber-base mastics with volatile solvents are preferred on counter tops because of their superior water resistance.

These mastics are applied with a ¹⁄₁₆-in. deep notched trowel similar to the procedure for installing ceramic floor tile. The same general procedure is recommended including a skim or brush coat of adhesive for waterproofing. All edges of the plywood or underlayment base should be sealed against moisture with the adhesive or a primer.

ROOF ADHESIVES

Nonflammable Roof Deck Adhesives

Since a disastrous automotive plant fire a few years ago, the nonflammable roof adhesives have been gaining in popularity. They bond the insulation to the roof deck. If a vapor barrier is used, they adhere the vapor barrier to the roof deck and the insulation to the vapor barrier. When hot, they will not burn, soften or drip through the joints of the deck onto the floor below, thus minimizing the possibility of a fire spreading. Most of these adhesives will only char at high temperatures.

There are two main types of adhesives used.

(a) Rubber-base liquid adhesives with non-flammable solvents and fire snuffing compounds.
(b) Asphalt-base mastics with fire-snuffing ingredient.

Application. The rubber-base liquid adhesives are semi-viscous so that they may be applied either by brushing with a push broom or by spreading beads with an applicator cart. Carts much like large hopper-type garden spreaders are available which will spread adhesive in the proper size beads continuously along the deck. The vapor barrier or insulation is placed directly into these beads of adhesive as soon after spreading as possible. The vapor barrier may be coated by applying adhesive with a special portable roll coating machine or by hand with a brush or a paint roller.

The asphalt adhesive is usually applied with a push broom or mopping technique, and the insulation or vapor barrier is pressed into the adhesive within the time recommended. The asphalt adhesives generally give longer working time than do the rubber-base mastics. The vapor barrier film is rolled with a heavy roller after application to the deck. The insulation, depending on its type, is generally rolled also.

Flammable Roof Deck Adhesives

The conventional types of adhesives that have been used for many years are usually the coal tars. These hot-melts are applied ordinarily by mopping or push brooming across the roof deck. The insulation is dropped into place while they are still tacky.

CEILING MATERIALS

Acoustical Tile Adhesives

There are many types of acoustical tile, including the vegetable fiber and mineral asbestos types. The same adhesives may be used to install most of these various types of tile.

(a) Resin-base mastics.
(b) Rubber-base mastics.
(c) Contact bond adhesives.

Of these, the resin-base mastics are most popular because of low cost and high initial strength.

The rubber-base mastics are used for specialty applications, where some special surface such as plastics or glass is involved. Rubber-base mastics have better adhesion to a greater variety of surfaces, good ultimate strength, and high shock resistance. Similarly the contact bond adhesives are used for special applications where quick strength is desired and where the surfaces are very flat and smooth.

Application. The base surface must be clean, dry and solid. All old adhesives or loose paint must be removed. The resin-base mastics and the rubber-base mastics are usually applied by pressing a portion of adhesive approximately the size of a golf ball about 2-in. in from each corner of the tile. The tile is then immediately pressed into position with a sliding motion to the proper level. The base surface, in some cases, should be primed or sized as recommended. This usually applies to bare plaster which may draw some of the oils from certain resin-base mastics and which also may be very dusty. On dusty tile such as some of the mineral asbestos types, the area on the back of the tile to receive the adhesive is first primed. This is done by drawing the edge of the trowel or putty knife applicator across this area of the tile, spreading a thin film of the adhesive to wet down the dust; then the gob of adhesive is placed over the primed area.

The contact bond adhesive is applied as described in previous sections of this chapter. Of course, tile bonded with this adhesive cannot be manipulated. It is most essential that the ceiling should not be disturbed for at least 48 hr. Some tile failures have resulted from premature installation of lighting, heating and air conditioning equipment after the tile is installed.

INSULATION

Insulation materials such as glass fiber, rock wool, cellular glass or cork are frequently bonded with adhesives to heating or cooling ducts, concrete walls, ceilings, etc. Adhesives include:

(a) Rubber-base liquid with solvent vehicle.
(b) Rubber-base liquid water dispersion.
(c) Rubber-base mastics with solvent vehicle.

The rubber-base liquid adhesives with a solvent vehicle are most popular because they are easily applied by brush or spray gun and provide high strength. There are some rubber types based on synthetic rubber (rather than reclaimed rubber) which have higher heat resistance and are consequently preferred on heating ducts. Although the rubber water dispersions have lower initial strengths, they are used where fire hazard is great. Rubber-base mastics are used on irregular surfaces such as concrete block walls.

Application. The liquid adhesives are brushable and occasionally sprayable. Usually a coat of adhesive is applied to the base surface and to the insulation; then, within a few minutes, the surfaces are joined with a firm hand pressure. The mastics are usually troweled or daubed on the base surface, after which within a short time, the insulation is pressed into the wet adhesive.

SANDWICH PANELS

Most of this chapter has referred to adhesives that are used on the job. Some adhesives, important to the building industry, are used in the factory, e.g., in making sandwich or laminated panels. These panels may fill a space in a curtain wall construction or, in some cases, support a structural load such as in roof panels, usually, they have some insulation value. They are often used for decorative purposes on the exterior or interior of buildings.

There are many adhesives that may be used for making sandwich panels depending on the facings and cores involved. Also there are panels composed of metal or porcelain enamel facings and insulated cores such as cellular glass foam, glass fiber or a paper or metal honeycomb. Some panels have ceramic tile or Portland cement facings with various types of core material. Some of the decorative plastic laminates with plastic facings such as polyester fiber glass have been introduced for interior panel work. These however are but a few

of the possibilities. The following are some of the adhesives that may be used with these combinations:

(a) Synthetic rubber adhesives with volatile solvents (Contact bond adhesive is one type).
(b) Synthetic rubber adhesive with water vehicle.
(c) Rubber-base mastics with solvent vehicle.
(d) Synthetic resin-water vehicle type.
(e) Synthetic resin, one or two part heat curing type bonding films or liquid adhesives.

Application. The synthetic rubber-solvent type is applied usually by spraying both surfaces with a paint type spray gun to give a continuous even film. After waiting the specified time for the solvent to evaporate, the bond is made by bringing the surfaces together with pressure applied with a rubber nip roll arrangement or with a cold press. Care must be taken not to exert more pressure than the facing or core will withstand, i.e., approximately 3 to 5 psi or 0.25 to 0.5 lb/in. These adhesives may also be applied by brushing or by applying with a paint roller to both surfaces. In some cases, large roll coating equipment is used to apply a smooth even film to a complete facing sheet. This technique has also been used on some core materials such as aluminum or paper honeycomb but is most satisfactory on flat sheet metal or board. The synthetic rubber-water vehicle type may be applied in a similar fashion. The roll coating technique is particularly useful. The rubber-base mastics are almost always applied with a notched spreader similar to those used for bonding ceramic tile.

The synthetic resin-water type, e.g., polyvinyl acetate, is limited to interior partitions by its poor water resistance. This adhesive may be applied by rolling with a paint roller, brushing, or spraying. The bond must be assembled quickly since the resin sets quite rapidly. The bond is usually held under pressure for some period of time until all of the water has evaporated and the bond has reached full strength.

Some newer types of adhesives such as the one or two-part synthetic resin (epoxy) types are being used where considerable structural strength is required. These may or may not require heat curing. They are usually applied with a roll coater or a knife coating arrangement. Many may be brushed, but a few can be sprayed. After assembling a panel, pressure is usually required for some time until the bond sets. In some cases, a heat cure is necessary to develop optimum strength.

— 55 —

Adhesives in Heat and Electrical Composites

D. V. Rosato

Telecomputing Corporation
Waltham, Massachusetts

Adhesives perform as major engineering materials in composites for heat insulation, electrical insulation, and friction. In these applications, the adhesives bond varied base materials such as metals, plastics, and rubber.

The universal problem in engineering design is the selection of the materials from which the various parts of the device, machine, or product are to be made. It is also the first problem because the materials selected will govern the allowable stresses, types of construction that might be adopted, the manufacturing methods employed, the assembly operations, the finishes that might be applied, the environmental conditions, and/or the cost and sales appeal of the product. In many of these designs, the commercial success or failure will depend on the adhesive and base materials selected.

The physical and other properties required usually determine which materials might be used. But the relative importance of the different properties will vary considerably for different types of design. The unit function or strength of the end item is in most cases directly related to the adhesive characteristic.

In addition to physical properties, corrosion resistance, heat conductivity, electrical conductivity, dielectric strength, friction properties, many others will enter into the problem. An example of the physical, electrical, and thermal properties of various plastics applicable in these composites are shown in Tables 1, 2, and 3. There is no formula or equation by which the material having the most suitable properties can be selected, nor is it always advisable to use the bonded material that has the highest values for the properties desired. Invariably, the final selection must be a compromise largely because two other important factors enter into the problem: the workability of the composites and its cost.

When a number of different materials have been selected, each possessing the desired properties to a satisfactory degree, the next step toward the final selection is the determination of the manufacturing methods that might be employed. Then the design must be analyzed for possible use of inserts, consolidation of different parts into one piece, use of standard purchased parts, etc. One must also consider the costs of machining, grinding, and other operations, which will vary greatly. Included in this category may be punching, hand reaming, rivoting, buffing, and polishing.

In the past two decades, development of new adhesives with improved properties has proceeded at an expanding rate. Impetus to the development of new products has been supplied by the acceptance of adhesives as reliable means of attachment and the need for adhesives with better properties.

Foamed or honeycomb insulators are most efficiently attached to surfaces by adhesives. Modern thinking concerning friction materials considers only adhesives as methods of fastening. The type of adhesives used include organic, inorganic, and ceramic matrixes.

INSULATION

Insulation is performed by a material used for cutting off or checking a spread of some form of

TABLE 1. COMPARISON OF PHYSICAL PROPERTIES OF PLASTIC MATERIALS.

Material	Description	Tensile Strength (psi × 10³)	Specific Tensile Strength (psi × 10³)	Flexural Strength (psi × 10³)	Compressive Strength (psi × 10³)
Phenol formaldehyde	Cast resin	5–10	6.6	4–10	8–20
Molded	Wood flour filler	6–11	6.0	8–16	16–35
Molded	Fabric filler	6–9	5.5	10–15	21–32
Molded	Mineral filler	5–6	3.7	8–18	18–36
Molded	Pulp preforms	1.7	12.6	25	22
Laminated	Paper-base X	12.5	8.7	21	20
Laminated	Paper-base XX	8.0	5.5	16	18
Laminated	Special	30.0	22.0	25	15 (edge)
Laminated	Canvas-base C	10.0	7.0	20	38
Laminated	Fine-weave fabric-L	10.0	7.0	20	35
Laminated	Asbestos base	.0	5.6	17	30
Laminated	Birch (compreg)	30.0 (with grain)	25.0	22.8	23
Laminated	Birch (compreg)	6.0 (vs. grain)	5.0 (vs. grain)	13	12
Urea formaldehyde	Alpha-cellulose filled	8–13	7.1	13.5–15	25–35
Melamine formaldehyde	Mineral-filled	5.5–7	3.5	7.5–16.5	27–37
Polystyrene	Molded	5.0–7.5	5.9	6.5–10.5	10–13.5
Polymethyl methacrylate	Sheet	6–8	5.8	12–16	11–15
Polyvinyl chloride-acetate	Molded, unfilled	8–10	6.7	10–13	11–12
Polyvinylidene chloride	Molded	4–7	3.2	15–17	—
Cellulose acetate	Sheet form	4–11	6.5	5–16	4–16
Cellulose acetate	Molded	3–10	4.5	5–10	12–17
Cellulose acetate-butyrate	Molded	2.5–7.5	4.23	2.8–13	7.5–17
Polyethylene	Sheet	1.7	1.85	1.7	15
Polyamide (nylon)	Molded	9.0	7.9	13.6	10–12
Ethyl cellulose	Molded	7–8.5	6.5	7–10	7–8
Cellulose nitrate	Sheet	5–10	5.0	5–10	21–23
Allyl type	Cast	5–6	4.17	8–10	40–50
Polyester	Laminated glass fiber	30–60	25	40–60	—
Aluminum	—	35	13	—	—
Steel	—	60	7.7	—	—

vibration such as, heat, cold, sound, electricity, etc. Materials used include glass, paper, porcelain, plastics, metals, ceramics, etc. Heat insulators usually involve glassy compositions, asbestos or mineral wool. For shutting out sounds and retaining heat, a closed-air space is a simple and effective medium. Various adhesives are used to retain, join or protect the insulation.

Heat Insulation

Heat is transmitted by radiation, conduction, and convection. Except in the semi-refractory and refractory fields where radiation is of great importance, the principal concern in the design of insulation for industrial equipment is the reduction of convection and conduction to negligible quantities. If it were practical, the perfect insulation for industrial equipment would be a vacuum, which would permit no transfer of convection or conduction heat since no material exists. The next best thing to a vacuum is dead or noncirculating air. In the manufacture of heat-insulating materials, a great number of tiny air spaces or pockets are trapped between fibers or crystals that make up the body of the insulation. The effectiveness of the insulation results from this the great number of small air spaces which reduce the cross-sectional area of the solid material and provide a multitude of surface resistance at the boundaries of the air spaces.

In preparing or manufacturing this type of insulation, the fibers or crystals can be bonded together either naturally or with adhesives. The basic adhesive can be a straight nonmodified phenol formaldehyde resin or furfural alcohol resin. Modified organic resin systems are also applicable.

Ceramic glass frit or adhesives are principally employed where the insulating materials are used at temperatures exceeding 200°F. The percentage of adhesive utilized is kept to a minimum (usually below 3 per cent by weight). When greater amounts of adhesives are required, modified adhesives with foaming agents are employed to develop more air spaces.

When reviewing the subject of insulation, it is important to consider both temperature and time

TABLE 2. COMPARATIVE ELECTRICAL PROPERTIES OF PLASTIC MATERIALS.

Material	Description	Short-Time Dielectric Strength (volts/mil)	60 cycles	Power factor (% 1000 cycles)	1000 kc
Phenol formaldehyde	Cast resin	75–250	25.0–50.0	20.0–30.0	9–10
Molded	Wood flour	300–375	3.0–12.0	3–6	3–5
Molded	Fabric-filled	200–325	10.0–25.0	4–10	4–6
Molded	Asbestos	300–350	15–35	10–25	5–10
Molded	Mica	350–500	1–2.5	0.7–1.5	0.5–0.9
Laminated	Paper, grade X	400–1000	—	—	2–8
Laminated	Fabric, grade C	150–600	—	—	2–8
Urea formaldehyde, molded	Alpha cellulose	300–400	3.5–10.0	3.5–5.0	2.7–4.0
Melamine, molded	Mineral-filled	390	7–17	—	4.1
Polymethyl methacrylate	Sheet	500	5–6	5–6	2–3
Polystyrene	Molded	500–700	0.006–0.05	0.005–0.05	0.01–0.05
Polyvinyl chloride-acetate	Sheet	400–425	0.7–1.0	1.1–1.3	1.8–1.9
Polyvinylidene chloride	Molded	350–400	3–8	3–15	3–5
Cellulose acetate	Molded (flow 286°F)	250–365	1–6	1–6	1–10
Cellulose acetate-butyrate	Molded (flow 286°F)	250–400	1–4	—	1–4
Polyethylene	Sheet	400–475	0.3–0.5	0.3–0.5	0.3–0.5
Polyester laminate	Fabric	200–600	—	—	—
Polyester laminate	Mat	250–500	—	—	—
Polyamide (nylon)	Molded	350–400	1.5–5.0	2–5	4–7
Ethyl cellulose	Molded	470–550	0.8–3.0	0.8–1.5	1.7–3.6
Cellulose nitrate	Sheet	300–600	6–15	—	7.0–10
Allyl resin	Cast	568	—	1.0	6.0
Isolantite	Ceramic	300–500	—	—	0.4
Fused quartz	—	—	—	—	0.022

TABLE 3. COMPARATIVE THERMAL PROPERTIES OF PLASTICS.

Material	Description	Thermal Conductivity (10^{-4} cal/sec/cm²/ °C/cm)	Heat-Distortion Temperature (°F)	Coefficient Thermal Expansion (X 10^{-5})
Phenol formaldehyde	Cast resin	3–5	104–140	5.7–15.0
Molded	Wood flour	4–7	260–300	3.0–3.5
Molded	Fabric filler	4–7	250–300	1.0–2.0
Molded	Asbestos	8–16	285–325	2.12
Laminated	Paper, grade X	5–8	>320	1.7–2.5
Laminated	Canvas, grade C	5–8	>320	1.7–3.0
Urea formaldehyde, molded	Alpha cellulose	7.0	—	2.5–3.0
Melamine formaldehyde	Mineral filler	—	266	2.0–4.5
Polymethyl methacrylate	Sheet	4.0–6.0	140	7.0–9.0
Polystyrene	Molded	1.8–2.0	168–176	6.0–8.0
Polyvinyl chlorideacetate	Rigid sheet	4.0–5.0	125	7.0
Polyvinylidene chloride	Molded	2.2	150–180	19.0
Cellulose acetate	Molded (flow 286°F)	4.0–8.0	118–144	8.0–16.0
Cellulose acetate	Sheet	4.0–6.0	150–175	6.0–16.0
Cellulose acetate-butyrate	Molded (flow 286°F)	4.0–8.0	114–134	11.0–17.0
Polyethylene	Sheet	8.0	115–122	18.0
Polyamide (nylon)	Molded	6.0	170	10.0
Ethyl cellulose	Molded	4.0–6.0	110–200	10.0–14.0
Cellulose nitrate	Sheet	3.1–5.1	110–150	9.0–16.0
Allyl resin	Cast	2.2	140–180	19.0
Polyester resin	Laminates	5.5–7.5	—	1.0–2.0
Steel	—	1130	—	1.1
Aluminum (24S-T)	—	5000	—	2.2
Brass	—	2000	—	1.8

conditions. Generally, insulation such as the type used for pipes and ovens must resist long time exposures which can range from 1 to 20 years; conversely insulation requirements also exist for such extreme short time conditions as those encountered in modern day rockets and missiles. These types of insulation products generally have no similarity to the longer time conventional type of insulators. Asbestos, glass, and other fibrous materials with phenolic resins typify molded plastic insulators presently used in missiles where temperature conditions ranging from 3000 to 20,000°F are encountered. Time durations range from seconds to minutes.[6] The extreme high temperature-short time heat insulation for missiles does not require the use of tiny air spaces or pockets. The basic consideration is that the materials themselves will not be destroyed under the operating time and temperature periods.

The principal function of adhesives in heat insulators is to join or bond the insulator to its mating surface. Two processes are used. In one, after the insulator is fabricated, it is bonded by applying the adhesive as a second step. Examples of this technique include roof insulation using a paper-type insulator with asphalt or pitch, thus bonding asbestos-cement insulator to heated pipe with sodium silicate, or bonding firebricks in kilns with a borosilicate adhesive. Usually the adhesive not only provides a method of joining but also meets other basic requirements, including heat resistance.

In the other process, the insulation is manufactured at the same time that it bonds to its mating surface. For example, the internal or external insulation of a rocket motor body is produced and bonded to the base metal or plastic structure in one operation. The actual insulation consists of a relatively solid plastic composed of a matrix and fiber (glass, asbestos, quartz, leached glass, etc.). The matrix is a heat-resistant organic resin such as a modified phenol formaldehyde. The phenolic resin meets the requirements of the matrix in the insulator and also provides the adhesion to the motor body.

Applications and Forms of Insulation

Typical industrial applications for insulators are as follows:

Application	Temperature (°F)
Heated Pipe	
Iron pipe or	60–500
Copper tubing	60–600
	60–1000
Steam-traced and	60–600
Nested lines	60–1000
Values and fittings	60–600
	60–500
Heated Equipment	
Breechings	
Condensers	60–500
Dryers	60–500
Ducts, process	60–500
evaporators	60–600
Heat exchangers	60–1000
Hydrators	60–1000
Kilns	
Ovens, industrial	
Stills	
Turbines	
Vessels, processing	
Heating and Ventilating Ducts	
Indoor exposed	60–450
	60–450
	60–450
	60–450
Indoor concealed	60–450
	60–450
	60–250
Outdoor exposed	60–150
	60–450

Application	Temperature (°F)
Air Conditioning Ducts	
Exterior application	30–250
	30–250
Interior application	30–250
	30–250
Cooled Pipes	
Dual-temperature lines	Sub-zero to 500
Cold water lines	Above 50
Ice water lines	50–35
Brine lines	34 to −30
Refrigerants	−31 to −60
Special process	−61 to −120

With continual increase in performance requirements of missiles and aircraft, the need for insulating materials capable of being utilized in high heat flux environments has also increased. At present, ablative-type plastics have been used in many of these applications. Re-entry nose cones and rocket exhaust areas are two of the most successful examples of this approach. Many organic resins and fibers contained in reinforced plastics interact with hyperthermal environments to form a residual surface char. This char, retained on the surface of the ablating material, is an effective barrier between the virgin plastic and the high temperature environment; thus there is partial protection of the plastic substrate from thermal, mechanical, and chemical effects of the environment.

This type of insulating material is usually bonded directly to a substruction such as stainless steel, molybdenum, titanium, or reinforced plastics. The adhesive used has to meet certain thermal, mechanical, and workable conditions. Straight or modified phenolics, epoxy-phenolics or inorganic (ceramic) type adhesives are applicable.

Application of insulators in the motor body area of missiles is a highly specialized field. Both rigid type insulators such as glass-phenolic or asbestos-phenolic plastics, and rubber or rubberlike materials are used. For the lower temperature requirements of e.g., below 2,000°F, rubberlike materials are applicable. Nitrile-rubber, vinyl-phenolic, and nylon-phenolic adhesives are used with the rubberlike insulators.

Insulation materials incorporate the use of basic materials such as magnesium carbonate, diatomaceous silica, calcium silicate, sodium silicate, asbestos fiber, glass fiber, Portland cement, sissal fiber, etc. In turn, these base materials are made into flexible blankets, rigid boards, loose construction, sprayable compounds, and molded in place forms. Various adhesives are applicable.

When the insulation is used in applications such as piping, furnaces, ducts, or roofing, special coverings are sometimes required. The insulation must be weather-proof, resist sunlight aging, resist abrasion, or provide an outer jacket which is chemical resistant. The outside surface can also be designed to reflect solar heat waves by using aluminum or other metallic foils.

These outer protective coverings can include canvas, asbestos paper, glass paper, cellulosic paper, wire screen, etc. The jackets can be made an integral part of the insulation by means of special type adhesives such as phenolic-rubber, asphalt, asbestos-cement, and sodium silicate.

Electrical Insulation

In the past, resistance to approximately 300°F was adequate for electrical insulation. Present industrial and military electronic material requirements considerably exceed the 300°F mark. Requirements exist for adhesives to bond insulators to the base electrical unit and also to bond electrical flakes (mica, glass, etc.), fibers, or powders to themselves, in turn providing electrical insulation.

The primary function of an electrical insulation is to confine the flow of electrical power. In performing this function, the insulation may also serve as a structural element by maintaining spacings or positions. Electrical insulation is also used to protect the surfaces of electronic components from adverse environments such as moisture, heat, and chemicals. They also fill spaces or voids where corona discharge is liable to occur.

The insulators can be organic, inorganic (ceramic, etc.), or combinations. Properties such as

TABLE 4. EPOXY CASTING AND POTTING RESINS.

Properties	ASTM Test Method	Value
Physical		
Specific gravity	D792–48T	1.11–1.23
Tensile strength, psi	D638–49T	12,000
Elongation	—	—
Modulus of elasticity		
in tension, psi $\times 10^5$	D638–49T	4.5
Flexural strength, psi	D790–49T	18,800
Flexural modulus, psi		—
Impact strength, Izod,		
ft-lb/in., notched	D256–47T	0.5–1.7
Thermal		
Conductivity,		
Btu/hr/ft^2/°F/in.		—
Specific heat		—
Coefficient of linear		
expansion, in/in/°F	D696–44	4.8×10^{-5}
Heat-distortion tem-		
perature, °F, 264 psi	D648–45T	302
Electrical		
Volume resistivity,		
ohm-cm	D257–49T	10^{16}–10^{17}
Dielectric strength,		
short-time, volts/mil	D149–44	400
Dielectric strength,		
step-by-step,		
volts/mil	D149–44	380
Dielectric constant		
60 cycles	D150–47T	3.89
10^3 cycles		3.67
10^6 cycles		3.62
Power factor		
60 cycles	D150–47T	0.0013
10^3 cycles		0.0024
10^6 cycles		0.019
Arc resistance, sec		50–180
Miscellaneous		
Water absorption, %		0.14
Parts Catalyst per		
100 of resin		
("Epon" 828-CL)		15
Cure schedule		
("Epon" 828-CL)		
Initial, 2 hr, 85°C		
Post cure, 4 hr, 150°C		

TABLE 5. POLYESTER MOLDING COMPOUNDS (ALKYDS).[a]

Properties	ASTM Test Method	Granular Type Mineral-Filled	Putty Type, Mineral-Filled	Glass-Filled
Physical				
Specific gravity	D792	2.18–2.25	1.80–1.83	1.7–2.0
Specific volume, in.^{3}/lb	D792	12.7–12.3	15.4–15.2	14.6
Tensile strength, psi	D638	3000–4000	3000–4000	4000–10,000
Elongation, %	D638	—	—	—
Modulus of elasticity in tension, psi $\times 10^5$	D638	25	15	16–20
Compressive strength, psi	D695	18,000–25,000	18,000–20,000	20,000–25,000
Flexural strength, psi	D790	7500–10,000	8000–10,000	5000–30,000
Impact strength, Izod, ft-lb/in.	D256	0.3–0.35	0.3–0.35	3–24
Hardness, Rockwell	D785	—	—	—
Thermal				
Conductivity, 10^{-4} cal/sec/cm^2/1°C/cm	C177	—	—	8–12
Specific heat, cal/°C/gm	—	0.25	0.25	—
Coefficient of thermal expansion, 10^{-5}, °C	D696	3.5	3.5	1.0–3.0
Resistance of heat, °F (continuous)	—	300–350	300–350	300
Heat-distortion temperature, °F	D648	350–400	375–425	400
Electrical				
Volume resistivity, ohm-cm	D257	10^{14}	10^{14}	10^{12}–10^{14}
Dielectric strength, short-time	D149	350–450	390–400	150–400
Dielectric strength, step-by-step	D149	300–350	325–335	315
Dielectric constant				
60 cycles	D150	6.0–7.5	5.9–6.4	5.2–6.0
10^3 cycles	D150	5.1–6.2	—	4.5–5.0
10^6 cycles	D150	4.6–5.5	4.8–5.1	4.0–4.5
Power factor				
60 cycles	D150	0.02–0.06	0.035–0.055	0.023–0.024
10^3 cycles	D150	0.02–0.03	—	0.015–0.020
10^6 cycles	D150	0.015–0.018	0.032–0.040	0.015–0.020
Arc resistance, sec	D495	190	175	100–180
Miscellaneous				
Water absorption, 24 hr, ⅛ in., %	D570	0.4–0.8	0.15	0.15–0.20
Effect of weak acids	D543	nil	nil	slight
Effect of strong acids	D543	nil	nil	attacked
Effect of weak alkalies	D543	attacked	attacked	attacked
Effect of strong alkalies	D543	decomposed	decomposed	decomposed
Effect of organic solvents	D543	nil	nil	nil
Machining qualities	—	fair	fair	fair

[a] Trade-names: "Bakelite," "Glaskyd," "Plaskon."

those described in Tables 4, 5, and 6 can be developed.

Usually the electrical insulation need not be bonded to the base materials. Materials can be directly sprayed, molded or potted so that complete encapsulation without a specific adhesive is applicable. However, adhesives or adhesive-like materials often are required to either form the insulating materials or provide adhesion between the insulator and the base unit. In these cases, the electrical properties of the adhesive become as important as its other properties.

Electrical tapes are a major use of adhesives. Electrical tapes are used to insulate, to hold, or to serve as spacers. They are commonly employed for wrapping coils or conductors, insulating splices, and for holding and bending insulating materials. Tapes are made from cloth, paper, plastic or rubber films, or composite laminated sheets. The basic fiber used in constructions of this type is glass. These tapes are generally used with a pressure-sensitive adhesive on one or both sides.

The adhesives generally have a dual purpose, i.e., they aid electrical insulation and bond the insulator to the unit. Adhesive materials used include vinyl-rubber, epoxy, cellulose acetate, polyvinylidene chloride, polyethylene and glass or ceramic frit.

Plastic electrical insulators (Tables 4 and 5) generally use filler materials: short fibers, chopped

TABLE 6. VINYL-CHLORIDE MOLDING COMPOUNDS.

Properties	ASTM Test Method	Rigid	Flexible, Unfilled	Flexible, Filled
Mechanical				
Specific gravity	D792	1.35–1.55	1.16–1.3	1.3–1.6
Specific volume, in.^{3}/lb	D792	20.5–17.8	22.2–20.5	21.3–16.3
Tensile strength, psi	D638	5000–9000	1500–3500	1000–3500
Elongation, %	D638	5.0–15.0	200–450	200–400
Modulus of elasticity, $10^5 \times$ psi	D638	5–6	—	—
Compressive strength, psi	D638	10,000–13,000	—	—
Flexural strength, psi	D790	8,000–16,000	—	—
Impact strength, Izod, ft-lb/in	D256	0.4–2.0	—[a]	—[a]
Thermal				
Conductivity, 10^{-4} cal/sec/cm^2/1°C/cm	C177	3.0–7.0	3.0–4.0	3.0–4.0
Specific heat, cal/°C/g	D696	0.2–0.28	0.3–0.5	0.3–0.5
Thermal expansion, 10^{-5}/°C	D696	5–6	—	—
Resistance to heat, °F (continuous)		130–160	150–175	150–175
Heat-distortion temperature, °F	D648	140–185	—	—
Electrical				
Volume resistivity, ohm-cm (50% relative humidity, 23°C)	D257	10^{16}	$(1–10)10^{12}$	$(4–7)10^{14}$
Dielectric strength, short-time, ⅛ in. thickness, volts/mil	D149	700–1300	800–1000	600–800
Dielectric strength, step-by-step, ⅛ in. thickness, volts/mil	D149	650–750	750–900	550–750
Dielectric constant				
60 cycles	D150	3.4–3.6	5.0–6.0	5.0–6.0
10^3 cycles	D150	3.0–3.3	4.0–5.0	4.0–5.0
10^6 cycles	D150	2.8–3.0	3.5–4.5	3.5–4.5
Arc resistance, sec	D495	60–80	—	—
Miscellaneous				
Water absorption, ⅛ in., 24 hr	D570	0.1–0.4	0.50–0.75	0.60–1.0
Machining qualities		Excellent	—	—
Effect of weak acids	D543	None	None	None
Effect of strong acids	D543	None	None to slight	—
Effect of weak and strong alkalies	D543	None	None	None
Effect of organic solvents	D543	Resists alcohols, hydrocarbons, and oils; soluble in ketones		

[a] Varies with plasticizer.

fabrics, and granular or flaked fillers (wood, mica, diatomaceous earth, asbestos, glass, etc.). Usually no secondary adhesive bonding operation is required.

When metal inserts are used with thermoplastic molded electrical thin wall insulators, the control on the base insulating material follows adhesive requirements rather than plastic molding requirements. The metal insert must be bonded or encapsulated without destructive side effects such as crazing, voids, etc. Differentiating between a plastic molded material and an adhesive material in this application is difficult. The basic constituents for either type material are similar. Fillers are generally used with these adhesives because they can increase heat stability, flexual and shear strengths, reduce cost of adhesives, provide blends of certain desirable chemical-electrical resins, etc.

In preparing mica insulators, the build-up of the mica flakes is made by bonding with natural or synthetic resins or with inorganic binders. Shellac is still used extensively as a binder; however a superior insulation is obtained with polyester or alkyd resin binders. Where cost permits, epoxy resin binders are used. The silicone resin binders are generally used where high temperature resistance combined with good electrical properties is required. Inorganic bonds for mica are achieved with ceramic or glass frit. The glass-bonded mica provides for high temperature operation of electrical insulators.

Ceramic dielectrics are used extensively as electrical insulators for electronic units. These ceramics can be used alone or to encapsulate electrical base units. When the ceramic insulator has to be attached to electronic units, ceramic adhesives are useful, e.g., sodium silicate, alkali borosilicate, aluminum phosphate, colloidal zirconia, colloidal silica, and calcium aluminate.

FRICTION MATERIALS

In the past decade, a major development in applying friction materials to base metal structures occurred as a result of the use of adhesives. The transition from rivoted or mechanically joined friction materials to adhesive-bonded units permitted lighter weight units, thinner friction materials, and lower cost units.

Previously, one of the most severe applications in the automotive industry was the attaching of linings to brake shoes. The relationship between the safety of the vehicle and the performance of the adhesive in this application has become apparent with the acceptance of heat-resistant, high-strength straight or modified phenolic adhesives. The nitrile rubber-phenolic adhesives, as well as unmodified phenolic adhesives, permit the bonds to operate at 600°F or higher.

The frictional heat normally reported in braking may be between 400 and 600°F for approximately one-half the lining thickness. Extremely high temperatures are theoretically obtained on the surface of friction material or on the surface of brake drums during the braking action of standard automobiles and trucks. Actual temperature readings are generally difficult to measure. Literature records temperatures from 2000 to 2500°F for very short periods of time. The actual temperature of the adhesive bonds normally does not exceed 400 to 600°F because of the low thermal conductivity of the friction-organic or inorganic materials.

Adhesive-bonded friction materials are now being used in automobile brake linings, automatic transmission parts, aircraft brake linings, automobile clutch plates, household automatic equipment such as washing machines, industrial automatic equipment such as hoists, etc. Some of the friction materials are completely inorganic (ceramic) such as brakes used in special heavy-duty trucks or aircraft. In the majority of these cases, ceramic adhesives are used as the bonding medium.

References

1. Baldrige, J. H., "Development of Rubber-Like Materials for Applications Involving Contact with Liquid Rocket Propellants," ASTIA Document No. AD 142205, Dec., 1957.
2. McClintock, R. M., and Hiza, M. J., "Epoxy Resins as Cryogenics Structural Adhesives," *Modern Plastics,* p. 172 (June 1958).
3. Merriam, J. C., "Adhesive Bonding," *Materials in Design Engineering,* Manual No. 162 (Sept. 1959).
4. Riley, M. W., "Joining and Fastening Plastics," *Materials in Design Engineering,* Manual No. 145, (Jan. 1958).
5. Robinson, H. E., "Thermal Resistance of Airspaces and Fibrous Insulations Bonded by Reflective Surfaces," U. S. Dept. of Commerce, Building Materials and Structures Report 151, Nov. 14, 1957.
6. Rosato, D. V., "Asbestos: Its Industrial Applications," New York, Reinhold Publishing Corp., 1959.
7. Rosato, D. V., "Plastics in Missiles—An Introduction to Current Uses of Plastics," *Brit. Plastics* pp. 369–374 (May 1952).
8. Roush, C. W., and Kearfott, A. J., "Properties of Some Heat Resistant Adhesives," *Mech. Eng.,* pp. 369–374 (May 1952).
9. "85% Magnesia Insulation Manual," The Magnesia Insulation Manufacturers Association, 1958.
10. "Electrical Insulation and Dielectrics," *Elec. Mfg.,* The Gage Publishing Company, 1955.

— 56 —

Adhesives
in the Electrical Industry

L. S. Kohn and A. F. Zavist

General Electric Company
Schenectady, New York

Many of the demands placed upon adhesives in the electrical industry are comparable to those encountered in other structural adhesive applications. An added consideration is that electrical as well as mechanical failure may occur. The attainment of adequate mechanical properties such as tensile and flexural strength, impact resistance, etc., is fundamental to satisfactory performance. However, since structural adhesive aspects are adequately covered in other chapters, the discussion here will concentrate on particular properties required of adhesives in electrical equipment which often are of little or no importance in other applications.

Classical methods of joining metals include riveting, soldering, brazing and welding. Since the metallic bonding agents employed in such operations are electrically conducting, the application of electrical insulation, if required, demands a separate and costly step. The particular fascination of organic adhesives for the electrical industry is that they perform not only the adhesion function, but if properly chosen, the insulation function as well. Therefore, adhesives to be generally useful in electrical equipment must be nonconducting.

There are, to be sure, some applications in which some degree of electrical conductivity is desirable and would be specified by the electrical designer.

To make optimum use of the inherent electrical insulation properties of modern organic adhesives, one should be aware of certain basic standards and concepts of the industry.

TEMPERATURE CLASSIFICATION

Electrical apparatus is usually guaranteed to operate at a specified maximum hot-spot temperature for the life of the equipment. The temperature limits for most rotating apparatus are:

Classification	Hot-Spot Temperature (°C)
Class O	90
Class A	105 Max.
Class B	130 Max.
Class F	155 Max.
Class H	180 Max.
Class C	Above 180

Slightly different limits have been established for other classes of electrical equipment. For an adhesive to be used in apparatus operating in any of these temperature classifications, it must be evaluated under appropriate conditions. The design and performance of such tests are of major concern to all in the electrical industry.

While Class A equipment is most important from many points of view, there is a definite trend toward Class B and higher temperature ratings for specific applications. The driving force for this change is that in many cases higher operating temperatures are accompanied by increased output for any machine size, or conversely, decreased size for a given output, and this is particularly important where space and weight are important factors. Of course, in missiles and related areas where weight saving is paramount, extremely high operating temperatures are often demanded even at greatly increased cost per unit of power output. In general, adhesives to be used at Class H or higher temperatures are chosen mainly for mechanical integrity and thermal endurance at the required temperatures. Equipment operating at such temperatures is usually designed for low voltage, and insulation needs are nominal.

The operating temperatures of modern electrical equipment often eliminate the use of practically all common thermoplastic resins as adhesives; hence the main emphasis in this chapter will be on synthetic thermosetting resin systems. Thermoplastics are often used to facilitate assembly and installation, but satisfactory operation of the apparatus is usually not dependent on permanency of these bonds. In addition, for many electronic applications which require only moderate operating temperatures, thermoplastics with "quick tack" are utilized to bond fine wires into coils, film materials to backers, etc. The rapid progress being made in polymer science guarantees that economical, high-melting thermoplastic adhesives will be available in the near future; futhermore their increasing use in electrical equipment is certain because of their inherent ease of application.

ELECTRICAL PROPERTIES

Volume Resistivity

While there is no sharp demarcation between electrical conductors and insulators, common practice defines conductors as those materials having a volume resistivity of less than 1 ohm-cm, insulators, a volume resistivity of greater than 10^6 ohm-cm, with materials in between loosely classified as semiconductors. For more critical insulation applications, specifically those involving high voltages or large currents, resistivities of better than 10^{12} ohm-cm are highly desirable. Resistivity is quite temperature dependent and almost always varies inversely with temperature. Polar or conducting impurities lower the volume resistivity significantly.

Surface resistivity is dependent not only on the nature of the material but on such environmental factors as cleanliness, moisture, dust, etc. Impurities drastically reduce the surface resistivity; however cleaning and drying procedures frequently restore a substantial part of the initial value.

The over-all electrical resistance of an adhesive layer serving as electrical insulation depends on the surface as well as volume resistivity.

Power factor is a measure of the relative dielectric loss in the insulation.

$$\text{Power factor} = \frac{\text{Energy loss in watts}}{\text{Volt ampere input to dielectric system considered as a condenser}}$$

$$= \text{cosine of dielectric phase angle}$$
$$= \text{sine of loss angle}$$
$$= \sin \delta$$

At low values $\sin \delta$ is approximately equal to $\tan \delta$ (dissipation factor).

The power factor is an indication of the loss of electrical energy as heat due to internal friction of the polar resin polymer as it attempts to line up with the changing field.

Dielectric Loss Factor is proportional to the rate at which electrical energy is transformed into heat in a dielectric subjected to a changing electrical field.

$$\text{Dielectric loss factor} = \text{Dielectric constant} \times \text{dissipation factor}$$

Power factor and dielectric loss are associated only with alternating fields. They are of no importance with d-c equipment. High power factor is characteristic of polar materials. Power factor generally increases with temperature and/or frequency with most materials but tends to decrease at very high frequencies. Typical curves are shown in Figs. 1 and 2.

While power factor itself may often be of limited importance in the choice of adhesive, a material should not be used at a temperature at which the power factor-temperature curve rises rapidly. Under such conditions, a thermal runaway and subsequent failure are possible.

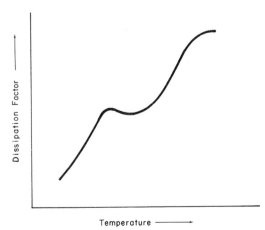

Fig. 1. Variation of dissipation factor with temperature for typical polar organic material (with second order transition temperature).

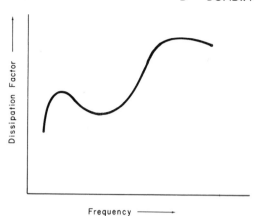

Fig. 2. Variation of dissipation factor with frequency for a typical polar organic material.

High loss factors are undesirable in certain high-frequency electronic applications such as radar wave guides, since for a given loss factor the power loss increases directly with frequency. Occasionally a certain degree of conductivity is desirable in the adhesive to help grade off voltage stresses; however this is usually accompanied by an increase in loss factor. While the increased loss is usually negligible with high-voltage rotating equipment, with power cables care must be taken not to get the losses so high as to affect cable efficiency. In general, dissipation factors can be decreased in either of two ways. The first is to use less polar materials. Naturally, the less polar the material, the less tendency do the dipoles have to move in the alternating electrical field. The second is to tie up the functional polar groups as much as possible in order to inhibit effectively their oscillation with the electrical field. Where very low power factors are important, nonpolar materials are almost mandatory.

Dielectric Constant

$$= \frac{\begin{array}{c}\text{capacitance of a capacitor}\\\text{containing material}\end{array}}{\text{capacitance of capacitor with vacuum*}}$$

The dielectric constant is not a constant. Typical values at 60 cycles are:

Asphalt	2–3
Phenolics	4–8
Glass	5–10
Water	1
Mica	2–7
Epoxies	3–6
Polyesters	3–6

* From a practical point of view, the capacitor with air instead of vacuum is sufficiently accurate.

One case in which the value of the dielectric constant is important is covered below.

Adhesives for Mica Insulation. One of the most basic materials for insulating rotating equipment is mica. It is particularly important in high-voltage equipment since it has exceptional long time dielectric strength and resistance to the ravages of corona. Mica is used in the form of relatively large, flat splittings on the order of 0.001 in. thick or reconstituted mica paper prepared from smaller splittings or platelets on conventional papermaking machinery. Mica is flexible and has excellent thermal and chemical stability. However, to facilitate application, the individual large splittings must be bonded together and the mica paper must be impregnated with a resinous adhesive to give interlaminar adhesion. The solvent content of the adhesive should be low to minimize formation of internal voids. The individual layers of mica insulation are applied as tapes or wrappers in multilayers on the equipment to be insulated. The unit is usually subjected to a vacuum-pressure processing cycle to form a void-free, compact, cured insulation layer.

From an electrical point of view it is desirable that the adhesive binder for the mica have a high dielectric constant. The mica flakes are far more capable of withstanding high-voltage stresses for long periods of time than the organic binders. In a mixed system the voltage stresses distribute themselves inversely as the dielectric constants of the individual components. By using a high dielectric constant adhesive, the voltage stresses are shifted to the mica, which is much more able to bear the load, and improved long time dielectric performance is obtained. As pointed out previously, care should be taken that the dielectric loss factors, which vary directly with dielectric constant, do not get so high that they approach a thermal runaway condition in the thicknesses used. The level of the dielectric loss itself is normally insignificant from a machine efficiency point of view since the losses in the copper and iron are much higher and dominate the efficiency (or loss) situation. In other words, as long as the rate of change of power factor is not too high, a higher dielectric constant (and therefore higher dielectric loss) material is more desirable when used with mica. In Fig. 3, adhesive A is preferable to adhesive B.

CHEMICAL RESISTANCE

In addition to mechanical and electrical properties, adhesives in most electrical apparatus must have a certain degree of chemical resistance. In rotating equipment, resistance to the lubricant is

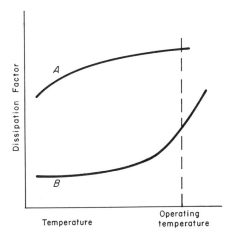

Fig. 3. Variation of dissipation factor with temperature. A. Compound with decreasing rate of change of dielectric loss with temperature. B. Compound with increasing rate of change.

required since contact cannot be avoided. A poor choice of adhesive can lead to softening and ultimate failure. Synthetic nonflammable lubricants, increasing in use, require adhesives of a higher order of chemical resistance. For hermetic refrigerant applications, it is critical that any adhesives have good resistance to the coolant with little or no extractibles or gas evolution during operation. In such applications, contamination of the refrigerant would ultimately lead to failure of the cooling system and possibly the electrical system.

Many installations, especially in the atomic energy field, require equipment that is capable of withstanding highly purified water at elevated temperatures and pressures. While resistance to cold water of even ordinary purity is difficult to attain, the use of highly purified water compounds the problem. Great care should be taken in extrapolating adhesive test results from water of one purity to a significantly purer grade. Pure water may in fact be considered as approaching a highly polar organic solvent which may swell many polymers.

In larger size transformers, adhesives must be resistant to hydrocarbon oils and chlorinated aromatic compounds which are employed as liquid insulation and heat transfer media. Very often the turns of the immersed coils are bonded with an adhesive, and any extractibles of a polar nature would lower the dielectric breakdown voltage of the liquid insulation.

The increased use of outdoor facilities in utilities and chemical plants requires choice of adhesives capable of resisting the combined factors of humidity, atmospheric dust and sunlight, and other weathering agents.

In specific situations, resistance to caustic and acids in paper-mill applications, detergents in home-sewage disposal units, acids in petroleum refineries, plasticizers in rubber and plastic compounding operations, etc. must be evaluated independently.

MOISTURE RESISTANCE

Many common adhesives absorb moisture from the atmosphere, especially at high relative humidity. The absorption of moisture by adhesives used to prepare printed circuit boards, for example, may cause a change in the volume and surface resistivity of the board as well as altering the electrical characteristics of the circuit. Moisture usually alters the surface resistivity much more markedly than the volume resistivity, particularly when surface impurities are present. The magnitude of change in resistivity from wet to dry conditions is frequently used as a measure of the quality of materials employed in production.

CHEMICAL CORROSIVITY

Certain ingredients in some adhesives may damage metallic and nonmetallic components in electrical equipment. Fine copper wire used in many electronic applications is susceptible to organic acids. Products formed during decomposition of some peroxides used to cure unsaturated polyesters can eventually cause open circuits by completely dissolving the wire. Of course, moisture accelerates this process. Many of the acidic or even the basic curing agents used with epoxy encapsulants and impregnant resin are similarly corrosive to copper. Certain curing agents, if chosen carefully and if thoroughly cured, perform satisfactorily. The choice of a coating varnish for printed circuits with thin copper components requires care for identical reasons. Aluminum components are attacked by moisture, especially under alkaline conditions.

Some wire enamels, including the polyesters, especially when employed in totally sealed systems, are sensitive to small amounts of water which lead to depolymerization and breakdown. Some adhesives such as the phenol-formaldehyde types and cellulosic types often used as backers for pressure-sensitive adhesives are generators of water upon heating and must be avoided. Often a thorough cure prior to sealing of the unit is sufficient to avoid subsequent insulation damage by hydrolysis. The same problems exist with the popular and ex-

TABLE 1. SELECTION OF ADHESIVES FOR ELECTRICAL APPLICATIONS.

Type of Application	Outstanding Requirements	Typical Adhesives	Remarks
Bonding formed small wire coils	Fast tack	Thermoplastics e.g., polyvinyl butyral; polyvinyl formal	Adhesive system must not attack wire enamel.
Bonding random packages of wires in rotating equipment	Good strength at elevated temperatures. Vibration resistance. Heat stability.	Epoxies Polyesters Phenolics	Must not attack wire enamel. Should bridge between wires and fill spaces well. Solventless systems preferable.
Bonding stator laminations	Bonded package must retain shape in service. Thin bond line preferable.	Epoxies Rubber phenolics	Too rigid an adhesive may increase magnetic losses. Low shrinkage during cure preferable.
Bonding of electrical grade laminates	High electrical resistivity. Good tracking resistance	Epoxies Polyesters Polyurethanes	Thin laminates require low modulus adhesives with good elongation.
Hermetic motors	Non-gassing. Resist attack by refrigerants. Adhesive should not contaminate refrigeration system.	Highly crosslinked, thermosetting materials.	Adhesives must be chosen specifically for each system, rather than by chemical class. Precautions must be taken to insure complete curing.
High frequency electronic applications	Low dielectric losses. Constant "q" or maintenance of electrical quality.	Non-polar adhesives	For less stringent applications, highly crosslinked, polar adhesive may be satisfactory.
Capacitors	Uniform, very thin bonding film	Polar adhesives	Low volatile evolution often a requirement. Preferably applicable to coating machinery.
Transformers	Low moisture pick-up. Resistance to transformer impregnants. Should not contaminate impregnant.	Crosslinked adhesives, e.g., epoxies modified phenolics, silicones.	Dielectric properties of adhesive more important in dry type transformers.
Switchgear Components	Non-tracking	Melamines, epoxies	Ionic impurities should be avoided. Certain fillers help tracking resistance.
Microwave applications	Transparency to microwave frequencies.	Non-polar adhesives	Low moisture pickup usually necessary.
Nuclear applications	Radiation resistance	Silicones, phenolics, epoxies, polystyrene, diallylphthalates, polyesters	Aromatic compounds generally have excellent radiation resistence. Materials should be evaluated after irradiation for maintenance of dielectric properties.

TABLE 1. SELECTION OF ADHESIVES FOR ELECTRICAL APPLICATIONS. (*cont'd.*)

Type of Application	Outstanding Requirements	Typical Adhesives	Remarks
High voltage insulation	Long time dielectric strength. Structural integrity at elevated temperatures for long periods of time.	Polyesters, epoxies	Final structure should be void-free.
Electronic Tube applications	Non-gassing. Structural integrity at high temperatures.	Epoxies, silicones	For some applications, good sealing and low vapor transmission are important.
Printed Circuitry	Maintenance of electrical & physical properties under varying conditions of humidity and thermal cycling.	Epoxies	Check for attack on copper.
Transient in-process adhesives	Provide temporary bond. Burn off cleanly leaving no residue.	Polyacrylates, Polyethylene oxides	Adhesive holds powders or inorganic components in place prior to subsequent high temperature processing.
High Temperature Applications 150–250 C	Retention of strength at elevated temperatures.	Silicones, epoxies, polyesters, diallylphthalates, phenolics, Aromatic polyamides and polyimides, ceramics	Difficult to obtain suitable elongation at very high temperatures.
Water resistant applications	Low water absorption. Maintenance of strength and electrical properties.	Non-polar thermoplastics, epoxies, polyesters	Difficult to maintain integrity in hot water, especially as purity of water increases.
Shock resistant applications	Resistance to thermal and mechanical shock.	Silicones, epoxies	For equipment used intermittently under extreme weather conditions.

tremely useful polyester films and fabrics. The rate of deterioration may be particularly significant with oriented films, where a relatively small amount of degradation markedly affects physical properties.

Oxidation inhibitors such as hydroquinone derivatives used in some adhesive formulations are corrosive to copper and other metals. Electrical contacts are particularly vulnerable to attack, which causes an increase in contact resistance.

Moisture or traces of organic solvents contained in some adhesives can foster the formation of small cracks perpendicular to the axis of some wire enamels. Annealing at elevated temperatures may heal such "crazing" in some cases, but often the damage is irreparable.

Since much electrical equipment involves materials with dissimilar coefficients of thermal expansion, it is frequently desirable to employ elastomeric or low modulus adhesives so that the electrical characteristics of the bonded units will not be altered during the thermal or mechanical cycling. Such requirements are often present in electronic circuitry. The use of silicone rubber encapsulants for electronic tubes depends on this concept. The use of too rigid materials often leads to crushing of encapsulated or potted vacuum tubes.

In some electrical apparatus it is required that a laminated core be prepared by bonding individual stampings of a magnetic steel with an organic adhesive. The magnetic characteristics of the core are quite different when bonded with a rigid adhesive as compared with a more flexible adhesive. Eddy current losses, for example, are greater when a rigid adhesive is used.

The preformed coils used in some large motor or generator stator windings often comprise mica bonded with flexible adhesives such as modified asphalts, etc. These insulating systems must be distorted as needed during insertion into the core without major damage to the coil insulation. Many random wound coils are held together by adhesives. Where the quality or "Q" of the coil must be maintained constant, e.g., in transducers, soft adhesives are needed.

ODORS

Adhesives used with household appliances should, of course, be nontoxic and essentially odorless. Because of the lack of ventilation in refrigerators and the recycling associated with automatic defrosting, a slight odor can become obnoxious after a period of time.

TRACKING RESISTANCE

Adhesives in electrical equipment may be subjected to high energy discharges and arcs. It is important to use materials which resist carbon formation upon exposure to such discharges; otherwise an electrical conducting path can be slowly formed. In general, adhesives which are non-aromatic seem to have superior arc resistance. It is possible to upgrade the tracking resistance of some adhesives by the additions of fillers such as hydrated alumina, which apparently helps convert any carbon formed to gaseous products. For thermal stability, it is desirable to choose materials with low rates of decomposition. For tracking or arc resistance, it is desirable that all the products of decomposition be gaseous or volatile, rather than to have the material undergo a gradual decrease in molecular weight with the formation of heavy, nonvolatile, carbonizing decomposition products.

There is no direct relationship between rate of decomposition and type of decomposition products. Polytetrafluoroethylene ("Teflon"*TFE), for example, has remarkable thermal stability and a very low rate of decomposition, yet decomposes to essentially gaseous products. Methacrylates also decompose to volatile fragments but show a very high rate of decomposition. Most other materials lie somewhere in between in thermal stability and

molecular weight of decomposition products. As pointed out previously, in cases where tracking resistance is necessary, it is important to avoid using aromatic organic materials in order to minimize the formation of conducting, carbon-containing residues, even at the risk of some loss in thermal stability.

PRIMERS

The use of primers to improve the adhesion of adhesives to certain nonmetallic surfaces which are used as insulators in electrical devices should be approached with care. Many of the common primers are polar in nature, and a conducting path may be formed under the adhesive which could act to short-circuit the insulation. The sodium naphthenate treatment of "Teflon" is a case in point, but it has been shown that adequate rinsing after treatment followed by careful drying will minimize any risk of contamination.

RADIATION RESISTANCE

The behavior of adhesives in electrical equipment to be used in the presence of high-energy radiation is under current study. The mechanical and electrical breakdown of many organic adhesives under severe radiation has been noted. Electrical failure may occur because of mechanical failure of the adhesive. However, reliance on the electrical insulation value of an adhesive as, for example, in a bonded coil, may lead to dielectric breakdown if the insulation value of the adhesive is altered or destroyed.

The destructive action of corona is caused by the presence of high-energy radiation, the formation of strong acids and the erosive action of ionic bombardment. In high-voltage equipment such as steam turbine-generators, the stator coils operate at voltages which may approach the corona starting level. Although much effort is expended toward completely filling the space between conductors, the micaceous insulation and interlaminar space, the presence of some voids is practically impossible to prevent; consequently it must be assumed that some corona will be present. Many materials such as epoxies, polyesters and asphalts give adequate life; but silicones are superior to all others in corona resistance. However, a consideration of many factors has prompted most large rotating electrical equipment manufacturers to favor the use of epoxies and polyesters for these applications.

* E. I. duPont de Nemours & Co., Inc.

LIBERATION OF GASEOUS PRODUCTS

The effects of gaseous products given off by some adhesives upon some insulation components have been described. In the case of sealed or canned units, especially those which have been evacuated, the liberation of any gases can change the environment within the unit or even cause rupture of the can. The volatile fragments are often corrosive in nature and may cause breaks in the electrical circuit or build-up on contacts to increase electrical resistance.

It has also been found that low-molecular weight fragments liberated by some silicone polymers will be converted to silica on the brushes and commutators of rotating equipment under some conditions and cause excessive brush wear. None of these situations is desirable, and usually extended prototype evaluation tests are required to bring the phenomena out into the open.

GENERAL PROCESSING REQUIREMENTS

A prime requirement for effective adhesive utilization is adequate shelf life and bondability Electrical equipment frequently requires complex assembly methods; the difficulty is greatest with very small and very large apparatus. Although a considerable interval of time may pass between application and final cure, the adhesive must not deteriorate significantly.

It is to be desired that all adhesives used in electrical equipment be solvent-free, if not during application, at least before final cure. The presence of solvents which can be liberated during operation of the equipment can only lead to trouble and possible failure. Plasticizers or modifiers which volatilize are similarly destructive.

Many of the adhesives used in electrical machinery are applied in tape form, usually with a fabric or film carrier. The use of separating layers to avoid blocking of adjacent layers is not a satisfactory procedure in many cases, and non-blocking adhesives are preferred.

One characteristic of the adhesive which is often an aid in effective bonding is a high viscosity. Frequently in large and occasionally in smaller equipment, the objects to be bonded do not mate perfectly. Good bonding and performance will then depend on the ability of the adhesive to bridge these gaps and yield a continuous bond line.

The choice of adhesive must be made while keeping in mind the need for process compatibility with the rest of the piece of equipment. The cure conditions should not be so severe as to injure other materials in the unit. In some cases, the adhesive may be subjected to destructive operations such as soldering; consequently ability to withstand a short time exposure to high temperatures without excessive damage becomes a prerequisite.

In some high-volume production items such as yoke coils for television sets or fluorescent light ballasts, an instantaneous tack bond is required to enable the coil to be immediately removed from the coil form without unwinding. Cure, if required, can be carried out after assembly.

Mechanical Performance

Most adhesive failures in electrical equipment are mechanical rather than electrical. Since adhesives are used to bond together dissimilar materials which are subjected to severe thermal expansion and centrifugal forces, they must be able to withstand the deterioration of the adhesive bond from fatigue associated with repeated stresses, sudden impact shocking, the effect of deteriorating chemicals, etc.

Most electrical equipment is subjected to cyclical vibrational stresses. To perform satisfactorily, an adhesive must often possess good fatigue resistance. All adhesives show deteriorating ultimate strength as the number of cycles increases. When a property such as maximum repeated stress is plotted against the logarithm of cycles (or time, with uniform cycling), a straight line is usually obtained initially. In most cases, but not necessarily always, the curve levels off and asymptotically approaches some finite value of repeated stress.

This leveling off greatly facilitates making more accurate predictions of service capability. Of course, the effect of statistical scatter and desirable

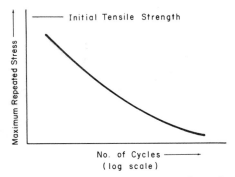

Fig. 4. Effect of repeated cycling or maximum bond strength.

safety margins must be considered. With no vibrational cycling, there is a similar effect of time on ultimate bond strength although the rate of deterioration is less severe. In most cases a plot of ultimate breaking strength versus time under loading will also show a leveling off.

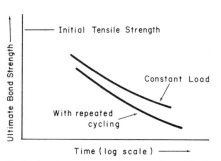

Fig. 5. Comparison of strength properties with time of loading, illustrating typical deteriorating effect of repeated cycling.

Preloading a sample diminishes the fatigue life for any given amplitude of stress. The maximum stress to which the bond is exposed is a prime controlling factor. Higher preimposed loads give higher maximum stresses, which result in shorter fatigue lives for any fixed amplitude of stress.

There is an interesting analogy between mechanical fatigue and electrical fatigue under high volt-

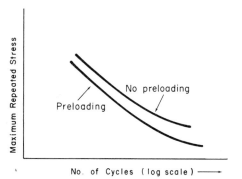

Fig. 6. Effect of preloading on fatigue life of adhesive bonds.

age stresses, particularly in the initial portion of the curve. A plot of breakdown voltage stress versus log time to failure (under constant cycles/sec) also gives a straight line (Fig. 7). With many systems, a leveling off also occurs.

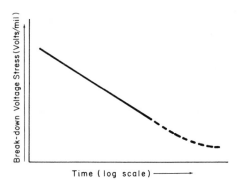

Fig. 7. Effect of time on dielectric break down strength.

The above examples are general statements of phenomena which have been observed. Naturally, any adhesive system for highly stressed cyclical applications should be evaluated carefully for the specific requirements involved. There are many complicating and influencing factors such as amplitude and frequency of vibration, modulus and extensibility of the adhesive, the effect of temperature on the physical properties of the adhesive, the bond strength to the adherends, etc., which are difficult to predict with any reasonable degree of precision. Performance characteristics for actual systems are best determined experimentally.

It has been our purpose in this chapter to point up those features or phenomena which are unique or particularly significant for the effective utilization of adhesives in electrical equipment. The products manufactured by the electrical industry are broad and varied. Electrical technology is fast-moving and ever-changing. It is hoped that the principles outlined and the problem situations described here will aid in solving the electrical adhesive problems of today and clarifying the solutions to future problems.

Adhesives in the Automobile Industry

Sumner B. Twiss

Cycleweld Chemical Products
Division of Chrysler Corporation
Trenton, Michigan

A number of different types of adhesives are currently used in the automobile industry. Thermosetting or structural adhesives are employed primarily for bonding brake linings and transmission bands. Thermoplastic adhesives are used primarily for bonding door weatherstrips and trim materials. A third type of material is sealants and sound deadeners. Although these are not, strictly speaking, bonding agents, they are required to have excellent adhesion to metal surfaces and form a barrier over spot welded joints and body seams to prevent entrance of air, water, dust, and noise.

APPLICATIONS OF THERMOSETTING ADHESIVES

Thermosetting adhesives undergo a chemical reaction in the process of forming a bond. The reaction may be produced by the application of heat, by catalysts, or by a combination of the two. They are generally an order of magnitude stronger than thermoplastic adhesives and sealants.

Since they offer advantages over other joining methods, the thermosetting or structural adhesives in automobiles will continue to grow in use. They not only join the two pieces, but also provide a continuous seal between them, giving noise and vibration dampening as well. They distribute the load over the entire bonded area, permitting the use of thinner sections and providing superior fatigue characteristics. They permit joining of dissimilar metals with little or no bimetallic corrosion. They allow the joining of materials such as aluminum and glass, which are difficult to join by other means. Finally, adhesive-bonded materials form smooth, protrusion-free joints without the need for countersinking or machining.

Bonding of Friction Materials

This is one of the earliest large-scale applications of thermosetting adhesives in the automobile industry. One manufacturer has bonded over 100 million shoes since 1949 without a single major brake failure attributable to the bonding process. Another manufacturer has successfully bonded over 150 million brake shoes as original equipment for passenger cars and trucks since 1951. The replacement market is probably ten times the original equipment market.

The major advantages of bonded brake linings are the longer life gained by wearing the friction material down to the metal shoe rather than just to the rivet heads, the increased area obtained by eliminating rivet holes and chamfers, and reduction of the possibility of scoring drums by rivets.

Success of the bonding process depends on a well controlled procedure. Important factors are cleanliness of brake linings and brake shoes, precise application of the adhesive, drying of the coated linings, correctly pressurized assembly and carefully controlled curing conditions. Figure 1 shows the first step—application of the adhesive

Fig. 1. Application of brake lining adhesive by extrusion process.

to the linings by an extrusion process and racking of the linings prior to entering the drying ovens.

Generally, the cure is carried out by passing the clamped assemblies through a hot-air circulating oven so that the bond line temperature will reach and maintain a temperature of 350°F for 20 to 25 min, with a pressure of 100 psi. In the "hot shot" bonding of replacement brake linings and original equipment transmission bands, pressures are raised to 200 to 300 psi and bond line temperature to 500°F. The time of bonding is thus reduced to 7 min, but requires very close control.

Rubber-resin and modified resin adhesives are used in bonding friction materials. The rubber-resin system in widest use is nitrile rubber-phenolic resin. In a typical shear test, this type of adhesive yields strengths of 2500 psi at room temperature and 600 to 900 psi at 400°F. In addition to strength, the adhesives must have closely controlled solids content and viscosity for either extrusion, roll coating, or spraying. They also need good storage stability, in both the wet and dry state.

Nitrile rubber-phenolic adhesives are also used extensively in bonding transmission bands. For bands or clutch facings, which encounter much

higher temperatures than normal, modified phenolic adhesives having higher heat resistance are available; but they also tend to be more brittle and less able to withstand shock loading. Typical shear strengths of modified phenolic adhesives for this application are values approaching 2500 psi at room temperature, 1500 to 2000 psi at 400°F and 1000 to 1500 psi at 600°F.

Improvement in bulk storage stability of the wet cement is a prime objective of current research on rubber-resin structural adhesives.

Bonding of Glass to Metal

The bonding of glass-to-metal in vent windows, movable side windows, and roll-type back lights in Suburbans requires adhesives with structural characteristics. The use of such adhesives has increased with the popularity of hard top and Suburban models. The cement must be thermosetting for permanence; yet it must allow sufficient flexibility to accommodate the different thermal expansion coefficients of glass and steel. The most successful adhesive for this application appears to be a nitrile rubber-epoxy resin cement.

The adhesive is manufactured in the form of a tape which forms an interference fit between the glass and the zinc die cast or steel channels. Once assembled, the windows are placed in the jig and held in an oven at 300 to 350°F for 20 to 30 min to cure the adhesive. Variations of this process are being investigated using induction heating to obtain shorter cure times and allow faster production.

Bonding of Body Sections

The bonding of large metal sections characterized by the body components of a car such as the floor pan, fenders, quarter panels, etc., is the subject of continuous work. In the case of the all-plastic body of the Chevrolet Corvette, the bonding of such body sections has been in production since 1954. The body parts such as the under body, the rear upper panel assembly consisting of upper panel, gasoline filler box and bulkhead, the front upper panel assembly, the dash panel, hinge pillar, instrument panel, etc., are all assembled by bonding. These sections carry flanges which can be drilled and riveted. The bonding resin is a polyester similar to that used in molding the plastic body components and contains chopped glass fiber. This resin mixed with catalyst is coated on the body flanges, and aluminum rivets are used to hold the parts together until the resin is cured at room temperature. It is necessary to disc grind the mating surfaces to ensure good mating and clean surfaces before bonding, and to smooth the body joints after bonding. The joint itself is covered by trim strips. The great disadvantage of this process compared with the high-speed gate line construction of steel bodies is the much longer time required for preparing the surfaces and curing the bond. Although it is the most satisfactory method for bonding plastic components on low production schedules, it is not competitive with the present method of assembling steel bodies.

Bonding of body sections of prototype aluminum military vehicles and trucks has been investigated with considerable success, although again, speed of construction presents a problem. The advantages of such a process are the formation of a continuous joint which seals out dust and water, elimination of protrusions caused by rivets, and the ability of the entire section to deform without breaking the bond or opening the joint. The application of bonding of side panels and roofs to reinforcing struts in the construction of trailers is becoming increasingly widespread.

Where heat and pressure can be used, the rubber-resin adhesives perform very well and give desired flexibility to the structure. Where only room temperature and contact pressure are available, the bonding of trailer sections must be carried out with neoprene-resin contact adhesive or with epoxy or polyurethane thermosetting materials.

A typical application for thermosetting cements is the bonding of resilient rubber engine mounts and other vibration dampeners. These secure the engine to the frame by floating the engine on rubber, thus isolating the vibration and preventing it from being carried through the frame to the body of the car. Formerly, the adhesives for this application were solutions of chlorinated rubber, which provided good bonding to the metal and the rubber. Cure was accomplished during the vulcanization of the engine mounts. In recent years, more exotic types of adhesives of proprietary composition are used, with tensile strengths up to 1000 psi after cure. Preparation of satisfactory bonds requires precise cleaning and bonderizing of the steel, as well as protection of the steel with the resin coating prior to bonding.

A different use of thermosetting cements is the application of extruded drops ("Hershey drops") between the inner and outer panels of hoods and deck lids, as shown in Fig. 2. Thirty-two drops or more are pattern extruded on to the hood panel; then the inner panel, in the form of a spider-reinforcing member, is installed and spot welded around the outer edges. During the paint-baking operation the drops are cured, under essentially contact pressure, and form spot bonds between the inner and outer panels. Important characteristics of an adhesive for this application are: (1) it must not cold-flow, and (2) it must not have excessive shrinkage. Since it is applied to oiled steel panels, it must be compatible with oil and drawing compounds. The adhesives used are based on either neoprene-resin blends or vinyl plastisols, although plasticized epoxy compositions have been investigated. Adhesives are essentially 100 per cent solids and must be capable of being pumped. Although bonding of the inner and outer panel is primarily to deaden sound and to prevent flutter of the hood, up-grading of the adhesive and the bond has resulted in a considerable increase in structural strength of this component.

APPLICATION OF THERMOPLASTIC ADHESIVES

Thermoplastic adhesives do not require heat or added catalyst to effect a cure, although heat may be utilized to accelerate removal of solvents and water. They are generally composed of natural or

Fig. 2. Application of adhesive drops and assembly of hood inner and outer panels.

synthetic rubbers, resins, oleoresinous materials and asphalt. There are two major types—solvent-dispersed and latex- or water-dispersed adhesives.

The solvent-based adhesives containing elastomers and resins are modified by tackifiers and plasticizers. The solvent acts as a viscosity-controlling agent, making the adhesive easy to apply, and also controls the open time of the cement. Completeness of solvent removal during application is very critical, particularly with nonporous surfaces such as metals or dense rubber parts. Care must also be taken in bonding materials which may remove the plasticizer from the cement or allow the cement to attract the plasticizer away from the material being bonded.

Two advantages of the water-dispersed adhesives are the elimination of fire hazards and their heat resistance, which allows their use on "body-in-white" and passage undamaged through primer and paint ovens. Water-dispersed adhesives are based on either reclaimed rubber and asphalt-water dispersions or polymer latices; moreover they may be applied by either spray or roll coater methods.

Weatherstrip Cements

Sponge rubber weatherstrip as a door seal has been used on cars since 1935. Since its inception, one of the primary means of attaching sponge rubber is by means of thermoplastic adhesives. Weatherstrip cements are applied in a variety of ways, but there are three principal methods:

(1) The one-coat system. The cement is applied to the metal door flanges, and the weatherstrip is pressed onto the flange after a partial evaporation of solvent, while the cement is still tacky.

(2) The two-coat system with reactivation. The adhesive is applied to the door flanges and the weatherstrip and allowed to dry. The cement on the weatherstrip or metal is then reactivated or made tacky with solvent and the weatherstrip pressed onto the coated door flange.

(3) The two-coat system without reactivation. The same cement is applied to the door flanges and the weatherstrip. Attachment is made without reactivation before the cement has dried. In this case the cement must possess a relatively long open time and have high initial bond strength. Figure 3 shows the application of the weatherstrip to the door flanges using the two-coat system.

Cement is generally applied by spray, roll coater or flow-gun. There are many factors which affect the installation of sponge weatherstrip:

(1) Quality of cement—control of viscosity and solids, drying rate, reactivation, softening temperature, high initial bond strength, aging characteristics, effect on paint and sponge rubber.

(2) Quality of weatherstrip—cleanliness of surface and nonbleeding plasticizers.

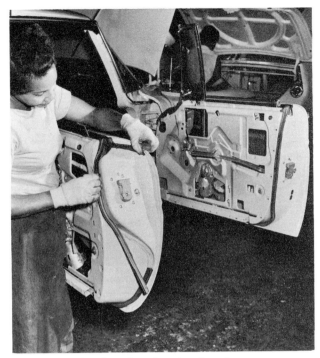

Fig. 3. Application of weatherstrip to door flange by two-coat process.

(3) Design of door and weatherstrip—no sharp inside curves, constant crosssection of weatherstrip for roll coater.

(4) Rate of installation of weatherstrip—affected by open time of cement, reactivation ease, effect of environmental conditions on drying rate, and physical space available for operation.

(5) Film thickness—optimum thickness is 10 mils.

(6) Attitude and ability of workmen—cements must be applied properly by skilled workmen.

Although reclaim rubber cements have been used for installation of weatherstrip in former times, at present the most satisfactory adhesives consist of formulations based on neoprene rubber and modified phenolic resins. Tackifiers and different solvents are employed to control open time, viscosity, and initial bond strengths.

Trim Adhesives for Fabrics

Generally, the installation of fabrics on seats and backs is simply a mechanical operation involving stretching the fabric over the foam cushion and springs and tying or hog ringing behind the seat or seat back. However, certain fabrics, notably nylon, are bonded to a thin plastic foam pad which holds the fabrics in place and gives a soft rich feel. The adhesive is generally a solvent-type cement. After joining the fabric and rubber pads, the parts are placed in a heated press for 1 min to complete the bonding and emboss the fabric.

Fabric headlining in the automobile is fastened to the frame of the back light, rear quarter windows and windshield by means of a cement and trim tabs which must hold the fabric in place until the garnish moldings are installed. The cement is usually a solvent-based GRS-resin type which must have high initial adhesion and long tack time.

Trim adhesives are also used for the bonding of vinyl to plastic or vinyl to foam in the construction of arm rests. Although the majority of the arm rests are currently manufactured by foaming polyurethane directly on vinyl film which has been preformed in vacuum molds, there is still some use of GRS latex cements to bond vinyl to foam, for interior trim.

Finally, the rear shelf, which is inserted between the back seat and the lower edge of the back light, generally consists of a vinyl film bonded to steel or to KB board, using again a rubber latex adhesive.

Trim Adhesives for Other Applications

There are many places in an automobile requiring bonding of films, fiber silencer pads, poly-

Fig. 4. Bonding of fiber silencer pads to underside of car roof.

ethylene and vinoleum to body parts. Figure 4 shows the bonding of fiber silencer pads to the underside of the roof section. These pads, usually consisting of sisal fiber, are effective in reducing noise and insulating the interior of the car to excessive heat or cold. A solvent-based GRS-resin adhesive is sprayed on the roof section, and before it dries, the fiber pad is pressed into place. In addition to having high initial tack, the cement must have sufficient temperature resistance to withstand the heat of paint ovens without softening.

A material widely used in surfacing the floors of Suburbans is vinoleum, which is a scuff-resistant, pigmented vinyl composition backed with asphalt felt. The cement for bonding die-cut and contoured vinoleum parts to metal is a neoprene-resin-solvent type which is applied both to the enameled surface and the asphalt felt backing. Immediately after application of the cement, the parts are brought together, heated to a relatively low temperature and repressurized to give a smooth continuous bonded section.

Similarly, the rear wheel housing in Suburbans are covered by a supported vinyl film bonded to enameled metal. A GRS latex cement is sprayed on the film back and the housing. The film is installed and pressurized manually.

As shown in Fig. 5, a very interesting trim ap-

Fig. 5. Bonding of PE film (shower curtain) to door inner panel.

plication is the bonding of polyethylene film inside doors to prevent ingress of water, dirt and air. This "shower curtain" is installed by spraying or flow brushing a GRS-resin-solvent adhesive around the edge of the door inner panel and pressing the polyethylene into place by hand.

Miscellaneous Applications of Thermoplastic Adhesives

Thermoplastic adhesives are used to hold shims, gaskets or parts in place until assembled. After assembly of the parts, the cement no longer has a functional requirement because the parts are mechanically retained. Such cements have moderate drying times, fair initial adhesion and good brushing qualities. They are generally based on GRS-resin-solvent and neoprene-solvent systems. Typical applications are the cementing of neoprene gaskets to the flanges of a heater housing, and the holding of metal head gaskets and miscellaneous paper and cork gaskets in engine assembly.

APPLICATIONS OF SEALERS AND SOUND DEADENERS

The primary requirement of sealers and sound deadeners is that they adhere well and remain in place for the life of the car. Generally the cohesive strength of such materials is low compared to adhesives. In contrast to adhseives, however, they frequently must have unique properties such as the ability to adhere to oily surfaces, non-slumping properties, heat expanding characteristics, etc. It is not easy to classify sealers either as thermosetting or thermoplastic materials; however the most important types, such as spot-welding sealers and seam sealers have thermosetting properties. They are required to set up or cure when the car bodies are passed through paint curing ovens. Sealers are based on combinations of asphalt and elastomeric or resinous polymers; moreover they contain fillers and other modifiers, particularly thixotropic agents.

Present day sealers and sound deadeners are essentially 100 per cent solids; yet they must be capable of being pumped from a central station to the use location by means of 40 to 1 or higher ratio pumps through a header system. At the point of use, the sealers are applied by the use of hand or foot-operated flow guns.

Seam Sealers

Seam sealers are employed on the underbody of the car to seal spot-welded seams on both horizontal and vertical surfaces (Fig. 6). After application of a bead, the sealer is generally brushed out to ensure bridging of gaps as large as ⅛ in. wide. They may be applied before or after the prime coat, and even when subjected to paint baking temperatures as high as 400°F, they must not flow, slump, or bubble. The resultant cured

Fig. 6. Application of 100% solids seam sealer by flow gun to underbody seams.

material must exhibit satisfactory adhesion and nonbrittleness at temperatures below −10°F and sufficient toughness to permit walking on the sealer in later trim operations. Vertical seams on the inside of the body are sealed with the same type of sealer; hence the thixotropic nonflow characteristic is important. Basically asphalt or Gilsonite, these sealers also contain plasticizing oils, powdered fillers and other modifiers.

Spot Welding Sealers

A difficult problem in the automotive industry has been the sealing of inaccessible seams formed by spot welding. This problem was solved by the application of spot welding sealers in the form of a bead to the welding flange of the metal surface. The welding flanges are then brought together and spot welded directly through the sealer.

In the past the major problems with this technique were to obtain a satisfactory spot weld, to keep the sealer in place until the parts are welded, and to seal large gaps. Today these problems have been almost completely eliminated by the use of spot-welding sealers capable of expanding or blowing upon application of heat to as much as 180 per cent of the original bead size. In addition, modern heat-expandable, weld-through sealers are essentially odor-free, adhere to oily surfaces, and have no flow after application; nevertheless they still can be pumped and applied by flow runs. A recent innovation in this type of sealer is the incorporation of nonflammable characteristics, which reduces the possibility of fires during the welding operation.

Exterior Seam Sealers

In addition to the spot-welded body seams, which can be sealed from the interior with an asphaltic type of seam sealer, there are welded body seams not accessible by this procedure. Where the depression is large, as in the joint between rear quarter panels and the rear trunk section or the roof, body solders are used for filling the gap. Where the gaps are smaller and the seam continuous, exterior organic seam sealers are employed.

The roof drip rail section where the roof and side rail are seam welded requires sealing to prevent corrosion of the welding flanges or leakage and to improve appearance. This section is sealed by applying through a flow gun a bead of sealer at the bottom of the trough formed by the drip rail extension of the side rail and the roof, as shown in Fig. 7. The drip rail sealer may be applied before prime or after prime, but before the application of

Fig. 7. Application of vinyl plastisol exterior seam sealer to drip rail.

the final top coat. The heat from the subsequent paint baking operation levels and sets up the sealer. On vertical exterior surfaces, a similar type of seam sealer is used which must have no flow after application.

The sealers presently used are based on vinyl plastisols having 100 per cent solids, no shrinkage, and controlled flow. These are most satisfactorily applied before prime, to produce better adhesion and reduce the tendency for the sealer to bleed through the top coat enamel if applied after prime.

Windshield Weatherstrip Sealers

Although the windshield and back light are mounted in rubber weatherstrips, sealers have been used for considerable time to seal out water completely. With the recent advent of the large wrap-around windshield, in addition to reducing movement of glass in the weatherstrip channel, the sealer should also possess the ability to reknit or reform broken bonds when movement occurs. The sealer used on the glass channel of the weatherstrip is a polybutene type which is applied to the weatherstrip channel before the glass is inserted and the weatherstrip laced up. A pumpable caulk sealer is also used to seal between the sheet metal fence of the body and the rubber weatherstrip. The two sealers are generally applied to the weatherstrip at the same time as shown in Fig. 8.

Fig. 8. Application of polybutene and pumpable caulk sealers to windshield weatherstrip.

Properties of the polybutene sealers are quite critical; moreover they must have limited flow, should not discolor painted surfaces or safety glass interliners, must not affect rubber, and should not be affected by water or windshield washer solutions.

Putty Sealers

As indicated, exterior seams which require a good surface finish and paint appearance are generally sealed with vinyl plastisols. Other sections of the body, which may be too large to be sealed with regular flow gun sealers and where appearance is not critical, are sealed with putties based on vinyl plastisols or drying oils. In addition, putties are employed as sealers where subassemblies are attached to the body such as the heater housing to the fire wall or the rear tail light housing to the body. The principal disadvantage of putty sealers lies in the necessity of manual application rather than the flow gun technique.

Thread Sealers

Natural and synthetic rubber latex and reclaimed rubber dispersions are used as stud bolt thread sealers to prevent oil, water and glycol leakage. Neoprene latex, of course, is required for sealing against oil leakage around bolts in engine blocks.

Sound Deadeners

Sound deadeners are used extensively in the automobile, primarily on the underbody, the door inner panels and the quarter panels. Generally applied by spraying, they have either a high solids content or essentially 100 per cent solids. They must have excellent adhesion and anti-sag characteristics in addition to their primary property of sound dampening. Generally, these materials are solvent cutbacks of asphalt containing a high proportion of dense fillers and other modifiers. A minimum density for a sound deadener is 13 lb/gal.

Body Solders and Glazing Compounds

Currently in the manufacture of automobiles, lead-tin solders are used to fill large exterior gaps in major body seams and joints. The lead solders are easily applied and worked; they require no setup time as do thermoplastic materials. Their chief disadvantages are the poisonous character of lead dust and their effect on body enamels which may come in contact with them; consequently vinyl glazing compounds are frequently applied over the lead solder after sanding to prevent interaction with alkyd type enamels.

Plastic body solders have the great advantage of being nontoxic, low density, and nonreactive with paint. Considerable use is made in auto repair shops of plastic solder based on polyester or epoxy resins; these are required to have excellent adhesion to steel, low shrinkage and good aging properties. In original equipment manufacture, where as many as 80 cars an hour may be produced on a production line, the application and cure time for plastic solders is excessive. Another disadvantage is shrinkage of the material on curing or aging. Some very satisfactory compositions have been developed for this use, but they all appear to be more difficult to apply or more time-consuming than the application of lead solders.

POTENTIAL APPLICATIONS

Although the automobile industry has come a long way in developing applications for adhesives and sealers in automotive manufacture, there is still much progress to be made, particularly in the use of thermosetting or structural cements.

At present, the outer panels of deck lids, hoods and doors are crimped over the inner panels and then spot welded. This is an ideal application for thermosetting adhesives, since the crimping exerts the necessary pressure and holds the structure together until the bond is cured. A continuous bead of adhesive applied around the outer edge, in addition to having the necessary strength, should seal the joint and have a sound dampening effect. A similar type of application is the attachment of the roof to the roof side rail, which is presently seam welded.

The success in sound deadening and improving structural rigidity of the hood through use of "Hershey drop" spot bonds between the inner and outer panels, suggests the possibility of achieving the same effect in bonding the roof bows to the car roof.

Designers feel that it would be very desirable for the windshield and back light to become more of a load-bearing structural component of the car body. This requires a stronger attachment of the glass to the body, which might be accomplished by actually bonding the windshield and back light to the body fence with thermosetting adhesives.

Much experimentation indicates the feasibility of using structural adhesives to bond parts of the transmission and the power train which cannot easily be welded or riveted. Particularly if the bonded joint is designed to perform in torsional shear, tensile shear or pure tension, with a minimum of peel stresses, it has been proved that existing rubber-resin or epoxy adhesives are more than adequate for the job.

With regard to body components, it is apparent now that body solders can be produced having the ease and speed of application and cure required for original equipment manufacture. Initial strength and hardness also appear adequate, but more time will be necessary to check out shrinkage and cracking characteristics on aging. In the more distant future, it is probable that adhesives and techniques will be perfected for the permanent attachment of trim strips and medallions to the exterior car body.

It is probable that continued advances will be made in all types of seam and body sealers. Particularly with regard to exterior seam sealers applied after prime, new sealers will be available which have better adhesion, will not bleed through paint, and can be cured at much lower temperatures than at present.

— 58 —

Nonwoven Fabrics

Francis Bozzacco*

Chemical Division,
Goodyear Tire & Rubber Co.
Akron, Ohio

Fabrics made without weaving are the oldest type of textile material known to man. The mechanical wool felts were made from animal fibers by the process of felting long before the time of recorded history. The nonwoven or bonded-fiber fabrics which are attracting so much attention today, however, are new products largely developed in the last ten years. They have been made possible by new developments in processing equipment and the availability of suitable polymeric binders. Bonded nonwoven fabrics represent a new phase of the textile industry that is in the early stages of its economic and technical development.

The manufacture of wool felt depends largely on the unique directional characteristics of the wool fiber. The nonwoven fabrics, however, have a structure produced by the formation of permanent bonds where individual fibers touch each other. This bonding may be produced by heat treating fiber blends containing a small percentage of thermoplastic fibers or by the application of an external polymeric binder. Wool fibers are not used to any great extent in bonded fiber fabrics in this country.

Nonwoven fabrics have the advantage that they can be made from almost any type of fiber. A number of different binder systems are available. By the proper selection of the fiber blend and binder system, a wide range of products can be made. The ability of nonwoven fabric manufacturers to engineer their products for specific end applications has been an important factor in the success of bonded-fiber fabrics.

Wool felts and nonwoven fabrics have similar characteristics. They both have a uniformity and

lack of woven structure which is an advantage in many types of fabrication. Both products are quite porous and indeed their application as a filter media has become important.

The absence of a woven structure in nonwovens results in a fabric which normally has a considerable degree of stretch. With the proper selection of binders, the stretched fabrics will show a high degree of elastic recovery. This property is partially responsible for the use of nonwoven fabrics for the backing of vinyl film and sheeting. The nonwoven backed vinyl has many of the desirable properties of vinyl sheeting backed with a knitted fabric, but at a lower cost.

Nonwoven fabrics are also being engineered to replace woven fabrics in garment-type applications. Here they provide an entirely new type of material for the textile designer to work with. In some respects, the nonwoven material perform like wool felt, but with greater resistance to deformation by washing and by wearing. Nonwovens have a considerable amount of strength, and consequently, can be made in light weights. Many unusual effects can be produced by printing and other special finishing operations.

SELECTING OF FIBER
OR FIBER BLEND

In selection of fibers for use in making a nonwoven fabric is governed by many factors among which are: desired finish properties, economic limitations and processing characteristics. Many

* Present address Enjay Chemical Co., Akron, Ohio.

fabrics will contain a blend of three or more basic types of fibers. Fibers being used today include cotton, viscose, rayon, nylon, and acetate rayon. Many types of nonwovens are made with re-used or reprocessed fibers. The fiber length plays an important part. A certain percentage of medium-to-long stable fiber is desirable to improve the handling properties of the unsaturated web. As most web-forming equipment has a relatively low through put, the effect of fiber blends on production rates must be considered.

In 1958 65,000,000 pounds of cellulosic and synthetic fibers were utilized in the manufacture of nonwoven fabrics. Cotton and rayon constituted 90 to 95 per cent of the total. The newer synthetic fibers, however, are becoming more prominent in the field and offer properties not entirely obtainable with cellulosics. Nylon and acetate are the two most frequently encountered synthetics.

The past few years have seen an increased amount of the newer synthetic fibers such as acrylics, polyesters, polyamides and inorganic fibers in nonwovens. Among the desirable features offered by these fibers are good chemical and electrical properties, increased resistance to creasing, good resilience, and also resistance to heat and light.

SELECTING AND COMPOUNDING OF BINDER

The very rapid growth of the nonwoven fabrics industry is due in a large extent to the availability of relatively new synthetic chemical bonding agents in almost an infinite number. Irrespective of what fiber is used or on what type of equipment it is produced, nonwoven fabrics are no better than the binder which holds the fiber web together. The bonding agents may be grouped under the following classifications:

(1) Emulsion binder systems.
(2) Solution binder systems.
(3) Thermoplastic fibers or heat-sensitive fibers.
(4) Thermoplastic and thermosetting powder resins.

In certain applications the binder system will be a combination of two or more of above systems.

The bonding agent constitutes the greater part of the weight of the nonwoven fabric. Major factors in the choice of binder for nonwoven fabrics are:

(1) Limitation of saturating and drying equipment.
(2) End use requirement.

(3) Fiber blend to be used.
(4) Cost and economy of binder.
(5) Mechanical stability, particle size and other latex and binder properties.
(6) Type of adhesion and heat sealability.
(7) Degree of firmness or softness imparted to the textile fabric.
(8) Migratory behavior of binder.
(9) Stability to ultraviolet light and heat.
(10) Abrasion, solvent and water resistance.

There are two classes of nonwovens based on binder content: (1) containing less than 25 per cent binder solids based on the fiber weight; and (2) containing from 30 to 300 per cent binder solids based on the fiber weight. In class (1) the fiber properties should predominate and form the strength of the system. In class (2) the nonwoven functions as carriers for the binder which not only is the adhesive but also the bulking agent. Most of the clothing-type nonwovens are in class (2) and do not allow use of cheap fillers which hurt the desired end properties.[1]

An ideal binder system should have the following properties.[2]

(1) Strength approaching that of the fiber.
(2) Binder location. If the binder could be located only at the points of contact of fibers, less binder would be required without impairing its contribution to fabric strength. Binder which merely coats the fiber length adds to the cost of the fabric, and increases its density, both undesirable characteristics. In one patented process a nonwoven manufacturer concentrates binder at the interface by applying a foamed emulsion binder first to one side of a web of fibers and then to the other.[3]
(3) Specific adhesion to fiber should be high. With the binders available at present, which have relatively low strength, specific adhesion is not yet a problem.
(4) Elastic recovery or the ability of the fabric to return to its original length after it has been stretched by a small amount.
(5) Other factors. The final requirements of a nonwoven fabric will determine which of the following properties are important.
   (a) Good resistance to damage by sunlight, laundering and dry cleaning.
   (b) High dimensional stability.
   (c) Freedom from discoloration during the life of the fabric.
   (d) Good crease resistance, crease recovery and resilience.

Emulsion Binder System

The water-based emulsion systems comprise by far the largest class of binders used in nonwoven fabrics. Synthetic materials used to produce an emulsion-binder system are of the thermoplastic or thermosetting types.

There are at least twenty chemical types of synthetic latices in addition to natural rubber latex. Some of these latices include polymers, copolymers, terepolymers or graft copolymers of the following: butadiene-styrene, butadiene-acrylonitrile, polybutadiene, polystyrene, neoprene, acrylic polymers, polyamides, polyesters, fluorocarbon polymers, vinyl acetals, vinyl chloride polymers, vinyl esters, vinyl pyridine polymers, vinylidene chloride polymers, rubber resin blend polymers and cross-linked carboxyl-type polymers.

Of all these synthetic polymers the ones in Table 1 represent those used in greatest volume for nonwoven fabric manufacture: butadiene-styrene, butadiene-acrylonitrile, polyvinyl acetate, acrylics and polyvinyl chloride.

It has been estimated that the butadiene-styrene types, both resin and rubber, supply the needs for more than 50 per cent of all the latex applications. Butadiene acryonitrile accounts for 25 per cent and polyvinyl acetate most of the remaining 25 per cent.

Butadiene-Styrene Latices. Polymers based on butadiene-styrene offer a factory of economy in industry. These polymers have an extreme range of properties from soft to hard and with varying degrees of tack. They are tough, durable and are compatible with many resins and modifiers. The range of properties is directly related to the proportion of styrene polymerized with butadiene, with styrene contributing hardness and butadiene contributing softness.

The butadiene-styrene latices are efficient binders for textile fibers. In general, latices having more than fifty parts of styrene are recommended and are considered as resinous-type latex binders.

A typical starting formula using a resin latex would be:

	Dry Wt.	% T.S.	Wet Wt.
Butadiene-styrene latex	100	48	208
Wingstay S emulsion[a]	1	60	1.7
Color pigment dispersion[b]	5–10	50	10.20

[a] Antioxidant, recommended to insure good aging if the latex does not contain antioxidant. See Table for supplier.

[b] Amount will vary considerably depending on the type of pigment used.

The permanence and wash resistance of the butadiene-styrene latex binders may be improved by utilizing a conventional type cure. The following formulation is given.

	Dry Wt.	% T.S.	Wet Wt.
Butadiene-styrene latex	100	48	208
Zinc oxide (dispersion)	5	50	10
Sulfur (dispersion)	1.45	73	2.0
"Wingstay S" (emulsion)	1.0	60	1.7
"Zetax" (dispersion)	2.0	30	4.0

T.S. = 46.5 per cent.

Cure 2–4 min at 280°F after web is dry.

* Accelerator (zinc mercaptobenzothiazole). R. T. Vanderbilt Co. Comparable materials are available from other manufacturers. See Table 3.

One-package curing dispersions are available from many suppliers (Table 3), e.g., R. T. Vanderbilt Co., General Latex & Chemical Co., Alco Oil & Chemical Co.

Various ratios of butadiene-styrene latices can be used. These vary from the high styrene resin latices to the rubber type latices depending upon the hand desired.

The incorporation of 5–10 parts of melamine resin (on dry basis) may also be considered to improve adhesion to synthetic fibers.

Butadiene-Acrylonitrile Latices. Polymerization of butadiene and acrylonitrile make various types of nitrile latices depending on proportions of the monomers used. The acrylonitrile copolymers are noted for their excellent resistance to hydrocarbons and other solvents used in dry cleaning, and their good binding and adhesive properties. These latices provide good to excellent tear strength on webs composed of cellulosic and synthetic fibers.

Several possible combinations of a copolymer of butadiene-acrylonitrile blend with a polyvinyl chloride copolymer are suitable binders. The following formulations are given.

	Dry Wt.	% T.S.	Wet Wt.
Butadiene-acrylonitrile latex	80	42.5	186.6
Polyvinyl chloride copolymer	20	52.0	38.5

T.S. = 44.5 per cent.

Saturated webs should be dried and subjected to fusion temperatures of 300 to 350°F for ½ to 1 min.

Either a high or medium acrylonitrile latex may be used. A medium acrylonitrile latex may be substituted for a high acrylonitrile latex to give a lower cost and a softer hand, but the product will also have lower solvent and oil resistance. By varying the ratio of acrylonitrile latex to vinyl chloride latex, a whole range of hand, as well as physical properties, can be obtained. Increasing the polyvinyl chloride latex content will give a stiffer hand, but with increased wet and dry tensile strength.

Bath solids should be adjusted by addition of soft water to give the desired binder content in the finished fabric.

Antifoaming agents may be added if foaming is excessive. The Silicone antifoams are very effective in the range of .01 per cent, on the total wet weight.

Curing agents may be incorporated in the formulation to impart special properties such as improved solvent or oil resistance.

Where necessary, wetting properties of the saturating bath may be improved by addition of surfactants such as "Emulphor" ON-870, "Tergitol" #4, etc. (See Table 3.)

Pigment color dispersions may be added to give a wide range of colors.

The binder system mentioned is suitable for use with webs of cotton fibers, or cotton and rayon blends. Products produced are used for industrial wiping cloths, filters, window cleaning cloths, etc.

A further modification of the first formulation is suggested to serve as a binder in nonwoven fabrics for other industrial applications:

	Dry Wt.	% T.S.	Wet Wt.
Butadiene-acrylonitrile latex	60.0	42.5	141.2
Polyvinylchloride latex	30.0	52.0	57.7
Dicapryl phthalate emulsion	10.0	50.0	20.0

% Total solids = 45.5.

Other suitable plasticizers would include "Flexol" TOF and DOP as primary plasticizers and "Conoco" H-300 as a secondary plasticizer. Selection of a plasticizer should be based in part on its minimum volatility during drying and fusion. (See Table 3.)

Drying should be followed by fusion at 300 to 350°F for ½ to 1 min.

Using this binder system with webs of cotton or cotton-synthetic blends, fabrics can be produced suitable for coating and lamination. These fabrics may be calendered or uncalendered, depending on the applications. This binder system exhibits good adhesion to vinyl films or sheeting in electronic sealing, heat lamination and other combining methods.

Cured Butadiene-acrylonitrile Latex Compounds. The usual techniques of compounding butadiene-acrylonitrile for cure may be used. A typical formulation is as follows:

	Dry Wt.	% T.S.	Wet Wt.
Butadiene-acrylonitrile latex	100.0	42.5	235.6
Ammonium caseinate			
(10% soln.)	1.0	10.0	10.0
Zinc oxide (dispersion)	3.0	50.0	6.0
Sulfur (dispersion)	2.0	73.0	2.75
"Rotax" (dispersion)	2.0	50.0	4.0
"Setsit" #5 (mix 1:1 with			
water before using)	1.0	50.0	2.0

% Total solids = 42.0.

"Rotax" is a mercaptobenzothiazole accelerator and "Setsit" #5 is a liquid dithiocarbamate accelerator. The "Setsit" #5 should be diluted with an equal amount of water before adding to the latex. Comparable materials from other manufacturers could be used. (See Table 3.)

The ammonium caseinate is effective as a dispersing agent or stabilizer to improve effectiveness of the curing

system. Therefore, the order of addition should be as given.

Adjust solids with soft water to control level of dry add-on.

It is difficult to give exact cure recommendations because curing and drying are usually done at the same time. The rate of drying will vary greatly with individual ovens. Until dry, the temperature of the web will not go much above 220°F. At this temperature curing would require about 15 to 20 min. As each degree rise in curing temperature will cut the curing time required approximately in half, a good rule of thumb is to provide for approximately 2 min in the oven at 280° after the web has become dry.

This type of formulation proves a suitable binder for webs of nylon or nylon blends. The fabric has application for garment use, as lining fabrics in women's and children's wear, and in men's suitings. With properties similar to crinoline but having a greater "bounce" and permanence, this fabric can stand repeated dry cleaning or laundering. Both the Stoddard solvent and perchlorethylene cleaning methods can be used due to the excellent solvent resistance of these latices.

Fabrics produced from nylon or from other synthetic fibers, using the above binder formulation, also are used by the coating trade for polyvinylchloride coatings. Differences in the fiber blends, fiber-to-binder ratio, and in the finishing or aftertreatment of the bonded web are introduced to meet various market requirements.

A modification of the conventional sulfur cure is often used to promote adhesion of the binder to the synthetic fibers. Thermosetting resins in a latex system have been used for a number of years for this purpose, and it is found that they also impart a "cure" similar to the conventional sulfur cure. In addition, they improve the light and heat aging of the latex binder.

A suggested starting formulation is:

	Dry Wt.	% T.S.	Wet Wt.
Butadiene-acrylonitrile latex	100.0	42.5	235.6
Ammonium caseinate			
(10% soln.)	1.5	10.0	15.0
Melamine resin	12.0	80.0	15.0
Melamine catalyst	0.6	35.0	1.7
Sulfur (dispersion)	1.0	73.0	1.4
Titanium dioxide (dispersion)	8.0	50.0	16.0
Zinc oxide (dispersion)	3.0	50.0	6.0
"Rotax" (dispersion)	2.0	50.0	4.0
"Setsit" 5 (mix 1:1 with			
water before adding)	1.0	50.0	2.0

% Total solids = 40.8.

(a) Suitable melamine resins are "Aerotex Resin" M-3 and "Resloom" M-75, (Table 3.)

(b) Suitable catalyst is Catalyst AC. (Table 3.)

(c) Cure: 2 to 4 min at 280°F. See note (c) and (d) of preceding formula.

(d) Further modification would include use of tinting colors, plasticizers, and surface-active materials to produce desired variations.

Acrylic Polymers. Acrylic polymers are based solely on acrylic monomers such as methyl acrylate, ethyl acrylate, methyl methacrylate, and so forth.

The acrylic polymers are internally plasticized and any degree of web stability can be obtained. The ratio of monomer is the determining factor in providing soft or firm film characteristics. These polymers provide good durability to laundering and dry cleaning. This durability is also enhanced by the use of thermosetting resins. These polymers are characterized by good clarity, stability to light and aging and resistance to water and solvent.

Polyvinyl Acetate. Webs bonded with polyvinyl acetate lack the resilience which in many cases is desirable in this field. The degree of recovery is relatively poor and adhesion to many of the synthetic fibers is marginal. Fastness to laundering and dry cleaning ranges from poor to fair.

Vinyl Chloride Polymers. Polymers of vinyl chloride show marked color changes and increasing stiffness unless stabilizers are used. As a class, the polyvinyl-chloride polymers are not resistant to oxidation which causes marked discoloration and stiffness. Recent work in graft copolymers has led to the development of newer and improved types which are internally plasticized and relatively resistant to degradation by ultraviolet light and heat.[4]

The polyvinyl-chloride polymers provide a low degree of elongation with fairly good tensile strength. Dry cleanability of this group will range from fair to good although wash fastness is in many cases marginal.

Solution Binders

Solution binder systems include both the aqueous and organic solvent systems. Materials such as starch, polyvinyl alcohol, amylose, glues, casings, alginates and cellulose xanthogenate can be prepared as aqueous solutions and applied to the web of fibers. Solvent solutions produce nonwoven fabrics which are resistant to degradation by water. These solutions are usually used as carriers for a binder; the solvent is flashed off and the polymeric binder coating remains. In some cases the solvents themselves function as binders by mildly attacking the fibers. The softened fibers can be pressed together forming a fiber-to-fiber bond network. Solutions of thermosetting resins such as the silicones and phenolic resins are also used in binding

inorganic fibers into the webs. These binders are costly, but may be needed for high heat resistance and electrical properties.

Cellulose dispersions such as cupra-ammonium cellulose or xanthate are somewhat more complicated than most other binding agents. Cellulose bonded fabrics have high wet strength. The bonding agent is insoluble in organic solvents and most inorganic solvents. Moreover the cellulose is odorless, tasteless and nontoxic and will not soften at elevated temperatures.

Thermoplastic Fiber Bonding

Thermoplastic fibers may be used as binder materials. The thermoplastic fibers are bonded with cellulose fibers in the picker, and the picker lap is carded into a web. The web is then pressed over heated rolls or oven-dried cans to soften the thermoplastic fibers, which bind the whole web together. Usually the thermoplastic fiber with a lower melting point than the base fiber makes up from 10 to 30 per cent of the weight of the finished fabric.

Fibers which are widely used in this manner are cellulose acetate and vinyl chloride-vinyl acetate copolymers. The softening point of copolymers of vinyl chloride-vinyl acetate is 170°F., and for cellulose acetate 350°F. Other thermoplastic fibers used are polyvinyl chloride, polyethylene, vinylidene chloride polymers and copolymers, and polyester fibers. According to one paper[5] the choice of thermoplastic fiber is of great importance in obtaining optimum properties of the nonwoven product desired. It was found that the best fabrics were produced when the binder fiber and the base fiber were chemically similar. The length of the binder was relatively important as long as the proportion by weight remained the same.

The thermoplastic fiber technique of binding is fairly costly when compared to other methods. Nonwoven fabrics made by fiber binder technique go into ribbons, tapes, decorative fabric and filter fabrics.

Thermoplastic and Thermosetting Resin Powders

Thermosetting and thermoplastic resins can be used in powder forms as a binder material and provide binding in somewhat the same manner as the thermoplastic binders. The powder is applied to the fibers during or after web formation. The bonding is produced when the web is passed through hot rolls or a flat press to produce a non-

TABLE 1. NONWOVEN BONDING AGENTS.

Types	Trade Name	Manufacturers
Butadiene-acrylonitrile	Chemigum	Goodyear Tire & Rubber Co.
	Hycar	B. F. Goodrich Chemical Co.
	Polyco	Borden Co.
	Nitrex	Naugatuck Chemical
Butadiene-styrene	Pliolite	Goodyear Tire & Rubber Co.
	Hycar	B. F. Goodrich Chemical Co.
	Tylac	International Latex
	Dow Latices	Dow Chemical
Acrylic resins	Rhoplex	Rohm & Haas
	Hycar	B. F. Goodrich Chemical Co.
	Gelva	Shawinigan Resins Corp.
Vinyl chloride	Pliovic	Goodyear Tire & Rubber Co.
	Geon	B. F. Goodrich Chemical Co.
	Dow	Dow Chemical Co.
Vinyl acetate	Elvacet	Du Pont
	Geon	B. F. Goodrich Chemical Co.
	Celanese	Celanese Corp. of America
	Polyco	Borden Co.
Phenolic resins	Synco	Bakelite Co.
		Synco Resins
Melamine resins	Aerotex	American Cyanamid
	Resloom	Monsanto Chemical
Urea formaldehyde	Durez	Durez Plastics
	Catalin	Catalin Corp.
	Synsize	Synco Resins
	Rhonite	Rohm & Haas
Vinyl alcohol	Elvanol	Du Pont
	Lemol	Borden Co.
Natural rubber latex	Natural Latex	General Latex & Chemical Corp.
		Firestone Tire & Rubber Co.

BINDER MANUFACTURERS

American Cyanamid Co.
Borden Co.
B. F. Goodrich Chemical Co.
Dow Chemical Co.
Dewey & Almy (Div. of W. R. Grace & Co.)
E I du Pont de Nemours & Co.
Firestone Tire & Rubber Co.
General Latex and Chemical Corp.

Goodyear Tire & Rubber Co., Chemical Div.
International Latex Corp.
Monsanto Chemical Corp.
National Starch and Chemical Products, Inc.
Naugatuck Chemical Div. U. S. Rubber Co.
Rohm & Haas Co.
Wica Chemical Inc.

woven fabric. Only a limited amount of work has been carried out to develop a powder-binder system. The problem of powder dusting out of the web before heat is applied and the uneven distribution of powder in the web makes this process difficult to use. Thermoplastic powders such as copolymers of vinyl chloride and vinyl acetate may be used effectively. Webs bonded with these resins generally contain from 15 to 30 per cent powder based on the final weight of the fabric.

Thermosetting resin powders such as melamine, melamine-urea, urea-formaldehyde, and phenol-formaldehyde condensates are also employed in this application.

WEB FORMATION AND EQUIPMENT

The choice of equipment which will be required for web formation depends on the types of nonwovens to be produced.[10-17] There are two

TABLE 2. FIBERS USED IN NONWOVEN FABRICS.

Synthetic Fibers

Nylon	a linear polymeric amide fiber	Du Pont American Enka Industrial Rayon
Acrylics	acrylonitrile polymers	Du Pont Chemstrand Corp. Dow Chemical Union Carbide & Chemical B. F. Goodrich Chemical Tennessee Eastman
Vinyl derivatives	vinyl chloride-vinyl acetate vinylidene chloride-vinyl chloride	American Viscose Corp. Dow Chemical Firestone
Polyesters		Beaunit Mills Inc. Du Pont Tennessee Eastman
Glass fibers		Owens Corning Johns Manville

Man-made Fibers

Rayon	Regenerated cellulose product manufactured from cotton linters and/or wood pulp	American Viscose Celanese Corp. of America American Enka Courtaulds North American Rayon Hartford Rayon
Acetate and triacetate	cellulose acetate fiber	Celanese Corp. of America

FIBER MANUFACTURERS

American Viscose Corp.	Eastman Chemical Products, Inc.
American Enka Corp.	E I du Pont de Nemours & Co., Inc.
American Bemberg	Industrial Rayon Corp.
Beaunit Mills Inc. Fibers Div.	North American Rayon Corp.
Chemstrand Corp.	The Saran Yarns Co.
Courtaulds Inc.	The Dow Chemical Co.
Celanese Corporation of America	Union Carbide Chemical Co.

basic fiber structures possible for nonwovens: oriented web structures and random web structures. In the former, the fibers are essentially parallelized, resulting in the nonwoven fabric with good strength properties in the machine direction, but little or no strength in the transverse direction.

The random web, on the other hand, is characterized by a complete lack of parallelism of the fibers, resulting in a fabric with equal strength in all directions.

A third type of nonwoven, called the cross-lay, represents the attempt to produce a fabric with good strength properties both machine direction and transverse direction, but utilizing the oriented fiber type of web formation. For cross-lay non-wovens, oriented webs are laid down along the machine direction, while other sets of oriented webs are laid down in the transverse direction. Equipment requirements for the cross-lay type of non-woven are essentially the same as for the oriented web type although placement of the equipment must be altered to achieve the web formation desired. The oriented web and the cross-lay non-woven are manufactured on conventional textile equipment. For their production openers, pickers and cards are required.

The first two operations, opening and picking, take the fibers as received in the bale and perform loosening and cleaning functions primarily, transforming the fibers into what is known as a

TABLE 3. MATERIAL SUPPLIERS.

Material	Suppliers
"Wingstay" S	Goodyear Tire & Rubber Co., Chemical Div., Akron
"Wingstay" S emulsions	General Latex & Chemical Corp., Cambridge, Mass.
"Zetax" (zinc mercaptobenzothiazole)	R. T. Vanderbilt Co., East Norwalk, Conn.
"Rotax" (mercaptobenzothiazole)	R. T. Vanderbilt Co., East Norwalk, Conn.
"Setsit" #5 (soluble dithiocarbamate)	R. T. Vanderbilt Co., East Norwalk, Conn.
Sulfur-curing dispersions	R. T. Vanderbilt Co., East Norwalk, Conn.
Melamine resins	
"Aerotex" M-3	American Cyanamid Co., Bound Brook, N. J.
"Resloom" M-75	Monsanto Chemical Co., Springfield, Mass.
"Catalyst AC"	Monsanto Chemical Co., Springfield, Mass.
Dioctyl phthalate (DOP)	Monsanto Chemical Co., Springfield, Mass.
"Concord" M-300	Continental Oil Co.
Dicapryl phthalate	Ohio Apex Co., Nitro, West Va.
"Flexol" TOF	Carbide & Carbon Chemical Co., New York, N. Y.
"Tergitol" #4	Carbide & Carbon Chemical Co., New York, N. Y.
"Triton" X-100	Rohm & Haas, Philadelphia, Pa.
Silicone antifoam	
DC Antifoam AF	Dow Corning, Midland, Mich.
GE 60 Antifoam	General Electric Co., Schenectady, N. Y.
Titanium dioxide dispersions	RBH Dispersions, Bound Brook, N. J.
	American Cyanamid Co., Bound Brook, N. J.
"Emulphor" ON-870	General Aniline & Film Corp., New York, N. Y.
Color dispersions	See Titanium Dioxide Dispersions

"picker lap" for feeding to the cards. Carding further cleans the trash from the fibers and forms a very light web of the essentially parallelized fibers, the web ranging in weight from 40 to 200 grains per sq ft.

Card webs form the basis of the oriented web and cross-lay nonwovens. For the oriented webs the card webs are superimposed on one another by means of conveyor systems, the number of such webs required depending on the weight fabric desired. For cross-lay nonwovens card webs are superimposed as before except that other card webs are laid at an angle to the machine direction.

The primary advantage of the oriented web and cross-lay system is that equipment familiar to all textile concerns may be utilized, and the producer need not design equipment completely foreign to him. On the other hand with such equipment for nonwoven manufacturers, the producer is restricted to the types of nonwovens where exceptionally high multi-direction strength is not a requirement, and cannot enter into many markets where nonwovens have proved successful.

The second basic type of nonwoven fabric has a completely disoriented or random web. Thus equipment requirements are completely changed and parallization of the fiber is to be avoided or at least limited to an initial process to be followed by disorienting the fibers. Pickers and cards may be used to clean the fibers and to tear apart hard

clumps which could not be handled subsequently. The randomness of the web is achieved by aerodynamic methods. While most producers of random web type nonwovens have designed their own equipment, a commercial unit is available for formation of the random web. This unit is the Curlator Rando-Feeder and Rando-Webber[6] shown in Fig. 1. The Rando-Feeder is essentially an opening unit, while the Rando-Webber produces the random web. Fibers are manipulated in the Rando-Webber by air pressure, and are ultimately placed in web form on an apron for transport to the fiber bonding unit. While the above unit may in many instances perform all the opening and cleaning required, in other instances it may be necessary to include pickers and/or cards as auxiliary equipment.

Another type being used for the manufacture of bonded type fabric is a modified card utilizing an air-doffer principle.[9] This unit involves feeding the open stock into a single card, or a duplex unit of two cards, feeding into a second of greater width, and then air-doffing to avoid distortion and obtain uniformity of the finished web. In addition to the Rando-Webber there are several other types of special air-lay random web machine being used by manufacturers today. Among these are Chicopee Mills, Kimberly-Clark, West Point Manufacturing Co., Pellon Corp., Owens-Corning Fiberglas Corp., and Proctor and Schwartz.

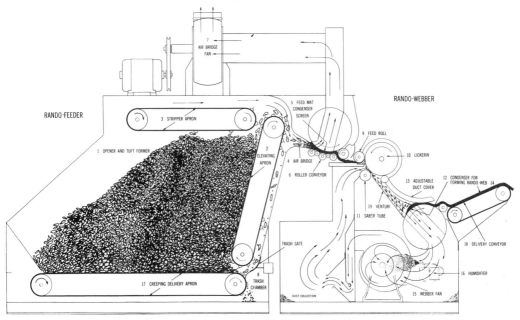

Fig. 1. Schematic flow diagram, combined Rando-Feeder and Rando-Webber. (*Courtesy Curlator Corp.*)

Another method of producing random laid fibers is the liquid system. Fibers are suspended in a liquid medium and deposited on a porous screen. Paper-making equipment can be and has been used for making nonwoven fabrics, but with textile fibers the major problem is to distribute and suspend them properly. So far the fibers have had to be cut short (¼ in. or less) to ensure proper processing. Uniformity and a higher rate of production are produced by this method although for nonwoven fabrics it is much less developed than the other methods given above. The disadvantage of this process is having to use such short fibers.

The principal advantage of random-web type nonwovens is their excellent multi-directional strength properties. This property has enabled nonwovens to enter successfully markets not available to the oriented web nonwovens, and will undoubtedly account for a higher proportion of the over-all nonwoven volume in the future. The necessity of equipment foreign to most textile concerns has been a drawback in the past. However as knowledge is acquired in this field and with commercial units becoming available, this drawback will be greatly minimized.

WEB BONDING AND EQUIPMENT

After the desired type of web has been produced, the fibers must be cemented together by a suitable binder. The binder may be applied from a solution, emulsion or dispersion, or it may already be present in the web in the form of thermoplastic or solvent-soluble resin fibers. As in the case of web formation, the equipment required for web bonding will vary according to the type of nonwovens being produced. Considering only liquid binders, whether they are aqueous or solvent solutions or emulsions, there are three basic bonding techniques in use today: discontinuous, continuous, and spray bonding. In the discontinuous, the bonding material is applied to the web in a definite pattern and it is not uniformly distributed throughout the web. Nonwovens made in this way generally have less than 50 per cent of web bonded. As a result there are fewer fiber-to-fiber bonding points. To impart the desired pattern to the web, an operation similar in principle to printing is necessary. Discontinuously bonded nonwovens are characterized by good drape and fabric-like hand, although with poor strength and tear-resistant properties, particularly in the transverse direction in the case of oriented webs.

The type of pattern employed will determine to a large extent the strength and elongation properties of the final product. For example, such patterns as bars and diamonds, at the optimum angle to the web and with optimum distribution, will impart higher transverse strength and elongation, even though the actual area bonded may be less than with other patterns. Discontinuously impregnated nonwoven fabrics have a multitude of disposable and semipermanent uses such as

TABLE 4. NONWOVEN MANUFACTURERS.

Name	Address
American Felt	Glenville, Conn.
Avondale Mills	Sylacauga, Ala.
Buresh Non Wovens	Westfield, Mass.
Callaway Mills	LaGrange, Ga.
Camden Fiber Mills, Inc.	Philadelphia, Pa.
Carlee Corp.	Rockleigh, N. J.
C. H. Dexter & Sons, Inc.	Windsor Locks, Conn.
The Felters Co.	Boston, Mass.
Gustin-Bacon Mfg. Co.	Kansas City, Mo.
Hollingsworth & Vose Co.	East Walpole, Mass.
Johnson & Johnson	New Brunswick, N. J.
Filter Products Div.	Chicago, Ill.
Chicopee Mfg. Corp.	Milltown, N. J.
The Kendall Co., Kendall Mills	Walpole, Mass.
Kimberly-Clark	Neenah, Wis.
Leshner Corporation	Hamilton, Ohio
Lowndes Products, Inc.	Greenville, S. C.
Minnesota Mining & Mfg. Co.	St. Paul, Minn.
National Automotive Fibers, Inc.	Cohoes, N. Y.
Pellon Corporation	Lowell, Mass.
Raybestos-Manhattan, Inc.	Manheim, Pa.
Rock River Cotton Co.	Janesville, Wis.
Sackner Products, Inc.	Grand Rapids, Mich.
St. Regis Paper Co.	New York, N. Y.
Scott Paper Co.	Chester, Pa.
Sherman Paper Products Corp.	Newton Upper Falls, Mass.
Standard Felt Co.	Alhambra, Calif.
Star Woolen Company	Cohoes, N. Y.
Stearns & Foster	Lockland, Ohio
Steralon Products, Inc.	Philadelphia, Pa.
Troy Blanket Mills	Troy, N. H.
Union Wadding Co.	Pawtucket, R. I.
West Point Mfg. Co.	West Point, Ga.
Wood Conversion Co.	Cloquet, Minn.

table cloths, cocktail napkins, guest towels, casket linings, and paddings and window drapes, to mention only a few.

Continuously bonded nonwovens will tend to display more of the properties of the bonded material. For this reason more consideration must be given to the choice of binder systems to be used so that desired fabric characteristics may be obtained.

Continuously bonded nonwovens are generally run through an impregnating bath for application of the bonding material, through squeeze rows for removal of the excess, and are then deposited on a belt feeding to the dryer. The fiber-bonding unit is a critical part of the entire range, and the most perfectly formed web can be easily distorted by improper handling. As in the case of web forming equipment, most producers of nonwovens have had to design their own bonding equipment, in the absence of commercially available equipment.

Today several equipment companies such as Rodney Hunt Machine Co. and John Waldron Corp. are making impregnators for applying a liquid binder to a web of fibers. The Rodney Hunt saturator consists of an impregnating bath, a conveyor system, and two squeeze rolls to remove surplus liquid. The conveyor system consists of two fine, woven, stainless steel wire endless belts which pick up the web of fibers, deliver to the impregnator, and carry the web between them into the impregnating bath. The wire belts then convey the impregnated web between squeeze rolls for removal of surplus liquid. Finally the web passes out of the impregnator for drying.[18]

The John Waldron impregnator consists of an impregnating bath, but employs only one open mesh-wire belt. The web of fibers is carried into the impregnator bath between this belt and a perforated drum. In this machine, surplus liquid is removed by vacuum extraction.[19]

Continuous binder application gives a relatively dense continuously bonded nonwoven fabric. Decorative fabrics, clothing, inner linings, vacuum fabrics for vinyl films, filter fabrics, laminating fabrics, wiping and polishing clothes, and a large number of nonwoven fabrics are made by this method.

Spraying of the liquid binder through a web of fibers gives a high-loft or bulky nonwoven fabric. Spraying is done by transporting the random web of fibers on a conveyor moving at the same rate the web is produced, through a spray chamber. The spray gun mounting moves back and forth across the width of the webs. Spans from 36 to 96 in. are available.

As many as four spray nozzles may be mounted on this carriage. The speed of the conveyor is governed by the amount of binder desired on the web. Careful adjustment of the height of the spray heads above the web, and spray pressure, is required to obtain the desired penetration of the binder into the web without distorting. Usually half the thickness of the web is sprayed on the first pass.

The web is then dried and cured as required. The direction of movement of the web is reversed on the second pass and it is run through the second spray chamber, dried and cured. These materials go into thermal insulation layers in clothing, padding or quilting and upholstering.[15]

DRYING EQUIPMENT

When the liquid bonding agents are used, some type of drying or heat-setting equipment is essen-

TABLE 5. MACHINERY SUPPLIERS.

Web-Forming Equipment

Cotton cards	Whitin Machine Works, Whitinsville, Mass.
	Saco-Lowell Shops, Boston, Mass.
Woolen cards	Davis & Furber Machine Co., North Andover, Mass.
	Proctor & Schwartz, Inc., Philadelphia, Pa.
Garnetts	James Hunter Machine Co., North Adams, Mass.
	Proctor & Schwartz, Inc., Philadelphia, Pa.
Platt lap converter	Atkinson, Haserick & Co., Boston, Mass.
Air-formed webs	Curlator Corp., East Rochester, N. Y.
	Turner Machine Co., Danbury, Conn.

Bonding and Drying Equipment

Calenders	Van Vlaanderen Machine Co., Paterson, N. J.
Dry cans	H. W. Butterworth & Sons Co., Bethayes, Pa.
Hot-air ovens	Industrial Ovens, Cleveland, Ohio
	National Drying Machinery Co., Philadelphia, Pa.
	Proctor & Schwartz, Inc., Philadelphia, Pa.
	Ross Engineering, Div. of
	Midland-Ross Corp., New York, N. Y.
	Lanly Co., Cleveland, Ohio
Infrared	Fostoria Pressed Steel Corp., Fostoria, Ohio
	Edwin L. Wiegand Co., Pittsburgh, Pa.
Impregnators	Rodney Hunt Machine Co., Orange, N. J.
	John Waldron Corp., New Brunswick, N. J.
Needle looms	James Hunter Machine Co., North Adams, Mass.
Spraying	De Vilbiss Co., Toledo, Ohio
	Paasche Air Brush Co., Chicago, Ill.
	Binks Mfg. Co., Chicago, Ill.

Dyeing and Finishing Equipment

Padders	Morrison Machine Co., Paterson, N. J.
Jigs	Van Vlaanderen Machine Co., Paterson, N. J.
Printing	Rice Barton Corp., Worcester, Mass.
Embossing	H. W. Butterworth & Sons Co., Bethayes, Pa.
	Van Vlaanderen Machine Co., Paterson, N. J.
Napping	Woonsocket Napping Machinery Co., Woonsocket, R. I.
Sueding	Woonsocket Napping Machinery Co., Woonsocket, R. I.

tial. This may consist of a series of dry cans, multiple-pass hot-air oven, and/or banks of infrared lights, calender rolls, or high frequency drying.

Several considerations govern the choice of drying equipment most suitable for nonwovens:

(1) The web as received from the fiber bonding unit has no strength and usually is supported on a belt through the drier.

(2) Migration of the bonding material is a problem best overcome by low initial temperature and fairly slow air movement. In air drying the early stages should be confined to a temperature of 200 to 260°F. Approximately 50 per cent of the water should be allowed to evaporate before the web is exposed to temperatures in excess of 300°F. In cases where thermoplastic polymers are used in conjunction with thermosetting resins, a temperature in excess of 280°F, is necessary to allow the thermosetting resin to crosslink with itself, the fiber; and in some cases the polymer.

(3) Stretch applied during drying will distort the web and destroy its iso-elasticity.

TABLE 6. PARTIAL LISTING OF PATENTS PERTAINING TO NONWOVENS.

Patent No.	Patentee	Date	Assignee	Summary
2,039,312	Goldman	5/5/36	Chicopee	Application of binder in parallel wavy lines
2,269,479	Reed	1/13/42	Kendall	Method for making nonwovens
2,277,049	Reed	3/24/42	Kendall	Process for manufacturing with thermoplastic fiber binders
2,437,689	Francis	3/16/48	AVC	Process for making needle felt
2,451,915	Buresh	10/19/48	Curlator	Machine for laying random web
2,459,803	Francis	1/25/49	AVC	Method of producing bonded felt
2,464,301	Francis	5/15/49	AVC	Textile fibrous product
2,477,675	Wilson Et Al	8/2/49	West Point	Air forming of web
2,478,148	Wilson Et Al	8/2/49	West Point	Machine for producing nonwovens
2,483,405	Francis	10/4/49	AVC	Method of producing fibrous product
2,486,803	Seymour	11/1/49	H. H. Frede Co.	Absorbent fibrous sheet
2,503,024	Boese	4/4/50	M. M. M.	Decorative rayon fabric
2,521,985	Lang	9/10/50	American Felt	Process for making bonded fibrous units
2,522,526	Manning	9/19/50	AVC	Spinning gun for producing nonwoven fabric
2,522,627	MacGregor	9/19/50	Courtaulds	Cyanoethylated fibers—nonwovens
2,528,129	Francis	10/31/50	AVC	Web and woven fabric base
2,531,594	Abrahams	11/28/56	Koffy-Pak	Nonwoven sealed coffee bag
2,535,919	Happey	12/26/50	Courtaulds	Acetylated fiber process for nonwovens
2,543,101	Francis	2/27/51	AVC	Random nonwoven of thermo- and non-thermoplastic fibers
2,537,631	Greenup	1/9/51	Firestone T & R Co.	Porous battery diaphragms
2,544,798	Lippman	3/13/51	Celanese	Sweatband of fibrous web
2,545,952	Goldman	3/20/51	Fiber Products	Unwoven flexible fabric
2,550,686	Goldman	5/1/51	Textron	Pile fabric using nonwoven fibers
2,560,332	Crane	7/10/51		Disposable diapers
2,569,765	Kellert	10/1/51		Nonwoven production
2,577,784	Lynam	12/11/51	Fiber Leather	Dispersing fiber in gaseous medium
BP663,732	Glover	12/27/51		Spray bonding cross-lay
2,581,069	Bertolet	1/1/52	Raybestos Manhattan	Apparatus for air-laid web
2,589,008	Lannon	3/11/52		Nonwoven manufacture
2,624,079	Duvall	1/6/53	Wood Conversion	Air-laid apparatus
2,626,883	Boese	1/27/53	M.M.M.	Web laminated to yarn
BP695,805	Brt. Cellophane	8/10/53		Cross-laid between parallel web and bonding
2,673,146	Kuznick	3/23/54	Raybestos Manhatton	Nonwoven abrasive product
2,673,819	Wendell	3/30/54		Batt bonded with dispersion of short fibers in resin
2,676,128	Piccard	4/20/54	DuPont	Nonwoven bonded with linear copolyester
2,676,363	Plummer	4/27/54	Chicopee	Isotropic nonwoven in air stream
2,697,678	Ness	12/51/54	Chicopee	Lacelike recticular nonwoven sinuous band bonded
2,698,271	Clark	12/28/54	Dick	Enclosed stream random collected
2,698,574	Dougherty	1/4/55	Visking	Pattern bonding apparatus
2,700,188	Buresh	1/25/55		Fiber web-forming machine
2,704,734	Draper	3/22/55	Glass Fibers	Method for nonwoven glass fibers
2,705,688	Ness	4/5/55	Chicopee	Oriented web; articulated binder
2,705,687	Petterson	4/5/55	Chicopee	Unidirectional web bonded in segmented patterns
2,705,692	Petterson	4/5/55	Chicopee	Two plies, obliquely dispersed lazy tong bonded
2,708,644	Dixon	4/17/55	American Cyanamid	Treatment with polymerized aldehyde

TABLE 6. PARTIAL LISTING OF PATENTS PERTAINING TO NONWOVENS. (*cont'd.*)

Patent No.	Patentee	Date	Assignee	Summary
BP703,251	Schroder	5/18/55	Steralon Process	Sodium carboxymethyl cellulose
BP731,077	Kaufman	6/1/55	Stearns & Foster	Carding to produce cotton batts
2,710,992	Goldman	6/21/55	Chicopee	Machine for making cross-laid nonwoven fabrics
2,719,337	Harwood	10/4/55		Making nonwoven fabric
2,719,795	Nottebohm	10/4/55	Pellon	Process for manufacturing
2,719,802	Nottebohm	10/4/55	Pellon	Process for manufacturing with resin
2,719,803	Nottebohm	10/4/55	Pellon	Foam binder
2,719,806	Nottebohm	10/4/55	Pellon	Foam binder
2,725,309	Rodman	11/29/55	DuPont	Coated nonwoven bonded with linear copolyester
2,726,423	Harwood	12/13/55	Kimberly-Clark	Nonwoven by combining drum and discharge forces
2,731,679	Kennette	1/24/56	Chicopee	Isotropic; pneumatically doffed
2,734,841	Merriman	2/14/56	Dunlap	Resilient nonwoven
2,748,429	Clark	6/5/56	A B Dick	Apparatus for forming fibrous structure
BP749,914	Bobkowicz	6/6/56		Fabric of adhesive yarns
2,750,317	Manning	6/12/56		Method for making nonwoven
2,765,247	Graham	10/22/56	DuPont	Nonwoven fabrics
2,766,137	Ashton	10/9/56		Nonwoven fabrics
2,774,687	Nottebohm	12/18/56	Pellon	Process
2,777,779	Harwood	1/15/57	Kimberly-Clark	Fiber bonded to woven fabric
2,782,833	Rusch	2/26/57		Nonwoven tubular fabric
2,784,139	Maisil	3/5/57	Fiber Bond	Air-permeable fibrous batt
2,786,790	Klein	3/28/57	Fiber Bond	On thermoplastic backings
2,787,571	Miller	4/2/57	Mohasco Ind	Nonwoven pile fabrics
2,787,572	Schwartz	4/2/57		Resilient fibrous mats
2,788,547	Kaufman	4/16/57	Stearns & Foster	High-speed carding machine
2,788,835	Brookes	4/16/57	Fabric Development	Nonwoven pile
2,791,529	Converse	5/7/57		Bonding nonwoven batt to a woven sheet
2,792,323	Ashcroft	5/14/57		Nonwoven pile fabrics
2,792,325	Downing	5/14/57	British Celanese	Cellulose acetate ribbon
2,795,524	Rodman	6/11/57	DuPont	Reinforced plastics
2,795,823	Wade	6/18/57		Fibrous filter batts
BP777,734	Gathling	6/26/57	Dunlap	Nonwoven fabrics
BP780,064	Bergin	7/31/57		Card webb
2,802,767	Mighton	8/13/57	DuPont	Nonwoven porous sheet
2,808,098	Chavanes	10/1/57	Permex Corp.	Powdered binder
2,813,806	Videen	11/19/57	Wood Conversion	Nonwoven fiber mats
2,820,716	Harmon	1/21/58	Chicopee	Nonwoven fabrics
2,820,721	Hitchcock	1/21/58	U. S. Rubber	Ironing board cloth
2,823,142	Sumner	2/11/58	Chicopee	Soft nonwoven
2,768,671	Schock	10/30/56	Alex Smith	Apparatus for making nonwovens
2,774,687	Nottebohm	12/18/56	Pellon	Process for manufacture
2,774,126	Secrist	12/18/56	Kendall	Process for felt-like product
2,774,127	Secrist	12/18/56	Kendall	Process for felt-like product
2,774,128	Secrist	12/18/56	Kendall	Process for felt-like product

AVC = American Viscose Corp.   CP = Canadian Patent
BP = British Patent   MMM = Minnesota Mining & Manufacturing Co.

(4) Many binder systems in use today require a cure, and provisions should be made for both drying and curing.

(5) Adequate exhaust systems are essential since ingredients in some binder systems are driven off during drying and cause unpleasant working conditions if not adequately exhausted from the room.

FINISHING EQUIPMENT

After the nonwoven fabric has been dried, it has a degree of strength and may be handled as a conventional woven fabric. Finishing operations which may be utilized to achieve desired effects include calendering, friction calendering, or saturating with a special finish. Dyeing, printing, and other finishings of the nonwoven fabric may be performed.

Nonwoven fabrics are mainly designed for a particular end use or for a relatively short-life cycle. Their average prices range between that of the high grade paper and medium quality woven fabric. These conditions require and permit the relatively low cost method of dyeing. Such dyeing may frequently be accomplished in a continuous operation with web production by incorporating color in the bonding agent. By starting with solution dyed man-made fibers a high degree of fastness to sunlight, laundering, dry cleaning, chlorine bleach, and salt water can be obtained. Nonwoven fabrics can also be dyed or printed in the same manner employed for woven or knitted fabrics.

TESTING OF NONWOVENS

No attempt will be made to describe the many tests which may be utilized to define the nonwoven fabric physical and chemical properties. The ASTM has made headway in establishing standard testing procedures for nonwovens. However, this program is in its initial phases and the approved tests represent only a small fraction of those commonly used. It is suggested that any nonwoven manufacturer consult ASTM and AATCC manuals for these approved testing procedures. Other tests commonly in use in the trade have been set up by nonwoven manufacturers and pertain to their specific fabrics.[20]

As in woven goods, some tests are utilized both to evaluate the suitability of nonwoven in any intended end usage, and for production control purposes. Such tests might include weight, gauge, tensile and tear strength, and elongation, all of which are standard woven textiles tests for which commercial testing equipment is available.

In addition to these tests, manufacturers must further define their products. For industrial fabrics, for example, such properties as Mullen bursting strength, abrasion, blocking, compression resilience, and heat sealability may be evaluated. Not all of these tests have been satisfactorily defined although all are important.

With the entrance of nonwovens into the apparel field, an additional series of tests became necessary. Besides tests already listed, manufacturers must consider such properties as washability, dry cleanability, hand (drape, softness, etc), light stability, flammability, air permeability, water spotting, gas fading, shrinkage, sewability, wrinkle resistance, and absorbency. All of these are important considerations of apparel goods. Naturally, some or all of these properties are also required for certain nonapparel uses.

One characteristic peculiar to nonwovens is their tendency to delaminate, or separate into layers. Delamination testing procedures are being evaluated by ASTM-AATCC to define this property in standard terms.

USE OF NONWOVENS

The physical and aesthetic properties of nonwoven fabrics can be varied over a wide range, dependent on the fiber and to a considerable extent on the binder or fiber used as a binder.

Present indications are that the nonwovens will emerge as a new industry. Its future potential will affect not only the textile, but also the paper, chemical, plastics and rubber industries.

At present the percentage of all nonwovens produced is only 1½ per cent of the entire textile consumption. This, according to estimates,[20] will rise to 5 per cent in the more distant future. Nonwoven uses can be roughly classified into three categories: disposable, semi-durable and durable.[2] Among the number of disposable uses are guest towels, bath mats, cocktail napkins, diaper liners, sanitary napkins, eye-glass tissues, medical dressings, hair-wave pads, and filters. Semi-durable end uses include window drapes, table cloths, vacuum-cleaner bags, and shoe-polishing cloths.

Durable uses are the largest, most important and most highly priced of the three categories. They include apparel, inner linings, backing for vinyl-coated fabrics and vinyl films, household and industrial wiping and polishing fabrics, electrical and thermal insulations, filtration fabrics, shoe inner liners, reinforcing for low- and high-pressure laminates and skirt fabrics, etc.

Nonwoven fabrics have three main advantages over their woven counterparts.[14] They provide:

(1) Diverse styling effects by incorporating features such as elasticity and recovery, porosity, wrinkle resistance, washability, and dry cleanability.

(2) Means for upgrading waste or other fiber

which is considered unsuitable for spinning into yarn.

(3) Means for converting fiber into fabric at a reduced cost per yard.

A nonwoven generally has at least twice the bulk and covering power of a woven fabric of equivalent weight. Other distinguishing characteristics of nonwovens are appearance (can be paper-like, felt-like or woven like); strength (can be varied from that of paper to a nonwoven fabric); porosity (wide range); hand (hard to soft); raveling (none); and fabrication (can be sewn, glued or heat bonded).

SUMMARY

The manufacture of nonwoven fabrics involves a considerable amount of closely held technical know-how in the selection of equipment, its operation, in the choice and compounding of binder systems, and in the fiber blend used. This is quite typical of a new industry. Products on the market today are the result of a number of years of development work on the part of experienced textile companies.

Nonwoven fabrics have been called chemically woven fabrics with good reason. The binder plays an important role in the success or failure of a nonwoven material. Formulations are given to illustrate a few of the many combinations which are possible. Each individual application has differences which make it difficult to be more specific. The formulations should only be considered as a starting point for work on nonwoven or other textile problems.

References*

1. Lynn, J. E., "Nonwoven Fabrics," 1957.
2. Coke, C. E., "Nonwoven Fabrics," *Chem. & Ind.,* pp. 1569–1576, (Nov. 29, 1958).
3. Nottebohm, (to Pellon Corp.), U.S. Patents No. 2,719,795; 2,719,802; 2,719,803; 2,719,806 (Oct. 4, 1955).
4. Bozzacco, F. A., *et al.,* U.S. Patent 2,849,419 (1958).
5. Moffett, R. P., "Nonwoven Fabrics—New Bonding Techniques," *Modern Textiles,* **37,** No. 10, 62–65 (1956).
6. Curlator Corp., East Rochester, New York.
7. West Point Manufacturing Co., Canadian Patents 479,794 and 479,795 (1951); 496,390 (1953).
8. Harwood, (to Kimberley-Clark Corp.), U.S. Patent 2,726,423 (Dec. 13, 1955).
9. Proctor and Schwartz Inc., Philadelphia, Pa.
10. Shearer, H. E., *American Digest Rep.,* **41,** 429 (1952).
11. Shearer, H. E., *idib.,* **44,** 464 (1955).
12. Shearer, H. E., *Modern Textiles,* (Nov.–Dec. 1958).
13. Leventhal, H. L., *American Digest Rep.,* **44,** 464 (1955).
14. Special Report on Nonwoven Textiles by various authors, *Text Bull.,* **83,** No. 10 (1957).
15. Buresh, F. M., *Textile Industry,* **84,** 48 (1958).
16. Hoffman, M. T., *Textile Industry,* **122,** 83 (1958).
17. Taylor, J. T., "Nonwoven Fabrics, the Chemical and Processing Techniques," *American Digest* Rep., June 17, 1957.
18. Rodney Hunt Machinery Co., Orange N. J.
19. John Waldron Corp., New Brunswick, N. J.
20. Rudo, S., "Nonwoven Volume Will Double in 3 Years," *Textile Industries* (Mar. 1958).
21. Steele, R., *Am. Dyestuff Rep.,* 329–335 (May 6, 1957).
22. Grove, C. S., Jr., Sheaffer, W. A., Vodonik, J. L., *Ind. Eng. Chem.,* **48.** No. 9, Part 2, 1721–1730 (Sept. 1956).

* See Table 6 for additional information on Patents.

Adhesives Guide for Designers

D. K. Rider

Bell Telephone Laboratories, Inc.
Murray Hill, New Jersey

PART I—INTRODUCTION

Scope

The purpose of this guide is to aid design engineers in the selection of adhesives for use in assembly applications. It must be recognized that no such compilation can be 100 per cent complete and correct for every application which may arise. The main problem lies in the difficulty of communicating the needs of the job in relation to the capabilities and limitations of the adhesive. Moreover, for each adhesive recommendation made, there may be several alternate suggestions equally acceptable under a slightly different specific set of conditions. Because of the wide variety of potential adhesive applications, the information in this guide must necessarily be supplemented with knowledge gained by the user through a more intimate association with his particular problem.

The author's primary intent is that this guide be useful to the designer of bonded assemblies involving a broad spectrum of substrates rather than, for example, to the paper converter concerned only with manufacturing gummed labels, or to the glass manufacturer interested in laminating safety glass; consequently most of the adhesives recommendations in this chapter have been restricted to compounds which are readily obtainable from adhesives manufacturers or formulators, rather than those requiring synthesis from basic raw materials. Most of the remaining compounds can be prepared by simple mixing without the need for highly specialized skills or equipment.

An infinite variety of formulations is possible, particularly in the categories of epoxies and solvent or bodied-solvent cements for thermoplastics. The recommendations in this chapter assume that the user will employ discretion in selecting specific compounds for a given job. Where, for example, a Neoprene, Type 1 cement has been recommended, this is because it is the author's opinion, based on years of experience, that a conventional neoprene solvent cement will do a good bonding job on the materials listed. It must be recognized, however, that many adhesives which fall in this broad category will not be of suitable quality to form an adequate bond. The success of any application requires that only quality adhesive products be employed in any instance.

Adhesive Selection

At this point it might be well to review very briefly the requirements for adhesion:

(1) The adhesive must be fluid at some stage of its application.
(2) While in this fluid state, it must wet the surface of each adherend.
(3) It must then cure or set sufficiently to provide resistance to displacement.

In many cases there will be a choice of adhesives for a given application, dependent on the means by which fluidity is achieved (Item 1) or the method by which setting occurs (Item 3). This guide is concerned primarily with Item 2, which deals with the matter of "compatibility" of various adhesive materials with the different adherends.

The adhesives engineer knows through experience that certain types of solvents will attack specific thermoplastics adversely; also he realizes that some epoxy adhesive compounds will corrode copper and its alloys and that a given adhesive may release from specific surfaces at relatively low stresses. Such factors serve to illustrate the degree of compatibility of various adhesive-adherend systems and have accordingly entered into the preparation of this guide. The apparent compatibility is, of course, affected markedly by the method of prebond treatment used on the substrates. The effective joining of an adhesive to the adherend is dependent on the cleanliness of the surfaces as well as on the chemical compatibility of the materials involved. In general, any surface to be bonded must be free of loose and nonadherent matter and sorbed contaminants which will prevent the fluid adhesive from wetting the surface.

Of equal importance in the selection of adhesives are available fabrication facilities, function of the final assembly, strength requirements, storage and service environments, etc. The suggested maximum service temperatures indicated in Part II for the various types of adhesives represent estimates based on many intangibles. The author has attempted to take into consideration such factors as the strength of the adhesive at elevated temperatures, any existing stresses likely to be encountered in service, the presumed design life of the assembly under consideration, the thermal stability of the adhesive, etc. In the interests of conservatism, an additional temperature derating has been applied to those assemblies expected to be stressed in service. Despite these considerations, it is not anticipated that there will exist anything approaching a unanimity of opinion among users of this guide regarding the temperatures suggested. Views of individuals must necessarily be colored by experience gained with specific adhesive formulations and applications possibly quite different from those considered by the author.

Use of Guide

The subsequent sections of this chapter are: Part II—Applications, an alphabetical listing of substrates and types of adhesives to be used in bonding them, and Part III—Adhesives Classification and Description, general descriptive information regarding the adhesive types listed in Part II.

The numbers indicated after the general adhesive class designations in Part II refer to specific adhesive types listed in Part III. In Part III the types are listed numerically under the alphabetically arranged general classes. This part comprises three tables: Table 1—General Listing, including all but Epoxy (Table 2) and Solvent (Table 3) classes. These latter two classes do not lend themselves to the form of tabulation employed in Table 1.

The epoxy resins are so versatile as to permit formulation with a wide variety of compounding ingredients, each of which may produce a marked effect on the final product. For this reason, a combination numerical and alphabetical coding is employed in Part II and is described in Table 2, Part III, to indicate the modifying agents, the fillers, and the curing agents employed with the epoxy resin. The ingredients listed should not be looked upon as restrictive in any sense, but rather should be viewed merely as providing sufficient diversity to satisfy the scope of this guide.

Like the epoxies, solvent cements also do not lend themselves to the form of tabulation employed in the General Listing (Table 1). Their type designations, however, are numerical, the only exceptions arising in the occasional use of the letter B following the number. This indicates the addition of some of the polymer being bonded as a means of providing "body" to the solvent.

In using Part II, then, one will look up the material he wishes to bond and (where listed) the conditions of service (i.e., temperature, moisture, electrical, nonstructural, etc.). On the right side will be found one or more adhesive recommendations listed by general class (e.g., Vinyl) and type under this class (e.g., 3). Referring then to Part III, Table 1, Vinyl will be found listed alphabetically between Urea and Vinyl-Phenolic. The numerical type designation (3) indicates that the particular adhesive recommended is a solution of polyvinyl acetate. Supplementary descriptive information is tabulated to aid the user in determining whether or not the particular recommendation is appropriate to his specific application. Where Epoxy or Solvent adhesives are referenced in Part II, information on the particular types specified will be found in Tables 2 and 3, respectively.

PART II—APPLICATIONS

ACETATE RAYON. *See* FABRICS
ACOUSTIC SILK
    to metal or thermoset plastic—Vinyl-Phenolic 3
ACRYLIC. *See* PLASTICS
ACRYLONITRILE RUBBER. *See* RUBBER, Buna N
AERODYNAMIC SMOOTHING COMPOUND—
    Epoxy 1Da
ALKYD. *See* PLASTICS, Thermoset
ALLYL. *See* PLASTICS
ALUMINUM. *See* METAL
ALUMINUM HONEYCOMB. *See* HONEYCOMB
ASBESTOS
    Board
        to asbestos or metal
            suggested maximum service temperature
            over 300°F—Inorganic 1
            300°F—Epoxy 3Fb
            200°F—Epoxy 1Be, 2Be; Vinyl-Phenolic 1
            175°F—Epoxy 1Ba, 2Ba
            160°F—Neoprene 2

        to composition board, wood, etc.
            suggested maximum service temperature
            300°F—Resorcinol 1
            160°F—Neoprene 2
    Fabric. *See* FABRICS
    Fiber (cloth, paper, tape). *See* FIBER

BASING, Lamp or Tube—Epoxy* 1Bd, 4Bc, 4Bch;
    Phenolic 1
BERYLLIUM COPPER. *See* METAL
BRAKE LINING. *See* FRICTION MATERIAL
BRASS. *See* METAL
BRONZE. *See* METAL
BUNA-N. *See* RUBBER
BUNA-S. *See* RUBBER, SBR
BUTYL RUBBER. *See* RUBBER

CELLOPHANE. *See* FILM
CELLULOID. *See* PLASTICS, Cellulose nitrate
CELLULOSE ACETATE. *See* FILM *or* PLASTICS
CELLULOSE ACETATE BUTYRATE. *See* FILM *or*
    PLASTICS
CELLULOSE PROPIONATE. *See* PLASTICS
CEMENT
    conductive
        suggested maximum service temperature
        200°F—Epoxy 1Ee
        175°F—Epoxy 1Ea
CERAMICS (glass, porcelain, stoneware, vitreous
    materials)
    to itself or metal

        electrical (i.e., high insulation resistance, high
        dielectric strength, noncorrosive)
            suggested maximum service temperature
            200°F—Epoxy 1Be†
            175°F—Epoxy 1 Ba†

        structural (i.e., highly stressed)
            suggested maximum service temperature
            over 300°F—Inorganic 1
            175°F—Epoxy 1Be

            150°F—Epoxy 1Ba
            125°F—Epoxy 4Bch

        nonstructural (i.e., unstressed or moderate
        temporary stress)
            suggested maximum service temperature
            275°F—Polysulfide 2
            175°F—Polysulfide 1
            150°F—Epoxy 1Ag

    to composition board, wood, etc.—Neoprene 2
CHLOROPRENE. *See* RUBBER, Neoprene
CHLOROSULFONATED POLYETHYLENE. *See*
    RUBBER
CLUTCH FACING. *See* FRICTION MATERIAL
COATED FABRICS
    to themselves, metal, thermoset plastic, etc.
        pyroxylin-coated—Cellulosic 1
        rubber-coated. *See* (specific) RUBBER
        vinyl-coated
            dark colored—Nitrile 1
            light colored—Vinyl 4
COMPONENTS. *See* CERAMICS, *to* itself or metal,
    electrical
COMPOSITION BOARD (hardboard, wood particle
    board)
        to itself or wood
            waterproof—Resorcinol 1
            moisture resistant—Urea 1, 2; Vinyl 2
            for dry service—Vinyl 1; Miscellaneous 1, 2

        to metal or porcelain enamel—Neoprene 2
COMPRESSED, RESIN-TREATED WOOD
    ("COMPREG"). *See* PLASTICS, Thermoset
CONCRETE
    composition board, plywood, or wood *to*—Neoprene
        1, 2; Reclaim 1
    metal *to*
        nonstructural—Neoprene 1, 3; Nitrile 3
        structural—Epoxy 1Ba, 1Da, 4Bc
CONDUCTIVE CEMENT. *See* CEMENT
COPPER or COPPER ALLOYS. *See* METAL
CORK
    to itself, composition board, plywood, or wood
        waterproof—Resorcinol 1
        moisture resistant—Miscellaneous 4; Neoprene 1,
            2; Reclaim 1; Vinyl 2
        for dry service—Miscellaneous 1; SBR 1; Vinyl 1
    to metal—Neoprene 1, 2; Reclaim 1; SBR 2
COTTON. *See* FABRICS, Other (uncoated)
COTTON HONEYCOMB. *See* HONEYCOMB
COUNTER TOPS
    to composition board, plywood, wood, etc.
        Linoleum—Miscellaneous 3; Neoprene 1;
            Reclaim 1
        Thermoset plastic
            waterproof—Resorcinol 1
            moisture resistant—Neoprene 1; Urea 1, 2;
                Vinyl 2
            for dry service—Vinyl 1
        Vinyl—Nitrile 1
CRYSTAL MOUNTING CEMENT—Miscellaneous 5

DIALLYL PHTHALATE. *See* Plastics

* Specific composition of epoxy basing cement is important factor.

† Specific formulation should be tested prior to use.

ELECTRICAL APPLICATIONS. *See* specific material
EPOXY. *See* PLASTICS, Thermoset
ETHYL CELLULOSE. *See* PLASTICS, Cellulosic

FABRICS. *See also* under material to which fabric is to
be bonded
Acetate rayon*
  to itself or wood—Acrylic 1; Vinyl 1
  to ceramics, metal, thermoset plastic, etc.—
    Neoprene 1
Asbestos or glass. *See* FIBER
Coated. *See* COATED FABRICS
Other (uncoated)*
  to itself or wood—Acrylic 1, 2; Vinyl 1, 2, 3, 4
  to ceramics, metal, thermoset plastics, etc.—
    Neoprene 1; Nitrile 1

FELT
  to itself, metal, or thermoset plastic
    high strength—Epoxy 1Ba†, 2Ba†
  to itself, metal, thermoset plastic, or wood
    moderate strength
      good oil resistance—Nitrile 1
      moderate oil resistance—Neoprene 1

FERRITE
  to itself or metal
    suggested maximum service temperature
    250°F—Nitrile-Phenolic 1, 2, 3
    200°F—Vinyl-Phenolic 1, 2; Epoxy 1Be
    175°F—Epoxy 1Ba
    125°F—Polyester 2, 3

FIBER
Asbestos or glass
  to itself, metal, or glass

    flexible
      suggested maximum service temperature
      over 300°F—Silicone 3‡
      275°F—Polysulfide 2
      175°F—Polysufide 1
      160°F—Neoprene 1; Nitrile 1

  to itself, metal, or glass

    rigid
      suggested maximum service temperature
      over 300°F—Inorganic 1
      200°F—Epoxy 1Ae, 1Ah
      175°F—Epoxy 1Aa

  to composition board, metal, plywood, etc.

    flexible
      suggested maximum service temperature
      160°F—Neoprene 1; Nitrile 1

Leather. *See* LEATHER
Textile. *See* COATED FABRICS *or* FABRICS
Vulcanized. *See* VULCANIZED FIBER
FIBER-GLASS HONEYCOMB. *See* HONEYCOMB
FILM. *See also* specific material
Cellulose acetate
  to itself, metal, thermoset plastic, etc.—Cellulosic 1,
    2; Nitrile 1; Solvent§ 1B, 2B, 4B, 5B
Cellulose acetate butyrate
  to itself, metal, thermoset plastic, etc.—Nitrile 1;
    Solvent§ 1B, 2B, 4B, 5B

Cellophane
  to itself or foreign surfaces. *See also* specific foreign
    surface—Cellulosic 1, 2
Fluorocarbon, bondable or cementable
  to itself, metal, thermoset plastic, etc.—Epoxy 1Aa,
    1Ag; Nitrile-Phenolic 1
"Mylar." *See* FILM, Polyester
Nylon
  to itself, metal, thermoset plastic, etc.—Nitrile 1;
    Solvent** 12B
Polycarbonate
  to itself, metal, thermoset plastic, etc.—Solvent§ 11B
Polyester
  to itself, metal, ferrite—Polyester 2, 3; Nitrile 1;
    SBR 3
Polyethylene
  to metal, thermoset plastic, etc.—Polyisobutylene 1
Polystyrene
  to itself or metal—SBR 3
Polyvinyl chloride
  to itself or metal—Vinyl 4; Nitrile 1
"Teflon." *See* FILM, Fluorocarbon
FLUOROCARBON. *See* FILM *or* PLASTICS
FOAM
Cellular cellulose acetate
  to itself—Epoxy 1Aa; Polyester 1
  to metal, thermoset plastic, etc.—Epoxy 1Aa, 1Ag,
    1Ba, 2Ba
Polystyrene
  to itself, metal—Epoxy 1Aa, 1Ag, 2Ba; Polysulfide 1††
  to composition board, fabric, paper, plywood, wood,
    etc. Vinyl 1; Acrylic 1; Reclaim 1‡‡; SBR 1
Polyurethane, flexible
  to metal—Nitrile 1‡‡
Polyurethane, rigid
  to itself, metal, thermoset plastics, etc.—Epoxy 1Aa,
    1Ba, 2Ba, 1Ag
FOIL. *See* METAL
FRICTION MATERIAL (brake lining, clutch facing)
  high strength, high-temperature cure—Nitrile-
    Phenolic 2
  low strength
    good oil resistance—Nitrile 1
    moderate oil resistance—Neoprene 1

GLASS. *See* CERAMICS *or* FIBER
GLASSINE. *See* PAPER
GR-S. *See* RUBBER, SBR

HARDBOARD. *See* COMPOSITION BOARD
HARD RUBBER. *See* RUBBER
HONEYCOMB (aluminum, cotton, fiberglass, paper,
stainless steel)§§
  nonstructural
    to composition board, metal, etc.—Neoprene 2

* Observe for staining by adhesive.
† Formulated to provide proper flow into felt.
‡ Prime adherend surfaces as required.
§ Solvent cement should be bodied to bond to foreign
surface.
** Not effective on all grades of nylon.
†† Avoid use of solvent-dispersed accelerator or sealer.
‡‡ Use care in choice of solvents.
§§ Use primers as recommended with specific adhesive
system.

structural
  metal (aluminum, stainless steel) primed with Nitrile-Phenolic 1 or Vinyl-Phenolic 1
    to composition board, laminated thermoset plastic facings, plywood—Resorcinol 1
    to glass-reinforced plastic facings
      suggested maximum service temperature
      over 300°F—Epoxy 3Fb
      175°F—Epoxy 1Ae, 2Be
      150°F—Epoxy 1Aa, 2Ba
      125°F—Epoxy 1Ag, 4Ac

  metal (aluminum, stainless steel)
    to metal facings
      suggested maximum service temperature
      over 300°F—Epoxy 3Fb
      250°F—Nitrile-Phenolic 4, 1, 2, 3
      200°F—Vinyl-Phenolic 1, 4
      175°F—Epoxy* 1Fe, 2Be
      150°F—Epoxy* 1Fa, 2Ba
      125°F—Epoxy 1Fg, 4Ac

structural
  metal (aluminum, stainless steel)
    to porcelainized metal
      Back up porcelainized metal with composition board bonded with Neoprene 2. Then prime and assemble as above (metal honeycomb *to* composition board, laminated thermoset plastic facings, plywood).
  cotton, paper
    to composition board facings, plywood—Resorcinol 1
    to glass-reinforced plastic facings—Epoxy 1Fg, 2BFa
    to metal facings
      suggested maximum service temperature
      200°F and under—*See* HONEYCOMB, metal *to* metal facings

fiber glass
  to glass-reinforced plastic†
  electrical
    suggested maximum service temperature
    175°F—Epoxy 1Fe; Polyester 1
    150°F—Epoxy 1Fa, 1Fg

structural
  fiber glass
    to metal facings‡
      suggested maximum service temperature
      over 300°F—Epoxy 3Fb
      250°F—Nitrile-Phenolic 2
      200°F—Vinyl-Phenolic 1, 4
      175°F—Epoxy 2BFe
      150°F—Epoxy 1AFa, 2BFa
      125°F—Epoxy 1Fg, 4Fc

IRON. *See* METAL

LABELS (designation plates, nameplates)
  Laminated thermoset plastic
    to **bare metal**, glass, porcelainized metal, thermoset **plastic**—Neoprene 3; Nitrile 3, 5
  Metal foil
    to bare metal, glass, porcelainized metal, thermoset plastic—SBR 4
  Metal plates
    to **bare metal**, composition board, glass, porcelainized

metal, thermoset plastic, wood—Neoprene 3, 4; Nitrile 3, 4, 5, 6
Paper
  to bare ferrous metal, porous metal castings—Vinyl 3
  to painted or nonferrous metal, thermoset plastic, wood—Vinyl 1, 2
Vinyl
  to bare metal, glass, porcelainized metal, thermoset plastic—Nitrile 1§

LAMINATED THERMOSET PLASTIC. *See* PLASTICS, Thermoset
LAMINATES. *See also* PLASTICS (specific material)
LEATHER
  to itself, composition board, wood—Neoprene 1; Nitrile 1; SBR 2
  to metal
    high strength—Epoxy 1Ag, 4Ac
    moderate strength—Neoprene 1; Nitrile 1; SBR 2
LINOLEUM. *See* COUNTER TOPS
"LUCITE." *See* PLASTICS, Acrylic

MAGNESIUM. *See* METAL
MELAMINE. *See* PLASTICS, Thermoset
METAL**
  to itself
    electrical†† (noncorrosive, high insulation resistance)—Epoxy 1Ff, 1Fa, 1Fe, 1Fd
  to itself
    structural (i.e., highly stressed)
      suggested maximum service temperature
      over 300°F—Epoxy 3Fb
      250°F—Nitrile-Phenolic 1, 2, 3
      200°F—Vinyl-Phenolic 1, 4
      175°F—Epoxy 2Be, 2BFe
      150°F—Epoxy 2Ba, 2BFa

    high peel strength—Nitrile-Phenolic 2, 3
    moderate peel strength—Vinyl-Phenolic 4
    semistructural (moderately stressed)
      suggested maximum service temperature
      175°F—Epoxy 2Ba, 1Ba
      150°F—Epoxy 1Ag, 4Ac, 1Bg, 4Bc

    nonstructural (unstressed or moderate temporary stress)—Neoprene 4; Nitrile 4, 6; Polysulfide 1
  to laminated thermoset plastic. *See* PLASTICS, Thermoset
  to other materials. *See* specific material (*to* metal)
Copper and high copper alloy foil
  to laminated thermoset plastic
    electrical—Vinyl-Phenolic 1; Nitrile-Phenolic 1§§
Other foil
  to polystyrene foam—SBR3; Polyisobutylene 1

* Facings primed with Nitrile-Phenolic 1 or Vinyl-Phenolic 1.
† Use peel-ply technique on facings to provide optimum bond.
‡ Prime facing with appropriate adhesive primer for best performance.
§ Observe for staining.
** Use primers as recommended with specific adhesive system.
†† Specific formulation should be tested prior to use.
§§ Some nitrile-phenolics have poor insulation resistance under humid conditions; others may react unfavorably with oxide coatings on copper.

METHACRYLATE. *See* PLASTICS, Acrylic
MICA
>   *to* itself or metal—Epoxy 4Ac, 1Ag; Nitrile-Phenolic
>   1; Vinyl-Phenolic 1
>   *to* metal or ferrite (low strength, heat resistant)—
>   Silicone 1

MOUNTING FIXTURE (Metal)
>   *to* plaster, concrete, tile, wood, composition board,
>   etc.—Neoprene 3, 4; Nitrile 3, 4

"MYLAR." *See* FILM, Polyester

NAMEPLATES. *See* LABELS
NATURAL RUBBER. *See* RUBBER
NEOPRENE. *See* RUBBER
NITROCELLULOSE. *See* PLASTICS, Cellulosic
NYLON. *See* PLASTICS

PAPER
>   *to* aluminum, die-cast or rough and porous—Vinyl 3
>   *to* ferrous metal—Vinyl 3
>   *to* nonferrous metal or laminates—Vinyl 1, 3
>   *to* organic finishes—Vinyl 1
>   *to* paper
>>   electrical—Acrylic 2; Cellulosic 1, 2
>>   nonelectrical—SBR 1; Vinyl 1, 2, 3

PLASTER (painted or unpainted)
>   metal *to*—Neoprene 3, 4; Nitrile 3, 4, 5, 6; Reclaim
>   1; SBR 2

PLASTICS
>   ABS Polymers. *See* PLASTICS, Polystyrene
>   Acetal ("Delrin")
>>   *to* itself or metal—Polyester 2; Epoxy 1Ag, 1Bg,
>>   4Ac; Nitrile 1
>   Acrylic
>>   *to* itself
>>>   electrical—Acrylic 5*
>>>   hermetic seal—Polysulfide 1†; Acrylic 5
>>>   other—Solvent‡ 14, 15, 20, 10; Acrylic 3
>>   *to* metal—Acrylic 5; Polysulfide† 1, 2§
>>   *to* fibrous materials—Acrylic 2, 5; SBR 2; Solvent
>>   10B, 13B
>>   *to* rubber—Acrylic 3; Polysulfide 1†; Reclaim 1;
>>   SBR 2
>   Acrylic-styrene copolymer (Methyl methacrylate
>   copolymer)
>>   *to* itself—Solvent‡ 6, 18
>   Alkyd. *See* PLASTICS, Thermoset
>   Allyl, cast
>>   *to* itself, metal or thermoset plastic—Epoxy 1Ag,
>>   1Bg; Polysulfide 1
>   Amino. *See* PLASTICS, Thermoset
>   Cellulosic
>>   Cellulose acetate, acetate butyrate, or propionate
>>>   *to* itself—Cellulosic 1, 2; Solvent‡ 1, 2, 5
>>>   *to* ethyl cellulose—Cellulosic 1; Solvent‡ 5
>>>   *to* fibrous materials—Cellulosic 1, 2; Vinyl 1, 2
>>>   *to* metal—Cellulosic 1, 2; Nitrile 1
>>>   *to* nitrocellulose—Cellulosic 1
>>   Cellulose nitrate
>>>   *to* itself—Cellulosic 1; Solvent‡ 1
>>>   *to* metal—Cellulosic 1
>>   Ethyl cellulose
>>>   *to* itself—Cellulosic 1; Solvent‡ 9
>>>   *to* metal or thermoset plastic—Cellulosic 1
>   Diallyl phthalate. *See* PLASTICS, Thermoset
>   Epoxy. *See* PLASTICS, Thermoset

Ethyl cellulose. *See* PLASTICS, Cellulosic
Fluorocarbon, bondable or cementable
>   *to* itself, metal, or thermoset plastic
>>   electrical
>>>   *suggested maximum service temperature*
>>>   200°F—Epoxy 1Ae**
>>>   175°F—Epoxy 1Aa**
>>   semistructural
>>>   *suggested maximum service temperature*
>>>   250°F—Nitrile-Phenolic 1, 2
>>>   200°F—Epoxy 1Ae, 2Be; Vinyl-Phenolic 1
>>>   175°F—Epoxy 1Aa, 1Ca, 2Ba
>>>   150°F—Epoxy 1Ag, 4Ac

Melamine. *See* PLASTICS, Thermoset
Nylon
>   *to* itself or thermoset plastic
>>   electrical
>>>   *suggested maximum service temperature*
>>>   200°F—Epoxy 1Ad**
>>>   175°F—Epoxy 1Aa**
>>>   150°F—Epoxy 1Bg,** 1 Cg**
>>   structural
>>>   *suggested maximum service temperature*
>>>   250°F—Resorcinol 1; Nitrile-Phenolic 2
>>>   175°F—Epoxy 1Ae
>>>   150°F—Epoxy 1Aa
>>>   125°F—Epoxy 1Ag, 4Ac
>>   temporary—Solvent 12B
>   *to* composition board or wood—Resorcinol 1
>   *to* ferrite—Nitrile-Phenolic 2
>   *to* metal
>>   electrical
>>>   *suggested maximum service temperature*
>>>   200°F—Epoxy 1Ae**
>>>   175°F—Epoxy 1Aa**
>>>   150°F—Epoxy 1Bg,** 1Cg**
>>   structural
>>>   *suggested maximum service temperature*
>>>   200°F—Nitrile-Phenolic 2
>>>   175°F—Epoxy 1Ae
>>>   150°F—Epoxy 1Aa
>>>   125°F—Epoxy 1Bg, 1Cg, 4Bc

Phenolic. *See* PLASTICS, Thermoset
"Plexiglas." *See* PLASTICS, Acrylic
Polyacetal. *See* PLASTICS, Acetal
Polycarbonate
>   *to* itself, metal, or thermoset plastic—Solvent‡ 10,
>   11, 13, 22, 24
Polyester. *See* FILM, Polyester, *or* PLASTIC,
>   Thermoset
Polyethylene
>   *to* itself, brass or brass-plated metal, or rubber—
>   Polybutadiene 1
Polyethylene (treated for bonding)
>   *to* metal, thermoset plastics, cyclized rubber, etc.—
>   Epoxy 1Ag, 4Ac, 2Ba

---

* Check specific compound for corrosion.
† Avoid use of solvent-dispersed accelerator or sealer.
‡ Solvent cement should be bodied for bonding to
poorly mated or foreign surfaces.
§ Use Type 2 in preference to Type 1 on anodic metals
exposed to corrosive environment.
** Specific formulation should be tested prior to use.

Polyformaldehyde. *See* PLASTICS, Acetal

Polystyrene. *See also* FILM *and* FOAM
  to itself or metal—Solvent* 21, 23, 25
  Copolymers or Polymer blends
    ABS Polymer
      to itself—Solvent* 16, 17, 18, 19
      to foreign surfaces—Nitrile 1; Epoxy 2Ba, 1Aa,
        1Ag; Solvent* 16, 17, 18, 19
    Styrene-acrylonitrile
      to itself—Solvent* 8, 16; Polyester 1
      to metal—Solvent* 8, 16
      to other foreign surfaces—Polyester 1; Solvent* 8,
        16
    Styrene-butadiene
      to itself—Solvent* 16, 18, 1
      to metal or other foreign surfaces—Nitrile 1;
        Solvent* 16, 18, 1
  Polyvinylidene chloride
    to itself or metal—Nitrile 1
  Polyvinyl chloride and copolymers. *See also* FILM
    to itself or metal—Nitrile 1; Solvent 7B; Vinyl 4
    to acrylic or polystyrene plastic—Nitrile 2
  Silicone. *See* PLASTICS, Thermoset
  Styrene and copolymers. *See* PLASTICS, Polystyrene
  Thermoset, cast, laminated, or molded
    Silicone
      to itself, silicone rubber, or metal
        suggested maximum service temperature
        over 300°F—Silicone 1, 2†, 3†, 5
        200°F—Silicone 4

    Other (e.g., alkyd, amino, diallyl phthalate, epoxy,
      melamine, phenolic, urea, etc.)
      to itself, other thermoset plastic, or metal

      electrical‡
        suggested maximum service temperature
        200°F—Epoxy 1Ae, 1Ff, 1Fh, 1Fe, 1Be;
          Vinyl-Phenolic 1, 2
        175°F—Epoxy 1Aa, 1Ba, 1Ca
        150°F—Epoxy 1Ag, 4Ac

      structural
        suggested maximum service temperature
        250°F—Nitrile-Phenolic 1, 2, 3
        200°F—Vinyl-Phenolic 1, 4
        175°F—Epoxy 1Fe, 2Be, 2BFe
        150°F—Epoxy 1Aa, 1Ba, 1Ca, 2Ba
        125°F—Epoxy 1Ag, 4Ac

      nonstructural—Neoprene 2
    Laminated
      to composition board, wood, etc.
      structural—Resorcinol 1
      semistructural—Neoprene 2; Urea 1, 2
      nonstructural—Vinyl 1, 2
    Urea. *See* PLASTICS, Thermoset

"PLEXIGLAS." *See* PLASTICS, Acrylic

PLYWOOD. *See* WOOD

POLYAMIDE. *See* PLASTICS, Nylon

POLYESTER. *See* PLASTICS *or* FILM

POLYETHYLENE. *See* FILM *or* PLASTICS

POLYSTYRENE. *See* FILM, FOAM, *or* PLASTICS

POLYSULFIDE. *See* RUBBER

POLYURETHANE. *See* FOAM *or* RUBBER

POLYVINYL ACETATE. *See* PLASTICS, Polyvinyl
  chloride and copolymers

POLYVINYL CHLORIDE. *See* FILM *or* PLASTICS

PORCELAIN. *See* CERAMICS

PRESSED BOARD. *See* COMPOSITION BOARD

PRINTED CIRCUIT BOARDS. *See* PLASTICS,
  Thermoset, electrical

RAYON. *See* FABRICS

RUBBER, Vulcanized
  to itself, ceramics, composition board, fabrics, metal,
    thermoset plastic, etc.
  Acrylonitrile. *See* RUBBER, Buna-N
  Buna-N. *See also* RUBBER, Cyclized—Nitrile 1
  Buna-S. *See* RUBBER, SBR
  Butyl—Neoprene 1
  Chlorosulfonated polyethylene—Nitrile 1
  Cyclized§
    to itself, metal, thermoset plastic, etc.—Epoxy 1Bg,
      2Ba, 4Ac
    to wood, composition board, etc.—Resorcinol 1
  GR-S. *See* RUBBER, SBR
  Hard
    electrical—Epoxy 1Aa, 1Ca
    structural
      suggested maximum service temperature
      150°F—Epoxy 1Aa, 1Ca, 2Ba
      125°F—Epoxy 1Ag, 4Ac

    nonstructural—Neoprene 2
  Natural. *See also* RUBBER, Cyclized—Neoprene 1
  Neoprene. *See also* RUBBER, Cyclized—Neoprene 1
  Nitrile. *See* RUBBER, Buna-N
  Polysulfide—Polysulfide 1, 2
  Polyurethane—Nitrile 1; Neoprene 1
  SBR. *See also* RUBBER, Cyclized—Neoprene 1
  Silicone
    to itself, or primed† foreign surfaces
      suggested maximum service temperature
      over 300°F—Silicone 2, 3
      200°F—Silicone 4

  "Thiokol." *See* RUBBER, Polysulfide

SILICONE. *See* PLASTICS *or* RUBBER

SILK. *See* FABRICS, Other (uncoated)

SILK, Acoustic. *See* ACOUSTIC SILK

STAINLESS STEEL. *See* METAL

STAKING SCREWS
  hermetic seal—Acrylic 4; Epoxy 1Ag, 4Ac; Polysulfide
    1, 2
  nonhermetic lock—Alkyd 1, 2

STONEWARE. *See* CERAMICS

STRUCTURAL PLASTIC. *See* PLASTICS, Thermoset

TABLE TOPS. *See* COUNTER TOPS

TEXTILES. *See* FABRICS

THERMOPLASTICS. *See* (specific) PLASTICS

THERMOSET PLASTICS. *See* PLASTICS, Thermoset

"THIOKOL" (Polysulfide). *See* RUBBER, Polysulfide

UREA. *See* PLASTICS, Thermoset

* Solvent cement should be bodied for bonding to
poorly mated or foreign surfaces.

† Prime metal with special primer available for use
with silicone adhesives.

‡ Specific formulation should be tested prior to use.

§ Buna-N, natural, neoprene, or SBR treated with sulfuric acid for structural bonding with thermosetting resin
adhesives.

VINYL. *See* COATED FABRICS, COUNTER TOPS,
LABELS, PLASTICS, POLYVINYL CHLORIDE
VITREOUS MATERIALS. *See* CERAMICS
VULCANIZED FIBER
 to itself, composition board, thermoset plastic, or
  wood—Resorcinol 1; Urea 1, 2; Vinyl 1, 2
 to metal
  for electrical use*

   suggested maximum service temperature
   200°F—Epoxy 1Ae, 1Ce
   175°F—Epoxy 1Aa, 1Ca
   150°F—Epoxy 4Ac

  structural
   suggested maximum service temperature
   175°F—Epoxy 2Be
   150°F—Epoxy 2Ba
   125°F—Epoxy 1Bg

  nonstructural
   suggested maximum service temperature
   160°F—Neoprene 1, 2; Nitrile 1
   140°F—SBR 2
   125°F—Reclaim 1

WALLBOARD. *See* COMPOSITION BOARD
WOOD (Plywood)
 to metal
  bare—Neoprene 2
  primed—Resorcinol 1
 to wood
  waterproof—Resorcinol 1
  moisture resistant—Vinyl 2
  for dry service—Miscellaneous 1, 2; Urea 1, 2;
   Vinyl 1
WOOD PARTICLE BOARD. *See* COMPOSITION
BOARD

  * Specific formulation should be tested prior to use.

PART III—ADHESIVES CLASSIFICATION AND DESCRIPTION

TABLE 1. GENERAL LISTING.

Class	Type	As Supplied	Description				Remarks
				Ready for Use			
			Color	Consistency or Film Thickness	% Nonvolatile	Setting or Curing Temp.	
Acrylic	1	Aqueous dispersion	Milky white	Watery	40–55	R.T.*	
	2	Ester(s) in aromatic or chlorinated solvent	Clear	Thin syrup	25–40	R.T.	
	3	Alkyl cyanoacrylate	Clear	Watery	Approx. 100	R.T.	
	4	Acrylic acid diester	(*See* Remarks)	Watery to very thin syrup	Approx. 100	R.T.–250°F	Color coded by strength grades.
	5	3-part	Clear	Medium syrup	Approx. 100	R.T.	Parts (*a*) and (*b*) may be mixed and held under refrigeration for several days prior to adding part (*c*).
		(*a*) Polymer in MMA† monomer plus polymerizing acid					
		(*b*) Peroxide catalyst					
		(*c*) Promoter					
Alkyd	1	Clear solution	Clear to light straw	Thin syrup	45–55	R.T.	
	2	Pigmented solution	(*See* Remarks)	Thin to medium syrup	40–80	R.T.	Color depends on pigmentation
Cellulosic	1	Nitrocellulose solution	Clear to amber	Thin to medium syrup	18–35	R.T.	Highly flammable.
	2	Cellulose acetate solution	Clear to amber	Thin to medium syrup	20–35	R.T.	
Epoxy		*See* Table 2					
Inorganic	1	Sodium silicate	Metallic gray	Heavy syrup to heavy paste	65–70	R.T.–250°F	

* R.T. = room temperature.
† MMA = methyl methacrylate.

							Remarks
Miscellaneous	1	Animal (including fish)	Tan	Thin syrup	25–32	R.T.	
	2	Casein (including soya and albumen)	Off-white to tan	Thin syrup	35–40	R.T.	
	3	Coumarone-indene solution	Tan to dark brown	Heavy syrup to thick paste	75–90	R.T.	
	4	Shellac solution	Amber	Thin syrup	40–60	R.T.	
	5	Shellac—hot melt, stick	Brown, black	Stick form	100	280°F	
Neoprene*	1	Solution	Tan to brown	Thin syrup to soft paste	20–53	R.T.–275°F	Generally corrosive to copper.
	2	Solution—contact bond	Tan to brown	Thin to medium syrup	18–36	R.T.–200°F	
	3	Supported film—solvent activated	Tan	0.005–0.040 in.	100	R.T.	
	4	Supported film—heat activated	Tan	0.015–0.030 in.	100	250–350°F	
Nitrile*	1	Solution	Tan to dark brown	Thin to medium syrup	20–37	R.T.–325°F	Effect on copper varies.
	2	Aqueous dispersion	Tan	Thin syrup to thin paste	38–60	R.T.	
	3	Supported film—solvent activated	Tan to brown	0.015–0.030 in.	100	R.T.	
	4	Supported film—heat activated	Tan to brown	0.015–0.030 in.	100	200–350°F	
	5	Free film—solvent activated	Tan to brown	0.002–0.008 in.	100	R.T.	
	6	Free film—heat activated	Tan to brown	0.002–0.008 in.	100	200–350°F	
Nitrile-Phenolic†	1	Solution	Amber to black	Thin to medium syrup	16–35	280–425°F	
	2	Free film	Tan to black	0.002–0.035 in.	100	280–425°F	
	3	Supported film	Tan to brown	0.010–0.020 in.	100	280–425°F	
	4	Composite film‡	(See Remarks)	0.013–0.016 in.	100	350°F	Tan on nitrile-phenolic side, off-white on epoxy side.

* Nominally thermoplastic; generally modified with phenolic or other synthetic resin.
† Thermosetting composition.
‡ 2-sided supported film for sandwich bonding: nitrile-phenolic toward facing, epoxy toward honeycomb core.

TABLE 1. GENERAL LISTING. (cont'd.)

Class	Type	As Supplied	Description		Ready for Use		Remarks
			Color	Consistency or Film Thickness	% Nonvolatile	Setting or Curing Temp.	
Phenolic (See also Resorcinol)	1	Solution	Dark brown, tan, or metallic	Heavy syrup to stiff paste	75-95	240-325°F	
Polybutadiene	1	Solution*	Off-white	Semigel at R.T.†	5-10	285-310°F	
Polyester	1	Unsaturated; styrene crosslinked‡	Light straw	Thin syrup	100	R.T.-250°F§	
	2	Terephthalate copolymer—resin	Clear	Thin syrup	15-30	200-350°F**	
	3	Terephthalate copolymer—film	Clear or dyed	0.00025 in.	100	325-350°F	
Polyisobutylene	1	Solution	Translucent	Medium syrup	25-35	R.T.	
Polysulfides††	1	Lead dioxide cure	Tan, black, metallic, etc.	Paste	Approx. 100	≥R.T.	
	2	Chromate cure		Paste	Approx. 100	≥R.T.	
Reclaim	1	Solution	Red-brown to black	Thin syrup to soft paste	38-78	R.T.	
Resorcinol‡‡	1	Aqueous or solvent dispersion§§	Red-brown	Thin syrup	54-72	R.T.-210°F	

* For composition refer to: Peters and Lockwood, *Rubber World*, **138**, 418-423 (1958).
† Thins to syrup at approximately 150°F.
‡ Requires peroxide catalyst.
§ Promoter required for room temperature cure.
** Varies with grade.
†† Solventless, 2-part.
‡‡ Including resorcinol-phenolic.
§§ 2-part; requires formaldehyde catalyst.

Type	No.	Form	Color	Consistency	Solids	Cure Temp.	Remarks
SBR**	1	Aqueous dispersion	Light cream	Medium syrup to soft paste	38–58	R.T.	
	2	Solution	Dark cream to black	Thin syrup to heavy paste	50–60	R.T.	
	3	Polyisobutylene modified—solution	Off-white, translucent	Thin syrup	31–37	R.T.	
	4	Pressure-sensitive film††	Clear	0.001 in.	100	R.T.	
Silicone	1	Pressure-sensitive—solution	Light straw	Medium syrup	40	160–210°F*	
	2	1-part, solventless	(See Remarks)	Heavy putty	100	225–250°F*	Color varies (white or colors).
	3	1-part, solution	(See Remarks)	Soft paste	Approx. 35	225–250°F*	Color varies (white or colors).
	4	2-part, solution	Clear to light straw	Thin syrup	75	R.T.	
	5	1-part, solventless	White	Paste	100	R.T.	
Solvent		——— See Table 3 ———					
Urea	1	Aqueous dispersion†	Milky white	Medium syrup	60–72	R.T.–250°F	
	2	Dry powder‡	Off-white to tan	Medium syrup	60–72	R.T.	
Vinyl		Polyvinyl acetate					
	1	Emulsion, 1-part	Milky white	Thin syrup	32–59	R.T.	
	2	Emulsion, 2-part	Off-white	Thin syrup	32–59	R.T.	
	3	Solution	Straw	Medium syrup	12–25	R.T.	
	4	Polyvinyl chloride—solution	Light straw	Thin syrup	4–10	R.T.	
Vinyl-Phenolic	1	Solution	Amber	Medium to heavy syrup	20–38	300–350°F	
	2	Free film—heat cured	(See Remarks)	0.001–0.002 in.	100	300–350°F	Natural color is amber, but dyes are normally added by manufacturer.
	3	Free film—solvent activated	(See Remarks)	0.001–0.002 in.	100	R.T.§	
	4	Support film	Amber	0.013–0.030 in.	100	300–350°F	

* Plus postcure.
† Catalyst required.
‡ Catalyst incorporated; water required.
§ Normally post-heated at 125–150°F to remove solvent.
** Styrene-butadiene rubber.
†† On removable backing.

TABLE 2. EPOXY ADHESIVES.

	Compounds				
Modifier*		Filler†		Curing Agent‡	
Type	Constituent	Type	Constituent	Type	Constituent
1	None	A	None	a	Primary aliphatic polya-
2	Polyvinyl acetate§	B	Mineral—extender		mine or amine adduct††
3	Phenolic resin	C	Mineral—thixotropic	b	Hexamethylenetetramine
4	Polysulfide liquid	D	Metal, powder or flake—	c	Tertiary amine
	polymer¶		nonconductive	d	Salt of tertiary amine
		E	Metal—silver flake**	e	Primary aromatic amine
		F	Glass fiber	f	Amide, short chain
				g	Polyamide
				h	Anhydride

	General Description	Remarks
Color	Clear to dark brown, or pigmented	All characteristics vary
Consistency or Film Thickness	Thin syrup to solid, or supported film	widely according to the combinations of compo- nents used.
% Nonvolatile	Approx. 100; may be diluted with solvents for specific applications.	
Setting or Curing Temperature	R. T. −400°F	

Note 1: For simplicity, epoxy recommendations are based on the use of polymers of epichlorohydrin and bis-phenol A.

Note 2: Although basically nonconductive, epoxies for electrical use should be tested for corrosion of copper and for electrical properties.

* Other modifiers (e.g., nitrile rubber, cashew oil derivatives, silicone resins, etc.) may also be employed. Polyamide resins are listed as curing agents since they also effect a cure.

† Color pigments may also be used.

‡ Combinations of curing agents may also be employed [e.g., (a) with (g), (c) with (h), etc.].

§ Corrosive to copper.

¶ Noxious odor until fully cured.

** Normally requires >25 % pigment volume concentration for dc conductivity.

†† Including cyanoethylation adducts of secondary aliphatic polyamines.

TABLE 3. SOLVENT ADHESIVES.

Type*	Composition†	Type*	Composition†
1	Acetone	13	Methylene chloride
2	Acetone—30:butyl acetate—50:methyl "Cellosolve" acetate—20	14	Methylene chloride—60:methyl methacrylate monomer—40
3	Acetone—90:ethyl lactate—10	15	Same as 14 but ratio changed to 50:50
4	Acetone—80:methoxyethyl acetate—20	16	Methylethyl ketone
5	Acetone—70:methyl "Cellosolve" acetate—30	17	Methylethyl ketone—50:toluene—50
6	n-Butyl acetate—38:methyl methacrylate monomer—62	18	Methyl isobutyl ketone
7	Cyclohexanone—20:tetrahydrofuran—80	19	Methyl isobutyl ketone—75:xylene—25
8	Ethyl acetate	20	Methyl methacrylate monomer
9	Ethyl alcohol—10:toluene—90	21	Perchloroethylene (tetrachloroethylene)
10	Ethylene dichloride	22	Tetrachloroethane
11	Ethylene dichloride—50:methylene chloride—50	23	Toluene
12	Fluoroalcohol (C3)	24	Trichloroethane (1, 1, 2)
		25	Trichloroethylene

* B following type number in Part II, Applications, indicates bodying of solvent with polymer being bonded (approximately 2 to 25% solids).

† Compositions are in parts by weight; proportions can be varied.

Index

Italics indicates initial page of major source of information and appears first.

Chapter 59, Adhesives Guide for Designers, has not been indexed, since it is itself largely an index, beginning on page 664.